GREAT BOOKS OF THE WESTERN WORLD

ROBERT MAYNARD HUTCHINS, *EDITOR IN CHIEF*

22.

CHAUCER

TROILUS AND CRESSIDA

AND

THE CANTERBURY TALES

BY GEOFFREY CHAUCER

WITH MODERN ENGLISH VERSIONS OF BOTH WORKS

WILLIAM BENTON, *Publisher*

ENCYCLOPÆDIA BRITANNICA, INC.

CHICAGO · LONDON · TORONTO

The Middle English versions of *Troilus and Criseyde* and *The Caunterbury Tales*
are reprinted from *The Complete Works of Geoffrey Chaucer*,
edited by W. W. Skeat, by arrangement with Oxford University Press

The Modern English version of *Troilus and Cressida*, translated by George Philip Krapp,
is reprinted by arrangement with
Random House, Inc. Copyright, 1932, by Random House, Inc.

The Modern English version of *The Canterbury Tales*, translated by J. U. Nicolson,
is reprinted by arrangement with Crown Publishers, New York.
Copyright, 1934, by Covici, Friede, Inc.

1955 Printing

BIOGRAPHICAL NOTE

Geoffrey Chaucer, c. 1340–1400

Chaucer was born when Edward III was achieving his first victories in the Hundred Years' War against France. The history of the Chaucer family to some extent mirrors the rise of the burgher class during these years. His father and grandfather were prosperous wine-merchants who had obtained some standing at court and were beginning to engage in public service. The poet for most of his life held government offices, and Thomas Chaucer, who was almost certainly the poet's son, rose to wealth and influence in the fifteenth century.

The extant records of Chaucer's life show that he was a busy and versatile man of affairs, but they disclose almost nothing of his personal life or of his literary career. Even the exact date of his birth is a matter of conjecture. From evidence he gave in a law-suit in 1386 it is known that he was then "forty years old and more and had borne arms for twenty-seven years." From an early age he evidently had intimate knowledge of the court; he served successively in the households of Lionel, Duke of Clarence, Edward III, and John of Gaunt, Duke of Lancaster. In 1359 he was a member of Lionel's division in the largest army which Edward III had so far led into France. Chaucer was taken prisoner and ransomed by the King. The following year he seems to have acted as diplomatic courier in the negotiations resulting in the Peace of Calais. He may then have been chosen to receive special training for government service, perhaps education at the Inns of Court, for by 1367 he had become a servant to the King with a pension for life.

Chaucer's social position was advanced by his marriage, perhaps in 1366, to Philippa de Roet, a lady in waiting on the Queen and sister of Katherine Swynford, afterwards the third wife of John of Gaunt, from whose issue the Tudors traced their descent. Chaucer had already begun to win some reputation as a poet and on the death of Gaunt's first wife in 1369, he wrote, supposedly at the Duke's request, the *Book of the Duchess*, in which he shows an intimate knowledge of the French court poetry.

During the first ten years of his service as a King's esquire Chaucer was frequently employed for diplomatic missions to the continent, "on the King's secret affairs." He went several times to France and the Low Countries, but perhaps the most important for his literary development were the two missions that he made to Italy in 1372 and 1378. The first of these took him to Genoa on a commercial assignment, but he also visited Florence and was there when the city was arranging for Boccaccio's lectures on Dante. On his second journey to Italy, regarding "certain affairs touching the expedition of the King's war," he visited Milan, where Petrarch had lived and worked the last twenty years of his life.

Even before his second Italian mission Chaucer had begun to receive offices at home. In 1374 he had been appointed Comptroller of Customs and Subsidy of Wools, Skins, and Hides. That same year he obtained rent-free the house above the city gate of Aldgate and was awarded by the King a daily pitcher of wine. A few years later he was also given charge of the customs on wines. In his position in the Custom House, which he held for almost twelve years, Chaucer came into close association with the great merchants who were then beginning to come into prominence, and seems to have been particularly intimate with the merchants who actually controlled the city government of London. Yet there is little indication that he ever became strongly partisan in politics. He received his first appointment under Edward III, when John of Gaunt was the power behind the throne; it was confirmed by Richard II, and Chaucer received several preferments from him; yet he also continued to receive favors from Henry IV after Richard's deposition.

The twelve years passed in the tower above Aldgate were among the most productive for Chaucer as a writer. Besides the two court poems, the *House of Fame* and the *Parliament of Fowls*, Chaucer, as the result of his Italian journeys and reading of Boccaccio and Petrarch was inspired to work upon "the storye of Palamon and Arcyte" and the *Troilus and Cressida*. The dedication of the *Troilus* to "moral Gower" and "philosophical Strode" disclose something of his intellectual friendships. He seem to have been rather intimate with Gower, for that poet acted as his deputy at the Custom

House during one of his missions. Strode, who was known for his work in logic at Oxford, was also associated with Chaucer in a business transaction. Chaucer's interest in philosophy is particularly shown in his translation of the *De Consolatione Philosophiæ* of Boethius, which provided the inspiration for several of his shorter poems. In the *Legend of Good Women* Chaucer proposed to atone to Love for his portrayal of the "false Cressida" by celebrating the lives of nineteen of "Cupid's saints," nine of which he completed.

In 1385, having obtained deputies for his comptrollerships, Chaucer appears to have retired to the country, perhaps to Greenwich. He became justice of the peace for Kent and the following year was elected to parliament as one of the knights of the shire. By the end of that year, however, Chaucer had ceased to work at the customs, perhaps because of the hostility of the Duke of Gloucester to the King's appointments, and for three years he was without employment. During this period of leisure it is probable that he began the *Canterbury Tales.*

Chaucer entered upon a new series of governmental posts in 1389 when Richard II assumed direct control of the government. As Clerk of the King's Works, he supervised the maintenance and repair of the royal buildings and parks, including the construction of scaffolds for the tournaments at Smithfield. In this office he was obliged to travel constantly and was twice robbed by highwaymen on the same day. His clerkship ceased in 1391, and he became administrative director of North Petherton forest in Somerset. This was his last regular office, and although he spent some time in Somerset, he was frequently in London, where he continued to enjoy royal favor. His pensions were somewhat irregular, for as was common at the time it was difficult to exact payment from the Exchequer, but there is little evidence that he suffered any real want. During his last years he presumably continued to work on the *Canterbury Tales*, and wrote a few minor poems and the *Treatise on the Astrolabe*, written for "litel Lowis my son."

In 1399, shortly after the coronation of Henry IV, Chaucer leased for fifty-three years a house in the garden of Westminster Abbey. He had previously received several gifts from Henry, and his pensions were approved and increased by the new King. Chaucer lived for less than a year in the Abbey garden. He died on October 25, 1400, and as a tenant of the grounds, was buried in Westminster Abbey in the place now known as the Poet's Corner.

GENERAL CONTENTS

. . .

MIDDLE ENGLISH

. . .

MODERN ENGLISH

. . .

CONTENTS

TROILUS AND CRESSIDA

TROILUS AND CRESSIDA

BOOK I

1

THE double sorwe of Troilus to tellen,
That was the king Priamus sone of Troye,
In lovinge, how his aventures fellen
Fro wo to wele, and after out of joye,
My purpos is, er that I parte fro ye.
Thesiphone, thou help me for t'endyte
Thise woful vers, that wepen as I wryte!

2

To thee clepe I, thou goddesse of torment,
Thou cruel Furie, sorwing ever in peyne;
Help me, that am the sorwful instrument
That helpeth lovers, as I can, to pleyne!
For wel sit it, the sothe for to seyne,
A woful wight to han a drery fere,
And, to a sorwful tale, a sory chere.

3

For I, that god of Loves servaunts serve,
Ne dar to Love, for myn unlyklinesse,
Preyen for speed, al sholde I therfor sterve,
So fer am I fro his help in derknesse;
But nathelees, if this may doon gladnesse
To any lover, and his cause avayle,
Have he my thank, and myn be this travayle!

4

But ye loveres, that bathen in gladnesse,
If any drope of pitee in yow be,
Remembreth yow on passed hevinesse
That ye han felt, and on the adversitee
Of othere folk, and thenketh how that ye
Han felt that Love dorste yow displese;
Or ye han wonne him with to greet an ese.

5

And preyeth for hem that ben in the cas
Of Troilus, as ye may after here,
That love hem bringe in hevene to solas,
And eek for me preyeth to god so dere,
That I have might to shewe, in som manere,
Swich peyne and wo as Loves folk endure,
In Troilus unsely aventure.

6

And biddeth eek for hem that been despeyred
In love, that never nil recovered be,
And eek for hem that falsly been apeyred
Thorugh wikked tonges, be it he or she;
Thus biddeth god, for his benignitee,
To graunte hem sone out of this world to pace,
That been despeyred out of Loves grace.

1

THE double sorrow of Troilus to tell,
Unhappy son of Priam, king of Troy,
And how he fared, when first in love he fell,
From woe to weal, then back again from joy,
Until we part my time I shall employ.
Tisiphone, now help me to endite
These woful lines, that weep e'en as I write!

2

On thee I call, Goddess malevolent,
Thou cruel Fury, grieving ever in pain!
Help me, who am the sorrowful instrument
That lovers use their sorrows to complain;
For truly this is not a saying vain,
A gloomy man should have a gloomy mate,
And faces sad, those who sad tales relate.

3

For I to serve Love's servants ever try,
Yet dare not seek, for my unlikeliness,
The aid of Love, although for love I die,
So far am I from prospect of success.
But yet if this may make the sorrows less
Of any lover, or may his cause avail,
The thanks be his and mine this toilsome tale.

4

But O ye lovers, bathed in bliss always,
If any drops of pity in you be,
Recall the griefs gone by of other days,
And think sometimes upon the adversity
Of other folk, forgetting not that ye
Have felt yourselves Love's power to displease,
Lest ye might win Love's prize with too great ease.

5

And pray for those who suffer in the plight
Of Troilus, as I shall tell you here,
Beseeching Love to bring them to delight;
And pray for me as well, to God so dear,
That I may have the skill to make appear,
In this unhappy tale of Troilus,
How dark may be love's ways and treacherous.

6

And pray for those that dwell in love's despair,
From which they never hope to be restored;
And pray for them who must the burden bear
Of slanderous tongue of lady or of lord;
Pray God that he the faithful may reward,
And to the hopeless grant a quick release
And bring them from unrest to lasting peace.

7

And pray for lovers all who are at ease,
That they may still continue to be so,
And pray that they their ladies still may please
And unto Love a reverent honor show;
For thus I trust my soul in truth shall grow,
Praying for those who Love's commands fulfill,
And setting forth their fates in all good will,

8

With pity and compassion in my heart,
As though I brother were to lovers all.
Now take, I pray, my story in good part;
Henceforth I shall endeavor to recall
What sorrows once on Troilus must fall
In loving Cressida, who first returned
His love, but for new love this old love spurned.

9

Well known the story, how the Greeks so strong
In arms, went with a thousand vessels sailing
To Troy, and there the Trojan city long
Besieged, and after ten years' siege prevailing,
In divers ways, but with one wrath unfailing,
Avenged on Troy the wrong to Helen done
By Paris, when at last great Troy was won.

10

Now so it chanced that in the Trojan town,
There dwelt a lord of rank and high degree,
A priest named Calchas, of such great renown
And in all science such proficiency,
That he knew what the fate of Troy would be,
For at the shrine at Delphi he had heard
Phoebus Apollo's dire foreboding word.

11

When Calchas found his priestly computation
Confirmed the oracle Apollo spake,
That with the Greeks came such a mighty nation,
That in the end the city they would take,
He straight resolved the Trojans to forsake;
For by his divinations well he knew
That Troy was doomed, for all that Troy might do.

12

With stealth to leave the city he prepared,
For cunning plans he knew well to devise;
In secret to the Grecian host he fared,
Where they received him in most courtly wise,
As one of high distinction in their eyes;
For they had hope that by his priestly skill,
He might ward off their future harm and ill.

13

Great cry arose when it was first made known
Through all the town, and everywhere was told,
That Calchas had turned traitor and had flown,
And to the Greeks his faithless honor sold;
And every Trojan, both the young and old,
Declared that Calchas, with his wicked kin,
Deserved to burn alive for this great sin.

14

Now Calchas left behind him when he fled,
Innocent of this so false and wicked deed,
His daughter, who in grief her life now led,
For mortal fear she felt in her great need,
And had no one in Troy her cause to plead,

7

And biddeth eek for hem that been at ese,
That god hem graunte ay good perseveraunce,
And sende hem might hir ladies so to plese,
That it to Love be worship and plesaunce.
For so hope I my soule best avaunce,
To preye for hem that Loves servaunts be,
And wryte hir wo, and live in charitee.

8

And for to have of hem compassioun
As though I were hir owene brother dere.
Now herkeneth with a gode entencioun,
For now wol I gon streight to my matere,
In whiche ye may the double sorwes here
Of Troilus, in loving of Criseyde,
And how that she forsook him er she deyde.

9

It is wel wist, how that the Grekes stronge
In armes with a thousand shippes wente
To Troye-wardes, and the citee longe
Assegeden neigh ten yeer er they stente,
And, in diverse wyse and oon entente,
The ravisshing to wreken of Eleyne,
By Paris doon, they wroughten al hir peyne.

10

Now fil it so, that in the toun ther was
Dwellinge a lord of greet auctoritee,
A gret devyn that cleped was Calkas,
That in science so expert was, that he
Knew wel that Troye sholde destroyed be,
By answere of his god, that highte thus,
Daun Phebus or Apollo Delphicus.

11

So whan this Calkas knew by calculinge,
And eek by answere of this Appollo,
That Grekes sholden swich a peple bringe,
Thorugh which that Troye moste been for-do,
He caste anoon out of the toun to go;
For wel wiste he, by sort, that Troye sholde
Destroyed been, ye, wolde who-so nolde.

12

For which, for to departen softely
Took purpos ful this forknowinge wyse,
And to the Grekes ost ful prively
He stal anoon; and they, in curteys wyse,
Him deden bothe worship and servyse,
In trust that he hath conning hem to rede
In every peril which that is to drede.

13

The noyse up roos, whan it was first aspyed,
Thorugh al the toun, and generally was spoken,
That Calkas traytor fled was, and allyed
With hem of Grece; and casten to ben wroken
On him that falsly hadde his feith so broken;
And seyden, he and al his kin at ones
Ben worthy for to brennen, fel and bones.

14

Now hadde Calkas left, in this meschaunce,
Al unwist of this false and wikked dede,
His doughter, which that was in gret penaunce,
For of hir lyf she was ful sore in drede,
As she that niste what was best to rede;

For bothe a widowe was she, and allone
Of any freend, to whom she dorste hir mone.

15

Criseyde was this lady name a-right;
As to my dome, in al Troyes citee
Nas noon so fair, for passing every wight
So aungellyk was hir natyf beautee,
That lyk a thing immortal semed she,
As doth an hevenish parfit creature,
That doun were sent in scorning of nature.

16

This lady, which that al-day herde at ere
Hir fadres shame, his falsnesse and tresoun,
Wel nigh out of hir wit for sorwe and fere,
In widewes habit large of samit broun,
On knees she fil biforn Ector a-doun;
With pitous voys, and tendrely wepinge,
His mercy bad, hir-selven excusinge.

17

Now was this Ector pitous of nature,
And saw that she was sorwfully bigoon,
And that she was so fair a creature;
Of his goodnesse he gladed hir anoon,
And seyde, "lat your fadres treson goon
Forth with mischaunce, and ye your-self, in
  joye,
Dwelleth with us, whyl you good list, in Troye.

18

And al th'onour that men may doon yow have,
As ferforth as your fader dwelled here,
Ye shul han, and your body shal men save,
As fer as I may ought enquere or here."
And she him thonked with ful humble chere,
And ofter wolde, and it hadde ben his wille,
And took hir leve, and hoom, and held hir stille.

19

And in hir hous she abood with swich meynee
As to hir honour nede was to holde;
And whyl she was dwellinge in that citee,
Kepte hir estat, and bothe of yonge and olde
Ful wel beloved, and wel men of hir tolde.
But whether that she children hadde or noon,
I rede it nought; therfore I lete it goon.

20

The thinges fellen, as they doon of werre,
Bitwixen hem of Troye and Grekes ofte;
For som day boughten they of Troye it derre,
And eft the Grekes founden no thing softe
The folk of Troye; and thus fortune onlofte,
And under eft, gan hem to wheelen bothe
After hir cours, ay whyl they were wrothe.

21

But how this toun com to destrucioun
Ne falleth nought to purpos me to telle;
For it were here a long disgressioun
Fro my matere, and yow to longe dwelle.
But the Troyane gestes, as they felle,
In Omer, or in Dares, or in Dyte,
Who-so that can, may rede hem as they wryte.

22

But though that Grekes hem of Troye shetten,
And hir citee bisegede al a-boute,

For she a widow was without a friend
Who might bear aid and helpful counsel lend.

15

Cressida was the name this lady bore,
And in the Trojan city, to my mind,
Was none so fair, for in her beauty more
Angelical she seemed than human kind,
As though a thing immortal were combined
Of all of heaven's gifts of choicest worth,
And sent down here in scorn of our poor earth.

16

This lady could in no way close her ears
To her own father's evil deed and fame,
And driven near distracted by her fears,
In widow's sober habit dressed, she came
Before great Hector, where she doth proclaim
Her loyalty with tearful voice and eye,
And pleads for grace and treason doth deny.

17

Now Hector was a man of kindly heart,
And when he saw how great was her distress,
And then her beauty likewise played a part,
These words of comfort to her did address:
"About your father's wicked deeds, the less
That's said the better! But you yourself in
  joy
Dwell here with us the while you will in Troy!

18

"And all respect that men owe unto you,
As though your father still were dwelling here,
That shall you have, and all regard that's due
Your person, I assure you without fear."
She humbly thanked him for these words of cheer,
And would have thanked him more had he desired,
And took her leave and to her home retired.

19

And there she dwelt with such a retinue
As fitting was for one of her high station,
And kept good house, as she was wont to do,
Enjoying love and honest reputation
As much as any in the Trojan nation;
But if she children had, I do not know,
I have not heard, and therefore let it go.

20

The fates of war were there exemplified
Between the Trojan and the Grecian forces,
For one day those of Troy were sorely tried,
But next the Greeks, for all their great resources,
Must yield; for Fortune hath uncertain courses,
And now her wheel goes up, and now goes down,
And now she wears a smile and now a frown.

21

But how this town came to its final end
Is not my purpose at this time to tell,
For much too far that lengthy tale would bend
Me from my point, and weary you as well;
But all the Trojan deeds, as there they fell,
Do Homer, Dares and Dictys all narrate,
For future time to read and contemplate.

22

Now though the Greeks the Trojan city hold,
Emprisoned by a siege set all around,

The Trojans still observe their customs old,
Honoring their gods with worshipping profound;
And of their relics one the most renowned
Was called Palladion, to which they prayed
In trust of heaven's protection and of aid.

23

And so it chanced when April heralds Spring,
And clothes the meadows with new pleasant green,
And when fresh flowers, white and red, now bring
Once more their fragrances so pure and clean,
The throngs of Trojan folk might then be seen,
All going forth Palladion's feast to hold,
According to their rites and customs old.

24

And to the temple in their very best,
The common folk came in from left and right,
And to Palladion themselves addressed;
And there came also many a lusty knight,
Many a lady fair and maiden bright,
All well arrayed, from greatest unto least,
In honor of the season and the feast.

25

Among the folk was Cressida that day,
All clothed in black, in widow's proper wise,
Yet as the alphabet begins with A,
So stood her beauty peerless in men's eyes;
And all folk gazed at her in glad surprise,
To see in her how fair the fairest are,
And under inky cloud, so bright a star

26

As was fair Cressida, so brightly shone
Her beauty there beneath her widow's weeds,
And yet she stood apart and all alone,
Behind the throng, which she but little heeds,
And by the door through which the crowd proceeds,
Quite simply dressed, but with the sprightly air
Of one who of herself can take good care.

27

Now Troilus, the leader of a band
Of youthful knights, went with them up and down
In this great temple, where on every hand
They eyed the beauties of the Trojan town;
For Troilus prized neither smile nor frown
Of one particular, and fancy free,
He praised or criticized impartially.

28

And as he roamed about, he kept an eye
On all the members of his retinue,
And if some knight or squire heaved a sigh,
Or longing glances towards some maiden threw,
Then he would smile and make a great ado,
And twit him thus, "God knows she sleepeth blithe,
For all of thee, though thou shalt twist and writhe!

29

"The fashion of you lovers I have heard,
And heard of all your foolish gaits and ways,
And what great toils to win love are incurred,
In keeping it, what dangers and dismays,
For when your prey is lost, come woful days!
What fools ye be, and in your folly blind,
Who can no lesson in each other find."

Hir olde usage wolde they not letten,
As for to honoure hir goddes ful devoute;
But aldermost in honour, out of doute,
They hadde a relik hight Palladion,
That was hir trist a-boven everichon.

23

And so bifel, whan comen was the tyme
Of Aperil, whan clothed is the mede
With newe grene, of lusty Ver the pryme,
And swote smellen floures whyte and rede,
In sondry wyses shewed, as I rede,
The folk of Troye hir observaunces olde,
Palladiones feste for to holde.

24

And to the temple, in al hir beste wyse,
In general, ther wente many a wight,
To herknen of Palladion the servyse;
And namely, so many a lusty knight,
So many a lady fresh and mayden bright,
Ful wel arayed, bothe moste and leste,
Ye, bothe for the seson and the feste.

25

Among thise othere folk was Criseyda,
In widewes habite blak; but nathelees,
Right as our firste lettre is now an A,
In beautee first so stood she, makelees;
Hir godly looking gladede al the prees.
Nas never seyn thing to ben preysed derre,
Nor under cloude blak so bright a sterre

26

As was Criseyde, as folk seyde everichoon
That hir bihelden in hir blake wede;
And yet she stood ful lowe and stille alloon,
Bihinden othere folk, in litel brede,
And neigh the dore, ay under shames drede,
Simple of a-tyr, and debonaire of chere,
With ful assured loking and manere.

27

This Troilus, as he was wont to gyde
His yonge knightes, ladde hem up and doun
In thilke large temple on every syde,
Biholding ay the ladyes of the toun,
Now here, now there, for no devocioun
Hadde he to noon, to reven him his reste,
But gan to preyse and lakken whom him leste.

28

And in his walk ful fast he gan to wayten
If knight or squyer of his companye
Gan for to syke, or lete his eyen bayten
On any woman that he coude aspye;
He wolde smyle, and holden it folye,
And seye him thus, "god wot, she slepeth softe
For love of thee, whan thou tornest ful ofte!

29

"I have herd told, pardieux, of your livinge,
Ye lovers, and your lewede observaunces,
And which a labour folk han in winninge
Of love, and, in the keping, which doutaunces;
And whan your preye is lost, wo and penaunces;
O verrey foles! nyce and blinde be ye;
Ther nis not oon can war by other be."

30

And with that word he gan cast up the browe,
Ascaunces, "lo! is this nought wysly spoken?"
At which the god of love gan loken rowe
Right for despyt, and shoop for to ben wroken;
He kidde anoon his bowe nas not broken;
For sodeynly he hit him at the fulle;
And yet as proud a pekok can he pulle.

31

O blinde world, O blinde entencioun!
How ofte falleth al th'effect contraire
Of surquidrye and foul presumpcioun;
For caught is proud, and caught is debonaire.
This Troilus is clomben on the staire,
And litel weneth that he moot descenden.
But al-day fayleth thing that foles wenden.

32

As proude Bayard ginneth for to skippe
Out of the wey, so priketh him his corn,
Til he a lash have of the longe whippe,
Than thenketh he, "though I praunce al biforn
First in the trays, ful fat and newe shorn,
Yet am I but an hors, and horses lawe
I moot endure, and with my feres drawe."

33

So ferde it by this fers and proude knight;
Though he a worthy kinges sone were,
And wende no-thing hadde had swiche might
Ayens his wil that sholde his herte stere,
Yet with a look his herte wex a-fere,
That he, that now was most in pryde above,
Wex sodeynly most subget un-to love.

34

For-thy ensample taketh of this man,
Ye wyse, proude, and worthy folkes alle,
To scornen Love, which that so sone can
The freedom of your hertes to him thralle;
For ever it was, and ever it shal bifalle,
That Love is he that alle thing may binde;
For may no man for-do the lawe of kinde.

35

That this be sooth, hath preved and doth yit;
For this trowe I ye knowen, alle or some,
Men reden not that folk han gretter wit
Than they that han be most with love y-nome;
And strengest folk ben therwith overcome,
The worthiest and grettest of degree;
This was, and is, and yet men shal it see.

36

And trewelich it sit wel to be so;
For alderwysest han ther-with ben plesed;
And they that han ben aldermost in wo,
With love han been conforted most and esed;
And ofte it hath the cruel herte apesed,
And worthy folk maad worthier of name,
And causeth most to dreden vyce and shame.

37

Now sith it may not goodly be withstonde,
And is a thing so vertuous in kinde,
Refuseth not to Love for to be bonde,
Sin, as him-selven list, he may yow binde.
The yerde is bet that bowen wole and winde

30

And with that word he lifteth up his brows,
As one should say, "Now is not this well spoken!"
And straight these vaunts the God of Love arouse
To wrath, of which he gives a dreadful token,
For now he shows his bow is far from broken,
And suddenly he hits him fair and full,
And all such peacocks' feathers he can pull.

31

O world so blind! O blind all man's contriving!
How often things fall out in ways contrary,
Through vain presumption and conceited striving!
The proud and humble both are caught unwary,
For Troilus, who now mounts up so airy,
Hath little thought of afterward descending;
But folly oft hath unexpected ending.

32

As Bayard, when he feels his oats, grows proud,
And dances and skips out of the travelled way,
Until the lash upon his flank cracks loud,
"Although I prance here first," he then doth say,
"A leader in the trace, and fat and gay,
Yet am I but a horse, and by the law
For horses made, I still must pull and draw."

33

So fared it with this rash and hardy knight,
Who was a king's son of most high degree,
For though he thought that nothing had the might
To curb the heart of such a one as he,
Yet with a look, no longer was he free,
And he who stood but now in pride above
All men, at once was subject most to Love.

34

And now I bid you profit by this man,
Ye worthy folk, and wise and proud withal,
And scorn not Love, he who so lightly can
The freedom of rebellious hearts enthral;
For still the common fate on you must fall,
That love, at nature's very heart indwelling,
Shall bind all things by nature's might compelling.

35

That this is true hath oftentimes been proved,
For well you know, and in wise books may read,
That men of greatest worth have deepest loved,
And none so powerful in word or deed,
But he the greater power of love must heed,
For all his fame or high nobility;
Thus hath it been and ever shall it be!

36

And fitting is it that it should be so,
For wisest men have most with love been pleased,
And those that dwelt in sorrow and in woe,
By love have often been consoled and eased,
And cruel wrath by love hath been appeased;
For love lends lustre to an honorable name,
And saves mankind from wickedness and shame.

37

And since you may not justly love deny,
Then take it as a virtue of the mind,
Delay not long with loving to comply,
For love at last must all constrain and bind;
And better the rod that bends, by force inclined,

Than one that breaks; and therefore pray take heed
To follow love, that best can guide and lead.

38

But now to leave attendant thoughts withal,
And come to Priam's son, of whom I told,
And passing by all things collateral,
My proper tale hereafter I shall hold,
Both of his joy and of his cares so cold,
And all the business of this sad affair,
As I began, I shall to you declare.

39

Within the fane this knight his wit
displayed,
Wandering at will and scattering jokes about,
And idly here, now there, his gazing strayed
On ladies of the town and from without;
And thus his roving eye, by chance no doubt,
Passed o'er the crowd and reached the very spot
Where Cressida stood, and then no further got.

40

And suddenly amazement came unbidden,
As more intent he bent on her his eyes.
"O Jupiter," he thought, "where has she hidden,
Whose beauty, shining bright, revealed now lies?"
And then his heart began to swell and rise,
But sighing soft that not a soul could hear,
He straight again began to laugh and jeer.

41

Among the small, this lady seemed not small,
She had a figure of proportioned kind,
Yet not the slightest mannish or too tall,
For nature had her frame so well designed,
And all her motions showed so well her mind,
That men could tell, in such there would reside
Honor and dignity and woman's pride.

42

And Troilus, the more he saw, the more
Was pleased with all her form and features clear,
But still she kept her eyes upon the floor,
Except she let one scornful glance appear,
As much as "Well, why shouldn't I stand here?"
But soon her eyes again grew soft and bright,
Which seemed to Troilus a goodly sight.

43

From eyes to heart in Troilus there passed
So great a longing, through this vision bred,
That in his deepest soul, fixed firm and fast,
This lady's image love did now imbed;
And he who once had held so high his head,
Must now draw in his horns and hold him low,
As one who knows not where to turn or go.

44

Lo, he who ne'er before had known defeat,
And scorned all who in Love's dominion lie,
He little was aware that love its seat
Hath in the glance and beaming of the eye;
Yet suddenly he felt within him die
All haughtiness of heart, by looking hurt,
And bless'd be love, which can men thus convert!

45

Thus still he stood, where he could well behold
This one in black, who hath his heart enchained,

Than that that brest; and therfor I yow rede
To folwen him that so wel can yow lede.

38

But for to tellen forth in special
As of this kinges sone of which I tolde,
And leten other thing collateral,
Of him thenke I my tale for to holde,
Bothe of his joye, and of his cares colde;
And al his werk, as touching this matere,
For I it gan, I wil ther-to refere.

39

With-inne the temple he wente him forth
pleyinge,
This Troilus, of every wight aboute,
On this lady and now on that lokinge,
Wher-so she were of toune, or of withoute:
And up-on cas bifel, that thorugh a route
His eye perced, and so depe it wente,
Til on Criseyde it smoot, and ther it stente.

40

And sodeynly he wex ther-with astoned,
And gan hire bet biholde in thrifty wyse:
"O mercy, god!" thoughte he, "wher hastow woned,
That art so fair and goodly to devyse?"
Ther-with his herte gan to sprede and ryse,
And softe sighed, lest men mighte him here,
And caughte a-yein his firste pleyinge chere.

41

She nas not with the leste of hir stature,
But alle hir limes so wel answeringe
Weren to womanhode, that creature
Was never lasse mannish in seminge.
And eek the pure wyse of here meninge
Shewede wel, that men might in hir gesse
Honour, estat, and wommanly noblesse.

42

To Troilus right wonder wel with-alle
Gan for to lyke hir mening and hir chere,
Which somdel deynous was, for she leet falle
Hir look a lite a-side, in swich manere,
Ascaunces, "what! may I not stonden here?"
And after that hir loking gan she lighte,
That never thoughte him seen so good a sighte.

43

And of hir look in him ther gan to quiken
So greet desir, and swich affeccioun,
That in his hertes botme gan to stiken
Of hir his fixe and depe impressioun:
And though he erst hadde poured up and doun,
He was tho glad his hornes in to shrinke;
Unnethes wiste he how to loke or winke.

44

Lo, he that leet him-selven so konninge,
And scorned hem that loves peynes dryen,
Was ful unwar that love hadde his dwellinge
With-inne the subtile stremes of hir yën;
That sodeynly him thoughte he felte dyen,
Right with hir look, the spirit in his herte;
Blessed be love, that thus can folk converte!

45

She, this in blak, lykinge to Troilus,
Over alle thing he stood for to biholde;

Ne his desir, ne wherfor he stood thus,
He neither chere made, ne worde tolde;
But from a-fer, his maner for to holde,
On other thing his look som-tyme he caste,
And eft on hir, whyl that servyse laste.

46

And after this, not fulliche al a-whaped,
Out of the temple al esiliche he wente,
Repentinge him that he hadde ever y-japed
Of loves folk, lest fully the descente
Of scorn fille on him-self; but, what he mente,
Lest it were wist on any maner syde,
His wo he gan dissimulen and hyde.

47

Whan he was fro the temple thus departed,
He streyght anoon un-to his paleys torneth,
Right with hir look thurgh-shoten and thurgh-
darted,
Al feyneth he in lust that he sojorneth;
And al his chere and speche also he borneth;
And ay, of loves servants every whyle,
Him-self to wrye, at hem he gan to smyle.

48

And seyde, "lord, so ye live al in lest,
Ye loveres! for the conningest of yow,
That serveth most ententiflich and best,
Him tit as often harm ther-of as prow;
Your hyre is quit ayein, ye, god wot how!
Nought wel for wel, but scorn for good servyse;
In feith, your ordre is ruled in good wyse!

49

In noun-certeyn ben alle your observaunces,
But it a sely fewe poyntes be;
Ne no-thing asketh so grete attendaunces
As doth your lay, and that knowe alle ye;
But that is not the worste, as mote I thee;
But, tolde I yow the worste poynt, I leve,
Al seyde I sooth, ye wolden at me greve!

50

But tak this, that ye loveres ofte eschuwe,
Or elles doon of good entencioun,
Ful ofte thy lady wole it misconstrue,
And deme it harm in hir opinioun;
And yet if she, for other enchesoun,
Be wrooth, than shalt thou han a groyn anoon;
Lord! wel is him that may be of yow oon!"

51

But for al this, whan that he say his tyme,
He held his pees, non other bote him gayned;
For love bigan his fetheres so to lyme,
That wel unnethe un-to his folk he feyned
That othere besye nedes him destrayned;
For wo was him, that what to doon he niste,
But bad his folk to goon wher that hem liste.

52

And whan that he in chaumbre was allone,
He doun up-on his beddes feet him sette,
And first he gan to syke, and eft to grone,
And thoughte ay on hir so, with-outen lette,
That, as he sat and wook, his spirit mette
That he hir saw a temple, and al the wyse
Right of hir loke, and gan it newe avyse.

Yet made no sign, and never a man he told
Why thus in that one station he remained,
But cunningly his purpose he maintained,
And now and then his gaze elsewhere extended,
Then back again, until the service ended.

46

And afterward, not dead but deadly smitten,
Out of the temple quietly he went,
Regretting all his jests and jibes hard bitten
At those in love, and fearing the descent
Of scorn upon himself, should he repent;
But lest this change of heart his friends might know,
With fine pretence he covered up his woe.

47

When from the temple all the folk depart,
Home to the palace he doth take his way,
Shot to the center by Love's flying
dart;
But lest his manner may his state bewray,
He cultivates a bearing light and gay,
And at Love's servants still doth jest and smile,
Driven at last to such deceit and guile.

48

"Good Lord," he says, "you lovers are well paid!
See how the cleverest one among you all,
Whose duty is most faithfully displayed,
Must bear the whips and scorns that on you fall!
You get your pay, if pay one can it call,
Not good for good, but scorn for duty done;
In faith, your order is a goodly one!

49

"How vain are all your worship and your rites,
What small return you get for prayer or plea!
Your creed demands attendance days and nights,
No other asks such assiduity.
From folly love indeed is never free;
If I should tell all love's absurdities,
You'd call them slanders and base calumnies.

50

"But lo, the things you lovers oft eschew,
Or what you do with very best intent,
Your lady will be sure to misconstrue,
And say she knows it was not kindly meant,
Whatever cause she has for discontent—
Or none; she always holds the whip in hand.
How lucky they who join your happy band!"

51

But nevertheless, when he found good occasion,
He held his peace, the best thing he could do!
For Love had clipped his wings, and no evasion
Could help his case. Yet many a tale untrue
He told his friends why he from them withdrew,
Or if they noted his abstracted airs,
He told them just to mind their own affairs.

52

When in his room at last he was alone,
He sat down at the foot-end of his bed,
And first began to sigh and then to moan,
And then, through waking visions in his head
By fancy and imagination bred,
He dreamed he saw her near the temple door,
In form and shape as she had been before.

53

And then he made a mirror of his mind,
In which he saw her features all complete,
And thought perhaps occasion he might find
For such a lady's favor to compete,
And maybe might with her approval meet,
Or win from her at least sufficient grace
To grant to him a humble servant's place.

54

And he surmised the effort were not vain,
That in her goodly service he might spend,
And love for such a one, he dared maintain,
If it were known, all persons would commend,
Especially those whose hopes on love depend—
This was at first his line of argument,
Unwarned by any sign or sad portent.

55

The art of love thus minded to pursue,
He thought he would begin first secretly,
And hide his new endeavor from all view,
That friend nor foe the least of it might see,
But leave him chance for his recovery,
Recalling, too, that love too widely known,
Yields bitter fruit, though sweetest seed be sown.

56

Yet more than this—he gave much careful thought
On what to speak and when he should hold in,
And plans for leading her to love he sought,
And thought a poem straight he would begin
Upon his love, as aid her love to win;
For now his highest hope was set and bent
On ways to love—too late now to repent!

57

The content of this song when it was sung,
As given by my author Lollius,
Except for variation in the tongue,
Was word for word the song of Troilus,
And every word he sang exactly thus,
As I shall say, and as you now may hear,
If you will grant me your attentive ear.

53

Thus gan he make a mirour of his minde,
In which he saugh al hoolly hir figure;
And that he wel coude in his herte finde,
It was to him a right good aventure
To love swich oon, and if he dide his cure
To serven hir, yet mighte he falle in grace,
Or elles, for oon of hir servaunts pace.

54

Imagininge that travaille nor grame
Ne mighte, for so goodly oon, be lorn
As she, ne him for his desir ne shame,
Al were it wist, but in prys and up-born
Of alle lovers wel more than biforn;
Thus argumented he in his ginninge,
Ful unavysed of his wo cominge.

55

Thus took he purpos loves craft to suwe,
And thoughte he wolde werken prively,
First, to hyden his desir in muwe
From every wight y-born, al-outrely,
But he mighte ought recovered be therby;
Remembring him, that love to wyde y-blowe
Yelt bittre fruyt, though swete seed be sowe.

56

And over al this, yet muchel more he thoughte
What for to speke, and what to holden inne,
And what to arten hir to love he soughte,
And on a song anoon-right to biginne,
And gan loude on his sorwe for to winne;
For with good hope he gan fully assente
Criseyde for to love, and nought repente.

57

And of his song nought only the sentence,
As writ myn autour called Lollius,
But pleynly, save our tonges difference,
I dar wel sayn, in al that Troilus
Seyde in his song; lo! every word right thus
As I shal seyn; and who-so list it here,
Lo! next this vers, he may it finden here.

THE SONG OF TROILUS

58

'If love is naught, O God, why feel I so?
If love is aught, what nature then hath he?
If love is good, whence cometh all my woe?
If love is bad, it seems then strange to me,
How every torment and adversity
That comes from love, itself with joy doth link,
For still I thirst the more, the more I drink.

59

"And if I burn but with my own desire,
Whence comes my lamentation and my
  plaint?
Why should I grieve, when I with grief conspire?
And why should I unweary be, yet faint?
O living death! O grief so sweet and quaint!
How can it come that love should in me grow
Except that I consent it shall be so?

60

"If I consent, with wrong I then complain!
Behold how to and fro I merely toss,

58

"If no love is, O god, what fele I so?
And if love is, what thing and whiche is he?
If love be good, from whennes comth my wo?
If it be wikke, a wonder thinketh me,
When every torment and adversitee
That cometh of him, may to me savory thinke;
For ay thurst I, the more that I it drinke.

59

And if that at myn owene lust I brenne,
Fro whennes cometh my wailing and my
  pleynte?
If harme agree me, wher-to pleyne I thenne?
I noot, ne why unwery that I feynte.
O quike deeth, o swete harm so queynte,
How may of thee in me swich quantitee,
But-if that I consente that it be?

60

And if that I consente, I wrongfully
Compleyne, y-wis; thus possed to and fro,

Al sterelees with-inne a boot am I
A-mid the see, by-twixen windes two,
That in contrarie stonden ever-mo.
Allas! what is this wonder maladye?
For hete of cold, for cold of hete, I dye."

61

And to the god of love thus seyde he
With pitous voys, "O lord, now youres is
My spirit, which that oughte youres be.
Yow thanke I, lord, that han me brought to this;
But whether goddesse or womman, y-wis,
She be, I noot, which that ye do me serve;
But as hir man I wole ay live and sterve.

62

Ye stonden in hire eyen mightily,
As in a place un-to your vertu digne;
Wherfore, lord, if my servyse or I
May lyke yow, so beth to me benigne;
For myn estat royal here I resigne
In-to hir hond, and with ful humble chere
Bicome hir man, as to my lady dere."

63

In him ne deyned sparen blood royal
The fyr of love, wher-fro god me blesse,
Ne him forbar in no degree, for al
His vertu or his excellent prowesse;
But held him as his thral lowe in distresse,
And brende him so in sondry wyse ay newe,
That sixty tyme a day he loste his hewe.

64

So muche, day by day, his owene thought,
For lust to hir, gan quiken and encrese,
That every other charge he sette at nought;
For-thy ful ofte, his hote fyr to cese,
To seen hir goodly look he gan to prese;
For ther-by to ben esed wel he wende,
And ay the neer he was, the more he brende.

65

For ay the neer the fyr, the hotter is,
This, trowe I, knoweth al this companye.
But were he fer or neer, I dar seye this,
By night or day, for wysdom or folye,
His herte, which that is his brestes yë,
Was ay on hir, that fairer was to sene
Than ever was Eleyne or Polixene.

66

Eek of the day ther passed nought an houre
That to him-self a thousand tyme he seyde,
"Good goodly, to whom serve I and
laboure,
As I best can, now wolde god, Criseyde,
Ye wolden on me rewe er that I deyde!
My dere herte, allas! myn hele and hewe
And lyf is lost, but ye wole on me rewe."

67

Alle othere dredes weren from him fledde,
Bothe of th'assege and his savacioun;
Ne in him desyr noon othere fownes bredde
But arguments to this conclusioun,
That she on him wolde han compassioun,
And he to be hir man, whyl he may dure;
Lo, here his lyf, and from the deeth his cure!

Within a boat upon the wayless main,
While vexing winds each other ever cross,
And leave me rudderless to stand at loss!
Alas, what sickness strange in me doth lie,
With chill of heat and heat of cold I die!"

61

Then to the God of Love anon he spake
With plaintive voice, "Thou, Lord, who solely hast
Taken my heart, and rightly dost it take,
I thank thee, Lord, for all that now hath passed!
For now that I have found my love at last,
My homage to her shall I ne'er deny,
But as her man, I still shall live and die!

62

"In her esteem thou hold'st a lofty place,
And for thy power such is rightly thine,
And therefore, Lord, turn not from me thy face,
But be thou gracious to me and benign;
For now my royal rank I all resign
Into her hands, and humbly standing here,
Become her man, and she my lady dear!"

63

No favor to his royal rank Love showed,
For from this flame no rank can ever save,
Nor parted from his customary mode,
For all he was a knight so bold and brave,
But held him in distress as thrall and slave,
And burned him in so many ways and new,
That sixty times a day he changed his hue.

64

So much from day to day his quickening thought
Now dwelt on her, and love thereby increase,
That every usual task he set at naught,
Yet often strove to make his burning cease
By sight of her, in hope to find release
From this uneasy burden that he bore—
But ever the nearer, ever he loved the more!

65

For ever the nearer, the hotter is the fire—
And this of course you know as well as I—
But were he farther off or were he nigher,
The eye of the heart that in the breast doth lie,
By day or night, with courage low or high,
Was still on her, with whom, she was so fair,
Helen nor Polyxena could compare.

66

And of the day there passed no single hour,
But to himself a thousand times he said,
"Thou good and gracious one, whom with all
power
I serve, some pity cast upon my head,
For with affliction I am nearly dead!
Dear heart, gone is my joy and gone my life,
Unless your pity end this mortal strife!"

67

All other thoughts from out his mind had fled—
The Greeks and all his warlike reputation;
Desire new no offspring in him bred,
But reasons leading to one consummation,
That she on him would show commiseration,
And as her man, let him through life endure—
O what a life, for death, O what a cure!

68

Not Hector's nor his other brothers' feats
Of arms, in many sharp attacks well proved,
Stirred him to such like charges or retreats;
Yet nevertheless, wherever peril moved,
There was he found, and as he fiercely loved,
So fiercely fought, such wondrous deeds achieving,
They seemed to men almost beyond believing.

69

But not for hatred of the Greeks he raged,
Nor yet to aid the rescue of the town,
But mightily in arms he battle waged
For this sole end, to cast opponents down
And win his lady's favor by renown;
And so his warlike valor shone so splendid,
That fear of death on all the Greeks descended.

70

And love that made him bold, made him to sleep
The less, and still his multiplying sorrow
Such hold upon his heart and soul doth keep,
It stood revealed with each returning morrow
Upon his face, and he was fain to borrow
The name of other ill, lest men might know
It was the fire of love that changed him so.

71

He said he had a fever, was not well,
Whatever shyness makes a man to say,
But to his lady not a word could tell,
Although perhaps she guessed it anyway;
The fact remained, he got but little pay
For all his service, since she gave no thought
To what he had or what he hadn't wrought.

72

And then there fell on him another woe
From which his troubled mind could not be freed,
The fear that she might love another so
That his poor suit she would in no wise heed;
But though the thought made him at heart to bleed,
Yet never a move, for all the world to win,
To make his sorrow known durst he begin.

73

But in his moments of relief from care,
Thus to himself he often would complain,
And say, "O fool, now art thou in the snare,
Who once did jest at love and all its pain!
Now art thou caught! Now go and gnaw thy chain!
Thou once wert wont that love to reprehend
From which thyself thou canst not now defend.

74

"What will now every lover say of thee,
If this be known, when thou art out of sight,
But laugh in scorn and say, 'Lo, there goes he
Who thought he dwelt alone on wisdom's height,
And held all lovers in such low despite!
But now, thank God, his place is in the dance
Of those whom Love delayeth to advance.'

75

"But O, thou woful Troilus, would God
(Since love thou must, by thy sad destiny)
That one who knows thy woe should hold the rod
O'er thee, although no pity in her be!
But cold in love thy lady is to thee,

68

The sharpe shoures felle of armes preve,
That Ector or his othere bretheren diden,
Ne made him only ther-fore ones meve;
And yet was he, wher-so men wente or riden,
Founde oon the best, and lengest tyme abiden
Ther peril was, and dide eek such travayle
In armes, that to thenke it was mervayle.

69

But for non hate he to the Grekes hadde,
Ne also for the rescous of the toun,
Ne made him thus in armes for to madde,
But only, lo, for this conclusioun,
To lyken hir the bet for his renoun;
Fro day to day in armes so he spedde,
That alle the Grekes as the deeth him dredde.

70

And fro this forth tho refte him love his sleep,
And made his mete his foo; and eek his sorwe
Gan multiplye, that, who-so toke keep,
It shewed in his hewe, bothe eve and morwe;
Therfor a title he gan him for to borwe
Of other syknesse, lest of him men wende
That the hote fyr of love him brende.

71

And seyde, he hadde a fever and ferde amis;
But how it was, certayn, can I not seye,
If that his lady understood not this,
Or feyned hir she niste, oon of the tweye;
But wel I rede that, by no maner weye,
Ne semed it [as] that she of him roughte,
Nor of his peyne, or what-so-ever he thoughte.

72

But than fel to this Troylus such wo,
That he was wel neigh wood; for ay his drede
Was this, that she som wight had loved so,
That never of him she wolde have taken hede;
For whiche him thoughte he felte his herte blede.
Ne of his wo ne dorste he not biginne
To tellen it, for al this world to winne.

73

But whanne he hadde a space fro his care,
Thus to him-self ful ofte he gan to pleyne;
He sayde, "O fool, now art thou in the snare,
That whilom japedest at loves peyne;
Now artow hent, now gnaw thyn owene cheyne;
Thou were ay wont eche lovere reprehende
Of thing fro which thou canst thee nat defende.

74

What wole now every lover seyn of thee,
If this be wist, but ever in thyn absence
Laughen in scorn, and seyn, 'lo, ther gooth he,
That is the man of so gret sapience,
That held us loveres leest in reverence!
Now, thonked be god, he may goon in the daunce
Of hem that Love list febly for to avaunce!'

75

But, O thou woful Troilus, god wolde,
Sin thow most loven thurgh thy destinee,
That thow beset were on swich oon that sholde
Knowe al thy wo, al lakkede hir pitee:
But al so cold in love, towardes thee,

Thy lady is, as frost in winter mone,
And thou fordoon, as snow in fyr is sone.

76

God wolde I were aryved in the port
Of deeth, to which my sorwe wil me lede!
A, lord, to me it were a greet comfort;
Then were I quit of languisshing in drede.
For by myn hidde sorwe y-blowe on brede
I shal bi-japed been a thousand tyme
More than that fool of whos folye men ryme.

77

But now help god, and ye, swete, for whom
I pleyne, y-caught, ye, never wight so faste!
O mercy, dere herte, and help me from
The deeth, for I, whyl that my lyf may laste,
More than my-self wol love yow to my laste.
And with som freendly look gladeth me, swete,
Though never more thing ye me bi-hete!"

78

This wordes and ful manye an-other to
He spak, and called ever in his compleynte
Hir name, for to tellen hir his wo,
Til neigh that he in salte teres dreynte.
Al was for nought, she herde nought his pleynte;
And whan that he bithoughte on that folye,
A thousand fold his wo gan multiplye.

79

Bi-wayling in his chambre thus allone,
A freend of his, that called was Pandare,
Com ones in unwar, and herde him grone,
And sey his freend in swich distresse and care:
"Allas!" quod he, "who causeth al this fare?
O mercy, god! what unhap may this mene?
Han now thus sone Grekes maad yow lene?

80

Or hastow som remors of conscience,
And art now falle in som devocioun,
And waylest for thy sinne and thyn offence,
And hast for ferde caught attricioun?
God save hem that bi-seged han our toun,
And so can leye our jolytee on presse,
And bring our lusty folk to holinesse!"

81

These wordes seyde he for the nones alle,
That with swich thing he mighte him angry maken,
And with an angre don his sorwe falle,
As for the tyme, and his corage awaken;
But wel he wiste, as fer as tonges spaken,
Ther nas a man of gretter hardinesse
Than he, ne more desired worthinesse.

82

"What cas," quod Troilus, "or what aventure
Hath gyded thee to see my languisshinge,
That am refus of every creature?
But for the love of god, at my preyinge,
Go henne a-way, for certes, my deyinge
Wol thee disese, and I mot nedes deye;
Ther-for go wey, ther is no more to seye.

83

But if thou wene I be thus syk for drede,
It is not so, and ther-for scorne nought;

As frost is cold beneath the winter moon;
Like snow in flame, so thou must perish soon!

76

"Would God I were arrived safe in the port
Of death, to which my sorrow will me lead!
That were for me the best and last resort,
Then were I of all fear and longing freed!
But if my hidden sorrow men should heed,
I shall be marked and mocked a great deal more
Than any fool for folly famed before!

77

"Now help, O God, and help, my lady sweet,
I am your prisoner caught and none so fast!
Have mercy now, and help me to defeat
This death! And I, until my days are past,
With more than life will love you to the last.
Now with some kindly glance my heart restore,
Although you never grant me favor more!"

78

These words, and more, within his room he spake,
And begged his lady, in his grief profound,
Some recognition of his love to make,
And wept salt tears in which he nearly drowned—
But all in vain, for not a single sound
She heard, not being present to do so,
Which made his griefs a thousandfold to grow.

79

Lamenting in his chamber thus alone,
A friend, whose name was Pandar, happened there,
And coming in by chance, he heard him groan,
And saw his friend in great distress and care.
"What ho, my friend!" he cried, "Why this despair?
What nasty trick does fortune on you serve?
Or have the naughty Greeks got on your nerve?

80

"Or is remorse of conscience cause of this,
And have you turned reluctant and devout,
Repenting all that you have done amiss,
For fear your guilt at last will find you out!
God curse the Greeks who lie in siege about
Our town, and turn our joy into distress
By driving jolly folk to holiness!"

81

He spoke these words, as I them to you say,
That Troilus to anger might be stirred,
And sorrow thus to anger giving way,
To deeds of courage once again be spurred;
For well he knew, and well all men have heard,
There was among the Trojans none more bold,
Or none whom men in higher honor hold.

82

"What chance," said Troilus, "what accident,
Hath led thee here to see my wretched state,
Where I deserted and alone lament?
But for God's sake, don't linger here too late,
But get thee gone, for surely my sad fate
Will be a painful sight, since I must die!
Then go, and let me here untroubled lie.

83

"But if you think that I am sick from fear,
It is not so, and therefore scorn me naught.

There's something else that touches me more near
Than anything the Greeks as yet have wrought,
And brings on me this sad and mortal
thought.
But though I may not now to thee confide it,
Please don't be vexed, 'tis best that I should hide it."

84

Then Pandar, yearning for this hapless youth,
Replied and said, "Alas, what can this be?
Good friend, if faithful love or constant truth
Now is or ever was twixt you and me,
Then do not treat me with such cruelty!
A confidential ear I'll glady lend,
For don't forget that Pandar is your friend.

85

"And I will gladly share with you your pain,
If it turn out I can no comfort bring;
For 'tis a friend's right, please let me explain,
To share in woful as in joyful things.
Through true or false report, I still shall cling
To you in faith forever firm and fast;
So tell your woe, for tell you must at last."

86

Troilus heaved a deep and mournful sigh,
And said to him, "Perhaps it may be best
If with your friendly wish I should comply,
And tear my secret from my aching breast,
Though well I know you can bring me no rest.
But lest you think I have no trust in thee,
I'll tell thee, friend, just how it stands with me.

87

"Lo, Love, against which he who most defendeth
Himself, the more thereby his effort faileth,
This Love so far his rule o'er me extendeth,
That now my heart to death a straight course saileth!
Love-longing over me so deep prevaileth,
That here to die for Love were greater joy
Than be both King of Greece and King of Troy.

88

"In what I've said, methinks to you I've told
More than enough about my cause of woe.
But for the love of God, my care so cold,
Conceal it well! For what you only know,
If further spread, great harms might after grow.
Now go, and live in joy and happiness,
And let me die, abandoned to distress."

89

"To hide this from me was unkindly done,"
Pandar replied, "and it was most unwise,
For maybe you have set your heart on one
Of whom I might with profit you advise."
"Maybe indeed," cried he in great surprise,
"In love you never had the slightest chance,
How can you then another's love advance?"

90

"Now listen, Troilus," replied his friend,
"Perhaps I am a fool, yet it is so,
That folly oft can helpful counsel lend,
Whereby the wise the better way may know.
For I myself have seen a blind man go,
Where he would fall who sees both far and wide;
Sometimes a fool can be the safest guide.

Ther is a-nother thing I take of hede
Wel more than ought the Grekes han y-wrought,
Which cause is of my deeth, for sorwe and
thought.
But though that I now telle thee it ne leste,
Be thou nought wrooth, I hyde it for the beste."

84

This Pandare, that neigh malt for wo and routhe,
Ful often seyde, "allas! what may this be?
Now freend," quod he, "if ever love or trouthe
Hath been, or is, bi-twixen thee and me,
Ne do thou never swiche a crueltee
To hyde fro thy freend so greet a care;
Wostow nought wel that it am I, Pandare?

85

I wole parten with thee al thy peyne,
If it be so I do thee no comfort,
As it is freendes right, sooth for to seyne,
To entreparten wo, as glad desport.
I have, and shal, for trewe or fals report,
In wrong and right y-loved thee al my lyve;
Hyd not thy wo fro me, but telle it blyve."

86

Then gan this sorwful Troilus to syke,
And seyde him thus, "god leve it be my beste
To telle it thee; for, sith it may thee lyke,
Yet wole I telle it, though myn herte breste;
And wel wot I thou mayst do me no reste.
But lest thow deme I truste not to thee,
Now herkne, freend, for thus it stant with me.

87

Love, a-yeins the which who-so defendeth
Him-selven most, him alder-lest avayleth,
With desespeir so sorwfully me offendeth,
That streyght un-to the deeth myn herte sayleth.
Ther-to desyr so brenningly me assaylleth,
That to ben slayn it were a gretter joye
To me than king of Grece been and Troye!

88

Suffiseth this, my fulle freend Pandare,
That I have seyd, for now wostow my wo;
And for the love of god, my colde care
So hyd it wel, I tele it never to mo;
For harmes mighte folwen, mo than two,
If it were wist; but be thou in gladnesse,
And lat me sterve, unknowe, of my distresse."

89

"How hastow thus unkindely and longe
Hid this fro me, thou fool?" quod Pandarus;
"Paraunter thou might after swich oon longe,
That myn avys anoon may helpen us."
"This were a wonder thing," quod Troilus,
"Thou coudest never in love thy-selven wisse;
How devel maystow bringen me to blisse?"

90

"Ye, Troilus, now herke," quod Pandare,
"Though I be nyce; it happeth ofte so,
That oon that exces doth ful yvele fare
By good counseyl can kepe his freend ther-fro.
I have my-self eek seyn a blind man go
Ther-as he fel that coude loke wyde;
A fool may eek a wys man ofte gyde.

91

A whetston is no kerving instrument,
And yet it maketh sharpe kerving-tolis.
And ther thow woost that I have ought miswent,
Eschewe thou that, for swich thing to thee scole is;
Thus ofte wyse men ben war by folis.
If thou do so, thy wit is wel biwared;
By his contrarie is every thing declared.

92

For how might ever sweetnesse have be knowe
To him that never tasted bitternesse?
Ne no man may be inly glad, I trowe,
That never was in sorwe or som distresse;
Eek whyt by blak, by shame eek worthinesse,
Ech set by other, more for other semeth;
As men may see; and so the wyse it demeth.

93

Sith thus of two contraries is a lore,
I, that have in love so ofte assayed
Grevaunces, oughte conne, and wel the more
Counsayllen thee of that thou art amayed.
Eek thee ne oughte nat ben yvel apayed,
Though I desyre with thee for to bere
Thyn hevy charge; it shal the lasse dere.

94

I woot wel that it fareth thus by me
As to thy brother Parys an herdesse,
Which that y-cleped was Oënone,
Wroot in a compleynt of hir hevinesse:
Ye sey the lettre that she wroot, y gesse?"
"Nay, never yet, y-wis," quod Troilus.
"Now," quod Pandare, "herkneth; it was thus.—

95

'Phebus, that first fond art of medicyne,'
Quod she, 'and coude in every wightes care
Remede and reed, by herbes he knew fyne,
Yet to him-self his conninge was ful bare;
For love hadde him so bounden in a snare,
Al for the doughter of the kinge Admete,
That al his craft ne coude his sorwe bete.'—

96

Right so fare I, unhappily for me;
I love oon best, and that me smerteth sore;
And yet, paraunter, can I rede thee,
And not my-self; repreve me no more.
I have no cause, I woot wel, for to sore
As doth an hauk that listeth for to pleye,
But to thyn help yet somwhat can I seye.

97

And of o thing right siker maystow be,
That certayn, for to deyen in the peyne,
That I shal never-mo discoveren thee;
Ne, by my trouthe, I kepe nat restreyne
Thee fro thy love, thogh that it were Eleyne,
That is thy brotheres wyf, if ich it wiste;
Be what she be, and love hir as thee liste.

98

Therfore, as freend fullich in me assure,
And tel me plat what is thyn enchesoun,
And final cause of wo that ye endure;
For douteth no-thing, myn entencioun
Nis nought to yow of reprehencioun

91

"A whetstone is no carving instrument,
And yet it maketh sharp the carving tool;
And if you see my efforts wrongly spent,
Eschew that course and learn out of my school;
For thus the wise may profit by the fool,
And edge his wit, and grow more keen and wary,
For wisdom shines opposed to its contrary.

92

"For how might sweetness ever have been known
To him who never tasted bitterness?
Felicity exists for those alone
Who first have suffered sorrow and distress;
Thus white by black, honor by shame's excess,
More brightly shines by what the other seems,
As all men see and as the wise man deems.

93

"By opposites does one in wisdom grow,
And though I have in love vain effort made,
Then all the better I thereby should know
To guide thee on thy path when thou hast strayed.
Spurn not with scorn, therefore, my proffered aid,
For I desire nothing but to share
Thy grief, and make it easier to bear.

94

"Indeed I am a quite good parallel
To what Oenone once, a shepherdess,
To your own brother Paris said so well,
Writing in grief of heart and heaviness;
You've seen the letter that she wrote, I guess?"
"No, that I haven't," answered Troilus.
"Then listen," Pandar said, "for it goes thus.

95

" 'Excelling in the art of medicine,
Phoebus could rightly find for each disease
A cure, through herbs that he was well versed in;
But to himself his skill could bring no ease,
When love on him did violently seize
For old Admetus' daughter, king of Greece,
Nor all his art could bid his sorrows cease.'

96

"So goes it now, unhappily, with me.
I love in vain, that's why my heart is sore,
And yet it may be I can counsel thee
And not myself. Reprove me now no more;
I have no cause, I know, on high to soar,
As doth a hawk, when he would sport and play,
But still, that doesn't mean I've naught to say.

97

"And one thing you may count a certainty,
I'd rather die in great and mortal pain,
Than breathe a word of what you say to me;
You need not fear that I would you restrain,
Though it were Helen's love you sought to gain,
Your brother's wife; whatever be her name,
For me I'll let you love her all the same.

98

"In my good friendship you can rest secure,
If to me you will only plainly mention
The source of all the grief that you endure;
For do not think I have the least intention
To speak to you by way of reprehension

In this affair; for no one can prevent
A man from loving, ere his love is spent.

99

"That both of these are vices is well seen—
To trust all men or all men disbelieve;
But no vice enters in the golden mean.
'Tis right the word of some men to receive,
And for this cause, it should not thee aggrieve
To take me fully in thy confidence,
For I mean only good and no offence.

100

"Solomon saith, 'Take heed who stands alone,
For if he falls, there's none to help him rise.'
But since thou hast a friend, to him make known
Thy grief, for we can better ways devise
To win thy love in more effective wise
Than lie and weep, like Niobe the queen,
Whose tears remain in marble to be seen.

101

"So now give o'er this lachrymose distress,
Of things that lighten grief now let us speak,
For thus thy time of sorrow may seem less.
Take not delight in woe thy woe to seek,
For fools alone sorrow with sorrow eke,
Who when they fall in some mishap and grief,
Neglect to look elsewhere for their relief.

102

"Men say that 'Misery loves company,'
And this is by no means a saying vain,
But one in which we both ought to agree,
For both of us with right on love complain.
I am so full of sorrow, I maintain
Another single drop could find no place
To sit on me, because there is no space.

103

"I take it thou art not afraid of me,
Lest of thy lady I should thee beguile.
You know yourself I am not fancy free,
But serve a lady dear for this long while;
And since you need fear neither trick nor wile,
And if your trust and confidence I hold,
Tell me as much as I to you have told."

104

Troilus answered not a single word,
And still as death he lay, though could but hear,
Yet afterward he sighed, and then he stirred,
Which showed that he had lent attentive ear,
And then cast up his eyes, so that great fear
Had Pandar, lest in sudden frenzy falling,
His soul might flit away beyond recalling.

105

"Wake up," he cried, with voice both loud and sharp,
"Hast thou in sleep by lethargy been struck?
Or art thou like the ass that hears a harp,
And hears the sound, when men the harp-strings pluck,
But from that sound no melody can suck
His heart to gladden in the very least,
Because he is a dull and brutish beast?"

106

Pandar from further speech with that refrained,
But not a word would Troilus reply,

To speke as now, for no wight may bireve
A man to love, til that him list to leve.

99

And witeth wel, that bothe two ben vyces,
Mistrusten alle, or elles alle leve;
But wel I woot, the mene of it no vyce is,
For for to trusten sum wight is a preve
Of trouthe, and for-thy wolde I fayn remeve
Thy wrong conceyte, and do thee som wight triste,
Thy wo to telle; and tel me, if thee liste.

100

The wyse seyth, 'wo him that is allone,
For, and he falle, he hath noon help to ryse;'
And sith thou hast a felawe, tel thy mone;
For this nis not, certeyn, the nexte wyse
To winnen love, as techen us the wyse,
To walwe and wepe as Niobe the quene,
Whos teres yet in marbel been y-sene.

101

Lat be thy weping and thy drerinesse,
And lat us lissen wo with other speche;
So may thy woful tyme seme lesse.
Delyte not in wo thy wo to seche,
As doon thise foles that hir sorwes eche
With sorwe, whan they han misaventure,
And listen nought to seche hem other cure.

102

Men seyn, 'to wrecche is consolacioun
To have an-other felawe in his peyne;'
That oughte wel ben our opinioun,
For, bothe thou and I, of love we pleyne;
So ful of sorwe am I, soth for to seyne,
That certeynly no more harde grace
May sitte on me, for-why ther is no space.

103

If god wole thou art not agast of me,
Lest I wolde of thy lady thee bigyle,
Thow wost thy-self whom that I love, pardee,
As I best can, gon sithen longe whyle.
And sith thou wost I do it for no wyle,
And sith I am he that thou tristest most,
Tel me sumwhat, sin al my wo thou wost."

104

Yet Troilus, for al this, no word seyde,
But longe he lay as stille as he ded were;
And after this with sykinge he abreyde,
And to Pandarus voys he lente his ere,
And up his eyen caste he, that in fere
Was Pandarus, lest that in frenesye
He sholde falle, or elles sone dye:

105

And cryde "a-wake" ful wonderly and sharpe;
"What? slombrestow as in a lytargye?
Or artow lyk an asse to the harpe,
That hereth soun, whan men the strenges plye,
But in his minde of that no melodye
May sinken, him to glade, for that he
So dul is of his bestialitee?"

106

And with that Pandare of his wordes stente;
But Troilus yet him no word answerde,

For-why to telle nas not his entente
To never no man, for whom that he so ferde.
For it is seyd, "man maketh ofte a yerde
With which the maker is him-self y-beten
In sondry maner," as thise wyse treten,

107

And namely, in his counseyl tellinge
That toucheth love that oughte be secree;
For of him-self it wolde y-nough out-springe,
But-if that it the bet governed be.
Eek som-tyme it is craft to seme flee
Fro thing which in effect men hunte faste;
Al this gan Troilus in his herte caste.

108

But nathelees, whan he had herd him crye
"Awake!" he gan to syke wonder sore,
And seyde, "freend, though that I stille lye,
I am not deef; now pees, and cry no more;
For I have herd thy wordes and thy lore;
But suffre me my mischef to biwayle,
For thy proverbes may me nought avayle.

109

Nor other cure canstow noon for me.
Eek I nil not be cured, I wol deye;
What knowe I of the quene Niobe?
Lat be thyne olde ensaumples, I thee preye."
"No," quod tho Pandarus, "therefore I seye,
Swich is delyt of foles to biwepe
Hir wo, but seken bote they ne kepe.

110

Now knowe I that ther reson in thee fayleth.
But tel me, if I wiste what she were
For whom that thee al this misaunter ayleth,
Dorstestow that I tolde hir in hir ere
Thy wo, sith thou darst not thy-self for fere,
And hir bisoughte on thee to han som routhe?"
"Why, nay," quod he, "by god and by my trouthe!"

111

"What? not as bisily," quod Pandarus,
"As though myn owene lyf lay on this nede?"
"No, certes, brother," quod this Troilus.
"And why?"—"For that thou sholdest never
spede."
"Wostow that wel?"—"Ye, that is out of drede,"
Quod Troilus, "for al that ever ye conne,
She nil to noon swich wrecche as I be wonne."

112

Quod Pandarus, "allas! what may this be,
That thou despeyred art thus causelees?
What? liveth not thy lady? *benedicite!*
How wostow so that thou art gracelees?
Swich yvel is not alwey botelees.
Why, put not impossible thus thy cure,
Sin thing to come is ofte in aventure.

113

I graunte wel that thou endurest wo
As sharp as doth he, Ticius, in helle,
Whos stomak foules tyren ever-mo
That highte volturis, as bokes telle.
But I may not endure that thou dwelle
In so unskilful an opinioun
That of thy wo is no curacioun.

For never once the thought he entertained
To tell for whom he thus must weep and sigh;
For it is said, "Man makes the stick whereby
The maker himself is beaten in his turn";
This bit of wisdom from the wise we learn.

107

And specially he planned few confidences
In love, for love should grow in secrecy,
Since of itself love breaks through all defences,
If one should fail to guard it zealously.
And sometimes it is art to seem to flee
The thing which in effect one is pursuing;
Such thoughts was Troilus in mind reviewing,

108

When thus so loudly he heard Pandar cry
"Wake up!"; then he began to sigh full sore,
And said, "Good friend, although so still I lie,
I am not deaf! Now peace, and say no more,
For I have heard your wisdom and your lore.
Leave me in peace my mishap to bewail,
For all your proverbs may me naught avail.

109

"You cannot find a remedy for me;
Besides I want no cure. I want to die!
And what care I for your queen Niobe?
You've told enough of old wives' tales, say I."
"Well, then," said Pandar, "let me but reply,
That fools alone their woes and griefs enjoy
And shun the remedies they might employ.

110

"It seems to me you must have lost your reason!
But tell me this, if I her name but knew,
In all good faith and with no taint of treason,
Durst I then tell her in her ear for you,
What you yourself have not the nerve to do,
And beg of her some little sign to show?"
"No, no," cried Troilus, "I tell you no!"

111

"What," said Pandar, "not even if I tried
As though it were my own affair and need?"
"Most surely not" sad Troilus replied.
"But why?" "Because you never could
succeed."
"How do you know?" "I know quite well indeed,"
Said Troilus, "when all is said and done,
She will by no such wretch as I be won."

112

"O well," said Pandar, "it may quite well be,
That without cause you are thus in despair.
For look, your lady is not dead, is she?
How can you tell beforehand how you'll fare?
Such evils are not oft beyond repair!
And why must you the worst always suppose,
Although the outcome you nor no one knows?

113

"I grant you well your grief is quite as sore
And sharp as that of Tityos in hell,
Whose heart continually the vultures tore,
According to the stories old books tell;
But still I can't permit you thus to dwell
Under the vain and baseless imputation
You've caught an ill for which there's no salvation.

114

"If you refuse to tell, just for faint heart,
And for your sloth and foolish wilfulness,
And will no slightest hint to me impart,
And why I should not help in your distress
You will not give a reason more or less,
But supine on your bed yourself you stretch—
I ask, what woman could love such a wretch?

115

"And how can she account then for your death,
If you thus die, and she knows nothing why,
Except for fear you breathed your final breath
Because the Greeks about our city lie?
What figure will you cut in the world's eye?
Then she and all will say in scornful tones,
'The wretch is dead, the devil have his bones.'

116

"You may here weep alone and pray and kneel,
But if the one you love of this knows naught,
How can she make return that you can feel—
Unknown, unkissed and lost, who is unsought!
Lo, many a man his love hath dearly bought,
And twenty years opined were not too much
To win the right his lady's lips to touch.

117

"But should he therefore fall in dark despair,
Or as a recreant himself demean,
Or slay himself, because his lady's fair?
No, no, let love be ever fresh and green,
Let each forever cherish his heart's queen,
And think it is love's guerdon but to serve,
A thousandfold more than he doth deserve."

118

To these wise words then Troilus took heed,
And saw the state of mind that he was in,
And thought what Pandar said was true indeed,
That just to die would not his lady win,
But would be both unmanly and a sin,
And useless, too, in every jot and tittle,
Since of his woe she knew still less than little.

119

At this sad thought, he sighed both loud and long,
And said, "Alas, what's best for me to do?"
And Pandar answered him, "You can't go wrong
In telling me your story whole and true;
I give my word, within a day or two,
I'll bring you news, the best you ever got,
Or have me drawn and quartered on the spot."

120

"That's what you say," cried Troilus, "alas,
But saying so, that will not make it so!
For my affairs have come to such a pass
That I perceive that Fortune is my foe,
And all who up and down this wide world go,
Must take whatever Fortune shall decree,
For as she will, she plays with bound and free."

121

"So then," said Pandar, "Fortune is to blame
For your own feelings! Now at last I see!
But don't you know that Fortune is the same
To all alive, in varying degree?
But of one comfort you have certainty,

114

But ones niltow, for thy coward herte,
And for thyn ire and folish wilfulnesse,
For wantrust, tellen of thy sorwes smerte,
Ne to thyn owene help do bisinesse
As muche as speke a resoun more or lesse,
But lyest as he that list of no-thing recche.
What womman coude love swich a wrecche?

115

What may she demen other of thy deeth,
If thou thus deye, and she not why it is,
But that for fere is yolden up thy breeth,
For Grekes han biseged us, y-wis?
Lord, which a thank than shaltow han of this!
Thus wol she seyn, and al the toun at ones,
'The wrecche is deed, the devel have his bones!'

116

Thou mayst allone here wepe and crye and knele;
But, love a woman that she woot it nought,
And she wol quyte that thou shalt not fele;
Unknowe, unkist, and lost that is unsought.
What! many a man hath love ful dere y-bought
Twenty winter that his lady wiste,
That never yet his lady mouth he kiste.

117

What? shulde he therfor fallen in despeyr,
Or be recreaunt for his owene tene,
Or sleen him-self, al be his lady fayr?
Nay, nay, but ever in oon be fresh and grene
To serve and love his dere hertes quene,
And thenke it is a guerdoun hir to serve
A thousand-fold more than he can deserve."

118

And of that word took hede Troilus,
And thoughte anoon what folye he was inne,
And how that sooth him seyde Pandarus,
That for to sleen him-self mighte he not winne,
But bothe doon unmanhod and a sinne,
And of his deeth his lady nought to wyte;
For of his wo, god woot, she knew ful lyte.

119

And with that thought he gan ful sore syke,
And seyde, "allas! what is me best to do?"
To whom Pandare answerde, "if thee lyke,
The best is that thou telle me thy wo;
And have my trouthe, but thou it finde so,
I be thy bote, or that it be ful longe,
To peces do me drawe, and sithen honge!"

120

"Ye, so thou seyst," quod Troilus tho, "allas!
But, god wot, it is not the rather so;
Ful hard were it to helpen in this cas,
For wel finde I that Fortune is my fo,
Ne alle the men that ryden conne or go
May of hir cruel wheel the harm withstonde;
For, as hir list, she pleyeth with free and bonde."

121

Quod Pandarus, "than blamestow Fortune
For thou art wrooth, ye, now at erst I see;
Wostow nat wel that Fortune is commune
To every maner wight in som degree?
And yet thou hast this comfort, lo, pardee!

That, as hir joyes moten over-goon,
So mote hir sorwes passen everichoon.

122

For if hir wheel stinte any-thing to torne,
Than cessed she Fortune anoon to be:
Now, sith hir wheel by no wey may sojorne,
What wostow if hir mutabilitee
Right as thy-selven list, wol doon by thee,
Or that she be not fer fro thyn helpinge?
Paraunter, thou hast cause for to singe!

123

And therfor wostow what I thee beseche?
Lat be thy wo and turning to the grounde;
For who-so list have helping of his leche,
To him bihoveth first unwrye his wounde.
To Cerberus in helle ay be I bounde,
Were it for my suster, al thy sorwe,
By my wil, she sholde al be thyn to-morwe.

124

Loke up, I seye, and tel me what she is
Anoon, that I may goon aboute thy nede;
Knowe ich hir ought? for my love, tel me this;
Than wolde I hopen rather for to spede."
Tho gan the veyne of Troilus to blede,
For he was hit, and wex al reed for shame;
"A ha!" quod Pandare, "here biginneth game!"

125

And with that word he gan him for to shake,
And seyde, "theef, thou shalt hir name telle."
But tho gan sely Troilus for to quake
As though men sholde han lad him in-to helle,
And seyde, "allas! of al my wo the welle,
Than is my swete fo called Criseyde!"
And wel nigh with the word for fere he deyde.

126

And whan that Pandare herde hir name nevene,
Lord, he was glad, and seyde, "freend so dere,
Now fare a-right, for Joves name in hevene,
Love hath biset thee wel, be of good chere;
For of good name and wysdom and manere
She hath y-nough, and eek of gentilesse;
If she be fayr, thow wost thy-self, I gesse.

127

Ne I never saw a more bountevous
Of hir estat, ne a gladder, ne of speche
A freendlier, ne a more gracious
For to do wel, ne lasse hadde nede to seche
What for to doon; and al this bet to eche,
In honour, to as fer as she may strecche,
A kinges herte semeth by hires a wrecche.

128

And for-thy loke of good comfort thou be;
For certeinly, the firste poynt is this
Of noble corage and wel ordeynè,
A man to have pees with him-self, y-wis;
So oughtest thou, for nought but good it is
To loven wel, and in a worthy place;
Thee oughte not to clepe it hap, but grace.

129

And also thenk, and ther-with glade thee,
That sith thy lady vertuous is al,
So folweth it that ther is some pitee

For as all joys on earth are short and brief,
So time will bring for sorrow its relief.

122

"Because if Fortune's wheel should cease to turn,
Then Fortune she at once no more would be;
And since in no fixed place she may sojourn,
It may chance, by mere mutability,
Such good luck she hath now in store for thee,
And such a boon to thee she soon will bring,
That for the joy of it, thy heart shall sing.

123

"And therefore do you know what I advise?
Look up! Don't keep your eyes upon the ground!
The sick must first unto the doctor's eyes
Reveal in what respect he is unsound.
To Cerberus in hell may I be bound,
If my own sister were thy cause of sorrow,
For all of me, she should be thine tomorrow.

124

"If I had something clear on which to go,
I'd surely find the remedy you need.
At least say this, your lady do I know?
For if I do, the fight is on indeed!"
Then Troilus at heart began to bleed,
For he was hit, and blushed with rosy shame;
"Aha!" cried Pandar, "now I smell the game!"

125

And then his victim he began to shake,
And said, "You thief, her name you've got to tell!"
Then hapless Troilus, with many a quake,
As though his soul were being led to hell,
Murmured, "Of all my woe the source and well
Is Cressida—and now you know her name!"
And with these words, he almost died for shame.

126

When Pandar heard who was his lady love,
Then he was glad and said, "My friend so dear,
Now all goes well, for by great Jove above,
You're lucky in your choice. Be of good cheer!
Of fame, wisdom and virtue never fear
She hath enough, and also gentle ways;
Her beauty you know, and I need not to praise.

127

"She hath besides a free and open hand
With all she owns, is affable in speech,
And how to do things well doth understand,
Yet never doth in doing overreach,
But gracious are her manners all and each.
Such truth and honor in her heart abide,
A king's heart seems a poor thing there beside.

128

"Good reason now you have to be content,
For half the battle is already gained
When courage dull inaction doth prevent,
And peace of heart within has been attained;
For love with every good is deep ingrained
When it is set upon a worthy place,
It is no evil then, but heaven's grace.

129

"You have this reason to be glad besides,
That since your lady hath these virtues all,
Then pity, also, in her heart resides,

Among these other things in general.
But take thou heed, whatever may befall,
That thou dishonor not an honest name,
For virtue never lends itself to shame.

130

"However, let us not be too austere,
For thou hast set thy heart in right good place;
But truth to tell, I always had a fear
That Love to you would never show his face.
And know you why? Because such vile disgrace
You heaped on Love, and Love did'st even call
'Saint Idiot, the lord of lovers all.'

131

"How often did you crack a foolish jest,
And say, 'Love's servants truly I disown,
For all are fools and God's apes at the best,
And some will munch their dreary food alone,
Lying abed with many a sigh and moan?'
White fever, you said, attacks the burning lover,
And often prayed such never might recover;

132

"And some, you said, lie shivering with the cold,
And on them turned your mockery full oft,
And laughed at those who fancied stories told
Of sleepless nights when they were resting soft.
With boasts, you said, they held their heads
aloft,
But for all that, must bend low at the last,
And many such like jests on love you passed.

133

"And you maintained that for the greater part,
All lovers loved but in a general way,
Because they thought it was the safer art
A dozen loves at one time to essay.
Now I might make such jests on you today,
But won't, because I'm quite convinced in mind
That you'll not be a lover of that kind.

134

"Now beat thy breast, and pray to God above,
'Thy mercy, Lord! For now I do repent
Of all I've said, and deeply now I love!'
Pray thus, that thus the God may now relent!"
"Ah, Lord," cried Troilus, "hear my lament,
Who pray to thee my jesting to forgive,
As I shall jest no more the while I live!"

135

"Well prayed," quoth Pandar. "Now it can be
said
Thou hast the God of Love in all appeased,
And since thou many a bitter tear hast shed,
And spoken things wherewith thy God is pleased,
I feel quite sure thou shalt in all be eased,
And she from whom arises all thy woe,
Through her thou shalt still further comfort know

136

"For that same ground that bears the useless weed,
Bears also wholesome herbs, and qute as oft;
And where the rough and stinging nettles breed,
Waxes the rose, so sweet and smooth and soft;
And next the valley, lifts the hill aloft,
And after night, then comes the glad tomorrow,
And so is joy the after end of sorrow.

Amonges alle thise othere in general;
And for-thy see that thou, in special,
Requere nought that is ayein hir name;
For vertue streccheth not him-self to shame.

130

But wel is me that ever I was born,
That thou biset art in so good a place;
For by my trouthe, in love I dorste have sworn,
Thee sholde never han tid thus fayr a grace;
And wostow why? for thou were wont to chace
At love in scorn, and for despyt him calle
'Seynt Idiot, lord of thise foles alle.'

131

How often hastow maad thy nyce japes,
And seyd, that loves servants everichone
Of nycetee ben verray goddes apes;
And some wolde monche hir mete alone,
Ligging a-bedde, and make hem for to grone;
And som, thou seydest, hadde a blaunche fevere,
And preydest god he sholde never kevere!

132

And some of hem toke on hem, for the colde,
More than y-nough, so seydestow ful ofte;
And some han feyned ofte tyme, and tolde
How that they wake, whan they slepen softe;
And thus they wolde han brought hem-self
a-lofte,
And nathelees were under at the laste;
Thus seydestow, and japedest ful faste.

133

Yet seydestow, that, for the more part,
These loveres wolden speke in general,
And thoughten that it was a siker art,
For fayling, for to assayen over-al.
Now may I jape of thee, if that I shal!
But nathelees, though that I sholde deye,
That thou art noon of tho, that dorste I seye.

134

Now beet thy brest, and sey to god of love,
'Thy grace, lord! for now I me repente
If I mis spak, for now my-self I love':
Thus sey with al thyn herte in good entente."
Quod Troilus, "a! lord! I me consente,
And pray to thee my japes thou foryive,
And I shal never-more whyl I live."

135

"Thow seyst wel," quod Pandare, "and now I
hope
That thou the goddes wratthe hast al apesed;
And sithen thou hast wepen many a drope,
And seyd swich thing wher-with thy god is plesed,
Now wolde never god but thou were esed;
And think wel, she of whom rist al thy wo
Here-after may thy comfort been al-so.

136

For thilke ground, that bereth the wedes wikke,
Bereth eek thise holsom herbes, as ful ofte
Next the foule netle, rough and thikke,
The rose waxeth swote and smothe and softe;
And next the valey is the hil a-lofte;
And next the derke night the glade morwe;
And also joye is next the fyn of sorwe.

137

Now loke that atempre be thy brydel,
And, for the beste, ay suffre to the tyde,
Or elles al our labour is on ydel;
He hasteth wel that wysly can abyde;
Be diligent, and trewe, and ay wel hyde.
Be lusty, free, persevere in thy servyse,
And al is wel, if thou werke in this wyse.

138

But he that parted is in every place
Is no-wher hool, as writen clerkes wyse;
What wonder is, though swich oon have no grace?
Eek wostow how it fareth of som servyse?
As plaunte a tre or herbe, in sondry wyse,
And on the morwe pulle it up as blyve,
No wonder is, though it may never thryve.

139

And sith that god of love hath thee bistowed
In place digne un-to thy worthinesse,
Stond faste, for to good port hastow rowed;
And of thy-self, for any hevinesse,
Hope alwey wel; for, but-if drerinesse
Or over-haste our bothe labour shende,
I hope of this to maken a good ende.

140

And wostow why I am the lasse afered
Of this matere with my nece trete?
For this have I herd seyd of wyse y-lered,
'Was never man ne woman yet bigete
That was unapt to suffren loves hete
Celestial, or elles love of kinde;'
For-thy som grace I hope in hir to finde.

141

And for to speke of hir in special,
Hir beautee to bithinken and hir youthe,
It sit hir nought to be celestial
As yet, though that hir liste bothe and couthe;
But trewely, it sete hir wel right nouthe
A worthy knight to loven and cheryce,
And but she do, I holde it for a vyce.

142

Wherfore I am, and wol be, ay redy
To peyne me to do yow this servyse;
For bothe yow to plese thus hope I
Her-afterward; for ye beth bothe wyse,
And conne it counseyl kepe in swich a wyse,
That no man shal the wyser of it be;
And so we may be gladed alle three.

143

And, by my trouthe, I have right now of thee
A good conceyt in my wit, as I gesse,
And what it is, I wol now that thou see.
I thenke, sith that love, of his goodnesse,
Hath thee converted out of wikkednesse,
That thou shalt be the beste post, I leve,
Of al his lay, and most his foos to-greve.

144

Ensample why, see now these wyse clerkes,
That erren aldermost a-yein a lawe,
And ben converted from hir wikked werkes
Thorugh grace of god, that list hem to him drawe,
Than arn they folk that han most god in awe,

137

"But hold with nicely tempered hand thy bridle,
And think that all things have their proper tide,
Or else thy labor is but vain and idle;
He makes most speed who can his time abide,
Who planneth well before he doth decide;
Be strong and free, and if you persevere,
All will be well, as I have made it clear.

138

"A man divided in a dozen places
Is nowhere whole, philosophy doth show,
For his own labor he himself effaces.
Do you know how this is? Why, just as though
You plant a tree or herb where it should grow,
And on the morrow pull it up alive—
No wonder if it thus should never thrive.

139

"And since the God of Love hath love bestowed
On thee full worthy of thy worthiness,
Stand fast, for to a good port hast thou rowed.
Let not thy hope and courage e'er grow less,
For only some great lack or some excess,
Or overhaste, can make our labor vain,
Whereby our happy end we shall attain.

140

"And know you why I am so well inclined
In this affair with my dear niece to treat?
Because 'tis sad, with truth, of all mankind,
That never one dwelt on this earthly seat
But he must feel in some degree the heat
Of love, or earthly or celestial,
For love is planted in us one and all.

141

"As for this lady we have now in mind,
By reason of her beauty and her youth,
Celestial love is not so well designed,
Although she could love in that way forsooth;
But now it seems to me, to tell the truth,
She ought to love some good and worthy knight,
If she would do what's suitable and right.

142

"Therefore I am and will be ready still
To help you in whatever way I can,
For what I do hereafter surely will
Give pleasure to you both; and all our plan
We can so closely hide that never a man
Shall be the wiser in the least degree,
And so in fact, we shall be glad all three.

143

"And now there comes to me a right good thougl
And that it's good I'm sure you will confess
When all my meaning you have fully caught.
I think that since Love hath, in due process,
Converted thee from all thy wickedness,
That thou shalt be a pillar and a post
In his support, and grieve his foes the most.

144

"To prove my point, recall how those great cler
Who most have erred against a certain law,
And are converted from their wicked works
By God's good grace that doth them to him dra
Are just the ones who hold God most in awe,

And grow into his most believing band,
For they know best all error to withstand."

145

To all this preaching Troilus assented,
Accepting likewise Pandar's proffered aid;
Then waned the woes by which he'd been
tormented,
But hotter waxed his love; and then he made
Reply, with joyful heart, but manner staid,
"Now, blessed Venus, let me never die,
Till all thy words, O Pandar, fructify!

146

"But friend, how shall my pain grow less acute
Till this is done? And also tell me first,
What thou wilt say of me and of my suit,
For I can look for nothing but the worst,
And all my hopes will like a bubble burst,
Since coming from her uncle, much I fear
That she to nothing of the sort will hear."

147

"Now, then," said Pandar, "what the need to worry
For fear the man might fall from out the moon!
Good Lord, why all this foolish fuss and hurry!
our time will come, not right away, but soon.
beg, for God's sake, grant me this one boon—
Let me alone! I know what's best to do!"
"All right," he said, "I leave it all to you.

148

"But listen, Pandar, one word ere you go!
Don't think that towards my lady I desire
The slightest impropriety to show,
Or to her harm in any way conspire;
For I would rather bear my sorrows dire
Than have her think it was not understood,
That all I mean is meant for her own good."

149

And I your backer," Pandar laughed, "O fie!
No need to tell me this, for all say so!
only wish that she were standing nigh
nd hearing all you say. But I must go.
dieu, be glad and see how things will grow!
this affair, I'll take the strain and stress,
nd yours be all the joy of my success."

150

en Troilus began to swell and boast,
friendly arm o'er Pandar's shoulders cast;
fig," he cried, "for all the Grecian host,
God will help us Trojans to the last!
d here I swear, that ere my days are past,
ny a Greek through me shall suffer sore—
such like boasting henceforth I deplore!

151

ow, Pandar, more than this I cannot say—
hou my guide, my confidant, my all,
life and death both in thy hands I lay!
now!" "Yes, not in vain on me you call."
y God reward you, let what may befall,
ll my fate on you doth now depend,
ake me live or meet my fatal end."

152

Pandar, eager now his friend to serve,
m in few and hasty words replied:

And strengest-feythed been, I understonde,
And conne an errour alder-best withstonde."

145

Whan Troilus had herd Pandare assented
To been his help in loving of Criseyde,
Wex of his wo, as who seyth,
untormented,
But hotter wex his love, and thus he seyde,
With sobre chere, al-though his herte pleyde,
"Now blisful Venus helpe, er that I sterve,
Of thee, Pandare, I may som thank deserve.

146

But, dere frend, how shal myn wo ben lesse
Til this be doon? and goode, eek tel me this,
How wiltow seyn of me and my destresse?
Lest she be wrooth, this drede I most, y-wis,
Or nil not here or trowen how it is.
Al this drede I, and eek for the manere
Of thee, hir eem, she nil no swich thing here."

147

Quod Pandarus, "thou hast a ful gret care
Lest that the cherl may falle out of the mone!
Why, lord! I hate of thee thy nyce fare!
Why, entremete of that thou hast to done!
For goddes love, I bidde thee a bone,
So lat me alone, and it shal be thy beste."—
"Why, freend," quod he, "now do right as thee leste.

148

But herke, Pandare, o word, for I nolde
That thou in me wendest so greet folye,
That to my lady I desiren sholde
That toucheth harm or any vilenye;
For dredelees, me were lever dye
Than she of me ought elles understode
But that, that mighte sounen in-to gode."

149

Tho lough this Pandare, and anoon answerde,
"And I thy borw? fy! no wight dooth but so;
I roughte nought though that she stode and herde
How that thou seyst; but fare-wel, I wol go.
A-dieu! be glad! god spede us bothe two!
Yif me this labour and this besinesse,
And of my speed be thyn al that swetnesse."

150

Tho Troilus gan doun on knees to falle,
And Pandare in his armes hente faste,
And seyde, "now, fy on the Grekes alle!
Yet, pardee, god shal helpe us at the laste;
And dredelees, if that my lyf may laste,
And god to-forn, lo, som of hem shal smerte;
And yet me athinketh that this avaunt me asterte!

151

Now, Pandare, I can no more seye,
But thou wys, thou wost, thou mayst, thou art al!
My lyf, my deeth, hool in thyn honde I leye;
Help now," quod he. "Yis, by my trouthe, I shal."
"God yelde thee, freend, and this in special,"
Quod Troilus, "that thou me recomaunde
To hir that to the deeth me may comaunde."

152

This Pandarus tho, desirous to serve
His fulle freend, than seyde in this manere,

"Far-wel, and thenk I wol thy thank deserve;
Have here my trouthe, and that thou shalt wel
here."—
And wente his wey, thenking on this matere,
And how he best mighte hir beseche of grace,
And finde a tyme ther-to, and a place.

153

For every wight that hath an hous to founde
Ne renneth nought the werk for to biginne
With rakel hond, but he wol byde a stounde,
And sende his hertes lyne out fro with-inne
Alderfirst his purpos for to winne.
Al this Pandare in his herte thoughte,
And caste his werk ful wysly, or he wroughte.

154

But Troilus lay tho no lenger doun,
But up anoon up-on his stede bay,
And in the feld he pleyde tho leoun;
Wo was that Greek that with him mette that day.
And in the toun his maner tho forth ay
So goodly was, and gat him so in grace,
That ech him lovede that loked on his face.

155

For he bicom the frendlyeste wight,
The gentileste, and eek the moste free,
The thriftieste and oon the beste knight,
That in his tyme was, or mighte be.
Dede were his japes and his crueltee,
His heighe port and his manere estraunge,
And ech of tho gan for a vertu chaunge.

156

Now lat us stinte of Troilus a stounde,
That fareth lyk a man that hurt is sore,
And is somdel of akinge of his wounde
Y-lissed wel, but heled no del
more;
And, as an esy pacient, the lore
Abit of him that gooth aboute his cure;
And thus he dryveth forth his aventure.

"Farewell, thy thanks I doubt not to deserve!
Have here my pledge, thou shalt be
satisfied!"
Then forth upon his thoughtful way he hied,
Considering how he might find time and place
Vicariously to win this lady's grace.

153

For any man who hath a house to found,
Runs not at once the labor to begin
With reckless hand, but first will look around,
And send his heart's line outward from within,
To see how best of all his end to win.
So Pandar in his contemplation thought,
And planned his work full wisely ere he wrought.

154

And Troilus, his sloth aside now laid,
Leaping upon his prancing gallant bay,
Upon the field the very lion played.
Woe to the Greek who met with him that day!
And in the town he made such fine display
Of goodly conduct, that in every place
All loved him who but looked upon his face.

155

For he became, as though but over night,
Most friendly, gentle, generous and free,
Most provident—in short the finest knight
That in his time or any time might be;
Gone now his jests, his boastful vanity,
His lofty ways and all his manner strange,
And all his vices into virtues change.

156

Now let us cease of Troilus to speak,
Who feels like one who has been wounded sore,
And from his wound still aching and still weak,
But grown more calm, though healed not thus the
more,
Submits in patience to the doctor's lore,
Who skilfully his ill investigates—
So Troilus the final end awaits.

HERE ENDETH THE FIRST BOOK

BOOK II

HERE BEGINNETH THE PROEM TO THE SECOND BOOK

1

Out of these blake wawes for to sayle,
O wind, O wind, the weder ginneth clere;
For in this see the boot hath swich travayle,
Of my conning that unnethe I it stere:
This see clepe I the tempestous matere
Of desespeyr that Troilus was inne:
But now of hope the calendes biginne.

2

O lady myn, that called art Cleo,
Thou be my speed fro this forth, and my
muse,
To ryme wel this book, til I have do;
Me nedeth here noon other art to use.
For-why to every lovere I me excuse,

1

Out of these billows black at last we sail,
O Wind, and now the breaking tempests clear!
In this wild sea my skill doth scarce avail
To save the boat that I attempt to steer,
This troubled sea, tempestuous and drear,
Of black despair that Troilus was in;
But lo, the kalends now of hope begin.

2

O lady mine, O Clio, glorious one,
Be thou henceforth my help, be thou my
muse,
To rhyme this book until the whole is done!
All other aid than thine I here refuse,
And therefore lovers all must me excuse,

If pure inventions I do not endite,
But only Latin into English write.

3

Then give me neither thank nor give me blame
For all this work, for meekly I deny
The fault, if anywhere my tale be lame,
For what my author sayeth, so say I.
And if unskilled in love my pen I ply,
No wonder that, for who would dare assert
A blind man should in colors be expert?

4

Remember in the forms of speech comes change
Within a thousand years, and words that then
Were well esteemed, seem foolish now and strange;
And yet they spake them so, time and again,
And thrived in love as well as any men;
And so to win their loves in sundry days,
In sundry lands there are as many ways.

5

If then the situation should arise,
That any captious lover in this place,
Who hears this tale, or reads it with his eyes,
How Troilus sued for his lady's grace,
Should think "I'd do not so in such a case,"
Or wonder at his words or at his acts,
He may—for me, I merely state the facts.

6

Travellers to Rome, as on their way they wend,
Hold not one path and not the self-same style;
And in some lands the game would quickly end,
If men made love as we do all the while,
As thus—so openly with glance or smile,
And visits, forms, and pretty speeches, too;
But when in Rome, do as the Romans do.

7

I doubt if in this land you could find three
Who'd act the same, if they in love should fall;
For what I like, to you may hateful be,
And yet we reach the same end, one and all,
Though some may carve on trees, some on a wall,
As it may chance.—But now where I began,
My story I must hasten as I can.

That of no sentement I this endyte,
But out of Latin in my tonge it wryte.

3

Wherfore I nil have neither thank ne blame
Of al this werk, but pray yow mekely,
Disblameth me, if any word be lame,
For as myn auctor seyde, so seye I.
Eek though I speke of love unfelingly,
No wonder is, for it no-thing of newe is;
A blind man can nat juggen wel in hewis.

4

Ye knowe eek, that in forme of speche is chaunge
With-inne a thousand yeer, and wordes tho
That hadden prys, now wonder nyce and straunge
Us thinketh hem; and yet they spake hem so,
And spedde as wel in love as men now do;
Eek for to winne love in sondry ages,
In sondry londes, sondry been usages.

5

And for-thy if it happe in any wyse,
That here be any lovere in this place
That herkeneth, as the story wol devyse,
How Troilus com to his lady grace,
And thenketh, so nolde I nat love purchace,
Or wondreth on his speche and his doinge,
I noot; but it is me no wonderinge;

6

For every wight which that to Rome went,
Halt nat o path, or alwey o manere;
Eek in som lond were al the gamen shent,
If that they ferde in love as men don here,
As thus, in open doing or in chere,
In visitinge, in forme, or seyde hir sawes;
For-thy men seyn, ech contree hath his lawes.

7

Eek scarsly been ther in this place three
That han in love seyd lyk and doon in al;
For to thy purpos this may lyken thee,
And thee right nought, yet al is seyd or shal;
Eek som men grave in tree, som in stoon wal,
As it bitit; but sin I have begonne,
Myn auctor shal I folwen, if I conne.

HERE ENDETH THE PROEM TO THE SECOND BOOK

HERE BEGINNETH THE SECOND BOOK

8

In May, mother of months, when all is gay,
When flowers, blue and white and red, now grow
Again, as winter's deadly hold gives way,
When balmy breezes o'er the meadows blow
And Phoebus with his brightest beams doth glow
In the white Bull, and of this month the third,
I now shall sing what great events occurred.

9

Wise Pandar then, for all his helpful speech,
Now felt, himself, the barb of love so keen,
That though he ne'er so well could others teach,
For thwarted love he turned a sickly green;
And all for nothing but this lover's spleen,
To bed he straightway went, and no time lost,
Where all the weary night he turned and tossed.

8

In May, that moder is of monthes glade,
That fresshe floures, blewe, and whyte, and rede,
Ben quike agayn, that winter dede made,
And ful of bawme is fletinge every mede;
Whan Phebus doth his brighte bemes sprede
Right in the whyte Bole, it so bitidde
As I shal singe, on Mayes day the thridde,

9

That Pandarus, for al his wyse speche,
Felte eek his part of loves shottes kene,
That, coude he never so wel of loving preche,
It made his hewe a-day ful ofte grene;
So shoop it, that him fil that day a tene
In love, for which in wo to bedde he wente,
And made, er it was day, ful many a wente.

10

The swalwe Proignè, with a sorwful lay,
Whan morwe com, gan make hir weymentinge,
Why she forshapen was; and ever lay
Pandare a-bedde, half in a slomeringe,
Til she so neigh him made hir chiteringe
How Tereus gan forth hir suster take,
That with the noyse of hir he gan a-wake;

11

And gan to calle, and dresse him up to ryse,
Remembringe him his erand was to done
From Troilus, and eek his greet empryse;
And caste and knew in good plyt was the mone
To doon viage, and took his wey ful sone
Un-to his neces paleys ther bi-syde;
Now Janus, god of entree, thou him gyde!

12

Whan he was come un-to his neces place,
"Wher is my lady?" to hir folk seyde he;
And they him tolde; and he forth in gan pace,
And fond, two othere ladyes sete and she
With-inne a paved parlour; and they three
Herden a mayden reden hem the geste
Of the Sege of Thebes, whyl hem leste.

13

Quod Pandarus, "ma dame, god yow see,
With al your book and al the companye!"
"Ey, uncle myn, welcome y-wis," quod she,
And up she roos, and by the hond in hye
She took him faste, and seyde, "this night thrye,
To goode mote it turne, of yow I mette!"
And with that word she doun on bench him sette.

14

"Ye, nece, ye shal fare wel the bet,
If god wole, al this yeer," quod Pandarus;
"But I am sory that I have yow let
To herknen of your book ye preysen thus;
For goddes love, what seith it? tel it us.
Is it of love? O, som good ye me lere!"
"Uncle," quod she, "your maistresse is not here!"

15

With that they gonnen laughe, and tho she seyde,
"This romaunce is of Thebes, that we rede;
And we han herd how that king Laius deyde
Thurgh Edippus his sone, and al that dede;
And here we stenten at these lettres rede,
How the bisshop, as the book can telle,
Amphiorax, fil thurgh the ground to helle."

16

Quod Pandarus, "al this knowe I my selve,
And al the'assege of Thebes and the care;
For her-of been ther maked bokes twelve:—
But lat be this, and tel me how ye fare;
Do wey your barbe, and shew your face bare;
Do wey your book, rys up, and lat us daunce,
And lat us don to May som observaunce."

17

"A! god forbede!" quod she, "be ye mad?
Is that a widewes lyf, so god you save?
By god, ye maken me right sore a-drad,
Ye ben so wilde, it semeth as ye rave!
It sete me wel bet ay in a cave

10

The swallow Progne, at the break of day,
In song began her still renewed lament
For her changed shape, but still great Pandar lay
Abed, and half asleep, though night was spent,
Until her plaints, as back and forth she went,
How Tereus her sister hence did take,
Aroused the knight and brought him wide awake.

11

He called aloud, now ready to arise,
Bethinking he must carry out ere noon
For Troilus his promised enterprise,
Reflecting, too, there was a right good moon
For such attempt, and took his way full soon
Unto his niece's palace there beside—
Now Janus, god of doorways, be his guide!

12

When he had been admitted at the door,
"Where is my lady, pray?" he briskly said;
And in the wake of him who went before,
Straight to her marbled parlor he was led,
Where she sat listening, while her maidens read
Aloud to her the famous ancient rime
Of all the siege of Thebes to pass the time.

13

"Madam," said Pandar, "and all this company,
How do you do, so busy with your book!"
"Why, uncle, pray come in," responded she,
And up she rose and by the hand him took,
And said, "For three nights now—but let's not look
For bad luck just from that—I've dreamed of you,"
And led him to a chair with great to-do.

14

"Why, niece, your dreams foretell to you some good,
For one whole year, I reckon," he replied.
"But I'm extremely sorry that I should
Thus interrupt when you are occupied.
What is your book? You can in me confide!
Is it a tale of love? Come, let's draw near!"
"Uncle," she said, "your sweetheart isn't here!"

15

They laughed, and Cressida stopped to explain,
"This is the tale of Thebes wherein we read,
About King Laius, stricken down and slain
By Oedipus his son, and all that deed.
We were at these red letters, whence proceed
The lines about Amphiorax to tell,
Who sank down in the ground and into hell."

16

"O yes, I know all that," Pandar replied,
"And all the siege of Thebes and that affair;
In twelve big books it has been versified.
But what's the news? What gossip's in the air?
Put off your gear and show your face all bare!
Lay by your book and let us take this chance
To celebrate the May with song and dance."

17

"O God forbid!" she cried, "you must be mad!
Is that the way a widow should behave?
Indeed your style of speech is shocking bad,
And almost like a crazy man you rave;
For it would fit me better in a cave

To pray the saints and read their holy lives!
Let maidens go and dance, and youthful wives."

18

"Well, I could tell," said Pandar with a laugh,
"A tale to make you want to sport and play!"
"Now, uncle dear," she said, "don't tease and chaff,
But tell us, do! Have the Greeks gone away?
I wish the siege would end this very day."
"No, no," says he, "I give my sacred word,
This thing beats any news you've ever heard."

19

"Heavens alive!" cried she, "what thing is that?
Why won't you tell? Indeed, you stagger me!
I can't imagine, uncle, what you're at!
Some joke, perhaps, that I shall never see,
Till you yourself reveal the mystery.
This talk is too much for my feeble brain,
I can't pretend to follow—please explain."

20

"Well, no," he said, "I really wouldn't dare,
Because it's not a tale on which you'd thrive."
"And pray why not?" she asked. "You aren't fair!"
"Dear niece," he said, "if this news should arrive
Unto your ears, no prouder woman alive
There could be found in all the town of Troy,
And no exaggeration I employ!"

21

This made her wonder more and ever more,
And downward thoughtfully her eyes she cast,
For ne'er in her born days had she before
So longed, with longing deep and unsurpassed,
To know a thing, but sighed and said at last,
"Well, uncle dear, of course I shan't insist,
And you can tell me when and what you list."

22

And after that with pleasant conversation
And friendly gossip, both of man and maid,
They keep the ball of speech in brisk rotation;
And when in deeper things they start to wade,
As friends will do when they enough have played,
Of Hector's health, the wall of Troy, she speaks,
That rod of wrath upon the wicked Greeks.

23

"He's well," said Pandar, "well as any other,
Thank God, except upon his arm a scratch,
And also Troilus, his younger brother,
To wise and worthy Hector nigh a match,
Such equal virtues to his name attach;
In truth and gentle birth he is not less,
In wisdom, honor, and ample worthiness."

24

"Good faith!" cried Cressida, "that pleases me!
I don't know where you'd find a better two!
I think it is the finest thing to see
A king's son, who in arms so well doth do,
And he a gentleman, all through and through;
For strength and moral virtue one can find
Not often in a character combined."

25

"Indeed," said Pandar, "that's the simple truth!
For verily, these princes are a pair,
Hector and Troilus, for all his youth,

To bidde, and rede on holy seyntes lyves:
Lat maydens gon to daunce, and yonge wyves."

18

"As ever thryve I," quod this Pandarus,
"Yet coude I telle a thing to doon you pleye."
"Now uncle dere," quod she, "tel it us
For goddes love; is than th'assege aweye?
I am of Grekes so ferd that I deye."
"Nay, nay," quod he, "as ever mote I thryve!
It is a thing wel bet than swiche fyve."

19

"Ye, holy god!" quod she, "what thing is that?
What? bet than swiche fyve? ey, nay, y-wis!
For al this world ne can I reden what
It sholde been; som jape, I trowe, is this;
And but your-selven telle us what it is,
My wit is for to arede it al to lene;
As help me god, I noot nat what ye mene."

20

"And I your borow, ne never shal, for me,
This thing be told to yow, as mote I thryve!"
"And why so, uncle myn? why so?" quod she.
"By god," quod he, "that wole I telle as blyve;
For prouder womman were their noon on-lyve,
And ye it wiste, in al the toun of Troye;
I jape nought, as ever have I joye!"

21

Tho gan she wondren more than biforn
A thousand fold, and doun hir eyen caste;
For never, sith the tyme that she was born,
To knowe thing desired she so faste;
And with a syk she seyde him at the laste,
"Now, uncle myn, I nil yow nought displese,
Nor axen more, that may do yow disese."

22

So after this, with many wordes glade,
And freendly tales, and with mery chere,
Of this and that they pleyde, and gunnen wade
In many an unkouth glad and deep matere,
As freendes doon, whan they ben met y-fere;
Til she gan axen him how Ector ferde,
That was the tounes wal and Grekes yerde.

23

"Ful wel, I thanke it god," quod Pandarus,
"Save in his arm he hath a litel wounde;
And eek his fresshe brother Troilus,
The wyse worthy Ector the secounde,
In whom that every vertu list abounde,
As alle trouthe and alle gentillesse,
Wysdom, honour, fredom, and worthinesse."

24

"In good feith, eem," quod she, "that lyketh me;
They faren wel, god save hem bothe two!
For trewely I holde it greet deyntee
A kinges sone in armes wel to do,
And been of good condiciouns ther-to;
For greet power and moral vertu here
Is selde y-seye in o persone y-fere."

25

"In good feith, that is sooth," quod Pandarus;
"But, by my trouthe, the king hath sones tweye,
That is to mene, Ector and Troilus,

That certainly, though that I sholde deye,
They been as voyde of vyces, dar I seye,
As any men that liveth under the sonne,
Hir might is wyde y-knowe, and what they conne.

26

Of Ector nedeth it nought for to telle;
In al this world ther nis a bettre knight
Than he, that is of worthinesse welle;
And he wel more vertu hath than might.
This knoweth many a wys and worthy wight.
The same prys of Troilus I seye,
God help me so, I knowe not swiche tweye."

27

"By god," quod she, "of Ector that is sooth;
Of Troilus the same thing trowe I;
For dredelees, men tellen that he dooth
In armes day by day so worthily,
And bereth him here at hoom so gentilly
To every wight, that al the prys hath he
Of hem that me were levest preysed be."

28

"Ye sey right sooth, y-wis," quod Pandarus;
"For yesterday, who-so hadde with him been,
He might have wondred up-on Troilus;
For never yet so thikke a swarm of been
Ne fleigh, as Grekes fro him gonne fleen;
And thorugh the feld, in every wightes ere,
Ther nas no cry but 'Troilus is there!'

29

Now here, now there, he hunted hem so faste,
Ther nas but Grekes blood; and Troilus,
Now hem he hurte, and hem alle doun he caste;
Ay where he wente it was arayed thus:
He was hir deeth, and sheld and lyf for us;
That as that day ther dorste noon withstonde,
Whyl that he held his blody swerd in honde.

30

Therto he is the freendlieste man
Of grete estat, that ever I saw my lyve;
And wher him list, best felawshipe can
To suche as him thinketh able for to thryve."
And with that word tho Pandarus, as blyve,
He took his leve, and seyde, "I wol go henne":
"Nay, blame have I, myn uncle," quod she thenne.

31

"What eyleth yow to be thus wery sone,
And namelich of wommen? wol ye so?
Nay, sitteth down; by god, I have to done
With yow, to speke of wisdom er ye go."
And every wight that was a-boute hem tho,
That herde that, gan fer a-wey to stonde,
Whyl they two hadde al that hem liste in honde.

32

Whan that hir tale al brought was to an ende
Of hire estat and of hir governaunce,
Quod Pandarus, "now is it tyme I wende;
But yet, I seye, aryseth, lat us daunce,
And cast your widwes habit to mischaunce:
What list yow thus your-self to disfigure,
Sith yow is tid thus fair an aventure?"

33

"A! wel bithought! for love of god," quod she,

That you might safely venture to compare,
So void of vice and full of virtues fair,
With any men that live beneath the sun,
So famous, too, for all that they have done.

26

"Of Hector there is nothing new to tell;
In all this world there is no better knight,
For of all good he is the fount and well,
One who excels in virtue more than might,
And yet stands strongest in all wise men's sight;
The same of Troilus I dare maintain,
In truth I know not such another twain."

27

"For Hector," answered she, "I quite agree,
And gladly think as well of Troilus,
For one hears every day how worthily
He bears himself in arms; so generous
He is at home, and ever courteous,
The highest priase and name he hath acquired
From those whose praise is most to be desired."

28

"Quite true, quite true," said Pandar in reply,
"For yesterday, as all the town agrees,
It was a sight to fill a wondering eye;
For never flew so thick a swarm of bees
As from him fled the Greeks with quaking knees,
And through the field in every person's ear
There was no cry but 'Troilus is here!'

29

"Now here, now there, he hunted them so fast,
There was but Grecian blood and Troilus;
For all were crushed or on the ground were cast,
And everywhere you could express it thus,
He was their death, and shield and life for us.
And all that day no man durst him withstand,
The while he held his bloody sword in hand.

30

"And yet he is the friendliest of souls,
For all his rank, that ever I have seen;
And if he likes a man, he straight enrols
That one in friendly love both firm and keen."
With that he rose with brisk and serious mien,
Prepared to go, and said, "Now I must run
Along." "What for?" said she. "What have I done?

31

"You really shouldn't be so quickly bored,
Especially with women. Must you go?
Sit down again, if you can time afford
About some business I would like to have you know."
The others all, on hearing her speak so,
Withdrew and at a distance took their stand,
And left them free for all they had on hand.

32

And when this consultation reached an end
And nothing seemed his going to prevent,
Said Pandar, "On my way now I must wend!
But first, let's dance, and pray won't you relent,
And put aside this sad habiliment?
Why dress yourself in this so mournful way,
When such good luck has chanced to you today?"

33

"O that reminds me," said she smilingly,

"Shall I not know the meaning of all this?"
"No, I must think it over," answered he,
"For I should never know a moment's bliss
If I should tell and you took it amiss.
And surely I had better far keep still
Than tell the truest truth against your will.

34

"For niece, by great Minerva, the divine,
And Jupiter, who makes the thunder sound,
And Venus, goddess most especially mine,
No other person on this world so round—
Sweethearts excepted—have I ever found,
That I love more than thee and least would grieve,
And this I think you know and well believe."

35

"O surely, uncle," said she, "and I'm duly
Grateful for all your long and friendly aid;
To no one have I been beholden truly
So much as you, and yet have less repaid;
You have then little cause to be afraid
That with intention I shall you offend,
And if I have done so, I shall amend.

36

"But now, dear uncle, let me please beseech,
And as I trust in you, let me insist,
That you leave off this strange mysterious speech,
And tell me clear and plain whate'er you list."
Then Pandar said, though first his niece he kissed,
"I will with pleasure, Cressida my dear,
But take it right, what I shall tell you here."

37

At that her eyes upon the ground she cast,
And Pandar, with a little cough polite,
Began, "Dear niece, lo, always at the last,
Though some men think their style is stale and trite
Unless with subtle artifice they write,
Beneath their little tricks you always find
The thing that from the first they had in mind.

38

"And since the point is always at the end,
And since the end is here not hard to see,
Why should I strive my story to extend,
Between old friends like us, especially?"
And pausing then as serious as could be,
He gazed intent and long into her face,
And said, "On such a mirror, heaven's grace!"

39

And to himself he thought, "If what I say
Seems hard to understand or to believe,
Then she will either no attention pay
Or think that I have something up my sleeve;
For simple minds fear all men will deceive,
When they hear something hard to understand,
And so I'll lead her gently by the hand."

40

His steady looking filled her with surprise,
She wondered why he should be gazing so,
And said, "Good Lord, don't eat me with your eyes!
You've seen me many a time before, you know."
"And better shall," he said, "before I go!
But I was wondering if you were to be
So fortunate, for now we soon shall see.

"Shal I not witen what ye mene of this?"
"No, this thing axeth layser," tho quod he,
"And eek me wolde muche greve, y-wis,
If I it tolde, and ye it toke amis.
Yet were it bet my tonge for to stille
Than seye a sooth that were ayeins your wille.

34

For, nece, by the goddesse Minerve,
And Juppiter, that maketh the thonder ringe,
And by the blisful Venus that I serve,
Ye been the womman in this world livinge,
With-oute paramours, to my witinge,
That I best love, and lothest am to greve,
And that ye witen wel your-self, I leve."

35

"Y-wis, myn uncle," quod she, "grant mercy;
Your freendship have I founden ever yit;
I am to no man holden trewely
So muche as yow, and have so litel quit;
And, with the grace of god, emforth my wit,
As in my gilt I shal you never offende;
And if I have er this, I wol amende.

36

But, for the love of god, I yow beseche,
As ye ben he that I most love and triste,
Lat be to me your fremde maner speche,
And sey to me, your nece, what yow liste":
And with that word hir uncle anoon hir kiste,
And seyde, "gladly, leve nece dere,
Tak it for good that I shal seye yow here."

37

With that she gan hir eyen doun to caste,
And Pandarus to coghe gan a lyte,
And seyde, "nece, alwey, lo! to the laste,
How-so it be that som men hem delyte
With subtil art hir tales for to endyte,
Yet for al that, in hir entencioun,
Hir tale is al for some conclusioun.

38

And sithen th'ende is every tales strengthe,
And this matere is so bihovely,
What sholde I peynte or drawen it on lengthe
To yow, that been my freend so feithfully?"
And with that word he gan right inwardly
Biholden hir, and loken on hir face,
And seyde, "on suche a mirour goode grace!"

39

Than thoughte he thus, "if I my tale endyte
Ought hard, or make a proces any whyle,
She shal no savour han ther-in but lyte,
And trowe I wolde hir in my wil bigyle.
For tendre wittes wenen al be wyle
Ther-as they can nat pleynly understonde;
For-thy hir wit to serven wol I fonde"—

40

And loked on hir in a besy wyse,
And she was war that he byheld hir so,
And seyde, "lord! so faste ye me avyse!
Sey ye me never er now? what sey ye, no?"
"Yes, yes", quod he, "and bet wole er I go;
But, by my trouthe, I thoughte now if ye
Be fortunat, for now men shal it see.

41

For to every wight som goodly aventure
Som tyme is shape, if he it can receyven;
And if that he wol take of it no cure,
Whan that it cometh, but wilfully it weyven,
Lo, neither cas nor fortune him deceyven,
But right his verray slouthe and wrecchednesse;
And swich a wight is for to blame, I gesse.

42

Good aventure, O bele nece, have ye
Ful lightly founden, and ye conne it take;
And, for the love of god, and eek of me,
Cacche it anoon, lest aventure slake.
What sholde I lenger proces of it make?
Yif me your hond, for in this world is noon,
If that you list, a wight so wel begoon.

43

And sith I speke of good entencioun,
As I to yow have told wel here-biforn,
And love as wel your honour and renoun
As creature in al this world y-born;
By alle the othes that I have yow sworn,
And ye be wrooth therfore, or wene I lye,
Ne shal I never seen yow eft with yë.

44

Beth nought agast, ne quaketh nat; wher-to?
Ne chaungeth nat for fere so your hewe;
For hardely, the werste of this is do;
And though my tale as now be to yow newe,
Yet trist alwey, ye shal me finde trewe;
And were it thing that me thoughte unsittinge,
To yow nolde I no swiche tales bringe."

45

"Now, my good eem, for goddes love, I preye,"
Quod she, "com of, and tel me what it is;
For bothe I am agast what ye wol seye,
And eek me longeth it to wite, y-wis
For whether it be wel or be amis,
Sey on, lat me not in this fere dwelle":
"So wol I doon, now herkneth, I shal telle:

46

Now, nece myn, the kinges dere sone,
The goode, wyse, worthy, fresshe, and free,
Which alwey for to do wel is his wone,
The noble Troilus, so loveth thee,
That, bot ye helpe, it wol his bane be.
Lo, here is al, what sholde I more seye?
Doth what yow list, to make him live or deye.

47

But if ye lete him deye, I wol sterve;
Have her my trouthe, nece, I nil not lyen;
Al sholde I with this knyf my throte kerve"—
With that the teres braste out of his yën,
And seyde, "if that ye doon us bothe dyen,
Thus giltelees, than have ye fisshed faire;
What mende ye, though that we bothe apeyre?

48

Allas! he which that is my lord so dere,
That trewe man, that noble gentil knight,
That nought desireth but your freendly chere,
I see him deye, ther he goth up-right,
And hasteth him, with al his fulle might,

41

"For every person hath his happy chance,
If good faith with his fortune he will hold.
But if he turns aside with scornful glance
When fortune comes, unwelcoming and cold,
Then for ill luck he may not fortune scold,
But his own sloth and feebleness of heart,
And he must take all blame from end to start.

42

"Good fortune, niece, hath lightly come thy way,
If thou wilt but accept it now as thine;
And for the love of God, without delay
Take hold of it, thy share do not decline.
But need I now say more along this line?
Give me your hand, for now it lies with you
To be the luckiest soul I ever knew.

43

"But let me speak again of my intention—
As I to you have often said before,
There is no living person I could mention
Whose honor and renown I cherish more;
By all the solemn oaths I ever swore,
If you are wroth at this, or think I lie,
I shan't have nerve to look you in the eye.

44

"Don't be so agitated! Pray, what for?
Don't look as though I meant some harm to you!
The worst is past and there is little more,
I've told the old and now must come the new.
Yet trust in me and you will find me true,
For never sure the least improper thing
Would I to your attention dare to bring."

45

"Now, uncle dear," she said, "for heaven's sake,
Hurry and tell me what it's all about,
For I am both so scared with fear I quake,
And eager, too, to have the whole thing out!
For be it thing of joy or thing of doubt,
Say on! This agony you must dispel!"
"So will I do," said Pandar, "listen well!

46

"Now, Cressida, my niece, the king's dear son,
The good, the wise, the worthy, fresh and free,
Who seeks the good and ever so hath done,
The noble Troilus so loveth thee,
That life or death for him you must decree.
So this is all! And as you shall reply,
Consider you will bid him live or die.

47

"But if you bid him die, you take my life,
For here this pledge, dear niece, I ratify,
That I will cut my throat with this my knife!"
And with these words and tears in either eye,
Pandar went on, "If both of us must die,
And guiltless both, 'twill be a sad affair,
And you alone the blame thereof must bear.

48

"Alas, that he who is my lord so dear,
That faithful man, that noble, gentle knight,
Who will to nothing but your welfare hear,
That I should see him perish in my sight,
And to his own destruction walk upright,

Hastening to a fate you might prevent!
Alas, that God such beauty to you sent!

49

"But if you will in careless cruelty
Insist that death at your hands he shall fetch,
A man of high and noble constancy,
As if he were some ordinary wretch,
I tell you all your beauty will not stretch
So far to make amends for such a deed—
And so, before it is too late, take heed!

50

"Woe to the precious gem that will not glow!
Woe to the herb that harms, but should work weal!
Woe to the power that will no mercy show!
Woe to the pride that treads all neath its heel!
And all ye fair, adorned with beauty's seal,
If therewith pity give not beauty worth,
'Twere pity you should dwell upon this earth!

51

"Now don't imagine any wrong I mean,
For I would rather thou and I and he
Were hanged, than I should be his go-between,
Or think of aught but what the world might see!
Remember who I am, for shame to me
As well as thee it were, should my endeavor
The least dishonor bring upon you ever.

52

"Of course you understand I would not bind
You to him in the very least degree;
But merely show yourself a little kind
And in such wise that he can plainly see,
Whereby at least his life assured will be.
Now here you have the whole of my intent,
And all I ever thought or ever meant.

53

"And sure there's nothing strange in this request,
And not a reason thereagainst to show.
Suppose the worst—that you are fearful lest
Some folk will talk, seeing him come and go.
But I can answer that, and will do so,
That every man, except the weak of mind,
Nothing but friendliness therein will find.

54

"For who supposes when he sees a man
Going to church, that he expects to eat
The images there! And think how well he can
Comport himself, so heedful and discreet,
A more considerate man you'll never
meet.
Besides he won't come here so frequently
But that the whole world might look on and see.

55

"Such friendship you will find in all this town—
A cloak, no doubt, if folk will use it so.
But as I hope to win salvation's crown,
I've given you the best advice I know.
You can, dear niece, alleviate his woe,
And if so be you can do nothing more,
His death, at least, will not lie at your door."

56

Cressida weighed these words, so doubtful wise,
And thought, "I'll see just what he's coming to!"

For to be slayn, if fortune wol assente;
Allas! that god yow swich a beautee sente!

49

If it be so that ye so cruel be,
That of his deeth yow liste nought to recche,
That is so trewe and worthy, as ye see,
No more than of a japere or a wrecche,
If ye be swich, your beautee may not strecche
To make amendes of so cruel a dede;
Avysement is good bifore the nede.

50

Wo worth the faire gemme vertulees!
Wo worth that herbe also that dooth no bote!
Wo worth that beautee that is routhelees!
Wo worth that wight that tret ech under fote!
And ye, that been of beautee crop and rote,
If therwith-al in you ther be no routhe,
Than is it harm ye liven, by my trouthe!

51

And also thenk wel, that this is no gaude;
For me were lever, thou and I and he
Were hanged, than I sholde been his baude,
As heye, as men mighte on us alle y-see;
I am thyn eem, the shame were to me,
As wel as thee, if that I sholde assente,
Thorugh myn abet, that he thyn honour shente.

52

Now understond, for I yow nought requere
To binde yow to him thorugh no beheste,
But only that ye make him bettre chere
Than ye han doon er this, and more feste,
So that his lyf be saved, at the leste
This al and som, and playnly our entente;
God helpe me so, I never other mente.

53

Lo, this request is not but skile, y-wis,
Ne doute of reson, pardee, is ther noon.
I sette the worste that ye dredden this,
Men wolden wondren seen him come or goon;
Ther-ayeins answere I thus a-noon,
That every wight, but he be fool of kinde,
Wol deme it love of freendship in his minde.

54

What? who wol deme, though he see a man
To temple go, that he the images eteth?
Thenk eek how wel and wysly that he can
Governe him-self, that he no-thing foryeteth,
That, wher he cometh, he prys and thank him
geteth;
And eek ther-to, he shal come here so selde,
What fors were it though al the toun behelde?

55

Swich love of freendes regneth al this toun;
And wrye yow in that mantel ever-mo;
And, god so wis be my savacioun,
As I have seyd, your beste is to do so.
But alwey, goode nece, to stinte his wo,
So lat your daunger sucred ben a lyte,
That of his deeth ye be nought for to wyte."

56

Criseyde, which that herde him in this wyse,
Thoughte, "I shal fele what he meneth, y-wis."

"Now, eem," quod she, "what wolde ye devyse,
What is your reed I sholde doon of this?"
"That is wel seyd," quod he, "certayn, best is
That ye him love ayein for his lovinge,
As love for love is skilful guerdoninge.

57

Thenk eek, how elde wasteth every houre
In eche of yow a party of beautee;
And therfore, er that age thee devoure,
Go love, for, olde, ther wol no wight of thee.
Lat this proverbe a lore un-to yow be;
'To late y-war,' quod Beautee, whan it paste;
And elde daunteth daunger at the laste.

58

The kinges fool is woned to cryen loude,
Whan that him thinketh a womman bereth hir hyë,
'So longe mote ye live, and alle proude,
Til crowes feet be growe under your yë,
And sende yow thanne a mirour in to pryë
In whiche ye may see your face a-morwe!'
Nece, I bid wisshe yow no more sorwe."

59

With this he stente, and caste adoun the heed,
And she bigan to breste a-wepe anoon.
And seyde, "allas, for wo! why nere I deed?
For of this world the feith is al agoon!
Allas! what sholden straunge to me doon,
When he, that for my beste freend I wende,
Ret me to love, and sholde it me defende?

60

Allas! I wolde han trusted, doutelees,
That if that I, thurgh my disaventure,
Had loved other him or Achilles,
Ector, or any mannes creature,
Ye nolde han had no mercy ne mesure
On me, but alwey had me in repreve;
This false world, allas! who may it leve?

61

What? is this al the joye and al the feste?
Is this your reed, is this my blisful cas?
Is this the verray mede of your beheste?
Is al this peynted proces seyd, allas!
Right for this fyn? O lady myn, Pallas!
Thou in this dredful cas for me purveye;
For so astonied am I that I deye!"

62

With that she gan ful sorwfully to syke;
"A! may it be no bet?" quod Pandarus;
"By god, I shal no-more come here this wyke,
And god to-forn, that am mistrusted thus;
I see ful wel that ye sette lyte of us,
Or of our deeth! Allas! I woful wrecche!
Mighte he yet live, of me is nought to recche.

63

O cruel god, O dispitouse Marte,
O Furies three of helle, on yow I crye!
So lat me never out of this hous departe,
If that I mente harm or vilanye!
But sith I see my lord mot nedes dye,
And I with him, here I me shryve, and seye
That wikkedly ye doon us bothe deye.

"Now, uncle," said she, "what would you advise?
In your opinion, what is best to do?"
"Well said," he answered, "now I'll tell you true!
Since love for love is but a fair return,
It were great wrong his proffered love to spurn.

57

"Remember time is wasting every hour
Some share of all the beauty now we see,
And thus, ere age shall all thy charms devour,
Go love, for old, none will have aught of thee!
This saying may a lesson to you be,
'It might have been,' said Beauty, beauty past,
For age will dull all edges at the last.

58

"The courtly fool is wont to cry aloud
When any woman holds her head too high,
'Long may you live and all ye beauties proud,
Til crowsfeet come to grow beneath your eye,
And in your mirror may you then descry
The face that you shall wear for many a morrow!'
I hope and pray for you no greater sorrow!"

59

With these few words he stopped and bowed his head,
While Cressida with weeping eyes replied:
"Alas, poor me! I wish that I were dead!
No honor in this world doth now abide;
For how shall I in strangers e'er confide,
When he who seemed to be my trusty friend
Would have me do what he should reprehend.

60

"In very deed and truth, I should have thought,
If I had loved, through chance unfortunate,
Him or Achilles or Hector, or shown aught
Of love to man of high or low estate,
Such conduct you would sternly reprobate,
And would me ever after discommend!
This faithless world, who may on it depend!

61

"Is this your fateful joy and happiness?
Is this your counsel, this my lucky chance?
Is this the care that you to me profess?
Is all thy pomp of speech and circumstance
But to this end? O Pallas, let thy glance
Now rest on me with sympathetic eye,
For I am so astounded I shall die!"

62

She paused and sighed with sorrow deep and sore,
And Pandar asked, "Is that all you can say?
Well, I'll be blessed if e'er again your door
I darken, if you doubt me in this way!
I see how little heed to us you pay,
Or to our death! Yet if it may but be
That he is saved, let fall what will on me!

63

"O cruel God, O most avenging Mars!
O Furies three of hell, on you I cry!
The door that to this house the entry bars
May I ne'er pass, if I meant harm thereby!
But since I see my lord and I must die,
Here let me say it with my final breath,
That wickedly you do us both to death.

64

"But since it pleases you to see me dead,
By Neptune, god of all the ocean free,
From this time forth I scorn all daily bread
Till with my eyes my own heart's blood I see,
For I shall end my days as soon as he!"
And then he started off like one distraught,
But with restraining hand his cloak she caught,

65

And though she almost passed away for fear,
For she at best was easy to affright,
At all the horrid things that she must hear,
And saw how deadly earnest was the knight,
And thought besides it maybe was all right,
And that she might stir harm up all the more,
Relenting just a bit and sighing sore,

66

She thought, "How often comes catastrophe
For love, and in such strange and dreadful way,
That men will treat themselves with cruelty.
And if here in my presence he should slay
Himself, there'd be a frightful price to pay!
What men would think of it, I do not know—,
Perhaps I'd better go a little slow."

67

Aloud with heartfelt sigh she then replied,
"Ah, Lord, what trouble on me thou has laid!
For my good name is periled on one side,
And thereagainst my uncle's life is weighed.
But for all that, perhaps with heaven's aid,
Some way to save my name I can devise
And your life, too." With that she dried her eyes.

68

"The less of two misfortunes I must choose,
Yet would I rather yield to Troilus,
With honor, than my uncle's life to lose.
Will you be satisfied to leave it thus?"
"Indeed yes," Pandar smiled, victorious.
"Well then," said she, "I'll see what I can do.
I shall my heart against my will construe,

69

"Yet will in no way raise his hopes too high,
For love a man I neither can nor may
Against my will, yet otherwise shall try
Honorably to please him day by day;
Nor had I once to all this thing said nay,
Were not my head so full of fantasies;
But stop the cause, you stop the whole disease!

70

"But here I make a solemn protestation,
That if you in this matter too far go,
Then certainly, for your nor his salvation,
Though both of you together die, and though
Each man alive become my deadly foe,
'Twill be the end of things twixt him and me."
"O certainly," said Pandar, "I agree."

71

"But tell me," said he, "can I trust in you
That all that you have promised to me here,
That all of this you faithfully will do?"
"Why yes," she said, "why not, my uncle dear?"
"And that you won't draw back from foolish fear

64

But sith it lyketh yow that I be deed,
By Neptunus, that god is of the see,
Fro this forth shal I never eten breed
Til I myn owene herte blood may see;
For certayn, I wole deye as sone as he"—
And up he sterte, and on his wey he raughte,
Til she agayn him by the lappe caughte.

65

Criseyde, which that wel neigh starf for fere,
So as she was the ferfulleste wight
That mighte be, and herde eek with hir ere,
And saw the sorwful ernest of the knight,
And in his preyere eek saw noon unright,
And for the harm that mighte eek fallen more,
She gan to rewe, and dradde hir wonder sore;

66

And thoughte thus, "unhappes fallen thikke
Alday for love, and in swich maner cas,
As men ben cruel in hem-self and wikke;
And if this man slee here him-self, allas!
In my presence, it wol be no solas.
What men wolde of hit deme I can nat seye;
It nedeth me ful sleyly for to pleye."

67

And with a sorwful syk she seyde thrye,
"A! lord! what me is tid a sory chaunce!
For myn estat now lyth in jupartye,
And eek myn emes lyf lyth in balaunce;
But nathelees, with goddes governaunce,
I shal so doon, myn honour shal I kepe,
And eek his lyf;" and stinte for to wepe.

68

"Of harmes two, the lesse is for to chese;
Yet have I lever maken him good chere
In honour, than myn emes lyf to lese;
Ye seyn, ye no-thing elles me requere?"
"No, wis," quod he, "myn owene nece dere."
"Now wel," quod she, "and I wol doon my peyne;
I shal myn herte ayeins my lust constreyne,

69

But that I nil not holden him in honde,
Ne love a man, ne can I not, ne may
Ayeins my wil; but elles wol I fonde,
Myn honour sauf, plese him fro day to day;
Ther-to nolde I nought ones have seyd nay,
But that I dredde, as in my fantasye;
But cesse cause, ay cesseth maladye.

70

And here I make a protestacioun,
That in this proces if ye depper go,
That certaynly, for no savacioun
Of yow, though that ye sterve bothe two,
Though al the world on o day be my fo,
Ne shal I never on him han other routhe."—
"I graunte wel," quod Pandare, "by my trouthe.

71

But may I truste wel ther-to," quod he,
"That, of this thing that ye han hight me here,
Ye wol it holden trewly un-to me?"
"Ye, doutelees," quod she, "myn uncle dere."
"Ne that I shal han cause in this matere,"

Quod he, "to pleyne, or after yow to preche?"
"Why, no, pardee; what nedeth more speche?"

72

Tho fillen they in othere tales glade.
Til at the laste, "O good eem," quod she tho,
"For love of god, which that us bothe made,
Tel me how first ye wisten of his wo:
Wot noon of hit but ye?" He seyde, "no."
"Can he wel speke of love?" quod she, "I preye,
Tel me, for I the bet me shal purveye."

73

Tho Pandarus a litel gan to smyle,
And seyde, "by my trouthe, I shal yow telle.
This other day, nought gon ful longe whyle,
In-with the paleys-gardyn, by a welle,
Gan he and I wel half a day to dwelle,
Right for to speken of an ordenaunce,
How we the Grekes mighte disavaunce.

74

Sone after that bigonne we to lepe,
And casten with our dartes to and fro,
Til at the laste he seyde, he wolde slepe,
And on the gres a-doun he leyde him tho;
And I after gan rome to and fro
Til that I herde, as that I welk allone,
How he bigan ful wofully to grone.

75

Tho gan I stalke him softely bihinde,
And sikerly, the sothe for to seyne,
As I can clepe ayein now to my minde,
Right thus to Love he gan him for to pleyne;
He seyde, "lord! have routhe up-on my peyn,
Al have I been rebel in myn entente;
Now, *mea culpa*, lord! I me repente.

76

O god, that at thy disposicioun
Ledest the fyn, by juste purveyaunce,
Of every wight, my lowe confessioun
Accepte in gree, and send me swich penaunce
As lyketh thee, but from desesperaunce,
That may my goost departe awey fro thee,
Thou be my sheld, for thy benignitee.

77

For certes, lord, so sore hath she me wounded
That stod in blak, with loking of hir yën,
That to myn hertes botme it is y-sounded,
Thorugh which I woot that I mot nedes dyen;
This is the worste, I dar me not bi-wryen;
And wel the hotter been the gledes rede,
That men hem wryen with asshen pale and dede.'

78

With that he smoot his heed adoun anoon,
And gan to motre, I noot what, trewely.
And I with that gan stille awey to goon,
And leet ther-of as no-thing wist hadde I,
And come ayein anoon and stood him by,
And seyde, 'a-wake, ye slepen al to longe;
It semeth nat that love dooth yow longe,

79

That slepen so that no man may yow wake.
Who sey ever or this so dul a man?'
'Ye, freend,' quod he, 'do ye your hedes ake

So that forever I shall have to preach?"
"Why no," she said, "what need of further speech?"

72

They talked of many things with right good cheer,
Till finally she said, "Before you go,
There's one thing, uncle, I should like to hear,
How of this matter you came first to know.
And is it spread abroad?" "By no means, no!"
"Is he well versed," she asked, "in these affairs?
Do tell—I might be taken unawares!"

73

Then Pandar answered with a little smile:
"I see no reason why I shouldn't tell!
The other day—'twas just a little while—
Within the palace garden, near a well,
Troilus and I in conversation fell
About some new and promising design
With which the Grecian force to undermine.

74

"And then we started in to jump and leap,
And cast our darts in practice to and fro,
Till Troilus said he would go and sleep,
And laid him down where soft the grass doth grow,
And I went farther off and left him so,
Until as I was walking there alone,
I heard him fearfully begin to groan.

75

"And then I stalked him softly from behind,
And heard all he was saying, clear and plain,
And just as I recall it now to mind,
Of love he spoke, and this was his refrain:
'O Lord, have pity now upon my pain!
Though I have been a rebel in intent,
Now, *mea culpa*, Lord I do repent!

76

" 'O God, who ever holdest in possession
The ends of things, in justice all comprising,
In thy good will accept my meek confession,
And send me penance at thy own devising;
Yet let not grief, from black despair arising,
Exile my spirit far away from thee,
But be my shield in thy benignity.

77

" 'For truly, Lord, the one who stood in black,
So deeply with the glancings of her eye
My heart on its foundations doth attack,
I know that from the wound I'm doomed to die.
And yet the worst is this, I can't reply,
And hotter grow the glowing coals so red,
When covered o'er with ashes pale and dead.'

78

"And then he laid his head upon the ground,
And muttered something which I couldn't hear,
And then I went away without a sound,
So that I might pretend to re-appear,
And soon came back again, and standing near,
I cried 'Awake from out this slumber deep!
It's plain that love cannot disturb your sleep!

79

" 'You sleep so sound I scarcely can you wake!
Who ever saw, forsooth, so dull a man?'
'Let lovers,' said he, 'love till their heads ache,

But let me get along as best I can!'
And though his face was wan beneath its tan,
Yet he put on a cheerful countenance,
As though all ready for a song or dance.

80

"So it continued, till the other day
It chanced that I came wondering all alone
Into his chamber, and found him where he lay
Upon his bed, and man so sorely groan
I never heard, but why he thus should moan
I did not know, for soon as he saw me,
He stopped his lamentation suddenly.

81

"You well may think, this made me grow suspicious,
And drawing near, I found him weeping sore,
And as I hope for grace from acts flagitious,
I never saw a sight that touched me more;
With all my wit and all my wisest lore,
This man I scarcely from his death could keep,
And even now my heart for him doth weep.

82

"God knows, not since the day that I was born,
Had I such need to any man to preach,
Nor ever was there man so deeply sworn
Ere he would tell me who might be his leech!
But bid me not rehearse again his speech,
And all his melancholy words repeat,
Or I shall drop and faint here at your feet.

83

"To save his life, and with no other thought,
Except no harm to you, thus am I driven!
And for God's love, who all the world have wrought,
See thou that life to both of us be given.
And now to you in full my heart I've shriven,
And since you see that it is pure and clean,
You know full well that I no evil mean.

84

"I pray to God, successful may you be,
Who such a fish hath caught without a net!
If you are wise, as you are fair to see,
Well in the ring then is the ruby set.
You two will make the best pair ever yet!
And heaven bless the day which well assures
That you are his as much as he is yours."

85

"Oho! I did not say that," answered she,
"Such talk as that will help things never a deal."
"O niece," said Pandar, "pray you, pardon me!
For though I merely spoke out as I feel,
I meant it well, by Mars with helm of steel!
So be not angry with me, dearest niece!"
"O well," she said, "for this time, I'll make peace."

86

And then he took his leave and homeward bent
His way, with progress made well satisfied,
And Cressida got up and straightway went
Into her private chamber close beside,
And still as a stone, she sat her down and tried
Each word that he had said to bring to mind,
And all interpretations of them find.

For love, and lat me liven as I can.'
But though that he for wo was pale and wan,
Yet made he tho as fresh a contenaunce
As though he shulde have led the newe daunce.

80

This passed forth, til now, this other day,
It fel that I com roming al allone
Into his chaumbre, and fond how that he lay
Up-on his bed; but man so sore grone
Ne herde I never, and what that was his mone,
Ne wiste I nought; for, as I was cominge,
Al sodeynly he lefte his compleyninge.

81

Of which I took somwhat suspecioun,
And neer I com, and fond he wepte sore;
And god so wis be my savacioun,
As never of thing hadde I no routhe more.
For neither with engyn, ne with no lore,
Unethes mighte I fro the deeth him kepe;
That yet fele I myn herte for him wepe.

82

And god wot, never, sith that I was born,
Was I so bisy no man for to preche,
Ne never was to wight so depe y-sworn,
Or he me tolde who mighte been his leche.
But now to yow rehersen al his speche,
Or alle his woful wordes for to soune,
Ne did me not, but ye wol see me swowne.

83

But for to save his lyf, and elles nought,
And to non harm of yow, thus am I driven;
And for the love of god that us hath wrought,
Swich chere him dooth, that he and I may liven.
Now have I plat to yow myn herte schriven;
And sin ye woot that myn entente is clene,
Tak hede ther-of, for I non yvel mene.

84

And right good thrift, I pray to god, have ye,
That han swich oon y-caught with-oute net;
And be ye wys, as ye ben fair to see,
Wel in the ring than is the ruby set.
Ther were never two so wel y-met,
Whan ye ben his al hool, as he is youre:
Ther mighty god yet graunte us see that houre!"

85

"Nay, therof spak I not, a, ha!" quod she,
"As helpe me god, ye shenden every deel!"
"O mercy, dere nece," anoon quod he,
"What-so I spak, I mente nought but weel,
By Mars the god, that helmed is of steel;
Now beth nought wrooth, my blood, my nece dere."
"Now wel," quod she, "foryeven be it here!"

86

With this he took his leve, and hoom he wente;
And lord, how he was glad and wel bi-goon!
Criseyde aroos, no lenger she ne stente,
But straught in-to hir closet wente anoon,
And sette here doun as stille as any stoon,
And every word gan up and doun to winde,
That he hadde seyd, as it com hir to minde;

87

And wex somdel astonied in hir thought,
Right for the newe cas; but whan that she
Was ful avysed, tho fond she right nought
Of peril, why she oughte afered be.
For man may love, of possibilitee,
A womman so, his herte may to-breste,
And she nought love ayein, but-if hir leste.

88

But as she sat allone and thoughte thus,
Th'ascry aroos at skarmish al with-oute,
And men cryde in the strete, "see, Troilus
Hath right now put to flight the Grekes route!"
With that gan al hir meynee for to shoute,
"A! go we see, caste up the latis wyde;
For thurgh this strete he moot to palays ryde;

89

For other wey is fro the yate noon
Of Dardanus, ther open is the cheyne."
With that com he and al his folk anoon
An esy pas rydinge, in routes tweyne,
Right as his happy day was, sooth to seyne,
For which, men say, may nought disturbed be
That shal bityden of necessitee.

90

This Troilus sat on his baye stede,
Al armed, save his heed, ful richely,
And wounded was his hors, and gan to blede,
On whiche he rood a pas, ful softely;
But swich a knightly sighte, trewely,
As was on him, was nought, with-outen faile,
To loke on Mars, that god is of batayle.

91

So lyk a man of armes and a knight
He was to seen, fulfild of heigh prowesse;
For bothe he hadde a body and a might
To doon that thing, as wel as hardinesse;
And eek to seen him in his gere him dresse,
So fresh, so yong, so weldy semed he,
It was an heven up-on him for to see.

92

His helm to-hewen was in twenty places,
That by a tissew heng, his bak bihinde,
His sheld to-dasshed was with swerdes and maces,
In which men mighte many an arwe finde
That thirled hadde horn and nerf and rinde;
And ay the peple cryde, "here cometh our joye,
And, next his brother, holdere up of Troye!"

93

For which he wex a litel reed for shame,
Whan he the peple up-on him herde cryen,
That to biholde it was a noble game,
How sobreliche he caste doun his yën.
Cryseyda gan al his chere aspyen,
And leet so softe it in hir herte sinke,
That to hir-self she seyde, "who yaf me drinke?"

94

For of hir owene thought she wex al reed,
Remembringe hir right thus, "lo, this is he
Which that myn uncle swereth he moot be deed,
But I on him have mercy and pitee";
And with that thought, for pure a-shamed, she

87

And she was somewhat troubled at the thought
Of all she'd heard and done, but still when she
Had weighed it well, it seemed that there was naught
To justify so great timidity;
For though a man with love near bursting be,
Nothing compels a woman to respond,
Unless, indeed, she should of him grow fond.

88

And as she sat alone, reflecting thus,
The noise arose of skirmishers without,
And men cried in the street, "Lo, Troilus
Hath put the coward Greeks to flight and rout!"
And all her household ran up with a shout,
"O let us see! Throw up the lattice wide!
As he goes home, he through this street will ride!

89

"There is no other way here from the gates
Of Dardanus where they've let down the chain."
And then he came, with all his battle mates,
All riding slowly in a double train;
And that it was his lucky day 'twas plain,
A day on which things turn out as they should,
And even bad luck turns at last to good.

90

Troilus rode upon his good bay steed,
All armed, except his head, in richest gear;
The wounds upon his charger still did bleed,
As slowly down the street the band drew near.
O what a noble sight did then appear!
Like Mars himself for battle all arrayed,
Troilus led the warlike cavalcade.

91

He was the picture of a warrior knight,
A man of greatest prowess in all ways,
For bold in mind, he strove with equal might
In deeds that won a universal praise.
It was pure joy upon this knight to gaze;
So fresh, so young, with such vitality,
He was, in truth, a heavenly sight to see.

92

His helm was hacked in twenty different places,
So that it hung by just a slender thread;
His shield was cut by strokes of swords and maces,
With arrows buried in it to the head,
Where horn and sinew made for them a bed.
And loud the people cried, "Here comes our joy,
And with his brother, great defence of Troy!"

93

And Troilus a little blushed for shame,
When thus he heard the people shout and cry;
To watch him was as good as any game,
How soberly he downward cast his eye;
And Cressida, intent on all to spy,
Felt in her heart a softly sinking motion,
And sighed, "Has some one given me a potion?"

94

And at this thought she blushed a rosy red,
Bethinking her, "This is the very he
Who loves me so, so hath my uncle said,
That he will die, unless help comes from me!"
And then in modest fear that he might see,

She drew back from the casement window fast
As Troilus and all his people passed.

95

And then in mind she canvassed up and down
The count of all his gracious qualities,
And all his rank and all his great renown,
His wit, his figure, all his knightly ease,
But that he loved her, most of all did please;
And then she said, "This man to death to do,
'Twere pity, if his mind and heart are true."

96

Now envious folk might make objection thus:
"This was a sudden love! How might it be
That she so quickly should love Troilus
At sight?" Why, such things happen frequently,
And if you doubt, just look about and see!
For all things slight beginnings first must know
Before to full completion they can grow.

97

For mark, not in the twinkling of an eye
She gave her love to him, but did incline
To like him first, and I have told you why,
And afterward, his qualities so fine
Made deepest love within her heart to mine,
And only then, for proper service done,
And not by sudden glance, her love was won.

98

Recall also that Venus, well arrayed,
Within her seventh house just then doth go,
With all kind aspects at that time displayed
To help poor Troilus in his deep woe;
And she was not in any case a foe
To Troilus from his first natal hour,
Whereby in love he had the greater power.

99

Let Troilus in peace his ways now go,
And let us turn to Cressida, shamefast
And pensive, sitting with her head bent low
And trying solitary to forecast
What courses she should follow at the last,
If Pandar persevering for his friend
Should push this suit unto the final end.

100

Then in her heart she started to debate
Of this affair, as I have to you told,
And over this and that to hesitate
Till she had twisted it in many a fold;
And now her heart was warm, now was it cold,
And some of what she thought I shall relate,
Though far too long were all of her debate.

101

And first she thought that Troilus she knew
At least by sight, and all about his birth,
So high she said, "Of course it would not do
To think of love, with one of such high worth,
But still 'twould be an honor, but in mirth
And in all innocence, for me to deal
With one like him, and mayhap for his weal.

102

"I don't forget he is my sovereign's son,
And since he seems in me to take delight,
If I all his advances harshly shun,

Gan in hir heed to pulle, and that as faste,
Whyl he and al the peple for-by paste,

95

And gan to caste and rollen up and doun
With-inne hir thought his excellent prowesse,
And his estat, and also his renoun,
His wit, his shap, and eek his gentilesse;
But most hir favour was, for his distresse
Was al for hir, and thoughte it was a routhe
To sleen swich oon, if that he mente trouthe.

96

Now mighte som envyous jangle thus,
"This was a sodeyn love, how mighte it be
That she so lightly lovede Troilus
Right for the firste sighte; ye, pardee?"
Now who-so seyth so, mote he never thee!
For every thing, a ginning hath it nede
Er al be wrought, with-outen any drede.

97

For I sey nought that she so sodeynly
Yaf him hir love, but that she gan enclyne
To lyke him first, and I have told yow why;
And after that, his manhod and his pyne
Made love with-inne hir for to myne,
For which, by proces and by good servyse,
He gat hir love, and in no sodeyn wyse.

98

And also blisful Venus, wel arayed,
Sat in hir seventhe hous of hevene tho,
Disposed wel, and with aspectes payed,
To helpen sely Troilus of his wo.
And, sooth to seyn, she nas nat al a fo
To Troilus in his nativitee;
God woot that wel the soner spedde he.

99

Now lat us stinte of Troilus a throwe,
That rydeth forth, and lat us tourne faste
Un-to Criseyde, that heng hir heed ful lowe,
Ther-as she sat allone, and gan to caste
Wher-on she wolde apoynte hir at the laste,
If it so were hir eem ne wolde cesse,
For Troilus, up-on hir for to presse.

100

And, lord! so she gan in hir thought argue
In this matere of which I have yow told,
And what to doon best were, and what eschue,
That plyted she ful ofte in many fold.
Now was hir herte warm, now was it cold,
And what she thoughte somwhat shal I wryte,
As to myn auctor listeth for to endyte.

101

She thoughte wel, that Troilus persone
She knew by sighte and eek his gentillesse,
And thus she seyde, "al were it nought to done,
To graunte him love, yet, for his worthinesse,
It were honour, with pley and with gladnesse,
In honestee, with swich a lord to dele,
For myn estat, and also for his hele.

102

Eek, wel wot I my kinges sone is he;
And sith he hath to see me swich delyt,
If I wolde utterly his sighte flee,

Paraunter he mighte have me in dispyt,
Thurgh which I mighte stonde in worse plyt;
Now were I wys, me hate to purchace,
With-outen nede, ther I may stonde in grace?

103

In every thing, I woot, ther lyth mesure.
For though a man forbede dronkenesse,
He nought for-bet that every creature
Be drinkelees for alwey, as I gesse;
Eek sith I woot for me is his distresse,
I ne oughte not for that thing him despyse,
Sith it is so, he meneth in good wyse.

104

And eek I knowe, of longe tyme agoon,
His thewes goode, and that he is not nyce.
Ne avauntour, seyth men, certein, is he noon;
To wys is he to do so gret a vyce;
Ne als I nel him never so cheryce,
That he may make avaunt, by juste cause;
He shal me never binde in swiche a clause.

105

Now set a cas, the hardest is, y-wis,
Men mighten deme that he loveth me:
What dishonour were it un-to me, this?
May I him lette of that? why nay, pardee!
I knowe also, and alday here and see,
Men loven wommen al this toun aboute;
Be they the wers? why, nay, with-outen doute.

106

I thenk eek how he able is for to have
Of al this noble toun the thriftieste,
To been his love, so she hir honour save;
For out and out he is the worthieste,
Save only Ector, which that is the beste
And yet his lyf al lyth now in my cure,
But swich is love, and eek myn aventure.

107

Ne me to love, a wonder is it nought;
For wel wot I my-self, so god me spede,
Al wolde I that noon wistë of this thought,
I am oon the fayreste, out of drede,
And goodlieste, who-so taketh hede;
And so men seyn in al the toun of Troye.
What wonder is it though he of me have joye?

108

I am myn owene woman, wel at ese,
I thanke it god, as after myn estat;
Right yong, and stonde unteyd in lusty lese,
With-outen jalousye or swich debat;
Shal noon housbonde seyn to me 'chek-mat!'
For either they ben ful of jalousye,
Or maisterful, or loven novelrye.

109

What shal I doon? to what fyn live I thus?
Shal I nat loven, in cas if that me leste?
What, *par dieux!* I am nought religious!
And though that I myn herte sette at reste
Upon this knight, that is the worthieste,
And kepe alwey myn honour and my name,
By alle right, it may do me no shame."

110

But right as whan the sonne shyneth brighte,

He might be angry with me, and with right,
Whereby I might fall in a still worse plight.
Would that be wise if I his hate incurred,
When I might have his love for just a word?

103

"In everything there should be moderation,
For though one might forbid all drunkenness,
One could not say that men through all creation
Should never drink—'twere folly, nothing less;
And since for me he feels all this distress,
No reason I should scorn him and despise,
That is, if he behaves in goodly wise.

104

"But well I know, and so does everyone,
That he in all affairs is most discreet,
And boaster, too, most surely he is none,
Nor idle tales or secrets would repeat;
But that's a point on which I need not treat,
For he shall have no chance to boast of me,
Or hold me by such bonds of secrecy.

105

"But now suppose the worst should come about
And men should gossip of his love for me,
Need that upon my name cast any doubt?
Can I stop him from that? Why, he is free!
I know, and every day I hear and see,
That men love women, yet no leave have they,
And when they want to stop, they can and may!

106

"Of course I know he is a splendid catch,
To get whom women all would do their best,
If no dishonor thereto did attach;
For he by far surpasses all the rest,
Save Hector only, who is worthiest,
And yet his life is subject to my glance!
But such is love, and such my lucky chance!

107

"That he should love me surely is no wonder,
For I am not so simple but I know
(Though naturally I say this only under
My breath) that I am fair, as women go,
Fairer than most, though I myself say so,
But plenty here in Troy will say the same;
If he thinks well of me, who can him blame?

108

"I am my master, too, here at my ease,
Thank God for that, and with a fair estate,
Right young and free to do just as I please,
With husband none to say to me 'Checkmate!'
Or worry me with troublesome debate.
For husbands all are full of jealousy,
And masterful, or hunting novelty!

109

"What should I do? Shall I not have some fun?
Shall I not even love, if so inclined?
Why not, I'd like to know! I'm not a nun!
What if my heart a resting place should find
Upon this knight, the best of all mankind,
If I preserve my honor and my name,
I see no cause in that of harm or blame!"

110

Now like the sun in March which shines out bright,

Though oft the March sun, too, doth hide his face,
For though the winds may put the clouds to flight,
Their courses soon again the clouds retrace,
So now a cloudy thought began to race
Across her heart, o'erspreading like a pall
Her sunny thoughts with shadowy thought withal.

111

The thought was this, "Alas, since I am free,
Should I now love and risk my happy state
And maybe put in bonds my liberty?
What folly such a course to contemplate!
Am I not satisfied to see the fate
Of others, with their fear and joy and pain?
Who loveth not, no cause hath to complain.

112

"For lovers ever lead a stormy life,
And have done so since loving was begun,
For always some distrust and foolish strife
There is in love, some cloud across the sun.
Then nothing by us women can be done,
But weep in wretchedness and sit and think,
'This is our lot, the cup of woe to drink!'

113

"And slanderous tongues, they are so very quick
To do us harm, and men are so untrue,
And once they're satisfied, they soon grow sick
Of ancient love and look for something new!
But when all's done, then what can women do!
These men at first their love like mad will spend,
But sharp attacks oft weaken at the end.

114

"Full often it hath been exemplified,
The treason that to women men will show;
And that's the end, when such a love hath died,
For what becomes of it, when it doth go,
No living creature on this earth can know,
For then there's nothing left to love or spurn;
What once was naught, to nothing doth return.

115

"And if I love, how busy must I be
To guard against all idle people's chatter,
And fool them that they see no fault in me,
For true or not, to them it doesn't matter,
If but their lying tales amuse or flatter;
For who can stop the wagging of a tongue,
Or sound of bells the while that they are rung!"

116

But when her cloudy thoughts began to clear,
She countered, "Nothing venture, nothing gain!
All things must have their price, or cheap or dear."
This thought brought dark forebodings in its train,
And hope and fear were linked in endless chain,
Now hot, now cold, and thus between the two
She started up, still doubtful what to do.

117

Down stairs along the garden paths she went,
And calling to her there her nieces three,
They rambled through the garden's whole extent,
Flexippe, Tarbe and Antigone,
A charming and a pleasant sight to see;
And others of her women came along,
And in the garden made a merry throng.

In March, that chaungeth ofte tyme his face,
And that a cloud is put with wind to flighte
Which over-sprat the sonne as for a space,
A cloudy thought gan thorugh hir soule pace,
That over-spradde hir brighte thoughtes alle,
So that for fere almost she gan to falle.

111

That thought was this, "allas! sin I am free,
Sholde I now love, and putte in jupartye
My sikernesse, and thrallen libertee?
Allas! how dorste I thenken that folye?
May I nought wel in other folk aspye
Hir dredful joye, hir constreynt, and hir peyne?
Ther loveth noon, that she nath why to pleyne.

112

For love is yet the moste stormy lyf,
Right of him-self, that ever was bigonne;
For ever som mistrust, or nyce stryf,
Ther is in love, som cloud is over the sonne:
Ther-to we wrecched wommen no-thing conne,
Whan us is wo, but wepe and sitte and thinke;
Our wreche is this, our owene wo to drinke.

113

Also these wikked tonges been so prest
To speke us harm, eek men be so untrewe,
That, right anoon as cessed is hir lest,
So cesseth love, and forth to love a newe:
But harm y-doon, is doon, who-so it rewe.
For though these men for love hem first to-rende,
Ful sharp biginning breketh ofte at ende.

114

How ofte tyme hath it y-knowen be,
The treson, that to womman hath be do?
To what fyn is swich love, I can nat see,
Or wher bicomth it, whan it is ago;
Ther is no wight that woot, I trowe so,
Wher it bycomth; lo, no wight on it sporneth;
That erst was no-thing, in-to nought it torneth.

115

How bisy, if I love, eek moste I be
To plesen hem that jangle of love, and demen,
And coye hem, that they sey non harm of me?
For though ther be no cause, yet hem semen
Al be for harm that folk hir freendes quemen;
And who may stoppen every wikked tonge,
Or soun of belles whyl that they be ronge?"

116

And after that, hir thought bigan to clere,
And seyde, 'he which that no-thing under-taketh,
No-thing ne acheveth, be him looth or dere."
And with an other thought hir herte quaketh;
Than slepeth hope, and after dreed awaketh;
Now hoot, now cold; but thus, bi-twixen tweye,
She rist hir up, and went hir for to pleye.

117

Adoun the steyre anoon-right tho she wente
In-to the gardin, with hir neces three,
And up and doun ther made many a wente,
Flexippe, she, Tharbe, and Antigone,
To pleyen, that it joye was to see;
And othere of hir wommen, a gret route,
Hir folwede in the gardin al aboute.

118

This yerd was large, and rayled alle the aleyes,
And shadwed wel with blosmy bowes grene,
And benched newe, and sonded alle the weyes,
In which she walketh arm in arm bitwene;
Til at the laste Antigone the shene
Gan on a Trojan song to singe clere,
That it an heven was hir voys to here.—

119

She seyde, "O love, to whom I have and shal
Ben humble subgit, trewe in myn entente,
As I best can, to yow, lord, yeve ich al
For ever-more, myn hertes lust to rente.
For never yet thy grace no wight sente
So blisful cause as me, my lyf to lede
In alle joye and seurtee, out of drede.

120

Ye, blisful god, han me so wel beset
In love, y-wis, that al that bereth lyf
Imaginen ne cowde how to ben bet;
For, lord, with-outen jalousye or stryf,
I love oon which that is most ententyf
To serven wel, unwery or unfeyned,
That ever was, and leest with harm distreyned.

121

As he that is the welle of worthinesse,
Of trouthe ground, mirour of goodliheed,
Of wit Appollo, stoon of sikernesse,
Of vertu rote, of lust findere and heed,
Thurgh which is alle sorwe fro me deed,
Y-wis, I love him best, so doth he me;
Now good thrift have he, wher-so that he be!

122

Whom sholde I thanke but yow, god of love,
Of al this blisse, in which to bathe I ginne?
And thanked be ye, lord, for that I love!
This is the righte lyf that I am inne,
To flemen alle manere vyce and sinne:
This doth me so to vertu for to entende,
That day by day I in my wil amende.

123

And who-so seyth that for to love is vyce,
Or thraldom, though he fele in it distresse,
He outher is envyous, or right nyce,
Or is unmighty, for his shrewednesse,
To loven; for swich maner folk, I gesse,
Defamen love, as no-thing of him knowe;
They speken, but they bente never his bowe.

124

What is the sonne wers, of kinde righte,
Though that a man, for feblesse of his yën,
May nought endure on it to see for brighte?
Or love the wers, though wrecches on it cryen?
No wele is worth, that may no sorwe dryen.
And for-thy, who that hath an heed of verre,
Fro cast of stones war him in the werre!

125

But I with al myn herte and al my might,
As I have seyd, wol love, un-to my laste,
My dere herte, and al myn owene knight,
In which myn herte growen is so faste,
And his in me, that it shal ever laste.

118

The place was large, and all the alleys railed,
And shaded well with flowery boughs, all green
With branches new, nor gravelled paths there failed
On which she walked, two nieces dear between,
The while Antigone, with cheerful mien,
Began to sing a Trojan lay, so clear
It was a heavenly joy her voice to hear:

119

"O God of Love, to whom I e'er have been
A humble subject, true in my intent
And will, through thee, O Love, I hope to win
What joy shall ever to my heart be sent!
For I opine that no one has been meant
By thy good grace a happier life to lead
Than I, whose joy by thee has been decreed.

120

"O blissful God, so happy is my state,
No creature on this earth, with creatures rife,
Could equal me in love or be my mate;
For Lord, with neither jealousy not strife,
I love one who is eager with his life
To serve me, tireless and unrestrained,
And with a love by no dishonor stained.

121

"For he whose mastership I here confess,
The ground of truth and virtue's looking-glass,
Apollo for wit, the rock of steadfastness,
The root of good, whose joys all joy surpass,
Who makes all sorrow wither as the grass—
I love him best, and so doth he love me;
Success to him, whoever he may be!

122

"Whom should I thank but thee, thou God above,
That now to bathe in bliss I may begin?
Have here my thanks, O Lord, that I may love!
The happy life is this that I dwell in,
The refuge here from every vice and sin!
Such virtue loving to my heart doth lend
That day by day I feel my life amend.

123

"And anyone who says that love is wrong,
Or slavery, then he is nothing less
Than envious, or in his wit not strong,
Or lacking power to love for crustiness;
And folk who talk of hardship and distress,
But slander love and nothing of him know;
They talk, but they have never bent his bow.

124

"For is the sun the worse in its own right
Because some man, for weakness of his eye,
May not endure its radiance so bright?
Or love the worse, though some against it cry?
No weal is well that sorrow can outvie,
And people in glass houses should be wary,
And specially of throwing stones be chary.

125

"But I with all my heart and all my might,
As I have said, with loving unsurpassed
Will love my love, my true and precious knight,
To whom my soul hath grown so firm and fast,
And his to me, our love shall ever last;

Though once with love I dreaded to begin,
Now well I know no peril lies therein."

126

When thus her song to happy end she brought,
Cressida spoke up, "Dearest niece," she said,
"Pray tell me who this pleasant ditty wrought?"
She gave no name but answered thus instead,
"Madam, the goodliest maid and highest bred
Of all maids in this pleasant town of Troy,
Who lived her life in honor and in joy."

127

"So it would seem, to judge her by her song,"
Said Cressida, and therewith paused and sighed,
"I wonder, doth such joy in truth belong
In love as by such ditties seems implied!"
"O yes" Antigone with rapture cried,
"For all the folk that dwell in mortal state
The joy of love in full could not relate.

128

"But 'tis not every humble creature knows
The perfect bliss of love! Most surely not!
For foolish men will foolish things suppose;
Most think it's love if only they are hot!
But ask the saints if you would know the lot
Of those in heaven, for they alone can tell,
And ask the devil if it's foul in hell."

129

Cressida to this said nothing in reply,
Observing but, "It's getting on toward night,"
Yet all these words within her memory lie,
Imprinted on her heart all clear and bright;
And now indeed of love she feels less fright
Than she had done, for now love sits at ease
Within her heart, with greater power to please.

130

The crown of day and heaven's brightest eye,
The foe of night (I merely mean the sun),
Westward and downward now began to hie,
For he the course of one full day had run,
And all things bright were turning drear and dun
For lack of light, while stars came out in scores,
And Cressida betook herself indoors.

131

And when at length time came to go to bed
And all the folk had left the house who ought,
To go to sleep she felt inclined she said,
And soon her women to her bed her brought;
And there in silence lay she still and thought
And thought, but all her thoughts I can't delay
To tell, and you can guess them anyway.

132

Upon a cedar green a nightingale,
Under the chamber wall near where she lay,
Full loudly sang against the moonlight pale,
A song perhaps of love, as birds well may,
For love alone could make a song so gay;
And listening long, this loving song sank deep
Within her heart before she fell asleep.

133

And as she slept, she dreamed, and dreaming saw
A wondrous eagle, feathered snowy white,
And from her breast he tore with curving claw

Al dredde I first to love him to biginne,
Now woot I wel, ther is no peril inne."

126

And of hir song right with that word she stente,
And therwith-al, "now, nece," quod Criseyde,
"Who made this song with so good entente?"
Antigone answerde anoon, and seyde,
"Ma dame, y-wis, the godlieste mayde
Of greet estat in al the toun of Troye;
And let hir lyf in most honour and joye."

127

"Forsothe, so it semeth by hir song,"
Quod tho Criseyde, and gan ther-with to syke,
And seyde, "lord, is there swich blisse among
These lovers, as they conne faire endyte?"
"Ye, wis," quod fresh Antigone the whyte,
"For alle the folk that han or been on lyve
Ne conne wel the blisse of love discryve.

128

But wene ye that every wrecche woot
The parfit blisse of love? why, nay, y-wis;
They wenen al be love, if oon be hoot;
Do wey, do wey, they woot no-thing of this!
Men mosten axe at seyntes if it is
Aught fair in hevene; why? for they conne telle;
And axen fendes, is it foul in helle."

129

Criseyde un-to that purpos nought answerde,
But seyde, "y-wis, it wol be night as faste."
But every word which that she of hir herde,
She gan to prenten in hir herte faste;
And ay gan love hir lasse for to agaste
Than it dide erst, and sinken in hir herte,
That she wex somwhat able to converte.

130

The dayes honour, and the hevenes yë,
The nightes fo, al this clepe I the sonne,
Gan westren faste, and dounward for to wrye,
As he that hadde his dayes cours y-ronne;
And whyte thinges wexen dimme and donne
For lak of light, and sterres for to appere,
That she and al hir folk in wente y-fere.

131

So whan it lyked hir to goon to reste,
And voyded weren they that voyden oughte,
She seyde, that to slepe wel hir leste.
Hir wommen sone til hir bed hir broughte.
Whan al was hust, than lay she stille, and thoughte
Of al this thing the manere and the wyse.
Reherce it nedeth nought, for ye ben wyse.

132

A nightingale, upon a cedre grene,
Under the chambre-wal ther as she lay,
Ful loude sang ayein the mone shene,
Paraunter, in his briddes wyse, a lay
Of love, that made hir herte fresh and gay.
That herkned she so longe in good entente,
Til at the laste the dede sleep hir hente.

133

And, as she sleep, anoon-right tho hir mette,
How that an egle, fethered whyt as boon,
Under hir brest his longe clawes sette,

And out hir herte he rente, and that a-noon,
And dide his herte in-to hir brest to goon,
Of which she nought agroos ne no-thing smerte,
And forth he fleigh, with herte left for herte.

Her heart, and then she saw a stranger sight;
Where hers had been, he put his heart forthright,
At which no fear she knew, nor pain nor smart,
And forth he flew, with heart exchanged for heart.

134

Now lat hir slepe, and we our tales holde
Of Troilus, that is to paleys riden,
Fro the scarmuch, of the whiche I tolde,
And in his chambre sit, and hath abiden
Til two or three of his messages yeden
For Pandarus, and soughten him ful faste,
Til they him founde, and broughte him at the
laste.

134

So let her sleep, and let us now give heed
To Troilus, who to the palace rides
From that same skirmish on his prancing steed,
And to his chamber goes, and there abides,
But sends his courier, and two or three besides,
To look for Pandar, whom they straightway sought
And found and to the palace quickly
brought.

135

This Pandarus com leping in at ones
And seide thus, "who hath ben wel y-bete
To-day with swerdes, and with slinge-stones,
But Troilus, that hath caught him an hete?"
And gan to jape, and seyde, "lord, so ye
swete!
But rys, and lat us soupe and go to reste";
And he answerde him, "do we as thee leste."

135

Pandar came running in at once and said,
"O what a day! What Trojan ever yet
Has had such storms of swords upon his head
As Troilus! It made you hot, I'll bet,"
And laughed and joking said, "Lord, how you
sweat!
But come, it's late, and time you should clean up."
"All right," said Troilus, "let's go and sup."

136

With al the haste goodly that they mighte,
They spedde hem fro the souper un-to bedde;
And every wight out at the dore him dighte,
And wher him list upon his wey he spedde;
But Troilus, that thoughte his herte bledde
For wo, til that he herde som tydinge,
He seyde, "freend, shal I now wepe or singe?"

136

In haste they went, in haste they also supped,
Then back again and so prepared for bed,
Sending away all who could interrupt
The confidential things that might be said;
And Troilus, whose very heart-strings bled
Until he heard what news his friend would bring,
Cried out, "Now tell me, shall I weep or sing?"

137

Quod Pandarus, "ly stille, and lat me slepe,
And don thyn hood, thy nedes spedde be;
And chese, if thou wolt singe or daunce or lepe;
At shorte wordes, thow shalt trowe me.—
Sire, my nece wol do wel by thee,
And love thee best, by god and by my trouthe,
But lak of pursuit make it in thy slouthe.

137

"O hush!" said Pandar, "let me go to sleep!
And you do, too! You have no need to worry,
But choose if you will dance or sing or leap.
Just trust in me and don't be in a hurry.
To tell the truth, she's in as great a flurry
As you are in, and near as resolute,
If only you don't slacken in pursuit.

138

For thus ferforth I have thy work bigonne,
Fro day to day, til this day, by the morwe,
Hir love of freendship have I to thee wonne,
And also hath she leyd hir feyth to borwe.
Algate a foot is hameled of thy sorwe."
What sholde I lenger sermon of it holde?
As ye han herd bifore, al he him tolde.

138

"For your affair I have so well begun
And carried on, that on this very day
Her loving friendship I for you have won
And her good faith against it she doth lay—
Your woe in one leg's crippled anyway!"
But why should I a longer discourse hold,
For all that you have heard, to him be told.

139

But right as floures, thorugh the colde of night
Y-closed, stoupen on hir stalkes lowe,
Redressen hem a-yein the sonne bright,
And spreden on hir kinde cours by rowe;
Right so gan tho his eyen up to throwe
This Troilus, and seyde, "O Venus dere,
Thy might, thy grace, y-heried be it here!"

139

And as the flowers, closed by cold at night,
Hang drooping on their stalks all limp and low,
But straighten up against the sunshine bright
And in their proper way expand and grow,
Troilus lifted up his eyes just so
And said, "O precious Venus, goddess mine,
All honor to thy grace and power divine!"

140

And to Pandare he held up bothe his hondes,
And seyde, "lord, al thyn be that I have;
For I am hool, al brosten been my bondes;
A thousand Troians who so that me yave,
Eche after other, god so wis me save,
Ne mighte me so gladen; lo, myn herte,
It spredeth so for joye, it wol to-sterte!

140

To Pandar then he held out both his hands,
And said, "Good sir, all that I have is thine!
For I am healed, and broken are my bands!
A thousand Troys, if thousand Troys were mine,
Could not together happily combine
To give me such a joy, for lo, my heart
So swells, it seems in fragments it must part.

141

"What shall I do? And how shall I survive?
And when again shall I my sweetheart see?
The tedious time away how shall I drive
Until you bring back further news to me?
'Tis easy quite to say 'Go slow,' but he
That's hanging by the neck in mortal pain
Has no desire hanging to remain."

142

"Now, now," said Pandar, "by the love of Mars,
You know that all things have their proper season,
And that the night immediate action bars;
But if you'll listen to a little reason,
I'll go the earliest hour that she agrees on;
In some things you must do just what I say,
Or on some other man your charges lay.

143

"For heaven knows, I ever yet have been
Ready at call, nor ever to this night
Have I held back, for though my wit be thin,
I've done my best, according to my might.
Do as I say, and it will be all right.
But if you won't, to me it's all the same,
Though in that case, I shall not bear the blame.

144

"I know that thou art wiser far than I,
But were I in the selfsame fix as thou,
I know the very plan that I would try.
With my own hand I'd go and write her now
A letter, telling her exactly how
The love of her had driven me near crazy.
Now stir yourself and don't be slack or lazy.

145

"And I myself will with your letter go,
And at the time that I am with her there,
In all your gear to make the bravest show,
Upon your courser to her street repair,
As though it were upon some chance affair,
And you will find us at a window-seat,
So shall I manage, looking in the street.

146

"And if you want, give us a brief salute,
But when you do, of course at me you'll glance,
And then ride on, as though on some pursuit
That called you hence. Don't stop, by any chance!
Just take it steady, and on your way advance,
And after you are gone, to her I'll turn
And tell her things will make your ears both burn.

147

"Respecting that letter, you are wise enough,
Only I wouldn't write in too high style,
Or spin fine arguments obscure and tough.
Don't write too neat, and use a little guile—
Let tear stains blot your words once in a while;
But if you find a word you think is clever,
Use it but once, don't harp on it forever!

148

"For though a harper were the best alive,
And had the best harp in the world to play,
And played it best with all his fingers five,
If he but touched one string or sang one lay,
However sharp his nails were filed away,

141

But lord, how shal I doon, how shal I liven?
Whan shal I next my dere herte see?
How shal this longe tyme a-wey be driven,
Til that thou be ayein at hir fro me?
Thou mayst answere, 'a-byd, a-byd,' but he
That hangeth by the nekke, sooth to seyne,
In grete disese abydeth for the peyne."

142

"Al esily, now, for the love of Marte,"
Quod Pandarus, "for every thing hath tyme;
So longe abyd til that the night departe;
For al so siker as thow lyst here by me,
And god toforn, I wol be there at pryme,
And for thy werk somwhat as I shal seye,
Or on som other wight this charge leye.

143

For pardee, god wot, I have ever yit
Ben redy thee to serve, and to this night
Have I nought fayned, but emforth my wit
Don al thy lust, and shal with al my might.
Do now as I shal seye, and fare a-right;
And if thou nilt, wyte al thy-self thy care,
On me is nought along thyn yvel fare.

144

I woot wel that thow wyser art than I
A thousand fold, but if I were as thou,
God helpe me so, as I wolde outrely,
Right of myn owene hond, wryte hir right now
A lettre, in which I wolde hir tellen how
I ferde amis, and hir beseche of routhe;
Now help thy-self, and leve it not for slouthe.

145

And I my-self shal ther-with to hir goon;
And whan thou wost that I am with hir there,
Worth thou up-on a courser right anoon,
Ye, hardily, right in thy beste gere,
And ryd forth by the place, as nought ne were,
And thou shalt finde us, if I may, sittinge
At som windowe, in-to the strete lokinge.

146

And if thee list, than maystow us saluwe,
And up-on me makë thy contenaunce;
But, by thy lyf, be war and faste eschuwe
To tarien ought, god shilde us fro mischaunce!
Ryd forth thy wey, and hold thy governaunce;
And we shal speke of thee som-what, I trowe,
Whan thou art goon, to do thyne eres glowe!

147

Touching thy lettre, thou art wys y-nough,
I woot thow nilt it digneliche endyte;
As make it with thise argumentes tough;
Ne scrivenish or craftily thou it wryte;
Beblotte it with thy teres eek a lyte;
And if thou wryte a goodly word al softe,
Though it be good, reherce it not to ofte.

148

For though the beste harpour upon lyve
Wolde on the beste souned joly harpe
That ever was, with alle his fingers fyve,
Touche ay o streng, or ay o werbul harpe,
Were his nayles poynted never so sharpe,

It shulde maken every wight to dulle,
To here his glee, and of his strokes fulle.

149

Ne jompre eek no discordaunt thing y-fere,
As thus, to usen termes of phisyk;
In loves termes, hold of thy matere
The forme alwey, and do that it be lyk;
For if a peyntour wolde peynte a pyk
With asses feet, and hede it as an ape,
It cordeth nought; so nere it but a jape."

150

This counseyl lyked wel to Troilus;
But, as a dreedful lover, he seyde this:—
"Allas, my dere brother Pandarus,
I am ashamed for to wryte, y-wis,
Lest of myn innocence I seyde a-mis,
Or that she nolde it for despyt receyve;
Thanne were I deed, ther mighte it no-thing
  weyve."

151

To that Pandare answerde, "if thee lest,
Do that I seye, and lat me therwith goon;
For by that lord that formed est and west,
I hope of it to bringe answere anoon
Right of hir hond, and if that thou nilt noon,
Lat be; and sory mote he been his lyve,
Ayeins thy lust that helpeth thee to thryve."

152

Quod Troilus, "*Depardieux*, I assente;
Sin that thee list, I will aryse and wryte;
And blisful god preye ich, with good entente,
The vyage, and the lettre I shal endyte,
So spede it; and thou, Minerva, the whyte,
Yif thou me wit my lettre to devyse":
And sette him doun, and wroot right in this
  wyse.—

153

First he gan hir his righte lady calle,
His hertes lyf, his lust, his sorwes leche,
His blisse, and eek this othere termes alle,
That in swich cas these loveres alle seche;
And in ful humble wyse, as in his speche,
He gan him recomaunde un-to hir grace;
To telle al how, it axeth muchel space.

154

And after this, ful lowly he hir prayde
To be nought wrooth, though he, of his folye,
So hardy was to hir to wryte, and seyde,
That love it made, or elles moste he dye,
And pitously gan mercy for to crye;
And after that he seyde, and ley ful loude,
Him-self was litel worth, and lesse he coude;

155

And that she sholde han his conning excused,
That litel was, and eek he dredde hir so,
And his unworthinesse he ay acused;
And after that, than gan he telle his wo;
But that was endeles, with-outen ho
And seyde, he wolde in trouthe alwey him holde;—
And radde it over, and gan the lettre folde.

156

And with his salte teres gan he bathe

His music would but make men dull and sad,
And only when he stopped would they be glad.

149

"And don't mix things that do not harmonize,
In love and medicine the same note strike,
But always use the style that best applies
To what you say, so that it seems life-like;
For if a painter painted finny pike
With asses' feet and headed them like apes,
He'd be no artist but a jack-a-napes."

150

Troilus thought this counsel very wise,
But timid lover that he was, replied,
"Pandar, alas, I see what you advise,
But I'm afraid to write, I must confide!
Such letters I have never seen nor tried,
And if she took amiss what I might say,
Goodnight for me—'twould be my fatal
  day!"

151

"Don't balk," said Pandar, "go ahead and write,
And let me with your letter to her go,
And by the Lord and his eternal might,
I'll have an answer soon that I can show
From her own hand. But if you won't do so,
I give it up. And heaven help the chap
Who tries to help you out of your mishap!"

152

"O Lord," his poor friend answered, "I give in!
Since you insist, I'll get up now and write!
May God help you your journey's end to win,
When, as and if my letter I endite!
Minerva, O thou goddess fair and bright,
Grant me the wit my letter to devise!"
Then down he sat and wrote her in this
  wise.

153

His only lady first he did her call,
Life of his heart, his joy, his sorrows' cure,
His bliss, and many other terms that all
Good lovers use their ladies to assure;
And then with humble words and with demure,
He begged that she would show to him some grace—
Of course to tell you all I haven't space.

154

Then next he begged in meek and humble fashion
That she would cast at least a pardoning eye
On what he dared to write, and said his passion
Left him no choice, except he wished to die,
Nor stopped with that at piling it on high;
Himself of small account he did profess,
And added that his deeds were worth still less,

155

And begged her to excuse his lack of skill,
And said it was because he feared her so,
And harped upon his subjugation still,
And on his sufferings too deep to show,
And said that they would even greater grow,
And then goodby, with pledges new and old,
And so his letter ready was to fold.

156

The ruby in his signet with his tears

He bathes, and when he hath it neatly set
Upon the wax, its impress there appears;
A thousand times then he did not forget
To kiss his missive with his kisses wet,
And said, "O letter, what a joy for thee!
Tomorrow thou my lady dear shalt see."

157

The letter in the morning Pandar took
To Cressida, as soon as he could start.
"Are you awake," he cried, "let's have a look!"
And then he laughed and joked, and said, "My
heart
Remains so fresh, for all love makes it smart,
I cannot sleep on such a May-time morrow!
I have a jolly woe, a lusty sorrow!"

158

Cressida greeted him with some surprise,
Eager to know, but also with some fear
Why he came there, she questions and replies,
"What lucky wind has brought you over
here
So early in the morning, uncle dear?
Tell us your jolly woe and your mischance!
What progress are you making in love's dance?"

159

"As ever," he said, "I'm limping far behind!"
At which she laughed as if her heart would burst.
"I hope," said Pandar, "you will always find
Me cause for mirth! But listen to me first—
There's come a stranger to this town accursed,
A Grecian spy, and he great tidings brings—
I thought you'd like to hear about these things.

160

"Let's go into the garden, you and I,
I'll tell you privately this latest news."
Then arm in arm, down from her chamber high
They walk into the garden cool, and choose
A quiet path where no one hears or views
The things they say or do, and thus concealed,
Pandar the precious letter straight revealed.

161

"He who is altogether yours," said he,
"Petitions you most humbly for your grace,
And sends to you this letter here by me.
Regard it well at fitting time and place,
And with your pen some goodly answer trace,
For now I tell you once for all and plain,
He cannot longer live in so great pain."

162

The letter she beheld, but stood quite still,
And took it not, till anger drove out fear,
And then she loudly cried, "Nor script nor bill,
For love of God, bring never to me here
From such a source! And also, uncle dear,
For my good name have more regard, I pray,
Than for your friend. What need I further say?

163

"Pray tell me, do you in your heart believe,
For all your guileful words and cunning speech,
That I could properly this note receive,
Or put in practice what you seem to preach,
And both of you so earnestly beseech,

The ruby in his signet, and it sette
Upon the wex deliverliche and rathe;
Ther-with a thousand tymes, er he lette,
He kiste tho the lettre that he shette,
And seyde, "lettre, a blisful destenee
Thee shapen is, my lady shal thee see."

157

This Pandare took the lettre, and that by tyme
A-morwe, and to his neces paleys sterte,
And faste he swoor, that it was passed pryme,
And gan to jape, and seyde, "y-wis, myn
herte,
So fresh it is, al-though it sore smerte,
I may not slepe never a Mayes morwe;
I have a joly wo, a lusty sorwe."

158

Criseyde, whan that she hir uncle herde,
With dreedful herte, and desirous to here
The cause of his cominge, thus answerde,
"Now by your feyth, myn uncle," quod she,
"dere,
What maner windes gydeth yow now here?
Tel us your joly wo and your penaunce,
How ferforth be ye put in loves daunce."

159

"By god," quod he, "I hoppe alwey bihinde!"
And she to-laugh, it thoughte hir herte breste.
Quod Pandarus, "loke alwey that ye finde
Game in myn hood, but herkneth, if yow leste;
Ther is right now come in-to toune a geste,
A Greek espye, and telleth newe thinges,
For which come I to telle yow tydinges.

160

Into the gardin go we, and we shal here,
Al prevely, of this a long sermoun."
With that they wenten arm in arm y-fere
In-to the gardin from the chaumbre doun.
And whan that he so fer was that the soun
Of that he speke, no man here mighte,
He seyde hir thus, and out the lettre plighte,

161

"Lo, he that is al hoolly youres free
Him recomaundeth lowly to your grace,
And sent to you this lettre here by me;
Avyseth you on it, whan ye han space,
And of som goodly answere yow purchace;
Or, helpe me god, so pleynly for to seyne,
He may not longe liven for his peyne."

162

Ful dredfully tho gan she stonde stille,
And took it nought, but al hir humble chere
Gan for to chaunge, and seyde, "scrit ne bille,
For love of god, that toucheth swich matere,
Ne bring me noon; and also, uncle dere,
To myn estat have more reward, I preye,
Than to his lust; what sholde I more seye?

163

And loketh now if this be resonable,
And letteth nought, for favour ne for slouthe,
To seyn a sooth; now were it covenable
To myn estat, by god, and by your trouthe,
To taken it, or to han of him routhe,

In harming of my-self or in repreve?
Ber it a-yein, for him that ye on leve!"

164

This Pandarus gan on hir for to stare,
And seyde, "now is this the grettest wonder
That ever I sey! lat be this nyce fare!
To deethe mote I smiten be with thonder,
If, for the citee which that stondeth yonder,
Wolde I a lettre un-to yow bringe or take
To harm of yow; what list yow thus it make?

165

But thus ye faren, wel neigh alle and some,
That he that most desireth yow to serve,
Of him ye recche leest wher he bicome,
And whether that he live or elles sterve.
But for al that that ever I may deserve,
Refuse it nought," quod he, and hente hir faste,
And in hir bosom the lettre doun he thraste,

166

And seyde hir, "now cast it away anoon,
That folk may seen and gauren on us tweye."
Quod she, "I can abyde til they be goon,"
And gan to smyle, and seyde him, "eem, I preye,
Swich answere as yow list your-self purveye,
For trewely I nil no lettre write."
"No? than wol I," quod he, "so ye endyte."

167

Therwith she lough, and seyde, "go we dyne."
And he gan at him-self to jape faste,
And seyde, "nece, I have so greet a pyne
For love, that every other day I faste"—
And gan his beste japes forth to caste;
And made hir so to laughe at his folye,
That she for laughter wende for to dye.

168

And whan that she was comen in-to halle,
"Now, eem," quod she, "we wol go dyne anoon";
And gan some of hir women to hir calle,
And streyght in-to hir chaumbre gan she goon;
But for hir besinesses, this was oon
A-monges othere thinges, out of drede,
Ful prively this lettre for to rede;

169

Avysed word by word in every lyne,
And fond no lak, she thoughte he coude good;
And up it putte, and went hir in to dyne.
And Pandarus, that in a study stood,
Er he was war, she took him by the hood,
And seyde, "ye were caught er that ye wiste";
"I vouche sauf," quod he, "do what yow liste."

170

Tho wesshen they, and sette hem doun and ete;
And after noon ful sleyly Pandarus
Gan drawe him to the window next the strete,
And seyde, "nece, who hath arayed thus
The yonder hous, that stant afor-yeyn us?"
"Which hous?" quod she, and gan for to biholde,
And knew it wel, and whos it was him tolde,

171

And fillen forth in speche of thinges smale,
And seten in the window bothe tweye.
Whan Pandarus saw tyme un-to his tale,

And not wreck all my good repute and fame?
Take it away, I bid in heaven's name!"

164

"Why, Cressida," he said, "you are quite droll!
Is this the first you've heard of this, I wonder!
Let Jove to depths infernal damn my soul,
Or strike me down with sudden stroke of thunder,
If for the town whose walls we're sitting under,
A harmful word to you I'd ever carry!
Your conduct seems to me extraordinary!

165

"But I suppose you think like all the rest,
That he deserves the least who most does try
To serve and aid you with his very best!
But though you reck not if he live or die,
And all my good intentions you deny,
You shan't refuse." And then he seized her gown
And in her bosom thrust the letter down.

166

"Now then," he said, "this note I dare you throw
Away, that folk may see your grand display!"
"O, I can wait," she said, "until you go!"
And then she smiled and added, "Uncle, pray,
Such answer as you will to him convey,
For truly, uncle, I shall write no letter."
"I'll dictate," said he, "if you think that's better."

167

She laughed at this and said, "Let's go and dine!"
And he agreed, assured the worst was past,
And said, "Dear niece, for love I peak and pine
So much, that every other day I fast!"
And told his jokes, some new, some old recast,
And made her laugh till she was out of breath.
And thought that she would laugh herself to death.

168

When they had come together to the hall,
"We'll dine," she said, "in just a minute or so,"
And her attendants coming at her call,
She said that to her room she'd have to go,
And there, as Pandar very well did know,
However pressing any other need,
Her letter first she would be sure to read.

169

She read it word by word and line by line,
And on the whole she thought it pretty good,
And put it up and then went in to dine.
Pandar apart in deep reflection stood,
And she came up and took him by the hood,
"Aha," she said, "a penny for your thought!"
"Have what you will," he said, "I'm fairly caught!"

170

And then they washed and set them down to eat,
And after dinner, Pandar with design,
Drew near the window looking on the street,
"Whose house is that," he asked, "decked out so fine,
A little further down across from thine?"
"Which house?" she answered, drawing near to see,
And knew it well, and told its history.

171

And there they stayed and talked of this and that,
Both sitting down within the window bay,
But after much such unimportant chat,

And when her women all were gone away,
Then Pandar turned and said, "Well, niece, I say,
How was the letter, good or just so-so?
How does he write? I'd really like to know."

172

At that she blushed a quick and rosy red,
But merely answered, "Hm! Of course you would"
"Now you must write a fair reply," he said,
"I'll sew your letter up all tight and good,
Across the middle, if you say I should,
And if you want, just make your letter small,
But let your uncle fold and sew it all."

173

"Perhaps I might," she murmured soft and slow,
"But if I should, I don't know what to say!"
"O niece," said Pandar, "such things quickly grow!
At least your grateful thanks you can convey,
And say some words his trouble to repay.
Indeed it's only decent courtesy
To grant at least so much to him and me."

174

"O dear," she said, "I hope it's quite all right!
I never thought to write a man a letter,
It really puts me in a nervous fright!"
Into her room she went to work the better,
And there alone her heart she doth unfetter
Out of the prison of disdain a while,
Striving a fitting letter to compile.

175

And what she wrote, in brief I mean to tell,
So far as I have heard or understand;
She thanked him first that he of her thought well,
But said she really could not take in hand
A serious answer to his chief demand,
But as a sister, if she could him please,
She'd gladly do her best his heart to ease.

176

She closed it then, while Pandar mused alone,
Beside the window looking on the street,
And brought it in, and sat upon a stone
Of jasper by him on a cushion seat,
With beaten gold embroidered, fair and neat,
And said, "I've never done a harder thing
Than write this letter which to you I bring!"

177

With thanks he took the letter and replied,
"You know from things with heavy heart begun,
Come happy endings. Niece, you may take pride
That you by him have not been lightly won,
For in the tale of sayings true, the one
That says the truest runs, 'Impressions light
Are always lightly ready to take flight.'

178

"But you have played the tyrant nigh too long,
And made your heart a hard thing to engrave;
So now relent and don't bear down too strong,
(Of course appearances we still must save),
And henceforth in a gentler way behave,
For manners cold and hard will soon or late
Turn every liking to dislike and hate."

179

And as they sat thus, friendly and confiding,

And saw wel that hir folk were alle aweye,
"Now, nece myn, tel on," quod he, "I seye,
How lyketh yow the lettre that ye woot?
Can he ther-on? for, by my trouthe, I noot."

172

Therwith al rosy hewed tho wex she,
And gan to humme, and seyde, "so I trowe."
"Aquyte him wel, for goddes love," quod he;
"My-self to medes wol the lettre sowe,"
And held his hondes up, and sat on knowe,
"Now, goode nece, be it never so lyte,
Yif me the labour, it to sowe and plyte."

173

"Ye, for I can so wryte," quod she tho;
"And eek I noot what I sholde to him seye."
"Nay, nece," quod Pandare, "sey not so;
Yet at the leste thanketh him, I preye,
Of his good wil, and doth him not to deye.
Now for the love of me, my nece dere,
Refuseth not at this tyme my preyere."

174

"*Depar-dieux*," quod she, "god leve al be wel!
God helpe me so, this is the firste lettre
That ever I wroot, ye, al or any del."
And in-to a closet, for to avyse hir bettre,
She wente allone, and gan hir herte unfettre
Out of disdaynes prison but a lyte;
And sette hir doun, and gan a lettre wryte,

175

Of which to telle in short is myn entente
Th'effect, as fer as I can understonde:—
She thonked him of al that he wel mente
Towardes hir, but holden him in honde
She nolde nought, ne make hir-selven bonde
In love, but as his suster, him to plese,
She wolde fayn, to doon his herte an ese.

176

She shette it, and to Pandarus gan goon,
There as he sat and loked in-to strete,
And doun she sette hir by him on a stoon
Of jaspre, up-on a quisshin gold y-bete,
And seyde, "as wisly helpe me god the grete,
I nevere dide a thing with more peyne
Than wryte this, to which ye me constreyne";

177

And took it him: he thonked hir and seyde,
"God woot, of thing ful ofte looth bigonne
Cometh ende good; and nece myn, Criseyde,
That ye to him of hard now ben y-wonne
Oughte he be glad, by god and yonder sonne!
For-why men seth, 'impressioun[e]s lighte
Ful lightly been ay redy to the flighte.'

178

But ye han pleyed tyraunt neigh to longe,
And hard was it your herte for to grave;
Now stint, that ye no longer on it honge,
Al wolde ye the forme of daunger save.
But hasteth yow to doon him joye have;
For trusteth wel, to longe y-doon hardnesse
Causeth despyt ful often, for distresse."

179

And right as they declamed this matere,

Lo, Troilus, right at the stretes ende,
Com ryding with his tenthe some y-fere,
Al softely, and thiderward gan bende
Ther-as they sete, as was his wey to wende
To paleys-ward; and Pandare him aspyde,
And seyde, 'nece, y-see who cometh here ryde!

180

O flee not in, he seeth us, I suppose;
Lest he may thinke that ye him eschuwe."
"Nay, nay," quod she, and wex as reed as rose.
With that he gan hir humbly to saluwe,
With dreedful chere, and ofte his hewes muwe;
And up his look debonairly he caste,
And bekked on Pandare, and forth he paste.

181

God woot if he sat on his hors a-right,
Or goodly was beseyn, that ilke day!
God woot wher he was lyk a manly knight!
What sholde I drecche, or telle of his aray?
Criseyde, which that alle these thinges say,
To telle in short, hir lyked al y-fere,
His persone, his aray, his look, his chere,

182

His goodly manere and his gentillesse,
So wel, that never, sith that she was born,
Ne hadde she swich routhe of his distresse;
And how-so she hath hard ben her-biforn,
To god hope I, she hath now caught a thorn.
She shal not pulle it out this nexte wyke;
God sende mo swich thornes on to pyke!

183

Pandare, which that stood hir faste by,
Felte iren hoot, and he bigan to smyte,
And seyde, "nece, I pray yow hertely,
Tel me that I shal axen yow a lyte.
A womman, that were of his deeth to wyte,
With-outen his gilt, but for hir lakked routhe,
Were it wel doon?" Quod she, "nay, by my
trouthe!"

184

"God helpe me so," quod he, "ye sey me sooth.
Ye felen wel your-self that I not lye;
Lo, yond he rit!" Quod she, "ye, so he dooth."
"Wel," quod Pandare, "as I have told yow thrye,
Lat be your nyce shame and your folye,
And spek with him in esing of his herte;
Lat nycetee not do yow bothe smerte."

185

But ther-on was to heven and to done;
Considered al thing, it may not be;
And why, for shame; and it were eek to sone
To graunten him so greet a libertee.
"For playnly hir entente," as seyde she,
"Was for to love him unwist, if she mighte,
And guerdon him with no-thing but with
sighte."

186

But Pandarus thoughte, "it shal not be so,
If that I may; this nyce opinioun
Shal not be holden fully yeres two."
What sholde I make of this a long sermoun?
He moste assente on that conclusioun

Lo, Troilus, along the lower end,
Came up the street with escort slowly riding,
And by this very house they must ascend
As to the palace on their way they wend.
Pandar at once beheld this fine array,
"Look, niece," he said, "who's riding up this way!

180

"Don't go away—he sees us I suppose—
'Twill look to him as though you feared pursuit!"
"No, no," she said, as red as any rose.
Troilus, riding by with grave salute,
And changing hue, and timidly and mute,
A gentle glance or two upon her cast,
Nodded to Pandar, and on his way he passed.

181

O Troilus, he was a goodly sight,
In goodly form he was that happy day!
He looked, and was in truth, a manly knight!
No need to stop and tell of his array,
And only one small thing I need to say,
That Cressida was favorably impressed,
By person, manner, look, and all the rest.

182

So well indeed, and by his gentleness,
That never since the day that she was born,
She felt so deep for any man's distress
As now for him upon this fateful morn!
To tell the truth, she hath picked up a thorn
At which she may full long and vainly pull!
God grant all hearts with such thorns may be full!

183

And Pandar, who was standing there near by,
Began to strike, feeling the iron hot.
"Dear niece," he said, "I wish you would untie
For me this simple little lovers' knot!
If this man guiltless through some woman got
His death, because her heart was hardened so,
Were it well done?" "I'd say," she answered,
"no!"

184

"And you'd say right," with ardor Pandar cried,
"With proper spirit you are now imbued.
Lo, forth he rides!" Says she, "Well, let him ride!"
"O come," said Pandar, "don't be such a prude!
Enough of this reluctant attitude!
Give him a hopeful word just for a start,
This holding off but frets and grieves the heart!"

185

With that the argument was on again!
"With what you say," she said, "I can't agree;
"Just think how all of Troy would talk! And then,
It's far too soon to grant a liberty!"
To this alone she would consent, said she,
To love him at a distance, as she might,
If he could be content but with her
sight.

186

But Pandar thought, "O that will never do!
She must get over such a foolish notion;
This matter can't run on a year or two."
But for the present he was all devotion
And thought it best to raise no great commotion,

And seeing all was well, at fall of eve,
He rose and said goodby and took his leave.

187

And on his homeward way full fast he sped,
And felt for very joy his heart must dance.
Troilus he found, extended on his bed,
Most lover-like, deep in a lover's trance,
Twixt hope of good and fear of evil chance,
And Pandar bursting in, began to sing,
A signal meaning, "Something good I bring."

188

"Who's buried here in bed," he cried, "so soon?"
A faint voice issued forth, "It's only me."
"Who? Troilus? Now by the sacred moon,"
Said Pandar, "get thee up and come and see
A wondrous charm that has been sent to thee,
To heal thee from all irksome grief and pain,
And make thee joyful, brisk and spry again."

189

"O yes, a miracle," said Troilus.
Then Pandar could no longer hold it back,
And said, "The Lord today hath favored us!
Bring here some light to look on all this black!"
Then joy and fear in turn made sharp attack
On Troilus, as he his letter read,
For in her words he found both hope and dread.

190

But in the end he took it for the best,
And thought that in her letter she had said
Some things at least on which his heart could
  rest,
Although between the lines they must be read;
And so to optimistic views thus led,
And trusting, too, in Pandar as his friend,
His deep despair began a bit to mend.

191

And as we may ourselves on all sides see,
The more the wood or coal, the more the fire;
As with increase of probability
There often comes an increase of desire;
As oaks from acorns grow and mount up higher,
So now this lover's flame more brightly burned,
His head by just one little letter turned.

192

And so it came to pass that day and night,
Troilus began to hunger more and more,
And as his hope increased, with all his
  might
He strove to put in practice Pandar's lore,
In writing to her of his sorrows sore;
Each day the effort new he made
In letters which by Pandar were conveyed.

193

To all proprieties he paid good heed
That to a lover in his case pertain;
And as the dice fell and as fate decreed,
His days were days of joy or days of pain,
Yet with his writing he did still proceed,
And echoing to the answers that he had,
His days took color, either glad or sad.

194

And Pandar ever was his great recourse.

As for the tyme; and whan that it was eve,
And al was wel, he roos and took his leve.

187

And on his wey ful faste homward he spedde,
And right for joye he felte his herte daunce;
And Troilus he fond alone a-bedde,
That lay as dooth these loveres, in a traunce,
Bitwixen hope and derk desesperaunce.
But Pandarus, right at his in-cominge,
He song, as who seyth, "lo! sumwhat I bringe."

188

And seyde, "who is in his bed so sone
Y-buried thus?" "It am I, freend," quod he.
"Who, Troilus? nay helpe me so the mone,"
Quod Pandarus, "thou shalt aryse and see
A charme that was sent right now to thee,
The which can helen thee of thyn accesse,
If thou do forth-with al thy besinesse."

189

"Ye, through the might of god!" quod Troilus.
And Pandarus gan him the lettre take,
And seyde, "pardee, god hath holpen us;
Have here a light, and loke on al this blake."
But ofte gan the herte glade and quake
Of Troilus, whyl that he gan it rede,
So as the wordes yave him hope or drede.

190

But fynally, he took al for the beste
That she him wroot, for sumwhat he biheld
On which, him thoughte, he mighte his herte
  reste,
Al covered she the wordes under sheld.
Thus to the more worthy part he held,
That, what for hope and Pandarus biheste,
His grete wo for-yede he at the leste.

191

But as we may alday our-selven see,
Through more wode or col, the more fyr;
Right so encrees of hope, of what it be,
Therwith ful ofte encreseth eek desyr;
Or, as an ook cometh of a litel spyr,
So through this lettre, which that she him sente,
Encresen gan desyr, of which he brente.

192

Wherfore I seye alwey, that day and night
This Troilus gan to desiren more
Than he dide erst, thurgh hope, and dide his
  might
To pressen on, as by Pandarus lore,
And wryten to hir of his sorwes sore
Fro day to day; he leet it not refreyde,
That by Pandare he wroot somwhat or seyde;

193

And dide also his othere observaunces
That to a lovere longeth in this cas;
And, after that these dees turnede on chaunces,
So was he outher glad or seyde "allas!"
And held after his gestes ay his pas;
And aftir swiche answeres as he hadde,
So were his dayes sory outher gladde.

194

But to Pandare alwey was his recours,

And pitously gan ay til him to pleyne,
And him bisoughte of rede and som socours;
And Pandarus, that sey his wode peyne,
Wex wel neigh deed for routhe, sooth to seyne,
And bisily with al his herte caste
Som of his wo to sleen, and that as faste;

195

And seyde, "lord, and freend, and brother dere,
God woot that thy disese doth me wo.
But woltow stinten al this woful chere,
And, by my trouthe, or it be dayes two,
And god to-forn, yet shal I shape it so,
That thou shalt come in-to a certayn place,
Ther-as thou mayst thy-self hir preye of grace.

196

And certainly, I noot if thou it wost,
But tho that been expert in love it seye,
It is oon of the thinges that furthereth most,
A man to have a leyser for to preye,
And siker place his wo for to biwreye;
For in good herte it moot som routhe impresse,
To here and see the giltles in distresse.

197

Paraunter thenkestow: though it be so
That kinde wolde doon hir to biginne
To han a maner routhe up-on my wo,
Seyth Daunger, 'Nay, thou shalt me never winne;
So reuleth hir hir hertes goost with-inne,
That, though she bende, yet she stant on rote;
What in effect is this un-to my bote?'

198

Thenk here-ayeins, whan that the sturdy ook,
On which men hakketh ofte, for the nones,
Receyved hath the happy falling strook,
The grete sweigh doth it come al at ones,
As doon these rokkes or these milne-stones.
For swifter cours cometh thing that is of wighte,
Whan it descendeth, than don thinges lighte.

199

And reed that boweth doun for every blast,
Ful lightly, cesse wind, it wol aryse;
But so nil not an ook whan it is cast;
It nedeth me nought thee longe to forbyse.
Men shal rejoysen of a greet empryse
Acheved wel, and stant with-outen doute,
Al han men been the lenger ther-aboute.

200

But, Troilus, yet tel me, if thee lest,
A thing now which that I shal axen thee;
Which is thy brother that thou lovest best
As in thy verray hertes privetee?"
"Y-wis, my brother Deiphebus," quod he.
"Now," quod Pandare, "er houres twyes twelve,
He shal thee ese, unwist of it him-selve.

201

Now lat me allone, and werken as I may,"
Quod he; and to Deiphebus wente he tho
Which hadde his lord and grete freend ben ay;
Save Troilus, no man he lovede so.
To telle in short, with-outen wordes mo,
Quod Pandarus, "I pray yow that ye be
Freend to a cause which that toucheth me."

And of his woes the sole recipient;
In him he found a never-failing source
Of aid, for Pandar could not rest content
To see his friend so languish and lament,
And ever in his mind he cast about
To find some fruitful way to help him out.

195

"My lord and friend," he said, "and brother dear,
It hurts me sore to see you take on so!
But do look up and be of better cheer,
For I've a little scheme I'd like to show,
Which I devised a day or two ago,
Whereby I'll bring you to a certain place,
And in her presence you can plead your case.

196

"I have no doubt this point is known to you,
But those who are expert in love declare
There's nothing like a personal interview
To help along a lagging love affair.
Just make her of your state of mind aware,
For every gentle heart it must impress
To see and hear the guiltless in distress.

197

"Perhaps you think, 'Though it may well be so,
That Nature doth constrain her to begin
To have some sort of pity on my woe,
Yet Will replies, "Thou shalt me never win!"
So doth her spirit rule her heart within,
That though she bend, she stands firm on her root.
What good, then, does all this to my poor suit?

198

"But on the other hand, the sturdy oak,
On which have been delivered many a blow,
Receives at last the happy falling stroke,
And all at once the whole tree down doth go,
Like heavy rocks or millstones falling low;
For things of weight come down with swifter flight
When they descend, than do things that are light.

199

"A reed that lowly bows before the blast,
After the wind again will lightly rise.
But not so when an oak-tree down is cast—
Of course you see what this exemplifies.
One should take pleasure in an enterprise
Of pith and moment placed beyond a doubt,
Though it took time to bring it all about.

200

"Now, Troilus, I have a slight request,
A little thing that I must ask of thee.
Which of thy brothers dost thou love the best
Within thy heart's most secret privacy?"
"Deiphebus it is," at once said he.
Said Pandar, "Ere another day shall end,
Unwittingly he shall thee well befriend!

201

"Leave it to me! I'll do the best I can!"
Then to Deiphebus he took his way,
Who was his lord and he his faithful man,
And more than this, long-standing friends were they,
And there arrived, he said his little say:
"I beg of you, my lord, that you will be
Friend to a cause that nearly touches me."

202

"O quite!" Deiphebus replied. "You know,
There's not a man within this mortal sphere
To whom a favor I'd more gladly show,
Troilus excepted, whom I hold most dear.
But first perhaps you'd better let me hear
What's weighing now so heavy on your mind,
And then the remedy we'll try to find."

203

Pandar his troubles thus doth then proclaim:
"My lord, there is a lady here in Troy,
My niece, and Cressida is her good name,
Whom certain men are trying to annoy,
And for themselves her property enjoy.
It is for her your aid I now beseech,
As I have told in plain and simple speech."

204

"Is she," he asked, "this lady in distress,
Of whom you speak in such a formal way,
My old friend Cressida?" Said Pandar, "Yes."
"Why, then," he cried, "there's nothing more to say!
For you can count on me in any fray
To champion her with sword or shaft or spear,
And this I'll say for all her foes to hear.

205

"But since you know the case, just tell me how
And what to do." Said Pandar, "Well, let's see!
If you, my gracious lord, would do me now
The honor to request my niece that she
Should come tomorrow, and here publicly
Present her case, I'm sure her enemies
Would hesitate to press their wicked pleas.

206

"And one thing more you might consent to do—
I wouldn't ask, except for her great need—
If some of your brothers could be here with you,
'Twould greatly help the case that she will plead
To have them all in her support agreed.
For with your aid and that of other friends,
She'll check her foes and thwart their wicked ends."

207

Deiphebus, who was by nature kind,
And glad to be a friendly instrument,
Replied, "It shall be done! And I can find
A better plan, which should her well content!
How would it be if I for Helen sent
To join with us? I'm sure that she will come,
And count for two, with Paris 'neath her thumb.

208

"And Hector, who to me is lord and brother,
No question but that he her friend will be!
For I have heard him, one time and another,
Commend her, and in such a high degree,
That she will need no assiduity
To win him to her side. Her only task
Will be, whatever she may want, to ask.

209

"And you yourself might speak to Troilus,
On my behalf, and ask him here to dine."
"O gladly," Pandar said, "I shall do thus!"
He took his leave and straight as any line,
He fastened forth to further his design,

202

"Yis, pardee," quod Deiphebus, "wel thow wost,
In al that ever I may and god to-fore,
Al nere it but for man I love most,
My brother Troilus; but sey wherfore
It is; for sith that day that I was bore,
I nas, ne never-mo to been I thinke,
Ayeins a thing that mighte thee for-thinke.

203

Pandare gan him thonke, and to him seyde,
"Lo, sire, I have a lady in this toun,
That is my nece, and called is Criseyde,
Which som men wolden doon oppressioun,
And wrongfully have hir possessioun:
Wherfor I of your lorship yow biseche
To been our freend, with-oute more speche."

204

Deiphebus him answerde, "O, is not this,
That thow spekest of to me thus straungely,
Criseÿda, my freend?" He seyde, "Yis."
"Than nedeth," quod Deiphebus, hardely,
"Na-more to speke, for trusteth wel, that I
Wol be hir champioun with spore and yerde;
I roughte nought though alle hir foos it herde.

205

But tel me, thou that woost al this matere,
How I might best avaylen?" "Now lat see,"
Quod Pandarus, "if ye, my lord so dere,
Wolden as now don this honour to me,
To prayen hir to-morwe, lo, that she
Com un-to yow hir pleyntes to devyse,
Hir adversaries wolde of hit agryse.

206

And if I more dorste preye as now,
And chargen yow to have so greet travayle,
To han som of your bretheren here with yow,
That mighten to hir cause bet avayle,
Than, woot I wel, she mighte never fayle
For to be holpen, what at your instaunce,
What with hir othere freendes governaunce."

207

Deiphebus, which that comen was, of kinde,
To al honour and bountee to consente,
Answerde, "it shal be doon; and I can finde
Yet gretter help to this in myn entente.
What wolt thow seyn, if I for Eleyne sente
To speke of this? I trow it be the beste;
For she may leden Paris as hir leste.

208

Of Ector, which that is my lord, my brother,
It nedeth nought to preye him freend to be;
For I have herd him, o tyme and eek other,
Speke of Criseyde swich honour, that he
May seyn no bet, swich hap to him hath she.
It nedeth nought his helpes for to crave;
He shal be swich, right as we wole him have.

209

Spek thou thy-self also to Troilus
On my bihalve, and pray him with us dyne."
"Sire, al this shal be doon," quod Pandarus;
And took his leve, and never gan to fyne,
But to his neces hous, as streght as lyne,

He com; and fond hir fro the mete aryse;
And sette him doun, and spak right in this wyse.

210

He seyde, "O veray god, so have I ronne!
Lo, nece myn, see ye nought how I swete?
I noot whether ye the more thank me conne.
Be ye nought war how that fals Poliphete
Is now aboute eft-sones for to plete,
And bringe on yow advocacyës newe?"
"I? no," quod she, and chaunged al hir hewe.

211

"What is he more aboute, me to drecche
And doon me wrong? what shal I do, allas?
Yet of him-self no-thing ne wolde I recche,
Nere it for Antenor and Eneas,
That been his freendes in swich maner cas;
But, for the love of god, myn uncle dere,
No fors of that, lat him have al y-fere;

212

With-outen that, I have ynough for us."
"Nay," quod Pandare, "it shal no-thing be so.
For I have been right now at Deiphebus,
And Ector, and myne othere lordes mo,
And shortly maked eche of hem his fo;
That, by my thirft, he shal it never winne
For ought he can, whan that so he biginne."

213

And as they casten what was best to done,
Deiphebus, of his owene curtasye,
Com hir to preye, in his propre persone,
To holde him on the morwe companye
At diner, which she nolde not denye,
But goodly gan to his preyere obeye.
He thonked hir, and wente up-on his weye.

214

Whanne this was doon, this Pandare up a-noon,
To telle in short, and forth gan for to wende
To Troilus, as stille as any stoon,
And al this thing he tolde him, word and ende;
And how that he Deiphebus gan to blende;
And seyde him, "now is tyme, if that thou conne,
To bere thee wel to-morwe, and al is wonne.

215

Now spek, now prey, now pitously compleyne;
Lat not for nyce shame, or drede, or slouthe;
Som-tyme a man not telle his owene peyne;
Bileve it, and she shal han on thee routhe;
Thou shalt be saved by thy feyth, in trouthe.
But wel wot I, thou art now in a drede;
And what it is, I leye, I can arede.

216

Thow thinkest now, 'how sholde I doon al this?
For by my cheres mosten folk aspye,
That for hir love is that I fare a-mis;
Yet hadde I lever unwist for sorwe dye.'
Now thenk not so, for thou dost greet folye.
For right now have I founden o manere
Of sleighte, for to coveren al thy chere.

217

Thow shalt gon over night, and that as blyve,
Un-to Deiphebus hous, as thee to pleye,
Thy maladye a-wey the bet to dryve,

To Cressida, whose dinner just was finished,
And straight began with ardor undiminished.

210

"O Lord," said he, "O what a way I've run!
Look, niece! Just gaze at what a sweat I'm in!
I hope I'll have your thanks for all I've done.
You know that Poliphete, that man of sin,
Is planning a new action to begin,
And open up fresh charges in your case?"
"I? No!" she cried, and grew pale in the face.

211

"What, will he never cease me to torment
And do me wrong? Alas, what shall I do!
For him alone I wouldn't care a cent,
But there's Antenor and Aeneas, too,
Both friends of his—in all, a wicked crew!
But I am weary, uncle, of this strife;
I'd give up all to have a peaceful life—

212

"A very little will suffice for us!"
"No, no," said Pandar, "I won't have it so!
But I've been talking with Deiphebus
And Hector, and with other lords you know,
And Poliphete will find in each a foe.
I pledge my word, this case he shall not win,
No matter when or what he may begin."

213

And as they sat considering this affair,
Deiphebus himself, most graciously,
In his own person came to see her there,
And ask the favor of her company
To dine next day. To this she did agree,
As proper was her lord thus to obey,
And he expressed his thanks and went his way.

214

Then Pandar left her with her thoughts alone,
For now on Troilus he must attend,
And while his friend sat still as any stone,
He told him all the tale from start to end,
How unawares Deiphebus would lend
His aid, and said to him, "Now if you can,
Is time to stir yourself and play the man!

215

"Speak up tomorrow, beg, beseech and pray,
And don't hold back for fear or modesty!
The time has come when you must say your say.
Don't lose your nerve, and you'll see what you'll see,
For as they say, the truth shall make thee free!
But something seems to stick still in your mind,
And what it is, I'll wager I can find.

216

"Perhaps you think, 'How shall I do all this?
For by my looks the folk will soon espy
And quickly guess that something is amiss,
And than they should do so, I'd rather die!'
But this is folly, and I'll tell you why;
For I've a scheme, it's something really bright,
To keep you safely out of all men's sight.

217

"To your dear brother's house I bid you go,
And say that you have come a while to stay,
And that by illness you've been troubled so,

But think a change may drive it all away.
Then go to bed, and when they ask you, say
You feel too ill and weak to dine or sup,
But lie right there, and wait for what turns up.

218

"And say your fever is cotidian,
And daily comes and goes at its own pleasure;
Just play the invalid the best you can,
And sick he is whose grief is out of measure.
Go, now! The time is past for idle leisure;
It's nerve will win the day in this affair.
Just keep your head and say goodby to care."

219

"In truth," said Troilus, "there is no need
To counsel me a sickness to pretend,
For I am sick in very fact and deed,
So sick it well may be my fatal end."
"That's good," said Pandar, "no time need you spend
On how to counterfeit the sick man's lot,
For one who sweats, is taken to be hot.

220

"Just hold you steady in your snug retreat,
And I the deer before your bow shall drive."
They parted then, though soon again to meet,
And each with other ready to connive.
Now Troilus is glad he is alive,
With Pandar's plan he is quite well content,
And to his brother's house at night he went.

221

With cordial welcome there he was received,
Deiphebus expressing sympathy,
And at his illness all were deeply grieved;
They covered him with bed-clothes carefully,
But still he seemed as sick as he could be;
He kept in mind what Pandar to him said,
And naught they did could budge him from his bed.

222

Before they from the sick man's room descend,
Deiphebus requested him to do her right
And be to Cressida a help and friend,
And Troilus agreed with words polite,
And said he would with all his will and might—
Of all requests this was as needless one
As bid a wild man leap and jump and run.

223

Recalling next day where she was to dine,
Helen the queen, the famous and the fair,
Informally and some time after nine,
Doth to her kindly brother's house repair,
Just to a little family dinner there,
And took it as a usual event,
Though God and Pandar knew what it all meant.

224

Cressida, unsuspecting, brought along
Antigone and Tarbe, sisters two—
In fact the diners numbered quite a throng;
But I don't mean to pass here in review
The names of guests and all they say and do,
For you can guess their greetings and their chatter,
And we'll proceed to more important matter.

For-why thou semest syk, soth for to seye.
Sone after that, doun in thy bed hee leye,
And sey, thow mayst no lenger up endure,
And lye right there, and byde thyn aventure.

218

Sey that thy fever is wont thee for to take
The same tyme, and lasten til a-morwe;
And lat see now how wel thou canst it make,
For, par-dee, syk is he that is in sorwe.
Go now, farewel! and, Venus here to borwe,
I hope, and thou this purpos holde ferme,
Thy grace she shal fully ther conferme."

219

Quod Troilus, "y-wis, thou nedelees
Counseylest me, that sykliche I me feyne!
For I am syk in ernest, doutelees,
So that wel neigh I sterve for the peyne."
Quod Pandarus, "thou shalt the bettre pleyne,
And hast the lasse nede to countrefete;
For him men demen hoot that men seen swete.

220

Lo, holde thee at thy triste cloos, and I
Shal wel the deer un-to thy bowe dryve."
Therwith he took his leve al softely,
And Troilus to paleys wente blyve.
So glad ne was he never in al his lyve;
And to Pandarus reed gan al assente,
And to Deiphebus hous at night he wente.

221

What nedeth yow to tellen al the chere
That Deiphebus un-to his brother made,
Or his accesse, or his syklich manere,
How men gan him with clothes for to lade,
Whan he was leyd, and how men wolde him glade?
But al for nought, he held forth ay the wyse
That ye han herd Pandare er this devyse.

222

But certeyn is, er Troilus him leyde,
Deiphebus had him prayed, over night,
To been a freend and helping to Criseyde.
God woot, that he it grauntede anon-right,
To been hir fulle freend with al his might.
But swich a nede was to preye him thenne,
As for to bidde a wood man for to renne.

223

The morwen com, and neighen gan the tyme
Of meel-tyd, that the faire quene Eleyne
Shoop hir to been, an houre after the pryme,
With Deiphebus, to whom she nolde feyne;
But as his suster, hoomly, sooth to seyne,
She com to diner in hir playn entente.
But god and Pandare wiste al what this mente.

224

Come eek Criseyde, al innocent of this,
Antigone, hir sister Tarbe also;
But flee we now prolixitee best is,
For love of god, and lat us faste go
Right to the effect, with-oute tales mo,
Why al this folk assembled in this place;
And lat us of hir saluinges pace.

225

Gret honour dide hem Deiphebus, certeyn,
And fedde hem wel with al that mighte lyke.
But ever-more, "allas!" was his refreyn,
"My goode brother Troilus, the syke,
Lyth yet"—and therwith-al he gan to syke;
And after that, he peyned him to glade
Hem as he mighte, and chere good he made.

226

Compleyned eek Eleyne of his syknesse
So feithfully, that pitee was to here,
And every wight gan waxen for accesse
A leche anoon, and seyde, "in this manere
Men curen folk; this charme I wol yow lere."
But there sat oon, al list hir nought to teche,
That thoughte, best coude I yet been his leche.

227

After compleynt, him gonnen they to preyse,
As folk don yet, whan som wight hath bigonne
To preyse a man, and up with prys him reyse
A thousand fold yet hyer than the sonne:—
"He is, he can, that fewe lordes conne."
And Pandarus, of that they wolde afferme,
He not for-gat hir preysing to conferme.

228

Herde al this thing Criseyde wel y-nough,
And every word gan for to notifye;
For which with sobre chere hir herte lough;
For who is that ne wolde hir glorifye,
To mowen swich a knight don live or dye?
But al passe I, lest ye to longe dwelle;
For for o fyn is al that ever I telle.

229

The tyme com, fro diner for to ryse,
And, as hem oughte, arisen everychoon,
And gonne a whyl of this and that devyse.
But Pandarus brak al this speche anoon,
And seyde to Deiphebus, "wole ye goon,
If yourë wille be, as I yow preyde,
To speke here of the nedes of Criseyde?"

230

Eleyne, which that by the hond hir held,
Took first the tale, and seyde, "go we blyve":
And goodly on Criseyde she biheld,
And seyde, "Joves lat him never thryve,
That dooth yow harm, and bringe him sone of lyve!
And yeve me sorwe, but he shal it rewe,
If that I may, and alle folk be trewe,"

231

"Tel thou thy neces cas," quod Deiphebus
To Pandarus, "for thou canst best it telle."—
"My lordes and my ladyes, it stant thus;
What solde I lenger," quod he, "do yow dwelle?"
He rong hem out a proces lyk a belle,
Up-on hir fo, that highte Poliphete,
So hëynous, that men mighte on it spete.

232

Answerde of this ech worse of hem than other,
And Poliphete they gonnen thus to warien,
"An-honged be swich oon, were he my
brother;
And so he shal, for it ne may not varien."

225

Deiphebus his guests doth entertain
With most delicious foods, the very pick,
But now and then, "Alas," was his refrain,
"That Troilus in bed is lying sick!"
Yet to this theme he did not always stick,
But often spoke of things more bright and cheery,
To keep his honored guests from growing weary.

226

And Helen, too, was really very nice
In warm expression of her sympathy,
And each one had some medical advice
To give—"I think the best treatment would be"—
"This charm indeed I recommend to thee"—
But to this lore that one made no addition
Who thought, " 'Tis I could be his best physician."

227

And then his praises they began to sing,
As folk will do when someone has begun;
A thousand variations there they ring
Upon this theme, and praise him to the sun,
"What he can do, there's mighty few have done!"
And all the flattering things of him they say,
Pandar confirms in most emphatic way.

228

Cressida heard, although she took no part,
And every syllable she kept in mind;
Though grave her look, she laughing was at heart,
For who alive would not great comfort find
To think she could about her finger wind
A knight like that! But now too long I dwell
And must proceed the end of this to tell.

229

The time came from the table to arise,
And thus they stood about, while each one spoke
By chance of one or other enterprise,
Till on the conversation Pandar broke
And said "Deiphebus, to all this folk,
May I now beg you somewhat to declare
Of Cressida's unfortunate affair?"

230

And Helen, holding Cressida's right hand,
Spoke first. "O, do!" with sympathy she cried,
As side by side together there they stand.
"By Jupiter, an evil fate betide
The wretches who to injure you have tried!
For sure, if I have anything to say,
They'll see good reason to regret the day."

231

"You state the case," remarked Deiphebus
To Pandar, "since you know it all so well."
"My lords and ladies all, it standeth thus,
No need," he said, "too long on it to dwell"—
Then rang them out a story like a bell
About this Poliphete, and made it stretch
So far, they felt like spewing on the wretch.

232

They all abused him, each worse than the other,
And right and left the scoundrel they did curse:
"He should and shall be hanged, were he my
brother!"
"And that's too good, if anything were worse!"

But why should I a lengthy tale rehearse?
For each and all assured her in the end,
They'd do their best and be her staunchest friend.

233

"O Pandar," Helen said, "pray tell to us,
Is my good lord and brother—Hector, I mean—
Informed of this affair? And Troilus?"
"Why, yes," he said, "but that reminds me, queen!
It seems to me, if Troilus can be seen,
It might be best, that is, if all assent,
If she herself saw him before she went.

234

"For he will have the matter more at heart,
If he should know the lady in the case,
And by your leave, right for his room I'll start,
And let you know within a second's space,
If he can hear her story in that place."
And in he ran and whispered in his ear,
"God bless thy soul, I've brought thy pillow
here!"

235

This joke drew forth a smile from Troilus,
And Pandar, lacking cause for long delay,
Went back to Helen and Deiphebus,
And said, "If she can come now right away,
But with no crowd, then come, he says, she may,
And he will hear what it is all about,
As long as he is able to hold out.

236

"But since you know the chamber is but small,
And people crowding in might make it hot,
I would not have the blame on me to fall
That I had added to his heavy lot,
No, not for all the arms and legs I've got.
Perhaps we'd better try some other day;
But that, of course, is all for you to say.

237

"But still, I think 'twill be the better plan
For none to go in first except you two,
And maybe me, who in a second can
Rehearse her case better than she can do;
And when you leave him, she can follow you
And ask for his support at no great length—
I don't think this will overtax his strength.

238

"Then, too, since she is strange, he might exert
Himself for her, but not for his own kin,
Besides I'm almost sure he will revert
To secret plans for helping Troy to win
Her way from out the siege that we are in."
And all unwitting of his deep intent,
Without ado to Troilus they went.

239

And Helen, always gently soft and sweet,
Began with him to chat and lightly play,
And said, "O, we'll soon have you on your feet!
Now, brother, for my sake, be well, I pray!"
And on his shoulder doth her white arm lay,
And strives with gentle art as one who fain
Would somewhat ease him on his couch of pain.

240

"We've come," she said, "to ask some help from you,

What sholde I lenger in this tale tarien?
Pleynly, alle at ones, they hir highten,
To been hir helpe in al that ever they mighten.

233

Spak than Eleyne, and seyde, "Pandarus,
Woot ought my lord, my brother, this matere,
I mene, Ector? or woot it Troilus?"
He seyde, "ye, but wole ye now me here?
Me thinketh this, sith Troilus is here,
It were good, if that ye wolde assente,
She tolde hir-self him al this, er she wente.

234

For he wole have the more hir grief at herte,
By cause, lo, that she a lady is;
And, by your leve, I wol but right in sterte,
And do yow wite, and that anoon, y-wis,
If that he slepe, or wole ought here of this."
And in he lepte, and seyde him in his ere,
"God have thy soule, y-brought have I thy
bere!"

235

To smylen of this gan tho Troilus,
And Pandarus, with-oute rekeninge,
Out wente anoon t'Eleyne and Deiphebus,
And seyde hem, "so there be no taryinge,
Ne more pres, he wol wel that ye bringe
Criseÿda, my lady, that is here;
And as he may enduren, he wole here.

236

But wel ye woot, the chaumbre is but lyte,
And fewe folk may lightly make it warm;
Now loketh ye, (for I wol have no wyte,
To bringe in prees that mighte doon him harm
Or him disesen, for my bettre arm),
Wher it be bet she byde til eft-sones;
Now loketh ye, that knowen what to doon is.

237

I sey for me, best is, as I can knowe,
That no wight in ne wente but ye tweye,
But it were I, for I can, in a throwe,
Reherce hir cas, unlyk that she can seye;
And after this, she may him ones preye
To ben good lord, in short, and take hir leve;
This may not muchel of his ese him reve.

238

And eek, for she is straunge, he wol forbere
His ese, which that him thar nought for yow;
Eek other thing, that toucheth not to here,
He wol me telle, I woot it wel right now,
That secret is, and for the tounes prow."
And they, that no-thing knewe of this entente,
With-oute more, to Troilus in they wente.

239

Eleyne in al hir goodly softe wyse,
Gan him saluwe, and womanly to pleye,
And seyde, "ywis, ye moste alweyes aryse!
Now fayre brother, beth al hool, I preye!"
And gan hir arm right over his sholder leye,
And him with al hir wit to recomforte;
As she best coude, she gan him to disporte.

240

So after this quod she, "we yow biseke,

My dere brother, Deiphebus, and I,
For love of god, and so doth Pandare eke.
To been good lord and freend, right hertely.
Un-to Criseyde, which that certeinly
Receyveth wrong, as woot wel here Pandare,
That can hir cas wel bet than I declare."

241

This Pandarus gan newe his tunge affyle,
And al hir cas reherce, and that anoon;
Whan it was seyd, sone after, in a whyle,
Quod Troilus, "as sone as I may goon,
I wol right fayn with al my might ben oon,
Have god my trouthe, hir cause to sustene."
"Good thrift have ye," quod Eleyne the quene.

242

Quod Pandarus, "and it your wille be,
That she may take hir leve, er that she go?"
"Or elles god for-bede," tho quod he,
"If that she vouche sauf for to do so."
And with that word quod Troilus, "ye two.
Deiphebus,and my suster leef and dere,
To yow have I to speke of o matere

243

To been avysed by your reed the bettre":—
And fond, as hap was, at his beddes heed,
The copie of a tretis and a lettre,
That Ector hadde him sent to axen reed,
If swich a man was worthy to ben deed,
Woot I nought who; but in a grisly wyse
He preyede hem anoon on it avyse.

244

Deiphebus gan this lettre to unfolde
In ernest greet; so dide Eleyne the quene;
And rominge outward, fast it gan biholde,
Downward a steyre, in-to an herber grene.
This ilke thing they redden hem bi-twene;
And largely, the mountaunce of an houre,
They gonne on it to reden and to poure.

245

Now lat hem rede, and turne we anoon
To Pandarus, that gan ful faste prye
That al was wel, and out he gan to goon
In-to the grete chambre, and that in hye,
And seyde, "god save al this companye!
Com, nece myn; my lady quene Eleyne
Abydeth yow, and eek my lordes tweyne.

246

Rys, take with yow your nece Antigone,
Or whom yow list, or no fors, hardily;
The lasse prees, the bet; com forth with me,
And loke that ye thonke humblely
Hem alle three, and, whan ye may goodly
Your tyme y-see, taketh of hem your leve,
Lest we to longe his restes him bireve."

247

Al innocent of Pandarus entente,
Quod tho Criseyde, "go we, uncle dere";
And arm in arm inward with him she wente,
Avysed wel hir wordes and hir chere;
And Pandarus, in ernestful manere,
Seyde, "alle folk, for goddes love, I preye,
Stinteth right here, and softely yow pleye.

My brother dear Deiphebus and I,
For love of—O, and so does Pandar, too,—
To be a friend to one whom we hold high,
To Cressida, who no one can deny
Has been much wronged, and Pandar over there,
Her case and situation can declare."

241

Then Pandar once again his tongue must file
To tell his tale convincingly yet brief;
When this was done, thinking a little while,
Troilus said, "When I have some relief,
Of all my duties that shall be the chief,
In Cressida's behalf to intervene."
"And all success to you!" replied the queen.

242

"Perhaps," said Pandar, "if you can her see
And say goodbye before she hence doth go"—
"O yes, of course she must," responded he,
"If she will be so good as to do so!"
Then turning, said, "To you I want to show,
Deiphebus and Helen, sister dear,
A matter of importance I have here,

243

"And ask you what course seems to you the better,"
And fished out from his bed a document,
And handed it, together with a letter
Which Hector to him recently had sent,
Whether a sentence of death he should prevent,
I know not whose, and with some agitation
He begged them give it their consideration.

244

Deiphebus first hastens to unfold
The letter, and then together with the queen
Downstairs he goes, a conference to hold,
And in a little quiet arbor green,
They talk the matter out themselves between
And for an hour's span, or less or more,
This document they read and on it pore.

245

So let them read, and let us turn again
To Pandar, now so jubilant to find
How well all went. He hastened out and when
He came into the room where they had dined,
He cried, "To all of you may heaven be kind!
But come, my niece, Queen Helen waits for you,
And both our gracious lords are waiting, too.

246

"Just take with you your niece Antigone,
Or whom you will—or rather come alone,
The less the crowd the better. Come now with me,
And when to them your gratitude you've shown,
With Troilus you breifly may condone,
And take your leave of him when you think best,
Though we must not disturb too long his rest."

247

Of Pandar's dark design all innocent,
Cressida said, "Come, uncle, let us go!"
And arm in arm out of the room they went,
With all decorum, dignified and slow,
And Pandar said, as they passed down the row,
"Good friends, your patience we shall not abuse,
If for a time yourselves you will amuse.

248

"But don't forget what folk are there within
And one of them, God help him, in what plight!"
"Dear niece," he murmured in her ear, "begin
But gently with this man and do him right,
And by the Lord who grants us life and light,
And by the crowning power of virtues twain,
Let him not lie here in this mortal
pain!

248

Aviseth yow what falk ben here with-inne,
And in what plyt oon is, god him amende!
And inward thus ful softely biginne;
Nece, I conjure and heighly yow defende,
On his half, which that sowle us alle sende,
And in the vertue of corounes tweyne,
Slee nought this man, that hath for yow this
peyne!

249

"Defy the devil! Keep Troilus in mind,
And in what state he lies! Don't sit so tight!
A chance once lost, you never again will find.
You'll both be glad when you give up the fight.
There's no suspicion yet, however slight,
About you two, and count it time well won
When all the world is blind to what is done.

249

Fy on the devel! thenk which oon he is,
And in what plyt he lyth; com of anoon;
Thenk al swich taried tyd, but lost it nis!
That wol ye bothe seyn, whan ye ben oon.
Secoundelich, ther yet devyneth noon
Up-on yow two; com of now, if ye conne;
Whyl folk is blent, lo, al the tyme is wonne!

250

"In hesitations, false starts and delays,
Men read deep meanings from a wagging straw.
For you at last are coming merry days,
Yet you hold back and timidly withdraw,
And of vain gossip stand in such great awe,
You waste the time you never can recover.
Have pity now upon this sorrowing lover!"

250

In titering, and pursuite, and delayes,
The folk devyne at wagginge of a stree;
And though ye wolde han after merye dayes,
Than dar ye nought, and why? for she, and she
Spak swich a word; thus lokd he, and he;
Lest tyme I loste, I dar not with yow dele;
Com of therfore, and bringeth him to hele."

251

But now I bid you, lovers far and near,
Regard poor Troilus and his sad state,
Who lay and all this whispering could hear,
And thought, "O Lord, I soon shall know my fate,
To live in love, or else to die in hate!"
His time was come now for her love to pray,
And, mighty God, what shall he do and say!

251

But now to yow, ye lovers that ben here,
Was Troilus nought in a cankedort,
That lay, and mighte whispringe of hem here,
And thoughte, "O lord, right now renneth my sort
Fully to dye, or han anoon comfort";
And was the firste tyme he shulde hir preye
Of love; O mighty god, what shal he seye?

HERE ENDETH THE SECOND BOOK

BOOK III

HERE BEGINNETH THE PROEM TO THE THIRD BOOK

1

O HAPPY light, of which the beams so clear
Illume the third expanse of heaven's air,
Loved of the sun, of Jove the daughter dear,
O Love's Delight, thou goodly one and fair,
In gentle hearts abiding everywhere,
Thou primal cause of joy and all salvation,
Exalted be thy name through all creation!

1

O BLISFUL light, of whiche the bemes clere
Adorneth al the thridde hevene faire!
O sonnes leef, O Joves doughter dere,
Pleasaunce of love, O goodly debonaire.
In gentil hertes ay redy to repaire!
O verray cause of hele and of gladnesse,
Y-heried be thy might and thy goodnesse!

2

In heaven and hell, on earth and salty sea,
All creatures answer to thy might supernal,
For man, bird, beast, fish, herb and leafy tree,
Their seasons know from thy breath ever vernal.
God loves, and grants that love shall be eternal.
All creatures in the world through love exist,
And lacking love, lack all that may persist.

2

In hevene and helle, in erthe and salte see
Is felt thy might, if that I wel descerne;
As man, brid, best, fish, herbe and grene tree
Thee fele in tymes with vapour eterne.
God loveth, and to love wol nought werne;
And in this world no lyves creature,
With-outen love, is worth, or may endure.

3

Mover of Jove to that so happy end,
Through which all earthly creatures live and be,
When mortal love upon him thou didst send,
For as thou wilt, the power lies with thee

3

Ye Joves first to thilke effectes glade,
Thorugh which that thinges liven alle and be,
Comeveden, and amorous him made
On mortal thing, and as yow list, ay ye

Yeve him in love ese or adversitee;
And in a thousand formes doun him sente
For love in erthe, and whom yow liste, he hente.

4

Ye fierse Mars apeysen of his ire,
And, as yow list, ye maken hertes digne;
Algates, hem that ye wol sette a-fyre,
They dreden shame, and vices they resigne;
Ye do hem corteys be, fresshe and benigne,
And hye or lowe, after a wight entendeth;
The joyes that he hath, your might him sendeth.

5

Ye holden regne and hous in unitee;
Ye soothfast cause of frendship been also;
Ye knowe al thilke covered qualitee
Of thinges which that folk on wondren so,
Whan they can not construe how it may jo,
She loveth him, or why he loveth here;
As why this fish, and nought that, cometh to were.

6

Ye folk a lawe han set in universe,
And this knowe I by hem that loveres be,
That who-so stryveth with yow hath the werse.
Now, lady bright, for thy benignitee,
At reverence of hem that serven thee,
Whos clerk I am, so techeth me devyse
Som joye of that is felt in thy servyse.

7

Ye in my naked herte sentement
Inhelde, and do me shewe of thy swetnesse.—
Caliope, thy vois be now present,
For now is nede; sestow not my destresse,
How I mot telle anon-right the gladnesse
Of Troilus, to Venus heryinge?
To which gladnes, who nede hath,
God him bringe!

Of ease in love or love's adversity,
And in a thousand forms is thy descent
On earth, in love to favor or prevent!

4

Fierce Mars for thee must subjugate his ire,
All hearts from thee receive their fates condign;
Yet ever when they feel thy sacred fire,
In dread of shame, their vices they resign,
And gentler grow, more brave and more benign;
And high or low, as each in his rank strives,
All owe to thee the joys of all their lives.

5

Houses and realms in greater unity,
And faith in friendship thou canst make to grow.
Thou understandest likings hard to see,
Which cause much wonder that they should be so,
As when in puzzlement, one seeks to know,
Why this loves that, why she by him is sought,
Why one and not the other fish is caught.

6

From thee comes law for all the universe,
And this I know, as all true lovers see,
That who opposeth, ever hath the worse.
Now, lady bright, in thy benignity,
Help me to honor those who honor thee,
And teach me, clerk of love, that I may tell
The joy of those who in thy service dwell.

7

True feeling in my naked heart infuse
That in my hands thy glory grow not less!
Calliope, thy voice let me now use,
For great my need! Now all my effort bless,
Who strive, in praise of Venus, this gladness
Of Troilus in fitting words to sing!
May God all lovers to such
gladness bring!

HERE ENDETH THE PROEM TO THE THIRD BOOK

HERE BEGINNETH THE THIRD BOOK

8

Lay al this mene whyle Troilus,
Recordinge his lessoun in this manere,
"Ma fey!" thought he, "thus wole I seye and thus;
Thus wole I pleyne un-to my lady dere;
That word is good, and this shal be my chere;
This nil I not foryeten in no wyse."
God leve him werken as he gan devyse.

9

And lord, so that his herte gan to quappe,
Heringe hir come, and shorte for to syke!
And Pandarus, that ladde hir by the lappe,
Com neer, and gan in at the curtin pyke,
And seyde, "god do bote on alle syke!
See, who is here yow comen to visyte;
Lo, here is she that is your deeth to wyte."

10

Ther-with it semed as he wepte almost;
"A ha," quod Troilus so rewfully,
"Wher me be wo, O mighty god, thou wost!
Who is al there? I see nought trewely."
"Sire," quod Criseyde, "it is Pandare and I."

8

Now all this time poor Troilus still lay,
Conning his lesson most industriously;
"I think," he planned, "just so and so I'll say;
Thus will I lead her my deep love to see;
This word sounds good, 'twill help in some degree,
And this by all means I must not neglect"—
And so on, all to much the same effect.

9

Hearing her come, how he begins to quake,
And how he sighs, with sighings short and quick,
While Pandar by the sleeve his niece doth take,
And peeping at him through the curtains thick,
He cries, "Now, God have mercy on the sick!
See who has come a visit here to pay!
Behold the fatal cause of all this fray!"

10

With tearful weeping Pandar's eyes o'erflow,
"Oh, Oh!" groans Troilus, most groanfully,
"How bad I feel, O Lord, no one does know!
Who all is there? It's hard for me to see."
"O, sir," said Cressida, "Pandar and me."

"What, you, my dear! Alas that I can't rise
And do you honor in a fitting wise."

11

He raised him up, but she at once drew nigh,
Her two restraining hands on him to lay.
"O, please," she cried, "for my sake please don't try!
(O, what was that I had in mind to say!)
Sir, here I come for two things, if I may,
To thank you first, then ask you as my lord
Your favor and protection to accord."

12

Hearing his lady to him humbly pray
For lordship, Troilus from shame near dead,
Had not a single word to her to say,
For he could think of none to save his head;
But suddenly he flushed a crimson red,
And all the clever things he'd counted on,
Fled from his mind, completely lost and gone.

13

Cressida understood this well enough,
For she was wise, and liked him none the less
Because he was not pert or quick and rough,
Nor yet so bold he lacked all humbleness.
But when his shame had passed its first excess,
His words, as in my way they can be told,
And as the old books say, I shall unfold.

14

With strange and trembling voice, from simple dread
Abashed, and blushing now from ear to ear,
But changing often too, now pale, now red,
To Cressida, his chosen lady dear,
Submissive standing at his side so near—
Lo, all he said when he his lips could part,
Was, twice, "O mercy, mercy, my sweetheart!"

15

He paused, and when he tried again at length,
His next word was, "God knows that I have been
All yours, with all I have of wit and strength,
And shall be yours, by him who saves from sin,
Until they dig my grave and put me in!
And though I'm slow of speech and hesitate,
My love by that you must not estimate.

16

"So much at present, O thou woman true,
I may declare, and if these words displease,
With my own life I'll make the payment due,
If by my death I may your wrath appease,
And bring your heart again to rest and ease.
For now that you have let me have my say,
I care not how or when I pass away."

17

Such manly sorrow in his bosom burned,
Tears from a heart of stone it would have drawn,
And Pandar wept as though to water turned,
And nudged his niece anon and yet anon,
And said, "Was ever man so woe-begone!
For God's sake, bring this matter to an end,
And slay us both, and on your ways then wend!"

18

"What's that?" cried she, "I know not for my part
Just what it is you're asking me to say!"
"What's that?" he said, "just show you have a heart,

"Ye, swete herte? allas, I may nought ryse
To knele, and do yow honour in som wyse."

11

And dressede him upward, and she right tho
Gan bothe here hondes softe upon him leye,
"O, for the love of god, do ye not so
To me," quod she, "ey! what is this to seye?
Sire, come am I to yow for causes tweye;
First, yow to thonke, and of your lorshipe eke
Continuaunce I wolde yow biseke."

12

This Troilus, that herde his lady preye
Of lordship him, wex neither quik ne deed,
Ne mighte a word for shame to it seye,
Al-though men sholde smyten of his heed.
But lord, so he wex sodeinliche reed,
And sire, his lesson, that he wende conne,
To preyen hir, is thurgh his wit y-ronne.

13

Criseyde al this aspyede wel y-nough,
For she was wys, and lovede him never-the-lasse,
Al nere he malapert, or made it tough,
Or was to bold, to singe a fool a masse.
But whan his shame gan somwhat to passe,
His resons, as I may my rymes holde,
I yow wol telle, as techen bokes olde.

14

In chaunged vois, right for his verrey drede,
Which vois eek quook, and ther-to his manere
Goodly abayst, and now his hewes rede,
Now pale, un-to Criseyde, his lady dere,
With look doun cast and humble yolden chere,
Lo, th'alderfirste word that him asterte
Was, twyes, "mercy, mercy, swete herte!"

15

And stinte a whyl, and whan he mighte out-bringe,
The nexte word was, "god wot, for I have,
As feythfully as I have had konninge,
Ben youres, also god my sowle save;
And shal, til that I, woful wight, be grave.
And though I dar ne can un-to yow pleyne,
Y-wis, I suffre nought the lasse peyne.

16

Thus muche as now, O wommanliche wyf,
I may out-bringe, and if this yow displese,
That shal I wreke upon myn owne lyf
Right sone, I trowe, and doon your herte an ese,
If with my deeth your herte I may apese.
But sin that ye han herd me som-what seye,
Now recche I never how sone that I deye."

17

Ther-with his manly sorwe to biholde,
It mighte han maad an herte of stoon to rewe;
And Pandare weep as he to watre wolde,
And poked ever his nece newe and newe,
And seyde, "wo bigon ben hertes trewe!
For love of god, make of this thing an ende,
Or slee us bothe at ones, er that ye wende."

18

"I? what?" quod she, "by god and by my trouthe,
I noot nought what ye wilne that I seye."
"I? what?" quod he, "that ye han on him routhe,

For goddes love, and doth him nought to deye."
"Now thanne thus," quod she, "I wolde him preye
To telle me the fyn of his entente;
Yet wiste I never wel what that he mente."

19

"What that I mene, O swete herte dere?"
Quod Troilus, "O goodly fresshe free!
That, with the stremes of your eyen clere,
Ye wolde som-tyme freendly on me see,
And thanne agreën that I may ben he,
With-oute braunche of vyce in any wyse,
In trouthe alwey to doon yow my servyse

20

As to my lady right and chief resort,
With al my wit and al my diligence,
And I to han, right as yow list, comfort,
Under your yerde, egal to myn offence,
As deeth, if that I breke your defence;
And that ye deigne me so muche honoure,
Me to comaunden ought in any houre.

21

And I to been your verray humble trewe,
Secret, and in my paynes pacient,
And ever-mo desire freshly newe,
To serven, and been y-lyke ay diligent,
And, with good herte, al holly your talent
Receyven wel, how sore that me smerte,
Lo, this mene I, myn owene swete herte."

22

Quod Pandarus, "lo, here an hard request,
And resonable, a lady for to werne!
Now, nece myn, by natal Joves fest,
Were I a god, ye sholde sterve as yerne,
That heren wel, this man wol no-thing yerne
But your honour, and seen him almost sterve,
And been so looth to suffren him yow serve."

23

With that she gan hir eyen on him caste
Ful esily, and ful debonairly,
Avysing hir, and hyed not to faste
With never a word, but seyde him softely,
"Myn honour sauf, I wol wel trewely,
And in swich forme as he can now devyse,
Receyven him fully to my servyse,

24

Biseching him, for goddes love, that he
Wolde, in honour of trouthe and gentilesse,
As I wel mene, eek mene wel to me,
And myn honour, with wit and besinesse,
Ay kepe; and if I may don him gladnesse,
From hennes-forth, y-wis, I nil not feyne:
Now beeth al hool, no lenger ye ne pleyne.

25

But nathelees, this warne I yow," quod she,
"A kinges sone al-though ye be, y-wis,
Ye shul na-more have soverainetee
Of me in love, than right in that cas is;
Ne I nil forbere, if that ye doon a-mis,
To wrathen yow; and whyl that ye me serve,
Cherycen yow right after ye deserve.

26

And shortly, derë herte and al my knight,

Nor this poor creature pitilessly slay!"
"Well, then," she said, "I'd ask him, if I may,
To tell me clearly what he has in mind,
For never yet his meaning could I find."

19

"Just what I have in mind, O sweetheart dear!"
Cried Troilus. "That thou so fair to see,
But with the beamings of thine eyes so clear
Sometimes wilt turn a kindly gaze on me,
And that, besides, to this thou wilt agree
That I in root and branch, and every way
In truth, may serve thee well from day to day,

20

"As rightful lady and my chief resort,
With all my wit and all my diligence,
And as you will, may have from you support,
According as you judge my competence—
Or death for any disobedience—
And that this honor you to me will show,
To seek my aid in all things high or low,

21

"And let me be your servant sworn and true,
Humble and secret, patient in endeavor,
Eager to find occasions fresh and new
To serve, and in my service slacken never,
And what you will and bid receiving ever
With good intent, however sore I smart—
Lo, this I have in mind, my own sweetheart!"

22

"Indeed," said Pandar, "that's a hard request,
And something any lady would deny!
My dearest niece, as I look to be blessed,
If I were God, I'd let you pine and die,
If honor, honor were your sole reply
To such a man, so faithfully approved,
By whom the hardest heart might well be moved!"

23

Though Cressida would not be pushed too fast,
Yet in a manner not at all severe,
A glance or two on Troilus she cast,
And answered soberly and plain and clear,
"Saving my honor, which I hold most dear,
With all formalities observed and kept,
This man into my service I accept,

24

"Beseeching him, for love of God, that he
By all the truth and honor of his birth,
As I mean well, may mean as well by me,
And ever hold my honor at high worth.
And if I may increase his joy and mirth,
In all good will, I shall thereto assent;
Take courage then, and cease your sad lament.

25

"But still this warning note I yet must sound—
A king's son though you be in all men's sight,
In love I shall be only so far bound
As would in any case be just and right;
And if you do amiss, I shall requite
With blame, yet also as you knightly serve,
Shall cherish you and praise as you deserve.

26

"In short, dear heart, and now my worthy knight,

Rejoice and put aside your fear and dread,
For truly I shall strive with all my might,
For bitter days to give you sweet instead,
And if through me to joy you can be led,
For each past woe you shall receive a bliss"—
And sealed her words with an embrace and kiss.

27

Fell Pandar on his knees, and up his eyes
To heaven cast, with hands extended high.
"Immortal God," he cried, "within the skies,
Cupid I mean, whom all men glorify,
And Venus, too, rejoice with melody!
Methinks in all the town, with no hand swinging,
To mark this miracle, the bells are ringing!

28

"But soft! we'll wait until another day,
Because Deiphebus will come back soon—
And hark, I hear them coming up this way.
But, Cressida, some morn or afternoon,
And Troilus, too, at season opportune,
A meeting at my house I shall arrange,
The remnant of your pledges to exchange,

29

"When you can ease your troubled hearts at leisure;
And let us see then which shall bear the bell
In boasts of love which love alone can measure,
For there you'll both have time your tale to tell."
"How long," asked Troilus, "am I to dwell
In this suspense?" "As soon as you get up,"
Said Pandar, "come to dine with me or sup."

30

With these words, Helen and Deiphebus
Appear, as they the topmost stairs ascend,
And now again deep groans from Troilus
Burst forth, as he bethinks him illness to pretend;
But Pandar says, "It's time for us to end
Our visit, niece, so take leave of all three,
And let them talk, and you come on with me."

31

She said goodbye in quite the proper way,
And they in turn, in polished manner, too,
The pleasant compliments of parting pay;
When she had left and closed the interview,
They still commended her with praises new,
Her wit, her charm and all her general style,
And Troilus listened with an inward smile.

32

Now to her palace let her wend her way
While we go back to Troilus in bed;
About the letter he had naught to say
That Helen and Deiphebus had read,
And wished that they would go, and soon he said
He thought perhaps it might for him be best
To try to sleep and get a little rest.

33

And Helen kissed him then and said goodby,
Deiphebus likewise his leave must take;
But Pandar soon, as straight as he could fly,
Came back, a couch beside his friend to make,
And Troilus and he, both wide awake,
Through all that confidential night there lay,
For they had many pressing things to say.

Beth glad, and draweth yow to lustinesse,
And I shal trewely, with al my might,
Your bittre tornen al in-to swetnesse;
If I be she that may yow do gladnesse,
For every wo ye shal recovere a blisse";
And him in armes took, and gan him kisse.

27

Fil Pandarus on knees, and up his yën
To hevene threw, and held his hondes hye,
"Immortal god!" quod he, "that mayst nought dyen,
Cupide I mene, of this mayst glorifye;
And Venus, thou mayst make melodye;
With-outen hond, me semeth that in towne,
For this merveyle, I here ech belle sowne.

28

But ho! no more as now of this matere,
For-why this folk wol comen up anoon,
That han the lettre red: lo, I hem here.
But I conjure thee, Criseyde, and oon,
And two, thou Troilus, whan thow mayst goon,
That at myn hous ye been at my warninge,
For I ful wel shal shape your cominge;

29

And eseth ther your hertes right y-nough;
And lat see which of yow shal bere the belle
To speke of love a-right!" ther-with he lough.
"For ther have ye a layser for to telle."
Quod Troilus, "how longe shal I dwelle
Er this be doon?" Quod he, "whan thou mayst ryse,
This thing shal be right as I yow devyse."

30

With that Eleyne and also Deiphebus
Tho comen upward, right at the steyres ende;
And lord, so than gan grone Triolus,
His brother and his suster for to blende.
Quod Pandarus, "it tyme is that we wende;
Tak, nece myn, your leve at alle three,
And lat hem speke, and cometh forth with me."

31

She took hir leve at hem ful thriftily,
As she wel coude, and they hir reverence
Un-to the fulle diden hardely,
And speken wonder wel, in hir absence,
Of hir, in preysing of hir excellence,
Hir governaunce, hir wit; and hir manere
Commendeden, it joye was to here.

32

Now lat hir wende un-to hir owne place,
And torne we to Troilus a-yein,
That gan ful lightly of the lettre passe
That Deiphebus hadde in the gardin seyn.
And of Eleyne and him he wolde fayn
Delivered been, and seyde, that him leste
To slepe, and after tales have reste.

33

Eleyne him kiste, and took hir leve blyve,
Deiphebus eek, and hoom wente every wight;
And Pandarus, as faste as he may dryve,
To Troilus tho com, as lyne right;
And on a paillet, al that glade night,
By Troilus he lay, with mery chere,
To tale; and wel was hem they were y-fere,

34

Whan every wight was voided but they two,
And alle the dores were faste y-shette,
To telle in short, with-oute wordes mo,
This Pandarus, with-outen any lette,
Up roos, and on his beddes syde him sette,
And gan to speken in a sobre wyse
To Troilus, as I shal yow devyse.

35

"Myn alderlevest lord, and brother dere,
God woot, and thou, that it sat me so sore,
When I thee saw so languisshing to-yere,
For love, of which thy wo wex alwey more;
That I, with al my might and al my lore,
Hath ever sithen doon my bisinesse
To bringe thee to joye out of distresse;

36

And have it brought to swich plyt as thou wost,
So that, thorugh me, thow stondest now in weye
To fare wel, I seye it for no bost,
And wostow why? for shame it is to seye,
For thee have I bigonne a gamen pleye
Which that I never doon shal eft for other,
Al-though he were a thousand fold my brother.

37

That is to seye, for thee am I bicomen,
Bitwixen game and ernest, swich a mene
As maken wommen un-to men to comen;
Al sey I nought, thou wost wel what I mene.
For thee have I my nece, of vyces clene,
So fully maad thy gentilesse triste,
That al shal been right as thy-selve liste.

38

But god, that al wot, take I to witnesse,
That never I this for coveityse wroughte,
But only for to abregge that distresse,
For which wel nygh thou deydest, as me thoughte.
But gode brother, do now as thee oughte,
For goddes love, and keep hir out of blame,
Sin thou art wys, and save alwey hir name.

39

For wel thou wost, the name as yet of here
Among the peple, as who seyth, halwed is;
For that man is unbore, I dar wel swere,
That ever wiste that she dide amis.
But wo is me, that I, that cause al this,
May thenken that she is my nece dere,
And I hir eem, and traytor eek y-fere!

40

And were it wist that I, through myn engyn,
Hadde in my nece y-put this fantasye,
To do thy lust, and hoolly to be thyn,
Why, al the world up-on it wolde crye,
And seye, that I the worste trecherye
Dide in this cas, that ever was bigonne,
And she for-lost, and thou right nought y-wonne.

41

Wher-fore, er I wol ferther goon a pas,
Yet eft I thee biseche and fully seye,
That privetee go with us in this cas,
That is to seye, that thou us never wreye;

34

When all had left the room except these two,
And firmly shut and barred was every door,
Their conversation they began anew,
And Pandar left his couch upon the floor,
And on the bed he sat, and now once more
Began to speak in his accustomed way
To Troilus, as I shall to you say.

35

"My lord most worshipful and brother dear,
God knows, and thou, what pain and grief I bore
To see thee languishing through all the year
For love that ever the longer grew the more!
Thus I with all my might and all my lore
Did ever since my time for you employ
To bring you back from sorrow into joy,

36

"And have so far my plannings carried out
That you to gain your end are in good way.
But there is nothing here to boast about,
And know you why? With shame I must it say,
For you I have begun a game to play,
The like of which I'd do for no one other,
Although he were a thousandfold my brother.

37

"That is to say, I've made myself for thee
Half jest, half earnest, such a go-between
As oft twixt man and maid the world doth see.
You know yourself what kind of thing I mean;
For thee I've made my niece, so pure and clean,
Such confidence and trust on thee bestow
That henceforth all just as thou wilt shall go.

38

"But God omniscient here I witness take,
For private ends in this I have not wrought,
But only strove thy sufferings to slake,
Which well nigh fatal were, or so I thought.
But, brother dear, remember that you ought,
In every manner, keep her free from blame,
And always strive to save her honest name.

39

"For well you know a woman's reputation
Among the people is a sacred thing,
And never man, I dare make affirmation,
A charge of wrong on her could justly bring;
But now the dreadful thought my heart doth wring,
That she should be my niece, so dear to me,
And I her uncle and her pimp should be.

40

"And were it known that I, through set design,
Had put my dearest niece in such a way
To follow thee and be all wholly thine,
Why, all the world would cry aloud and say,
That no such treachery for many a day
Was in this fashion planned and done,
And she be lost, and for thee nothing won!

41

"And so before a further step we take,
No matter what befall, I ask again
For secrecy, for hers and for my sake;
Do not disgrace me in the eyes of men!

And be not wroth at me if now and then,
I beg for privacy in this affair,
For well you know how urgent is my prayer.

42
"And think what woes of old have come to pass
From boastful speech, and how today men lead
Their lives in griefs that burden and harass,
From hour to hour, for that same wicked deed.
And in the wisest clerks you well may read
This proverb, useful to the old and young,
'The highest virtue is to hold your tongue.'

43
"And if I would not now abbreviate
Diffusiveness in speech, I could almost
A thousand ancient tales to you relate
Of women lost through false and foolish boast.
Such proverbs you yourself must know a host;
All boastful blabbers are but fools forsooth,
Even if what they say seems like the truth.

44
"One tongue, alas, hath often made to mourn
And caused full many a lady bright of hue
To cry, 'Alas the day that I was born!'
And many a maid her sorrow to renew;
And yet the things are twisted all askew
Of which men boast, if they were brought to
proof;
Boasters by nature are from truth aloof.

45
"A boaster and a liar, all is one!
For now suppose a woman granteth me
Her love, as to no other she hath done,
And I am sworn to sacred secrecy,
And then I go and talk to two or three,
Then I'm a boaster and a liar both,
For I have broken all my plighted troth.

46
"You see right well how much they are to blame,
Such sort of folk—or scamps would be more pat—
Who boast of women, even by their name,
Who never promised them nor this nor that,
Nor knew them any more than my old hat!
I ask you, is it any wonder then
That women fear to get involved with men?

47
"I don't say this especially of you—
I hope you're not in need of all I've said.
I'm thinking of the harm that people do
By heedlessness, and not by malice led;
For well I know no woman need to dread
The vice of boasting in a man of sense;
The wise learn from the fools to shun offence.

48
"But to the point! Now my good brother dear,
Keep all these things that I have said in mind,
And ponder well. But now, be of good cheer,
And doubt not at the proper time to find
Me true, for I shall work in such a kind
That you therewith shall be well satisfied,
For all shall be as you yourself decide.

49
"I have no doubt of thy integrity,

And be nought wrooth, though I thee ofte preye
To holden secree swich an heigh matere;
For skilful is, thow wost wel, my preyere.

42
And thenk what wo ther hath bitid er this,
For makinge of avauntes, as men rede;
And what mischaunce in this world yet ther is,
Fro day to day, right for that wikked dede;
For which these wyse clerkes that ben dede
Han ever yet proverbed to us yonge,
That 'firste vertu is to kepe tonge.'

43
And, nere it that I wilne as now t'abregge
Diffusioun of speche, I coude almost
A thousand olde stories thee alegge
Of wommen lost, thorugh fals and foles bost;
Proverbes canst thy-self y-nowe, and wost,
Ayeins that vyce, for to been a labbe,
Al seyde men sooth as often as they gabbe.

44
O tonge, allas! so often here-biforn
Hastow made many a lady bright of hewe
Seyd, 'welawey! the day that I was born!'
And many a maydes sorwes for to newe;
And, for the more part, al is untrewe
That men of yelpe, and it were brought to
preve;
Of kinde non avauntour is to leve.

45
Avauntour and a lyere, al is on;
As thus: I pose, a womman graunte me
Hir love, and seyth that other wol she non,
And I am sworn to holden it secree,
And after I go telle it two or three;
Y-wis, I am avauntour at the leste,
And lyere, for I breke my biheste.

46
Now loke thanne, if they be nought to blame,
Swich maner folk; what shal I clepe hem, what,
That hem avaunte of wommen, and by name,
That never yet bihighte hem this ne that,
Ne knewe hem more than myn olde hat?
No wonder is, so god me sende hele,
Though wommen drede with us men to dele.

47
I sey not this for no mistrust of yow,
Ne for no wys man, but for foles nyce,
And for the harm that in the world is now,
As wel for foly ofte as for malyce;
For wel wot I, in wyse folk, that vyce
No womman drat, if she be wel avysed;
For wyse ben by foles harm chastysed.

48
But now to purpos; leve brother dere,
Have al this thing that I have seyd in minde,
And keep thee clos, and be now of good chere,
For at thy day thou shalt me trewe finde.
I shal thy proces sette in swich a kinde,
And god to-forn, that it shall thee suffyse,
For it shal been right as thou wolt devyse.

49
For wel I woot, thou menest wel, parde;

Therfore I dar this fully undertake.
Thou wost eek what thy lady graunted thee,
And day is set, the chartres up to make.
How now good night, I may no lenger wake;
And bid for me, sin thou art now in blisse,
That god me sende deeth or sone lisse."

And therefore all this task I undertake.
Thou knowest that thy lady grants to thee
A day on which thy settlement to make!
And now goodnight! I cannot keep awake.
And pray for me, since heaven doth thee bless,
God send me death, or make my sorrow less!"

50

Who mighte telle half the joye or feste
Which that the sowle of Troilus tho felte,
Heringe th'effect of Pandarus biheste?
His olde wo, that made his herte swelte,
Gan tho for joye wasten and to-melte,
And al the richesse of his sykes sore
At ones fledde, he felte of hem no more.

50

Now who could tell one half the jubilation
Which Troilus within his heart then felt,
Hearing the end of Pandar's protestation!
The wounds that grief unto his heart had dealt
Began for joy to vanish and to melt,
And all his multitude of sighings sore
Dispersed and fled away forevermore.

51

But right so as these holtes and these hayes,
That han in winter dede been and dreye,
Revesten hem in grene, whan that May is,
Whan every lusty lyketh best to pleye:
Right in that selve wyse, sooth to seye,
Wex sodeynliche his herte ful of joye,
That gladder was ther never man in Troye.

51

As when the woods and hedges everywhere,
Which through the winter waited dead and dry,
Reclothe themselves in green, so fresh and fair,
And all the folk rejoice with spirits high,
The same thing now in him you might descry;
His heart with joy to blossom so began
That in all Troy there was no happier man.

52

And gan his look on Pandarus up caste
Ful sobrely, and frendly for to see,
And seyde, "freend, in Aprille the laste,
As wel thou wost, if it remembre thee,
How neigh the deeth for wo thou founde me;
And how thou didest al thy bisinesse
To knowe of me the cause of my distresse.

52

Then Troilus his eye on Pandar cast,
Most soberly, yet in a friendly way,
And said, "O friend, remember April last,
For I am sure you can't forget the day,
How nearly mortal sorrow did me slay,
And how you long and earnestly did press
Me there to tell the cause of my distress?

53

Thou wost how longe I it for-bar to seye
To thee, that art the man that I best triste;
And peril was it noon to thee by-wreye,
That wiste I wel; but tel me, if thee liste,
Sith I so looth was that thy-self it wiste,
How dorste I mo tellen of this matere,
That quake now, and no wight may us here?

53

"You know how long to speak I then forbore,
Although you were the man I trusted best,
And nothing hindered me then to declare
The truth to you. Now tell me, I request,
Since nothing of my love I then confessed,
How durst I babble in the general ear,
And tremble now, with no one by to hear?

54

But natheles, by that god I thee swere,
That, as him list, may al this world governe,
And, if I lye, Achilles with his spere
Myn herte cleve, al were my lyf eterne,
As I am mortal, if I late or yerne
Wolde it biwreye, or dorste, or sholde conne,
For all the good that god made under sonne;

54

"But by the God omnipotent I swear,
By him who deals to every man his fate,
And if I lie, may not Achilles spare
To cleave my heart, that I shan't divulgate,
Though I should live forever, soon or late,
A word of this, or hint to anyone,
For all the gifts of God beneath the sun.

55

That rather deye I wolde, and determyne,
As thinketh me, now stokked in presoun,
In wrecchednesse, in filthe, and in vermyne,
Caytif to cruel king Agamenoun;
And this, in alle the temples of this toun,
Upon the goddes alle, I wol thee swere'
To-morwe day, if that thee lyketh here.

55

"The rather would I end my days withal,
Fettered in prison cell would rather be,
In wretchedness where filthy vermin crawl,
In Agamemnon's harsh captivity;
And this in all our temples faithfully,
By all our Gods tomorrow I will swear,
And you can go along and witness bear.

56

And that thou hast so muche y-doon for me,
That I ne may it never-more deserve,
This knowe I wel, al mighte I now for thee
A thousand tymes on a morwen sterve,
I can no more, that that I wol thee serve
Right as thy sclave, whider-so thou wende,
For ever-more, un-to my lyves ende!

56

"That thou hast done so very much for me
That all thy service I can ne'er repay,
I understand quite well, although for thee
I died a thousand times and more a day;
But as thy slave, and what more can I say,
Upon thy wish and will I shall attend,
Till death shall bring my life unto its end.

57

"But let me now with all my heart beseech
That you assign me no such attribute,
As I might fairly gather from your speech,
That you supposed that all my honest suit
Was but a bawdy thing of ill repute.
I'm not a scholar, but I'm not a fool,
I've learned a thing or two outside of school.

58

"A man who this affair should undertake
For gold or profit, call him what you will!
But what you've done, you did for pity's sake,
Through goodness of your heart and not for ill.
Regard it so, for men of any skill
All know that the distinctions subtle are
Between two things a good deal similar.

59

"And here's another thing that I declare
To wipe from all your act the shameful blot;
Behold my sister Polyxena fair,
Cassandra, Helen, or any of the lot,
Though she be fair with never a stain or spot,
Just tell me which of these you'd like to be
Your very own, and leave the rest to me!

60

"But since thou hast helped me in this wise
To save my life, and not for hope of meed,
So, for the love of God, this great emprise
Carry thou out, for now there is much need;
In high and low, in every single deed
All thy commands I faithfully will keep,
And so good night, and let us go to sleep."

61

Thus each with other was well satisfied,
No better friends in all the world could be;
The next day, early up and dressed, each hied
Him to his regular activity;
And Troilus, although he longed to see
The one on whom depended all his joy,
Took heed all right precautions to employ,

62

And every reckless action to restrain
With manly will, and each unbridled look;
There was no man alive could entertain
The least suspicion, such good care he took
That none might nose him out by hook or crook.
He held himself as lonely as a cloud,
From policy, and not that he was proud.

63

And all this time of which I now relate,
He daily strove with valor and with might
The service high of Mars to cultivate
In deeds of arms befitting a true knight;
And on his couch when darkness followed light
He lay, and thought how he might serve
His lady best, and thus her thanks deserve.

64

I will not say, although his couch was soft,
That he in heart was fully at his ease,
Or that he turned not on his pillow oft,
Nor longed to grasp what was too far to seize.
Such lonely nights have little power to please—

57

But here, with al myn herte, I thee biseche,
That never in me thou deme swich folye
As I shal seyn; me thoughte, by thy speche,
That this, which thou me dost for companye,
I sholde wene it were a bauderye;
I am nought wood, al-if I lewed be;
It is not so, that woot I wel, pardee.

58

But he that goth, for gold or for richesse,
On swich message, calle him what thee list;
And this that thou dost, calle it gentilesse,
Compassioun, and felawship, and trist;
Departe it so, for wyde-where is wist
How that there is dyversitee requered
Bitwixen thinges lyke, as I have lered.

59

And, that thou knowe I thenke nought ne wene
That this servyse a shame be or jape,
I have my faire suster Polixene,
Cassandre, Eleyne, or any of the frape;
Be she never so faire or wel y-shape,
Tel me, which thou wilt of everichone,
To han for thyn, and lat me thanne allone.

60

But sin that thou hast don me this servyse,
My lyf to save, and for noon hope of mede,
So, for the love of god, this grete empryse
Parforme it out; for now is moste nede.
For high and low, with-outen any drede,
I wol alwey thyne hestes alle kepe;
Have now good night, and lat us bothe slepe."

61

Thus held him ech with other wel apayed,
That al the world ne mighte it bet amende;
And, on the morwe, whan they were arayed,
Ech to his owene nedes gan entende.
But Troilus, though as the fyr he brende
For sharp desyr of hope and of plesaunce,
He not for-gat his gode governaunce.

62

But in him-self with manhod gan restreyne
Ech rakel dede and ech unbrydled chere,
That alle tho that liven, sooth to seyne,
Ne sholde han wist, by word or by manere,
What that he mente, as touching this matere.
From every wight as fer as is the cloude
He was, so wel dissimulen he coude.

63

And al the whyl which that I yow devyse,
This was his lyf; with al his fulle might,
By day he was in Martes high servyse,
This is to seyn, in armes as a knight;
And for the more part, the longe night
He lay, and thoughte how that he mighte serve
His lady best, hir thank for to deserve.

64

Nil I nought swerë, al-though he lay softe,
That in his thought he nas sumwhat disesed,
Ne that he tornede on his pilwes ofte,
And wolde of that him missed han ben sesed;
But in swich cas man is nought alwey plesed,

For ought I wot, no more than was he;
That can I deme of possibilitee.

65

But certeyn is, to purpos for to go,
That in this whyle, as writen is in geste,
He say his lady som-tyme; and also
She with him spak, whan that she dorste or leste,
And by hir bothe avys, as was the beste,
Apoynteden ful warly in this nede,
So as they dorste, how they wolde procede.

66

But it was spoken in so short a wyse,
In swich awayt alwey, and in swich
fere,
Lest any wyght divynen or devyse
Wolde of hem two, or to it leye an ere,
That al this world so leef to hem ne were
As that Cupido wolde hem grace sende
To maken of hir speche aright an ende.

67

But thilke litel that they speke or wroughte,
His wyse goost took ay of al swich hede,
It semed hir, he wiste that she thoughte
With-outen word, so that it was no nede
To bidde him ought to done, or ought forbede;
For which she thoughte that love, al come it late,
Of alle joye hadde opned hir the yate.

68

And shortly of this proces for to pace,
So wel his werk and wordes he bisette,
That he so ful stood in his lady grace,
That twenty thousand tymes, or she lette,
She thonked god she ever with him mette;
So coude he him governe in swich servyse,
That al the world ne mighte it bet devyse.

69

For-why she fond him so discreet in al,
So secret, and of swich obëisaunce,
That wel she felte he was to hir a wal
Of steel, and sheld from every displesaunce;
That, to ben in his gode governaunce,
So wys he was, she was no more afered,
I mene, as fer as oughte ben requered.

70

And Pandarus, to quike alwey the fyr,
Was ever y-lyke prest and diligent;
To ese his frend was set al his desyr.
He shoof ay on, he to and fro was sent;
He lettres bar whan Troilus was absent.
That never man, as in his freendes nede,
Ne bar him bet than he, with-outen drede.

71

But now, paraunter, som man wayten wolde
That every word, or sonde, or look, or chere
Of Troilus that I rehersen sholde,
In al this whyle, un-to his lady dere;
I trowe it were a long thing for to here;
Or of what wight that stant in swich disjoynte,
His wordes alle, or every look, to poynte.

72

For sothe, I have not herd it doon er this,
In storye noon, ne no man here, I wene;

So I've been told,—and so thought he maybe;
I note it as a possibility.

65

But this is sure, in order not to stray
Too far among reflections manifold,
He saw his lady, yet not every day,
And spoke with her, although too rash or bold
They neither were, and always strove to hold
Themselves in hand, for each one felt the need
With proper care and caution to proceed.

66

And when they spoke, they spoke so quick and
brief,
With great reserve and with oppressive fear,
(For folk are prone to jump at some belief,
And strain to gather something through the ear),
That all would think that nothing was so dear
To them as this, that Cupid should them send
An opportunity their speech to end.

67

But though they spake but little or spake naught,
His spirit was so tuned in every deed,
It seemed to her he knew of all her thought
Without a word, so that there was no need
To caution or for aught to intercede;
For so it seemed that love, though come so late,
To all their joy had opened up the gate.

68

In short, to bring the matter to a close,
So faithfully he did on her attend,
That high in his dear lady's grace he rose,
And twenty thousand times or more on end
She thanked the Lord that she had such a friend,
Who could conduct himself in all his ways
So well, he merited the highest praise.

69

In truth she found him so discreet withal,
So secret ever and obedient,
She felt he was to her a very wall
Of steel and shield from fear or discontent;
And when she saw how nicely all things went,
She felt she had no need to be so wary—
I mean, of course, no more than necessary.

70

And Pandar, ready still to feed the fire,
Was ever diligent and close at hand.
To please his friend was now his sole desire,
He urged him on, was ready at command
To carry letters, or for him to stand,
When Troilus was busy or away—
In short, the perfect confidant to play.

71

But if you think that I should now relate
Each word of Troilus, each hope and fear,
The little nothings, sweet and intimate,
That he meant only for his lady's ear,
I couldn't do it if I took a year;
To tell you every passage of his wooing
Would be a labor scarcely worth the doing.

72

I do not find that ever anyone
In telling such details has been minute—

'Twould be appalling if it were all done!
In letters thousands of verses I compute
They wrote, on which my author is quite mute;
He was too sensible and wise to try
To write all lovers say, and so am I.

73

But to the great result! As things stood thus,
These two in concord and in peace complete,
These lovers Cressida and Troilus,
Were well content in all this time so sweet,
Except that only rarely they could meet,
And had so little time their joys to tell,
I now proceed to say what next befell.

74

Good Pandar, striving still with all his might
To lead this matter to a happy end,
Thought how to bring unto his house some night
His niece so dear, and his still dearer friend,
That at their leisure they might there attend
To this great love by which they both were bound,
And finally a fitting time he found.

75

He made his plans with great deliberation,
Providing for all things that might avail
To help them realize their expectation,
However great the toil this might entail,
And worked it out so that it could not fail,
And that for anyone through it to see,
Would be a sheer impossibility.

76

To fool all folk his plan was well designed,
The spoil-sports and the gossips, all the same;
He had no doubts, for all the world is blind,
In such affairs, the wild ones and the tame!
And now the timbers ready are to frame!
There's nothing lacking now except to know
The hour at which to his house she should go.

77

And Troilus, who all this plotting knew,
And patiently in silent waiting lay,
Had also planned with care what he would do,
And also, for excuse, that he would say,
If he were not about some night or day,
That to a certain temple he would go,
His duty to the deity to show,

78

And solitary there would watch and wake,
If some sign from Apollo he might see,
Or might behold the holy laurel shake,
Or hear Apollo speaking from the tree,
To tell him when the Greeks would homeward
flee;
And therefore let him as he will pretend,
And pray Apollo bring all to good end.

79

And now we're coming to the point right soon!
For Pandar up and with no great ado,
But when there was a changing of the moon
And lightless is the world a night or two,
And when the clouds foretold a rain in view,
To Cressida, his niece's house he went,
And you well know the whole of his intent.

And though I wolde I coude not, y-wis;
For ther was som epistel hem bitwene,
That wolde, as seyth myn auctor, wel contene
Neigh half this book, of which him list not wryte;
How sholde I thanne a lyne of it endyte?

73

But to the grete effect: than sey I thus,
That stonding in concord and in quiete
Thise ilke two, Criseyde and Troilus,
As I have told, and in this tyme swete,
Save only often mighte they not mete,
Ne layser have hir speches to fulfelle,
That it befel right as I shal yow telle,

74

That Pandarus, that ever dide his might
Right for the fyn that I shal speke of here.
As for to bringe to his hous som night
His faire nece, and Troilus y-fere,
Wher-as at leyser al this heigh matere,
Touching hir love, were at the fulle up-bounde,
Hadde out of doute a tyme to it founde.

75

For he with greet deliberacioun
Hadde every thing that her-to mighte avayle
Forn-cast, and put in execucioun,
And neither laft for cost ne for travayle;
Come if hem lest, hem sholde no-thing fayle;
And for to been in ought espyed there,
That, wiste he wel, an inpossible were.

76

Dredelees, it cleer was in the wind
Of every pye and every lette-game;
Now al is wel, for al the world is blind
In this matere, bothe fremed and tame.
This timber is al redy up to frame;
Us lakketh nought but that we witen wolde
A certain houre, in whiche she comen sholde.

77

And Troilus, that al this purveyaunce
Knew at the fulle, and waytede on it ay,
Hadde here-up-on eek made gret ordenaunce,
And founde his cause, and ther-to his aray,
If that he were missed, night or day,
Ther-whyle he was aboute this servyse,
That he was goon to doon his sacrifyse,

78

And moste at swich a temple alone wake,
Answered of Appollo for to be;
And first, to seen the holy laurer quake,
Er that Apollo spak out of the tree,
To telle him next whan Grekes sholden
flee;
And forthy lette him no man, god forbede,
But preye Apollo helpen in this nede.

79

Now is ther litel more for to done,
But Pandare up, and shortly for to seyne,
Right sone upon the chaunging of the mone,
Whan lightles is the world a night or tweyne,
And that the welken shoop him for to reyne,
He streight a-morwe un-to his nece wente;
Ye han wel herd the fyn of his entente.

80

When he was come, he gan anoon to pleye
As he was wont, and of him-self to jape;
And fynally, he swor and gan hir seye,
By this and that, she sholde him not escape,
Ne lenger doon him after hir to gape;
But certeynly she moste, by hir leve,
Come soupen in his hous with him at eve.

81

At whiche she lough, and gan hir faste excuse,
And seyde, "it rayneth; lo, how sholde I goon?"
"Lat be," quod he, "ne stond not thus to muse;
This moot be doon, ye shal be ther anoon."
So at the laste her-of they felle at oon,
Or elles, softe he swor hir in hir ere,
He nolde never come ther she
were.

82

Sone after this, to him she gan to rowne,
And asked him if Troilus were there?
He swor hir, "nay, for he was out of towne,"
And seyde, "nece, I pose that he were,
Yow thurfte never have the more fere.
For rather than men mighte him ther aspye,
Me were lever a thousand-fold to dye."

83

Nought list myn auctor fully to declare
What that she thoughte whan he seyde so,
That Troilus was out of town y-fare,
As if he seyde ther-of sooth or no;
But that, with-oute awayt, with him to go,
She graunted him, sith he hir that bisoughte,
And, as his nece, obeyed as hir oughte.

84

But nathelees, yet gan she him biseche,
Al-though with him to goon it was no fere,
For to be war of goosish peples speche,
That dremen thinges whiche that never were,
And wel avyse him whom he broughte there;
And seyde him, "eem, sin I mot on yow triste,
Loke al be wel, and do now as yow liste."

85

He swor hir, "yis, by stokkes and by stones,
And by the goddes that in hevene dwelle,
Or elles were him lever, soule and bones,
With Pluto king as depe been in helle
As Tantalus!" What sholde I more telle?
Whan al was wel, he roos and took his leve,
And she to souper com, whan it was eve,

86

With a certayn of hir owene men,
And with hir faire nece Antigone,
And othere of hir wommen nyne or ten;
But who was glad now, who, as trowe ye,
But Troilus, that stood and mighte it see
Thurgh-out a litel windowe in a stewe,
Ther he bishet, sin midnight, was in mewe,

87

Unwist of every wight but of Pandare?
But to the poynt; now whan she was y-come
With alle joye, and alle frendes fare,
Hir eem anoon in armes hath hir nome,

80

When he arrived, in his accustomed way
He joked and jested at his own expense,
But finally he paused and made display
Of earnestness and of great exigence,
And said for no excuse and no pretence,
He'd let her off, but come she must that eve
To supper at his house by her good leave.

81

At this she laughed and in excuse replied,
"It's raining, look! So how then could I go?"
"That's nothing," said he. "Just let me decide.
You've got to come—I will not take a no!"
And so at last they left the matter so,
For he had whispered softly in her ear,
"Don't come if you won't, but for it you'll pay
dear!"

82

But she was not quite ready to give way,
And asked if maybe Troilus was there.
"O no," he said, "he's out of town today!
But, niece, I say, supposing that he were,
You have no slightest cause for fear or care,
Indeed a thousand times I'd rather die,
Than have folk on him at my house to spy."

83

Explicitly no one has set it down,
Just what she thought when Pandar told her so,
That Troilus was that day out of town,
If Cressida believed his tale or no;
But that she went with him to sup we know,
At least, as he so urgently besought,
No matter what she knew or what she thought.

84

But nevertheless she did again beseech,
Although to go she had no hesitation,
That he forget not foolish people's speech,
Who dream what never was in all creation,
And that he give this full consideration;
"For, uncle," said she, "since in you I trust,
Take heed, for follow where you lead I must."

85

To do all this he swore by sticks and stones,
And all the gods that high in heaven dwell,
Or let him be, said he, both skin and bones,
As deep as Tantalus in lowest hell
Where Pluto reigns! What is there more to tell?
All thus arranged, he rose and took his leave,
And she to supper came when it was eve,

86

Along with certain of her household men,
And with her charming niece Antigone,
And others of her women, nine or ten.
Who now was glad? Who other can it be
But Troilus, who stood where he could see,
Right through a little window in a room,
Where he till midnight hid in lonely gloom,

87

To all the folk save Pandar quite unknown?
But to the point! When she had come at last,
With all her friends, as I before have shown,
Her uncle with his arm about her cast,

Together with his guests to supper passed,
And when they all were seated happily,
The dainties served there were a sight to see.

88

When from the supper table they arose,
At ease in mind and heart was man and maid,
And each for her his freshest stories chose,
While Pandar his most sparkling wit displayed.
He sang; she played; he told the tale of Wade,
But everything at last must have an end,
And she prepared her homeward way to wend.

89

Thou Chance, executrix of each man's weird!
O Influences dwelling in the sky!
All under God, our fates by these are steered,
Though we poor brutes the cause cannot descry;
For though she said that homeward she would hie,
The Gods had willed it in another way,
And willy-nilly, there she had to stay.

90

The curving moon, with her two horns all pale,
And Saturn, Jove and Cancer so united
That all the rains of heaven now assail
The earth, and all these ladies were affrighted,
Who by the smoky rain were thus benighted;
But Pandar only laughed at them, and cried,
" 'Tis fine for ducks and ladies now outside!

91

"But now, good niece, I hope that you will please
Accept my humble hospitality,
As well for mine as for your greater ease,
And all remain here overnight with me.
Pray let my house for once your own house be;
For if you went out now, I'd feel to blame,
And take it as an insult and a shame."

92

And Cressida, who saw how matters stood
As well as anyone, had naught to say,
For since the flooding rain had come for good,
She thought, "I might as well, if I must stay,
Accept the matter in a cheerful way,
And have his thanks, as grumble and remain,
For home we cannot go just now, that's plain."

93

"That's very kind," she said, "my uncle dear,
And if you really wish, it shall be so.
We're glad to have the chance of staying here.
'Twas but a joke when I said I would go."
"I thank you, niece," he answered, bowing low,
"Joking or not, the simple truth to tell,
I am relieved that with me you will dwell."

94

So far, so good! Then they began anew
The conversation in a merry strain,
But Pandar kept the main point still in view,
And he to get them soon to bed was fain.
"Good Lord," he said, "this is a mighty rain!
It's just the weather for a good long sleep!
Let other things until tomorrow keep!

95

"And, niece, I have a place for you to stay,
Right here, where we shan't be too far asunder,

And after to the souper, alle and some,
Whan tyme was, ful softe they hem sette;
God wot, ther was no deyntee for to fette.

88

And after souper gonnen they to ryse,
At ese wel, with hertes fresshe and glade,
And wel was him that coude best devyse
To lyken hir, or that hir laughen made.
He song; she pleyde; he tolde tale of Wade.
But at the laste, as every thing hath ende,
She took hir leve, and nedes wolde wende.

89

But O, Fortune, executrice of wierdes,
O influences of thise hevenes hye!
Soth is, that, under god, ye ben our hierdes,
Though to us bestes been the causes wrye.
This mene I now, for she gan hoomward hye,
But execut was al bisyde hir leve,
At the goddes wil; for which she moste bleve.

90

The bente mone with hir hornes pale,
Saturne, and Jove, in Cancro joyned were,
That swich a rayn from hevene gan avale,
That every maner womman that was there
Hadde of that smoky reyn a verray fere;
At which Pandare tho lough, and seyde thenne,
"Now were it tyme a lady to go henne!

91

But goode nece, if I mighte ever plese
Yow any-thing, than prey I yow," quod he,
"To doon myn herte as now so greet an ese
As for to dwelle here al this night with me,
For-why this is your owene hous, pardee.
For, by my trouthe, I sey it nought a-game,
To wende as now, it were to me a shame."

92

Criseyde, whiche that coude as muche good
As half a world, tok hede of his preyere;
And sin it ron, and al was on a flood,
She thoughte, as good chep may I dwellen here,
And graunte it gladly with a freendes chere,
And have a thank, as grucche and thanne abyde;
For hoom to goon it may nought wel bityde.

93

"I wol," quod she, "myn uncle leef and dere,
Sin that yow list, it skile is to be so;
I am right glad with yow to dwellen here;
I seyde but a-game, I wolde go,"
"Y-wis, graunt mercy, nece!" quod he tho;
"Were it a game or no, soth for to telle,
Now am I glad, sin that yow list to dwelle."

94

Thus al is wel; but tho bigan aright
The newe joye, and al the feste agayn;
But Pandarus, if goodly hadde he might,
He wolde han hyed hir to bedde fayn,
And seyde, "lord, this is an huge rayn!
This were a weder for to slepen inne;
And that I rede us sone to biginne.

95

And nece, woot ye wher I wol yow leye,
For that we shul not liggen fer asonder,

And for ye neither shullen, dar I seye,
Heren noise of reynes nor of thonder?
By god, right in my lyte closet yonder.
And I wol in that outer hous allone
Be wardeyn of your wommen everichone.

96

And in this middel chaumbre that ye see
Shul youre wommen slepen wel and softe;
And ther I seyde shal your-selve be;
And if ye liggen wel to-night, com ofte,
And careth not what weder is on-lofte.
The wyn anon, and whan so that yow leste,
So go we slepe, I trowe it be the beste.'

97

Ther nis no more, but here-after sone,
The voydè dronke, and travers drawe anon,
Gan every wight, that hadde nought to done
More in that place, out of the chaumber gon.
And ever-mo so sternelich it ron,
And blew ther-with so wonderliche loude,
That wel neigh no man heren other coude.

98

Tho Pandarus, hir eem, right as him oughte,
With women swiche as were hir most aboute,
Ful glad un-to hir beddes syde hir broughte,
And took his leve, and gan ful lowe loute,
And seyde, "here at this closet-dore withoute,
Right over-thwart, your wommen liggen alle,
That, whom yow liste of hem, ye may here
calle."

99

So whan that she was in the closet leyd,
And alle hir wommen forth by ordenaunce
A-bedde weren, ther as I have seyd,
There was no more to skippen nor to traunce,
But boden go to bedde, with mischaunce,
If any wight was steringe any-where,
And late hem slepe that a-bedde were.

100

But Pandarus, that wel coude eche a del
The olde daunce, and every poynt therinne,
Whan that he sey that alle thing was wel,
He thoughte he wolde up-on his werk biginne,
And gan the stewe-dore al softe un-pinne,
And stille as stoon, with-outen lenger lette,
By Troilus a-doun right he him sette.

101

And, shortly to the poynt right for to gon,
Of al this werk he tolde him word and ende,
And seyde, "make thee redy right anon,
For thou shalt in-to hevene blisse wende."
"Now blisful Venus, thou me grace sende,"
Quod Troilus, "for never yet no nede
Hadde I er now, ne halvendel the drede."

102

Quod Pandarus, "ne drede thee never a del,
For it shal been right as thou wilt desyre;
So thryve I, this night shal I make it wel,
Or casten al the gruwel in the fyre."
"Yit blisful Venus, this night thou me enspyre,"
Quod Troilus, "as wis as I thee serve,
And ever bet and bet shal, til I sterve.

And where you shan't hear in the slightest way
The noise of raining or the din of thunder.
My little room will suit you to a wonder,
And in that outer place alone I'll sleep,
And watch and guard upon your women keep.

96

"And in this room between, that here you see,
Shall all your women sleep both well and soft,
And snug within, yourself alone shall be.
And if you sleep well, come back soon and oft,
No matter what the weather be aloft!
Just one last drink! And when you feel inclined,
Now all of you know just where your bed to find!"

97

The night cup to the company was passed,
And all the curtains then were closely drawn,
And so it was not long until the last
Of all the folk from out the room had gone.
But still the pelting rain kept on and on,
And such a storm of wind blew all around,
You could not hear a single other sound.

98

Fair Cressida was to her chamber brought,
Together with a personal maid or two,
And Pandar, doing all a good host ought,
With many a bow, to her then said adieu,
But added, "At this door not far from you,
Your women will be lodged across the hall,
And if you want them, you need only
call."

99

So Cressida was safely tucked in bed,
And all disposed of, just as Pandar planned,
And I have carefully explained and said;
If any then would tramp about, or stand
And talk, the rest did scold and all demand
That those who made the racket should keep still,
And let the others sleep who had the will.

100

Now Pandar knew the game he had to play,
And how to manage every point therein,
And all in a preliminary way
Now being well, was ready to begin;
And first the little door he doth unpin,
And entering there as still as any stone,
By Troilus he sat him down alone.

101

And then he had a story to relate
Of all these things, from very start to end.
"Get ready," said he, "heaven's joys await
On thee, if thou wilt but attend!"
"Saint Venus," Troilus replied, "now send
Thy aid, for never have I had such need,
Nor ever felt such fright for any deed!"

102

Said Pandar, "Don't be in the least afraid,
For all shall turn out just as you desire;
Tonight I say your fortune shall be made,
Or else tonight the fat be in the fire."
"O blessed Venus, now my heart inspire,"
Cried Troilus, "and in thy service high
My time forever I shall occupy!

103

"And if there reigned, O Venus, queen of mirth,
Aspects of Saturn, or of Mars malign,
Or thou wert quenched or hindered at my birth,
Thy father pray that he this harm of mine
Will turn aside, and grant me joy divine,
For love of him for whom thou felt'st love's pain,
Adonis, by the fateful wild boar slain!

104

"O Jove, thou lover of Europa fair,
Who as a bull didst carry her away,
Now help! O Mars, who bloody cloak dost bear,
For love of Venus, hinder me not I pray!
O Phoebus, think how Daphne pined one day
Beneath the bark, and to a laurel grew,
And help me now, for love of her so true!

105

"O Mercury, I beg in Herse's name,
Though Pallas was against Aglauros set,
Now help! Diana, let not modest shame
Dissuade thee now to aid me and abet!
O Fatal Sisters, ere my nurse made yet
My swaddling clothes, my destiny ye spun,
So help me in this work that is begun!"

106

Said Pandar, "O, you chicken-hearted wretch!
Are you afraid because you think she'll bite?
Put something on—this over-cloak just fetch
Along, and follow me to see a sight!
But wait, I'll go ahead, to make all right!"
Then he undid a little secret door,
And Troilus waiting, he went on before.

107

The wind so roared and rumbled round about,
No other sound could anywhere be heard,
And those whose beds stood near the door without,
They slept and not a single person stirred,
For none had caught a whisper or a word.
Then Pandar found the door, without a light,
Where they all lay, and softly shut it tight.

108

He came again, quite still and stealthily,
But Cressida awoke and cried, "Who's there?"
"Dear niece," he softly said, "it's only me!
I hope I haven't given you a scare!"
And whispering low, he begged her to beware;
"No word," he said, "that curious folk can hear!
We don't want meddlers now to interfere!"

109

"How in the world," she asked, "did you get here,
And they not know a thing about it all?"
"At this trap-door," he answered, drawing near.
"Perhaps," said Cressida, "I'd better call."
"What, God forbid!" he answered still and small.
"If we by anyone should thus be caught,
They might think what they never would have
thought.

110

"Like sleeping dogs, you know—just let them sleep!
Don't ever give a chance for vague surmise.
Your women are in slumber sunk so deep,
You might pull down the town before their eyes,

103

And if I hadde, O Venus ful of mirthe,
Aspectes badde of Mars or of Saturne,
Or thou combust or let were in my birthe,
Thy fader pray al thilke harm disturne
Of grace, and that I glad ayein may turne,
For love of him thou lovedest in the shawe,
I mene Adoon, that with the boor was slawe.

104

O Jove eek, for the love of faire Europe,
The whiche in forme of bole away thou fette;
Now help, O Mars, thou with thy blody cope,
For love of Cipris, thou me nought ne lette;
O Phebus, thenk whan Dane hir-selven shette
Under the bark, and laurer wex for drede,
Yet for hir love, O help now at this nede!

105

Mercurie, for the love of Hiersè eke,
For which Pallas was with Aglauros wrooth,
Now help, and eek Diane, I thee biseke,
That this viage be not to thee looth.
O fatal sustren, which, er any clooth
Me shapen was, my destenè me sponne,
So helpeth to this werk that is bi-gonne!"

106

Quod Pandarus, "thou wrecched mouses herte,
Art thou agast so that she wol thee byte?
Why, don this furred cloke up-on thy sherte,
And folowe me, for I wol han the wyte;
But byd, and lat me go bifore a lyte."
And with that word he gan un-do a trappe,
And Troilus he broughte in by the lappe.

107

The sterne wind so loude gan to route
That no wight other noyse mighte here;
And they that layen at the dore withoute,
Ful sikerly they slepten alle y-fere;
And Pandarus, with a ful sobre chere,
Goth to the dore anon with-outen lette,
Ther-as they laye, and softely it shette.

108

And as he com ayeinward prively,
His nece awook, and asked "who goth there?"
"My dere nece," quod he, "it am I;
Ne wondreth not, ne have of it no fere";
And ner he com, and seyde hir in hir ere,
"No word, for love of god I yow biseche;
Lat no wight ryse and heren of our speche."

109

"What! which wey be ye comen, *benedicite?*"
Quod she, "and how thus unwist of hem alle?"
"Here at this secree trappe-dore," quod he.
Quod tho Criseyde, "lat me som wight calle."
"Ey! god forbede that it sholde falle,"
Quod Pandarus, "that ye swich foly wroughte!
They mighte deme thing they never er
thoughte!

110

It is nought good a sleping hound to wake,
Ne yeve a wight a cause to devyne;
Your wommen slepen alle, I under-take,
So that, for hem, the hous men mighte myne;

And slepen wolen til the sonne shyne.
And whan my tale al brought is to an ende,
Unwist, right as I com, so wol I wende.

111

Now nece myn, ye shul wel understonde,"
Quod he, "so as ye wommen demen alle,
That for to holde in love a man in honde,
And him hir 'leef' and 'dere herte' calle,
And maken him an howve above a calle,
I mene, as love an other in this whyle,
She doth hir-self a shame, and him a gyle.

112

Now wherby that I telle yow al this?
Ye woot your-self, as wel as any wight,
How that your love al fully graunted is
To Troilus, the worthieste knight,
Oon of this world, and ther-to trouthe plyght,
That, but it were on him along, ye nolde
Him never falsen, whyl ye liven sholde.

113

Now stant it thus, that sith I fro yow wente,
This Troilus, right platly for to seyn,
Is thurgh a goter, by a privè wente,
In-to my chaumbre come in al this reyn,
Unwist of every maner wight, certeyn,
Save of my-self, as wisly have I joye,
And by that feith I shal Pryam of Troye!

114

And he is come in swich peyne and distresse
That, but he be al fully wood by this,
He sodeynly mot falle in-to wodnesse,
But-if god helpe; and cause why this is,
He seyth him told is, of a freend of his,
How that ye sholde love oon that hatte Horaste,
For sorwe of which this night shalt been his laste."

115

Criseyde, which that al this wonder herde,
Gan sodeynly aboute hir herte colde,
And with a syk she sorwfully answerde,
"Allas! I wende, who-so tales tolde,
My dere herte wolde me not holde
So lightly fals! allas! conceytes wronge,
What harm they doon, for now live I to longe!

116

Horaste! allas! and falsen Troilus?
I knowe him not, god helpe me so," quod she;
"Allas! what wikked spirit tolde him thus?
Now certes, eem, to-morwe, and I him see,
I shal ther-of as ful excusen me
As ever dide womman, if him lyke";
And with that word she gan ful sore syke.

117

"O god!" quod she, "so worldly selinesse,
Which clerkes callen fals felicitee,
Y-medled is with many a bitternesse!
Ful anguisshous than is, god woot," quod she,
"Condicioun of veyn prosperitee;
For either joyes comen nought y-fere,
Or elles no wight hath hem alwey here.

118

O brotel wele of mannes joye unstable!

And will sleep so until the sun shall rise;
And when I've told you what I have to say,
As silent as I came, I'll go away.

111

"Dear niece, I'm sure you quite well understand,
And all, I think, agree in this," he said,
"That if you have a certain man in hand,
Whose hopes with honeyed words you long have fed,
And yet you set a fool's cap on his head,
I mean, with someone else you are too thick,—
Why, that's a shameful and a nasty trick.

112

"Now let me tell why I say this to you.
You know yourself as well as any wight,
That all your love is promised and is due
To Troilus, that good and noble knight,
And with such pledges you your faith did plight,
You never would your love to him deny,
Unless, indeed, the fault in him should lie.

113

"But here's the point, that since to bed I went,
This Troilus, with something on his brain,
Has by a gutter, through a secret vent,
Into my chamber come in all this rain,
Of course unknown to all, let me explain,
Save me alone in all the town of Troy,
I swear as I have hope of heaven's joy.

114

"Now he has come this night in such great grief
That I'm afraid lest he may lose his mind,
For he is hurt and wild beyond belief,
And now the reason for all this I find,
His faith in you a friend has undermined,
Who says you love a fellow named Horast,
For grief of which this night may be his last."

115

Cressida heard this tale with great surprise,
And therewithal she felt her heart grow cold,
And suddenly exclaimed, with tears and sighs,
"Alas, I thought, whatever tales were told,
My sweetheart would not me so lightly hold
For false! Alas, they'll drive me to my death,
These liars with their foul and poisoned breath!

116

"Horast! And me be false to Troilus!
Indeed I never knew him," answered she.
"Alas, what wicked spirit told him thus!
But Troilus tomorrow I shall see,
And from these charges I myself shall free,
In his and in the eyes of all good men,"
And thereupon she sighed and sighed again.

117

"O God," she cried, "these blessings temporal,
Which scholars falsely call felicity,
With bitterness are mingled and with gall!
God only knows what anguish then hath he
Who sees his empty joys before him flee!
For either joys arrive inopportune,
Or else they flit and vanish all too soon!

118

"O fickle fate! O worldly joy unstable!

Of men thou makest but a sport and play!
All know that they to hold their joy are able,
Or know it not—there is no other way.
Now if one knows it not, how may he say
That he of perfect joy perceives the spark,
If ignorance still leaves him in the dark?

119

"But if he knows that joy is transitory,
Since joy in every worldly thing must flee,
This troubling thought diminishes the glory
Of earthly joy, and so in such degree,
Imperfect must be his felicity;
If loss of joy he fears a jot or tittle,
This proves that earthly joy is worth but little.

120

"And so this problem I must thus decide,
That verily, for aught that I can see,
No perfect joy can in this world abide.
But O, thou viper, wicked jealousy!
O folly, faithless, envious of me!
Why hast thou bred in Troilus distrust,
And I in all things ever true and just!"

121

"You know," said Pandar, "that of Troilus"—
"Why, uncle dear," she cried, "who told him so?
Alas, why does my sweetheart treat me thus?"
"O, well," he said, "the way of the world, you
know.
But what's gone wrong, we'll make the right way
go.
The way to stop all this with you doth rest,
And everything will turn out for the best."

122

"So shall I do tomorrow," answered she,
"And in a way I'm sure will satisfy."
"Tomorrow?" he cried, "as well eternity!
No, no, we cannot let this thing slip by!
Old clerks have written in their widsom high
That peril with delaying, strikes within.
No, such delayings are not worth a pin!

123

"There comes a fitting time for everything,
And when a room's afire or a hall,
It's better folk at once some help should bring,
Than stand and argufy amongst them all,
'How chanced this candle in the straw to fall?'
The harm is done the while they thus debate,
To lock the stable door is then too late.

124

"And niece, one thing I hope you'll let me say,
If all the night you leave him in this state,
Your love for him has been but vain display.
That's how it seems to me at any rate.
You can't abandon him to such a fate,
You know yourself, 'twould be the height of folly
To leave him in this dangerous melancholy."

125

"My love a vain display! You never loved
As I have loved," indignantly she cried.
"Well, that," he said, "remains yet to be proved!
But since by me you think you're justified,
I wouldn't let him in this sorrow bide,

With what wight so thou be, or how thou pleye,
Either he woot that thou, joye, art muable,
Or woot it not, it moot ben oon of tweye;
Now if he woot it not, how may he seye
That he hath verray joye and seliness,
That is of ignoraunce ay in derknesse?

119

Now if he woot that joye is transitorie,
As every joye of worldly thing mot flee,
Than every tyme he that hath in memorie,
The drede of lesing maketh him that he
May in no parfit selinesse be.
And if to lese his joye he set a myte,
Than semeth it that joye is worth ful lyte.

120

Wherfore I wol deffyne in this matere,
That trewely, for ought I can espye,
Ther is no verray wele in this world here.
But O, thou wikked serpent Jalousye,
Thou misbeleved and envious folye,
Why hastow Troilus me mad untriste,
That never yet agilte him, that I wiste?"

121

Quod Pandarus, "thus fallen is this cas."
"Why, uncle myn," quod she, "who tolde him this?
Why doth my dere herte thus, allas?"
"Ye woot, ye nece myn," quod he,
"what is;
I hope al shal be wel that is
amis.
For ye may quenche al this, if that yow leste,
And doth right so, for I holde it the beste."

122

"So shal I do to-morwe, y-wis" quod she,
"And god to-forn, so that it shal suffyse."
"To-morwe? allas, that were a fayr," quod he,
"Nay, nay, it may not stonden in this wyse;
For, nece myn, thus wryten clerkes wyse,
That peril is with drecching in y-drawe;
Nay, swich abodes been nought worth an hawe.

123

Nece, al thing hath tyme, I dar avowe;
For whan a chaumber a-fyr is, or an halle,
Wel more nede is, it sodeynly rescowe
Than to dispute, and axe amonges alle
How is this candel in the straw y-falle?
A! *benedicite!* for al among that fare
The harm is doon, and fare-wel feldefare!

124

And, nece myn, ne take it not agreef,
If that ye suffre him al night in this wo,
God help me so, ye hadde him never leef,
That dar I seyn, now there is but we two;
But wel I woot, that ye wol not do so;
Ye been to wys to do so gret folye,
To putte his lyf al night in jupartye."

125

"Hadde I him never leef? By god, I wene
Ye hadde never thing so leef," quod she.
"Now by my thrift," quod he, "that shal be sene;
For, sin ye make this ensample of me,
If I al night wolde him in sorwe see

For al the tresour in the toun of Troye,
I bidde god, I never mote have joye!

126

Now loke thanne, if ye, that been his love,
Shul putte al night his lyf in jupartye
For thing of nought! Now, by that god above,
Nought only this delay comth of folye,
But of malyce, if that I shal nought lye.
What, platly, and ye suffre him in distresse,
Ye neither bountee doon ne gentilesse!"

127

Quod tho Criseyde, "wole ye doon o thing,
And ye therwith shal stinte al his disese;
Have here, and bereth him this blewe ring,
For ther is no-thing mighte him bettre plese,
Save I my-self, ne more his herte apese;
And sey my dere herte, that his sorwe
Is causeles, that shal be seen to-morwe."

128

"A ring?" quod he, "ye, hasel-wodes shaken!
Ye, nece myn, that ring moste han a stoon
That mighte dede men alyve maken;
And swich a ring, trowe I that ye have noon.
Discrecioun out of your heed is goon;
That fele I now," quod he, "and that is routhe;
O tyme y-lost, wel maystow cursen slouthe!

129

Wot ye not wel that noble and heigh corage
Ne sorweth not, ne stinteth eek for lyte?
But if a fool were in a jalous rage,
I nolde setten at his sorwe a myte,
But feffe him with a fewe wordes whyte
Another day, whan that I mighte him finde:
But this thing stont al in another kinde.

130

This is so gentil and so tendre of herte,
That with his deeth he wol his sorwes wreke;
For trusteth wel, how sore that him smerte,
He wol to yow no jalouse wordes speke.
And for-thy, nece, er that his herte breke,
So spek your-self to him of this matere;
For with o word ye may his herte stere.

131

Now have I told what peril he is inne,
And his coming unwist is t' every wight;
Ne, pardee, harm may ther be noon ne sinne;
I wol my-self be with yow al this night.
Ye knowe eek how it is your owne knight,
And that, by right, ye moste upon him triste,
And I al prest to fecche him whan yow liste."

132

This accident so pitous was to here,
And eek so lyk a sooth, at pryme face,
And Troilus hir knight to hir so dere,
His privè coming, and the siker place,
That, though that she dide him as thanne a grace,
Considered alle thinges as they stode,
No wonder is, sin she dide al for gode.

133

Cryseyde answerde, "as wisly god at reste
My sowle bringe, as me is for him wo!
And eem, y-wis, fayn wolde I doon the beste,

I swear by Jove who in Olympus reigns,
No, not for all the gold that Troy contains!

126

"Now, look, if you who are his only love,
Shall put his life all night in jeopardy,
Just for a trifle, by the God above,
Both inconsiderate this act would be
And show in you a bad propensity.
If you abandon him, I'm frank to say,
Nor wisdom nor yet kindness you display."

127

"At least," said Cressida, "this can I do,
And that will bring him some relief and ease.
Convey to him this ring with stone of blue,
For there is nothing will him better please,
Except myself, or more his wrath appease,
And say to my sweetheart that all his sorrow
Is without ground, as he shall see tomorrow."

128

"O pshaw," said he, "a fig for all your ring!
The sort of ring he needs must have a stone
With power enough the dead to life to bring,
And such a ring, dear niece, you do not own.
Discretion from your head seems to have flown!
O time, O wasted opportunity,
O cursed sloth, O heedless sluggardy!

129

"Do you not know that men of courage high,
Feel strongly and are quick and sharp in action?
A fool in jealous rage one might pass by,
For shallow minds are shallow in distraction;
A few fair words will give them satisfaction,
They'll wait until you're ready to be kind,
But this is quite another thing, you'll find.

130

"This man is of such high and gentle heart,
His sorrows with his death he well may wreak;
Be sure, however sorely he may smart,
No jealous word to you he'll ever speak.
And now no further subterfuges seek,
Insist no longer on your wilful pride,
But say the word his heart to cheer and guide.

131

"I've told you now the peril he is in,
And not a soul of him has caught a sight.
Besides there need be neither harm nor sin,
For I shall be at hand through all the night.
You know he never will transgress his right,
And as your knight, you must in him confide.
I'll fetch him here as soon as you decide."

132

Now so distressing was all this to hear,
And seemed, besides, so likely on its face,
And Troilus, her knight, to her so dear,
So secret, too, his coming and the place,
That though there was a risk of some disgrace,
Considering everything, just how it stood,
No wonder if she took it all for good.

133

"God knows," said Cressida, "it makes me sad
To hear of my dear love's distress and woe;
To help him in his sorrow I'd be glad,

If what was best to do I could but know;
But whether you should stay or for him go,
I am, till heaven some direction send,
But at Dulcarnon, at my wits' last end."

134

"Dulcarnon"? said he, "let me tell you, dear,
That means, 'last hope of those of feeble mind.'
Such persons in their heads are never clear,
But stay for very sloth perversely blind,
And for such folk this saying is designed;
But you are wise, and what we have in hand,
Calls for no subtle wit to understand."

135

"Well, uncle," said she, "do as you think best!
But let me first, before he comes, arise.
And since my trust in you two all doth rest,
And since you both are most discreet and wise,
I beg you will this matter so devise,
My honor and his wish to satisfy,
For everything in your hands now doth lie."

136

"Well spoken that," he said, "my niece so dear!
You've shown you have a wise and gentle heart!
But just lie still and let him come right here,
Your messages you can as well impart,
And may you ease each other's pain and smart.
And now at last, O Venus, praise to thee,
For soon some happy times we here shall see."

137

Troilus now beside his lady kneeling,
Full soberly beside his lady's bed,
Extends to her his greetings with such feeling,
She waxes all at once a rosy red;
She could not speak a word, to save her head,
On seeing him so sudden and unbidden,
Come from the place in which he had been hidden.

138

But Pandar always knew just what to do,
And now to break the ice, his jokes began,
And said, "See how this lord doth kneel to you!
Just rest your eyes upon this gentleman!"
And quickly then, he for a cushion ran,
And said, "Take this, and on it kneel your fill!
And may your hearts be purged of every ill!"

139

Just why she did not order him to rise,—
If sorrow drove the thought out of her mind,
I cannot say, or kneeling in this wise
She thought as manners only was designed,
But this I know, she was in so far kind,
That though she sighed, nevertheless she kissed him
And to a seat beside her did assist him.

140

"All's ready now," said Pandar, "to begin!
That's right, dear niece, these curtains interfere,
Just let him sit upon your bed within;
It's easier so each other's words to hear."
Then he withdrew and left the way all clear,
And took a light and sat down by the fire,
As though to read he felt a great desire.

If that I hadde grace to do so.
But whether that ye dwelle or for him go,
I am, til god me bettre minde sende,
At Dulcarnon, right at my wittes ende."

134

Quod Pandarus, "ye, nece, wol ye here?
Dulcarnon called is 'fleminge of wrecches';
It semeth hard, for wrecches wol not lere
For verray slouthe or othere wilful tecches;
This seyd by hem that be not worth two fecches.
But ye ben wys, and that we han on honde
Nis neither hard, ne skilful to withstonde."

135

"Thanne, eem," quod she, "doth her-of as yow list;
But er he come I wil up first aryse;
And, for the love of god, sin al my trist
Is on yow two, and ye ben bothe wyse,
So wircheth now in so discreet a wyse,
That I honour may have, and he plesaunce;
For I am here al in your governaunce."

136

"That is wel seyd," quod he, "my nece dere,
Ther good thrift on that wyse gentil herte!
But liggeth stille, and taketh him right here,
It nedeth not no ferther for him sterte;
And ech of yow ese otheres sorwes smerte,
For love of god; and, Venus, I thee herie;
For sone hope I we shulle ben alle merie."

137

This Troilus ful sone on knees him sette
Ful sobrely, right by hir beddes heed,
And in his beste wyse his lady grette;
But lord, so she wex sodeynliche reed!
Ne, though men sholden smyten of hir heed,
She coude nought a word a-right out-bringe
So sodeynly, for his sodeyn cominge.

138

But Pandarus, that so wel coude fele
In every thing, to pleye anoon bigan,
And seyde, "nece, see how this lord can knele!
Now, for your trouthe, seeth this gentil man!"
And with that word he for a quisshen ran,
And seyde, "kneleth now, whyl that yow leste,
Ther god your hertes bringe sone at reste!"

139

Can I not seyn, for she bad him not ryse,
If sorwe it putte out of hir remembraunce,
Or elles if she toke it in the wyse
Of duëtee, as for his observaunce;
But wel finde I she dide him this plesaunce,
That she him kiste, al-though she syked sore;
And bad him sitte a-doun with-outen more.

140

Quod Pandarus, "now wol ye wel beginne;
Now doth him sitte, gode nece dere,
Upon your beddes syde al there withinne,
That ech of yow the bet may other here."
And with that word he drow him to the fere,
And took a light, and fond his contenaunce
As for to loke up-on an old romaunce.

141

Criseyde, that was Troilus lady right,
And cleer stood on a ground of sikernesse,
Al thoughte she, hir servaunt and hir knight
Ne sholde of right non untrouthe in hir gesse,
Yet nathelees, considered his distresse,
And that love is in cause of swich folye,
Thus to him spak she of his jelousye:

142

"Lo, herte myn, as wolde the excellence
Of love, ayeins the which that no man may,
Ne oughte eek goodly maken resistence;
And eek bycause I felte wel and say
Your grete trouthe, and servyse every day;
And that your herte al myn was, sooth to seyne,
This droof me for to rewe up-on your peyne.

143

And your goodnesse have I founde alwey yit,
Of whiche, my dere herte and al my knight,
I thonke it yow, as fer as I have wit,
Al can I nought as muche as it were right;
And I, emforth my conninge and my might,
Have and ay shal, how sore that me smerte,
Ben to yow trewe and hool, with al myn herte;

144

And dredelees, that shal be founde at preve.—
But, herte myn, what al this is to seyne
Shal wel be told, so that ye noght yow greve,
Though I to yow right on your-self compleyne.
For ther-with mene I fynally the peyne,
That halt your herte and myn in hevinesse,
Fully to sleen, and every wrong redresse.

145

My goode, myn, not I for-why ne how
That Jalousye, allas! that wikked wivere,
Thus causelees is cropen in-to yow;
The harm of which I wolde fayn delivere!
Allas! that he, al hool, or of him slivere,
Should have his refut in so digne a place,
Ther Jove him sone out of your herte arace.

146

But O, thou Jove, O auctor of nature,
Is this an honour to thy deitee,
That folk ungiltif suffren here injure,
And who that giltif is, al quit goth he?
O were it leful for to pleyne on thee,
That undeserved suffrest jalousye,
And that I wolde up-on thee pleyne and crye!

147

Eek al my wo is this, that folk now usen
To seyn right thus, 'ye, Jalousye is Love!'
And wolde a busshel venim al excusen,
For that o greyn of love is on it shove!
But that wot heighe god that sit above,
If it be lyker love, or hate, or grame;
And after that, it oughte bere his name.

148

But certeyn is, som maner jalousye
Is excusable more than som, y-wis.

141

And Cressida, assured that all was right,
And that she stood on safe and solid ground,
Yet thinking as her servant and her knight
No lack of faith in her he should have found,
Now felt herself constrained in duty bound,
Though faithful love had caused this thing to be,
To speak to him about his jealousy.

142

"Though love," she said, "should be of such a kind,
That no true lover ever ought or may
Encourage opposition in his mind,
Yet still, because I've seen in every way
Your faithfulness and service day by day,
And that your heart was mine has been so plain,
This led me to have pity on your pain.

143

"And since I've ever found you good and wise,
For which, my precious heart and my true knight,
I thank you now as far as in me lies,
Though not as much, perhaps, as were your right,
Yet still according to my wit and might,
Whatever grief hereafter may befall,
My heart is yours and shall be all in all.

144

"And that, I'm sure, you do and will believe.
To say this, sweetheart, goes against the grain,
But you must not thereat too deeply grieve,
Although I seem upon you to complain;
For in the end this present grief and pain
That holds your heart and mine in heaviness,
I shall remove and every harm redress.

145

"But precious one, I know not how nor why
That viper jealousy, insidious thief,
Should thus into your bosom creep so sly,
The which to both of us is cause of grief.
Alas, that thou shouldst thus beyond belief
Exalt low jealousy to such a place!
May Jove such thoughts from out your heart erase!

146

"But O, thou Jove, from whom all things have life,
Is this an honor to thy deity,
That guiltless folk should suffer here in strife
And yet the guilty one all free goes he?
O, were it lawful to complain on thee,
This charge I'd bring against thy mighty name,
Of causeless jealousy I bear the blame.

147

"Another shame is this, that folk abuse
True love and say, 'Yea, jealousy is love!'
A bushel of venom such folk will excuse
If but a grain of love therein they shove.
But God knows this, who lives and reigns above,
If it be liker love or liker hate,
And by its name we should it designate.

148

"Some sorts of jealousy, I will confess,
Are more excusable than other kinds,

As when there's cause, or when folk long repress
Some harsh fantastic notion in their minds,
Which in expression no free outlet finds,
And on itself it thus doth grow and feed;
For such repression is a gentle deed.

149

"And some are filled with fury and despite
So full that it surpasses all restraint—
But, sweetheart, you are not in such plight,
Thank God, and all your grieving and your plaint,
I call it an illusive lover's taint
From love's excess, and from anxiety,
From which this long time you have not been free,

150

"At which I grieve, but do no anger feel.
But now, if this will set your heart at rest,
Just as you will, by oath or by ordeal,
By lot, or any way you think the best,
I'm ready here to undergo the test.
If I am guilty, take my life away!
What more, alas, is there that I can say?"

151

Some tears with that, like shining drops of dew,
Fell from her eyes, but only two or three,
"Thou knowest, God, that Cressida untrue
To Troilus is not, nor e'er shall be!"
And then upon her couch she laid her head,
And sighing sore, covered it with the sheet,
And held her peace in silence quite complete.

152

May heaven bring relief for all this sorrow!
There's ground for hope, for such is heaven's way;
For I have seen on many a misty morrow
Following oft a merry summer's day,
And after winter, comes along the May.
'Tis known, and vouched for by authorities,
That storms are presages of victories.

153

Poor Troilus, when he heard how she spoke,
Imagine how her chiding words struck deep!
A heavy stick it was that struck this stroke,
To hear and see his lady-love thus weep;
The cramp of death he felt upon him creep,
And every tear he saw his lady shed,
Strangled his heart till it lay cold and
dead.

154

And mentally the hour he did curse
That he came there, or that when he was born!
For what was bad, was now turned into worse,
And for love's labors lost, he could but mourn,
And count him of all creatures most forlorn.
O Pandar, thought he, all thy cunning guile,
Has come to naught but this, alack the while!

155

At these sad thoughts he humbly hung his head,
And fell upon his knees and deeply sighed,
What could he say? All life from him had fled,
Her chiding words his grief so magnified,
But when he could, at last he thus replied:
"When all is known, I swear in heaven's name,
Then you will see that I am not to blame."

As whan cause is, and som swich fantasye
With pietee so wel repressed is,
That it unnethe dooth or seyth amis,
But goodly drinketh up al his distresse;
And that excuse I, for the gentilesse.

149

And som so ful of furie is and despyt,
That it sourmounteth his repressioun;
But herte myn, ye be not in that plyt,
That thanke I god, for whiche your passioun
I wol not calle it but illusioun,
Of habundaunce of love and bisy cure,
That dooth your herte this disese endure.

150

Of which I am right sory, but not wrooth;
But, for my devoir and your hertes reste,
Wher-so yow list, by ordal or by ooth,
By sort, or in what wyse so yow leste,
For love of god, lat preve it for the beste!
And if that I be giltif, do me deye,
Allas! what mighte I more doon or seye?"

151

With that a fewe brighte teres newe
Out of hir eyen fille, and thus she seyde,
"Now god, thou wost, in thought ne dede untrewe
To Troilus was never yet Criseyde."
With that hir heed doun in the bed she leyde,
And with the shete it wreigh, and syghed sore,
And held hir pees; not a word spak she more.

152

But now help god to quenchen al this sorwe,
So hope I that he shal, for he best may;
For I have seyn, of a ful misty morwe
Folwen ful ofte a mery someres day;
And after winter folweth grene May.
Men seen alday, and reden eek in stories,
That after sharpe shoures been victories.

153

This Troilus, whan he hir wordes herde,
Have ye no care, him liste not to slepe;
For it thoughte him no strokes of a yerde
To here or seen Criseyde his lady wepe;
But wel he felte aboute his herte crepe,
For every teer which that Criseyde asterte,
The crampe of deeth, to streyne him by the
herte.

154

And in his minde he gan the tyme acurse
That he cam therë, and that he was born;
For now is wikke y-turned in-to worse,
And al that labour he hath doon biforn,
He wende it lost, he thoughte he nas but lorn.
"O Pandarus," thoughte he, "allas! thy wyle
Serveth of nought, so weylawey the whyle!"

155

And therwithal he heng a-doun the heed,
And fil on knees, and sorwfully he sighte;
What mighte he seyn? he felte he nas but deed,
For wrooth was she that shulde his sorwes lighte.
But nathelees, whan that he speken mighte,
Than seyde he thus, "god woot, that of this game,
Whan al is wist, than am I not to blame!"

156

Ther-with the sorwe so his herte shette.
That from his eyen fil ther not a tere,
And every spirit his vigour in-knette,
So they astoned and oppressed were.
The feling of his sorwe, or of his fere,
Or of ought elles, fled was out of towne;
And doun he fel al sodeynly a-swowne.

157

This was no litel sorwe for to see;
But al was hust, and Pandare up as faste,
"O nece, pees, or we be lost," quod he,
"Beth nought agast"; but certeyn, at the laste,
For this or that, he in-to bedde him caste,
And seyde, "O theef, is this a mannes herte?"
And of he rente al to his bare sherte;

158

And seyde, "nece, but ye helpe us now,
Allas, your owne Troilus is lorn!"
"Y-wis, so wolde I, and I wiste how,
Ful fayn," quod she; "alas! that I was born!"
"Ye, nece, wol ye pullen out the thorn
That stiketh in his herte?" quod Pandare;
"Sey 'al foryeve,' and stint is all this fare!"

159

"Ye, that to me," quod she, "ful lever were
Than al the good the sonne aboute gooth";
And therwith-al she swoor him in his ere,
"Y-wis, my dere herte, I am nought wrooth,
Have here my trouthe and many another ooth;
Now speek to me, for it am I, Criseyde!"
But al for nought; yet mighte he not a-breyde.

160

Therwith his pous and pawmes of his hondes
They gan to frote, and wete his temples tweyne,
And, to deliveren him from bittre bondes,
She ofte him kiste; and, shortly for to seyne,
Him to revoken she dide al hir peyne.
And at the laste, he gan his breeth to drawe,
And of his swough sone after that adawe,

161

And gan bet minde and reson to him take,
But wonder sore he was abayst, y-wis.
And with a syk, whan he gan bet a-wake,
He seyde, 'O mercy, god, what thing is this?"
"Why do ye with your-selven thus amis?"
Quod tho Criseyde, "is this a mannes game?
What, Troilus! wol ye do thus, for shame?"

162

And therwith-al hir arm over him she leyde,
And al foryaf, and ofte tyme him keste.
He thonked hir, and to hir spak, and seyde
As fil to purpos for his herte reste.
And she to that answerde him as hir leste;
And with hir goodly wordes him disporte
She gan, and ofte his sorwes to comforte.

163

Quod Pandarus, "for ought I can espyen,
This light nor I ne serven here of nought;
Light is not good for syke folkes yën.
But for the love of god, sin ye be brought
In thus good plyt, lat now non hevy thought

156

Though sorrow at his heart so sternly pressed,
There fell not from his eye a single tear,
His inmost nature was so strained and stressed
No movement of his spirit could appear;
Sensation now of sorrow or of fear
Or aught beside, all fled was out of town,
And in a swoon he suddenly fell down.

157

O, what a dreadful thing this was to see!
How still he lay, but Pandar got up fast,
"Hush, niece! Keep still or we are lost!" said he;
"Don't be afraid!" and took him at the last,
And tearing off his clothes, he quickly cast
Him in her bed. "O Cressida," he cried,
"Have you a human heart in your inside!

158

"Dear niece, unless you try to help us now,
Your Troilus is ever lost and lorn."
"That would I gladly do if I knew how,"
She cried. "Alas that I was ever born!"
"There's naught to do except pull out the thorn
That sticketh in his heart," wise Pandar said.
"Say 'All's forgiven,' and raise him from the dead."

159

"That were to me," she said, "a thing more dear
Than all the gold the circling sun goes round."
And thereupon she swore him in his ear,
"By all the oaths by which I can be bound,
I am not angry,"—yet he made no sound.
"It's Cressida, O speak, my precious heart!"
But from his trance she could not make him start.

160

His wrists and palms they then began to chafe,
With water both his temples they did lave,
From out his bitter bonds to bring him safe,
And many a loving kiss to him she gave,
To call him from his lethargy so grave,
Until a breath he drew, and none too soon,
And so began to come out of his swoon.

161

And when some notice he began to take,
Full sore he was abashed and mortified,
And with a sigh, when he was quite awake,
"Where am I?" first with feeble voice he cried.
"What trouble for you all I've made," he sighed.
"O Troilus, now be a man!" said she.
"Why do you act like this? For shame on thee!"

162

Her arm around his neck she gently laid,
Forgiving him with many a soft embrace,
And his apologies he humbly made,
In manner fitting to the time and place.
These she received at once with right good grace,
And spoke to him so kindly and so well,
Her loving words his sorrow soon dispel.

163

"This candle and I, so far as I can spy,"
Said Pandar, "are no longer here required!
The light is harmful to a sick man's eye!
But now you have the chance so long desired,
Before the fleeting time shall be expired,

Let joy alone within your hearts abide,"—
And took his candle to the chimney-side.

164

At last this lady's mind was set and clear!
Since he all oaths she could or would devise
Had sworn to her and banished all her fear,
She saw no reason now to bid him rise.
Yet less than oaths quite often satisfies
In such a case as this, for every man
Who loveth well, will do the best he can.

165

At first she asked, insisting she would know,
What man, and where, and also why,
He jealous was, and no cause to be so,
And also all the signs he judged her by
She bade him tell and not a thing deny,
Or else, she said, she saw no other way,
She'd have to think a trick he tried to play.

166

And when he saw she would not be denied,
Or if she were, her doubts would be increased,
Choosing the lesser evil, he replied,
"It was," he said, "at such and such a feast"—
And thought she might have looked at him at
least—
O, I don't know, he said some thing or other,
'Twas all as well, one answer or another.

167

"My dearest heart," she said, "though it were true,
Why such an imputation must you draw?
For by the God above who made us two,
No harm in that I ever meant or saw!
Your vain suspicions are not worth a straw!
Such childish reasons scarce deserve the thanking,
You really ought to have a right good spanking!"

168

Then Troilus began again to sigh,
And new fears at his heart began to twine.
"Alas," he said, "my errors heavy lie
Upon my conscience, precious sweetheart mine,
But now all foolish thoughts I will resign,
And shall hereafter not again offend.
Do what you will—I'm yours unto the end!"

169

"True mercy," said she, "is not slow or strained,
Forgiven and forgotten be the past!
But let this night in mind be long retained;
Of jealous doubts, let this one be the last!"
"O yes, dear heart!" he promised quick and fast.
"And now," she said, "the pain I've given thee,
Sweetheart, I beg that you forgive it me!"

170

Troilus felt such glad relief at this,
With trust in God and in his lady's grace,
And courage drawn from his so sudden bliss,
He seized and held her in a close embrace.
And Pandar, feeling somewhat out of place,
Lay down to sleep and said, "If you are wise,
Don't swoon again, or others may arise!"

171

The helpless lark, what can it do or say
After the hawk hath caught it in his claw?

Ben hanginge in the hertes of yow tweye":
And bar the candel to the chimeneye.

164

Sone after this, though it no nede were,
Whan she swich othes as hir list devyse
Hadde of him take, hir thoughte tho no fere,
Ne cause eek non, to bidde him thennes ryse.
Yet lesse thing than othes may suffyse
In many a cas; for every wight, I gesse,
That loveth wel meneth but gentilesse.

165

But in effect she wolde wite anoon
Of what man, and eek where, and also why
He jelous was, sin ther was cause noon;
And eek the signe, that he took it by,
She bad him that to telle hir bisily,
Or elles, certeyn, she bar him on honde,
That this was doon of malis, hir to fonde.

166

With-outen more, shortly for to seyne,
He moste obeye un-to his lady heste;
And for the lasse harm, he moste feyne.
He seyde hir, whan she was at swiche a feste
She mighte on him han loked at the
leste;
Not I not what, al dere y-nough a risshe,
As he that nedes moste a cause fisshe.

167

And she answerde, "swete, al were it so,
What harm was that, sin I non yvel mene?
For, by that god that boughte us bothe two,
In alle thinge is myn entente clene.
Swich arguments ne been not worth a bene;
Wol ye the childish jalous contrefete?
Now were it worthy that ye were y-bete."

168

Tho Troilus gan sorwfully to syke,
Lest she be wrooth, him thoughte his herte deyde;
And seyde, "allas! upon my sorwes syke
Have mercy, swete herte myn, Criseyde!
And if that, in tho wordes that I seyde,
Be any wrong, I wol no more trespace;
Do what yow list, I am al in your grace."

169

And she answerde, "of gilt misericorde!
That is to seyn, that I foryeve al this;
And ever-more on this night yow recorde,
And beth wel war ye do no more amis."
"Nay, dere herte myn," quod he, "y-wis."
"And now," quod she, "that I have do yow smerte,
Foryeve it me, myn owene swete herte."

170

This Troilus, with blisse of that supprysed,
Put al in goddes hond, as he that mente
No-thing but wel; and, sodeynly avysed,
He hir in armes faste to him hente.
And Pandarus, with a ful good entente,
Leyde him to slepe, and seyde, "if ye ben wyse,
Swowneth not now, lest more folk aryse."

171

What mighte or may the sely larke seye,
Whan that the sparhauk hath it in his foot?

I can no more, but of thise ilke tweye,
To whom this tale sucre be or soot,
Though that I tarie a yeer, som-tyme I moot,
After myn auctor, tellen hir gladnesse,
As wel as I have told hir hevinesse.

172

Criseyde, which that felte hir thus y-take,
As writen clerkes in hir bokes olde,
Right as an aspes leef she gan to quake,
Whan she him felte hir in his armes folde.
But Troilus, al hool of cares colde,
Gan thanken tho the blisful goddes sevene;
Thus sondry peynes bringen folk to hevene.

173

This Troilus in armes gan hir streyne,
And seyde, "O swete, as ever mote
  I goon,
Now be ye caught, now is ther but we tweyne;
Now yeldeth yow, for other boot is noon."
To that Criseyde answerde thus anoon,
"Ne hadde I er now, my swete herte dere,
Ben yolde, y-wis, I were now not here!"

174

O! sooth is seyd, that heled for to be
As of a fevre or othere greet syknesse,
Men moste drinke, as men may often see,
Ful bittre drink; and for to han gladnesse,
Men drinken often peyne and greet distresse;
I mene it here, as for this aventure,
That thourgh a peyne hath founden al his cure.

175

And now swetnesse semeth more swete,
That bitternesse assayed was biforn;
For out of wo in blisse now they flete.
Non swich they felten, sith they were born;
Now is this bet, than bothe two be lorn!
For love of god, take every womman hede
To werken thus, if it comth to the nede.

176

Criseyde, al quit from every drede and tene,
As she that juste cause hadde him to triste,
Made him swich feste, it joye was to sene,
Whan she his trouthe and clene entente wiste.
And as aboute a tree, with many a twiste,
Bitrent and wryth the sote wode-binde,
Gan eche of hem in armes other winde.

177

And as the newe abaysshed nightingale,
That stinteth first whan she biginneth singe,
Whan that she hereth any herde tale,
Or in the hegges any wight steringe,
And after siker dooth hir voys out-ringe;
Right so Criseyde, whan hir drede stente,
Opned hir herte, and tolde him hir entente.

178

And right as he that seeth his deeth y-shapen,
And deye moot, in ought that he may gesse,
And sodeynly rescous doth him escapen,
And from his deeth is brought in sikernesse,
For al this world, in swich present gladnesse
Was Troilus, and hath his lady swete;
With worse hap god lat us never mete!

Not otherwise it was with her that day;
Like it or not, this is all nature's law.
And though my tale throughout a year I draw,
Lo, I, as does my author, still must tell,
After their grief, their time of joy as well.

172

Cressida in his arms thus boldly taken,
As all wise clerks have said in books of old,
Shook like an aspen leaf by breezes shaken,
As his strong arms about her body fold;
And Troilus, all freed of care so cold,
Gave thanks to those bright Gods, glorious seven—
In sundry ways thus folk are brought to heaven

173

Troilus in arms his love doth hold and strain,
And whispers, "Precious heart, now are you
  caught!
In all the world there liveth but we twain!
Now you must yield, evasion helpeth naught!"
But of evasion she had little thought;
"Had I not yielded," said she, "sweetheart dear,
Before this night, I would not now be here!"

174

O true it is, before they can be cured,
Whether of fever or other great disease,
The sick must drink, for all they have endured,
Full bitter drink, and for their better ease,
Must oft partake of things that do not please.
All this to Troilus may be applied,
Who after pain is glad and satisfied.

175

And sweetness now seemed more than ever sweet,
For all the bitterness that went before;
And now the time goes by on winged feet,
In joy so great, it never could be more,
Or better pay for all the griefs they bore.
And here I beg that lovers all will heed
This good example at their time of need!

176

And Cressida, from fear and dread all free,
With faith and trust in him now absolute,
Made him such feast that it was good to see
Such faithful service bear such happy fruit.
And as the woodbine, growing near its root,
Doth clasp the tree with tendrils intertwined,
So they their arms about each other wind.

177

And like the hushed expectant nightingale,
Who ceases after she begins to sing
If sound of voices loud her ears assail,
Or in the hedges stirreth anything,
But then thereafter lets her song out-ring,
So Cressida, released from all her fear,
Opened her heart for him to look and hear.

178

And like the man who sees his death impending,
And die he must, for aught that he can tell,
Yet sudden rescue brings a happy ending,
And all the things he dreaded, turn out well,
So now to Troilus like fortune fell,
For now at last he hath his lady sweet—
God grant we may with no worse fortune meet!

179

Her slender arms, her back so straight and soft,
Her yielding sides, so long and smooth and bright,
He gently stroked, nor failed to note full oft
Her snowy throat, her rounding breasts so white,
Whereon he gazed in heavenly delight.
Such joy he felt he scarce knew what to do,
A thousand kisses seemed to him but few.

180

"O Love," exclaimeth he, "O Charity!
Thy mother also, Citherea sweet,
After thyself exalted may she be,
O Venus, gracious planet, I repeat,
And next to Venus, Hymen, I thee greet!
For never man was to you Gods more bound
Than I, who from my cares relief have found.

181

"O Love benign, thou holy bond of things,
All they who seek thy grace, but scorn thy aid,
Their love shall fly but feebly without wings.
By thy goodwill man's fortune must be made;
For faithful service ne'er so well displayed,
Were all for naught, this dare I well assert,
Did not thy gift surpass our poor desert.

182

"And since that I, who merited the least
To win thy gracious favor and support,
Have had my joys extended and increased
And am exalted in such lofty sort
That widest bounds to hold my joys fall short,
What can I do, but words of reverent praise
Unto thy bounty and thy goodness raise!"

183

His prayer he ended with a kiss or two,
Which part of it at least was well received,
And then he said, "I would to God I knew
How you of every grief might be relieved!
Was ever man," he said, "so little grieved
As I, on whom the fairest and the best
Deigneth her loving heart to bring to rest!

184

"Here one may see that mercy passeth right,
As my experience tells me feelingly,
Who am unworthy of you, lady bright;
But sweetheart mine, in your benignity,
Believe that all unworthy though I be,
Yet needs I must amend and still improve,
But through the lofty virtue of my love.

185

"One favor more, dear heart, I beg beside,
Since God hath wrought me but to do thy will,
Be thou my ever-present, helpful guide,
For thou hast power of good and power of ill.
So teach me, sweetheart mine, that I may still
Deserve thy thanks, and thy good counsel lend
To save me from all acts that may offend.

186

"For truly, fairest of all womankind,
This dare I say, that truth and diligence
Through all my life thou shalt within me find;
And if I sin with injury prepense,
Present or absent, I shall waive defence,

179

His armes smale, hir streyghte bak and softe,
Hir sydes longe, fleshly, smothe, and whyte
He gan to stroke, and good thrift bad ful ofte
Hir snowish throte, hir brestes rounde and lyte;
Thus in this hevene he gan him to delyte,
And ther-with-al a thousand tyme hir kiste;
That, what to done, for joye unnethe he wiste.

180

Than seyde he thus, "O, Love, O, Charitee,
Thy moder eek, Citherea the swete,
After thy-self next heried be she,
Venus mene I, the wel-willy planete;
And next that, Imenëus, I thee grete;
For never man was to yow goddes holde
As I, which ye han brought fro cares colde.

181

Benigne Love, thou holy bond of thinges,
Who-so wol grace, and list thee nought honouren,
Lo, his desyr wol flee with-outen winges.
For, noldestow of bountee hem socouren
That serven best and most alwey labouren,
Yet were al lost, that dar I wel seyn, certes,
But-if thy grace passed our desertes.

182

And for thou me, that coude leest deserve
Of hem that nombred been un-to thy grace,
Hast holpen, ther I lykly was to sterve,
And me bistowed in so heygh a place
That thilke boundes may no blisse pace,
I can no more, but laude and reverence
Be to thy bounte and thyn excellence!"

183

And therwith-al Criseyde anoon he kiste,
Of which, certeyn, she felte no disese.
And thus seyde he, "now wolde god I wiste,
Myn herte swete, how I yow mighte plese!
What man," quod he, "was ever thus at ese
As I, on whiche the faireste and the beste
That ever I say, deyneth hir herte reste.

184

Here may men seen that mercy passeth right;
The experience of that is felt in me,
That am unworthy to so swete a wight.
But herte myn, of your benignitee,
So thenketh, though that I unworthy be,
Yet mot I nede amenden in som wyse,
Right thourgh the vertu of your heyghe servyse.

185

And for the love of god, my lady dere,
Sin god hath wrought me for I shal yow serve,
As thus I mene, that ye wol be my stere,
To do me live, if that yow liste, or sterve,
So techeth me how that I may deserve
Your thank, so that I, thurgh myn ignoraunce,
Ne do no-thing that yow be displesaunce.

186

For certes, fresshe wommanliche wyf,
This dar I seye, that trouthe and diligence,
That shal ye finden in me al my lyf,
Ne I wol not, certeyn, breken your defence;
And if I do, present or in absence,

For love of god, lat slee me with the dede,
If that it lyke un-to your womanhede."

187

"Y-wis," quod she, "myn owne hertes list,
My ground of ese, and al myn herte dere,
Graunt mercy, for on that is al my trist;
But late us falle awey fro this matere;
For it suffyseth, this that seyd is here.
And at o word, with-outen repentaunce,
Wel-come, my knight, my pees, my suffisaunce!"

188

Of hir delyt, or joyes oon the leste
Were impossible to my wit to seye;
But juggeth, ye that han ben at the feste
Of swich gladnesse, if that hem liste pleye!
I can no more, but thus thise ilke tweye
That night, be-twixen dreed and sikernesse,
Felten in love the grete worthinesse.

189

O blisful night, of hem so longe y-sought,
How blithe un-to hem bothe two thou were!
Why ne hadde I swich on with my soule y-bought,
Ye, or the leeste joye that was there?
A-wey, thou foule daunger and thou fere,
And lat hem in this hevene blisse dwelle,
That is so heygh, that al ne can I telle!

190

But sooth is, though I can not tellen al,
As can myn auctor, of his excellence,
Yet have I seyd, and, god to-forn, I shal
In every thing al hoolly his sentence.
And if that I, at loves reverence,
Have any word in eched for the beste,
Doth therwith-al right as your-selven leste.

191

For myne wordes, here and every part,
I speke hem alle under correccioun
Of yow, that feling han in loves art,
And putte it al in your discrecioun
T' encrese or maken diminucioun
Of my langage, and that I yow bi-seche;
But now to purpos of my rather speche.

192

Thise ilke two, that ben in armes laft,
So looth to hem a-sonder goon it were,
That ech from other wende been biraft,
Or elles, lo, this was hir moste fere,
That al this thing but nyce dremes were;
For which ful ofte ech of hem seyde, "O swete,
Clippe ich yow thus, or elles I it mete?"

193

And, lord! so he gan goodly on hir see,
That never his look ne bleynte from hir face,
And seyde, "O dere herte, may it be
That it be sooth, that ye ben in this place?"
"Ye, herte myn, god thank I of his grace!"
Quod tho Criseyde, and therwith-al him kiste,
That where his spirit was, for joye he niste.

194

This Troilus ful ofte hir eyen two
Gan for to kisse, and seyde, "O eyen clere,

And yield myself to thee at that same hour,
As humbly subject to thy womanly power."

187

"Enough," she cried, "O thou my richest treasure,
My ground of ease, and all I hold most dear,
I trust in thee beyond all bound and measure!
But let us talk no more of future fear,
There needs no more than thou hast promised here.
I am content, befall what may befall;
Welcome, my knight, my peace, my all in all!"

188

To tell the limits of their great delight
For me were sheer impossibility,
But all can guess who such a festal night
Have ever known, I trust, in some degree;
And of these lovers twain, I merely say to thee,
That night twixt joy and fear they realize
How love may be a serious enterprise.

189

O night of love, by them so long time sought,
So happy now at last in consummation,
With my own soul I gladly would have bought
The least division of its delectation!
Away now every check to inclination,
And let them in this bliss of heaven dwell,
Too great for mortal tongue to sing or tell.

190

But though I cannot tell you everything,
As might my author with his greater gift,
The burden of his song yet shall I sing,
And all his thought employ with proper thrift,
And if I've added to his general drift
In praise of love, I leave it in your hand,
Remove it from my tale or let it stand.

191

For all my words, in this and every part,
Are spoken under your correction all,
Who better know the secrets of the heart
Than I, and therefore I upon you call
To change or take away in general,
Such words as seem to you were best omitted;
But now to come back where our tale we quitted.

192

These two whom we have left in love's embrace,
Could not endure the thought of separation;
They scarce believed that they were in that place,
Or else were filled with fear and consternation
That all this night was but hallucination,
And oft they said, for doubt this was but seeming,
"O art thou there, or am I only dreaming?"

193

With such intentive look he on her gazed,
His eyes were fixed unmoving on her face;
"O sweetheart," he exclaimed, "the Gods be praised,
And is it true that thou art in this place?"
"Yes, sweetheart mine, and all by heaven's grace!"
She says, and therewithal a kiss bestows,
That where his spirit is, he scarcely knows.

194

And he neglected not to kiss her eyes,
And when he did, he said, "O eyes so clear,

In you the cause of all my sorrow lies,
Ye double weapons of my lady dear!
Though mercy seemeth to be written here,
The text, forsooth, is very hard to find.
How is it, without bonds thou couldst me bind?"

195

Within his arms his lady he doth take,
And full a thousand times he gently sighed,
Not sighs of sorrow, such as sad men make
From grief, or when by sickness they are tried,
But easy sighs, which showed how satisfied
He was, and how his love was deeply seated,
Such sighs he drew, and oft and oft repeated.

196

And then they spoke of many varied things,
As in this situation would arise,
And playfully they interchanged their rings,
But what the mottoes were, you may surmise;
A brooch of gold, as azure as the skies,
Set with a ruby heart, she gave him too,
And pinned it to his shirt as love pledge true.

197

Do you suppose that any grasping wretch,
Who chides at love and holds it in despite,
From all the profit he from gold can fetch,
Was ever so enriched with pure delight
As these two knew, in measure infinite?
Nay, they can never know, so God me save,
Such perfect joy who niggardly behave.

198

And if they say they do, they merely lie,
Those busy wretches, full of woe and dread;
They call love madness and against it cry,
But ever they in grief shall make their bed,
Nor yet have joy of money, white nor red!
So let them live in grief and in mischance,
But lovers' joys may heaven still enhance.

199

Would God that all those wretches who despise
The gentle works of love had ears as long
As Midas had, that king so penny-wise;
Or might be served with drink as hot and strong
As Crassus drank, for deeds so harsh and wrong;
For greed is vice, as all old stories show,
And love is virtue, let who will say no.

200

These happy two, whose joys I've been reporting,
Who now at last in love were so secure,
They fell to talking, and in playful sporting
They told how, when and where they first were sure
They knew each other, and how they did endure
The griefs now passed; for all that might annoy
This night was turned at last to perfect joy!

201

If in their talk of joy they came abrupt
On any woe of times now past and gone,
With kisses all their tale they interrupt,
And thus again to joy are brought anon.
One thing alone their hearts were set upon,
To free their joy from all its base alloys,
And former grief with joy to counterpoise.

It were ye that wroughte me swich wo,
Ye humble nettes of my lady dere!
Though ther be mercy writen in your chere,
God wot, the text ful hard is, sooth, to finde,
How coude ye with-outen bond me binde?"

195

Therwith he gan hir faste in armes take,
And wel an hundred tymes gan he syke,
Nought swiche sorwful sykes as men make
For wo, or elles whan that folk ben syke,
But esy sykes, swiche as been to lyke,
That shewed his affeccioun with-inne;
Of swiche sykes coude he nought bilinne.

196

Sone after this they speke of sondry thinges,
As fil to purpos of this aventure,
And pleyinge entrechaungeden hir ringes,
Of which I can nought tellen no scripture;
But wel I woot a broche, gold and asure,
In whiche a ruby set was lyk an herte,
Criseyde him yaf, and stak it on his sherte.

197

Lord! trowe ye, a coveitous, a wrecche,
That blameth love and holt of it despyt,
That, of tho pens that he can mokre and kecche,
Was ever yet y-yeve him swich delyt,
As is in love, in oo poynt, in som plyt?
Nay, doutelees, for also god me save,
So parfit joye may no nigard have!

198

They wol sey "yis," but lord! so that they lye,
Tho bisy wrecches, ful of wo and drede!
They callen love a woodnesse or folye,
But it shal falle hem as I shal yow rede;
They shul forgo the whyte and eke the rede,
And live in wo, ther god yeve hem mischaunce,
And every lover in his trouthe avaunce!

199

As wolde god, tho wrecches, that dispyse
Servyse of love, hadde eres al-so longe
As hadde Myda, ful of coveityse;
And ther-to dronken hadde as hoot and stronge
As Crassus dide for his affectis wronge,
To techen hem that they ben in the vyce,
And loveres nought, al-though they holde hem nyce!

200

Thise ilke two, of whom that I yow seye,
Whan that hir hertes wel assured were,
Tho gonne they to speken and to pleye,
And eek rehercen how, and whanne, and where,
They knewe hem first, and every wo and fere
That passed was; but al swich hevinesse,
I thanke it god, was tourned to gladnesse.

201

And ever-mo, whan that hem fel to speke
Of any thing of swich a tyme agoon,
With kissing al that tale sholde breke,
And fallen in a newe joye anoon,
And diden al hir might, sin they were oon,
For to recoveren blisse and been at ese,
And passed wo with joye countrepeyse.

202
Reson wil not that I speke of sleep,
For it accordeth nought to my matere;
God woot, they toke of that ful litel keep,
But lest this night, that was to hem so dere,
Ne sholde in veyn escape in no manere,
It was biset in joye and bisinesse
Of al that souneth in-to gentilnesse.

203
But whan the cok, comune astrologer,
Gan on his brest to bete, and after crowe,
And Lucifer, the dayes messager,
Gan for to ryse, and out hir bemes throwe;
And estward roos, to him that coude it knowe,
Fortuna maior, than anoon Criseyde,
With herte sore, to Troilus thus seyde:—

204
"Myn hertes lyf, my trist and my plesaunce,
That I was born, allas! what me is wo,
That day of us mot make desseveraunce!
For tyme it is to ryse, and hennes go,
Or elles I am lost for evermo!
O night, allas! why niltow over us hove,
As longe as whonne Almena lay by Jove?

205
O blake night, as folk in bokes rede,
That shapen art by god this world to hyde
At certeyn tymes with thy derke wede,
That under that men mighte in reste abyde,
Wel oughte bestes pleyne, and folk thee chyde,
That there-as day with labour wolbe us breste,
That thou thus fleest, and deynest us nought reste!

206
Thou dost, allas! to shortly thyn offyce,
Thou rakel night, ther god, makere of kinde,
Thee, for thyn hast and thyn unkinde vyce,
So faste ay to our hemi-spere binde,
That never-more under the ground thou winde!
For now, for thou so hyest out of Troye,
Have I forgon thus hastily my joye!"

207
This Troilus, that with tho wordes felte,
As thoughte him tho, for piëtous distresse,
The blody teres from his herte melte,
As he that never yet swich hevinesse
Assayed hadde, out of so greet gladnesse,
Gan therwith-al Criseyde his lady dere
In armes streyne, and seyde in this manere:—

208
"O cruel day, accusour of the joye
That night and love han stole and faste y-wryen,
A-cursed be thy coming in-to Troye,
For every bore hath oon of thy bright yën!
Envyous day, what list thee so to spyen?
What hastow lost, why sekestow this place,
Ther god thy lyght so quenche, for his grace?

209
Allas! what han thise loveres thee agilt,
Dispitous day? thyn be the pyne of helle!
For many a lovere hastow shent, and wilt;
Thy pouring in wol no-wher lete hem dwelle.
What proferestow thy light here for to selle?

202
You'll scarce expect that I should speak of sleep,
The topic seems, indeed, not pertinent.
A night of vigil they were glad to keep,
And lest this time, that so much to them meant,
Should slip away before they could prevent,
The happy hours were fully occupied
With all the gentle arts to love allied.

203
The cock, astrologer in his own way,
Began to beat his breast and then to crow,
And Lucifer, the messenger of day,
Began to rise and forth her beams to throw,
And eastward rose, as you perhaps may know,
Fortuna Major—for the night was fled,
And Cressida to Troilus thus said:

204
"Life of my heart, my trust and my delight,
That I was born, alas, to such a woe!
For we must part with parting of the night.
'Tis time that thou must rise and hence must go,
Or I am lost, and ever shall be so!
O night, why wilt thou not above us hover,
As long as when Jove was Alcmena's lover?

205
"O night so black, as one in old books reads,
Thou wert designed by God this world to hide
At certain seasons with thy inky weeds,
That men might then in rest and peace abide;
Yet beasts may well lament and men may chide,
That though by toil through all the day distressed,
Away thou flee'st and grantest them no rest!

206
"Thou dost, alas, thy time too quickly waste,
O heedless night! The maker of mankind
Curse thee for thy unnecessary haste,
And to our hemisphere so firm thee bind,
Thy way below thou ne'er again shalt find!
For through thy heedless hieing out of Troy
Thus have we hastily foregone our joy!"

207
Troilus, too, at these sad bodings felt
The weight of heavy sorrow on him press;
His heart began in bloody tears to melt,
For never yet such grievous heaviness
He e'er had known or woe so comfortless;
And Cressida, his lady, he did take
Within his arms, and in this manner spake:

208
"O cruel day, denouncer of the joy
That night and love have stolen and concealed,
Accursed by thy coming into Troy,
For all to thy bright eyes is now revealed!
Envious day, what will thy spying yield?
What hast thou lost, and hunt for in this place?
May God put out thy light in dark disgrace!

209
"Alas, with wrong thou chargest love of guilt,
Thou hateful day! May thine be all the pain of hell!
For many a lover hast thou slain, and wilt
Yet slay, for light grants them no place to dwell!
Why must thou proffer here thy light to sell?

Go sell to them who tiny seals engrave!
We want thee not, we need no daylight save!"

210

Titan, the sun, in like words did he chide,
And said, "O fool, well may men thee despise,
Thou hast all night fair Daybreak at thy side,
And yet permittest her so soon to rise
And so distress all lovers in this wise!
What, stay in bed, thou Titan, with thy
Morrow!
May heaven grant the both of you have sorrow!"

211

He sighed and said, for yet he was not done,
"My lady true, and of my weal and woe
The very root, thou fair and goodly one,
Must I arise? Alas, and must I so?
My heart is cleft in twain that I must go!
Since all the joy I have abides with you,
With my poor life what then is left to do?

212

"What hope is left? In truth I know not how
Or when, alas, I may occasion see
To be again with thee as I am now!
God knows, 'twill be a heavy weird to dree!
And if desire now so tortures me,
I seem but dead till to thy arms I turn,
How shall I longer time from thee sojourn?

213

"But nevertheless, my precious lady bright,
If I were sure beyond the slightest doubt,
That I, your servant and your faithful knight,
Within your heart were compassed round about
As you in mine, so naught can shut me out,
The world for me could hold no greater gain,
And that good thought would lighten all my pain."

214

To this fair Cressida replied anon,
And sighing said, "Beloved sweetheart dear,
The game in very truth is so far gone
That Phoebus first shall fall from out his sphere,
And doves and eagles as true friends appear,
And every rock from out its station start,
Ere Troilus from Cressida's poor heart!

215

"Love doth thee in my heart so deep engrave,
That though I would expel thee from my thought,
As heaven's grace my weary soul shall save,
Though I should die, I could accomplish naught!
And for the love of him who hath us wrought,
Let no such fancy creep within your brain,
To cause me thus to perish with the pain.

216

"If you hold me as firmly in your mind
As I hold you, I'll be content and glad,
And if it turn out so, then I shall find
No further happiness for heaven to add!
But, love, let's talk no more of glad and sad,
Be true to me, there's nothing more to say,
For I am thine, forever and a day!

217

"Be thus content, and cast away all fear!
Thou hast what ne'er shall have another man.

Go selle it hem that smale seles graven,
We wol thee nought, us nedeth no day haven."

210

And eek the sonne Tytan gan he chyde,
And seyde, "O fool, wel may men thee dispyse,
That hast the Dawing al night by thy syde,
And suffrest hir so sone up fro thee ryse,
For to disesen loveres in this wyse.
What! hold your bed ther, thou, and eek thy Mor-
we!
I bidde god, so yeve yow bothe sorwe!"

211

Therwith ful sore he sighte, and thus he seyde,
"My lady right, and of my wele or wo
The welle and rote, O goodly myn, Criseyde,
And shal I ryse, allas! and shal I go?
Now fele I that myn herte moot a-two!
For how sholde I my lyf an houre save,
Sin that with yow is al the lyf I have?

212

What shal I doon, for certes, I not how,
Ne whanne, allas! I shal the tyme see,
That in this plyt I may be eft with yow;
And of my lyf, god woot how that shal be,
Sin that desyr right now so byteth me,
That I am deed anoon, but I retourne.
How sholde I longe, allas! fro you sojourne?

213

But nathelees, myn owene lady bright,
Yit were it so that I wiste outrely,
That I, your humble servaunt and your knight,
Were in your herte set so fermely
As ye in myn, the which thing, trewely,
Me lever were than thise worldes tweyne,
Yet sholde I bet enduren al my peyne."

214

To that Criseyde answerde right anoon,
And with a syk she seyde, "O herte dere,
The game, y-wis, so ferforth now is goon,
That first shal Phebus falle fro his spere,
And every egle been the dowves fere,
And every roche out of his place sterte,
Er Troilus out of Criseydes herte!

215

Ye be so depe in-with myn herte grave,
That, though I wolde it turne out of my thought,
As wisly verray god my soule save,
To dyen in the peyne, I coude nought!
And, for the love of god that us hath wrought,
Lat in your brayn non other fantasye
So crepe, that it cause me to dye!

216

And that ye me wolde han as faste in minde
As I have yow, that wolde I yow bi-seche;
And, if I wiste soothly that to finde,
God mighte not a poynt my joyes eche!
But, herte myn, with-oute more speche,
Beth to me trewe, or elles were it routhe;
For I am thyn, by god and by my trouthe!

217

Beth glad for-thy, and live in sikernesse;
Thus seyde I never er this, ne shal to mo;

And if to yow it were a gret gladnesse
To turne ayein, soone after that ye go,
As fayn wolde I as ye, it were so,
As wisly god myn herte bringe at reste!"
And him in armes took, and ofte keste.

218

Agayns his wil, sin it mot nedes be,
This Troilus up roos, and faste him cledde,
And in his armes took his lady free
An hundred tyme, and on his wey him spedde,
And with swich wordes as his herte bledde,
He seyde, "farewel, my dere herte swete,
Ther god us graunte sounde and sone to mete!"

219

To which no word for sorwe she answerde,
So sore gan his parting hir destreyne;
And Troilus un-to his palays ferde,
As woo bigon as she was, sooth to seyne;
So hard him wrong of sharp desyr the peyne
For to ben eft there he was in plesaunce,
That it may never out of his remembraunce.

220

Retorned to his rëal palais, sone
He softe in-to his bed gan for to slinke,
To slepe longe, as he was wont to done,
But al for nought; he may wel ligge and winke,
But sleep ne may ther in his herte sinke;
Thenkinge how she, for whom desyr him brende,
A thousand-fold was worth more than he wende.

221

And in his thought gan up and doun to winde
Hir wordes alle, and every contenaunce,
And fermely impressen in his minde
The leste poynt that to him was plesaunce;
And verrayliche, of thilke remembraunce,
Desyr al newe him brende, and lust to brede
Gan more than erst, and yet took he non hede.

222

Criseyde also, right in the same wyse,
Of Troilus gan in hir herte shette
His worthinesse, his lust, his dedes wyse,
His gentilesse, and how she with him mette,
Thonkinge love he so wel hir bisette;
Desyring eft to have hir herte dere
In swich a plyt, she dorste make him chere.

223

Pandare, a-morwe which that comen was
Un-to his nece, and gan hir fayre grete,
Seyde, "al this night so reyned it, allas!
That al my drede is that ye, nece swete,
Han litel layser had to slepe and mete;
Al night," quod he, "hath reyn so do me wake,
That som of us, I trowe, hir hedes ake."

224

And ner he com, and seyde, "how stont it now
This mery morwe, nece, how can ye fare?"
Criseyde answerde, "never the bet for yow,
Fox that ye been, god yeve your herte care!
God helpe me so, ye caused al this fare,
Trow I," quod she, "for alle your wordes whyte;
O! who-so seeth yow knoweth yow ful lyte!"

And if it be thy will, O sweetheart dear,
Come back again as soon as e'er you can,
Thy pleasure here shall be no greater than
My own, so may I hope for heaven's bliss!—"
And took him in her arms with many a kiss.

218

So willy-nilly, since the day was near,
Troilus got up and dressed beside the bed,
And in his arms he took his lady dear,
A hundred times, ere on his way he sped,
And with a voice as though at heart he bled,
He cried aloud, "Farewell, my precious sweeting!
God grant us soon a safe and happy meeting!"

219

To this no word for sorrow she replied,
And grief that thus they must be rent in twain;
And Troilus unto the palace hied,
As woe-begone as she, I dare maintain.
So heavy was the burden of the pain
Of joys remembered, but so sudden vanished,
He felt as one from heaven sternly banished.

220

He reached the palace as the daylight grew,
And softly to his bed he planned to slink
And sleep as late as he was wont to do—
But planned in vain, for not a single wink
Of sleep into his heart might gently sink,
For pondering she who now his life controlled
Was better than he guessed a thousandfold.

221

About his loving thoughts now twist and wind
Her every word and every loving glance,
Impressing clear and firm upon his mind
Each slightest point and circumstance;
And at the memory of his happy chance,
Love bursts anew in flames of high desire,
Though little feels he now the burning fire.

222

Cressida, also, in the selfsame wise,
The worth, the gaiety, and every deed
Of Troilus recalled before her eyes,
And all remembrances for him so plead,
That from this love she never can be freed;
She longs again to have him in such plight
That she alone may bring to him delight.

223

Now Pandar, seeing day was there at last,
Came to his niece, and fairly doth her greet.
"All night," he said, "it rained so hard and fast,
That I am dreadfully afraid, my sweet,
Your dreams will not be pleasant to repeat.
All night the rain kept me quite wide awake,
I greatly fear it's made our heads all ache."

224

Then he drew near and said, "How do you do
This sunny morn? How do you feel today?"
Cressida answered, "None the better for you,
Fox that you are! The Lord will you repay!
For you have managed things in your own way,
I now can see, for all your words so fair!
You fooled me well with your deceptive air!"

225

Cressida strove her blushing face to hide
Behind the sheet, and grew for shame all red.
But Pandar underneath the bedclothes pried,
"Dear Cressida, if I must die," he said,
"Have here a sword and smite off my poor head!"
He thrust his arm beneath her neck to twist
The covers off, and then his niece he kissed.

226

No need to tell how they were reconciled!
If God forgave his death, then should not she
Forgive her uncle? Thus the time they whiled
Away in great amicability,
As good friends now as anyone could be,
Till in good time to her own house she went
And left her uncle very well content.

227

To Troilus let us now turn again,
Who long abed in wakeful tossing lay;
For Pandar soon he sent some of his men
To bid him hasten thither right away,
And Pandar came without a no or nay,
And greeting him in manner dignified,
Upon his bed he sat down at his side.

228

And Troilus, moved by the deep affection
Which for his friend within his heart now lies,
Falls on his knees in absolute subjection,
Nor from that humble place he will arise,
But thank with grateful thank he multiplies,
A thousand times, and oft the day doth bless
His friend was born to save him from distress.

229

"O friend," he said, "of friends the very best
That ever was or ever was heard tell,
Thou hast in heaven brought my soul to rest
From Phlegethon, the fiery flood of hell;
A thousand times a day if I should sell
Myself to serve and honor only thee,
Enough reward and pay it would not be.

230

"The sun, which moves above in all man's sight,
Saw never yet, this dare I will aver,
A fairer than my dearest lady bright,
And to my death I shall be bound to her;
The thanks for all this favor I refer
To Love, who honors me with kind assistance,
And also, Pandar, to thy wise persistence.

231

"What thou hast given is no little thing,
And I shall pay thee thanks forever and aye!
And why? Because thy faithful help did bring
Me back to life, who else were dead this day"—
And then upon his bed again he lay.
Soberly Pandar listened at his side
Till he was through, and thus replied:

232

"My dearest friend, if aught I've done for thee,
God knows it is to me a great relief,
And I'm as glad of it as you can be.
But now take heed that we come not to grief,
For there is danger still of this mischief,

225

With that she gan hir face for to wrye
With the shete, and wex for shame al reed;
And Pandarus gan under for to prye,
And seyde, "nece, if that I shal ben deed,
Have here a swerd, and smyteth of myn heed."
With that his arm al sodeynly he thriste
Under hir nekke, and at the laste hir kiste.

226

I passe al that which chargeth nought to seye,
What! God foryaf his deeth, and she al-so
Foryaf, and with hir uncle gan to pleye,
For other cause was ther noon than so.
But of this thing right to the effect to go,
Whan tyme was, hom til hir hous she wente,
And Pandarus hath fully his entente.

227

Now torne we ayein to Troilus,
That restelees ful longe a-bedde lay,
And prevely sente after Pandarus,
To him to come in al the haste he may.
He com anoon, nought ones seyde he "nay,"
And Troilus ful sobrely he grette,
And doun upon his beddes syde him sette.

228

This Troilus, with al the affeccioun
Of frendes love that herte may devyse,
To Pandarus on kneës fil adoun,
And er that he wolde of the place aryse,
He gan him thonken in his beste wyse;
A hondred sythe he gan the tyme blesse,
That he was born to bringe him fro distresse.

229

He seyde, "O frend, of frendes th' alderbeste
That ever was, the sothe for to telle,
Thou hast in hevene y-brought my soule at reste
Fro Flegiton, the fery flood of helle;
That, though I mighte a thousand tymes selle,
Upon a day, my lyf in thy servyse,
It mighte nought a mote in that suffyse.

230

The sonne, which that al the world may see,
Saw never yet, my lyf, that dar I leye,
So inly fair and goodly as is she,
Whos I am al, and shal, til that I deye;
And, that I thus am hires, dar I seye,
That thanked be the heighe worthinesse
Of love, and eek thy kinde bisinesse.

231

Thus hastow me no litel thing y-yive,
Fo which to thee obliged be for ay
My lyf, and why? for thorugh thyn help I live;
For elles deed hadde I be many a day."
And with that word doun in his bed he lay,
And Pandarus ful sobrely him herde
Til al was seyd, and thanne he him answerde:

232

"My dere frend, if I have doon for thee
In any cas, god wot, it is me leef;
And am as glad as man may of it be,
God help me so; but tak now not a-greef
That I shal seyn, be war of this myscheef,

That, there-as thou now brought art in-to blisse,
That thou thy-self ne cause it nought to misse.

233

For of fortunes sharp adversitee
The worst kinde of infortune is this,
A man to have ben in prosperitee,
And it remembren, whan it passed is.
Thou art wys y-nough, for-thy do nought amis;
Be not to rakel, though thou sitte warme,
For if thou be, certeyn, it wol thee harme.

234

Thou art at ese, and hold thee wel ther-inne.
For also seur as reed is every fyr,
As greet a craft is kepe wel as winne;
Brydle alwey wel thy speche and thy desyr.
For worldly joye halt not but by a wyr;
That preveth wel, it brest alday so ofte;
For-thy nede is to werke with it softe."

235

Quod Troilus, "I hope, and god toforn,
My dere frend, that I shal so me bere,
That in my gilt ther shal no thing be lorn,
N' I nil not rakle as for to greven here;
It nedeth not this matere ofte tere;
For wistestow myn herte wel, Pandare,
God woot, of this thou woldest litel care."

236

Tho gan he telle him of his glade night.
And wher-of first his herte dredde, and how,
And seyde, "freend, as I am trewe knight,
And by that feyth I shal to god and yow,
I hadde it never half so hote as now;
And ay the more that desyr me byteth
To love hir best, the more it me delyteth.

237

I noot my-self not wisly what it is;
But now I fele a newe qualitee,
Ye, al another than I dide er this."
Pandare answerde, and seyde thus, that he
That ones may in hevene blisse be,
He feleth other weyes, dar I leye,
Than thilke tyme he first herde of it seye.

238

This is o word for al; this Troilus
Was never ful, to speke of this matere,
And for to preysen un-to Pandarus
The bountee of his righte lady dere,
And Pandarus to thanke and maken chere.
This tale ay was span-newe to biginne
Til that the night departed hem a-twinne.

239

Sone after this, for that fortune it wolde,
I-comen was the blisful tyme swete,
That Troilus was warned that he sholde,
Ther he was erst, Criseyde his lady mete;
For which he felte his herte in joye flete;
And feythfully gan alle the goddes herie;
And lat see now if that he can be merie.

240

And holden was the forme and al the wyse,
Of hir cominge, and eek of his also,
As it was erst, which nedeth nought devyse.

That now that thou art settled in thy bliss,
Thyself may cause affairs to go amiss.

233

"Of fickle fortune's sharp adversities,
The very worst misfortune of them all,
Is this, to know and lose all joy and ease,
And have but bitter memories to recall.
Exert thy wisdom such fate to forestall;
Be not too rash, nor of thyself too sure,
Or harm will quickly come and long endure.

234

"Thou art at ease, and hold thee well therein,
For just as true that red is every fire,
To keep demands as much skill as to win.
Then bridle well thy speech and thy desire,
For worldly joys hang by a subtle wire,
And for sad proof, it breaketh quick and oft,
Wherefore the need to walk both light and soft."

235

"I hope," said Troilus, "before men's eyes,
Dear friend, that I such heed shall take,
That through my fault no danger shall arise,
And rashness I abjure for her dear sake.
You need not fear my promise I shall break,
If you but knew the secrets of my mind,
Then mighty little cause for fear you'd find."

236

And then he told him of his happy night,
And how at first he was afraid, and why,
And said, "I swear upon my honor bright
And by my faith in you and God on high,
I never knew what loving did imply;
For as my heart's desires rose in height,
The greater grew my love and my delight.

237

"To me myself it is a mystery,
For now I feel in me a nature new,
A thing that makes a different man of me."
And Pandar said, "Yes, I suppose it's true,
That he who once in heaven's bliss may be,
He feels it all in quite another way
Than when he knew it only by hear-say."

238

But now enough—though Troilus indeed
To speak of this doth never stop or tire,
And still to praise his lady would proceed,
Exalting all her bounty higher and higher,
And thanking Pandar all he could require,
Then in again bran-new he ever starts,
Until his friend at night homeward departs.

239

Soon after this, by great good luck, it fell
He had a chance his night-watch to repeat,
For Pandar came the happy news to tell,
That Cressida, his lady, he should meet.
How then his heart with sudden joy doth beat!
His thanks to all the Gods he then did pay,
And you can guess if he was glad and gay!

240

The manner of this meeting was again
Somewhat as I have told and as you know,
And so I shall not bother to explain,

But to the end now let us straightway go;
For Pandar still his faithful aid did show
And brought them to the place they liked the best,
And there they are in quiet and in rest.

241

You have no need, now they again are met,
To ask of me if they were happy there.
For what was good before, grows better yet
A thousandfold, with goodness still to spare.
And now they know no sorrow or no care,
For joy as great to them the kind Gods send
As any human heart may comprehend.

242

This is no trifling thing that now I say,
'Tis something no man's wit can all comprise;
For each to other's will doth so obey
That all the joys which ancient clerks so wise
Have praised, counted as nothing in their eyes;
Their joy may not be written down in ink,
For it surpasses all that heart may think!

243

But cruel day, alack the fateful hour,
Again returns, as they by signs well knew,
And they must yield to sorrow's greater power.
Full sad they were, full sad and pale of hue,
Reviling day with scornings ever new,
Calling it traitor, envious and worse—
O, bitterly the light of day they curse!

244

"Alas," said Troilus, "now is it plain
That Pyroeis and his team-mates three,
Which draw the bright sun's chariot in their train,
Have gone some short cut in despite of me,
And that is why the night so soon doth flee;
And if the sun will hasten thus the day,
No offerings on his altar shall I lay."

245

But day must come, and they must separate,
And after all was said that could be said,
They finally submit to their sad fate,
Yet for a meeting set a time ahead;
And thus for many a night their lives they led
As Fortune gave to them this ample joy,
To Cressida and Troilus of Troy.

246

In great content, in sport and merry songs,
Troilus passes now his happy days.
He spends, he jousts, his feastings he prolongs,
Himself in gaudy garments he arrays,
He has a world of folk about always,
The freshest and the best that he can find,
As suiting one of his so noble kind.

247

Such name and fame of him now circulate
Throughout the world, his honor and largess,
It mounts and rings at heaven's very gate;
And through his love he knows so great gladness
That in his heart he ever doth profess,
No lover in the world is more at ease
Or hath a love with greater power to please.

248

Though other ladies were both fair and kind,

But playnly to the effect right for to go,
In joye and seurte Pandarus hem two
A-bedde broughte, whan hem bothe leste,
And thus they ben in quiete and in reste.

241

Nought nedeth it to yow, sin they ben met,
To aske at me if that they blythe were;
For if it erst was wel, tho was it bet
A thousand-fold, this nedeth not enquere.
A-gon was every sorwe and every fere;
And bothe, y-wis, they hadde, and so they wende,
As muche joye as herte may comprende.

242

This is no litel thing of for to seye,
This passeth every wit for to devyse;
For eche of hem gan otheres lust obeye;
Felicitee, which that thise clerkes wyse
Commenden so, ne may not here suffyse.
This joye may not writen been with inke,
This passeth al that herte may bithinke.

243

But cruel day, so wel-awey the stounde!
Gan for to aproche, as they by signes knewe,
For whiche hem thoughte felen dethes wounde;
So wo was hem, that changen gan hir hewe,
And day they gonnen to dispyse al newe,
Calling it traytour, envyous, and worse,
And bitterly the dayes light they curse.

244

Quod Troilus, "allas! now am I war
That Pirous and tho swifte stedes three,
Whiche that drawen forth the sonnes char,
Han goon som by-path in despyt of me;
That maketh it so sone day to be;
And, for the sonne him hasteth thus to ryse,
Ne shal I never doon him sacrifyse!"

245

But nedes day departe moste hem sone,
And whanne hir speche doon was and hir chere,
They twinne anoon as they were wont to done,
And setten tyme of meting eft y-fere;
And many a night they wroughte in this manere.
And thus Fortune a tyme ladde in joye
Criseyde, and eek this kinges sone of Troye.

246

In suffisaunce, in blisse, and in singinges,
This Troilus gan al his lyf to lede;
He spendeth, justeth, maketh festeyinges;
He yeveth frely ofte, and chaungeth wede,
And held aboute him alwey, out of drede,
A world of folk, as cam him wel of kinde,
The fressheste and the beste he coude finde;

247

That swich a voys was of him and a stevene
Thorugh-out the world, of honour and largesse,
That it up rong un-to the yate of hevene.
And, as in love, he was in swich gladnesse,
That in his herte he demede, as I gesse,
That there nis lovere in this world at ese
So wel as he, and thus gan love him plese.

248

The godlihede or beautee which that kinde

In any other lady hadde y-set
Can not the mountaunce of a knot unbinde,
A-boute his herte, of al Criseydes net.
He was so narwe y-masked and y-knet,
That it undoon on any manere syde,
That nil not been, for ought that may betyde.

249

And by the hond ful ofte he wolde take
This Pandarus, and in-to gardin lede,
And swich a feste and swich a proces make
Him of Criseyde, and of hir womanhede,
And of hir beautee, that, with-outen drede,
It was an hevene his wordes for to here;
And thanne he wolde singe in this manere:

250

"Love, that of erthe and see hath governaunce,
Love, that his hestes hath in hevene hye,
Love, that with an holsom alliaunce
Halt peples joyned, as him list hem gye,
Love, that knetteth lawe of companye,
And couples doth in vertu for to dwelle,
Bind this acord, that I have told and telle;

251

That that the world with feyth, which that is stable,
Dyverseth so his stoundes concordinge,
That elements that been so discordable
Holden a bond perpetuely duringe,
That Phebus mote his rosy day forth bringe,
And that the mone hath lordship over the nightes,
Al this doth Love; ay heried be his mightes!

252

That that the see, that gredy is to flowen,
Constreyneth to a certeyn ende so
His flodes, that so fersly they ne growen
To drenchen erthe and al for ever-mo;
And if that Love ought lete his brydel go,
Al that now loveth a-sonder sholde lepe,
And lost were al, that Love halt now to-hepe.

253

So wolde god, that auctor is of kinde,
That, with his bond, Love of his vertu liste
To cerclen hertes alle, and faste binde,
That from his bond no wight the wey out wiste.
And hertes colde, hem wolde I that he twiste
To make hem love, and that hem leste ay rewe
On hertes sore, and kepe hem that ben trewe."

254

In alle nedes, for the tounes werre,
He was, and ay the firste in armes dight;
And certeynly, but-if that bokes erre,
Save Ector, most y-drad of any wight;
And this encrees of hardinesse and might
Cam him of love, his ladies thank to winne,
That altered his spirit so with-inne.

255

In tyme of trewe, on haukinge wolde he ryde,
Or elles hunten boor, bere, or lyoun;
The smale bestes leet he gon bi-syde.
And whan that he com rydinge in-to toun,
Ful ofte his lady, from hir window doun,
As fresh as faucon comen out of muwe,
Ful redy was, him goodly to saluwe.

Yet all the virtues in their natures set
About his heart one knot could not unbind
Of Cressida's so subtly woven net.
Enmeshed he was, and never shall he get
His freedom, nor a single part of it,
For no man's skill this net can e'er unknit.

249

And Pandar by the hand he oft would take,
And in the garden find a quiet place,
And such a glorious anthem there they'd make
Of Cressida and all her woman's grace,
And of the beauty of her form and face,
It was a heavenly joy his praise to hear,
And thus he sang unto his lady dear:

250

"O love, that dost the earth and sea control,
O Love, that dost command the heavens high,
O Love, of blessed harmony the soul,
All nations rest beneath thy guiding eye!
Thou with whose law societies comply,
Thou in whose virtue loving couples dwell,
O Love, bind this accord of which I tell!

251

"The world that stands so firm on its foundation,
With all its many harmonies diverse;
The elements with all their contentation,
Yet held in bonds that nothing can disperse;
Phoebus that doth the earth in light immerse;
The moon that hath the lordship over night—
All these depend on Love and on his might.

252

"The sea that never falters in its flowing,
Restrains its floods to such a certain end,
However fiercely tempests may be blowing,
To drown the earth it never can ascend;
If aught the bridle from Love's hand should rend,
All harmonies at once would burst asunder,
And scatter all that Love now holdeth under.

253

"God grant, the author of all natural kind,
That with the bond of Love he will consent
In circling love all hearts so firm to bind,
Escape therefrom no man shall e'er invent;
And loveless hearts, let them by Love be bent
To learn to love, and thus in pity grow,
But faithful hearts may Love keep ever so!"

254

In all events that at the siege occurred,
Troilus was ready now for fray or fight,
He was, indeed, unless the books have erred,
Save Hector, Troy's most celebrated knight,
And this increase of valor and of might,
All came from love, his lady's thanks to win,
Which thus had changed his heart and soul within.

255

In times of truce, a-hawking he would ride,
Or hunt the boar or lion or the bear;
From smaller beasts he always turned aside.
And when he on his homeward way would fare,
Full oft his lady at her window there,
As fresh as falcon just freed of its hood,
Smiled salutations down from where she stood.

256

Now most of love and virtue was his speech,
And he despised all actions mean and low,
Nor failed to practice what some men but preach,
To honor those who first did honor show,
And comfort those in sorrow and in woe;
And when he heard that any man fared well
In love, such news he liked to hear and tell.

256

And most of love and vertu was his speche,
And in despyt hadde alle wrecchednesse;
And doutelees, no nede was him biseche
To honouren hem that hadde worthinesse,
And esen hem that weren in distresse.
And glad was he if any wight wel ferde,
That lover was, whan he it wiste or herde.

257

He held each man in estimation slight,
Unless he were engaged in love's emprise—
I mean the men who ought to be of right.
Love fancies he himself could well devise
And dress himself in such a dashing wise
That all the youth there in the city thought
That all was well, whate'er he said or wrought.

257

For sooth to seyn, he lost held every wight
But-if he were in loves heigh servyse,
I mene folk that oughte it been of right.
And over al this, so wel coude he devyse
Of sentement, and in so unkouth wyse
Al his array, that every lover thoughte,
That al was wel, what-so he seyde or wroughte.

258

And though he was himself of royal race,
He treated no man with unkindly pride;
Benign he was to each in every place,
For which he won high praise on every side.
For love demanded by its native grace,
That he should shun all envy, pride and ire,
All avarice and other base desire.

258

And though that he be come of blood royal,
Him liste of pryde at no wight for to chase;
Benigne he was to ech in general,
For which he gat him thank in every place.
Thus wolde Love, y-heried be his grace,
That Pryde, Envye, Ire, and Avaryce
He gan to flee, and every other vyce.

259

O daughter to Dione, lady bright,
And Cupid, too, thy blind and winged son;
Ye sisters nine, who on Parnassus' height
Abide beside the fountain Helicon,
Thus far, with you to guide, my tale hath won!
And now since ye on other ways will wend,
Honor and praise be yours, world without end!

259

Thou lady bright, the doughter to Dione,
Thy blinde and winged sone eek, daun Cupyde;
Ye sustren nyne eek, that by Elicone
In hil Parnaso listen for to abyde,
That ye thus fer han deyned me to gyde,
I can no more, but sin that ye wol wende,
Ye heried been for ay, with-outen ende!

260

Your aid hath helped me in my song to tell
How Troilus to joy at last attained,
Though with his joy there was some grief as well,
Just as my author in his day explained.
My third book by your aid its end hath gained,
And Troilus we leave in peace and joy,
And Cressida, within the town of Troy.

260

Thourgh you have I seyd fully in my song
Th'effect and joye of Troilus servyse,
Al be that ther was som disese among,
As to myn auctor listeth to devyse.
My thridde book now ende ich in this wyse;
And Troilus in luste and in quiete
Is with Criseyde, his owne herte swete.

HERE ENDETH THE THIRD BOOK

BOOK IV

[*PROEM*]

1

Too short a fleeting time, alas the while,
Great joy endures, and Fortune wills it so,
Who truest seems when most she will beguile,
And most allures when she will strike a blow,
And from her wheel some hapless victim throw;
For when some wretch slips down and disappears,
She laughs at him and comforts him with jeers.

1

But al to litel, weylawey the whyle,
Lasteth swich joye, y-thonked be Fortune!
That semeth trewest, whan she wol bygyle,
And can to foles so hir song entune,
That she hem hent and blent, traytour comune;
And whan a wight is from hir wheel y-throwe,
Than laugheth she, and maketh him the mowe.

2

From Troilus she now began to turn
Her face, and paid to him but little heed;
She made his lady her true lover spurn,
And on her wheel she set up Diomede;
At which, in truth, my heart begins to bleed,

2

From Troilus she gan hir brighte face
Awey to wrythe, and took of him non hede,
But caste him clene oute of his lady grace,
And on hir wheel she sette up Diomede;
For which right now myn herte ginneth blede,

And now my penne, allas! with which I wryte,
Quaketh for drede of that I moot endyte.

And now my pen, with which I faltering write,
Trembles for fear of what I must endite.

3

For how Criseyde Troilus forsook,
Or at the leste, how that she was unkinde,
Mot hennes-forth ben matere of my book,
As wryten folk thorugh which it is in minde.
Allas! that they shulde ever cause finde
To speke hir harm; and if they on hir lye,
Y-wis, hem-self sholde han the vilanye.

3

How Cressida her Troilus forsook,
Or at the least, how she became unkind,
Henceforth must be the matter of my book,
As ancient records bring the tale to mind.
Alas, that ever they a cause should find
To speak her harm! But if the records lie,
Shame on the head of slanderers I cry!

4

O ye Herines, Nightes doughtren three,
That endelees compleynen ever in pyne,
Megera, Alete, and eek Thesiphone;
Thou cruel Mars eek, fader to Quiryne,
This ilke ferthe book me helpeth fyne,
So that the los of lyf and love y-fere
Of Troilus be fully shewed here.

4

Ye daughters of black night! Ye furies three,
Ye who lament in everlasting pain,
Megaera, Alecto and Tisiphone!
Thou cruel Mars, Quirinus' father, deign
To aid my fourth book to its end to gain
And tell how loss of love and loss of life
May be the final end of lovers' strife!

HERE ENDETH THE PROEM.

HERE BEGINNETH THE FOURTH BOOK

5

LIGGINGE in ost, as I have seyd er this,
The Grekes stronge, aboute Troye toun,
Bifel that, whan that Phebus shyning is
Up-on the brest of Hercules Lyoun,
That Ector, with ful many a bold baroun,
Caste on a day with Grekes for to fighte,
As he was wont to greve hem what he mighte.

5

The Grecian hosts, as I before have told,
Still lay in siege about the Trojan wall;
And when within the Lion beams of gold
From Phoebus on the Lion's breast first fall,
Then Hector doth his barons to him call,
And plan to meet the Greeks in open fight,
And work such injury as there they might.

6

Not I how longe or short it was bitwene
This purpos and that day they fighte mente;
But on a day wel armed, bright and shene,
Ector, and many a worthy wight out wente,
With spere in hond and bigge bowes bente;
And in the berd, with-oute lenger lette,
Hir fomen in the feld anoon hem mette.

6

I do not know how long it was between
The day they made their plan and when they meant
To fight, but with their arms all bright and keen,
With spears in hand and great bows tautly bent,
Hector with many a worthy warrior went
Before the town, for battle ready set,
And on the field their foeman soon they met.

7

The longe day, with speres sharpe y-grounde,
With arwes, dartes, swerdes, maces felle,
They fighte and bringen hors and man to grounde,
And with hir axes out the braynes quelle.
But in the laste shour, sooth for to telle,
The folk of Troye hem-selven so misledden,
That with the worse at night homward they fledden.

7

The whole long day with all spears sharply ground,
With arrows, darts, with swords and heavy maces,
They fiercely fight, and horse and man confound,
While axes dash out brains and cleave men's faces;
But at the last the Trojan host retraces
Its steps, faltering where their captains led,
And in defeat at night they homeward fled.

8

At whiche day was taken Antenor,
Maugre Polydamas or Monesteo,
Santippe, Sarpedon, Polynestor,
Polyte, or eek the Trojan daun Ripheo,
And othere lasse folk, as Phebuseo.
So that, for harm, that day the folk of Troye
Dredden to lese a greet part of hir joye.

8

That day Antenor yielded in the fight,
And Polydamas nor yet Menestheus,
Xanthippus, Sarpedon or Polynestor might,
Polites nor the Trojan Sir Ripheus
Withstand the Greeks, still less Sir Phebuseus,
And all his like; the harm that day done Troy
The city's hopes did very near destroy.

9

Of Pryamus was yeve, at Greek requeste,
A tyme of trewe, and tho they gonnen trete,
Hir prisoneres to chaungen, moste and leste,
And for the surplus yeven sommes grete.
This thing anoon was couth in every strete,
Bothe in th'assege, in toune, and everywhere,
And with the firste it cam to Calkas ere.

9

Thereafter the Greeks a truce agreed to make,
As Priam asked, the purpose to debate
Of changing prisoners in a give and take,
And for the surplus, money payments great.
This news at once began to circulate
Among both Greeks and Trojans far and near,
And very soon it came to Calchas' ear.

10

Assured that all was true as it was told,
Into the Greek assembly Calchas pressed,
Where sat the Grecian lords so wise and old,
And took his rightful place among the rest,
And solemnly he made them this request,
That they would do him so much reverence
To stop their noise and give him audience.

11

"My lords, I was a Trojan in past days,"
He said, "as doubtless all of you know well,
And know that Calchas merits Grecian praise,
For I came here your troubles to dispel,
And all your future conquest to foretell;
For you shall surely burn the Trojan town,
And all its walls the Greeks shall batter down.

12

"And how at last the Greeks shall win this prize
And seize the town and conquest full achieve,
You've heard me often in detail previse;
All this you know, my lords, as I believe,
And how the Grecian fortunes to retrieve,
I came in my own person here from Troy,
On your behalf my knowledge to employ,

13

"Renouncing all my treasure, well content
If I could but contribute to your ease.
Thus all my goods I left with free consent,
My only thought, my lords, was you to please;
Nor grieve I now at loss of these,
Nor shall I much be troubled at the cost
If all my property in Troy is lost—

14

"Except a daughter, whom I left behind,
Sleeping at home the night I slipped away.
How could a father be so far unkind,
So hard of heart! Rather than let her stay,
Had I but dragged her forth in night array!
And so, my lords, except you heed my sorrow,
Methinks I ne'er shall see another morrow.

15

"And I so long, my lords, have held my peace,
Because I saw no way to bring her here;
But now or never must come her release,
And soon I hope to see my daughter dear!
To beg your aid before you I appear!
Have pity on an old man in distress,
For you are cause of all my heaviness.

16

"Trojans enough you have as captives caught,
With one of these, if so your will it be,
Redemption for my daughter may be bought.
I beg you in your generosity,
One of so many captives give to me!
Why should you such a little thing refuse,
Since all the town and folk are yours to choose?

17

"For here again I faithfully will swear,
Just as Apollo hath it to me told,
And as the stars above likewise declare,
And auspices and auguries of old,
I swear by all these signs so manifold,

10

Whan Calkas knew this tretis sholde holde,
In consistorie, among the Grekes, sone
He gan in thringe forth, with lordes olde,
And sette him there-as he was wont to done;
And with a chaunged face hem bad a bone,
For love of god, to don that reverence,
To stinte noyse, and yeve him audience.

11

Thanne seyde he thus, "lo! lordes myne, I was
Trojan, as it is knowen out of drede;
And if that yow remembre, I am Calkas,
That alderfirst yaf comfort to your nede,
And tolde wel how that ye sholden spede.
For dredelees, thorugh yow, shal, in a stounde,
Ben Troye y-brend, and beten doun to grounde.

12

And in what forme, or in what maner wyse
This town to shende, and al your lust to acheve,
Ye han er this wel herd it me devyse;
This knowe ye, my lordes, as I leve.
And for the Grekes weren me so leve,
I com my-self in my propre persone,
To teche in this how yow was best to done;

13

Havinge un-to my tresour ne my rente
Right no resport, to respect of your ese.
Thus al my good I loste and to yow wente,
Wening in this you, lordes, for to plese.
But al that lose ne doth me no disese.
I vouche-sauf, as wisly have I joye,
For you to lese al that I have in Troye,

14

Save of a doughter, that I lafte, allas!
Slepinge at hoom, whanne out of Troye I sterte.
O sterne, O cruel fader that I was!
How mighte I have in that so hard an herte?
Allas! I ne hadde y-brought hir in hir sherte!
For sorwe of which I wol not live to morwe,
But-if ye lordes rewe up-on my sorwe.

15

For, by that cause I say no tyme er now
Hir to delivere, I holden have my pees;
But now or never, if that it lyke yow,
I may hir have right sone, doutelees.
O help and grace! amonges al this prees,
Rewe on this olde caitif in destresse,
Sin I through yow have al this hevinesse!

16

Ye have now caught and fetered in prisoun
Trojans y-nowe; and if your willes be,
My child with oon may have redempcioun.
Now for the love of god and of bountee,
Oon of so fele, allas! so yeve him me.
What nede were it this preyere for to werne,
Sin ye shul bothe han folk and toun as yerne?

17

On peril of my lyf, I shal not lye,
Appollo hath me told it feithfully;
I have eek founde it by astronomye,
By sort, and by augurie eek trewely,
And dar wel seye, the tyme is faste by,

That fyrn and flaumbe on al the toun shal sprede;
And thus shal Troye turne in asshen dede.

18

For certeyn, Phebus and Neptunus bothe,
That makeden the walles of the toun,
Ben with the folk of Troye alwey so wrothe,
That thei wol bringe it to confusioun,
Right in despyt of king Lameaudoun.
By-cause he nolde payen hem hir hyre,
The toun of Troye shal ben set on-fyre."

19

Telling his tale alwey, this olde greye,
Humble in speche, and in his lokinge eke,
The salte teres from his eyën tweye
Ful faste ronnen doun by eyther cheke.
So longe he gan of socour hem by-seke
That, for to hele him of his sorwes sore,
They yave him Antenor, with-oute more.

20

But who was glad y-nough but Calkas tho?
And of this thing ful sone his nedes leyde
On hem that sholden for the tretis go,
And hem for Antenor ful ofte preyde
To brigen hoom king Toas and Criseyde;
And whan Pryam his save-garde sente,
Th'embassadours to Troye streyght they wente.

21

The cause y-told of hir cominge, the olde
Pryam the king ful sone in general
Let here-upon his parlement to holde,
Of which the effect rehersen yow I shal.
Th'embassadours ben answered for fynal,
Th'eschaunge of prisoners and al this nede
Hem lyketh wel, and forth in they procede.

22

This Troilus was present in the place,
Whan axed was for Antenor Criseyde,
For which ful sone chaungen gan his face,
As he that with tho wordes wel neigh deyde.
But nathelees, he no word to it seyed,
Lest men sholde his affeccioun espye;
With mannes herte he gan his sorwes drye.

23

And ful of anguish and of grisly drede
Abood what lordes wolde un-to it seye;
And if they wolde graunte, as god forbede,
Th'eschaunge of hir, than thoughte he thinges tweye,
First, how to save hir honour, and what weye
He might best th'eschaunge of hir withstonde;
Ful faste he caste how al this mighte stonde.

24

Love him made al prest to doon hir byde,
And rather dye than she sholde go;
But resoun seyde him, on that other syde,
"With-oute assent of hir ne do not so,
Lest for they werk she wolde by thy fo,
And seyn, that thorugh thy medling is y-blowe
Your bother love, there it was erst unknowe."

25

For which he gan deliberen, for the beste,
That though the lordes wolde that she wente,

That fire and flame on all the town shall spread,
And Troy shall turn to ashes, cold and dead.

18

"Phoebus on high, and watery Neptune, too,
Who gave its walls unto the Trojan town,
Are angry at the Trojan folk untrue,
And eager now to tear those same walls down;
Laomedon, who bore the royal crown,
Refused to pay to them their proper hire,
For which their city shall be burned with fire."

19

Rehearsing thus his tale, this old man gray
And feeble to the Greeks doth humbly speak,
With tears as salty as the ocean spray
Fast running down on either withered cheek.
So long he begs and earnestly doth seek,
That at the last, to stop his long lament,
To give to him Antenor they consent.

20

When thus the long debate was brought to close,
Calchas arrangements with the legates made
Whom for their embassy the Grecians chose,
To give Antenor and take back in trade
His daughter and King Thoas, as he prayed;
And when King Priam had safe-conduct sent,
To Troy the legates on their mission went.

21

The purpose of their embassy they told,
And Priam listened with attentive ear;
A parliament he bade the Trojans hold,
Which I but briefly need to dwell on here,
For with one voice the Trojans spoke out clear,
That they approved of this proposed exchange,
And all details were ready to arrange.

22

Now Troilus was present in the place,
When Cressida was being bargained for,
At which it might be gathered from his face
That this request had touched him deep and sore;
Yet he in silence this disaster bore,
And lest his speech his secret should reveal,
Manfully strove his sorrow to conceal.

23

Thus full of anguish and of ghastly fear,
He waited what the other lords would say,
And if from their debate it should appear,
That Cressida from Troy must go away,
Two things he planned to do without delay,
Both save her honest name, and keep her still
In Troy, if strength availed thereto or skill.

24

For if she longer might not there abide,
Then naught was left for him except to die,
But Reason told him on the other side,
That first for her advice he must apply;
For if he brought her in the public eye,
She might complain his meddling had revealed
Their love, that otherwise had been concealed.

25

To this decision thus he came at last,
That if the lords decreed that she must go,

He would assent to any law they passed,
And then his lady seek and let her know,
And what she bade him do, he would do so,
Cost what it might in labor or in strife,
For what she willed, was dearer than his life.

26

Now Hector, who had heard the Greeks' demand,
For Cressida Antenor to restore,
Against this spoke and firmly took his stand:
"Sirs, she is not a prisoner of war!
I know not what you want this lady for,
But for my part, you can go back and tell
Your friends, we have no women here to sell!"

27

You can't imagine what a stir this made,
For all the folk blazed up like straw on fire;
Their luck against them in this matter played,
They got their wish and their confusion dire.
"Hector," they said, "what's this that you require,
To shield this woman and cause us thus to lose
Antenor, whom you should the rather choose,

28

"Who is so wise and of such great renown,
And we have need of men, as you can see,
And he among the greatest in this town!
O Hector, let such foolish fancies be!
And Priam, king of Troy, hear our decree,
That we will have Antenor, yes or no,
And Cressida to her Greek friends may go!"

29

O Juvenal, how truly thou didst say,
The people never know for what they seek,
For what they want seems right in every way,
And clouds of error ever render weak
Their judgments, in whate'er they do or speak;
For though Antenor now had every voice,
In time the Trojans shall repent their choice.

30

For later his own city he betrayed!
Alas, they brought him back to Troy too soon!
O foolish world, with error over-laid!
Poor harmless Cressida they now repugn,
And now her song of joy must change its tune,
For now to have Antenor all are bound,
And she must go, declare both hare and hound.

31

And so it was decreed in parliament,
At end of much debate and wild uproar,
And thus announced there by their president,
Though Hector did this action much deplore;
But finally he could do nothing more,
For folk and all in this were quite agreed,
And by the parliament it was decreed.

32

Discussion ended, home the Trojans went,
And Troilus, as well, with footsteps slow,
And then about their tasks his men he sent,
While he into his chamber straight did go;
But first he told his men, to hide his woe,
That he would rest and sleep an hour or two,
And on his lonely bed himself he threw.

He wolde late hem graunte what hem leste,
And telle his lady first what that they mente.
And whan that she had seyd him hir entente,
Ther-after wolde he werken also blyve,
Though al the world ayein it wolde stryve.

26

Ector, which that wel the Grekes herde,
For Antenor how they wolde han Criseyde,
Gan it withstonde, and sobrely answerde:—
"Sires, she nis no prisoner," he seyde;
"I noot on yow who that this charge leyde,
But, on my part, ye may eft-sone him telle,
We usen here no wommen for to selle."

27

The noyse of peple up-stirte thanne at ones,
As breme as blase of straw y-set on fyre;
For infortune it wolde, for the nones,
They sholden hir confusioun desyre.
"Ector," quod they, "what goost may yow enspyre,
This womman thus to shilde and doon us lese
Daun Antenor?—a wrong wey now ye chese—

28

That is so wys, and eek so bold baroun,
And we han nede of folk, as men may see;
He is eek oon, the grettest of this toun;
O Ector, lat tho fantasyës be!
O king Pryam," quod they, "thus seggen we,
That al our voys is to for-gon Criseyde";
And to deliveren Antenor they preyde.

29

O Juvenal, lord! trewe is thy sentence,
That litel witen folk what is to yerne
That they ne finde in hir desyr offence;
For cloud of errour lat hem not descerne
What best is; and lo, here ensample as yerne.
This folk desiren now deliveraunce
Of Antenor, that broughte hem to mischaunce!

30

For he was after traytour to the toun
Of Troye; allas! they quitte him out to rathe;
O nyce world, lo, thy discrecioun!
Criseyde, which that never dide hem skathe,
Shal now no lenger in hir blisse bathe;
But Antenor, he shal com hoom to toune,
And she shal out: thus seyden here and howne.

31

For which delibered was by parlement,
For Antenor to yelden up Criseyde,
And it pronounced by the president,
Al-theigh that Ector "nay" ful ofte preyde.
And fynaly, what wight that it withseyde,
It was for nought; it moste been, and sholde;
For substaunce of the parlement it wolde.

32

Departed out of parlement echone,
This Troilus, with-oute wordes mo,
Un-to his chaumbre spedde him faste allone,
But-if it were a man of his or two,
The whiche he bad out faste for to go,
By-cause he wolde slepen, as he seyde,
And hastely up-on his bed him leyde.

33

And as in winter leves been biraft,
Eche after other, til the tree be bare,
So that ther nis but bark and braunche y-laft,
Lyth Troilus, biraft of ech wel-fare,
Y-bounden in the blake bark of care,
Disposed wood out of his wit to breyde,
So sore him sat the chaunginge of Criseyde.

34

He rist him up, and every dore he shette
And windowe eek, and tho this sorweful man
Up-on his beddes syde a-doun him sette,
Ful lyk a deed image pale and wan;
And in his brest the heped wo bigan
Out-breste, and he to werken in this wyse
In his woodnesse, as I shal you devyse.

35

Right as the wilde bole biginneth springe
Now here, now there, y-darted to the herte,
And of his deeth roreth in compleyninge,
Right so gan he aboute the chaumbre sterte,
Smyting his brest ay with his festes smerte;
His heed to the wal, his body to the grounde
Ful ofte he swapte, him-selven to confounde.

36

His eyen two, for pitee of his herte,
Out stremeden as swifte wells tweye;
The heighe sobbes of his sorwes smerte
His speche him rafte, unnethes mighte he seye,
"O deeth, allas! why niltow do me deye?
A-cursed be the day which that nature
Shoop me to ben a lyves creature!"

37

But after, whan the furie and the rage
Which that his herte twiste and faste threste,
By lengthe of tyme somwhat gan asswage,
Up-on his bed he leyde him doun to reste;
But tho bigonne his teres more out-breste,
That wonder is, the body may suffyse
To half this wo, which that I yow devyse.

38

Than seyde he thus, "Fortune! allas the whyle!
What have I doon, what have I thus a-gilt?
How mightestow for reuthe me bigyle?
Is ther no grace, and shal I thus be spilt?
Shal thus Criseyde awey, for that thou wilt?
Allas! how maystow in thyn herte finde
To been to me thus cruel and unkinde?

39

Have I thee nought honoured al my lyve,
As thou wel wost, above the goddes alle?
Why wiltow me fro joye thus depryve?
O Troilus, what may men now thee calle
But wrecche of wrecches, out of honour falle
In-to miserie, in which I wol biwayle
Criseyde, allas! til that the breeth me fayle?

40

Allas, Fortune! if that my lyf in joye
Displesed hadde un-to thy foule envye,
Why ne haddestow my fader, king of Troye,
By-raft the lyf, or doon my bretheren dye,
Or slayn my-self, that thus compleyne and crye,

33

And as the leaves in winter blow away,
By one and one, leaving the tree all bare,
And only bark and branch the winds withstay,
So now unhappy Troilus doth fare,
Close bound within the dismal bark of care,
And wild with fear lest he dare not refuse
The vote by which he Cressida must lose.

34

Then up he rose and fastened every door,
And window, too, and then this wretched man
Upon his bedside sat him down once more,
And sat as still as any image can,
And looked as wan, until his woe began
At last to break forth in a raging storm,
And how he acted, I shall you inform.

35

Not otherwise than as the fierce wild bull
Doth roar and leap and spring, when from his heart
The huntsman forth the fatal spear doth pull,
So Troilus doth from his bedside start,
And beat his breast, and here and yonder dart,
Striking his head full hard against the wall,
And to the floor his body oft doth fall.

36

His eyes for very sorrow turned to fountains,
From which the tears in double streamlets well,
And from his breast, as if from bursting mountains,
The sobs broke forth, scarce leaving breath to tell
His grief. "O death," he said, "thou traitor fell,
Why must I stay alive who curse the day
That I was born this hapless part to play!"

37

But when the fury and the blinding rage
Which thus his heart afflicted and oppressed,
With time began a little to assuage,
Upon his bed he laid him down to rest,
And now the flood of tears attained its crest;
It was a marvel that the body could
Endure the woe and grief in which he stood.

38

"O Fortune," he exclaimed, "alas the while!
What have I done? What crime have I committed?
How didst thou have the heart me to beguile?
Shall I by thee be evermore outwitted?
Must thou so strong 'gainst Cressida be pitted?
Alas, that thou, so cruel and unkind,
Shouldst towards me cherish such a hostile mind!

39

"To honor thee do I not ever strive,
Above the other Gods and powers all?
Why dost thou of my blessing me deprive?
O Troilus, well may mankind thee call
Most wretched of all wretches, who dost fall
To such a depth, in which thou must bewail
Lost Cressida, till thy last breath shall fail.

40

"Fortune, alas, was it for my delight
In love that I have lost thy favor high?
Why didst thou not my father in despite
Deprive of life, or let my brother die,
Or me myself, who on thee thus do cry?

I, cumber-world, whose happy days are sped,
Forever dying, yet never fully dead!

41

"If Cressida alone to me were left,
I'd care not, Fortune, what course you might steer!
But of my love you have me now bereft,
For 'tis your way, to keep man still in fear,
To rob him of the one he holds most dear.
You prove your strength by wanton violence,
And thus I'm lost, all hopeless of defence.

42

"O Lord of love! O very God on high!
Thou knowest best my heart and all my thought;
What shall I do my life to occupy,
If I forego what I so dear have bought?
Since thou my love and me hast safely brought
Into thy hand, and both our hearts hast sealed,
How could thy act then ever be repealed?

43

"What shall I do? And shall I never master
The living torment and the cruel pain
Of this so unforeseen and great disaster?
Alone in solitude let me complain,
And never see it shine or see it rain,
But in the dark, like Oedipus of old,
End both my life and sorrows manifold!

44

"O weary spirit, wandering to and fro,
When wilt thou seek elsewhere a place of rest
And let this body to destruction go?
O lurking soul, fly forth from out thy nest!
Abandon this sad heart and weary breast,
And follow Cressida, thy lady dear,
For now thy proper home no more is here.

45

"O weary eyes, since all your bliss and joy
Was but in Cressida's reflected light,
What will ye do, since I cannot employ
You as I would, but weep out all your sight?
Since she is quenched who was my lamp so bright,
From this time forth, my eyes are but in vain,
And all their virtue can me nothing gain.

46

"O Cressida, my sovereign lady dear,
Unto this grieving soul that thus doth cry,
Who shall give comfort when thou art not here?
Alas, no one! But when my heart shall die,
My spirit straight to thee alone shall fly,
To serve thee as thy everlasting slave,
While I shall lie forgotten in my grave.

47

"O all ye lovers, high upon the wheel
Of Fortune set in joy and bliss secure,
God grant that ye may find your love of steel,
And may your joyous life full long endure;
And when ye come upon my sepulture,
Remember that your comrade resteth there,
For I loved, too, though sorrow was my share.

48

"O, old, enfeebled, mis-behaving man—
Calchas I mean—what wickedness led thee
To leave thy Troy and join the Grecian clan?

I, combre-world, that may of no-thing serve,
But ever dye, and never fully sterve?

41

If that Criseyde allone were me laft,
Nought roughte I whider thou woldest me stere;
And hir, allas! than hastow me biraft.
But ever-more, lo! this is thy manere,
To reve a wight that most is to him dere,
To preve in that thy gerful violence.
Thus am I lost, ther helpeth no defence.

42

O verray lord of love, O god, allas!
That knowest best myn herte and al my thought,
What shal my sorwful lyf don in this cas
If I for-go that I so dere have bought?
Sin ye Cryseyde and me han fully brought
In-to your grace, and bothe our hertes seled,
How may ye suffre, allas! it be repeled?

43

What I may doon, I shal, whyl I may dure
On lyve in torment and in cruel peyne,
This infortune or this disaventure,
Allone as I was born, y-wis, compleyne;
Ne never wil I seen it shyne or reyne;
But ende I wil, as Edippe, in derknesse
My sorwful lyf, and dyen in distresse.

44

O wery goost, that errest to and fro,
Why niltow fleen out of the wofulleste
Body, that ever mighte on grounde go?
O soule, lurkinge in this wo, unneste,
Flee forth out of myn herte, and lat it breste,
And folwe alwey Criseyde, thy lady dere;
Thy righte place is now no lenger here!

45

O wofulle eyen two, sin your disport
Was al to seen Criseydes eyen brighte,
What shal ye doon but, for my discomfort,
Stonden for nought, and wepen out your sighte?
Sin she is queynt, that wont was yow to lighte,
In veyn fro-this-forth have I eyen tweye
Y-formed, sin your vertue is a-weye.

46

O my Criseyde, O lady sovereyne
Of thilke woful soule that thus cryeth,
Who shal now yeven comfort to my peyne?
Allas, no wight; but when myn herte dyeth,
My spirit, which that so un-to yow hyeth,
Receyve in gree, for that shal ay yow serve;
For-thy no fors is, though the body sterve.

47

O ye loveres, that heighe upon the wheel
Ben set of Fortune, in good aventure,
God leve that ye finde ay love of steel,
And longe mot your lyf in joye endure!
But whan ye comen by my sepulture,
Remembreth that your felawe resteth there;
For I lovede eek, though I unworthy were.

48

O olde unholsom and mislyved man,
Calkas I mene, allas! what eyleth thee
To been a Greek, sin thou art born Trojan?

O Calkas, which that wilt my bane be,
In cursed tyme was thou born for me!
As wolde blisful Jove, for his joye,
That I thee hadde, where I wolde, in Troye!"

49

A thousand sykes, hottere than the glede,
Out of his brest ech after other wente,
Medled with pleyntes newe, his wo to fede,
For which his woful teres never stente;
And shortly, so his peynes him to-rente,
And wex so mat, that joye nor penaunce
He feleth noon, but lyth forth in a traunce.

50

Pandare, which that in the parlement
Hadde herd what every lord and burgeys seyde,
And how ful graunted was, by oon assent,
For Antenor to yelden so Criseyde,
Gan wel neigh wood out of his wit to breyde,
So that, for wo, he niste what he mente;
But in a rees to Troilus he wente.

51

A certeyn knight, that for the tyme kepte
The chaumbre-dore, un-dide it him anoon;
And Pandare, that ful tendreliche wepte,
In-to the derke chaumbre, as stille as stoon,
Toward the bed gan softely to goon,
So confus, that he niste what to seye;
For verray wo his wit was neigh aweye.

52

And with his chere and loking al to-torn,
For sorwe of this, and with his armes folden,
He stood this woful Troilus biforn,
And on his pitous face he gan biholden;
But lord, so often gan his herte colden,
Seing his freend in wo, whos hevinesse
His herte slow, as thoughte him for distresse.

53

This woful wight, this Troilus, that felte
His freend Pandare y-comen him to see,
Gan as the snow ayein the sonne melte,
For which this sorwful Pandare, of pitee,
Gan for to wepe as tendreliche as he;
And specheles thus been thise ilke tweye,
That neyther mighte o word for sorwe seye.

54

But at the laste this woful Troilus,
Ney deed for smert, gan bresten out to rore,
And with a sorwful noyse he seyde thus,
Among his sobbes and his sykes sore,
"Lo! Pandare, I am deed, with-outen more.
Hastow nought herd at parlement," he seyde,
"For Antenor how lost is my Criseyde?"

55

This Pandarus, ful deed and pale of hewe,
Ful pitously answerde and seyde, "yis!
As wisly were it fals as it is trewe,
That I have herd, and wot al how it is.
O mercy, god, who wolde have trowed this?
Who wolde have wend that, in so litel a throwe,
Fortune our joye wolde han over-throwe?

56

For in this world ther is no creature,

O Calchas, thou my fatal bane wilt be,
For thou wast born to be a curse to me!
O would that Jove would grant the happy hour
That thou wert here in Troy and in my power!"

49

A thousand sighs as hot as glowing embers
Forth from his breast in swift succession rise,
When thus his sorrows freshly he remembers;
And streams of burning tears break from his eyes,
The burden of his heart to signalize,
Till nature yielding to the heavy stress
Of grief, he lies in dim unconsciousness.

50

Now Pandar likewise at the parliament
Had heard what every lord and burgess said,
And how with one opinion they assent
That Cressida should to the Greeks be led,
And straightway he completely lost his head;
So shocked he was, his wits went all astray,
And off to Troilus he rushed away.

51

A certain knight who kept the chamber door
Permitted him to enter in the room,
And Pandar, weeping silently but sore,
Slipped in the chamber, dark as any tomb,
And to the bed he went in silent gloom,
So deeply agitated and dismayed,
One word he could not summon to his aid.

52

His heart by pity and compassion torn,
He stands, and on his breast his arms doth fold,
And gazes thus on Troilus forlorn,
Whose face a dreadful thing is to behold;
And Pandar feels his very heart grow cold
At sight of him thus prostrate in despair
Whose great affliction he would gladly share.

53

And Troilus, reviving when he felt
That Pandar was come there with sympathy,
Began like snow against the sun to melt,
And down their cheeks the tears ran copiously
Of these two comrades in adversity;
Yet speechless stood they there, these weeping two,
Nor yet had thought of anything to do.

54

But finally this woful Troilus,
Half dead with sorrow, burst out in a roar,
And with a strangely sounding voice spoke thus,
Mid sobs and moans and other noises more:
"The world hath nothing now for me in store!
Hast thou not heard how by parliament,
Away from Troy my Cressida is sent?"

55

And Pandar, ghastly now and pale of hue,
Most pitifully spoke and answered, "Yes!
Would God it were as false as it is true!
I've heard it all, and must it all confess!
This end, O how could any person guess!
Who would have thought with such a sudden fling
Fortune our joy to this sad end would bring!

56

"In all this world no creature ever saw

Ruin so sudden and so undesigned,
So strange and utterly beyond all law!
But every accident can't be divined—
So goes the world! This lesson here I find,
Let no man think that he's exceptional,
For Fortune will desert us one and all.

57

"But tell me why you thus beyond all reason
Lament and lie upon your bed supine,
For had you not your joy in its good season?
Give thanks for joy, yourself to loss resign!
But I that ne'er in love, as thou in thine
Hast prospered, nor ever knew a friendly eye,
'Tis I who might thus weep and wail and sigh!

58

"And here's another thing—I dare aver
This town is full of ladies round about,
Fairer indeed than any twelve like her;
And if you want me, I can pick one out,
Yes, more than one or two, without a doubt.
Be glad, therefore, my own dear chosen brother,
If she is lost, why, we can get another.

59

"The Lord forbid that you should never glance
At things which have not been your chief delight!
If one can sing, another well can dance!
One may be fair, another gay and bright,
And virtue lack of beauty may requite!
Each by her excellences should be measured,
For heroner and falcon both are treasured.

60

"As Zanzis wrote, who was so very wise,
A new love expediteth oft the old.
Adapt yourself as new conditions rise,
And ever on your heart maintain your hold;
No fire so hot but time will make it cold;
And since all pleasures are but accidental,
New accidents are nothing detrimental.

61

"For just as sure as day comes after night,
Some new love, some new task, or some new woe,
Or even seldom having her in sight,
These all assist affections old to go.
And one of these you're bound to have, you know,
For out of sight, she'll soon be out of mind,
Whereby new comfort you shall quickly find."

62

These wise and cheering words good Pandar spoke
To help his friend as helpless he there lay,
As one who any measures would invoke,
No matter how much nonsense he might say.
But Troilus did slight attention pay
To all this rigmarole or what it meant,
In one and out the other ear it went.

63

At last he said, as on his arm he leaned,
"This medicine and cure proposed by you,
Were well enough if I were but a fiend!
Be false to Cressida, to me so true!
That's something, Pandar, I shall never do!
But slay me rather here upon the spot
Than I should add this shame to my sad lot.

As to my doom, that ever saw ruyne
Straungere than this, thorugh cas or aventure.
But who may al eschewe or al devyne?
Swich is this world; for-thy I thus defyne,
Ne truste no wight finden in Fortune
Ay propretee; hir yeftes been comune.

57

But tel me this, why thou art now so mad
To sorwen thus? Why lystow in this wyse,
Sin thy desyr al holly hastow had,
So that, by right, it oughte y-now suffyse?
But I, that never felte in my servyse
A frendly chere or loking of an yë,
Lat me thus wepe and wayle, til I dye.

58

And over al this, as thou wel wost thy-selve,
This town is ful of ladies al aboute;
And, to my doom, fairer than swiche twelve
As ever she was, shal I finde, in som route,
Ye, oon or two, with-outen any doute.
For-thy be glad, myn owene dere brother,
If she be lost, we shul recovere another.

59

What, god for-bede alwey that ech plesaunce
In o thing were, and in non other wight!
If oon can singe, another can wel daunce;
If this be goodly, she is glad and light;
And this is fayr, and that can good a-right.
Ech for his vertu holden is for dere,
Bothe heroner and faucon for rivere.

60

And eek, as writ Zanzis, that was ful wys,
'The newe love out chaceth ofte the olde';
And up-on newe cas lyth newe avys.
Thenk eek, thy-self to saven artow holde;
Swich fyr, by proces, shal of kinde colde.
For sin it is but casuel plesaunce,
Som cas shal putte it out of remembraunce.

61

For al-so seur as day cometh after night,
The newe love, labour or other wo,
Or elles selde seinge of a wight,
Don olde affecciouns alle over-go.
And, for thy part, thou shalt have oon of tho
To abrigge with thy bittre peynes smerte;
Absence of hir shal dryve hir out of herte."

62

Thise wordes seyde he for the nones alle,
To helpe his freend, lest he for sorwe deyde.
For doutelees, to doon his wo to falle,
He roughte not what unthrift that he seyde.
But Troilus, that neigh for sorwe deyde,
Tok litel hede of al that ever he mente;
Oon ere it herde, at the other out it wente:—

63

But at the laste answerde and seyde, "freend,
This lechecraft, or heled thus to be,
Were wel sitting, if that I were a feend,
To traysen hir that trewe is unto me!
I pray god, lat this consayl never y-thee;
But do me rather sterve anon-right here
Er I thus do as thou me woldest lere.

64

She that I serve, y-wis, what so thou seye,
To whom myn herte enhabit is by right,
Shal han me holly hires til that I deye.
For, Pandarus, sin I have trouthe hir hight,
I wol not been untrewe for no wight;
But as hir man I wol ay live and sterve,
And never other creature serve.

65

And ther thou seyst, thou shalt as faire finde
As she, lat be, make no comparisoun
To creature y-formed here by kinde.
O leve Pandare, in conclusioun,
I wol not be of thyn opinioun,
Touching al this; for whiche I thee biseche,
So hold thy pees; thou sleest me with thy speche.

66

Thow biddest me I sholde love another
Al freshly newe, and lat Criseyde go!
It lyth not in my power, leve brother.
And though I mighte, I wolde not do so.
But canstow pleyen raket, to and fro,
Netle in, dokke out, now this, now that, Pandare?
Now foule falle hir, for thy wo that care!

67

Thow farest eek by me, thou Pandarus,
As he, that whan a wight is wo bi-goon,
He cometh to him a pas, and seyth right thus,
'Thenk not on smert, and thou shalt fele noon.'
Thou most me first transmuwen in a stoon,
And reve me my passiounes alle,
Er thou so lightly do my wo to falle.

68

The deeth may wel out of my brest departe
The lyf, so longe may this sorwe myne;
But fro my soule shal Criseydes darte
Out never-mo; but doun with Proserpyne,
Whan I am deed, I wol go wone in pyne;
And ther I wol eternally compleyne
My wo, and how that twinned be we tweyne.

69

Thow hast here maad an argument, for fyn,
How that it sholde lasse peyne be
Criseyde to for-goon, for she was myn,
And live in ese and in felicitee.
Why gabbestow, that seydest thus to me
That 'him is wors that is fro welle y-throwe,
Than he hadde erst non of that wele y-knowe?'

70

But tel me now, sin that thee thinketh so light
To chaungen so in love, ay to and fro,
Why hastow not don bisily thy might
To chaungen hir that doth thee al thy wo?
Why niltow lete hir fro thyn herte go?
Why niltow love an-other lady swete,
That may thyn herte setten in quiete?

71

If thou hast had in love ay yet mischaunce,
And canst it not out of thyn herte dryve,
I, that livede in lust and in plesaunce
With hir as muche as creature on-lyve,
How sholde I that foryete, and that so blyve?

64

"I'll serve her still, for all your worldly lore,
To whom my heart is bound by every right,
And shall do so until I breathe no more!
That humble faith which I to her did plight,
That shall I keep, and faith with faith requite;
As her true man I'll be forever bound,
And serve no other on this whole world round.

65

"But when you say that others you can find
As fair as she, compare her not, I pray,
With any creature formed of human kind!
And Pandar dear, I've only this to say
To your advice, and that is plainly, Nay!
And therefore I politely must request
That you will let these other ladies rest.

66

"You counsel me that I should love another,
And start afresh, and Cressida let go!
That lies not in my power, friend and brother!
And if I could, I never would do so.
And if you play the ball thus to and fro,
Now in, now out, now new love ousting old,
What claim on love can you expect to hold!

67

"Indeed what you have said seems thus to me,
As you should tell one sick with ills severe,
Who seeks your aid in his adversity,
'Don't think of pain, and pain will disappear,'—
As though a stone dwelt in my bosom here!
Against all feeling you must me insure
Before such medicine can work a cure.

68

"Let life from out this wretched breast depart,
And with my life, let thus my sorrows end,
Yet Cressida shall hold me, soul and heart,
And down with Proserpina I shall wend,
When heaven this relief to me shall send,
And there I will eternally complain
The bitter woe that cleft us two in twain!

69

"But for that argument of yours so fine,
That resignation lighter grief should be
Because my lady one time has been mine
And we have known the meaning of felicity—
What nonsense! Trulier once you said to me,
His lot is worse who out of joy is thrown
Than his who never any joy hath known.

70

"But tell me, since you take it thus so light,
To change your love and pass aye to and fro,
Why have you never exercised this right,
And left the one who brings you naught but woe?
If love comes light, it may as lightly go!
Why do you not hunt up another love,
And from your heart the cruel old one shove?

71

"If you, who never yet in love fared well,
Forth from your heart your old love cannot drive,
Can I, who once in heaven's joy did dwell
In bliss as great as any man alive,
Can I forget, though earnestly I strive?

O Pandar, tell me where you went to school,
Who argue thus so futilely by rule!

72

"'Tis nothing, Pandar, all that you have said!
I know quite well, whatever may befall,
My soul must now be numbered with the dead!
O death, thou certain end of sorrows all,
Come now, nor bid me oftener on thee call;
For blessed is the death so long time sought
By which an end to pain and grief is brought.

73

"Time was when life on earth to me was sweet,
And death a hateful need and danger dire,
But now his coming I would gladly greet,
For nothing in this world I more desire.
O death, O soul, with anguish set afire,
Let falling tears the flames of sorrow drench,
Or thy cold stroke this mortal fever quench.

74

"O thou, who slayest in such sundry ways,
Against men's wills, unsought, by day or night,
Grant this request to one who humbly prays:
Relieve this world of him who doth but blight
Existence with his sorrows infinite!
The time has come for me to leave this earth,
For fate hath made my life but little worth."

75

Salt tears the eyes of Troilus distil,
Like liquid from alembic falling fast,
And Pandar held his tongue and kept him still,
And downward to the ground his eyes he cast;
This silence, though, could not forever last,
And rather than his friend should pass away,
Pandar was minded something more to say.

76

"Good friend, since you thus dwell in great distress,
And since you find so much in me to blame,
Why don't you make an effort to redress
Your griefs, and strength and manhood thus
proclaim?
Take her by force and hold her so! For shame!
Or either let her go in peace elsewhere,
Or keep her here and banish all your care!

77

"Art thou in Troy, and dost thou lack the nerve
To take a woman who's in love with thee,
And would love more if thou more shouldst deserve?
A greater folly never did I see!
Get up at once, and let thy weeping be,
And show thou art a man, with manly powers,
You'll see that Cressida shall still be ours."

78

To these words Troilus made answer soft
And said, "In truth, my friend and brother dear,
All this I've thought myself, reflecting oft,
And more indeed than you've suggested here;
But many reasons thereagainst appear,
Which I will tell, if you good heed will pay,
And then your own opinion you may say.

79

"You know this town is now involved in war
Because a woman was borne off by force,

O where hastow ben hid so longe in muwe,
That canst so wel and formely arguwe?

72

Nay, nay, god wot, nought worth is al thy reed,
For which, for what that ever may bifalle,
With-outen wordes mo, I wol be deed.
O deeth, that endere art of sorwes alle,
Com now, sin I so ofte after thee calle;
For sely is that deeth, soth for to seyne,
That, ofte y-cleped, cometh and endeth peyne.

73

Wel wot I, whyl my lyf was in quiete,
Er thou me slowe, I wolde have yeven hyre;
But now thy cominge is to me so swete,
That in this world I no-thing so desyre.
O deeth, sin with this sorwe I am a-fyre,
Thou outher do me anoon in teres drenche,
Or with thy colde strook myn hete quenche!

74

Sin that thou sleest so fele in sondry wyse
Ayens hir wil, unpreyed, day and night,
Do me, at my requeste, this servyse,
Delivere now the world, so dostow right,
Of me, that am the wofulleste wight
That ever was; for tyme is that I sterve,
Sin in this world of right nought may I serve."

75

This Troilus in teres gan distille,
As licour out of alambyk ful faste;
And Pandarus gan holde his tunge stille,
And to the ground his eyen doun he caste.
But nathelees, thus thoughte he at the laste,
"What, parde, rather than my felawe deye,
Yet shal I som-what more un-to him seye":

76

And seyde, "freend, sin thou hast swich distresse,
And sin thee list myn arguments to blame,
Why nilt thy-selven helpen doon redresse,
And with thy manhod letten al this
grame?
Go ravisshe hir ne canstow not for shame!
And outher lat hir out of toune fare,
Or hold hir stille, and leve thy nyce fare.

77

Artow in Troye, and hast non hardiment
To take a womman which that loveth thee,
And wolde hir-selven been of thyn assent?
Now is not this a nyce vanitee?
Rys up anoon, and lat this weping be,
And kyth thou art a man, for in this houre
I wil be deed, or she shal bleven oure."

78

To this answerde him Troilus ful softe,
And seyde, "parde, leve brother dere,
Al this have I my-self yet thought ful ofte,
And more thing than thou devysest here.
But why this thing is laft, thou shalt wel here;
And whan thou me hast yeve an audience,
Ther-after mayst thou telle al thy sentence.

79

First, sin thou wost this toun hath al this werre
For ravisshing of wommen so by might,

It sholde not be suffred me to erre,
As it stant now, ne doon so gret unright.
I sholde han also blame of every wight,
My fadres graunt if that I so withstode,
Sin she is chaunged for the tounes goode.

80

I have eek thought, so it were hir assent,
To aske hir at my fader, of his grace;
Than thenke I, this were hir accusement,
Sin wel I woot I may hir not purchace.
For sin my fader, in so heigh a place
As parlement, hath hir eschaunge enseled,
He nil for me his lettre be repeled.

81

Yet drede I most hir herte to pertourbe
With violence, if I do swich a game;
For if I wolde it openly distourbe,
It moste been disclaundre to hir name.
And me were lever deed than hir defame,
As nolde god but-if I sholde have
Hir honour lever than my lyf to save!

82

Thus am I lost, for ought that I can see;
For certeyn is, sin that I am hir knight,
I moste hir honour lever han than me
In every cas, as lovere oughte of right.
Thus am I with desyr and reson twight;
Desyr for to distourben hir me redeth,
And reson nil not, so myn herte dredeth."

83

Thus wepinge that he coude never cesse,
He seyde, "allas! how shal I, wrecche, fare?
For wel fele I alwey my love encresse,
And hope is lasse and lasse alwey, Pandare!
Encressen eek the causes of my care;
So wel-a-wey, why nil myn herte breste?
For, as in love, ther is but litel reste."

84

Pandare answerde, "freend, thou mayst, for me,
Don as thee list; but hadde ich it so hote,
And thyn estat, she sholde go with me;
Though al this toun cryede on this thing by note,
I nolde sette at al that noyse a grote.
For when men han wel cryed, than wol they
roune;
A wonder last but nyne night never in toune.

85

Devyne not in reson ay so depe
Ne curteysly, but help thy-self anoon;
Bet is that othere than thy-selven wepe,
And namely, sin ye two been al oon.
Rys up, for by myn heed, she shal not goon;
And rather be in blame a lyte y-founde
Than sterve here as a gnat, with-oute wounde.

86

It is no shame un-to yow, ne no vyce
Hir to with-holden, that ye loveth most.
Paraunter, she mighte holden thee for nyce
To lete hir go thus to the Grekes ost.
Thenk eek Fortune, as wel thy-selven wost,
Helpeth hardy man to his empryse,
And weyveth wrecches, for hir cowardyse.

And as things stand, 'twould cause a great uproar,
If to such methods I should have recourse;
I'm sure 'twould be a very fruitful source
Of blame, if I my father's act withstood,
Since she's to be exchanged for Troy's own good.

80

"I've also thought, of course with her consent,
To ask my father for her as a favor,
But that to treason were equivalent,
For never would he in his duty waver,
Since in so high a public place he gave her
As parliament, and hath the edict sealed,
Which for his son could scarcely be repealed.

81

"And I'm afraid my lady 'twould disturb
If by such violence I should her claim;
The tongue of the world is very hard to curb,
And it might seem a slander on her name,
And I would rather die than cause her shame.
Her honor I hold dearer in my sight
Than anything beneath the heavens bright.

82

"All hope is lost, for aught that I can see!
For true it is, that as her faithful knight,
Her honor still my first concern must be;
Such service do I owe to her of right.
Desire and Reason in me ever fight;
Desire insists, Let force control the day,
But Reason counsels quite the other way!"

83

He wept as though his tears would never cease,
And said, "Alas, what course shall I pursue?
For all the while I feel my love increase,
And hope grow less and less, as it must do,
Since my distress itself doth still renew.
O heart, why will you not break in my breast!
Alas, a lover's heart hath seldom rest!"

84

"You may," said Pandar, "as far as I'm concerned,
Let your heart break! But were I in so deep,
A man like you, I'd take her, if it turned
The whole town topsy-turvy in a heap.
The more they talked, the stiller you could keep,
And to their hearts' content, just let them
shout,
For nine days always wears a wonder out.

85

"Don't get involved in reasonings too deep
Or precious. Help yourself the first of all!
If some must weep, then let the others weep!
You two are one, you need no aid to call;
Get up, she shall not go, whate'er befall!
For some small blame 'tis better to incur,
Than die here like a gnat and never stir.

86

"Don't call it force, but follow my advice;
Firm action I would call it at the most.
No doubt she'd think that you were over-nice
To let them send her to the Grecian host.
Remember, too, it is no idle boast
That fortune helps the brave in his emprise,
But from the coward wretch she ever flies.

87

"Your lady may at first a little grieve,
But peace with her you easily can make.
To tell the truth, I can't at all believe
That she the very least offence will take.
Why then should you in fear and trembling quake?
You know what Paris did—follow your brother;
What's good for one, is good, too, for another.

88

"And Troilus, this also here I swear,
If Cressida, as we indeed suppose,
An equal love and faith with you doth share,
She'll thank you if she can escape her foes,
No matter what disturbance from it grows;
But on the other hand, if she abandons you,
Then she is false and fickle, through and through.

89

"Take courage then, recall you are a knight!
True love, you know, hath no regard for law.
Exhibit now your valor and your might,
And stand not here in trembling and in awe,
While griefs and fears your very vitals gnaw.
Despise the world and all the planets seven,
And if you die a martyr, go to heaven!

90

"And for your aid, I'll faithfully stand by,
With all my kin, throughout the country round,
Though on the street like dogs we all shall lie,
Stricken with many a wide and bloody wound;
Whatever falls, your friend I shall be found.
But if you'd rather die here like a wretch,
Farewell, to hell the devil may you fetch!"

91

These vigorous words made Troilus revive;
"Enough," he cried, "I give my full assent.
You need no further urge me on, or strive
To speak in terms so stern and vehement.
For here I tell you fully my intent:
Abduct her, that is what I mean to do,
But only so if she consents thereto."

92

"Let that," said Pandar, "be as be it may!
Have you inquiries of her ever made?"
And Troilus could answer naught but "Nay."
"Well, then," said Pandar, "why are you afraid?
You don't know if she'd be at all dismayed
To be abducted! Why then all this fear,
Unless some angel told it in your ear?

93

"Get up, pretend that nothing has occurred,
And wash your face, and on the king attend;
He'll wonder why from you he hasn't heard.
Yourself from all surmise you must defend,
Or unexpected he may sometime send
For you. In short, be glad, my brother dear,
You really haven't anything to fear.

94

"For I shall try to bring it so about,
Tonight you'll see your lady in some way,
And then you two can thresh the whole thing out,
And you can tell from what she has to say,
Just what part each of you must plan and play,

87

And though thy lady wolde a litel hir greve,
Thou shalt thy pees ful wel here-after make,
But as for me, certayn, I can not leve
That she wolde it as now for yvel take.
Why sholde than for ferd thyn herte quake?
Thenk eek how Paris hath, that is thy brother,
A love; and why shaltow not have another?

88

And Troilus, o thing I dar thee swere,
That if Criseyde, whiche that is thy leef,
Now loveth thee as wel as thou dost here,
God helpe me so, she nil not take a-greef,
Though thou do bote a-noon in this mischeef.
And if she wilneth fro thee for to passe,
Thanne is she fals; so love hir wel the lasse.

89

For-thy tak herte, and thenk, right as a knight,
Thourgh love is broken alday every lawe.
Kyth now sumwhat thy corage and thy might,
Have mercy on thy-self, for any awe.
Lat not this wrecched wo thin herte gnawe,
But manly set the world on sixe and sevene;
And, if thou deye a martir, go to hevene.

90

I wol my-self be with thee at this dede,
Though ich and al my kin, up-on a stounde,
Shulle in a strete as dogges liggen dede,
Thourgh-girt with many a wyd and blody wounde.
In every cas I wol a freend be founde.
And if thee list here sterven as a wrecche,
A-dieu, the devel spede him that it recche!"

91

This Troilus gan with tho wordes quiken,
And seyde, "freend, graunt mercy, ich assente;
But certaynly thou mayst not me so priken,
Ne peyne noon ne may me so tormente,
That, for no cas, it is not myn entente,
At shorte wordes, though I dyen sholde,
To ravisshe hir, but-if hir-self it wolde."

92

"Why, so mene I," quod Pandarus, "al this day.
But tel me than, hastow hir wel assayed,
That sorwest thus?" And he answerde, "nay."
"Wher-of artow," quod Pandare, "than a-mayed,
That nost not that she wol ben yvel apayed
To ravisshe hir, sin thou hast not ben there,
But-if that Jove tolde it in thyn ere?

93

For-thy rys up, as nought ne were, anoon,
And wash thy face, and to the king thou wende,
Or he may wondren whider thou art goon.
Thou most with wisdom him and othere blende;
Or, up-on cas, he may after thee sende
Er thou be war; and shortly, brother dere,
Be glad, and lat me werke in this matere.

94

For I shal shape it so, that sikerly
Thou shalt this night som tyme, in som manere,
Com speke with thy lady prevely,
And by hir wordes eek, and by hir chere,
Thou shalt ful sone aparceyve and wel here

Al hir entente, and in this cas the beste;
And fare now wel, for in this point I reste."

95

The swifte Fame, whiche that false thinges
Egal reporteth lyk the thinges trewe,
Was thorugh-out Troye y-fled with preste winges
Fro man to man, and made this tale al newe,
How Calkas doughter, with hir brighte hewe,
At parlement, with-oute wordes more,
I-graunted was in chaunge of Antenore.

96

The whiche tale anoon-right as Criseyde
Had herd, she which that of hir fader roughte,
As in this cas, right nought, ne whanne he deyde,
Ful bisily to Juppiter bisoughte
Yeve him mischaunce that this tretis broughte.
But shortly, lest thise tales sothe were,
She dorste at no wight asken it, for fere;

97

As she that hadde hir herte and al hir minde
On Troilus y-set so wonder faste,
That al this world ne mighte hir love unbinde,
Ne Troilus out of hir herte caste;
She wol ben his, whyl that hir lyf may laste.
And thus she brenneth bothe in love and drede,
So that she niste what was best to rede.

98

But as men seen in toune, and al aboute,
That wommen usen frendes to visyte,
So to Criseyde of wommen com a route
For pitous joye, and wenden hir delyte;
And with hir tales, dere y-nough a myte,
These wommen, whiche that in the cite dwelle,
They sette hem doun, and seyde as I shal telle.

99

Quod first that oon, "I am glad, trewely,
By-cause of yow, that shal your fader see."
A-nother seyde, "y-wis, so nam not I;
For al to litel hath she with us be."
Quod tho the thridde, "I hope, y-wis, that she
Shal bringen us the pees on every syde,
That, whan she gooth, almighty god hir gyde!"

100

Tho wordes and tho wommannisshe thinges,
She herde hem right as though she thennes were;
For, god it wot, hir herte on other thing is,
Although the body sat among hem there.
Hir advertence is alwey
elles-where;
For Troilus ful faste hir soule soughte;
With-outen word, alwey on him she thoughte.

101

Thise wommen, that thus wenden hir to plese,
Aboute nought gonne alle hir tales spende;
Swich vanitee ne can don hir non ese,
As she that, al this mene whyle, brende
Of other passioun than that they wende,
So that she felte almost hir herte dye
For wo, and wery of that companye.

102

For which no lenger mighte she restreyne
Hir teres, so they gonnen up to welle,

And so decide what action seems the best.
Farewell, for at this point I pause and rest."

95

Swift Rumor, which repeateth untrue things
With equal speed as she repeateth true,
Had flown through Troy, with ever-ready wings,
From man to man, to tell this marvel new,
How Calchas' daughter, fair and bright of hue,
By sentence passed in highest parliament,
Forth to her ancient father should be sent.

96

To Cressida arrived this dreadful news,
But on her father she had little thought,
Except he could go hang when he might choose;
And Jupiter she earnestly besought
To curse the hour which this bad luck had brought;
But if the news that thus came to her ear
Were true or not, she dared not ask for fear.

97

For she had set her heart and mind
On Troilus long since, so firm and fast,
That all the world her love might not unbind,
Or Troilus from out her bosom cast,
For she was his, as long as life shall last.
And thus distracted both by love and terror,
She scarce could tell the truth apart from error.

98

It is the common custom in each land
For ladies to indulge in calls polite,
And now there came to Cressida a band,
Both glad and sad, as seemed to them but right;
And with their gossipings unwelcome quite,
These ladies, who in hapless Troy did dwell,
They sat them down and said as I shall tell.

99

"O, I'm so glad," the one of them doth cry,
"That now your father you so soon shall see!"
Another said, "Indeed, so am not I,
For all too little now in Troy she'll be!"
"Indeed I hope," the third one said, "that she
Shall bring us happy peace on every side,
And when she goes, may heaven be her guide!"

100

These words, and other female blandishments,
She hears, but in her thoughts they have no share;
Another picture quite her heart presents,
Although in body she is sitting there.
God knows her thought and mind are placed
elsewhere,
And Troilus alone her spirit sought,
For whom she had no words, but all her thought.

101

These ladies with no wish but how to please,
Their breath in idle gossiping expend,
Wherein poor Cressida can find no ease,
Nor with her burning heart thereto attend
Scarce long enough a courteous ear to lend;
She felt that she was ready to expire,
With all this talk that doth her bore and tire.

102

And in the end, she might no more restrain
Her tears, for upward they began to well

As signs of all the inward bitter pain
In which her wretched spirit now must dwell,
Reflecting from what heaven to what hell
She fallen was, since she hath lost the joy
That she had known with Troilus in Troy.

103

And all the silly fools that sat about
Supposed she wept and sighed so long and sore,
Because from Troy she soon must now set out,
And their society enjoy no more!
And all the ladies there, almost a score,
They saw her weep, and loved her tender heart,
And in the weeping all of them took part.

104

And all endeavored with her to condole,
But little knew the things of which she thought,
Or what alone could cheer her and console;
And to be glad they often her besought,
Which to her grief such mitigation brought
As for a splitting headache one might feel
If one were kindly rubbed upon the heel.

105

When they had said all they could think to say,
They took their leave and home departed all,
And Cressida, oppressed with sad dismay,
Into her chamber went from out the hall,
And like one dead, upon her bed doth fall,
Borne down by all this heavy weight of grief,
From which she saw no prospect of relief.

106

The bitter tears from out her eyes down pour,
Like April showers falling full and fast;
Her breast so white she beat, and evermore
She called on death to take her at the last,
Such heavy sorrow now her soul harassed,
Her lover lost, who was her only hope,
Forlorn in black despair so left to grope.

107

Her rippling hair, as golden as the sun,
She tore, and wrung her hands with fingers small,
But no relief from sorrow thus she won,
Nor yet from death, on whom she oft doth call;
Her hue so bright lay hidden neath a pall,
In testimony of this hard distraint,
And thus with sobs she uttered this sad plaint:

108

"Alas, sent forth from out my home and nation,
I, woful wretch, bereft of all delight,
And born beneath a cursed constellation,
Must now depart from my beloved's sight!
Woe worth the day, and specially the night,
When first I saw him with my eyes so plain,
Who causes me, as I cause him, such pain!

109

"What shall he do? And what indeed shall I?
How shall I now my life anew begin?
And O, dear heart, for whom I'd gladly die,
Who shall relieve the sorrow you are in?
O Calchas, father, thine is all this sin!
I curse the day my mother dear, Argive,
Brought me into this wretched world
alive!

That yeven signes of the bitter peyne
In whiche hir spirit was, and moste dwelle;
Remembring hir, fro heven unto which helle
She fallen was, sith she forgoth the sighte
Of Troilus, and sorowfully she sighte.

103

And thilke foles sittinge hir aboute
Wenden, that she wepte and syked sore
By-cause that she sholde out of that route
Departe, and never pleye with hem more.
And they that hadde y-knowen hir of yore
Seye hir so wepe, and thoughte it kindenesse,
And eche of hem wepte eek for hir distresse;

104

And bisily they gonnen hir conforten
Of thing, god wot, on which she litel thoughte;
And with hir tales wenden hir disporten,
And to be glad they often hir bisoughte.
But swich an ese ther-with they hir wroughte
Right as a man is esed for to fele,
For ache of heed, to clawen him on his hele!

105

But after al this nyce vanitee
They took hir leve, and hoom they wenten alle.
Criseyde, ful of sorweful pitee,
In-to hir chaumbre up wente out of the halle,
And on hir bed she gan for deed to falle,
In purpos never thennes for to ryse;
And thus she wroughte, as I shal yow devyse.

106

Therwith the teres from hir eyen two
Doun fille, as shour in Aperill, ful swythe;
Hir whyte brest she bet, and for the wo
After the deeth she cryed a thousand sythe,
Sin he that wont hir wo was for to lythe,
She mot for-goon; for which disaventure
She held hir-self a forlost creature.

107

Hir ounded heer, that sonnish was of hewe,
She rente, and eek hir fingres longe and smale
She wrong ful ofte, and bad god on hir rewe,
And with the deeth to doon bote on hir bale.
Hir hewe, whylom bright, that tho was pale,
Bar witnes of hir wo and hir constreynte;
And thus she spak, sobbinge, in hir compleynte:

108

"Alas!" quod she, "out of this regioun
I, woful wrecche and infortuned wight,
And born in corsed constellacioun,
Mot goon, and thus departen fro my knight;
Wo worth, allas! that ilke dayes light
On which I saw him first with eyen tweyne,
That causeth me, and I him, al this peyne!"

109

She seyde, "how shal he doon, and I also?
How sholde I live, if that I from him twinne?
O dere herte eek, that I love so,
Who shal that sorwe sleen that ye ben inne?
O Calkas, fader, thyn be al this sinne!
O moder myn, that cleped were Argyve,
Wo worth that day that thou me bere on
lyve!

110

To what fyn sholde I live and sorwen thus?
How sholde a fish with-oute water dure?
What is Criseyde worth, from Troilus?
How sholde a plaunte or lyves creature
Live, with-oute his kinde noriture?
For which ful oft a by-word here I seye,
That, 'rotelees, mot grene sone deye.'

111

I shal don thus, sin neither swerd ne darte
Dar I non handle, for the crueltee,
That ilke day that I from yow departe,
If sorwe of that nil not my bane be,
Than shal no mete or drinke come in me
Til I my soule out of my breste unshethe;
And thus my-selven wol I do to dethe.

112

And, Troilus, my clothes everichoon
Shul blake been, in tokeninge, herte swete,
That I am as out of this world agoon,
That wont was yow to setten in quiete;
And of myn ordre, ay til deeth me mete,
The observaunce ever, in your absence,
Shal sorwe been, compleynte, and abstinence.

113

Myn herte and eek the woful goost ther-inne
Biquethe I, with your spirit to compleyne
Eternally, for they shul never twinne.
For though in erthe y-twinned be we tweyne,
Yet in the feld of pitee, out of peyne,
That hight Elysos, shul we been y-fere,
As Orpheus and Erudice his fere.

114

Thus herte myn, for Antenor, allas!
I sone shal be chaunged, as I wene.
But how shul ye don in this sorwful cas,
How shal your tendre herte this sustene?
But herte myn, for-yet this sorwe and tene,
And me also; for, soothly for to seye,
So ye wel fare, I recche not to deye."

115

How mighte it ever y-red ben or y-songe,
The pleynte that she made in hir distresse?
I noot; but, as for me, my litel tonge,
If I discreven wolde hir hevinesse,
It sholde make hir sorwe seme lesse
Than that it was, and childishly deface
Hir heigh compleynte, and therfore I it pace.

116

Pandare, which that sent from Troilus
Was to Criseyde, as ye han herd devyse,
That for the beste it was accorded thus,
And he ful glad to doon him that servyse,
Un-to Criseyde, in a ful secree wyse,
Ther-as she lay in torment and in rage,
Com hir to telle al hoolly his message.

117

And fond that she hir-selven gan to trete
Ful pitously; for with hir salte teres
Hir brest, hir face y-bathed was ful wete;
The mighty tresses of hir sonnish heres,

110

"To what end should I live and sorrow thus?
Shall fishes without water long endure?
What worth is Cressida if Troilus
Is gone? For must not every plant procure
Its proper food, existence to assure?
Many a time I've heard the old wives say,
'Withdrawn from earth, things green all pass away.'

111

"And now, since either sword or pointed dart
Would be a rather cruel end for me,
The day that I from Troilus depart,
If simple grief my slayer will not be,
From that day on, all food and drink I'll flee,
Until my soul shall breathe its final breath,
Starvation bringing me a welcome death.

112

"And Troilus, let me be dressed in black,
In tokening, my precious sweetheart dear,
That I am gone and never can come back,
Who once was all your consolation here.
And so I'll live, till I lie on my bier,
As one from whom joy doth itself absent,
In sorrow, solitude and deep lament.

113

"My heart and soul and all that dwells therein,
Bequeathe I with your spirit to remain
Eternally, for each is other's twin.
And though on earth we parted were in twain,
Yet in that blessed field, all freed from pain,
Where Pluto rules, we shall together be,
As Orpheus was with his Eurydice.

114

"Thus, sweetheart, by a stern decree of state,
Troy must I leave and with the Greeks abide,
And how canst thou survive this dreadful fate?
Why should this grief your tender heart betide?
But sweetheart mine, forget this woe so wide,
And me as well! For truly I can say,
If you are happy, let me go my way!"

115

Who might, as I cannot, the tale have sung
Which plaintively she made of her distress?
But as for me and for my feeble tongue,
In that attempt, I'd have such slight success
'Twould make her sorrows seem far less
Than they should seem, and weakly would I show
Her high lament, and so I let it go.

116

As emissary sent by Troilus
To Cressida, as you have heard me say,
And as before it was agreed on thus,
The first step in the plans that they would lay,
Came Pandar now, by some quite secret way,
Prepared his message wholly to explain
To her reclined upon her couch of pain.

117

Poor Cressida, she was a woful sight,
Her breasts tear-stained with falling drops that made
Their way unheeded down her cheeks so white!
Her golden hair in bright disorder strayed

About her ears, escaped from out its braid,
Undoubted signal of the martyrdom
Of death, which none too soon for her may come.

118

At sight of him, she strove for shame anon
Her tearful face behind her arms to hide,
At which good Pandar was so woe-begone,
He scarcely in the chamber might abide,
At her sad look he was so horrified;
And now her flood of woe broke out anew
And by release a thousandfold it grew.

119

Then thus with words to sorrow she gave voice:
"My uncle Pandar, cause of causes first
That in the light of love I did rejoice,
My joy to sudden woe is now reversed!
Shouldst thou be welcomed here or be accursed,
Who thus hast guided me in love's emprise,
To end, alas, in this so wretched wise!

120

"Must love then end in woe? Yes, or men lie,
And every worldly joy, it seems to me,
For grief the place of joy must occupy!
And he who doubts if such the end must be,
Let him behold my grievous fate and see
How I from bad must ever pass to worse,
And thus am led my hateful birth to curse.

121

"Who looks at me, beholdeth sorrows all,
All pain, all torture, woe and all distress;
I have no need on other harms to call,
As anguish, languor, cruel bitterness,
Discomfort, dread, and madness more and less;
Methinks from heaven above the tears must rain
In pity for my harsh and cruel pain."

122

"I grant, dear lady, that your lot is hard,"
Said Pandar, "yet what do you plan to do?
For to yourself you should have more regard,
And not some vain and useless course pursue;
But now I want to say a word or two—
A message I must briefly now present
From Troilus, whose heart with pain is rent."

123

Her face she turned to him, so deathly pale,
It was a most distressing sight to see.
"Alas," she said, "can words for aught avail?
What can my precious sweetheart say to me
Since we are lost through all eternity?
Will he have news of all the tears I've shed?
They are enough, at least that can be said."

124

Her grief exacts from her a dreadful price,
She looks like one to her last bier consigned;
Her face, the image once of Paradise,
Is changed completely to another kind.
The play, the laughter men were wont to find
In her, and all her varied wit renewed,
Have fled, and left her mute in solitude.

125

About her eyes there stands a purple ring,
A silent token of her grief and pain,

Unbroyden, hangen al aboute hir eres;
Which yaf him verray signal of martyre
Of deeth, which that hir herte gan desyre.

118

Whan she him saw, she gan for sorwe anoon
Hir tery face a-twixe hir armes hyde,
For which this Pandare is so wo bi-goon,
That in the hous he mighte unnethe abyde,
As he that pitee felte on every syde.
For if Criseyde hadde erst compleyned sore,
Tho gan she pleyne a thousand tymes more.

119

And in hir aspre pleynte than she seyde,
"Pandare first of joyes mo than two
Was cause causinge un-to me, Criseyde,
That now transmuwed been in cruel wo.
Wher shal I seye to yow 'welcome' or no,
That alderfirst me broughte in-to servyse
Of love, allas! that endeth in swich wyse?

120

Endeth than love in wo? Ye, or men lyeth!
And alle worldly blisse, as thinketh me,
The ende of blisse ay sorwe it occupyeth;
And who-so troweth not that it so be,
Lat him upon me, woful wrecche, y-see,
That my-self hate, and ay my birthe acorse,
Felinge alwey, fro wikke I go to worse.

121

Who-so me seeth, he seeth sorwe al at ones,
Peyne, torment, pleynte, wo, distresse.
Out of my woful body harm ther noon is,
As anguish, langour, cruel bitternesse,
A-noy, smert, drede, fury, and eek siknesse.
I trowe, y-wis, from hevene teres reyne,
For pitee of myn aspre and cruel peyne!"

122

"And thou, my suster, ful of discomfort,"
Quod Pandarus, "what thenkestow to do?
Why ne hastow to thy-selven som resport,
Why woltow thus thy-selve, allas, for-do?
Leef al this werk and tak now hede to
That I shal seyn, and herkne, of good entente,
This, which by me thy Troilus thee sente."

123

Torned hir tho Criseyde, a wo makinge
So greet that it a deeth was for to see:—
"Allas!" quod she, "what wordes may ye bringe?
What wol my dere herte seyn to me,
Which that I drede never-mo to see?
Wol he have pleynte or teres, er I wende?
I have y-nowe, if he ther-after sende!"

124

She was right swich to seen in hir visage
As is that wight that men on bere binde;
Hir face, lyk of Paradys the image,
Was al y-chaunged in another kinde.
The pleye, the laughtre men was wont to finde
In hir, and eek hir joyes everychone,
Ben fled, and thus lyth now Criseyde allone.

125

Aboute hir eyen two a purpre ring
Bi-trent, in sothfast tokninge of hir peyne,

That to biholde it was a dedly thing,
For which Pandare mighte not restreyne
The teres form his eyen for to reyne.
But nathelees, as he best mighte, he seyde
From Troilus thise wordes to Criseyde.

126

"Lo, nece, I trowe ye han herd al how
The king, with othere lordes, for the beste,
Hath mad eschaunge of Antenor and yow,
That cause is of this sorwe and this unreste.
But how this cas doth Troilus moleste,
That may non erthely mannes tonge seye;
For verray wo his wit is al aweye.

127

For which we han so sorwed, he and I,
That in-to litel bothe it hadde us slawe;
But thurgh my conseil this day, fynally,
He somwhat is fro weping now withdrawe.
And semeth me that he desyreth fawe
With yow to been al night, for to devyse
Remede in this, if ther were any wyse.

128

This, short and pleyne, th'effect of my message,
As ferforth as my wit can comprehende.
For ye, that been of torment in swich rage,
May to no long prologe as now entende;
And her-upon ye may answere him sende.
And, for the love of god, my nece dere,
So leef this wo er Troilus be here."

129

"Gret is my wo," quod she, and sighte sore,
As she that feleth dedly sharp distresse;
"But yet to me his sorwe is muchel more,
That love him bet than he him-self, I gesse.
Allas! for me hath he swich hevinesse?
Can he for me so pitously compleyne?
Y-wis, this sorwe doubleth al my peyne.

130

Grevous to me, god wot, is for to twinne,"
Quod she, "but yet it hardere is to me
To seen that sorwe which that he is inne;
For wel wot I, it wol my bane be;
And deye I wol in certayn," tho quod she;
"But bidde him come, er deeth, that thus me threteth,
Dryve out that goost, which in myn herte beteth."

131

Thise wordes seyd, she on hir armes two
Fil gruf, and gan to wepe pitously.
Quod Pandarus, "allas! why do ye so,
Syn wel ye wot the tyme is faste by,
That he shal come? Arys up hastely,
That he yow nat biwopen thus ne finde,
But ye wol han him wood out of his minde!

132

For wiste he that ye ferde in this manere,
He wolde him-selve slee; and if I wende
To han this fare, he sholde not come here
For al the good that Pryam may despende.
For to what fyn he wolde anoon pretende,
That knowe I wel; and for-thy yet I seye,
So leef this sorwe, or platly he wol deye.

Wherein to gaze was a distressing thing,
And Pandar was unable to restrain
His tears, which from his eyes began to rain;
But still things couldn't last forever thus,
And soon he spoke to her for Troilus:

126

"You know, dear niece, that it is sadly true,
The king and other lords have thought it best
To take Antenor in exchange for you,
From which comes all this woe and this unrest;
And how all this doth Troilus molest,
It is beyond the power of human tongue
To tell, such deadly grief his heart hath wrung.

127

"For this we both have sorrowed, he and I,
And both have felt the pangs of mortal pain,
But through my counsel he at length doth try
Somewhat from useless weeping to abstain;
And now, it seems, that Troilus would fain
Be all night with you in convenient wise,
Some remedy to plan and to devise.

128

"Of this I've come you briefly to inform,
If I his message rightly comprehend,
And you, who now indulge in such a storm
Of grief, may wisely to his words attend,
And back to him a proper answer send;
But let me ask above all things, my dear,
Leave off these tears ere Troilus comes here."

129

"Great is my grief," she said, still sighing sore,
As one who felt the pangs of dire distress,
"Yet his great sorrow grieves me even more,
And by comparison, mine seems the less.
Alas, that love and woe together press
Upon his heart, where joy cannot remain!
The grief he feels doth double all my pain.

130

"God knows 'tis hard from him to separate,
But harder yet than this it is to know
That he is suffering in such sorrow great!
The thought alone the chill of death doth blow
Upon my heart and sorrows new there grow.
Then bid him come, or in his stead let death
Drive out my soul and its last lingering breath!"

131

Burying her face within her arms, she gave
Herself again to tears most copiously.
"O now," said Pandar, "why can't you behave
More sensibly? A moment or two and he
Will come, and what a sight then will he see?
I would not have him find you thus in tears
'Twould add too much to all his other fears.

132

"For if he knew you took things in this way,
He'd kill himself, and so he must not know;
I'd never let him come here, night or day,
For all the wealth that Priam could bestow!
Were he here now, I know how things would go!
To what I say, I beg you then attend,
These tears and cries you must bring to an end.

133

"Strive rather now his sorrow to relieve
And not to magnify it, dearest niece;
Hard measures will not joy retrieve,
But soft and gentle ways will bring you peace.
What use are tears, though tears should never cease,
And you were drowned in them? Far better sure
Than tears are all the happy means of cure.

134

"Now, my advice is, when your plans are made,
Since you are wise and both of one assent,
Arrange for your departure to evade,
Or quick return, if that you can't prevent.
Women do best without long argument,
Let's see now what your woman's wit avails,
And I'll be there to help you when it fails."

135

"Go then," said Cressida, "and truly I
Shall do my best all weeping to restrain
While he is here, and earnestly shall try
To make him glad, and free him of his pain,
Through all his heart in every coursing vein.
If any salve for him I can discover,
I shall be found not lacking to my lover."

136

Then Pandar went, and Troilus he sought,
And found him in a temple all alone,
Weary of life and much in mind distraught,
And there he prayed and made his bitter moan,
And of his prayers, this was the constant tone,
That end of life might bring him end of grief,
For well he thought this was his sole relief.

137

And in his mind, the simple truth to tell,
He was so fallen in despair that day,
He thought no longer in this world to dwell,
And argued of it in the following way:
"I am," he said, "but done for, so to say;
For all that comes, comes by necessity,
Thus to be done for is my destiny.

138

"I must believe and cannot other choose,
That Providence, in its divine foresight,
Hath known that Cressida I once must lose,
Since God sees everything from heaven's height
And plans things as he thinks both best and right,
According to their merits in rotation,
As was arranged for by predestination.

139

"But still I don't quite know what to believe!
For there have been great scholars, many a one,
Who say that destined fate we must receive,
Yet others prove that this need not be done,
And that free choice hath been denied to none.
Alack, so sly they are, these scholars old,
I can't make out what doctrine I should hold!

140

"For some declare, what God perceives before,
(And God of course can never be misled)
All that must be, though men may it deplore,
Because foreordination hath so said;
Wherefore the thought still lingers in my head,

133

And shapeth yow his sorwe for to abregge,
And nought encresse, leve nece swete;
Beth rather to him cause of flat than egge,
And with som wysdom ye his sorwes bete.
What helpeth is to wepen ful a strete,
Or though ye bothe in salte teres dreynte?
Bet is a tyme of cure ay than of pleynte.

134

I mene thus; whan I him hider bringe,
Sin ye ben wyse, and bothe of oon assent,
So shapeth how distourbe your goinge.
Or come ayen, sone after ye be went.
Wommen ben wyse in short avysement;
And lat sen how your wit shal now avayle;
And what that I may helpe, it shal not fayle."

135

"Go," quod Criseyde, "and uncle, trewely,
I shal don al my might, me to restreyne
From weping in his sight, and bisily,
Him for to glade, I shal don al my peyne,
And in myn herte seken every veyne;
If to this soor ther may be founden salve,
It shal not lakken, certain, on myn halve."

136

Goth Pandarus, and Troilus he soughte,
Til in a temple he fond him allone,
As he that of his lyf no lenger roughte;
But to the pitouse goddes everichone
Ful tendrely he preyde, and made his mone,
To doon him sone out of this world to pace;
For wel he thoughte ther was non other grace.

137

And shortly, al the sothe for to seye,
He was so fallen in despeyr that day,
That outrely he shoop him for to deye.
For right thus was his argument alwey:
He seyde, he nas but loren, waylawey!
"For al that comth, comth by necessitee;
Thus to be lorn, it is my destinee.

138

For certaynly, this wot I wel," he seyde,
"That for-sight of divyne purveyaunce
Hath seyn alwey me to for-gon Criseyde,
Sin god seeth every thing, out of doutaunce,
And hem desponeth, thourgh his ordernaunce,
In hir merytes sothly for to be,
As they shul comen by predestinee.

139

But nathelees, allas! whom shal I leve?
For ther ben grete clerkes many oon,
That destinee thorugh argumentes preve;
And som men seyn that nedely ther is noon;
But that free chois is yeven us everichoon.
O, welaway! so sleye arn clerkes olde,
That I not whos opinion I may holde.

140

For som men seyn, if god seth al biforn,
Ne god may not deceyved ben, pardee,
Than moot it fallen, though men hadde it sworn,
That purveyaunce hath seyn bifore to be.
Wherfor I seye, that from eterne if he

Hath wist biforn our thought eek as our dede,
We have no free chois, as these clerkes rede.

141

For other thought nor other dede also
Might never be, but swich as purveyaunce,
Which may not ben deceyved never-mo,
Hath feled biforn, with-outen ignoraunce.
For if ther mighte been a variaunce
To wrythen out fro goddes purveyinge,
Ther nere no prescience of thing cominge;

142

But it were rather an opinioun
Uncerteyn, and no stedfast forseinge;
And certes, that were an abusioun,
That god shuld han no parfit cleer witinge
More than we men that han doutous weninge.
But swich an errour up-on god to gesse
Were fals and foul, and wikked corsednesse.

143

Eek this is an opinioun of somme
That han hir top ful heighe and smothe y-shore;
They seyn right thus, that thing is not to come
For that the prescience hath seyn bifore
That it shal come; but they seyn, that therfore
That it shal come, therfore the purveyaunce
Wot it biforn with-outen ignoraunce;

144

And in this manere this necessitee
Retorneth in his part contrarie agayn.
For needfully bihoveth it not to be
That thilke thinges fallen in certayn
That ben purveyed; but nedely, as they seyn,
Bihoveth it that thinges, whiche that falle,
That they in certayn ben purveyed alle.

145

I mene as though I laboured me in this,
To enqueren which thing cause of which thing be;
As whether that the prescience of god is
The certayn cause of the necessitee
Of thinges that to comen been, pardee;
Or if necessitee of thing cominge
Be cause certeyn of the purveyinge.

146

But now ne enforce I me nat in shewinge
How the ordre of causes stant; but wel wot I,
That it bihoveth that the bifallinge
Of thinges wist biforen certeynly
Be necessarie, al seme it not ther-by
That prescience put falling necessaire
To thing to come, al falle it foule or faire.

147

For if ther sit a man yond on a see,
Than by necessittee bihoveth it
That, certes, thyn opinioun soth be,
That wenest or conjectest that he sit;
And ferther-over now ayenward yit,
Lo, right so it is of the part contrarie,
As thus; (now herkne, for I wol not tarie):

148

I seye, that if the opinioun of thee
Be sooth, for that he sit, than seye I this,
That he mot sitten by necessitee;

If God foreknows the thought and act of each
Of us, we have no choice, as scholars preach.

141

"For neither thought nor deed might ever be,
Or anything, unless foreordination,
In which there may be no uncertainty,
Perceives it without shade of variation;
For if there were the slightest hesitation
Or any slip in God's foreordering,
Foreknowledge then were not a certain thing,

142

"But rather one would call it expectation,
Unsteadfast, not foreknowledge absolute;
And that, indeed, were an abomination,
For God's foreknowledge thus to substitute
Imperfect human doubts and mere repute;
In God such human error to imply
Were false and foul and cursed treason high.

143

"Then there is this opinion held by some,
Whose tonsured foreheads quite imposing shine;
They say whatever happens does not come
Because foreknowledge sees with fixed design
That come it must, but rather they incline
To say that come it will, and reason so,
That such foreknowledge doth but merely know.

144

"But there resides here a perplexity
That in some proper way must be explained,
That things that happen do not have to be
Merely because they may be foreordained;
Yet still this truth at least must be maintained,
That all the things that ever shall befall,
Must surely be ordained, both one and all.

145

"You see that I am trying to find out
Just what is cause and what is consequence.
Is God's foreknowledge cause beyond a doubt
As necessary in his plan prepense
Of all the human things we call events,
Or does necessity in them reside
And thus ordaining cause for them provide?

146

"I must confess I can't pretend to show
Just how the reasons stand, but this I'll say,
That every thing that happens, must do so,
And must have been foreknown in such a way
That made it necessary, though it may
Be that foreknowledge did not so declare
That it must happen, be it foul or fair.

147

"But if a man is sitting on a chair,
Then this necessity you can't evade,
That true it is that he is sitting there,
And thus a truthful judgment you have made;
And furthermore against this may be laid
A supplement to this and its contrary,
As thus—pray heed, and just a moment tarry.

148

"I say if that opinion which you hold
That he sits there is true, then furthermore
He must be sitting there, as I have told;

There's thus necessity on either score,
That he must sit, as we agreed before,
And you must think he does, and so say I,
Necessity on both of you doth lie.

149

"But you may urge, this man, he does not sit
Because your judgment on this may be true,
But rather, since he sat ere you thought it,
Your judgment from his sitting doth ensue;
But I say, though your judgment may be due
To his first sitting there, necessity
To judge and sit distributed must be.

150

"These arguments I think I may advance,
And make apply, for so it seems to me,
To God's foreknowledge and foreordinance,
In all the happenings that come to be.
And by these arguments you well may see,
That all the things that on the earth befall,
By plain necessity they happen all.

151

"Though things to come must all be foreordained,
Their cause therein you cannot simply find,
For these two points apart must be maintained,
But yet foreordinance cannot be blind,
And God must foreordain with truthful mind,
Or else whatever foreordained should be,
Would come to pass through blind necessity.

152

"But no more arguments I need display
To show that free choice is an idle dream.
Yet this, however, 'tis quite false to say,
That temporal things one should esteem
As cause of God's foreknowledge aye supreme;
From such opinion only errors grow,
That things that happen cause him to foreknow.

153

"I must suppose then, had I such a thought,
That God ordains each thing that is to come
Because it is to come, and for else naught!
Why, then, I might believe things, all and some,
From ages past, whate'er they issued from,
Are cause of God's high power that before
Hath known all things and nothing doth ignore!

154

"I have just one more point to add hereto,
That when I know that there exists a thing,
I know my knowing of that thing is true,
And so, whatever time to pass shall bring,
Those things I know must come; the happening
Of things foreknown ere their appointed hour,
Can be prevented by no human power.

155

"Almighty Jove, supreme upon thy throne,
O thou who knowst all things false and true,
In pity let me perish here alone,
Or Cressida and me no more pursue
With woe!" He paused, and scarcely was he through
With this request, when Pandar doth appear
Within the door, and speaks as you shall hear.

156

"Almighty Jove," he echoed, "on thy throne,

And thus necessitee in either is.
For in him nede of sitting is, y-wis,
And in thee nede of sooth; and thus, forsothe,
Ther moot necessitee ben in yow bothe.

149

But thou mayst seyn, the man sit not therfore,
That thyn opinion of sitting soth is;
But rather, for the man sit ther bifore,
Therfore is thyn opinion sooth, y-wis.
And I seye, though the cause of sooth of this
Comth of his sitting, yet necessitee
Is entrechaunged, bothe in him and thee.

150

Thus on this same wyse, out of doutaunce,
I may wel maken, as it semeth me,
My resoninge of goddes purveyaunce,
And of the thinges that to comen be;
By whiche reson men may wel y-see,
That thilke thinges that in erthe falle,
That by necessitee they comen alle.

151

For al-though that, for thing shal come, y-wis,
Therfore is it purveyed, certaynly,
Nat that it comth for it purveyed is:
Yet nathelees, bihoveth it nedfully,
That thing to come be purveyed, trewely;
Or elles, thinges that purveyed be,
That they bityden by necessitee.

152

And this suffyseth right y-now, certeyn,
For to destroye our free chois every del.—
But now is this abusion to seyn,
That fallinge of the thinges temporel
Is cause of goddes prescience eternel.
Now trewely, that is a fals sentence,
That thing to come sholde cause his prescience.

153

What mighte I wene, and I hadde swich a thought.
But that god purveyth thing that is to come
For that it is to come, and elles nought?
So mighte I wene that thinges alle and some,
That whylom been bifalle and over-come,
Ben cause of thilke sovereyn purveyaunce,
That for-wot al with-outen ignoraunce.

154

And over al this, yet seye I more herto,
That right as whan I woot ther is a thing,
Y-wis, that thing mot nedefully be so;
Eek right so, whan I woot a thing coming,
So mot it come; and thus the bifalling
Of thinges that ben wist bifore the tyde,
They mowe not been eschewed on no syde."

155

Than seyde he thus, "almighty Jove in trone,
That wost of al this thing the soothfastnesse,
Rewe on my sorwe, or do me deye sone,
Or bring Criseyde and me fro this distresse."
And whyl he was in al this hevinesse,
Disputinge with him-self in this matere,
Com Pandare in, and seyde as ye may here.

156

"O mighty god," quod Pandarus, "in trone,

Ey! who seigh ever a wys man faren so?
Why, Troilus, what thenkestow to done?
Hastow swich lust to been thyn owene fo?
What, parde, yet is not Criseyde a-go!
Why lust thee so thy-self for-doon for drede,
That in thyn heed thyn eyen semen dede?

157

Hastow not lived many a yeer biforn
With-outen hir, and ferd ful wel at ese?
Artow for hir and for non other born?
Hath kind thee wroughte al-only hir to plese?
Lat be, and thenk right thus in thy disese:
That, in the dees right as ther fallen chaunces,
Right so in love, ther come and goon plesaunces.

158

And yet this is a wonder most of alle,
Why thou thus sorwest, sin thou nost not yit,
Touching hir goinge, how that it shal falle,
Ne if she can hir-self distorben it.
Thou hast not yet assayed al hir wit.
A man may al by tyme his nekke bede
Whan it shal of, and sorwen at the nede.

159

For-thy take hede of that that I shal seye;
I have with hir y-spoke and longe y-be,
So as accorded was bitwixe us tweye.
And ever-mo me thinketh thus, that she
Hath som-what in hir hertes prevetee,
Wher-with she can, if I shal right arede,
Distorbe al this, of which thou art in drede.

160

For which my counseil is, whan it is night,
Thou to hir go, and make of this an ende;
And blisful Juno, thourgh hir grete mighte,
Shal, as I hope, hir grace un-to us sende.
Myn herte seyth, "certeyn, she shal not wende;"
And for-thy put thyn herte a whyle in reste;
And hold this purpos, for it is the beste."

161

This Troilus answerde, and sighte sore,
"Thou seyst right wel, and I wil do right so";
And what him liste, he seyde un-to it more.
And whan that it was tyme for to go,
Ful prevely him-self, with-outen mo,
Un-to hir com, as he was wont to done;
And how they wroughte, I shal yow telle sone.

162

Soth is, that whan they gonne first to mete,
So gan the peyne hir hertes for to twiste,
That neither of hem other mighte grete,
But hem in armes toke and after kiste.
The lasse wofulle of hem bothe niste
Wher that he was, ne mighte o word out-bringe,
As I seyde erst, for wo and for sobbinge.

163

Tho woful teres that they leten falle
As bittre weren, out of teres kinde,
For peyne, as is ligne-aloës or galle.
So bittre teres weep nought, as I finde,
The woful Myrra through the bark and rinde.
That in this world ther nis so hard an herte,
That nolde han rewed on hir peynes smerte.

Who ever saw a grown man acting so?
Can't you do something else than weep and moan?
Why, Troilus, you are your own worst foe!
Good heavens, Cressida may never go,
So why afflict yourself with needless dread
And almost cry your eyes out of your head?

157

"Recall how many years you've lived, dear brother,
Without her, yet you got along with ease!
You weren't made for her and nary other!
There's plenty more who know the art to please.
Among your helpful thoughts you might place these,
That as the chance in dice falls when you throw,
Just so in love, your pleasures come and go.

158

"But this to me is cause of great surprise,
That you disturb your soul, and yet don't know,
Touching her going, what in the future lies,
Nor if she can't devise some way to throw
Them off the track, and so not need to go;
To meet the ax a man his neck may stretch,
But why should that give pleasure to the wretch?

159

"And now I'll tell you what I have to say.
I've been with her and told her your petition,
As we agreed between ourselves today,
And Troilus, I have a shrewd suspicion,
That in her heart she's got a proposition,
Though what it was she didn't fully mention,
That will repay the carefullest attention.

160

"And so, if you'll take my advice, tonight
Just go to her and bring this to an end,
For blessed Juno, through her ample might,
Shall, as I hope, her favor to us send.
I'm quite convinced your lady will attend
To this affair, so set your mind at rest,
For all at last will turn out for the best."

161

Troilus replied, as Pandar reached the door,
"Perhaps you're right, I might as well do so—"
Although, of course, he said a great deal more,
And when the time arrived for him to go,
Most secretly, so not a soul should know,
He came to her, as he was wont to do
Their usual occupations to pursue.

162

And truly at the first, when there they meet,
Sorrow about their hearts doth wind and twist,
So neither may in words the other greet,
But each in other's arms, each other kissed;
Thus silently they keep this mournful tryst,
For gathering woe in both their hearts so throbs,
No words can find a place among their sobs.

163

The precious tears that there descend and fall
Were bitter tears, of an unnatural kind,
As though of aloes mingled or of gall.
The woful Myrrha wept through bark and rind
No tears like these, as I her story find.
In all this world, no heart could be so hard
For such despair to lack as deep regard.

164

But when their wandering weary spirits twain
Returned were to the hearts where they should dwell,
And long lament had lightened so their pain,
When, too, the bitter tears ebbed in their well,
And less the sorrows in their bosoms swell,
To Troilus then Cressida thus spoke,
With hoarse and halting voice that often broke:

165

"O Jove! O God! Thy mercy I beseech!
Help, Troilus!" And therewithal her face
Upon his breast she laid, bereft of speech,
Her woful spirit ready to retrace
Its course back to its starting place;
And thus she lies, her face all pale and green,
Though fairest once, and freshest to be seen.

166

And Troilus who doth her thus behold,
Calling her name to wake her from the dead,
And feeling all her limbs grow stiff and cold,
And both her eyes cast upward in her head,
This Troilus was filled with mortal dread,
And many a time her lips so cold he kissed,
And prayed the Gods with comfort to assist.

167

Her body on her couch he straightly laid,
For now her cheeks with life no longer glow;
Good reason now has he to be dismayed,
And now his song is but a song of woe.
For when he saw her lying speechless so,
With voice and tears and sobs together blended,
He cried, "Her sorrows are at last all ended!"

168

From loud lament he could not be restrained,
And wrung his hands and said what was to say,
And on his heaving breast the salt tears rained;
But finally his tears he wiped away,
And for her flitting soul he thus doth pray:
"O God, established on thy throne above,
Grant me that I shall follow soon my love!"

169

How cold she was, how robbed of all sensation,
Nor trace of tender breathing could he feel,
Which was for him the final declaration,
As there beside her he did sadly kneel,
That she had suffered now the last ordeal;
And so the body of his lady dear
He placed as one does bodies for the bier.

170

And after this, with sternly hardened heart,
His shining sword from out its sheath he drew,
To slay himself and from this life to part,
So that his soul might quickly hers pursue,
And both receive from Minos judgment due,
Since love and cruel fortune so decide
That he may in this world no longer bide.

171

His life resigned, he voiced his high disdain:
"O cruel Jove, and Fortune so adverse,
I can but say that falsely ye have slain
My love, and since ye can do nothing worse,

164

But whan hir woful wery gostes tweyne
Retorned been ther-as hem oughte dwelle,
And that som-what to wayken gan the peyne
By lengthe of pleynte, and ebben gan the welle
Of hire teres, and the herte unswelle,
With broken voys, al hoors for-shright, Criseyde
To Troilus thise ilke wordes seyde:

165

"O Jove, I deye, and mercy I beseche!
Help, Troilus!" and ther-with-al hir face
Upon his brest she leyde, and loste speche;
Hir woful spirit from his propre place,
Right with the word, alwey up poynt to pace.
And thus she lyth with hewes pale and grene,
That whylom fresh and fairest was to sene.

166

This Troilus, that on hir gan biholde,
Clepinge hir name, (and she lay as for deed,
With-oute answere, and felte hir limes colde,
Hir eyen throwen upward to hir heed),
This sorwful man can now noon other reed,
But ofte tyme hir colde mouth he kiste;
Wher him was wo, god and him-self it wiste!

167

He rist him up, and long streight he hir leyde;
For signe of lyf, for ought he can or may,
Can he noon finde in no-thing on Criseyde,
For which his song ful ofte is "weylaway!"
But whan he saugh that specheles she lay,
With sorwful voys, and herte of blisse al bare,
He seyde how she was fro this world y-fare!

168

So after that he longe hadde hir compleyned,
His hondes wronge, and seyd that was to seye,
And with his teres salte hir brest bireyned,
He gan tho teres wypen of ful dreye,
And pitously gan for the soule preye,
And seyde, "O lord, that set art in thy trone,
Rewe eek on me, for I shal folwe hir sone!"

169

She cold was and with-outen sentement,
For aught he woot, for breeth ne felte he noon;
And this was him a preignant argument
That she was forth out of this world agoon;
And whan he seigh ther was non other woon,
He gan hir limes dresse in swich manere
As men don hem that shul be leyd on bere.

170

And after this, with sterne and cruel herte,
His swerd a-noon out of his shethe he twighte,
Him-self to sleen, how sore that him smerte,
So that his sowle hir sowle folwen mighte,
Ther-as the doom of Mynos wolde it dighte;
Sin love and cruel Fortune it ne wolde,
That in this world he lenger liven sholde.

171

Thanne seyde he thus, fulfild of heigh desdayn,
"O cruel Jove, and thou, Fortune adverse,
This al and som, that falsly have ye slayn
Criseyde, and sin ye may do me no werse,

Fy on your might and werkes so diverse!
Thus cowardly ye shul me never winne;
Ther shal no deeth me fro my lady twinne.

172

For I this world, sin ye han slayn hir thus,
Wol lete, and folowe hir spirit lowe or hye;
Shal never lover seyn that Troilus
Dar not, for fere, with his lady dye;
For certeyn, I wol bere hir companye.
But sin ye wol not suffre us liven here,
Yet suffreth that our soules ben y-fere.

173

And thou, citee, whiche that I leve in wo,
And thou, Pryam, and bretheren al y-fere,
And thou, my moder, farewel! for I go;
And Attropos, make redy thou my bere!
And thou, Criseyde, o swete herte dere,
Receyve now my spirit!" wolde he seye,
With swerd at herte, al redy for to deye.

174

But as god wolde, of swough therwith she abreyde,
And gan to syke, and "Troilus" she cryde;
And he answerde, "lady myn Criseyde,
Live ye yet?" and leet his swerd doun glyde.
"Ye, herte myn, that thanked be Cupyde!"
Quod she, and ther-with-al she sore sighte;
And he bigan to glade hir as he mighte;

175

Took hir in armes two, and kiste hir ofte,
And hir to glade he dide al his entente;
For which hir goost, that flikered ay on-lofte,
In-to hir woful herte ayein it wente.
But at the laste, as that hir eyen glente
A-syde, anoon she gan his swerd aspye,
As it lay bare, and gan for fere crye,

176

And asked him, why he it hadde out-drawe?
And Troilus anoon the cause hir tolde,
And how himself ther-with he wolde have slawe.
For which Criseyde up-on him gan biholde,
And gan him in hir armes faste folde,
And seyde, "O mercy, god, lo, which a dede!
Allas! how neigh we were bothe dede!

177

Thanne if I ne hadde spoken, as grace was,
Ye wolde han slayn your-self anoon?" quod she.
"Ye, douteless"; and she answerde, "allas!
For, by that ilke lord that made me,
I nolde a forlong wey on-lyve han be,
After your deeth, to han be crowned quene
Of al the lond the sonne on shyneth shene.

178

But with this selve swerd, which that here is,
My-selve I wolde have slayn!"—quod she tho;
"But ho, for we han right y-now of this,
And late us ryse and streight to bedde go,
And therë lat us speken of our wo.
For, by the morter which that I see brenne,
Knowe I ful wel that day is not fer henne."

179

Whan they were in hir bedde, in armes folde,
Nought was it lyk tho nightes here-biforn;

Your might and all your evil works I curse!
Ye shall naught in this coward fashion gain,
For death shall never separate us twain!

172

"Now all this world, since ye have slain her thus,
I here renounce, and after her will hie;
No lover true shall say that Troilus
To share his lady's death did e'er deny.
Together to one fate we two will fly,
And since ye will not suffer us to live,
One stroke of death to our two spirits give!

173

"And O thou city, where I live in woe,
And Priam, and my brothers dwelling here,
And thou, my mother, farewell, for I go!
And Atropos, make ready now my bier!
And blessed Cressida, my sweetheart dear,
Receive my soul!"—he was about to say,
With sword at heart, prepared himself to slay,

174

But, thanks to God, she woke up from her swoon,
And drew a breath, and "Troilus!" she sighed,
And "Sweetheart, Cressida!" he answered soon,
"Are you alive?" and let his weapon slide;
"Yes, sweetheart, thanks to Venus!" she replied,
And therewithal a mighty sigh she heaved,
And Troilus now felt somewhat relieved.

175

He took her in his arms and kissed her oft,
To make her glad was now his sole intent,
Until her spirit, flickering aye aloft,
Again into its harbor softly went;
But then it chanced, her glances sidelong bent,
His sword upon the floor she did espy,
As it lay bare, which drew from her a cry.

176

She asked him why his sword he thus had drawn,
And Troilus the reason straightway told,
How he would slay himself therewith anon;
And she with wide eyes doth her knight behold
And him in arms most lovingly enfold;
"O mercy God! What an escape!" she cried,
"Alas, 'twere little but we both had died!

177

"And if I hadn't spoken, by good chance,
You would have slain yourself with it?" asked she;
"Quite right!" he answered with a loving glance,
And she replied, "By Him who fashioned me,
I would not living on this planet be
After thy death, if I were crowned the queen
Of all the land the sun hath ever seen.

178

"But straight thy very bloody sword I'd seize
And after thee, myself I'd slay! But ho!
Enough of such sad possibilities!
Arise and straight to bed now let us go,
Where we can peacefully discuss our woe.
For by the night-light now so lowly burning,
I know the day is not far from returning."

179

Though in her bed reclined in love's embrace,
Unlike was this to nights that went before,

For sadly they behold each other's face
As though their joy was flown forevermore,
And their misfortune often they deplore.
But Cressida at last took things in hand,
And thus to him her thoughts she did expand:

180

"Lo, sweetheart, this you know most certainly,
That if a man does nothing but complain,
And seeks no way from trouble to be free,
That is but folly and increase of pain;
And since we've come together here, we twain,
To find a way out of the way we're in,
It seems to me, it's high time to begin.

181

"I'm but a woman, as of course you know,
But my opinion I will tell you free
And frank, just as it comes in its first glow,
That neither you nor I, it seems to me,
Need get excited in such high degree,
Because there must be some way of redress
For all this wrong that causes us distress.

182

"As it now stands, the thought that we most
hate,
The thought that robs us of all hope of bliss,
Is merely that we two must separate,
And all in all, there's nothing more amiss!
And what is then the remedy for this?
But that we manage soon again to meet!
That's all there is to it, my precious sweet!

183

"Now that I certainly can bring about,
To come back soon again if I must go,
Of this I do not have the slightest doubt,
For at the most within a week or so,
I shall be back, and now I shall you show,
Just briefly, and in simple words and few,
How I shall carry my proposal through.

184

"But I don't want to make a long discourse,
For time once lost cannot recovered be,
And if you'll only trust to my resource,
'Twill be the best, as soon I think you'll see.
And, sweetheart, pray you now, forgive it me,
If what I say, seems somewhat hard to you,
For truly, 'tis the best that we can do.

185

"So let me here most earnestly protest
That the intent of all that I shall say
Is but to show what I regard the best,
And I believe, in fact the only way
To help ourselves—and take it so, I pray!
But in the end, whatever you require,
That will I do—it is my sole desire.

186

"Now listen! You of course will understand,
I go away by act of parliament,
And both of us must yield to that command.
There is no earthly way to circumvent
This act, and thus we may as well assent,
And so with that, dismiss it from our mind
And look about some better way to find.

For pitously ech other gan biholde,
As they that hadden al hir blisse y-lorn,
Biwaylinge ay the day that they were born.
Til at the last this sorwful wight Criseyde
To Troilus these ilke wordes seyde:—

180

"Lo, herte myn, wel wot ye this," quod she,
"That if a wight alwey his wo compleyne,
And seketh nought how holpen for to be,
It nis but folye and encrees of peyne;
And sin that here assembled be we tweyne
To finde bote of wo that we ben inne,
It were al tyme sone to bigenne.

181

I am a womman, as ful wel ye woot,
And as I am avysed sodeynly,
So wol I telle yow, whyl it is hoot.
Me thinketh thus, that neither ye nor I
Oughte half this wo to make skilfully.
For there is art y-now for to redresse
That yet is mis, and sleen this hevinesse.

182

Sooth is, the wo, the whiche that we ben
inne,
For ought I woot, for no-thing elles is
But for the cause that we sholden twinne.
Considered al, ther nis no-more amis.
But what is thanne a remede un-to this,
But that we shape us sone for to mete?
This al and som, my dere herte swete.

183

Now that I shal wel bringen it aboute
To come ayein, sone after that I go,
Ther-of am I no maner thing in doute.
For dredeles, with-inne a wouke or two,
I shal ben here; and, that it may be so
By alle right, and in a wordes fewe,
I shal yow wel an heep of weyes shewe.

184

For which I wol not make long sermoun,
For tyme y-lost may not recovered be;
But I wol gon to my conclusioun,
And to the beste, in ought that I can see.
And, for the love of god, for-yeve it me
If I speke ought ayein your hertes reste;
For trewely, I speke it for the beste;

185

Makinge alwey a protestacioun,
That now these wordes, whiche that I shal seye,
Nis but to shewe yow my mocioun,
To finde un-to our helpe the beste weye;
And taketh it non other wyse, I preye.
For in effect what-so ye me comaunde,
That wol I doon, for that is no demaunde.

186

Now herkeneth this, ye han wel understonde,
My going graunted is by parlement
So ferforth, that it may not be with-stonde
For al this world, as by my jugement.
And sin ther helpeth noon avysement
To letten it, lat it passe out of minde;
And lat us shape a bettre wey to finde.

187

The sothe is, that the twinninge of us tweyne
Wol us disese and cruelliche anoye.
But him bihoveth som-tyme han a peyne,
That serveth love, if that he wol have joye.
And sin I shal no ferthere out of Troye
Than I may ryde ayein on half a morwe,
It oughte lasse causen us to sorwe:

188

So as I shal not so ben hid in muwe,
That day by day, myn owene herte dere,
Sin wel ye woot that it is now a truwe,
Ye shul ful wel al myn estat y-here.
And er that truwe is doon, I shal ben here,
And thanne have ye bothe Antenor y-wonne
And me also; beth glad now, if ye conne;

189

And thenk right thus, 'Criseyde is now agoon,
But what! she shal come hastely ayeyn'";
And whanne, allas? by god, lo, right anoon,
Er dayes ten, this dar I saufly seyn.
And thanne at erste shul we been so fayn,
So as we shulle to-gederes ever dwelle,
That al this world ne mighte our blisse telle.

190

I see that ofte, ther-as we ben now,
That for the beste, our conseil for to hyde,
Ye speke not with me, nor I with yow
In fourtenight; ne see yow go ne ryde.
May ye not ten dayes thanne abyde,
For myn honour, in swich an aventure?
Y-wis, ye mowen elles lyte endure!

191

Ye knowe eek how that al my kin is here,
But-if that onliche it my fader be;
And eek myn othere thinges alle y-fere
And nameliche, my dere herte, ye,
Whom that I nolde leven for to see
For al this world, as wyd as it hath space;
Or elles, see ich never Joves face!

192

Why trowe ye my fader in this wyse
Coveiteth so to see me, but for drede
Lest in this toun that folkes me dispyse
By-cause of him, for his unhappy dede?
What woot my fader what lyf that I lede?
For if he wiste in Troye how wel I fare,
Us neded for my wending nought to care.

193

Ye seen that every day eek, more and more,
Men trete of pees; and it supposed is,
That men the quene Eleyne shal restore,
And Grekes us restore that is mis.
So though ther nere comfort noon but this,
That men purposen pees on every syde,
Ye may the bettre at ese of herte abyde.

194

For if that it be pees, myn herte
dere,
The nature of the pees mot nedes dryve
That men moste entrecomunen y-fere,
And to and fro eek ryde and gon as blyve

187

"Of course it's true, the parting of us twain
Most dreadfully will both of us annoy;
But every lover must endure some pain,
Or he would not appreciate his joy.
And since I go no farther out of Troy
Then I can ride again in half a morrow,
There's not much reason here to grieve or sorrow.

188

"For sure the Greeks will not me so immure,
But day by day, my darling sweetheart dear,
(You know this truce for some time will endure),
Of all my doings you shall fully hear.
And ere the truce is o'er, I'll reappear;
If you will keep an eye on your demeanor,
You shall have me, and Troy shall have Antenor!

189

"And think, 'What though my Cressida is gone,
'Twill not be long before she's back again.' "
"But when, alas!" "I swear it, right anon,
Or maybe several days, or nine or ten.
And when I come, you'll be so happy then,
That we shall evermore together dwell,
In greater bliss than all the world can tell.

190

"You know with things arranged as they are now,
We're oft compelled our private life to hide,
And dare no trysts or conference allow—
A fortnight thus our patience oft is tried—,
And can't you then a mere ten days abide,
My honest reputation to insure?
Of course you can, or yet much more endure!

191

"And don't forget that all my kin are here,
Except my father, who of course is not,
And all my property, which I hold dear,
And thou, dearer than all the wealth I've got,
Whom I would not exchange for any lot
On all this earth, so wide as earth hath space,
I swear it in the sight of great Jove's face!

192

"Do you suppose my father, who is wise,
Desires to see me, but that he's afraid
Lest folk mistrust me here or me despise,
Because of all the trouble he has made?
But why should he suppose I need his aid?
If he knew how content I am in Troy,
He would his wits in other ways employ.

193

"You see, besides, how each day more and more
Men treat of peace, and everywhere they say
The Trojans will Queen Helen soon restore
And then the Greeks will quickly sail away,
And that will be for us a blessed day;
And so you may with ease of heart abide,
Because they treat of peace on either side.

194

"And when the peace shall come, my sweetheart
dear,
You know the town and place will be alive
With Grecian messengers who will come here,
And some will go and new ones will arrive,

As thick as honey-bees about a hive,
And everyone will then be free to go
Wherever he will, and no one care or know.

195

"And even though the plans for peace fall through,
I must come back, for could I anywhere
Or either go or stay away from you?
And I could never stand it living there
Within a camp devoted to warfare;
And so if you regard what I have said,
I don't see why you need have any dread.

196

"But I've another plan that's sure to hold
If what I've spoken of should not suffice.
My father Calchas is now growing old,
And greed you know, is still an old man's vice.
And if I wanted to, I could entice
Him to our net, and I dare make the vaunt
That we shall have him doing what we want.

197

"'Tis hard, so doth the ancient proverb go,
To fill the wolf and hold intact the sheep,
Which is to say, that often men must throw
Away a part, if they the rest will keep.
With gold it's very easy to cut deep
Into the heart of him who's set on gain,
And what I plan to do, I'll now explain.

198

"The ready cash I have here in this town,
I'll take it to my father and I'll say,
'Tis sent to him by friends to salt it down
And keep it safe against a rainy day,
And that these friends most fervently do pray
Him send for more, and the first chance embrace,
Because this town is such a risky place.

199

"And what's to come shall be a huge amount—
So shall I say—and lest it be espied,
It must be sent by me on their account;
And then I'll show him, that if peace betide,
What friends I have at court on every side,
Who Priam's wrath will help to mitigate
And him in Trojan favor reinstate.

200

"So what for all the things I'll to him tell,
I'll so enchant him, as I said before,
He'll think he doth in heaven surely dwell.
That for Apollo, or for his clerkly lore,
Or for his calculations by the score!
Desire of gold shall so his priestcraft blind,
I shall him 'round my finger lightly wind.

201

"And if he puts to test by priestly skill
If I am lying, I'll pull him by the sleeve
And in his divinations doubt instil,
So that at last I'll lead him to believe
The oracles he wrongly doth receive.
The Gods all speak in amphibologies,
And twenty times more lies than truths in these.

202

"Fear made the Gods at first, so shall I say,
And now again that same fear in his heart

Alday as thikke as been flen from an hyve;
And every wight han libertee to bleve
Wher-as him list the bet, with-outen leve.

195

And though so be that pees ther may be noon,
Yet hider, though ther never pees ne were,
I moste come; for whider sholde I goon,
Or how mischaunce sholde I dwelle there
Among tho men of armes ever in fere?
For which, as wisly god my soule rede,
I can not seen wher-of ye sholden drede.

196

Have here another wey, if it so be
That al this thing ne may yow not suffyse.
My fader, as ye knowen wel, pardee,
Is old, and elde is ful of coveityse.
And I right now have founden al the gyse,
With-oute net, wher-with I shal him hente;
And herkeneth how, if that ye wole assente.

197

Lo, Troilus, men seyn that hard it is
The wolf ful, and the wether hool to have;
This is to seyn, that men ful ofte, y-wis,
Mot spenden part, the remenaunt for to save.
For ay with gold men may the herte grave
Of him that set is up-on coveityse;
And how I mene, I shal it yow devyse.

198

The moeble which that I have in this toun
Un-to my fader shal I take, and seye,
That right for trust and for savacioun
It sent is from a freend of his or tweye,
The whiche freendes ferventliche him preye
To senden after more, and that in hye,
Whyl that this toun stant thus in jupartye.

199

And that shal been an huge quantitee,
Thus shal I seyn, but, lest it folk aspyde,
This may be sent by no wight but by me;
I shal eek shewen him, if pees bityde,
What frendes that ich have on every syde
Toward the court, to doon the wrathe pace
Of Priamus, and doon him stonde in grace.

200

So, what for o thing and for other, swete,
I shal him so enchaunten with my sawes,
That right in hevene his sowle is, shal he mete!
For al Appollo, or his clerkes lawes,
Or calculinge avayleth nought three hawes;
Desyr of gold shal so his sowle blende,
That, as me lyst, I shal wel make an ende.

201

And if he wolde ought by his sort it preve
If that I lye, in certayn I shal fonde
Distorben him, and plukke him by the sleve,
Makinge his sort, and beren him on honde,
He hath not wel the goddes understonde.
For goddes speken in amphibologyes,
And, for a sooth, they tellen twenty lyes.

202

Eek drede fond first goddes, I suppose,
Thus shal I seyn, and that his coward herte

Made him amis the goddes text to glose,
Whan he for ferde out of his Delphos sterte.
And but I make him sone to converte,
And doon my reed with-inne a day or tweye,
I wol to yow oblige me to deye."

203

And treweliche, as writen wel I finde,
That al this thing was seyd of good entente;
And that hir herte trewe was and kinde
Towardes him, and spak right as she mente,
And that she starf for wo neigh, whan she wente,
And was in purpos ever to be trewe;
Thus writen they that of hir werkes knewe.

204

This Troilus, with herte and eres spradde,
Herde al this thing devysen to and fro;
And verraylich him semed that he hadde
The selve wit; but yet to lete hir go
His herte misforyaf him ever-mo.
But fynally, he gan his herte wreste
To trusten hir, and took it for the beste.

205

For which the grete furie of his penaunce
Was queynt with hope, and ther-with hem
bitwene
Bigan for joye the amorouse daunce.
And as the briddes, whan the sonne is shene,
Delyten in hir song in leves grene,
Right so the wordes that they spake y-fere
Delyted hem, and made hir hertes clere.

206

But natheles, the wending of Criseyde,
For al this world, may nought out of his minde;
For which ful ofte he pitously hir preyde,
That of hir heste he might hir trewe finde.
And seyde hir, "certes, if ye be unkinde,
And but ye come at day set in-to Troye,
Ne shal I never have hele, honour, ne joye.

207

For al-so sooth as sonne up-rist on morwe,
And, god! so wisly thou me, woful wrecche,
To reste bringe out of this cruel sorwe,
I wol my-selven slee if that ye drecche.
But of my deeth though litel be to recche,
Yet, er that ye me cause so to smerte,
Dwel rather here, myn owene swete herte!

208

For trewely, myn owene lady dere,
Tho sleightes yet that I have herd yow stere
Ful shaply been to failen alle y-fere.
For thus men seyn, 'that oon thenketh the bere,
But al another thenketh his ledere.'
Your sire is wys, and seyd is, out of drede,
'Men may the wyse at-renne, and not at-rede.'

209

It is ful hard to halten unespyed
Bifore a crepul, for he can the craft;
Your fader is in sleighte as Argus yëd;
For al be that his moeble is him biraft,
His olde sleighte is yet so with him laft,
Ye shal not blende him for your womanhede,
Ne feyne a-right, and that is al my drede.

Made him report their omens the wrong way,
When he in fear from Delphi did depart.
You'll see that I shall give him such a start
That he will turn completely round about;
Within a day or two, you'll find this out."

203

I can but think, as I it written find,
That all of this was said with good intent,
And that her heart withal was true and kind,
And what she said, all that she truly meant,
And of her grief no part did she invent,
And ever thought to him she would be true,
But of her heart, not all of it she knew.

204

Poor Troilus, with heart and ears outspread,
Drank in this tale of plotting to and fro,
And almost was convinced by what she said,
But nevertheless to let her from him go,
That gave him many a pang of doubt and woe;
But finally, against his better mind,
He trusted her and all his doubts resigned.

205

The tempest of his grief somewhat abated,
Despair gave way to hope, and new
delight
Of love was for old sorrow reinstated;
And as the birds against the sun so bright
Sing on the branch, though hidden from all sight,
So were their words to this so loving pair
Songs of delight, their solace to declare.

206

Yet still the thought that Cressida must go,
Troilus could not drive from out his mind,
And all his words his dark forebodings show
That truth in her he might not ever find;
"If e'er to me," he said, "you are unkind,
And if you come not on your day to town,
Farewell my health, my honor and renown!

207

"For just as sure as morrow's sun shall rise,
If your returning you should long delay,
No other refuge open to me lies,
But black despair at once my heart will slay;
And though the thought of death brings no dismay,
Rather than such grief on us both should fall,
Sweetheart, I beg, don't go away at all!

208

"To tell the truth, my precious sweetheart dear,
Those little tricks of yours of which you've told,
They fill me not with hope, but ghastly fear.
'The bear thinks one thing,' goes the saying old,
'Although his leader other views may hold!'
Your sire is wise, you must look out for it,
'One may the wise outrun, but not outwit.'

209

"It's very hard to limp and not be spied
Before a cripple—that's his specialty.
In tricks your father sure is Argus-eyed,
And though his gold took wings and forth did flee,
His cunning still is left in full degree.
You won't fool him, for all your woman's ways,
And grave doubts in my mind you merely raise.

210

"I do not know if peace shall e'er be made,
But peace or no, it's really all the same,
For Calchas by his turning renegade
Hath so besmirched and so defiled his name,
He dare not come to Troy again for shame,
And so that plan, so far as I can see,
Is nothing but a pleasing fantasy.

211

"You'll see—your father shall you so persuade,
You'll marry there, for he knows how to preach;
For some fine Greek he'll have his plans well laid,
And carry you away with his soft speech,
Or make you wed by force, his end to reach;
And Troilus may then go hang forsooth,
For all his innocence and all his truth!

212

"Yet more—your father doth us all despise,
And says our city is but lost and lorn,
That from this siege we never shall arise,
Since all the Greeks most solemnly have sworn
We shall be slain, and down our walls be torn;
Such fearsome words he will unto you say,
That in the end among the Greeks you'll stay!

213

"And you will see so many a lusty knight
Among the Greeks, and of such mansuetude,
And each of them with heart and wit and might
To please you well abundantly imbued,
That soon you'll weary of the manners rude
Of simple Trojans, loosing from your mind
The bonds that our two hearts together bind.

214

"And this to me so grievous is to think,
That from my breast the very soul 'twill rend,
To lowest depths I feel my heart doth sink,
But at the thought that you from Troy will wend;
Against your father's cunning, heaven defend!
So if you go away, as I have said,
You may as well count me among the dead.

215

"So now, with humble, true and faithful heart,
A thousand times your pardon here I pray;
Regard the matter, sweetheart, from my part,
And do somewhat as I shall to you say,
And let us two in silence steal away;
Bethink 'tis naught but folly pure and plain,
To lose the great, some minor point to gain.

216

"I mean that since we may, ere break of day,
Steal forth and be together ever so,
What need for such uncertainty to stay,
If you hence to the Grecian army go,
Of your returning here again or no?
Why should we put in pawn a joy secure
For far-off prospects, doubtful and unsure?

217

"And now to speak of low, material things
Like money, each of us can take along
Enough to buy what pleasures money brings,
Till death shall take us with his power strong.
This do I urge, this choice cannot be wrong,

210

I noot if pees shal ever-mo bityde;
But, pees or no, for ernest ne for game,
I woot, sin Calkas on the Grekes syde
Hath ones been, and lost so foule his name,
He dar no more come here ayein for shame;
For which that weye, for ought I can espye,
To trusten on, nis but a fantasye.

211

Ye shal eek seen, your fader shal yow glose
To been a wyf, and as he can wel preche,
He shal som Greek so preyse and wel alose,
That ravisshen he shal yow with his speche,
Or do yow doon by force as he shal teche.
Ane Troilus, of whom ye nil han routhe,
Shal causeles so sterven in his trouthe!

212

And over al this, your fader shal despyse
Us alle, and seyn this citee nis but lorn;
And that th'assege never shal aryse,
For-why the Grekes han it alle sworn
Til we be slayn, and doun our walles torn.
And thus he shal you with his wordes fere,
That ay drede I, that ye wol bleve there.

213

Ye shul eek seen so many a lusty knight
A-mong the Grekes, ful of worthinesse,
And eche of hem with herte, wit, and might
To plesen yow don al his besinesse,
That ye shul dullen of the rudenesse
Of us sely Trojanes, but-if routhe
Remorde yow, or vertue of your trouthe.

214

And this to me so grevous is to thinke,
That fro my brest it wol my soule rende;
Ne dredeles, in me ther may not sinke
A good opinioun, if that ye wende;
For-why your faderes sleighte wol us shende.
And if ye goon, as I have told yow yore,
So thenk I nam but deed, with-oute more.

215

For which, with humble, trewe, and pitous herte,
A thousand tymes mercy I yow preye;
So reweth on myn aspre peynes smerte,
And doth somwhat, as that I shal yow seye,
And lat us stele away bitwixe us tweye;
And thenk that folye is, whan man may chese,
For accident his substaunce ay to lese.

216

I mene this, that sin we mowe er day
Wel stele away, and been to-gider so,
What wit were it to putten in assay,
In cas ye sholden to your fader go,
If that ye mighte come ayein or no?
Thus mene I, that it were a gret folye
To putte that sikernesse in jupartye.

217

And vulgarly to speken of substaunce
Of tresour, may we bothe with us lede
Y-nough to live in honour and plesaunce,
Til in-to tyme that we shul ben dede;
And thus we may eschewen al this drede.

For everich other wey ye can recorde,
Myn herte, y-wis, may not ther-with acorde.

218

And hardily, ne dredeth no poverte,
For I have kin and freendes elles-where
That, though we comen in our bare sherte,
Us sholde neither lakke gold ne gere,
But been honoured whyl we dwelten there.
And go we anoon, for, as in myn entente,
This is the beste, if that ye wole assente."

219

Criseyde, with a syk, right in this wyse
Answerde, "y-wis, my dere herte trewe,
We may wel stele away, as ye devyse,
And finde swiche unthrifty weyes newe;
But afterward, ful sore it wol us rewe.
And help me god so at my moste nede
As causeles ye suffren al this drede!

220

For thilke day that I for cherisshinge
Or drede of fader, or of other wight,
Or for estat, delyt, or for weddinge
Be fals to yow, my Troilus, my knight,
Saturnes doughter, Juno, thorugh hir might,
As wood as Athamante do me dwelle
Eternaly in Stix, the put of helle!

221

And this on every god celestial
I swere it yow, and eek on eche goddesse,
On every Nymphe and deite infernal,
On Satiry and Fauny more and lesse,
That halve goddes been of wildernesse;
And Attropos my threed of lyf to-breste
If I be fals; now trowe me if thow leste!

222

And thou, Simoys, that as an arwe clere
Thorugh Troye rennest ay downward to the see,
Ber witnesse of this word that seyd is here,
That thilke day that ich untrewe be
To Troilus, myn owene herte free,
That thou retorne bakwarde to thy welle,
And I with body and soule sinke in helle!

223

But that ye speke, awey thus for to go
And leten alle your freendes, god forbede,
For any womman, that ye sholden so,
And namely, sin Troye hath now swich nede
Of help; and eek of o thing taketh hede,
If this were wist, my lif laye in balaunce,
And your honour; god shilde us fro mischaunce!

224

And if so be that pees her-after take,
As alday happeth, after anger, game,
Why, lord! the sorwe and wo ye wolden make,
That ye ne dorste come ayein for shame!
And er that ye juparten so your name,
Beth nought to hasty in this hote fare;
For hasty man ne wanteth never care.

225

What trowe ye the peple eek al aboute
Wolde of it seye? It is ful light to arede.
They wolden seye, and swere it, out of doute,

With any other plan or other plea,
I cannot in my heart or mind agree.

218

"Of poverty you need have not a fear,
For I have hosts of kin and friends elsewhere,
And though in our bare shirts we did appear,
In all their gold and gear they'd give us share,
And honor us the while we rested there.
So let us go, and go without delay,
I wait but till the happy word you say!"

219

Cressida paused, and said with many sighs,
"In very truth, my precious sweetheart true,
We might thus steal away, as you advise,
Or try some other thriftless plans and new,
But afterward we would it surely rue,
And let me say again, as I have said,
There is no ground for all your fear and dread.

220

"If it should come, at any day or hour,
Through fear of parent or of other wight,
For rank or pride or thought of marriage dower,
That I am false, my Troilus, my knight,
Let Juno, Saturn's daughter, through her might,
Send me, as mad as Athamas, to dwell
Eternally in Styx, the pit of hell!

221

"And this I swear, by every God supernal,
And swear it, too, by every bright Goddess,
By every Nymph and Deity infernal,
By every Faun and Satyr, more and less,
Those demi-gods that haunt the wilderness,
That Atropos may snip her fatal shears
If I am false or justify your fears!

222

"Thou, Simois, that like an arrow clear
Through Troy aye runnest downward to the sea,
Bear witness of the pledge that I speak here,
And on the day that I untrue shall be
To Troilus, who holds my heart in fee,
Flow backward to thy primal source and well,
And let me soul and body sink to hell!

223

"What you propose, to slip away and go,
And leave your friends, a lonely life to lead,
No woman should induce you to do so,
Especially as Troy hath now such need
Of help; and of another thing take heed,
If this were known, the state would have my life,
And death dishonored end all earthly strife.

224

"And if sometime the armies should make peace,
For wildest moments must give way to tame,
Your lamentations then would never cease,
Because you couldn't come back here for shame;
And so before you peril thus your name,
Be not too hot, or on rash action bent;
The hasty man must many times repent.

225

"What think you all the people round about
Would say of it? 'Tis easy to surmise!
They'd say, and think it true beyond a doubt,

Not love impelled you to such enterprise,
But lust and coward fear, and such like lies.
And thus were lost, sweetheart so dear,
Your honest name, which shines now bright and
clear.

That love ne droof yow nought to doon this dede,
But lust voluptuous and coward drede.
Thus were al lost, y-wis, myn herte dere,
Your honour, which that now shyneth so
clere.

226

"And also think a moment on my name,
Flourishing yet, but with how dark a blot
And with what stains it would be brought to
shame,
If I should flee to some forbidden spot;
Never till death should end my mortal lot
Could I again fair reputation win;
Thus were I lost, and lost in shame and sin.

226

And also thenketh on myn honestee,
That floureth yet, how foule I sholde it shende,
And with what filthe it spotted sholde
be,
If in this forme I sholde with yow wende.
Ne though I livede un-to the worldes ende,
My name sholde I never ayeinward winne;
Thus were I lost, and that were routhe and sinne.

227

"Let rashness then to reason make way here!
Men say, 'To patience comes the victory,'
And too, 'Who will be dear, he must hold dear.'
Thus make a virtue of necessity!
Be patient! Think that Fortune's lord is he
Who asks no help from her in his pursuits;
The coward wretch alone she persecutes.

227

And for-thy slee with reson al this hete;
Men seyn, "the suffraunt overcometh," pardee;
Eek "who-so wol han leef, he leef mot lete";
Thus maketh vertue of necessitee
By pacience, and thenk that lord is he
Of fortune ay, that nought wol of hir recche;
And she ne daunteth no wight but a wrecche.

228

"Believe, sweetheart, with perfect confidence,
Before Lucina, Phoebus' sister dear,
Her path beyond the Lion shall commence,
Without a doubt again I shall be here—
I mean that when the tenth day shall appear,
No power short of death can so prevail
To make me in my promised coming fail."

228

And trusteth this, that certes, herte swete,
Er Phebus suster, Lucina the shene,
The Leoun passe out of this Ariete,
I wol ben here, with-outen any wene.
I mene, as helpe me Juno, hevenes quene,
The tenthe day, but-if that deeth me assayle,
I wol yow seen, with-outen any fayle."

229

"So must it be," said Troilus at last,
"And since I must, I will await that day,
For well I see, time of debate is past!
But for the love of God, once more I pray,
Let us tonight in secret steal away,
Together forever, forever so at rest,
The counsels of the heart are ever best."

229

"And now, so this be sooth," quod Troilus,
"I shal wel suffre un-to the tenthe day,
Sin that I see that nede it moot be thus.
But, for the love of god, if it be may,
So lat us stele prively away;
For ever in oon, as for to live in reste,
Myn herte seyth that it wol been the beste."

230

"O now," cried Cressida distressedly,
"Alas, you drive me wild with all your fears!
It seems you have but little trust in me,
And by your words it patently appears!
In Cynthia's name, so bright among the spheres,
Mistrust me not, for thou hast little reason
To lay against me any taint of treason.

230

"O mercy, god, what lyf is this?" quod she;
"Allas, ye slee me thus for verray tene!
I see wel now that ye mistrusten me;
For by your wordes it is wel y-sene.
Now, for the love of Cynthia the shene,
Mistrust me not thus causeles, for routhe;
Sin to be trewe I have yow plight my trouthe.

231

"Bethink you well that often it is art
To lose some time a better time to gain,
And though we for a day or two must part,
I'm not yet lost, nor shall I lost remain,
And from such foolish thoughts, I beg, refrain.
Now trust in me and banish all this sorrow,
Or grief will end my days before tomorrow.

231

And thenketh wel, that som tyme it is wit
To spende a tyme, a tyme for to winne;
Ne, pardee, lorn am I nought fro yow yit,
Though that we been a day or two a-twinne.
Dryf out the fantasyes yow with-inne;
And trusteth me, and leveth eek your sorwe,
Or here my trouthe, I wol not live til morwe.

232

"For if you knew how much I am oppressed
By this, you'd cease your argument;
The very spirit weepeth in my breast
To hear you grieve and bitterly resent
That with the Greeks a few days must be spent!
Though I myself, did I not know the cure,
Such fate with fortitude could not endure.

232

For if ye wiste how sore it doth me smerte,
Ye wolde cesse of this; for god, thou wost,
The pure spirit wepeth in myn herte,
To see yow wepen that I love most,
And that I moot gon to the Grekes ost.
Ye, nere it that I wiste remedye
To come ayein, right here I wolde dye!

233

But certes, I am not so nyce a wight
That I ne can imaginen a way
To come ayein that day that I have hight.
For who may holde thing that wol a-way?
My fader nought, for al his queynte pley.
And by my thrift, my wending out of Troye
Another day shal torne us alle to joye.

234

For-thy, with al myn herte I yow beseke,
If that yow list don ought for my preyere,
And for the love which that I love yow eke,
That er that I departe fro yow here,
That of so good a comfort and a chere
I may you seen, that ye may bringe at reste
Myn herte, which that is at point to breste.

235

And over al this, I pray yow," quod she tho,
"Myn owene hertes soothfast suffisaunce,
Sin I am thyn al hool, with-outen mo,
That whyl that I am absent, no plesaunce
Of othere do me fro your remembraunce.
For I am ever a-gast, for-why men rede,
That 'love is thing ay ful of bisy drede.'

236

For in this world ther liveth lady noon,
If that ye were untrewe, as god defende!
That so bitraysed were or wo bigoon
As I, that alle trouthe in yow entende.
And douteles, if that ich other wende,
I nere but deed; and er ye cause finde,
For goddes love, so beth me not unkinde."

237

To this answerde Troilus and seyde,
"Now god, to whom ther nis no cause y-wrye,
Me glade, as wis I never un-to Criseyde,
Sin thilke day I saw hir first with yë,
Was fals, ne never shal til that I dye.
At shorte wordes, wel ye may me leve;
I can no more, it shal be founde at preve."

238

"Graunt mercy, goode myn, y-wis," quod she,
"And blisful Venus lat me never sterve
Er I may stonde of plesaunce in degree
To quyte him wel, that so wel can deserve;
And whyl that god my wit wol me conserve,
I shal so doon, so trewe I have yow founde,
That ay honour to me-ward shal rebounde.

239

For trusteth wel, that your estat royal
Ne veyn delyt, nor only worthinesse
Of yow in werre, or torney marcial,
Ne pompe, array, nobley, or eek richesse,
Ne made me to rewe on your distresse;
But moral vertue, grounded upon trouthe,
That was the cause I first hadde on yow routhe!

240

Eek gentil herte and manhod that ye hadde,
And that ye hadde, as me thoughte, in despyt
Every thing that souned in-to badde,
As rudenesse and poeplish appetyt;

233

"But I am not of such a simple mind
That I can't ferret out some easy way,
A speedy time for my return to find,
For who can hold what hath a will to stray?
My father can't, whatever tricks he play!
And take it so, my going forth from Troy
But antecedent is to greater joy!

234

"With all my heart I therefore you beseech,
If anything you'll ever grant to me,
And for the love that we have each for each,
Ere from my presence you tonight must flee,
A smile upon your features I may see,
As cheering witness to my troubled breast
That once again our hearts in union rest.

235

"And finally," she said, "one thing I pray,
My soul's delight and only satisfaction,
Since I am wholly thine, while I'm away,
Seek not elsewhere for pleasure and distraction,
Nor let love grow oblivious from inaction!
For still I fear, since often it is said,
'In love there always lies a cause for dread.'

236

"This world cannot another lady show,
If thou shouldst be untrue (as God defend),
Who would be cast in deeper depths of woe,
Than I, who shall be true unto the end;
Should any fate like that on me descend,
I could not live, and till just cause you find,
I pray to God, be not to me unkind!"

237

"By all the Gods," cried Troilus, "above,
And all that dwell below this solid earth,
I've never swerved an instant in my love
From that first moment when it had its birth,
Nor ever shall I hold thee at less worth;
I can but say, to you I'm ever bound,
And truth thereof will in the end be found."

238

"Have all my thanks," she said, "O sweetheart mine,
And blessed Venus, ere I end my days,
Fulfil in Cressida thy great design,
And quit him well who merits all my praise!
As long as soul with living body stays,
I shall so strive, so true you've ever been,
That love with lasting honor we shall win.

239

"Believe me well that neither vain delight,
Nor royal rank, nor yet the high respect
Of you in war, or in the tourney fight,
Nor pomp, nor wealth, nor dress, did aught affect
My heart, and thy sole image there erect—
No, moral virtue, firmly set and true,
That was the reason why I first loved you.

240

"The gentle heart and manhood that you had,
And nobly cherished, ever in despite
Of all things leaning to the low and bad,
All coarseness and all vulgar appetite,

So that your reason bridled your delight—
For this I was above all others yours,
And shall be so, as long as life endures.

And that your reson brydled your delyt,
This made, aboven every creature,
That I was your, and shal, whyl I may dure.

241

"Through length of years my love I'll not forsake,
Nor Fortune, mutable, shall e'er deface
My heart! But Jupiter, who well can make
The wretched glad, give us the happy grace
To meet again in ten nights in this place;
But now, alas, how swift the hour flies!
Farewell, dear heart, for now you must arise."

241

And this may lengthe of yeres not for-do,
Ne remuable fortune deface;
But Juppiter, that of his might may do
The sorwful to be glad, so yeve us grace,
Er nightes ten, to meten in this place,
So that it may your herte and myn suffyse;
And fareth now wel, for tyme is that ye ryse."

242

'Tis thus they end their long lamentings sad,
And kiss, and each in other's arms enfold;
But daylight breaks, and Troilus now clad,
Full sadly doth his lady's face behold,
As one who feels the breath of death so cold,
And with a grief that heavy on him bore,
Of last goodbyes he said to her a score.

242

And after that they longe y-pleyned hadde,
And ofte y-kist and streite in armes folde,
The day gan ryse, and Troilus him cladde,
And rewfulliche his lady gan biholde,
As he that felte dethes cares colde.
And to hir grace he gan him recomaunde;
Wher him was wo, this holde I no demaunde.

243

I doubt if any head imagine can,
Or judgment weigh, or any tongue could tell
The cruel anguish of this woful man,
Surpassing all the torments dire of hell;
Since with his lady he no more may dwell,
His heart perturbed and dark with dread portent,
Forth from her chamber, silently he went.

243

For mannes heed imaginen ne can,
Ne entendement considere, ne tonge telle
The cruel peynes of this sorwful man,
That passen every torment doun in helle.
For whan he saugh that she ne mighte dwelle,
Which that his soule out of his herte rente,
With-outen more, out of the chaumbre he wente.

HERE ENDETH THE FOURTH BOOK

BOOK V

HERE BEGINNETH THE FIFTH BOOK

1

THE end approacheth of the destiny
Which Jove so long hath had in preparation,
And you, O Parcae, angry sisters three,
He trusteth with the fatal consummation!
Now Cressida must suffer love's probation,
And Troilus to grief himself resign
While Lachesis his thread of life shall twine.

1

APROCHEN gan the fatal destinee
That Joves hath in disposicioun,
And to yow, angry Parcas, sustren three,
Committeth, to don execucioun;
For which Criseyde moste out of the toun,
And Troilus shal dwelle forth in pyne
Til Lachesis his threed no lenger twyne.—

2

The gold-crowned Phoebus, high in heaven aloft,
Three times upon the earth below had seen
The molten snows, and Zephyrus as oft
Had brought again the tender leaflets green,
Since first the son of Hecuba the queen,
Began to cherish her for whom this sorrow
Had come, that she must leave him on the morrow.

2

The golden-tressed Phebus heighe on-lofte
Thryës hadde alle with his bemes shene
The snowes molte, and Zephirus as ofte
Y-brought ayein the tendre leves grene,
Sin that the sone of Ecuba the quene
Bigan to love hir first, for whom his sorwe
Was al, that she departe sholde a-morwe.

3

Before the hour of nine came Diomede,
With him now Cressida from Troy must go;
The sorrows of her suffering heart exceed
All sorrow she had ever thought to know;
Yet all this inner grief she may not show,
But forth from out the Trojan town must fare,
And all the weight of woe in silence bear.

3

Ful redy was at pryme Dyomede,
Criseyde un-to the Grekes ost to lede,
For sorwe of which she felte hir herte blede,
As she that niste what was best to rede.
And trewely, as men in bokes rede,
Men wiste never womman han the care,
Ne was so looth out of a toun to fare.

4

And Troilus, a lost and wandering sprite,
From whose sad heart all happiness was fled,

4

This Troilus, with-outen reed or lore,
As man that hath his joyes eek forlore,

Was waytinge on his lady ever-more
As she that was the soothfast crop and more
Of al his lust, or joyes here-tofore.
But Troilus, now farewel al thy joye,
For shaltow never seen hir eft in Troye!

5

Soth is, that whyl he bood in this manere,
He gan his wo ful manly for to hyde,
That wel unnethe it seen was in his chere;
But at the yate ther she sholde oute ryde
With certeyn folk, he hoved hir t'abyde,
So wo bigoon, al wolde he nought him pleyne,
That on his hors unnethe he sat for peyne.

6

For ire he quook, so gan his herte gnawe,
Whan Diomede on horse gan him dresse,
And seyde un-to him-self this ilke sawe,
"Allas," quod he, "thus foul a
  wrecchednesse
Why suffre ich it, why nil ich it redresse?
Were it not bet at ones for to dye
Than ever-more in langour thus to drye?

7

Why nil I make at ones riche and pore
To have y-nough to done, er that she go?
Why nil I bringe al Troye upon a rore?
Why nil I sleen this Diomede also?
Why nil I rather with a man or two
Stele hir a-way? Why wol I this endure?
Why nil I helpen to myn owene cure?"

8

But why he nolde doon so fel a dede,
That shal I seyn, and why him liste it spare:
He hadde in herte alwey a maner drede,
Lest that Criseyde, in rumour of this fare,
Sholde han ben slayn; lo, this was al his care.
And elles, certeyn, as I seyde yore,
He hadde it doon, with-outen wordes more.

9

Criseyde, whan she redy was to ryde,
Ful sorwfully she sighte, and seyde "allas!"
But forth she moot, for ought that may bityde,
And forth she rit ful sorwfully a pas.
Ther nis non other remedie in this cas.
What wonder is though that hir sore smerte,
Whan she forgoth hir owene swete herte?

10

This Troilus, in wyse of curteisye,
With hauke on hond, and with an huge route
Of knightes, rood and dide hir companye,
Passinge al the valey fer with-oute.
And ferther wolde han riden, out of doute,
Ful fayn, and wo was him to goon so sone;
But torne he moste, and it was eek to done.

11

And right with that was Antenor y-come
Out of the Grekes ost, and every wight
Was of it glad, and seyde he was welcome.
And Troilus, al nere his herte light,
He peyned him with al his fulle might
Him to with-holde of wepinge at the leste,
And Antenor he kiste, and made feste.

Had thoughts but of his lady, fair and bright,
Who now as ever, was the fountain-head
Of all his hope, the cure for all his dread.
But Troilus, farewell to hope of joy,
For thou shalt never seek her back in Troy!

5

And since he could do nothing now but wait,
Full manfully he strove his grief to hide
From curious eyes, and at the city gate,
Whence forth upon her journey she should ride,
He and her friends to do her honor bide,
Though on his horse his seat he scarcely kept,
For grief unknown, unspoken and unwept.

6

What anger at his heart began to gnaw
When Diomede upon his steed drew near!
But anger now must yield to higher law,
Checked by his promised pledge, though not
  by fear.
"Alas," he sighed, "that I stand idle here!
Were it not better death should end this anguish,
Than evermore in lonely grief to languish?

7

"Why do I not the world and all defy,
And put a stop to this so hateful deed?
Why do I not all Trojan power deny?
Why do I not destroy this Diomede?
And carry her away upon my steed?
Why do I this misfortune so endure?
Why do I not risk all for my own cure?"

8

But there was reason why he could not do
These things, and must them sadly all resign;
For in his heart the fear of danger grew,
Not to himself, but fear lest any sign
Of violence should make the Greeks combine,
And in the wild disorder of the fray,
His helpless lady they in wrath would slay.

9

Now Cressida is ready forth to ride,
Though far more gladly she would stay than go;
But to the Greeks she must whate'er betide,
And to the world a willing face must show;
Thus forth she paces, statelily and slow,
And who can wonder that her heart should grieve,
Since all her love and joy she now must leave!

10

And Troilus by way of courtesy,
With hawk on hand, and with an escort strong
Of knights, this lady doth accompany;
Across the valley rode the noble throng,
And even farther Troilus did long
To ride, but though it grieved him to do so,
Return he must, he may no farther go.

11

For at that moment forth Antenor came
From out the Grecian host, and those of Troy
Rejoiced and greeted him with loud acclaim;
And Troilus, though sharing not their joy,
Took heed restraining caution to employ,
And let no sign of sorrow mar his face,
But met Antenor with a kind embrace.

12

Such greetings made, his leave he now must take;
On Cressida he cast his lingering eye,
And to her side his way doth sadly make,
And took her hand to say a last goodbye,
While she, alas, doth naught but weep and sigh;
One word he softly said beneath his breath,
"Now hold your day, on that hangs life and death!"

13

His courser then he wheeled and rode away,
With face all pale, and unto Diomede
No word did he or any Trojan say,
Of which the son of Tydeus took heed,
Who knew a thing or two not in the Creed;
He took the lady's bridle at his side,
While back to Troy lone Troilus must ride.

14

Now Diomede, who held her horse's bridle,
When all the folk of Troy had gone away,
Reflected, "All my labor shan't be idle,
If I have anything in this to say;
'Twill help at least at putting in the day.
I've heard it said, and read it in a book,
'He is a fool who doth himself o'erlook.'"

15

But Diomede was wise, with wit enough,
And mused, "I shall, I'm sure, accomplish naught
If I begin too soon, or treat her rough;
For if that man is dwelling in her thought
Whom I suppose, so soon he can't be brought
Out of her mind; but I shall find a way,
So she shan't guess what game I mean to play."

16

Then Diomede, attending at her side,
Remarked to her, she seemed a trifle sad,
And hoped she would not weary of the ride,
And anything she wanted, he'd be glad
To get for her, and do whate'er she bade,
For he was hers to order and command,
Till at her father's tent-door she should stand.

17

He swore upon his honor as a knight,
That nothing in the world would him more
please,
Than to exert himself with will and might
To add unto her pleasure and her ease,
And hoped she would grow gladder by degrees,
"Because," he said, "we Greeks will all enjoy
Your company as much as those of Troy.

18

"Just now," he said, "You feel a little strange—
No wonder, since it's all so fresh and new,
From Trojan friends to Grecian friends to change,
Who all as yet are quite unknown to you;
But take my word for it, that just as true
A Greek you shall among our people find
As any Trojan, and just as well inclined.

19

"And since your friend I'll be, forever steady,
As I have sworn, to help you all I can,
And since we're old acquaintances already,
And since you know me best of any man—

12

And ther-with-al he moste his leve take,
And caste his eye upon hir pitously,
And neer he rood, his cause for to make,
To take hir by the honde al sobrely.
And lord! so she gan wepen tendrely!
And he ful softe and sleighly gan hir seye,
"Now hold your day, and dooth me not to deye."

13

With that his courser torned he a-boute
With face pale, and un-to Diomede
No word he spak, ne noon of al his route;
Of which the sone of Tydeus took hede,
As he that coude more than the crede
In swich a craft, and by the reyne hir hente;
And Troilus to Troye homwarde he wente.

14

This Diomede, that ladde hir by the brydel,
Whan that he saw the folk of Troye aweye,
Thoughte, "al my labour shal not been on ydel,
If that I may, for somwhat shal I seye.
For at the worste it may yet shorte our weye.
I have herd seyd, eek tymes twyës twelve,
'He is a fool that wol for-yete himselve.'"

15

But natheles this thoughte he wel ynough,
"That certaynly I am aboute nought
If that I speke of love, or make it tough;
For douteles, if she have in hir thought
Him that I gesse, he may not been y-brought
So sone awey; but I shal finde a mene,
That she not wite as yet shal what I mene."

16

This Diomede, as he that coude his good,
Whan this was doon, gan fallen forth in speche
Of this and that, and asked why she stood
In swich disese, and gan hir eek biseche,
That if that he encrese mighte or eche
With any thing hir ese, that she sholde
Comaunde it him, and seyde he doon it wolde.

17

For trewely he swoor hir, as a knight,
That ther nas thing with whiche he mighte hir
plese,
That he nolde doon his peyne and al his might
To doon it, for to doon hir herte an ese.
And preyede hir, she wolde hir sorwe apese,
And seyde, "y-wis, we Grekes con have joye
To honouren yow, as wel as folk of Troye."

18

He seyde eek thus, "I woot, yow thinketh straunge,
No wonder is, for it is to yow newe,
Th'aqueintaunce of these Trojanes to chaunge,
For folk of Grece, that ye never knewe.
But wolde never god but-if as trewe
A Greek ye shulde among us alle finde
As any Trojan is, and eek as kinde.

19

And by the cause I swoor yow right, lo, now,
To been your freend, and helply, to my might,
And for that more aqueintaunce eek of yow
Have ich had than another straunger wight,

So fro this forth I pray yow, day and night,
Comaundeth me, how sore that me smerte,
To doon al that may lyke un-to your herte;

20

And that ye me wolde as your brother trete,
And taketh not my frendship in despyt;
And though your sorwes be for thinges grete,
Noot I not why, but out of more respyt,
Myn herte hath for to amende it greet delyt.
And if I may your harmes not redresse,
I am right sory for your hevinesse.

21

And though ye Trojans with us Grekes wrothe
Han many a day be, alwey yet, pardee,
O god of love in sooth we serven bothe.
And, for the love of god, my lady free,
Whom so ye hate, as beth not wroth with me.
For trewely, ther can no wight yow serve,
That half so looth your wraththe wolde deserve.

22

And nere it that we been so neigh the tente
Of Calkas, which that seen us bothe may,
I wolde of this yow telle al myn entente;
But this enseled til another day.
Yeve me your hond, I am, and shal ben ay,
God help me so, whyl that my lyf may dure,
Your owene aboven every creature.

23

Thus seyde I never er now to womman born;
For god myn herte as wisly glade so,
I lovede never womman here-biforn
As paramours, ne never shal no mo.
And, for the love of god, beth not my fo;
Al can I not to yow, my lady dere,
Compleyne aright, for I am yet to lere.

24

And wondreth not, myn owene lady bright,
Though that I speke of love to you thus blyve;
For I have herd or this of many a wight,
Hath loved thing he never saugh his lyve.
Eek I am not of power for to stryve
Ayens the god of love, but him obeye
I wol alwey, and mercy I yow preye.

25

Ther been so worthy knightes in this place,
And ye so fair, that everich of hem alle
Wol peynen him to stonden in your grace.
But mighte me so fair a grace falle,
That ye me for your servaunt wolde calle,
So lowly ne so trewely you serve
Nil noon of hem, as I shal, til I sterve."

26

Criseide un-to that purpos lyte answerde,
As she that was with sorwe oppressed so
That, in effect, she nought his tales herde,
But here and there, now here a word or two.
Hir thoughte hir sorwful herte brast a-two.
For whan she gan hir fader fer aspye,
Wel neigh doun of hir hors she gan
to sye.

27

But natheles she thonked Diomede

I mean of course among the Grecian clan—,
I hope that you will always feel quite free,
In case of any need, to call on me.

20

"Regard me as your brother, let me pray,
And take my friendship kindly, as 'tis meant;
And if perhaps some griefs upon you weigh,
I know not why, but all my heart is bent
On aiding you, if you will but consent;
And if your troubles deep I can't amend,
For sympathy at least on me depend.

21

"You Trojans towards us Greeks are filled with hate,
But so in every case it need not be;
For Greeks and Trojans likewise venerate
The God of Love as their divinity.
Hate whom you will, but be not wroth with me,
For no man living, you may well believe,
If you were angry, would more deeply grieve.

22

"But now we're drawing near your father's tent,
Whose eyes, I have no doubt, are turned this way;
With what I've said, I now must be content,
And leave the rest until some other day.
Give me your hand! I am, and shall be aye,
So heaven help me, while my life shall last,
In friendship yours, forever firm and fast.

23

"Such words to woman never have I spoken,
For by my hope of earthly happiness,
No woman have I given any token
Of love, and shall hereafter give still less,
If with your friendship, you my soul will bless;
Forgive me if my thought I rudely blurt,
For in these matters I am not expert.

24

"And do not be surprised, my lady bright,
That thus I speak to you of love so soon;
For I have heard of many a noble knight
Who, sight unseen, hath sought the lover's boon;
Nor have I power in me to oppugn
The God of Love, but must his will obey,
And ever shall, and for your mercy pray.

25

"There are such knights, so worthy, in this place,
And you so fair, that they will one and all
Bestir themselves to stand high in your grace;
But if such fortune to my lot should fall,
That me your humble servant you will call,
I promise here that I will serve as true
And faithfully as any man can do."

26

This blarney Cressida but vaguely heard,
So grievously at heart she was oppressed,
Although she could not help but catch a word
Or two, which she thought briefly it were best
To answer, letting so the matter rest;
But when at last her father came in sight,
Down from her horse she almost slipped from
fright.

27

But still she spoke her thanks to Diomede

For all his trouble and his kindly care,
And for his proffered friendship, which indeed
She now accepted with a gracious air,
And hoped they'd meet again sometime somewhere,
And said she thought he was a trusty knight,
And down from off her horse did then alight.

28

Within his arms her father hath her taken,
And twenty times he kissed his daughter sweet.
"Welcome," he cried, "O daughter mine forsaken!"
And she, she said, was glad that they should meet
Again, and stood, submissive and discreet.
And here I leave her, her new life to lead,
For back to Troilus I now must speed.

29

To Troy this woful Troilus returned,
Sorrow of sorrows now his hapless lot;
With angry brow all dallying he spurned,
But down from his horse without delay he got,
And to his chamber hastened like a shot;
His comrades were afraid a word to say,
For he did slight attention to them pay.

30

To all the woes that he so long had checked,
He had at last a chance to give free rein;
He cursed the Gods for all his hopes thus wrecked,
Jove and Apollo and Cupid, time and again,
Ceres, Bacchus and Venus, with might and main,
His birth, himself, his fate, the world so blind,
And save his lady, all of human kind.

31

To bed he goes, and tosses there and turns,
As does Ixion, suffering deep in hell,
And through the sleepless night he there sojourns;
But then his heart a little doth unswell,
Relieved by floods of tears that upward well;
His lady he began now to invoke,
And to himself these sorrowing words he spoke:

32

"O where is now my lovely lady dear?
Where are her breasts so white, O where, O where?
Where are her arms and where her eyes so clear,
Which yesternight were solace to my care?
Now I must weep alone in dark despair,
And blindly grope, but nothing in this place,
Except a pillow, find I to embrace!

33

"What shall I do? When will she come again?
God knows, alas! Why did I let her go?
O, would that I had perished there and then!
O precious heart, O Cressida, sweet foe,
O lady mine, my weeping eyes o'erflow!
With all my life and soul I thee endow,
But though I die, you can not aid me now!

34

"Who looks upon you now, my bright lodestar?
Who maketh now to thee his compliments?
Who comforts you, away from me so far?
Now I am gone, whom give you audience?
Who troubleth now to speak in my defence?
Alas, no man! And though I grieve and pine,
As evil is your fortune as is mine!

Of al his travaile, and his goode chere,
And that him liste his friendship hir to bede;
And she accepteth it in good manere,
And wolde do fayn that is him leef and dere;
And trusten him she wolde, and wel she mighte,
As seyde she, and from hir hors she alighte.

28

Hir fader hath hir in his armes nome,
And tweynty tyme he kiste his doughter swete,
And seyde, "O dere doughter myn, welcome!"
She seyde eek, she was fayn with him to mete,
And stood forth mewet, mildë, and mansuete.
But here I leve hir with hir fader dwelle,
And forth I wol of Troilus yow telle.

29

To Troye is come this woful Troilus.
In sorwe aboven alle sorwes smerte,
With felon look, and face dispitous.
Tho sodeinly doun from his hors he sterte,
And thorugh his paleys, with a swollen herte,
To chambre he wente; of no-thing took he hede,
Ne noon to him dar speke a word for drede.

30

And there his sorwes that he spared hadde
He yaf an issue large, and "deeth!" he cryde;
And in his throwes frenetyk and madde
He cursed Jove, Appollo, and eek Cupyde,
He cursed Ceres, Bacus, and Cipryde,
His burthe, him-self, his fate, and eek nature,
And, save his lady, every creature.

31

To bedde he goth, and weyleth there and torneth
In furie, as dooth he, Ixion, in helle;
And in this wyse he neigh til day sojorneth.
But tho bigan his herte a lyte unswelle
Thorugh teres which that gonnen up to welle;
And pitously he cryde up-on Criseyde,
And to him-self right thus he spak, and seyde:—

32

"Wher is myn owene lady lief and dere,
Wher is hir whyte brest, wher is it, where?
Wher been hir armes and hir eyen clere,
That yesternight this tyme with me were?
Now may I wepe allone many a tere,
And graspe aboute I may, but in this place,
Save a pilowe, I finde nought t'enbrace.

33

How shal I do? Whan shal she com ayeyn?
I noot, allas! why leet ich hir to go?
As wolde god, ich hadde as tho be sleyn!
O herte myn, Criseyde, O swete fo!
O lady myn, that I love and no mo!
To whom for ever-mo myn herte I dowe;
See how I deye, ye nil me not rescowe!

34

Who seeth yow now, my righte lodesterre?
Who sit right now or stant in your presence?
Who can conforten now your hertes werre?
Now I am gon, whom yeve ye audience?
Who speketh for me right now in myn absence?
Allas, no wight; and that is al my care;
For wel wot I, as yvel as I ye fare.

35

How shulde I thus ten dayes ful endure,
Whan I the firste night have al this tene?
How shal she doon eek, sorwful creature?
For tendernesse, how shal she this sustene,
Swich wo for me? O pitous, pale, and grene
Shal been your fresshe wommanliche face
For langour, er ye torne un-to this place."

36

And whan he fil in any slomeringes,
Anoon biginne he sholde for to grone,
And dremen of the dredfulleste thinges
That mighte been; as, mete he were allone
In place horrible, makinge ay his mone,
Or meten that he was amonges alle
His enemys, and in hir hondes falle.

37

And ther-with-al his body sholde sterte,
And with the stert al sodeinliche awake,
And swich a tremour fele aboute his herte,
That of the feer his body sholde quake;
And there-with-al he sholde a noyse make,
And seme as though he sholde falle depe
From heighe a-lofte; and than he wolde wepe,

38

And rewen on him-self so pitously,
That wonder was to here his fantasye.
Another tyme he sholde mightily
Conforte him-self, and seyn it was folye,
So causeles swich drede for to drye,
And eft biginne his aspre sorwes newe,
That every man mighte on his sorwes rewe.

39

Who coude telle aright or ful discryve
His wo, his pleynte, his langour, and his pyne?
Nought al the men that han or been onlyve.
Thou, redere, mayst thy-self ful wel devyne
That swich a wo my wit can not defyne.
On ydel for to wryte it sholde I swinke,
Whan that my wit is wery it to thinke.

40

On hevene yet the sterres were sene,
Al-though ful pale y-waxen was the mone;
And whyten gan the orisonte shene
Al estward, as it woned is to done.
And Phebus with his rosy carte sone
Gan after that to dresse him up to fare,
Whan Troilus hath sent after Pandare.

41

This Pandare, that of al the day biforn
Ne mighte have comen Troilus to see,
Al-though he on his heed it hadde y-sworn,
For with the king Pryam alday was he,
So that it lay not in his libertee
No-where to gon, but on the morwe he wente
To Troilus, whan that he for him sente.

42

For in his herte he coude wel devyne,
That Troilus al night for sorwe wook;
And that he wolde telle him of his pyne,
This knew he wel y-nough, with-oute book.
For which to chaumbre streight the wey he took,

35

"And how shall I for ten whole days survive,
If I the first night suffer all this pain?
And how shall she, my sweetheart, keep alive?
How shall her tender heart such woe sustain?
What sorry signs of grief must still remain
Imprinted on her fair and gracious face
Until time brings her back unto this place!"

36

And if he fell in any slumbering,
He did not cease to toss about and groan,
Or dream perhaps of some most dreadful thing,
As thus, that he must lie and ever moan,
Abandoned in some frightful place alone,
Or that he was among his foes withal,
And in their cruel hands about to fall.

37

And then convulsively he up would start,
And with the shock would suddenly awake,
While such a tremor ran throughout his heart,
The fear of it made all his body quake,
And horrid gasping sounds his breath would make,
For so it seemed, he fell from some high place,
Down to the lowest depths of endless space.

38

Upon his wretched state when he took thought,
His grief was greater than he well could bear,
But then he took himself in hand, and sought
To brighten up, and said he borrowed care,
And causeless was his grief and his despair,
Yet such devices brought but respite brief,
And hope soon yielded way to fear and grief.

39

O, who could all his woe relate,
His long-enduring sorrow and his pain?
Not all the men on earth incorporate!
Thus, reader, you will see why I refrain
To carry to its end this plaintive strain,
For how may this by my weak art be phrased,
When at the simple thought I stand amazed?

40

The stars still lingered in the morning sky,
But the horizon eastward glimmered gray,
And pale and thin the moon had climbed on high—
In short the dawn came in its usual way,
And Phoebus, ushering in the rosy day,
Brightened the eastern sky as up he went,
And Troilus for faithful Pandar sent.

41

Now Pandar, all the livelong day before,
Had found no chance to proffer sympathy,
Although he knew his friend was suffering sore,
Because all day about the court he had to be,
But now at his first moment's liberty,
He quickly came, responsive to command,
Prepared by his afflicted friend to stand.

42

For in his heart he readily could guess
How Troilus, awake all night, would look,
And how he longed his sorrows to confess—
He knew this well enough without the book!
So to his chamber straight his way he took,

And there most sombrely his friend he greeted
And by him on his bed himself he seated.

43

"My Pandar," then said Troilus, "the sorrow
Within my heart I may no more endure;
Today will be my last, or else tomorrow—
And of some final things I would make sure,
And most about my formal sepulture;
And will you please dispose of my estate,
As your good judgment may to you dictate.

44

"And of the fire and all the funeral flames,
To which my lifeless body thou shalt feed,
And of the feast and the palaestral games
To celebrate my wake, I pray take heed
That they be good; and offer Mars my steed,
My sword, my helmet, and, O brother dear,
My shield to Pallas give, the bright and clear.

45

"The powdered ash to which my heart shall
  burn,
I pray thee take and let it be confined
Within the vessel which men call an urn,
One made of gold, which then shall be consigned
To my fair lady, thus to keep in mind
My love and death, and bid my lady dear
Preserve it as a final souvenir.

46

"For now I feel approach the mortal throes,
And by my dreams, both old and new, I know
My time on earth is drawing near its close;
Besides the boding owl, Ascaphilo,
Two nights hath shrieked for me, the third I go!
To thee, O Mercury, I now confide
My wandering soul, to be its final guide."

47

To this speech Pandar answered, "Troilus,
Dear friend, as I have told you oft before,
'Tis folly so, and most egregious,
To grieve, and now of this I'll say no more;
For he who heeds advice nor other lore,
He may for all that I shall say or do,
Alone in his own juice forever stew.

48

"But Troilus, I pray thee, tell me now,
Do you believe that any such delight
In love a living man hath known as thou?
Why, yes, God knows! And many a worthy wight
Has lacked his lady for a whole fortnight,
And hath not made one half the stir and fuss!
Why must you then be so tempestuous?

49

"For you yourself, on any day, may see,
How one must leave his lady-love or wife,
Through some compulsion or necessity,
Though she were dear to him as his own life,
Yet will not make such great to-do and strife;
For one takes such things as one takes the weather,
The best of friends can't always be together.

50

"And think upon the chaps whose loves are married
By force to other men, as happens oft,

And Troilus tho sobreliche he grette,
And on the bed ful sone he gan him sette.

43

"My Pandarus," quod Troilus, "the sorwe
Which that I drye, I may not longe endure.
I trowe I shal not liven til to-morwe;
For whiche I wolde alwey, on aventure,
To thee devysen of my sepulture
The forme, and of my moeble thou dispone
Right as thee semeth best is for to done.

44

But of the fyr and flaumbe funeral
In whiche my body brenne shal to glede,
And of the feste and pleyes palestral
At my vigile, I pray thee take good hede
That al be wel; and offre Mars my stede,
My swerd, myn helm, and, leve brother dere,
My sheld to Pallas yef, that shyneth clere.

45

The poudre in which myn herte y-brend shal
  torne,
That preye I thee thou take and it conserve
In a vessel, that men clepeth an urne,
Of gold, and to my lady that I serve,
For love of whom thus pitously I sterve,
So yeve it hir, and do me this plesaunce,
To preye hir kepe it for a remembraunce.

46

For wel I fele, by my maladye,
And by my dremes now and yore ago,
Al certeinly, that I mot nedes dye.
The owle eek, which that hight Ascaphilo,
Hath after me shright alle thise nightes two.
And, god Mercurie! of me now, woful wrecche,
The soule gyde, and, whan thee list, it fecche!"

47

Pandare answerde, and seyde, "Troilus,
My dere freend, as I have told thee yore,
That it is folye for to sorwen thus,
And causeles, for whiche I can no-more.
But who-so wol not trowen reed ne lore,
I can not seen in him no remedye,
But lete him worthen with his fantasye.

48

But Troilus, I pray thee tel me now,
If that thou trowe, er this, that any wight
Hath loved paramours as wel as thou?
Ye, god wot, and fro many a worthy knight
Hath his lady goon a fourtenight,
And he not yet made halvendel the fare.
What nede is thee to maken al this care?

49

Sin day by day thou mayst thy-selven see
That from his love, or elles from his wyf,
A man mot twinnen of necessitee,
Ye, though he love hir as his owene lyf;
Yet nil he with him-self thus maken stryf.
For wel thow wost, my leve brother dere,
That alwey freendes may nought been y-fere.

50

How doon this folk that seen hir loves wedded
By freendes might, as it bi-tit ful ofte,

And seen hem in hir spouses bed y-bedded?
God woot, they take it wysly, faire and softe.
For-why good hope halt up hir herte on-lofte,
And for they can a tyme of sorwe endure;
As tyme hem hurt, a tyme doth hem cure.

51

So sholdestow endure, and late slyde
The tyme, and fonde to ben glad and light.
Ten dayes nis so long not t'abyde.
And sin she thee to comen hath bihight,
She nil hir hestes breken for no wight.
For dred thee not that she nil finden weye
To come ayein, my lyf that dorste I leye.

52

Thy swevenes eek and al swich fantasye
Dryf out, and lat hem faren to mischaunce;
For they procede of thy malencolye,
That doth thee fele in sleep al this penaunce.
A straw for alle swevenes signifiaunce!
God helpe me so, I counte hem not a bene,
Ther woot no man aright what dremes mene.

53

For prestes of the temple tellen this,
That dremes been the revelaciouns
Of goddes, and as wel they telle, y-wis,
That they ben infernals illusiouns;
And leches seyn, that of complexiouns
Proceden they, or fast, or glotonye.
Who woot in sooth thus what they signifye?

54

Eek othere seyn that thorugh impressiouns,
As if a wight hath faste a thing in minde,
That ther-of cometh swiche avisiouns;
And othere seyn, as they in bokes finde,
That, after tymes of the yeer by kinde,
Men dreme, and that th'effect goth by the mone;
But leve no dreem, for it is nought to done.

55

Wel worth of dremes ay thise olde wyves,
And treweliche eek augurie of thise foules;
For fere of which men wenen lese her lyves,
As ravenes qualm, or shryking of thise oules.
To trowen on it bothe fals and foul is.
Allas, allas, so noble a creature
As is a man, shal drede swich ordure!

56

For which with al myn herte I thee beseche,
Un-to thy-self that al this thou foryive;
And rys up now with-oute more speche,
And lat us caste how forth may best be drive
This tyme, and eek how freshly we may live
Whan that she cometh, the which shal be right sone;
God help me so, the beste is thus to done.

57

Rys, lat us speke of lusty lyf in Troye
That we han lad, and forth the tyme dryve;
And eek of tyme cominge us rejoye,
That bringen shal our blisse now so blyve;
And langour of these twyës dayes fyve
We shal ther-with so foryete or oppresse,
That wel unnethe it doon shal us duresse.

And to a watchful husband's house are carried!
Hard hit such lovers are, but take it soft,
For hope survives to hold their hearts aloft;
Their needful time of sorrow they endure,
For time brings sorrow, and brings sorrow's cure.

51

"So take things as they come and let time slide,
And cultivate a joyous heart and light!
Ten days is not so long a time to bide.
For her return she pledged her honor bright,
And I am sure that she will come all right;
You need not fear but she will find a way,
I'm quite prepared my life on that to lay.

52

"And all your dreams and other such like folly,
To deep oblivion let them be consigned;
For they arise but from your melancholy,
By which your health is being undermined.
A straw for all the meaning you can find
In dreams! They aren't worth a hill of beans,
For no one knows what dreaming really means.

53

"Priests in the temples sometimes choose to say
That dreams come from the Gods as revelations;
But other times they speak another way,
And call them hellish false hallucinations!
And doctors say they come from complications,
Or fast or surfeit, or any other lie,
For who knows truly what they signify?

54

"And others say that through impressions deep,
As when one has a purpose firm in mind,
There come these visions in one's sleep;
And others say that they in old books find,
That every season hath its special kind
Of dream, and all depends upon the moon;
But all such folk are crazy as a loon!

55

"Dreams are the proper business of old wives,
Who draw their auguries from birds and fowls,
For which men often fear to lose their lives,
The raven's croak or mournful shriek of owls!
O why put trust in bestial shrieks and howls!
Alas, that noble man should be so brash
To implicate his mind in such like trash!

56

"And so with all my heart I thee beseech,
Against these melancholy thoughts to strive;
And pray get up, I've ended now my speech,
And let us plan something to help us drive
Dull care away, and keep us both alive
Till she returns, which won't be very long;
To waste the time in moping is all wrong.

57

"Come, let us think of those good times in Troy
That we have had, to pass the time away;
And think, besides, of those we shall enjoy
At some not very distant happy day.
These twice five days we'll fill with sport and play,
And so amuse ourselves with many things
That time will fly on self-oblivious wings.

58

"This town is full of nobles here and there,
The truce will last, besides, for yet some while,
I say, let's straightway to Sarpedon fare,
The distance to his house is but a mile;
And there we can the time at ease beguile,
Until there rolls around that happy morrow
When she returns, whose absence is thy sorrow.

59

"Get up then, friend and brother Troilus,
For truly it is scarcely worthy thee,
Upon thy bed to weep and cower thus;
For one thing certain you can take from me,
If thus you lie a day or two or three,
The folk will say you have a coward's heart,
And but for fear you play the sick man's part."

60

"O brother dear," Troilus replied,
"They know, whose heavy hearts have suffered pain,
When times of grief and sorrow shall betide
And deep affliction burns in every vein,
Then one cannot from cries of grief abstain;
And though I wept forever, I have good right,
For I have lost the source of all delight.

61

"But since I have to get up in the end,
I shall do so without too great delay,
And meantime pray that God will kindly send
As quickly as he can the glad tenth day!
For never was there bird as fain of May,
As I shall be when she comes back to Troy
Who causes all my grief as well as joy.

62

"But where do you suggest that we should go,
And where can we ourselves the best amuse?"
"My counsel is," said Pandar, "as you know,
To let Sarpedon counteract your blues."
After exchange of arguments and views,
Troilus at last thereto gave his assent,
And forth to good Sarpedon's house they went.

63

Sarpedon was a man in arms most able,
And famed throughout all Troy for living high;
And every costly dainty for the table
For daily entertainment he would buy,
And nothing to his guests he would deny,
Who always said, the greatest and the least,
They never had sat down to such a feast.

64

And in this world there was no instrument,
Sweet with the blast of air or touch of chord,
That skill of man could anywhere invent
For sounds that pleasure to the ear afford,
But it was heard around his festal board;
And ladies, too, to dance at his command
Were there, and ne'er was seen so fair a band.

65

But what avails all this to Troilus,
Whose inward grief absorbs his every thought
And rules his heart with will imperious!
His lady's memory he ever sought,

58

This toun is ful of lordes al aboute,
And trewes lasten al this mene whyle.
Go we pleye us in som lusty route
To Sarpedon, not hennes but a myle.
And thus thou shalt the tyme wel bigyle,
And dryve it forth un-to that blisful morwe,
That thou hir see, that cause is of thy sorwe.

59

Now rys, my dere brother Troilus;
For certes, it noon honour is to thee
To wepe, and in thy bed to jouken thus.
For trewely, of o thing trust to me,
If thou thus ligge a day, or two, or three,
The folk wol wene that thou, for cowardyse,
Thee feynest syk, and that thou darst not ryse."

60

This Troilus answerde, "O brother dere,
This knowen folk that han y-suffred peyne,
That though he wepe and make sorwful chere,
That feleth harm and smert in every veyne,
No wonder is; and though I ever pleyne,
Or alwey wepe, I am no-thing to blame,
Sin I have lost the cause of al my game.

61

But sin of fyne force I moot aryse,
I shal aryse, as sone as ever I may;
And god, to whom myn herte I sacrifyse,
So sende us hastely the tenthe day!
For was ther never fowl so fayn of May,
As I shal been, whan that she cometh in Troye,
That cause is of my torment and my joye.

62

But whider is thy reed," quod Troilus,
"That we may pleye us best in al this toun?"
"By god, my conseil is," quod Pandarus,
"To ryde and pleye us with king Sarpedoun."
So longe of this they speken up and doun,
Til Troilus gan at the laste assente
To ryse, and forth to Sarpedoun they wente.

63

This Sarpedoun, as he that honourable
Was ever his lyve, and ful of heigh prowesse,
With al that mighte y-served been on table,
That deyntee was, al coste it greet richesse,
He fedde hem day by day, that swich noblesse,
As seyden bothe the moste and eek the leste,
Was never er that day wist at any feste.

64

Nor in this world ther is non instrument
Delicious, through wind, or touche, or corde,
As fer as any wight hath ever y-went,
That tonge telle or herte may recorde,
That at that feste it nas wel herd acorde;
Ne of ladies eek so fayr a companye
On daunce, er tho, was never y-seyn with yë.

65

But what avayleth this to Troilus,
That for his sorwe no-thing of it roughte?
For ever in oon his herte piëtous
Ful bisily Criseyde his lady soughte.

On hir was ever al that his herte thoughte.
Now this, now that, so faste imagininge,
That glade, y-wis, can him no festeyinge.

66

These ladies eek that at this feste been,
Sin that he saw his lady was a-weye,
It was his sorwe upon hem for to seen,
Or for to here on instrumentz so pleye.
For she, that of his herte berth the keye,
Was absent, lo, this was his fantasye,
That no wight sholde make melodye.

67

Nor ther nas houre in al the day or night,
Whan he was ther-as no wight mighte him here,
That he ne seyde, "O lufsom lady bright,
How have ye faren, sin that ye were here?
Wel-come, y-wis, myn owene lady dere."
But welaway, al this nas but a mase;
Fortune his howve entended bet to glase.

68

The lettres eek, that she of olde tyme
Hadde him y-sent, he wolde allone rede,
An hundred sythe, a-twixen noon and pryme;
Refiguringe hir shap, hir womanhede,
With-inne his herte, and every word and dede
That passed was, and thus he droof to an ende
The ferthe day, and seyde, he wolde wende.

69

And seyde, "leve brother Pandarus,
Intendestow that we shul herë bleve
Til Sarpedoun wol forth congeyen us?
Yet were it fairer that we toke our leve.
For goddes love, lat us now sone at eve
Our leve take, and homward lat us torne;
For trewely, I nil not thus sojorne."

70

Pandare answerde, "be we comen hider
To fecchen fyr, and rennen hoom ayeyn?
God helpe me so, I can not tellen whider
We mighten goon, if I shal soothly seyn,
Ther any wight is of us more fayn
Than Sarpedoun; and if we hennes hye
Thus sodeinly, I holde it vilanye,

71

Sin that we seyden that we wolde bleve
With him a wouke; and now, thus sodeinly,
The ferthe day to take of him our leve,
He wolde wondren on it, trewely!
Lat us holde forth our purpos fermely;
And sin that ye bihighten him to byde,
Hold forward now, and after lat us ryde."

72

Thus Pandarus, with alle peyne and wo,
Made him to dwelle; and at the woukes ende,
Of Sarpedoun they toke hir leve tho,
And on hir wey they spedden hem to wende.
Quod Troilus, "now god me grace sende,
That I may finden, at myn hom-cominge,
Criseyde comen!" and ther-with gan he singe.

73

"Ye, hasel-wode!" thoughte this Pandare,
And to him-self ful softely he seyde,

And longing such imagination wrought
Of this and that, his mind was never free
To take delight in this festivity.

66

The ladies, too, in throngs assembled there,
Since his was not, among the number gay,
Gave him no ease of heart, though all were fair;
And on sweet instruments to hear men play,
While she was absent who hath borne away
The key of his heart, to him seemed blasphemy,
And vain abuse of such sweet melody.

67

Nor was there hour of all the day or night
When he said not, though not to listening ear,
"O Cressida, my lovely lady bright,
How have you fared since you have not been here?
O welcome back, my precious lady dear!"
Vain words were these, except his breath to cool,
For he was doomed to be but fortune's fool!

68

And all the letters old that she had sent
To him, he read them when he was alone,
And all the morning period thus he spent,
And in his fancy now her beauty shone
Afresh, and in his mind he caught the tone
Of her dear voice; four days he managed so,
And then resolved back home at once to go.

69

"Pandar," said he, "what are you thinking about?
Do you intend to keep on staying here,
Until Sarpedon tells us to get out?
I'm sure 'twill more considerate appear
For us to go; and now as eve draws near,
Let's say goodbye, and homeward let us turn,
For I just cannot longer here sojourn."

70

"Did we come here," said Pandar, "fetching fire,
To turn and run straight home with it again?
What better place than this can you desire?
We're with the most hospitable of men,
Sarpedon will but take it sadly when
We go, and your so hasty attitude
Would be, I think, unpardonably rude.

71

"Because we said that we had come to stay
A week with him, and now in so great haste
And on the fourth day thus to go away
Would hurt his feelings and be shocking taste;
He has himself at our disposal placed,
And since we've promised here a week to bide,
We should do so, and homeward then may ride."

72

Thus Pandar, both with force and argument,
Held him until the week had reached its end;
Sarpedon then they thanked and homeward went,
For Troilus would not his stay extend.
"Now God," he said, "this favor to me send,
That Cressida will be my welcoming,
When I get home," and so began to sing.

73

"Yes, in your eye," was what wise Pandar thought,
And to himself he said, quite soft and low,

"O, you'll cool off, my boy, if I know aught,
Ere Calchas lets his daughter from him go!"
But still of confidence he made a show,
And said that something told him in his heart
That she would come as soon as she could start.

74

And when at eve they reached the palace gate,
Down from their horses quickly they alight,
And to the room of Troilus go straight,
And sit them down and talk till almost night,
Which talk was all of Cressida the bright,
And afterward, when so they felt inclined,
They went to bed, though first of course they
  dined.

75

Next day, before the morning lights shone clear,
Troilus awoke, and leaping from his bed,
He routed Pandar out, his brother dear,
"For love of God," most plaintively he said,
"I cannot rest until I've visited
Her house, and though my eyes I cannot feast
On her, I can her palace see at least."

76

He found some way his household to mislead,
And he and Pandar to the town then go,
And to his lady's house at once proceed,
But, Lord, he only hastened to his woe!
He thought his heart with grief must overflow,
For when he saw the doors still bolted tight,
Upon his horse he scarce could sit upright.

77

For with one fatal glance his eyes behold
That shut is every window of the place,
And at the sight his heart like ice grows cold;
Without a word, and deadly pale of face,
Forth by the palace doth he madly race;
He spurs his horse and rides away full speed,
And of no man he takes the slightest heed.

78

"O palace desolate," he then began,
"O house, of houses once most dear to sight!
O palace, empty and accursed of man!
O lantern, wherein now is quenched the light!
O dwelling, once my day, now turned to night!
Why dost thou stand, while all my joys decay,
And she is gone, who was my hope and stay.

79

"O palace, once the crown of houses all,
Illumined with the sun of every bliss!
O ring, from which the ruby now doth fall!
O cause of woe, but cause of joy ere this!
Yet lacking better, fain now would I kiss
Thy doorways cold, if folk were not about!
Yet farewell, shrine, from which the saint is out!"

80

On Pandar then he cast his mournful eye,
With face all drawn and dreadful to behold,
And interrupted oft with many a sigh,
To him the devastating tale he told,
Of sorrow new and former joys grown old;
And pain sat on his countenance so grim,
No heart so hard but must have pitied him.

"God woot, refreyden may this hote fare
Er Calkas sende Troilus Criseyde!"
But natheles, he japed thus, and seyde,
And swor, y-wis, his herte him wel bihighte,
She wolde come as sone as ever she mighte.

74

Whan they un-to the paleys were y-comen
Of Troilus, they doun of hors alighte,
And to the chambre hir wey than han they nomen.
And in-to tyme that it gan to nighte,
They spaken of Criseÿde the brighte.
And after this, whan that hem bothe leste,
They spedde hem fro the soper un-to
  reste.

75

On morwe, as sone as day bigan to clere,
This Troilus gan of his sleep t'abreyde,
And to Pandare, his owene brother dere,
"For love of god," ful pitously he seyde,
"As go we seen the paleys of Criseyde;
For sin we yet may have namore feste,
So lat us seen hir paleys at the leste."

76

And ther-with-al, his meynee for to blende,
A cause he fond in toune for to go,
And to Criseydes hous they gonnen wende.
But lord! this sely Troilus was wo!
Him thoughte his sorweful herte braste a-two.
For whan he saugh hir dores sperred alle,
Wel neigh for sorwe a-doun he gan to falle.

77

Therwith whan he was war and gan biholde
How shet was every windowe of the place,
As frost, him thoughte, his herte gan to colde;
For which with chaunged deedlich pale face,
With-outen word, he forth bigan to pace;
And, as god wolde, he gan so faste ryde,
That no wight of his contenaunce aspyde.

78

Than seyde he thus, "O paleys desolat,
O hous, of houses whylom best y-hight,
O paleys empty and disconsolat,
O thou lanterne, of which queynt is the light,
O paleys, whylom day, that now art night,
Wel oughtestow to falle, and I to dye,
Sin she is went that wont us was to gye!

79

O paleys, whylom croune of houses alle,
Enlumined with sonne of alle blisse!
O ring, fro which the ruby is out-falle,
O cause of wo, that cause hast been of lisse!
Yet, sin I may no bet, fayn wolde I kisse
Thy colde dores, dorste I for this route;
And fare-wel shryne, of which the seynt is oute!"

80

Ther-with he caste on Pandarus his yë
With chaunged face, and pitous to biholde;
And whan he mighte his tyme aright aspye,
Ay as he rood, to Pandarus he tolde
His newe sorwe, and eek his joyes olde,
So pitously and with so dede an hewe,
That every wight mighte on his sorwe rewe.

81

Fro thennesforth he rydeth up and doun,
And every thing com him to remembraunce
As he rood forth by places of the toun
In whiche he whylom hadde al his plesaunce.
"Lo, yond saugh I myn owene lady daunce;
And in that temple, with hir eyen clere,
Me caughte first my righte lady dere.

82

And yonder have I herd ful lustily
My dere herte laughe, and yonder pleye
Saugh I hir ones eek ful blisfully.
And yonder ones to me gan she seye,
'Now goode swete, love me wel, I preye.'
And yond so goodly gan she me biholde,
That to the deeth myn herte is to hir holde.

83

And at that corner, in the yonder hous,
Herde I myn alderlevest lady dere
So wommanly, with voys melodious,
Singen so wel, so goodly, and so clere,
That in my soule yet me thinketh I here
The blisful soun; and, in that yonder place,
My lady first me took un-to hir grace."

84

Thanne thoughte he thus, "O blisful lord Cupyde,
Whanne I the proces have in my memorie,
How thou me hast werreyed on every syde,
Men mighte a book make of it, lyk a storie.
What nede is thee to seke on me victorie,
Sin I am thyn, and hooly at thy wille?
What joye hastow thyn owene folk to spille?

85

Wel hastow, lord, y-wroke on me thyn ire,
Thou mighty god, and dredful for to greve!
Now mercy, lord, thou wost wel I desire
Thy grace most, of alle lustes leve.
And live and deye I wol in thy bileve;
For which I n'axe in guerdon but a bone,
That thou Criseyde ayein me sende sone.

86

Distreyne hir herte as faste to retorne
As thou dost myn to longen hir to see;
Than woot I wel, that she nil not sojorne.
Now, blisful lord, so cruel thou ne be
Un-to the blood of Troye, I preye thee,
As Juno was un-to the blood Thebane,
For which the folk of Thebes caughte hir bane."

87

And after this he to the yates wente
Ther-as Criseyde out-rood a ful good paas,
And up and doun ther made he many a wente,
And to him-self ful ofte he seyde "allas!
From hennes rood my blisse and my solas!
As wolde blisful god now, for his joye,
I mighte hir seen ayein come in-to Troye.

88

And to the yonder hille I gan hir gyde,
Allas! and there I took of hir my leve!
And yond I saugh hir to hir fader ryde,
For sorwe of which myn herte shal to-cleve.
And hider hoom I com whan it was eve;

81

And then distraught, he rode there up and down,
And everything came back in memory
As he rode by the places in the town
In which he once had known felicity.
"Lo, yonder last I did her dancing see!
And in that temple by her eyes so clear,
First was I caught by my own lady dear!

82

"And yonder once I heard her laugh so bright,
And yonder once I saw her lightly play
And never since have seen so goodly sight!
And yonder once she came to me to say,
'O sweetheart mine, now love me well, I pray!'
And yonder such a loving glance she gave,
The thought of it will cheer me in my grave.

83

"And at that corner house upon this street,
I heard my most beloved lady dear,
With woman's voice so gentle and so sweet,
Singing withal so goodly and so clear
That in my soul methinks I yet can hear
The blissful sound! And in that yonder place
My dearest lady did I first embrace!

84

"O Cupid," then he thought, "O blessed Lord,
When all these things in memory I see,
How thou against me on all sides hast warred,
It seems just like a book of history!
But yet, why seek a conquest over me,
Since I am thine and wholly at thy will?
What joy hast thou, thy subjects thus to kill?

85

"Thou hast, O Lord, avenged on me thy ire,
Thou God of might, and dangerous to grieve!
Have mercy, Lord! Thou knowest I desire
Nothing but thy good favor to receive;
Living and dying I shall in thee believe,
For all of which I beg a single boon,
That thou wilt send me Cressida back soon.

86

"Constrain her heart as quickly to return
As thou dost mine with longing her to see,
Then well I know she will not long sojourn.
Now, blessed Lord, show not such cruelty
Unto the blood of Troy, perilled in me,
As Juno showed unto the Theban race,
Nor let me perish here in lone disgrace!"

87

Forth to the city's open gates he rode,
Whence Cressida had started on her way,
And up and down there many a time he strode,
And often to himself "Alas!" did say,
"'Twas here I lost my bliss that fatal day,
And as she went, so may I have the joy
To see her now come riding back to Troy.

88

"As far as yonder hill, I was her guide,
And there I took of her my final leave,
And there I saw her to her father ride,
The thought of which my heart in two will cleave;
And hither came I home when it was eve,

And here bereft of every joy I dwell,
And must so bide till time makes all things well."

89

Sick in his fancy, he imagined oft
That he was looking gaunt and pale and thin,
And that men noticed it and whispered soft,
"What can it be? What trouble is he in?
It must be bad, because he looks like sin!"
But this was all by melancholy bred,
Which spun such foolish fancies in his head.

90

At other times, in his fantastic brain,
He thought that every man along the way
Gave him such pitying looks as said quite plain,
"Poor Troilus, he's nearing his last day!"
'Twas so he passed his time in sad dismay,
And in these troubled days his life he led,
Still wavering in mind twixt hope and dread.

91

Some little joy he took in song to show
The reason for his grief, as best he might,
For heavy hearts when they in words o'erflow,
By such discharge may sometimes grow more light;
And so, when he was out of all men's sight,
With gentle voice unto his lady dear,
Though absent, yet sang as you shall hear:

92

"O star, now I have lost thy cheering light,
With grief unsending may I well bewail,
That in dark torment ever night by night
Toward certain death with favoring wind I sail!
And if the sacred tenth night there should fail
Thy beams to guide me through that fatal hour,
Charybdis shall my ship and me devour!"

93

When he had sung his song, thereafter soon
He fell again into his sighings old,
And every night he gazed upon the moon,
Shining with light so clear, but pale and cold,
And all his sorrow to the moon he told,
And said, "When thy two horns again are new,
I shall be glad, if all the world holds true.

94

"Thy horns were old upon that luckless morrow
When from this place rode forth my lady dear,
The cause of all my torment and my sorrow.
And O Lucina, bright and ever clear,
Run fast, I beg, about thy circling sphere,
For when thy horns anew begin to spring,
To Troy again my lady shall they bring."

95

The days stretched out, and longer every night
Seemed to this mind increasingly to grow,
And that the sun ran on his course unright,
By longer way than it was wont to go.
"In truth," he said, "I fear it must be so,
That Phaeton, son of the sun, alive,
Doth still amiss his father's chariot drive!"

96

And on the city's walls he oft would walk,
And gaze where he could see the Grecian host,
And to himself in this wise would he talk,

And here I dwelle out-cast from alle joye,
And shal, til I may seen hir eft in Troye."

89

And of him-self imagined he ofte
To ben defet, and pale, and waxen lesse
Than he was wont, and that men seyde softe,
"What may it be? who can the sothe gesse
Why Troilus hath al this hevinesse?"
And al this nas but his malencolye,
That he hadde of him-self swich fantasye.

90

Another tyme imaginen he wolde
That every wight that wente by the weye
Had of him routhe, and that they seyen sholde,
"I am right sory Troilus wol deye."
And thus he droof a day yet forth or tweye.
As ye have herd, swich lyf right gan he lede,
As he that stood bitwixen hope and drede.

91

For which him lyked in his songes shewe
Th'encheson of his wo, as he best mighte,
And make a song of wordes but a fewe,
Somwhat his woful herte for to lighte.
And whan he was from every mannes sighte,
With softe voys he, of his lady dere,
That was absent, gan singe as ye may here.

92

"O sterre, of which I lost have al the light,
With herte soor wel oughte I to bewayle,
That ever derk in torment, night by night,
Toward my deeth with wind in stere I sayle;
For which the tenthe night if that I fayle
The gyding of thy bemes brighte an houre,
My ship and me Caribdis wol devoure."

93

This song when he thus songen hadde, sone
He fil ayein in-to his sykes olde;
And every night, as was his wone to done,
He stood the brighte mone to beholde,
And al his sorwe he to the mone tolde;
And seyde, "y-wis, whan thou art horned newe,
I shal be glad, if al the world be trewe!

94

I saugh thyn hornes olde eek by the morwe,
Whan hennes rood my righte lady dere,
That cause is of my torment and my sorwe;
For whiche, O brighte Lucina the clere,
For love of god, ren faste aboute thy spere!
For whan thyn hornes newe ginne springe,
Than shal she come, that may my blisse bringe!"

95

The day is more, and lenger every night,
Than they be wont to be, him thoughte tho;
And that the sonne wente his course unright
By lenger wey than it was wont to go;
And seyde, "y-wis, me dredeth ever-mo,
The sonnes sone, Pheton, be on-lyve,
And that his fadres cart amis he dryve."

96

Upon the walles faste eek wolde he walke,
And on the Grekes ost he wolde see,
And to him-self right thus he wolde talke,

"Lo, yonder is myn owene lady free,
Or elles yonder, ther tho tentes be!
And thennes comth this eyr, that is so sote,
That in my soule I fele it doth me bote.

97

And hardely this wind, that more and more
Thus stoundemele encreseth in my face,
Is of my ladyes depe sykes sore.
I preve it thus, for in non othere place
Of al this toun, save onliche in this space,
Fele I no wind that souneth so lyk peyne;
It seyth, 'allas! why twinned be we tweyne?'"

98

This longe tyme he dryveth forth right thus,
Til fully passed was the nynthe night;
And ay bi-syde him was this Pandarus,
That bisily dide alle his fulle might
Him to comforte, and make his herte light;
Yevinge him hope alwey, the tenthe morwe
That she shal come, and stinten al his sorwe.

99

Up-on that other syde eek was Criseyde,
With wommen fewe, among the Grekes stronge;
For which ful ofte a day "allas!" she seyde,
"That I was born! Wel may myn herte longe
After my deeth; for now live I to longe!
Allas! and I ne may it not amende;
For now is wors than ever yet I wende.

100

My fader nil for no-thing do me grace
To goon ayein, for nought I can him queme;
And if so be that I my terme passe,
My Troilus shal in his herte deme
That I am fals, and so it may wel seme.
Thus shal I have unthank on every syde;
That I was born, so weylawey the tyde!

101

And if that I me putte in jupartye,
To stele awey by nighte, and it bifalle
That I be caught, I shal be holde a spye;
Or elles, lo, this drede I most of alle,
If in the hondes of som wrecche I falle,
I am but lost, al be myn herte trewe;
Now mighty god, thou on my sorwe rewe!"

102

Ful pale y-waxen was hir brighte face,
Hir limes lene, as she that al the day
Stood whan she dorste, and loked on the place
Ther she was born, and ther she dwelt hadde ay.
And al the night wepinge, allas! she lay.
And thus despeired, out of alle cure,
She ladde hir lyf, this woful creature.

103

Ful ofte a day she sighte eek for destresse,
And in hir-self she wente ay portrayinge
Of Troilus the grete worthinesse,
And alle his goodly wordes recordinge
Sin first that day hir love bigan to springe.
And thus she sette hir woful herte a-fyre
Thorugh remembraunce of that she gan desyre.

104

In al this world ther nis so cruel herte

"Lo, yonder lies the one I love the most!
Lo, yonder the tent whence like a pining ghost,
There comes this sighing breeze so gently blowing,
New life upon my lifeless soul bestowing.

97

"And verily this wind, that more and more
Increases steadily upon my face,
Is from my lady's sighs, so deep and sore;
In proof of which, there is no other space
Of all this town, but only in this place
I feel a wind that soundeth so like pain;
It saith, 'Alas, why parted are we twain!'"

98

The tedious time he passes in this way
And thus survives until the last ninth night;
And Pandar still was his support and stay,
Striving with all his patience and his might
To cheer his friend and make his heart more light,
Feeding his hope that on the tenth tomorrow,
Cressida would come again and end his sorrow.

99

Now Cressida, upon the other side,
In exile lone among the Greeks must dwell,
And many a time a day, "Alas," she cried,
"That I was born! My wretched heart may well
Long for the tolling of my burial bell!
Alas, that fortune such hostility
Should single out to show to harmless me!

100

"My father will not grant me my request,
For anything that I can do or say,
And Troilus as treason self-confessed
Will take it, if too long from Troy I stay,
Nor could he see it any other way!
Thus shall I have the worst on every side,
Alas, that such fate should to me betide.

101

"And if the risky project I should try,
To steal away by night, then were I caught,
I should be taken surely for a spy;
Or else, indeed a still more dreadful thought
Into some ruffian's hands I might be brought.
So am I lost, whichever way I turn,
Nor find the peace for which my heart doth yearn!"

102

Now pale and wan had grown her lovely face,
Her body, too, with grief doth waste away;
From dawn to night she gazed upon the place,
Which was her home for many a happy day,
And all the sleepless night she weeping lay;
No remedy she knew for all her care,
And day and night were sunk in black despair.

103

In all this time she found her greatest ease
In keeping in her heart the image bright
Of Troilus, and his fair qualities
And all his goodly words she would recite
Since first she took him for her loving knight,
Cherishing in her woful heart the fires
Of love by such fond thoughts as love inspires.

104

In all this world so wide, no heart of stone

But must have melted at her grievous sorrow,
As there she wept, abandoned and alone;
At thought of Troilus at eve and morrow,
She had no need of others' tears to borrow,
And this was yet the worst of all her grief,
That she could tell no one for her relief.

105

With sad and mournful eyes she looked on Troy,
On every tower high and every hall.
"Alas," she said, "the pleasure and the joy
Which I have known within that city wall,
But now all turned to bitterness and gall!
O Troilus, what art thou doing now?
Art thou still faithful to thy lover's vow?

106

"Would I had done as you did once require,
Had fled with you to some security,
Then would I not in lonely grief expire!
That it was right, O who would not agree
With such a one as Troilus to flee;
But when the corpse is ready to put in
The grave, too late to think of medicine!

107

"Too late, too late, the evil to repair!
Prudence, alas, one of thy triple eyes
I lacked in management of this affair!
Of time long past I was aware and wise,
And present things could at their value prize,
But future time, ere I was fairly caught,
I could not see, and so thus low am brought.

108

"But now I say, betide what may betide,
I shall tomorrow night, by hook or crook,
Steal from this camp, and when I get outside,
With Troilus I'll seek some happy nook
Where we can dwell; I care not how men look
At it, or how the gossips' tongues may wag,
True love they always in the mire will drag.

109

"If every gossip's word you were to heed,
Or rule yourself by other people's wit,
'Twould be a pretty life that you would lead;
Whate'er you do, some will find fault with it,
Yet others think it proper, right and fit;
And in such matters of dubiety,
My happiness will compensate for me.

110

"I know, then, now at last, what I shall do,
I'll go to Troy, and thus the matter end!"
But time would come, and ere a month or two,
When quite another way her mind would tend!
Troilus and Troy together she would send
Their way quite readily would let them slide,
And happily among the Greeks abide.

111

Now Diomede, of whom I spoke before,
Hath still his mind intent upon one thing,
Which in his inmost heart he ever bore,
How he with some device encompassing,
Cressida's heart into his net might bring.
To catch this lady was his sole design,
And to this end he laid out hook and line.

That hir hadde herd compleynen in hir sorwe,
That nolde han wopen for hir peynes smerte,
So tendrely she weep, bothe eve and morwe.
Hir nedede no teres for to borwe.
And this was yet the worste of al hir peyne,
Ther was no wight to whom she dorste hir pleyne.

105

Ful rewfully she loked up-on Troye,
Biheld the toures heighe and eek the halles;
"Allas!" quod she, "the plesaunce and the joye
The whiche that now al torned in-to galle is,
Have I had ofte with-inne yonder walles!
O Troilus, what dostow now," she seyde;
"Lord! whether yet thou thenke up-on Criseyde?

106

Allas! I ne hadde trowed on your lore,
And went with yow, as ye me radde er this!
Thanne hadde I now not syked half so sore.
Who mighte have seyd, that I had doon a-mis
To stele awey with swich on as he is?
But al to late cometh the letuarie,
Whan men the cors un-to the grave carie.

107

To late is now to speke of this matere;
Prudence, allas! oon of thyn eyen three
Me lakked alwey, er that I cam here;
On tyme y-passed, wel remembred me;
And present tyme eek coude I wel y-see.
But futur tyme, er I was in the snare,
Coude I not seen; that causeth now my care.

108

But natheles, bityde what bityde,
I shal to-morwe at night, by est or weste,
Out of this ost stele on som maner syde,
And go with Troilus wher-as him leste.
This purpos wol I holde, and this is beste.
No fors of wikked tonges janglerye,
For every on love han wrecches had envye.

109

For who-so wole of every word take hede,
Or rewlen him by every wightes wit,
Ne shal he never thryven, out of drede.
For that that som men blamen ever yit,
Lo, other maner folk commenden it.
And as for me, for al swich variaunce,
Felicitee clepe I my suffisaunce.

110

For which, with-outen any wordes mo,
To Troye I wol, as for conclusioun."
But god it wot, er fully monthes two,
She was ful fer fro that entencioun.
For bothe Troilus and Troye toun
Shal knotteles through-out hir herte slyde;
For she wol take a purpos for t'abyde.

111

This Diomede, of whom yow telle I gan,
Goth now, with-inne him-self ay arguinge
With al the sleighte and al that ever he can,
How he may best, with shortest taryinge,
In-to his net Criseydes herte bringe.
To this entente he coude never fyne;
To fisshen hir, he leyde out hook and lyne.

112

But natheles, wel in his herte he thoughte,
That she nas nat with-oute a love in Troye.
For never, sithen he hir thennes broughte,
Ne coude he seen her laughe or make joye.
He niste how best hir herte for t'acoye.
"But for t'assaye," he seyde, "it nought ne greveth;
For he that nought n'assayeth, nought n'acheveth."

113

Yet seide he to him-self upon a night,
"Now am I not a fool, that woot wel how
Hir wo for love is of another wight,
And here up-on to goon assaye hir now?
I may wel wite, it nil not been my prow.
For wyse folk in bokes it expresse,
'Men shal not wowe a wight in hevinesse.'

114

But who-so mighte winnen swich a flour
From him, for whom she morneth night and day,
He mighte seyn, he were a conquerour."
And right anoon, as he that bold was ay,
Thoughte in his herte, "happe, how happe may,
Al sholde I deye, I wole hir herte seche;
I shal no more lesen but my speche."

115

This Diomede, as bokes us declare,
Was in his nedes prest and corageous;
With sterne voys and mighty limes square,
Hardy, testif, strong, and chevalrous
Of dedes, lyk his fader Tideus.
And som men seyn, he was of tunge large;
And heir he was of Calidoine and Arge.

116

Criseyde mene was of hir stature,
Ther-to of shap, of face, and eek of chere,
Ther mighte been no fairer creature.
And ofte tyme this was hir manere,
To gon y-tressed with hir heres clere
Doun by hir coler at hir bak bihinde,
Which with a threde of gold she wolde binde.

117

And, save hir browes joyneden y-fere,
Ther nas no lak, in ought I can espyen;
But for to speken of hir eyen clere,
Lo, trewely, they writen that hir syen,
That Paradys stood formed in hir yën.
And with hir riche beautee ever-more
Strof love in hir, ay which of hem was more.

118

She sobre was, eek simple, and wys with-al,
The beste y-norisshed eek that mighte be,
And goodly of hir speche in general,
Charitable, estatliche, lusty, and free;
Ne never-mo ne lakkede hir pitee;
Tendre-herted, slydinge of corage;
But trewely, I can not telle hir age.

119

And Troilus wel waxen was in highte,
And complet formed by proporcioun
So wel, that kinde it not amenden mighte;

112

But he was wary, since he surely thought
That she had left some love in Troy behind,
For ever since she from that town was brought,
She seemed to carry something on her mind,
Some loss to which she could not be resigned.
"But still," he said, "to try is worth the pains,
For he who nothing ventures, nothing gains."

113

And so he said unto himself one day,
"Now I am not a fool! I see well how
She's sad because her lover is away;
If I should be too brisk with her just now,
It wouldn't do; I must some time allow;
Wise folk in books this matter thus express,
'Do not make love to those in great distress.'

114

"But such a flower for yourself to win
From him for whom she mourneth night and day,
That were a conquest one might glory in!"
And boldly then, for he loved not delay,
"Let happen," he declared, "whatever may,
I'll try her out, and if she should refuse,
I've nothing but a little breath to lose."

115

This Diomede, as all the books attest,
Was quick in action, also brave and bold,
And stern of voice, with mighty arms and chest;
For feats adventurous he was extolled,
High as his father Tydeus of old;
Some say his word could not be counted on,
This prince of Argos and of Calydon.

116

Cressida was in frame of even height,
And in her shape, her look and all her face,
No fairer creature ever blessed man's sight.
Following the custom of her time and place,
She wore her hair all braided in a lace,
Down by her collar at her back hehind,
And with a thread of gold she did it bind.

117

Her curving brows beneath her forehead met,
And in all things men counted her most fair;
Her eyes within their frame were brightly set,
And all who saw her with one voice declare
That Paradise in truth was written there;
Beauty and love in her were so create,
That which the greater, one could but debate.

118

Sedate she was, simple and wise withal,
Instructed in the arts most carefully,
Goodly of speech, whatever might befall,
With kindly grace, both dignified and free;
Nor lacked her heart in sensibility
In all the things which sympathy engage,
But I regret I cannot tell her age.

119

And Troilus was more than middle height,
But well-proportioned and of figure neat;
In short, he seemed in everything just right,

Young, fresh, and quick as a lion on his feet,
And true as steel his heart within its seat;
He was with all the qualities endowed,
That to our human nature are allowed.

120

In all the histories it is related
That Troilus was never in men's sight
In lower rank than with the highest rated,
In noble deeds pertaining to a knight;
Though not a giant in his body's might,
His heart was ever equal to the best,
In deeds that knightly competence attest.

121

But now let us return to Diomede.
The tenth day came since that sad parting day
When to the Greeks this lady he did lead,
And Diomede, fresh as the flowers in May,
Came to the tent where wise old Calchas lay,
And feigned that he had business with the priest,
But of his plans, the business was the least.

122

Now Cressida, in all things neat and nice,
Received him there, and bade him take a seat,
Nor had she any need to ask him twice;
And in the proper way a guest to treat,
Spices and wine she served in manner meet;
In friendly conversation then they fell,
A part of which I shall proceed to tell.

123

First of the war he then began to speak
Between the Greeks and the besieged in Troy,
And her opinion doth he humbly seek
What methods in the siege one should employ;
And then he asked her if she did enjoy
Her life among the Greeks, and if their ways
Seemed strange, and how she passed her days,

124

And why her father should delay so long
To marry her to some good worthy knight.
But Cressida, who felt the pain still strong
For absent Troilus, her heart's delight,
Gave answer to his questions as she might,
But of his deeper purpose and intent,
Perhaps she had no inkling what he meant.

125

But nevertheless the dauntless Diomede
Pressed bravely on, and this attempt essayed:
"If I have rightly of you taken heed,
Dear Cressida, I'm very much afraid,
Since hand upon your bridle first I laid,
When you came forth from Troy upon that morrow,
You have been sore oppressed by some deep sorrow.

126

"I cannot say just what the cause may be,
Unless perhaps some Trojan you hold dear,
Yet let me say, it truly would grieve me
If you for any Trojan, far or near,
Should ever spill a quarter of a tear,
Or let one from your face drive off the smile,
For, Cressida, it isn't worth the while.

127

"The Trojans, one might say, both all and some,

Yong, fresshe, strong, and hardy as lyoun;
Trewe as steel in ech condicioun;
On of the beste enteched creature,
That is, or shal, whyl that the world may dure.

120

And certainly in storie it is y-founde,
That Troilus was never un-to no wight,
As in his tyme, in no degree secounde
In durring don that longeth to a knight.
Al mighte a geaunt passen him of might,
His herte ay with the firste and with the beste
Stod paregal, to durre don that him leste.

121

But for to tellen forth of Diomede:—
It fil that after, on the tenthe day,
Sin that Criseyde out of the citee yede,
This Diomede, as fresshe as braunche in May,
Com to the tente ther-as Calkas lay,
And feyned him with Calkas han to done;
But what he mente, I shal yow telle sone.

122

Criseyde, at shorte wordes for to telle,
Welcomed him, and doun by hir him sette;
And he was ethe y-nough to maken dwelle.
And after this, with-outen longe lette,
The spyces and the wyn men forth hem fette;
And forth they speke of this and that y-fere,
As freendes doon, of which som shal ye here.

123

He gan first fallen of the werre in speche
Bitwixe hem and the folk of Troye toun;
And of th'assege he gan hir eek byseche,
To telle him what was hir opinioun.
Fro that demaunde he so descendeth doun
To asken hir, if that hir straunge thoughte
The Grekes gyse, and werkes that they wroughte?

124

And why hir fader tarieth so longe
To wedden hir un-to som worthy wight?
Criseyde, that was in hir peynes stronge
For love of Troilus, hir owene knight,
As fer-forth as she conning hadde or might,
Answerde him tho; but, as of his entente,
It semed not she wiste what he mente.

125

But natheles, this ilke Diomede
Gan in him-self assure, and thus he seyde,
"If ich aright have taken of yow hede,
Me thinketh thus, O lady myn, Criseyde,
That sin I first hond on your brydel leyde,
Whan ye out come of Troye by the morwe,
Ne coude I never seen yow but in sorwe.

126

Can I not seyn what may the cause be
But-if for love of som Troyan it were,
The which right sore wolde athinken me
That ye, for any wight that dwelleth there,
Sholden spille a quarter of a tere,
Or pitously your-selven so bigyle;
For dredelees, it is nought worth the whyle.

127

The folk of Troye, as who seyth, alle and some

In preson been, as ye your-selven see;
For thennes shal not oon on-lyve come
For al the gold bitwixen sonne and see.
Trusteth wel, and understondeth me,
Ther shal not oon to mercy goon on-lyve,
Al were he lord of worldes twyës fyve!

128

Swich wreche on hem, for fecching of Eleyne,
Ther shal be take, er that we hennes wende,
That Manes, which that goddes ben of peyne,
Shal been agast that Grekes wol hem shende.
And men shul drede, un-to the worldes ende,
From hennes-forth to ravisshe any quene,
So cruel shal our wreche on hem be sene.

129

And but-if Calkas lede us with ambages,
That is to seyn, with double wordes slye,
Swich as men clepe a 'word with two visages,'
Ye shul wel knowen that I nought ne lye,
And al this thing right seen it with your yë,
And that anoon; ye nil not trowe how sone;
Now taketh heed, for it is for to done.

130

What wene ye your wyse fader wolde
Han yeven Antenor for yow anoon,
If he ne wiste that the citee sholde
Destroyed been? Why, nay, so mote I goon!
He knew ful wel ther shal not scapen oon
That Troyan is; and for the grete fere,
He dorste not, ye dwelte lenger there.

131

What wole ye more, lufsom lady dere?
Lat Troye and Troyan fro your herte pace!
Dryf out that bittre hope, and make good chere,
And clepe ayein the beautee of your face,
That ye with salte teres so deface.
For Troye is brought in swich a jupartye,
That, it to save, is now no remedye.

132

And thenketh wel, ye shal in Grekes finde
A more parfit love, er it be night,
Than any Troyan is, and more kinde,
And bet to serven yow wol doon his might.
And if ye vouche sauf, my lady bright,
I wol ben he to serven yow my-selve,
Ye, lever than be lord of Greces twelve!"

133

And with that word he gan to waxen reed,
And in his speche a litel wight he quook,
And caste a-syde a litel wight his heed,
And stinte a whyle; and afterward awook,
And sobreliche on hir he threw his look,
And seyde, "I am, al be it yow no joye,
As gentil man as any wight in Troye.

134

For if my fader Tydeus," he seyde,
"Y-lived hadde, I hadde been, er this,
Of Calidoine and Arge a king, Criseyde!
And so hope I that I shal yet, y-wis.
But he was slayn, allas! the more harm is,
Unhappily at Thebes al to rathe,
Polymites and many a man to scathe.

Are prisoners, and never shall be free,
For out of Troy not one alive shall come,
For all the gold between the sun and sea;
You can take this for utter certainty,
No single one shall come from thence alive,
Although he were the lord of worlds twice five.

128

"The rape of Helen we shall so repay,
Ere we upon our homeward way shall wend,
The Manes, Gods of pain, shall be afraid
Lest Grecian wrath with theirs should e'er contend;
And men shall fear, until this world shall end,
Henceforth forever to abduct a queen,
Such vengeance on the Trojans shall be seen.

129

"For either Calchas tricks us with ambages,
That is, with words of double meaning sly,
Such as we call a word with two visages,
Or that I speak the truth, none can deny;
For all of this you'll see with your own eye,
And you shan't need to wait for many a moon,
Mind what I say, you'll be surprised how soon!

130

"Do you suppose your father, old and wise,
Would give Antenor for you in this war,
Unless he knew just how the matter lies,
And what fate for the Trojans is in store?
He knows full well that there is no hope for
A single Trojan, and so he didn't dare
To let you stay among them over there.

131

"What further can you ask ,my lady dear?
Both Troy and Trojans from your heart erase!
Drive out this futile hope and make good cheer,
Restore again your beauty to its place,
Which with the salt of tears you now deface!
For Troy is brought at last to such a state,
To save her now, it is too late a date.

132

"Besides, you shall among us Grecians find
A love more perfect, and a truer knight
Than any Trojan is, and one more kind,
To honor you with all his strength and might;
If you will listen to me, lady bright,
Myself will be the man, and for the price,
A dozen Greeces I would sacrifice."

133

And with that word he blushed a bashful red,
And as he spoke, his voice trembled and shook,
The while he turned aside and bowed his head,
And paused, but soon new courage took,
And with a serious, but gentle look,
He said, "I am, though this gives you no joy,
As good a gentleman as dwells in Troy.

134

"For if my father Tydeus," he said,
"Had longer lived, I would have been ere this
Of Calydon and Argos king and head,
And shall be yet, unless my guess I miss.
But he was slain, and lost all earthly bliss,
At Thebes, where Polynices and his men
Good reason had to grieve in sorrow then.

135

"But, lady dear, since now I am your man,
And in my heart you hold the chiefest place,
And I shall serve you every way I can,
As long as I exist in time and space,
So look upon me with a kindly face,
And grant that I may come again tomorrow
And tell you more at leisure of my sorrow."

136

Why should I all his pretty speeches tell?
He spoke enough for one day, that is sure,
And what he said to her, he said so well,
That her consent he doth at last procure
To come again, though first she did adjure
Him not to raise the topic he had broached,
At which, no doubt, he felt himself reproached!

137

But still her heart was set on Troilus,
And his dear image she could not erase
From out her mind, and so she answered thus:
"O Diomede, I love that happy place
Where I was born! May heaven in its grace
Deliver it from out its sorry state
And grant to hapless Troy a happy fate!

138

"And that the Greeks on Troy their wrath would wreak,
I know that very well! But after all,
It may not happen as you say and speak,
And God forbid that such thing should befall;
I know my father did me to him call,
And that he dearly bought me, as you say,
And for all this, I shall him well repay!

139

"And that the Greeks are men of high renown,
I know that, too; but truly you shall find
As worthy folk within the Trojan town,
As able, too, as perfect and as kind,
As any twixt the Orcades and Ind.
And that some lady gladly would receive
Your service, that I'm ready to believe.

140

"But as for love," she said, and gently sighed,
"I had a lord, and I his wedded wife,
To whom my heart was pledged until he died;
But other love than that in all my life
There hath not been, nor shall I seek love's strife.
And that you are of high and noble birth,
That have I heard, and know you for your worth.

141

"And for that reason now I wonder,
That any woman you should trouble so!
For love and I are very far asunder,
And I am more inclined, as things now go,
To spend my life in mourning and in woe,
Though how my heart may change, I cannot tell;
The future may, of course, my grief dispel.

142

"But now I am afflicted and cast down,
And you in arms are busy day by day;
But later, when you Greeks have won the town,
There's just a chance that then it happen may,

135

But herte myn, sin that I am your man,
And been the ferste of whom I seche grace,
To serven you as hertely as I can,
And ever shal, whyl I to live have space,
So, er that I departe out of this place,
Ye wol me graunte, that I may to-morwe,
At bettre leyser, telle yow my sorwe."

136

What shold I telle his wordes that he seyde?
He spak y-now, for o day at the meste;
It preveth wel, he spak so that Criseyde
Graunted, on the morwe, at his requeste,
For to speken with him at the leste,
So that he nolde speke of swich matere;
And thus to him she seyde, as ye may here:

137

As she that hadde hir herte on Troilus
So faste, that ther may it noon arace;
And straungely she spak, and seyde thus,
"O Diomede, I love that ilke place
Ther I was born; and Joves, for his grace,
Delivere it sone of al that doth it care!
God, for thy might, so leve it wel to fare!

138

That Grekes wolde hir wraththe on Troye wreke,
If that they mighte, I knowe it wel, y-wis.
But it shal not bifallen as ye speke;
And god to-forn, and ferther over this,
I wot my fader wys and redy is;
And that he me hath bought, as ye me tolde,
So dere, I am the more un-to him holde.

139

That Grekes been of heigh condicioun,
I woot eek wel; but certein, men shal finde
As worthy folk with-inne Troye toun,
As conning, and as parfit and as kinde,
As been bitwixen Orcades and Inde.
And that ye coude wel your lady serve,
I trowe eek wel, hir thank for to deserve.

140

But as to speke of love, y-wis," she seyde,
"I hadde a lord, to whom I wedded was,
The whos myn herte al was, til that he deyde;
And other love, as helpe me now Pallas,
Ther in myn herte nis, ne never was.
And that ye been of noble and heigh kinrede,
I have wel herd it tellen, out of drede.

141

And that doth me to han so gret a wonder,
That ye wol scornen any womman so.
Eek, god wot, love and I be fer a-sonder;
I am disposed bet, so mote I go,
Un-to my deeth, to pleyne and maken wo.
What I shal after doon, I can not seye;
But trewely, as yet me list not pleye.

142

Myn herte is now in tribulacioun,
And ye in armes bisy, day by day.
Here-after, whan ye wonnen han the toun,
Paraunter, thanne so it happen may,

That whan I see that I never er say,
Than wole I werke that I never wroughte!
This word to yow y-nough suffysen oughte.

143

To-morwe eek wol I speke with yow fayn,
So that ye touchen nought of this matere.
And whan yow list, ye may come here ayeyn;
And, er ye gon, thus muche I seye yow here:
As helpe me Pallas with hir heres clere,
If that I sholde of any Greek han routhe,
It sholde be your-selven, by my trouthe!

144

I sey not therfore that I wol yow love,
Ne I sey not nay, but in conclusioun,
I mene wel, by god that sit above":—
And ther-with-al she caste hir eyen doun,
And gan to syke, and seyde, "O Troye toun,
Yet bidde I god, in quiete and in reste
I may yow seen, or do myn herte breste."

145

But in effect, and shortly for to seye,
This Diomede al freshly newe ayeyn
Gan pressen on, and faste hir mercy preye;
And after this, the sothe for to seyn,
Hir glove he took, of which he was ful fayn
And fynally, whan it was waxen eve,
And al was wel, he roos and took his leve.

146

The brighte Venus folwede and ay taughte
The wey, ther brode Phebus doun alighte;
And Cynthea hir char-hors over-raughte
To whirle out of the Lyon, if she mighte;
And Signifer his candeles shewed brighte,
Whan that Criseyde un-to hir bedde wente
In-with hir fadres faire brighte tente.

147

Retorning in hir soule ay up and doun
The wordes of this sodein Diomede,
His greet estat, and peril of the toun,
And that she was allone and hadde nede
Of freendes help; and thus bigan to brede
The cause why, the sothe for to telle,
That she tok fully purpos for to dwelle.

148

The morwe com, and goostly for to speke,
This Diomede is come un-to Criseyde,
And shortly, lest that ye my tale breke,
So wel he for him-selve spak and seyde,
That alle hir sykes sore adoun he leyde.
And fynally, the sothe for to seyne,
He refte hir of the grete of al hir peyne.

149

And after this the story telleth us,
That she him yaf the faire baye stede,
The which he ones wan of Troilus;
And eek a broche (and that was litel nede)
That Troilus was, she yaf this Diomede.
And eek, the bet from sorwe him to releve,
She made him were a pencel of hir sleve.

150

I finde eek in the stories elles-where,

If things turn out in unexpected way,
That I shall do what I ne'er thought to do,
And what I've said should be enough for you.

143

"Come back tomorrow, if you so desire,
But do not push this matter now too far.
Come when you want, if that's all you require!
But ere you go, at least I'll say, you are,
So help me Pallas, gleaming like a star,
The one of all within the Grecian city
Who first could rouse my heart to throbs of pity.

144

"I do not say I promise what you seek,
Nor yet deny. So do not fret nor frown,
For thou hast need to fear no other Greek!"
Pausing at these concessions, she looked down
And deeply sighing said, "O Trojan town,
Pray God that thou shalt be in safety first,
Or else my wretched heart in grief shall burst!"

145

But Diomede was not all dismayed,
And brought forth arguments all fresh and new,
And with insistence for her favor prayed,
And thereupon, the most that he could do,
He took her glove, and called it love-pledge true,
And finally, when it drew on towards eve,
And all was well, he rose and took his leave.

146

Bright Venus soon appeared to point the way
Where Phoebus, wide and round, should down alight,
And now her chariot horses Cynthia
Whirls out of the Lion, driven by her might,
And Signifer displays his candles bright;
Then Cressida unto her nigh-rest went
Within her father's fair and shining tent,

147

Debating in her soul aye up and down
The words of this impetuous Diomede,
His high estate, the peril of the town,
Her loneliness and all her pressing need
Of friendly help, and thus began to breed
The reasons why, the simple truth to tell,
She thought it best among the Greeks to dwell.

148

The morrow came, and like a confessor
Came Diomede, who cunningly displayed
His arguments and added many more,
And such an all-persuasive case he made,
That her misgivings were almost allayed,
And finally, to state the matter plain,
She found in him a surcease from her pain.

149

And afterward, the story telleth us,
She gave him back the bay, the noble steed
Which once he won from hapless Troilus;
A brooch besides—and that was little need—
Her lover's gift, she gave to Diomede,
And as her knight she doth him now receive,
And made for him a pennant of her sleeve.

150

And elsewhere in the story it is told,

When deeply wounded once was Diomede,
By Troilus, she wept tears manifold
When she beheld his wide wounds freshly bleed,
And in the care of him she took great heed,
And then, to heal his wound in every part,
Men say, men say she gave to him her heart.

151

And yet the story also telleth us,
No woman ever did so deep lament
For love betrayed as she for Troilus!
"Alas," she cried, "forever lost and spent
Is all my truth in love's high sacrament!
The gentlest man, the noblest ever made
Have I in falsehood wilfully betrayed!

152

"Alas, of me unto the world's last end,
There shall be neither written nor yet sung
A kindly word! No one will me defend!
O rolled shall be my name on many a tongue,
Throughout the world my bell shall wide be rung,
And women will despise me most of all!
Alas, that such a fate on me should fall!

153

"And they will say, in scorning of all this,
That I dishonored them, alack the day;
Though I were not the first that did amiss,
That will not wipe the blot of shame away!
But since what's done, must so forever stay,
And since my former guilt I can't undo,
To Diomede at least I shall be true.

154

"But Troilus, since I can do no more,
And since our paths henceforth must separate,
May heaven to its favor thee restore!
O Troilus, the best and gentlest mate
Who e'er his heart to love did consecrate,
What other love can stand in thy dear stead!"
She broke down then, and bitter tears she shed.

155

"Of this I'm sure, that I shall hate you never,
A friend's love you shall have at least of me,
And my good word, though I should live forever!
And truly I should grieve if I should see
You ever fall into adversity.
That you are guiltless, no one need me tell!
God's will be done! And thus I say farewell!"

156

How long a time it was that lay between
Ere she forsook him for bold Diomede,
No author tells, so far as I have seen,
And no man, let him ne'er so widely read,
Shall find a further record of this deed;
But Diomede, though quick enough to woo,
Before he won her, had yet more to do.

157

Nor shall I now this woman further chide
Than from her simple story doth arise;
Her name, alas, is published far and wide,
Her guilt is plain enough to all men's eyes;
And if I could condone in any wise
Her deed, in pity's name I would assent,
For of her sin she did at least repent.

Whan through the body hurt was Diomede
Of Troilus, tho weep she many a tere,
Whan that she saugh his wyde woundes blede;
And that she took to kepen him good hede,
And for to hele him of his sorwes smerte.
Men seyn, I not, that she yaf him hir herte.

151

But trewely, the story telleth us,
Ther made never womman more wo
Than she, whan that she falsed Troilus.
She seyde, "allas! for now is clene a-go
My name of trouthe in love, for ever-mo!
For I have falsed oon, the gentileste
That ever was, and oon the worthieste!

152

Allas, of me, un-to the worldes ende,
Shal neither been y-writen nor y-songe
No good word, for thise bokes wol me shende,
O, rolled shal I been on many a tonge!
Through-out the world my belle shal be ronge;
And wommen most wol hate me of alle.
Allas, that swich a cas me sholde falle!

153

They wol seyn, in as muche as in me is,
I have hem doon dishonour, weylawey!
Al be I not the firste that dide amis,
What helpeth that to do my blame awey?
But sin I see there is no bettre way,
And that to late is now for me to rewe,
To Diomede algate I wol be trewe.

154

But Troilus, sin I no better may,
And sin that thus departen ye and I,
Yet preye I god, so yeve yow right good day
As for the gentileste, trewely,
That ever I say, to serven feithfully,
And best can ay his lady honour kepe":—
And with that word she brast anon to wepe.

155

"And certes, yow ne haten shal I never,
And freendes love, that shal ye han of me,
And my good word, al mighte I liven ever.
And, trewely, I wolde sory be
For to seen yow in adversitee.
And giltelees, I woot wel, I yow leve;
But al shal passe; and thus take I my leve."

156

But trewely, how longe it was bitwene,
That she for-sook him for this Diomede,
Ther is non auctor telleth it, I wene.
Take every man now to his bokes hede;
He shal no terme finden, out of drede.
For though that he bigan to wowe hir sone,
Er he hir wan, yet was ther more to done.

157

Ne me ne list this sely womman chyde
Ferther than the story wol devyse.
Hir name, allas! is publisshed so wyde,
That for hir gilt it oughte y-now suffyse
And if I mighte excuse hir any wyse.
For she so sory was for hir untrouthe,
Y-wis, I wolde excuse hir yet for routhe.

158

This Troilus, as I biforn have told,
Thus dryveth forth, as wel as he hath might.
But often was his herte hoot and cold,
And namely, that ilke nynthe night,
Which on the morwe she hadde him byhight
To come ayein: god wot, ful litel reste
Hadde he that night; no-thing to slepe him leste.

159

The laurer-crouned Phebus, with his hete,
Gan, in his course ay upward as he wente,
To warmen of th' est see the wawes wete;
And Nisus doughter song with fresh entente,
Whan Troilus his Pandare after sente;
And on the walles of the toun they pleyde,
To loke if they can seen ought of Criseyde.

160

Til it was noon, they stoden for to see
Who that ther come; and every maner wight,
That cam fro fer, they seyden it was she,
Til that they coude knowen him a-right,
Now was his herte dul, now was it light;
And thus by-japed stonden for to stare
Aboute nought, this Troilus and Pandare.

161

To Pandarus this Troilus tho seyde,
"For ought I wot, bi-for noon, sikerly,
In-to this toun ne comth nought here Criseyde.
She hath y-now to done, hardily,
To winnen from hir fader, so trowe I;
Hir olde fader wol yet make hir dyne
Er that she go; god yeve his herte pyne!"

162

Pandare answerde, "it may wel be, certeyn;
And for-thy lat us dyne, I thee biseche;
And after noon than mayst thou come ayeyn."
And hoom they go, with-oute more speche;
And comen ayein, but longe may they seche
Er that they finde that they after cape;
Fortune hem bothe thenketh for to jape.

163

Quod Troilus, "I see wel now, that she
Is taried with hir olde fader so,
That er she come, it wol neigh even be.
Com forth, I wol un-to the yate go.
Thise portours been unkonninge ever-mo;
And I wol doon hem holden up the yate
As nought ne were, al-though she come late."

164

The day goth faste, and after that comth eve,
And yet com nought to Troilus Criseyde.
He loketh forth by hegge, by tree, by greve,
And fer his heed over the wal he leyde.
And at the laste he torned him, and seyde,
"By god, I woot hir mening now, Pandare!
Al-most, y-wis, al newe was my care.

165

Now douteles, this lady can hir good;
I woot, she meneth ryden prively.
I comende hir wysdom, by myn hood!
She wol not maken peple nycely
Gaure on hir, whan she comth; but softely

158

Poor Troilus, as I before have told,
Now lived along in any way he might,
But often was his heart now hot, now cold,
And most of all upon that last ninth night,
For still he hoped next day his lady bright
Would come again; but yet he had, God knows,
Throughout that wakeful night but slight repose.

159

Phoebus, the laurel-crowned, now shiningly
Upon his course aye higher upward went
To warm the wide waves of the eastern sea,
And Nisus' daughter sang the day's advent,
When Troilus his word for Pandar sent,
And on the city walls they walked about,
To keep for Cressida a far lookout.

160

Till noon they kept their place and looked to see
Who came, and every one, they said, as long
As he was far away, was surely she,
Till nearer view showed they were always wrong,
For she was never one in any throng;
And thus befooled, this fond expectant pair
Stand on the Trojan walls and vainly stare.

161

Said Troilus, "Unless she comes quite soon,
I must believe she couldn't get away
And won't arrive in town till afternoon.
No doubt she had enough to do and say
To get from under her old father's sway.
I think, perhaps, he wanted her to dine
Before she left, and she could not decline."

162

Pandar to this replied, "That may well be,
And let us do the same, I might suggest,
And then come back, to see what we can see."
So home they go and dine and briefly rest,
Then back again upon their hopeless quest.
They cannot see, for all their straining eyes,
That fortune hides from them a sad surprise.

163

"It looks," said Troilus, "as though something
Has happened, or else her father keeps her so
She can't arrive till nearly evening.
Come on, and to the city gates let's go!
These gatemen are such stupid dolts, you know,
They wouldn't hesitate to shut the gate
And keep her out, if she chanced to be late."

164

The day goes fast, night falls on land and sea,
And "Cressida, she cometh not," he said.
He gazes forth on hedge and grove and tree,
And from the city wall he hangs his head,
But still she tarries, still his hopes he fed.
"I know," he cried, "what she intends to do!
Almost I feared that she would prove untrue!

165

"But now I know just what she doth intend—
She means to travel here incognito,
And her good sense therein I must commend.
She will not make herself a public show,
But quietly, and so that none may know,

By night into the town she means to ride,
And her good pleasure we must so abide.

166

"In fact there's nothing else that we can do.
But Pandar, look! What is it there I see?
She's come at last, it's too good to be true!
Lift up your eyes, old man! Is not that she?"
"Well, no," said Pandar, "sorry I can't agree!
You're wrong again, my boy, and for my part,
All I can see is some poor farmer's cart."

167

"Too true, it's but too true," said Troilus,
"But still I cannot think it's all for naught
That in my heart I feel uplifted thus.
Some good must be foreshadowed by my thought,
Since consolation comes to me unsought;
I never felt such comfort, truth to say,
And that she'll come tonight, my life I'll lay."

168

"It may be," answered Pandar, "well enough,"
Nor any of his empty hopes denied,
Though in his heart he thought it silly stuff,
And with straight face said to himself aside,
"You might as well give up and let things slide,
For all the good you'll get by waiting here.
Yes, farewell to the snows of yesteryear!"

169

The warden of the gates began to call
The folk without the fosses to prepare
To drive into the town their cattle all,
Or through the night they must remain out
there;
And in the dusk, with heart oppressed by care,
Troilus turns at last homeward to ride,
For now why should he longer there abide!

170

But still he took some hope in thinking this,
That he perhaps had counted wrong the day.
"I must," he said, "have taken her amiss,
For I recall I heard her that night say,
'I shall be back again, if so I may,
Before the silver moon, my own sweetheart,
Shall pass the Lion and from the Ram depart,'

171

"And so it may yet turn out for the best."
And on the morrow, to the gate he went,
And up and down, to east and then to west,
Beyond the city walls his gaze he bent,
But nothing gained from weary time thus spent,
And so at night, when he could see no more,
He went back home in disappointment sore.

172

Now hope delusive took its final flight,
For all that he had sought had turned out wrong;
Upon his heart there fell a deadly blight,
So were his silent sorrows sharp and strong,
For when he saw she stayed away so long,
He dared not to himself or think or say
Why she should fail to keep her promised day.

173

The third, the fourth, the fifth, the sixth succeed,
Since the appointed ten days by had rolled,

By nighte in-to the toun she thenketh ryde.
And, dere brother, thenk not longe t' abyde.

166

We han nought elles for to doon, y-wis.
And Pandarus, now woltow trowen me?
Have here my trouthe, I see hir! yond she is.
Heve up thyn eyen, man! maystow not see?"
Pandare answerde, "nay, so mote I thee!
Al wrong, by god; what seystow, man, wher art?
That I see yond nis but a fare-cart."

167

"Allas, thou seist right sooth," quod Troilus;
"But hardely, it is not al for nought
That in myn herte I now rejoyse thus.
It is ayein som good I have a thought.
Noot I not how, but sin that I was wrought,
Ne felte I swich a confort, dar I seye;
She comth to-night, my lyf, that dorste I leye!"

168

Pandare answerde, "it may be wel, y-nough";
And held with him of al that ever he seyde;
But in his herte he thoughte, and softe lough,
And to him-self ful sobrely he seyde:
"From hasel-wode, ther Joly Robin pleyde,
Shal come al that that thou abydest here;
Ye, fare-wel al the snow of ferne yere!"

169

The wardein of the yates gan to calle
The folk which that with-oute the yates were,
And bad hem dryven in hir bestes alle,
Or al the night they moste bleven
there.
And fer with-in the night, with many a tere,
This Troilus gan hoomward for to ryde;
For wel he seeth it helpeth nought t'abyde.

170

But natheles, he gladded him in this;
He thoughte he misacounted hadde his day,
And seyde, "I understonde have al a-mis.
For thilke night I last Criseyde say,
She seyde, 'I shal ben here, if that I may,
Er that the mone, O dere herte swete!
The Lyon passe, out of this Ariete.'

171

For which she may yet holde al hir biheste."
And on the morwe un-to the yate he wente,
And up and down, by west and eek by este,
Up-on the walles made he many a wente.
But al for nought; his hope alwey him blente;
For which at night, in sorwe and sykes sore
He wente him hoom, with-outen any more.

172

This hope al clene out of his herte fledde,
He nath wher-on now lenger for to honge;
But for the peyne him thoughte his herte bledde,
So were his throwes sharpe and wonder stronge.
For when he saugh that she abood so longe,
He niste what he juggen of it mighte,
Sin she hath broken that she him bihighte.

173

The thridde, ferthe, fifte, sixte day
After tho dayes ten, of which I tolde,

Bitwixen hope and drede his herte lay,
Yet som-what trustinge on hir hestes olde.
But whan he saugh she nolde hir terme holde,
He can now seen non other remedye,
But for to shape him sone for to dye.

174

Ther-with the wikked spirit, god us blesse,
Which that men clepeth wode jalousye,
Gan in him crepe, in al this hevinesse;
For which, by-cause he wolde sone dye,
He ne eet ne dronk, for his malencolye,
And eek from every companye he fledde;
This was the lyf that al the tyme he ledde.

175

He so defet was, that no maner man
Unnethe mighte him knowe ther he wente;
So was he lene, and ther-to pale and wan,
And feble, that he walketh by potente;
And with his ire he thus him-selven shente.
And who-so axed him wher-of him smerte,
He seyde, his harm was al aboute his herte.

176

Pryam ful ofte, and eek his moder dere,
His bretheren and his sustren gonne him freyne
Why he so sorwful was in al his chere,
And what thing was the cause of al his peyne?
But al for nought; he nolde his cause pleyne,
But seyde, he felte a grevous maladye
A-boute his herte, and fayn he wolde dye.

177

So on a day he leyde him doun to slepe,
And so bifel that in his sleep him thoughte,
That in a forest faste he welk to wepe
For love of hir that him these peynes wroughte;
And up and doun as he the forest soughte,
He mette he saugh a boor with tuskes grete,
That sleep ayein the bright sonnes hete.

178

And by this boor, faste in his armes folde,
Lay kissing ay his lady bright Criseyde:
For sorwe of which, whan he it gan biholde,
And for despyt, out of his slepe he breyde,
And loude he cryde on Pandarus, and seyde,
"O Pandarus, now knowe I crop and rote!
I nam but deed, ther nis non other bote!

179

My lady bright Criseyde hath me bitrayed,
In whom I trusted most of any wight,
She elles-where hath now hir herte apayed;
The blisful goddes, through hir grete might,
Han in my dreem y-shewed it ful right.
Thus in my dreem Criseyde I have biholde"—
And al this thing to Pandarus he tolde.

180

"O my Criseyde, allas! what subtiltee,
What newe lust, what beautee, what science,
What wratthe of juste cause have ye
 to me?
What gilt of me, what fel experience
Hath fro me raft, allas! thyn advertence?
O trust, O feyth, O depe aseürance,
Who hath me reft Criseyde, al my plesaunce?

And hope and dread still battle for the lead,
Nor could he quite reject her pledges old;
But then he saw her word she would not hold,
And this last woe completely filled his cup,
And he had nothing now to keep his courage up.

174

The dark and wicked mood of jealousy,
Which drives men on until they grow insane,
Crept in his heart to keep grief company,
And from all food and drink he did abstain,
As one who on this earth would not remain;
A lonely, melancholy life he led,
And from companionship he turned and fled.

175

A sick man now, his body's powers fail,
He seems a stranger even to his friends;
So thin and gaunt, of face so wan and pale,
Upon a staff he weakly now depends,
For thus black care achieves its evil ends;
And if one asked him how it all did start,
He said he had some trouble with his heart.

176

Priam inquired, and so his mother dear,
His brothers and his sisters, too, did ask,
Why he should always be so sad and drear,
And for his good they took him oft to task;
But still his grief he ever sought to mask,
And said about his heart he felt such pain
As mortal body could not long sustain.

177

It chanced one day he laid him down to sleep,
And in his restless slumber, so he thought,
Within a wood he went to walk and weep,
For love of her who all this wrong had wrought,
And down a path, his eyes a vision caught;
A tusked boar appeared in his sad dreams,
Asleep and lying in the bright sunbeams,

178

And by this boar, whom in her arms she held,
Lay Cressida, kissing the fearsome beast.
And suddenly this vision strange expelled
All sleep, and from his dreaming thus released,
Troilus knew all hope for him had ceased.
"O Pandar," cried he, "now I know the worst!
I am a man abandoned and accursed!

179

"My lady Cressida hath me betrayed,
In whom was all my trust and my delight;
Her love she hath elsewhere conveyed!
The blessed Gods above through their great might
Have in my dreams revealed it to my sight!
Thus in my dreams I did my love behold—"
And all the tale to Pandar he then told.

180

"O Cressida, what baseless treachery,
What lust of heart, what beauty or what wit—,
What wrath with just cause have you felt
 towards me?
What guilt in me, what thoughts or deeds unfit
Have caused thy heart away from me to flit?
O trust! O faith! O hopes that life inspire!
O who hath robbed me of my heart's desire!

181

"Alas, why did I ever let you go?
O, by what folly was I thus misled?
What faith on oaths can I henceforth bestow!
God knows I was convinced in heart and head,
That every word was Gospel that you said.
But treason oft doth show its hateful face
In those in whom the greatest trust we place.

182

"What shall I do? What now is left for me?
There falls on me anew so sharp a pain,
For which there can be found no remedy,
Better to kill myself with these hands twain
Than in this life of misery remain!
Death at the least a final peace will send,
But life is daily death that hath no end!"

183

Then Pandar answered him, "Alas the while
That I was born! Have I not said ere this,
That dreams all sorts of folk all times beguile?
And why? They all interpret them amiss!
To charge her false on dreams is cowardice,
Because your dreams rise only from your fear,
And what they mean, you never can make clear.

184

"This dream that you have had about a boar,
It well may be that it doth signify
Her father, old and of his head so hoar,
Who near his death doth in the warm sun lie,
While she for natural grief must weep and cry,
And kiss him as he lies there on the ground—
This is the way you should your dream expound."

185

"Perhaps," said Troilus. "I wish I knew
For certain how to judge my dream aright."
"I'll tell you then," said Pandar, "what to do!
Since you know well enough how to endite,
Bestir yourself and to your lady write.
I know no better way of finding out
The truth and freeing so your mind of doubt.

186

"That way you'll know just how things stand, for better
Or worse; for if untrue she means to be,
She will not send an answer to your letter;
And if she writes, then you can quickly see
If she to come again to Troy is free,
And if she's let and hindered in some way,
She will explain it all as clear as day.

187

"You have not written her since forth she went,
Nor has she written you, and I dare say
Some little things her coming back prevent,
And when you know just what they are, you may
Decide she's acted in the wisest way.
Go then and write; of all plans that's the best
To ease your mind and set your doubts at rest."

188

Troilus to this advice can but agree,
For other plan he has none to propose,
Nor long delays, but sits down hastily,
Debating in his heart the cons and pros

181

Allas! why leet I you from hennes go,
For which wel neigh out of my wit I breyde?
Who shal now trowe on any othes mo?
God wot I wende, O lady bright, Criseyde,
That every word was gospel that ye seyde!
But who may bet bigylen, if him liste,
Than he on whom men weneth best to triste?

182

What shal I doon, my Pandarus, allas!
I fele now so sharpe a newe peyne,
Sin that ther is no remedie in this cas,
That bet were it I with myn hondes tweyne
My-selven slow, than alwey thus to pleyne.
For through my deeth my wo sholde han an ende,
Ther every day with lyf my-self I shende."

183

Pandare answerde and seyde, "allas the whyle
That I was born; have I not seyd er this,
That dremes many a maner man bigyle?
And why? for folk expounden hem a-mis.
How darstow seyn that fals thy lady is,
For any dreem, right for thyn owene drede?
Lat be this thought, thou canst no dremes rede.

184

Paraunter, ther thou dremest of this boor,
It may so be that it may signifye
Hir fader, which that old is and eek hoor,
Ayein the sonne lyth, on poynt to dye,
And she for sorwe ginneth wepe and crye,
And kisseth him, ther he lyth on the grounde;
Thus shuldestow thy dreem a-right expounde."

185

"How mighte I thanne do?" quod Troilus,
"To knowe of this, ye, were it never so lyte?"
"Now seystow wysly," quod this Pandarus,
"My reed is this, sin thou canst wel endyte,
That hastely a lettre thou hir wryte,
Thorugh which thou shalt wel bringen it aboute,
To knowe a sooth of that thou art in doute.

186

And see now why; for this I dar wel seyn,
That if so is that she untrewe be,
I can not trowe that she wol wryte ayeyn.
And if she wryte, thou shalt ful sone see,
As whether she hath any libertee
To come ayein, or elles in som clause,
If she be let, she wol assigne a cause.

187

Thou hast not writen hir sin that she wente,
Nor she to thee, and this I dorste leye,
Ther may swich cause been in hir entente,
That hardely thou wolt thy-selven seye,
That hir a-bood the beste is for yow tweye.
Now wryte hir thanne, and thou shalt fele sone
A sothe of al; ther is no more to done."

188

Acorded been to this conclusioun,
And that anoon, these ilke lordes two;
And hastely sit Troilus adoun,
And rolleth in his herte to and fro,

How he may best discryven hir his wo.
And to Criseyde, his owene lady dere,
He wroot right thus, and seyde as ye may here.

189

"Right fresshe flour, whos I have been and shal,
With-outen part of elles-where servyse,
With herte, body, lyf, lust, thought, and al;
I, woful wight, in every humble wyse
That tonge telle or herte may devyse,
As ofte as matere occupyeth place,
Me recomaunde un-to your noble grace.

190

Lyketh it yow to witen, swete herte,
As ye wel knowe how longe tyme agoon
That ye me lafte in aspre peynes smerte,
Whan that ye wente, of which yet bote noon
Have I non had, but ever wers bigoon
Fro day to day am I, and so mot dwelle,
While it yow list, of wele and wo my welle!

191

For which to yow, with dredful herte trewe,
I wryte, as he that sorwe dryfth to wryte,
My wo, that every houre encreseth newe,
Compleyninge as I dar or can endyte.
And that defaced is, that may ye wyte
The teres, which that fro myn eyen reyne,
That wolde speke, if that they coude, and pleyne.

192

Yow first biseche I, that your eyen clere
To look on this defouled ye not holde;
And over al this, that ye, my lady dere,
Wol vouche-sauf this lettre to biholde.
And by the cause eek of my cares colde,
That sleeth my wit, if ought amis me asterte,
For-yeve it me, myn owene swete herte.

193

If any servant dorste or oughte of right
Up-on his lady pitously compleyne,
Than wene I, that ich oughte be that wight,
Considered this, that ye these monthes tweyne
Han taried, ther ye seyden, sooth to seyne,
But dayes ten ye nolde in ost sojourne,
But in two monthes yet ye not retourne.

194

But for-as-muche as me mot nedes lyke
Al that yow list, I dar not pleyne more,
But humblely with sorwful sykes syke;
Yow wryte ich myn unresty sorwes sore,
Fro day to day desyring ever-more
To knowen fully, if your wil it were,
How ye han ferd and doon, whyl ye be there.

195

The whos wel-fare and hele eek god encresse
In honour swich, that upward in degree
It growe alwey, so that it never cesse;
Right as your herte ay can, my lady free,
Devyse, I prey to god so mote it be.
And graunte it that ye sone up-on me rewe
As wisly as in al I am yow trewe.

196

And if yow lyketh knowen of the fare
Of me, whos wo ther may no wight discryve,

How he may best portray to her his woes,
And thus to Cressida, his lady dear,
He wrote this letter as follows here:

189

"Flower of my life, whom I do rightly call
Sole sovereign of my every act and deed,
With body and soul, with will and thought and all,
I, wretched man, answering every need
That tongue may tell or heart may ever plead,
As far as matter occupieth space,
I, wretched man, beseech of you your grace!

190

"And let me now recall, my own sweetheart,
How long a lonely time has passed away,
Since you left me, pierced with the bitter dart
Of pain, for which no help nor stay
Have I yet had, but ever worse from day
To day, and so must I forever dwell
Until you come my sorrow to dispel.

191

"With heart oppressed by fear, yet firm and true,
As one by need hard driven now I write,
And all my grief that ever grows anew,
With such skill as I have, I here endite,
And all these stains upon this parchment white
Are tears which from my eyes upon it rain,
And let them plead my sorrow not in vain!

192

"The first I beg is that with eyes so clear
You'll look at this, and hold it not defiled;
And yet again, that you, my lady dear,
Will read it with a gentle heart and mild.
And if my words should seem abrupt or wild,
Bethink that from my grief they all do start,
And so forgive them me, my own sweetheart.

193

"If any lover ever durst with right
Upon his lady chargefully complain,
Then surely I am that unlucky wight,
Considering how you have for these months twain
Delayed, although you said, time and again,
But ten days with the Greeks you would sojourn—
Yet in two months, you do not yet return.

194

"But since in all things I must to you yield,
I may say nothing further on this score,
Yet humbly and with sorrow unconcealed,
I here set forth all my affliction sore,
From day to day desiring ever more
To know in full how with the Greeks you fare,
And what you have been doing over there.

195

"Your health and fortune may the Lord increase,
And may your honor upward in degree
Advance, and in its growing never cease;
The hopes you cherish, every wish and plea,
The Gods grant them to you all utterly!
And may some pity thereamongst shine through
Towards me, thy faithful knight and ever true.

196

"And if you would know how in Troy I fare,
Whose griefs now at their pinnacle arrive,

I can but say, that borne upon by care,
The time I wrote this, I was yet alive,
Yet ready, too, with swift death to connive,
Which I hold off, and from me briefly fend,
Until I see what word to me you send.

197

"My eyes, now useless your fair face to see,
Of bitter tears are but two flowing wells,
My song is but of my adversity,
My happy heavens turn to bitter hells,
And no relief my weight of woe dispels;
I am my own accursed adversary,
And every joy turns into its contrary.

198

"But when you come back home again to Troy,
All this affliction you may soon redress,
For then indeed you shall revive my joy,
For never yet did heaven a heart so bless
As you shall mine, when all my long distress
Shall come to end; if not by pity stirred,
Stern duty bids you hold at least your word.

199

"But if I've earned this fate by doing wrong,
Or if my face you ne'er again will see,
In mere reward that I have served you long,
I beg that you will be both frank and free,
And quickly write and send word back to me
And tell me so, my only lodestar bright,
That I may end my life in death and night.

200

"Or if some other cause makes you to dwell,
Then in your letter make of this report,
For though to me your absence is a hell,
My woe to needful patience can resort,
And hope against my black despair retort.
Pray write then, sweet, and make the matter plain,
With hope, or death, deliver me from pain!

201

"But I must warn you, my own sweetheart true,
When you again your Troilus shall see,
So much has changed his frame and all his hue,
That Cressida shall scarcely know it's he.
In truth, light of my world, my lady free,
So thirsts my heart your beauty to behold,
My grasp on life I scarce can longer hold.

202

"I say no more, though more I well could write,
And still leave boundless volumes yet to say;
With life or death my love you may requite,
Yet heaven grant you joy in every way!
So fare thee well, my love, and have good day!
My life or death I take as you shall send
And to your truth myself I still commend,

203

"With such good will, that if you grant to me
The same good will, there's nothing else I crave;
For in you lies, if so you'll have it be,
The doom that men shall dig for me my grave,
Or in you lies the might my life to save,
And bid all grief and pain from me depart!
And now a last farewell, my own sweetheart!

Le vostre T."

I can no more but, cheste of every care,
At wrytinge of this lettre I was on-lyve,
Al redy out my woful gost to dryve;
Which I delaye, and holde him yet in honde,
Upon the sight of matere of your sonde.

197

Myn eyen two, in veyn with which I see,
Of sorweful teres salte arn waxen welles;
My song, in pleynte of myn adversitee;
My good in harm; myn ese eek waxen helle is.
My joye, in wo; I can sey yow nought elles,
But turned is, for which my lyf I warie,
Everich joye or ese in his contrarie.

198

Which with your cominge hoom ayein to Troye
Ye may redresse, and, more a thousand sythe
Than ever ich hadde, encresen in me joye.
For was ther never herte yet so blythe
To han his lyf, as I shal been as swythe
As I yow see; and, though no maner routhe
Commeve yow, yet thinketh on your trouthe.

199

And if so be my gilt hath deeth deserved,
Or if you list no more up-on me see,
In guerdon yet of thatI have you served,
Biseche I yow, myn hertes lady free,
That here-upon ye wolden wryte me,
For love of god, my righte lode-sterre,
Ther deeth may make an ende of al my werre.

200

If other cause aught doth yow for to dwelle,
That with your lettre ye me recomforte;
For though to me your absence is an helle,
With pacience I wol my wo comporte,
And with your lettre of hope I wol desporte.
Now wryteth, swete, and lat me thus not pleyne;
With hope, or deeth, delivereth me from peyne.

201

Y-wis, myn owene dere herte trewe,
I woot that, whan ye next up-on me see,
So lost have I myn hele and eek myn hewe,
Criseyde shal nought conne knowe me!
Y-wis, myn hertes day, my lady free,
So thursteth ay myn herte to biholde
Your beautee, that my lyf unnethe I holde.

202

I sey no more, al have I for to seye
To you wel more than I telle may;
But whether that ye do me live or deye,
Yet pray I god, so yeve yow right good day.
And fareth wel, goodly fayre fresshe may,
As ye that lyf or deeth me may comaunde;
And to your trouthe ay I me recomaunde

203

With hele swich that, but ye yeven me
The same hele, I shal noon hele have.
In you lyth, whan yow list that it so be,
The day in which me clothen shal my grave.
In yow my lyf, in yow might for to save
Me from disese of alle peynes smerte;
And fare now wel, myn owene swete herte!

Le vostre T."

204

This lettre forth was sent un-to Criseyde,
Of which hir answere in effect was this;
Ful pitously she wroot ayein, and seyde,
That al-so sone as that she might, y-wis,
She wolde come, and mende al that was mis.
And fynally she wroot and seyde him thanne,
She wolde come, ye, but she niste whanne.

204

To Cressida this letter straight was sent,
To which her answer was to this effect:
Her long delay she sadly did lament,
And said that she would come when good prospect
She found, and what was wrong would all correct,
And finally she wrote and told him then
That she would come, O yes, but knew not when.

205

But in hir lettre made she swich festes,
That wonder was, and swereth she loveth him best,
Of which he fond but botmelees bihestes.
But Troilus, thou mayst now, est or west,
Pype in an ivy leef, if that thee lest;
Thus gooth the world; god shilde us fro
mischaunce,
And every wight that meneth trouthe avaunce!

205

But still her letter seemed most cordial,
Though in the end he found it vague and cold,
And yet she swore she loved him best of all!
But Troilus, when all the tale is told,
Cressida hath left thee here the bag to hold!
Thus goes the world! God shield us from
disaster,
And of our fates may each of us be master!

206

Encresen gan the wo fro day to night
Of Troilus, for taryinge of Criseyde;
And lessen gan his hope and eek his might,
For which al doun he in his bed him leyde;
He ne eet, ne dronk, ne sleep, ne word he seyde,
Imagininge ay that she was unkinde;
For which wel neigh he wex out of his minde.

206

The grief of Troilus grew greater night
And day, so long his lady from him stayed,
And feebler grew his hope and body's might,
For which upon his bed himself he laid,
Nor ate, nor drank, nor slept, nor speech essayed,
And thought upon the curse of fortune blind,
Until all reason fled from out his mind.

207

This dreem, of which I told have eek biforn,
May never come out of his remembraunce;
He thoughte ay wel he hadde his lady lorn,
And that Joves, of his purveyaunce,
Him shewed hadde in sleep the signifiaunce
Of hir untrouthe and his disaventure,
And that the boor was shewed him in figure.

207

This dream, of which I have already told,
He never from his fancy could expel,
Nor could he doubt his lady had grown cold,
Nor yet that Jove had taken means to tell
By dreams, when heavy sleep upon him fell,
Of her untruth and his disastrous fate—
All which the boar was meant to indicate.

208

For which he for Sibille his suster sente,
That called was Cassandre eek al aboute;
And al his dreem he tolde hir er he stente,
And hir bisoughte assoilen him the doute
Of the stronge boor, with tuskes stoute;
And fynally, with-inne a litel stounde,
Cassandre him gan right thus his dreem expounde.

208

Then for his sister Sibly straight he sent,
Known also as Cassandra round about,
And told his dream to her just at it went,
And asked her to resolve his mind of doubt,
Concerning this great boar with tusks so stout;
And soon as she the meaning of it found,
She thus began his vision to expound.

209

She gan first smyle, and seyde, "O brother dere,
If thou a sooth of this desyrest knowe,
Thou most a fewe of olde stories here,
To purpos, how that fortune over-throwe
Hath lordes olde; through which, with-inne a
throwe,
Thou wel this boor shalt knowe, and of what kinde
He comen is, as men in bokes finde.

209

Smiling a prophet's smile, "O brother dear,"
She said, "if you the truth will really know,
Then you must first a few old stories hear,
Which tell how fortune once did overthrow
Some lords of old, and thereby I shall
show
And tell you whence this boar, and of what kind,
As in the books the story you may find.

210

Diane, which that wrooth was and in ire
For Grekes nolde doon hir sacrifyse,
Ne encens up-on hir auter sette a-fyre,
She, for that Grekes gonne hir so dispyse,
Wrak hir in a wonder cruel wyse.
For with a boor as greet as oxe in stalle
She made up frete hir corn and vynes alle.

210

"Diana, filled with anger and with ire,
Because the Greeks withheld her sacrifice,
Nor on her altar set incense afire,
In vengeance made them pay a cruel price,
And this, in long and short, was her device,
She let a boar, as great as ox in stall,
Devour their growing corn and vines and all.

211

To slee this boor was al the contree reysed,
A-monges which ther com, this boor to see,
A mayde, oon of this world the best y-preysed;

211

"To slay this boar the countryside was raised,
And thereamong came one, the boar to see,
A maiden whom all in that region praised;

And Meleager, lord of that country,
So loved this maiden, fair and fresh and free,
That into battle with this boar he went,
And killing it, its head unto her sent.

212

"From this, as ancient writers tell to us,
There rose a contest and a warfare high,
And from this lord descended Tydeus,
By line direct, as no one can deny;
But how this Meleager came to die
Through his own mother, that I shall not tell,
For on that tale it were too long to dwell."

213

How Tydeus made warfare Sibyl told,
At Thebes, that ancient city and so strong,
Maintaining that to Polynices bold,
The Theban city did by right belong,
And that Eteocles, his brother, wrong
Had done, in holding Thebes by strength—
All this she told to him and at great length.

214

She also told about Haemonides,
When Tydeus slew fifty knights so stout,
And told of all the wondrous prophecies,
And how the seven kings for Thebes set out,
And then besieged the city round about,
And of the holy serpent and the well,
And of the Furies, all this did she tell;

215

And Archemorus' death and funeral plays,
And how Amphiorax fell through the ground,
How Tydeus was slain and closed his days,
And also how Ipomedon was drowned,
And Parthenope final death wound found,
And how Capaneus, the strong and proud,
Was slain by stroke of thunder, sounding loud.

216

And then she told the tale how either brother,
Eteocles and Polynices true,
How each of them in skirmish killed the other,
And how Argia wept and made ado;
The burning of the town did she review,
And so descended down from stories old
To Diomede, and of him thus she told.

217

"This boar you dreamed of stands for Diomede,
Tydeus' son, of Meleager's line,
Who killed the boar and won fame by that deed;
Thy lady, if in fact she once was thine,
With Diomede in love doth now combine;
Be glad or sad, but there can be no doubt,
This Diomede is in and you are out."

218

"That isn't true," he cried, "thou sorceress!
False is the spirit of thy prophecy,
And all the priestly cunning you profess!
Your wickedness is plain and clear to see,
To stain a lady's name with falsity!
Away," he cried, "may Jove increase your sorrow,
For you are false today and false tomorrow!

219

"As well defame the beautiful Alceste,

And Meleagre, lord of that contree,
He lovede so this fresshe mayden free
That with his manhod, er he wolde stente,
This boor he slow, and hir the heed he sente;

212

Of which, as olde bokes tellen us,
Ther roos a contek and a greet envye;
And of this lord descended Tydeus
By ligne, or elles olde bokes lye;
But how this Meleagre gan to dye
Thorugh his moder, wol I yow not telle,
For al to long it were for to dwelle."

213

She toldë eek how Tydeus, er she stente,
Un-to the stronge citee of Thebes,
To cleyme kingdom of the citee, wente,
For his felawe, daun Polymites,
Of which the brother, daun Ethyocles,
Ful wrongfully of Thebes held the strengthe;
This tolde she by proces, al by lengthe.

214

She tolde eek how Hemonides asterte,
Whan Tydeus slough fifty knightes stoute.
She tolde eek al the prophesyes by herte,
And how that sevene kinges, with hir route,
Bisegeden the citee al aboute;
And of the holy serpent, and the welle,
And of the furies, al she gan him telle.

215

Of Archimoris buryinge and the pleyes,
And how Amphiorax fil through the grounde,
How Tydeus was slayn, lord of Argeyes,
And how Ypomedoun in litel stounde
Was dreynt, and deed Parthonope of wounde;
And also how Cappanëus the proude
With thonder-dint was slayn, that cryde loude.

216

She gan eek telle him how that either brother,
Ethyocles and Polimyte also,
At a scarmyche, eche of hem slough other,
And of Argyves wepinge and hir wo;
And how the town was brent she tolde eek tho.
And so descendeth doun from gestes olde
To Diomede, and thus she spak and tolde.

217

"This ilke boor bitokneth Diomede,
Tydeus sone, that doun descended is
Fro Meleagre, that made the boor to blede.
And thy lady, wher-so she be, y-wis,
This Diomede hir herte hath, and she his.
Weep if thou wolt, or leef; for, out of doute,
This Diomede is inne, and thou art oute."

218

"Thou seyst nat soth," quod he, "thou sorceresse,
With al thy false goost of prophesye!
Thou wenest been a greet devyneresse;
Now seestow not this fool of fantasye
Peyneth hir on ladyes for to lye?
Awey," quod he, "ther Joves yeve thee sorwe!
Thou shalt be fals, paraunter, yet to-morwe!

219

As wel thou mightest lyen on Alceste,

That was of creatures, but men lye,
That ever weren, kindest and the beste.
For whanne hir housbonde was in jupartye
To dye him-self, but-if she wolde dye,
She chees for him to dye and go to helle,
And starf anoon, as us the bokes telle."

220

Cassandre goth, and he with cruel herte
For-yat his wo, for angre of hir speche;
And from his bed al sodeinly he sterte,
As though al hool him hadde y-mad a leche.
And day by day he gan enquere and seche
A sooth of this, with al his fulle cure;
And thus he dryeth forth his aventure.

221

Fortune, whiche that permutacioun
Of thinges hath, as it is hir committed
Through purveyaunce and disposicioun
Of heighe Jove, as regnes shal ben flitted
Fro folk in folk, or whan they shal ben smitted,
Gan pulle awey the fetheres brighte of Troye
Fro day to day, til they ben bare of joye.

222

Among al this, the fyn of the parodie
Of Ector gan approchen wonder blyve;
The fate wolde his soule sholde unbodie,
And shapen hadde a mene it out to dryve;
Ayeins which fate him helpeth not to stryve;
But on a day to fighten gan he wende,
At which, allas! he caughte his lyves ende.

223

For which me thinketh every maner wight
That haunteth armes oughte to biwayle
The deeth of him that was so noble a knight;
For as he drough a king by th'aventayle,
Unwar of this, Achilles through the mayle
And through the body gan him for to ryve;
And thus this worthy knight was brought of lyve.

224

For whom, as olde bokes tellen us,
Was maad swich wo, that tonge it may not telle;
And namely, the sorwe of Troilus,
That next him was of worthinesse welle.
And in this wo gan Troilus to dwelle,
That, what for sorwe, and love, and for unreste,
Ful ofte a day he bad his herte breste.

225

But natheles, though he gan him dispeyre,
And dradde ay that his lady was untrewe,
Yet ay on hir his herte gan repeyre.
And as these loveres doon, he soughte ay newe
To gete ayein Criseyde, bright of hewe.
And in his herte he wente hir excusinge,
That Calkas causede al hir taryinge.

226

And ofte tyme he was in purpos grete
Him-selven lyk a pilgrim to disgyse,
To seen hir; but he may not contrefete
To been unknowen of folk that weren wyse,
Ne finde excuse aright that may suffyse,
If he among the Grekes knowen were;
For which he weep ful ofte many a tere.

Who was, unless all history doth lie,
Of human kind the truest and the best,
For when her husband was about to die,
Unless his place she would herself supply,
For him she chose to die and go to hell,
And in his stead, among the dead to dwell."

220

Cassandra goes, and he with hardened heart
At anger of her speech forgot his woe,
And from his bed now suddenly doth start,
As one who had been sick, but well doth grow;
For nothing now he cares except to know
The truth of what he must henceforth endure,
And in the truth to find his death or cure.

221

Fortune, controller of the permutation
Of things entrusted to her will and sway,
Yet subject to great Jove's administration,
Now making kingdoms slip and slide away,
And all things follow their appointed day,
Began to pluck the feathers bright of Troy,
And left both Troy and Trojans bare of joy.

222

Great Hector drew near to his period's end,
Which all too soon for Troy must now arrive;
Forth from his body fate his soul would send,
And sought a means upon its way to drive
It hence, against which he in vain might strive;
For into battle on a day he went,
Which ended only when his life was spent.

223

Now every man, it seems to me but right,
Who follows arms, should heartily bewail
The death of such a perfect noble knight!
As with his sword he did a king assail,
Achilles, unseen, pierced him through the mail,
And through his body drove the fatal dart
That stopped the beating of his knightly heart.

224

For this knight's death, so brave and generous,
The grief the Trojans felt no tongue can tell,
And least of all the grief of Troilus,
Who next to him was honor's source and well;
Such dark despair on Troilus now fell,
So utterly all joys his heart forsook,
For no day of relief he now doth look.

225

Nevertheless for all his grim despair,
For all his fear his lady was untrue,
Yet still his mind and thought turned ever there,
And like all lovers, still he sought anew
To justify his lady, bright of hue,
And to excuse her, he would often say,
That Calchas was the cause of this delay.

226

He even planned, should time and place permit,
To go and see her in a pilgrim's guise,
But feared he could not so well counterfeit,
That he might risk the test of searching eyes,
Nor find excuse for what men might surmise,
If he among the Greeks were ever caught,
And so he must relinquish this vain thought.

227

To Cressida he often wrote anew,
For not the faintest chance he would neglect,
Beseeching her that since he still was true,
His love, long proved, she should not thus reject;
And Cressida, for pity, I suspect,
Wrote him, as I shall tell, a parting word,
Which was the last he ever from her heard:

228

"Thou son of Cupid, model of all that's good,
Thou sword of knighthood, valor's primal source,
Pray how may she who long herself hath stood
In torment, sorrow from thy heart divorce?
Behold me, sad and sick, with no recourse,
Since you with me nor I with you may deal,
But helpless grief within me to conceal.

229

"Your letters ample and your paper plaints
Have deeply moved my heart to sympathy;
The stains of tears that broke their long restraints,
These have I seen, but what you ask of me,
To come to Troy, just now that cannot be,
Yet why, since someone may this letter seize,
I cannot here explain to you with ease.

230

"Grievous to me, God knows, is your unrest,
And what the Gods have ordered and ordained,
It seems you take it not as for the best,
And all the thought you have in mind retained
Is but of present pleasure unrestrained;
But for all that, I say 'tis only fear
Of wicked tongues that makes me linger here.

231

"For I have heard things much to my surprise,
Concerning you and me, and how we stand,
Which calls for cautious action and for wise;
And I have heard that you have merely planned
To hold me at your beck and your command;
But let that pass—I can but in you see
All truth, and gentleness and honesty.

232

"Yes, I will come! But times are out of joint,
And as things stand with me, what year or day
That this shall be, I cannot now appoint.
But still, whatever happens, let me pray
To have your goodwill and your friendship aye,
For truly while my living days endure,
My friendship to you I do here assure.

233

"And I must ask you that you do not take
It ill, if I so briefly to you write;
I dare not, where I am, distrust awake,
Nor ever had I skill well to endite.
Brief words may cover more than meets the sight.
The meaning counts, and not the letters' space.
So fare you well! God grant to you his grace!

La vostre C."

234

This letter Troilus thought rather strange,
And read it with a sad and thoughtful sigh,
For therein saw he many signs of change,

227

To hir he wroot yet ofte tyme al newe
Ful pitously, he lefte it nought for slouthe,
Biseching hir that, sin that he was trewe,
She wolde come ayein and holde hir trouthe.
For which Criseyde up-on a day, for routhe,
I take it so, touchinge al this matere,
Wrot him ayein, and seyde as ye may here.

228

"Cupydes sone, ensample of goodlihede,
O swerd of knighthod, sours of gentilesse!
How mighte a wight in torment and in drede
And helelees, yow sende as yet gladnesse?
I hertelees, I syke, I in distresse;
Sin ye with me, nor I with yow may dele,
Yow neither sende ich herte may nor hele.

229

Your lettres ful, the papir al y-pleynted,
Conseyved hath myn hertes piëtee;
I have eek seyn with teres al depeynted
Your lettre, and how that ye requeren me
To come ayein, which yet ne may not be.
But why, lest that this lettre founden were,
No mencioun ne make I now, for fere.

230

Grevous to me, god woot, is your unreste,
Your haste, and that, the goddes ordenaunce,
It semeth not ye take it for the beste.
Nor other thing nis in your remembraunce,
As thinketh me, but only your plesaunce.
But beth not wrooth, and that I yow biseche;
For that I tarie, is al for wikked speche.

231

For I have herd wel more than I wende,
Touchinge us two, how thinges han y-stonde;
Which I shal with dissimulinge amende.
And beth nought wrooth, I have eek understonde,
How ye ne doon but holden me in honde.
But now no fors, I can not in yow gesse
But alle trouthe and alle gentilesse.

232

Comen I wol, but yet in swich disjoynte
I stonde as now, that what yeer or what day
That this shal be, that can I not apoynte.
But in effect, I prey yow, as I may,
Of your good word and of your friendship ay.
For trewely, whyl that my lyf may dure,
As for a freend, ye may in me assure.

233

Yet preye I yow on yvel ye ne take,
That it is short which that I to yow wryte;
I dar not, ther I am, wel lettres make.
Ne never yet ne coude I wel endyte.
Eek greet effect men wryte in place lyte.
Th'entente is al, and nought the lettres space;
And fareth now wel, god have you in his grace!

La vostre C."

234

This Troilus this lettre thoughte al straunge,
Whan he it saugh, and sorwefully he sighte;
Him thoughte it lyk a kalendes of chaunge;

But fynally, he ful ne trowen mighte
That she ne wolde him holden that she highte;
For with ful yvel wil list him to leve
That loveth wel, in swich cas, though him greve.

235

But natheles, men seyn that, at the laste,
For any thing, men shal the sothe see;
And swich a cas bitidde, and that as faste,
That Troilus wel understood that she
Nas not so kinde as that hir oughte be.
And fynally, he woot now, out of doute,
That al is lost that he hath been aboute.

236

Stood on a day in his malencolye
This Troilus, and in suspecioun
Of hir for whom he wende for to dye.
And so bifel, that through-out Troye toun,
As was the gyse, y-bore was up and doun
A maner cote-armure, as seyth the storie,
Biforn Deiphebe, in signe of his victorie,

237

The whiche cote, as telleth Lollius,
Deiphebe it hadde y-rent from Diomede
The same day; and whan this Troilus
It saugh, he gan to taken of it hede,
Avysing of the lengthe and of the brede,
And al the werk; but as he gan biholde,
Ful sodeinly his herte gan to colde.

238

As he that on the coler fond with-inne
A broche, that he Criseyde yaf that morwe
That she from Troye moste nedes twinne,
In remembraunce of him and of his sorwe:
And she him leyde ayein hir feyth to borwe
To keep it ay; but now, ful wel he wiste,
His lady nas no lenger on to triste.

239

He gooth him hoom, and gan ful sone sende
For Pandarus; and al this newe chaunce,
And of this broche, he tolde him word and ende,
Compleyninge of hir hertes variaunce,
His longe love, his trouthe, and his penaunce;
And after deeth, with-outen wordes more,
Ful faste he cryde, his reste him to restore.

240

Than spak he thus, "O lady myn Criseyde,
Wher is your feth, and wher is your biheste?
Wher is your love, wher is your trouthe?" he seyde;
"O Diomede have ye now al this feste!
Allas, I wolde have trowed at the leste,
That, sin ye nolde in trouthe to me stonde,
That ye thus nolde han holden me in honde!

241

Who shal now trowe on any othes mo?
Allas, I never wolde han wend, er this,
That ye, Criseyde, coude han chaunged so;
Ne, but I hadde a-gilt and doon amis,
So cruel wende I not your herte, y-wis,
To sele me thus; allas, your name of trouthe
Is now for-doon, and that is al my routhe.

242

Was ther non other broche yow liste lete

Yet to himself continued to deny
That she her faith and name would stultify.
However much their ladies may them grieve,
That they are false, what lover can believe!

235

But ever must a time come at the last
When truth will out for every man to see;
For now the day approaches, sure and fast,
When Troilus must realize that she
Was not as constant as she ought to be,
And that the love and faith that seemed so sure,
Were not so true that they could long endure.

236

One day he stood in melancholy thought,
For now his doubts of her he could not down,
But still they came unchallenged and unsought,
When through the length of all the Trojan town,
As happened oft with trophies of renown,
Before Deiphebus for all to see
An armor cloak was born in victory.

237

This cloak, as Lollius explains to us,
Deiphebus had torn from Diomede
That day, and in the throng was Troilus,
Regarding it with keen attentive heed;
Its length, its breadth, the work on it, their meed
Of praise he gave to all, and taking hold
Of it, he saw what made his blood run cold.

238

For on the collar lay hid there within,
A brooch which he to Cressida had given
Ere she left Troy, and on her breast did pin,
In witness of his love with sorrow riven;
And she an equal faith to show had striven,
And pledged to keep it aye, but now he knew
That to her word and him she was untrue.

239

He hastened home and straight for Pandar sent,
Recounting to him all the sad details
About the fatal brooch and what it meant;
His lady's falsity he then bewails
Against which love nor honor aught avails,
For death alone can heal this wound so sore,
And peace unto his shattered heart restore.

240

"O Cressida," he cried, "O lady bright,
Where is your faith, where is your promised word!
Where are the love and truth that you did plight!
All these on Diomede are now conferred!
Alas, by shame you should have been deterred
From this, for though you might have been untrue,
No need was there such hateful deed to do!

241

"What man shall ever trust in oaths again?
I never dreamed that thou couldst alter so,
O Cressida, unless it might be then,
If I the first inconstancy should show!
O that thy tender heart could deal such blow!
Alas, the hateful deed that thou hast done,
An evil eminence for thee hath won!

242

"Was there no other brooch that you might use

With which your new love you might usher in,
But only that endeared one you must choose,
Which on your faithless breast I once did pin?
What end could you expect thereby to win,
Except with needless cruelty to tell
That in your heart I now no longer dwell?

243

"For now I see you utterly have cast
Me from your thought, and yet I cannot find
It in my heart, in spite of all that's passed,
To drive you for a moment from my mind!
O what a fate unnatural and blind,
That I must love the best on all this earth
The one who holds me of the slightest worth!

244

"O God above, this favor I request,
That I may meet, and soon, this Diomede,
For gladly would I try with him a test
Of strength and see his life's heart bleed!
O God, who ever dost and shouldst take heed
To further virtue and to punish wrong,
Take thou thy vengeance on him swift and strong!

245

"Thou, Pandar, who didst often fret and chide,
Because my dreams seemed credible to me,
O, would that more on them I had relied,
For now you see your niece's falsity!
In sundry ways both joy and misery
The Gods reveal in sleep for our behoof,
And here my dreams provide for this a proof.

246

"But now of this what need I further speak?
From this time forth I shall in warlike fray
My death embrace, in fight with any Greek,
And none too soon for me shall come that day!
But Cressida, whom I shall love for aye,
With one last word, I will myself defend,
My love hath merited a better end."

247

All these things Pandar heard and none denied,
For now the end was far too evident;
With only silence therefore he replied,
Sorrow for Troilus doth speech prevent,
And shame for Cressida's ill management;
Still as a stone he stood, nor answer made,
By grief and shame all utterly dismayed.

248

But at the last he spoke as best he could,
"My brother dear, I fear your trouble lies
Beyond my aid, and I am through for good
With Cressida, and her I now despise.
What I have done for you in this emprise,
Regarding not my honor nor my rest,
I did it, Troilus, all for the best.

249

"If anything I did still pleases thee,
Then I am glad, and for this treason now,
God knows it is a heavy blow to me.
If anything could ease your heart, I vow
That I would serve you, if I knew but how,
And as for Cressida, the while I live,
Her perjury I never shall forgive."

To feffe with your newe love," quod he,
"But thilke broche that I, with teres wete,
Yow yaf, as for a remembraunce of me?
Non other cause, allas, ne hadde ye
But for despyt, and eek for that ye mente
Al-outrely to shewen your entente!

243

Through which I see that clene out of your minde
Ye han me cast, and I ne can nor may,
For al this world, with-in myn herte finde
T' unloven yow a quarter of a day!
In cursed tyme I born was, weylaway!
That ye, that doon me al this wo endure,
Yet love I best of any creature.

244

Now god," quod he, "me sende yet the grace
That I may meten with this Diomede!
And trewely, if I have might and space,
Yet shal I make, I hope, his sydes blede.
O god," quod he, "that oughtest taken hede
To fortheren trouthe, and wronges to punyce,
Why niltow doon a vengeaunce on this vyce?

245

O Pandare, that in dremes for to triste
Me blamed hast, and wont art ofte upbreyde,
Now maystow see thy-selve, if that thee liste,
How trewe is now thy nece, bright Criseyde!
In sondry formes, god it woot," he seyde,
"The goddes shewen bothe joye and tene
In slepe, and by my dreme it is now sene.

246

And certaynly, with-oute more speche,
From hennes-forth, as ferforth as I may
Myn owene deeth in armes wol I seche;
I recche not how sone be the day!
But trewely, Criseyde, swete may,
Whom I have ay with al my might y-served,
That ye thus doon, I have it nought deserved."

247

This Pandarus, that alle these thinges herde,
And wiste wel he seyde a sooth of this,
He nought a word ayein to him answerde;
For sory of his frendes sorwe he is,
And shamed, for his nece hath doon a-mis;
And stant, astoned of these causes tweye,
As stille as stoon; a word ne coude he seye.

248

But at the laste thus he spak, and seyde,
"My brother dere, I may thee do no-more.
What shulde I seyn? I hate, y-wis, Criseyde!
And god wot, I wol hate hir evermore!
And that thou me bisoughtest doon of yore,
Havinge un-to myn honour ne my reste
Right no reward, I dide al that thee leste.

249

If I dide ought that mighte lyken thee,
It is me leef; and of this treson now,
God woot, that it a sorwe is un-to me!
And dredelees, for hertes ese of yow,
Right fayn wolde I amende it, wiste I how.
And fro this world, almighty god I preye,
Delivere hir sone; I can no-more seye."

250

Gret was the sorwe and pleynt of Troilus;
But forth hir cours fortune ay gan to holde.
Criseyde loveth the sone of Tydeus,
And Troilus mot wepe in cares colde.
Swich is this world; who-so it can biholde,
In eche estat is litel hertes reste;
God leve us for to take it for the beste!

251

In many cruel batayle, out of drede,
Of Troilus, this ilke noble knight,
As men may in these olde bokes rede,
Was sene his knighthod and his grete might.
And dredelees, his ire, day and night,
Ful cruelly the Grekes ay aboughte;
And alwey most this Diomede he soughte.

252

And ofte tyme, I finde that they mette
With blody strokes and with wordes grete,
Assaying how hir speres weren whette;
And god it woot, with many a cruel hete,
Gan Troilus upon his helm to-bete.
But natheles, fortune it nought ne wolde,
Of otheres hond that either deyen sholde.—

253

And if I hadde y-taken for to wryte
The armes of this ilke worthy man,
Than wolde I of his batailles endyte.
But for that I to wryte first bigan
Of his love, I have seyd as that I can.
His worthy dedes, who-so list hem here,
Reed Dares, he can telle hem alle y-fere.

254

Bisechinge every lady bright of hewe,
And every gentil womman, what she be,
That al be that Criseyde was untrewe,
That for that gilt she be not wrooth with me.
Ye may hir gilt in othere bokes see;
And gladlier I wol wryten, if yow leste,
Penelopeës trouthe and good Alceste.

255

Ne I sey not this al-only for these men,
But most for wommen that bitraysed be
Through false folk; god yeve hem sorwe, amen!
That with hir grete wit and subtiltee
Bitrayse yow! and this commeveth me
To speke, and in effect yow alle I preye,
Beth war of men, and herkeneth what I seye!—

256

Go, litel book, go litel myn tregedie,
Ther god thy maker yet, er that he dye,
So sende might to make in som comedie!
But litel book, no making thou n'envye,
But subgit be to alle poesye;
And kis the steppes, wher-as thou seest pace
Virgile, Ovyde, Omer, Lucan, and Stace.

257

And for ther is so greet diversitee
In English and in wryting of our tonge,
So preye I god that noon miswryte thee,
Ne thee mismetre for defaute of tonge.
And red wher-so thou be, or elles songe,

250

This brought but slight relief to Troilus,
Whose final fortunes quickly now unfold.
Cressida loves the son of Tydeus,
And Troilus hath naught but comfort cold!
Such is the world! Wherever you behold,
The common state of man is one of woe,
And in the end we all must take it so!

251

In daily battles, as the days go by,
Doth Troilus, the noblest Trojan knight,
With courage by despair exalted high,
Exhibit all his valor and his might;
Now doth his wrath upon the Greeks alight,
But most of all he looked for Diomede,
For hate of him doth other hates exceed.

252

And oftentimes these two opponents met,
With bloody strokes and with exchange of speech;
Spear against spear they often thus did whet,
Yet neither pierced so deeply as to reach
The other's life, so matched was each to each;
This neat exchange blind fortune would not send
That either one the other's life should end.

253

And if my purpose here had been to write
The arms of Troilus, and not the man,
Then could I of his battles much endite;
But of his love I've told since I began,
And shall continue so, as best I can.
His deeds of arms, if you would of them hear,
Read Dares, where they all in full appear.

254

O gentle ladies all, so bright of hue,
Let me beseech, although it had to be
That I should write of one who was untrue,
Put not the blame for what she did on me,
For all the books tell her iniquity;
Penelope the true, if I but could,
I'd rather praise, or fair Alceste the good.

255

And O ye men, of you naught need be said,
Except that ladies men have oft betrayed!
Bad luck to them and curses on their head,
Who with feigned words and plots so subtly laid
On simple minds their evil tricks have played!
Beware of wiles, O ladies, and take heed,
What lesson in my story you may read.

256

Go, little book, my little tragedy!
God grant thy maker, ere his ending day,
May write some tale of happy poetry!
But, little book, of any poet's lay
Envy of heart here shalt thou not display,
But kiss the steps where pass through ages spacious,
Vergil and Ovid, Homer, Lucan and Statius.

257

And since there is so great diversity
In English, and in the writing of our tongue,
I pray to God that no man miswrite thee,
Or get thy meter wrong and all unstrung;
But everywhere that thou art read or sung,

I trust all men will take thee as they should—
But now to come back where my story stood.

258

The wrath of Troilus, as I have said,
The Grecian warriors had to pay for dear,
And hosts of Greeks his valiant hand struck dead;
Though in his time he was without a peer
Within the city, yet the fatal spear
Of bold Achilles, as the Gods had willed,
At early last this Trojan hero killed.

259

And when his final earthly breath he drew,
His spirit from his body lightly went,
And to the eighth sphere's hollow concave flew,
Leaving in convex every element,
And then he saw, in glorious ascent,
The wandering stars, and heard the harmony
Of all the spheres in heavenly melody.

260

And down from thence he cast his spirit's eyes
Upon this spot of earth, that with the sea
Is bound, and now doth heartily despise
This wretched world, with all its vanity,
In contrast with the joy in full degree
Of heaven above; and at the very last
His gaze where he was slain, he downward cast.

261

Silently he laughed to see the grief and woe
Of those who weep within this earthly space,
Renouncing all men's works, who only know
Those earthly joys which time shall soon efface;
In peace content with heaven's lasting grace,
His way he went, in rest no tongue can tell,
Where Mercury appointed him to dwell.

262

Thus ended, lo, the love of Troilus,
Thus ended, lo, this model of mankind;
His royal rank led to such end, and thus
Ended his high nobility of mind,
For this false world, so mutable and blind.
'Twas thus his love for Cressida began,
And thus until he died its full course ran.

263

Ye youth, so happy at the dawn of life,
In whom love springs as native to your days,
Estrange you from the world and its vain strife,
And let your hearts their eyes to him upraise
Who made you in his image! Give him praise,
And think this world is but a passing show,
Fading like blooms that all too briefly blow.

264

And love ye him who on the cross did buy
Our souls from timeless death to live for aye,
Who died and rose and reigns in heaven high!
Your deepest love his love will ne'er betray,
Your faith on him I bid you safely lay;
And since his love is best beyond compare,
Love of the world deny with all its care.

265

Here, lo, the vanity of pagan rites!
Lo, here, how little all their shrines avail!
Lo, here the end of worldly appetites!

That thou be understonde I god beseche!
But yet to purpos of my rather speche.—

258

The wraththe, as I began yow for to seye,
Of Troilus, the Grekes boughten dere;
For thousandes his hondes maden deye,
As he that was with-outen any pere,
Save Ector, in his tyme, as I can here.
But weylaway, save only goddes wille,
Dispitously him slough the fiers Achille.

259

And whan that he was slayn in this manere,
His lighte goost ful blisfully is went
Up to the holownesse of the seventh spere,
In convers letinge every element;
And ther he saugh, with ful avysement,
The erratik sterres, herkeninge armonye
With sownes fulle of hevenish melodye.

260

And doun from thennes faste he gan avyse
This litel spot of erthe, that with the see
Enbraced is, and fully gan despyse
This wrecched world, and held al vanitee
To respect of the pleyn felicitee
That is in hevene above; and at the laste,
Ther he was slayn, his loking doun he caste;

261

And in him-self he lough right at the wo
Of hem that wepten for his deeth so faste;
And dampned al our werk that folweth so
The blinde lust, the which that may not laste,
And sholden al our herte on hevene caste.
And forth he wente, shortly for to telle,
Ther as Mercurie sorted him to dwelle.—

262

Swich fyn hath, lo, this Troilus for love,
Swich fyn hath al his grete worthinesse;
Swich fyn hath his estat real above,
Swich fyn his lust, swich fyn hath his noblesse;
Swich fyn hath false worldes brotelnesse.
And thus bigan his lovinge of Criseyde,
As I have told, and in this wyse he deyde.

263

O yonge fresshe folkes, he or she,
In which that love up groweth with your age,
Repeyreth hoom from worldly vanitee,
And of your herte up-casteth the visage
To thilke god that after his image
Yow made, and thinketh al nis but a fayre
This world, that passeth sone as floures fayre.

264

And loveth him, the which that right for love
Upon a cros, our soules for to beye,
First starf, and roos, and sit in hevene a-bove;
For he nil falsen no wight, dar I seye,
That wol his herte al hoolly on him leye.
And sin he best to love is, and most meke,
What nedeth feyned loves for to seke?

265

Lo here, of Payens corsed olde rytes,
Lo here, what alle hir goddes may availle;
Lo here, these wrecched worldes appetytes;

Lo here, the fyn and guerdon for travaille
Of Jove, Appollo, of Mars, of swich rascaille!
Lo here, the forme of olde clerkes speche
In poetrye, if ye hir bokes seche.—

266

O moral Gower, this book I directe
To thee, and to the philosophical Strode,
To vouchen sauf, ther nede is, to corecte,
Of your benignitees and zeles gode.
And to that sothfast Crist, that starf on rode,
With al myn herte of mercy ever I preye;
And to the lord right thus I speke and seye:

267

Thou oon, and two, and three, eterne on-lyve,
That regnest ay in three and two and oon,
Uncircumscript, and al mayst circumscryve,
Us from visible and invisible foon
Defende; and to thy mercy, everychoon,
So make us, Jesus, for thy grace, digne,
For love of mayde and moder thyn benigne! Amen.

Lo, here, how all the Gods at last shall fail,
Apollo, Jove and Mars and all the tale!
Lo, here the song that time hath held in fee,
Rescued from crumbling, grey antiquity!

266

O moral Gower, to thee this book I send,
And to thee, too, thou philosophical Strode,
And beg, if need be, ye will it amend,
And have my thanks, for all such care bestowed.
To Christ, the crucified, whose blood hath flowed
For us, for mercy now I humbly pray,
And to the highest Lord these words I say:

267

O Thou Eternal Three and Two and One,
Reigning forever in One and Two and Three,
Boundless, but binding all through Father and Son,
From foes unseen and seen deliver me;
And blessed Jesus, turn our love to thee,
And through thy maiden Mother, meek and mild,
Let all our hearts to thee be reconciled!

HERE ENDETH THE BOOK OF
TROILUS AND CRESSIDA

CONTENTS

THE CANTERBURY TALES

THE CANTERBURY TALES

∴

THE PROLOGUE

HERE BEGINNETH THE BOOK OF THE TALES OF CANTERBURY

WHAN that Aprille with his shoures sote
The droghte of Marche hath perced to the rote,
And bathed every veyne in swich licour,
Of which vertu engendred is the flour;
Whan Zephirus eek with his swete breeth
Inspired hath in every holt and heeth
The tendre croppes, and the yonge sonne
Hath in the Ram his halfe cours y-ronne,
And smale fowles maken melodye,
That slepen al the night with open yë,
(So priketh hem nature in hir corages):
Than longen folk to goon on pilgrimages
(And palmers for to seken straunge strondes)
To ferne halwes, couthe in sondry londes;
And specially, from every shires ende
Of Engelond, to Caunterbury they wende,
The holy blisful martir for to seke,
That hem hath holpen, whan that they were seke.
  Bifel that, in that seson on a day,
In Southwerk at the Tabard as I lay
Redy to wenden on my pilgrimage
To Caunterbury with ful devout corage,
At night was come in-to that hostelrye
Wel nyne and twenty in a companye,
Of sondry folk, by aventure y-falle
In felawshipe, and pilgrims were they alle,
That toward Caunterbury wolden ryde;
The chambres and the stables weren wyde,
And wel we weren esed atte beste.
And shortly, whan the sonne was to reste,
So hadde I spoken with hem everichon,
That I was of hir felawshipe anon,
And made forward erly for to ryse,
To take our wey, ther as I yow devyse.
  But natheles, whyl I have tyme and space,
Er that I ferther in this tale pace,
Me thinketh it acordaunt to resoun,
To telle yow al the condicioun
Of ech of hem, so as it semed me,
And whiche they weren, and of what degree;
And eek in what array that they were inne:
And at a knight than wol I first biginne

WHEN April with his showers sweet with fruit
The drought of March has pierced unto the root
And bathed each vein with liquor that has power
To generate therein and sire the flower;
When Zephyr also has, with his sweet breath,
Quickened again, in every holt and heath,
The tender shoots and buds, and the young sun
Into the Ram one half his course has run,
And many little birds make melody
That sleep through all the night with open eye
(So Nature pricks them on to ramp and rage)—
Then do folk long to go on pilgrimage,
And palmers to go seeking out strange strands,
To distant shrines well known in sundry lands.
And specially from every shire's end
Of England they to Canterbury wend,
The holy blessed martyr there to seek
Who helped them when they lay so ill and weak.
  Befell that, in that season, on a day
In Southwark, at the Tabard, as I lay
Ready to start upon my pilgrimage
To Canterbury, full of devout homage,
There came at nightfall to that hostelry
Some nine and twenty in a company
Of sundry persons who had chanced to fall
In fellowship, and pilgrims were they all
That toward Canterbury town would ride.
The rooms and stables spacious were and wide,
And well we there were eased, and of the best.
And briefly, when the sun had gone to rest,
So had I spoken with them, every one,
That I was of their fellowship anon,
And made agreement that we'd early rise
To take the road, as you I will apprise.
  But none the less, whilst I have time and space,
Before yet farther in this tale I pace,
It seems to me accordant with reason
To inform you of the state of every one
Of all of these, as it appeared to me,
And who they were, and what was their degree,
And even how arrayed there at the inn;
And with a knight thus will I first begin.

THE KNIGHT

  A knight ther was, and that a worthy man,
That fro the tyme that he first bigan
To ryden out, he loved chivalrye,
Trouthe and honour, fredom and curteisye.

  A knight there was, and he a worthy man,
Who, from the moment that he first began
To ride about the world, loved chivalry,
Truth, honour, freedom and courtesy.

Full worthy was he in his liege-lord's war,
And therein had he ridden (none more far)
As well in Christendom as heathenesse,
And honoured everywhere for worthiness.
At Alexandria, he, when it was won;
Full oft the table's roster he'd begun
Above all nations' knights in Prussia.
In Latvia raided he, and Russia,
No christened man so oft of his degree.
In far Granada at the siege was he
Of Algeciras, and in Belmarie.[1]
At Ayas was he and at Satalye[2]
When they were won; and on the Middle Sea
At many a noble meeting chanced to be.
Of mortal battles he had fought fifteen,
And he'd fought for our faith at Tramissene[3]
Three times in lists, and each time slain his foe.
This self-same worthy knight had been also
At one time with the lord of Palatye[4]
Against another heathen in Turkey:
And always won he sovereign fame for prize.
Though so illustrious, he was very wise
And bore himself as meekly as a maid.
He never yet had any vileness said,
In all his life, to whatsoever wight.
He was a truly perfect, gentle knight.
But now, to tell you all of his array,
His steeds were good, but yet he was not gay.
Of simple fustian wore he a jupon
Sadly discoloured by his habergeon;
For he had lately come from his voyage
And now was going on this pilgrimage.

Ful worthy was he in his lordes werre,
And therto hadde he riden (no man ferre)
As wel in Cristendom as hethenesse,
And ever honoured for his worthinesse.
At Alisaundre he was, whan it was wonne;
Ful ofte tyme he hadde the bord bigonne
Aboven alle nacioun in Pruce.
In Lettow hadde he reysed and in Ruce,
No Cristen man so ofte of his degree.
In Gernade at the sege eek hadde he be
Of Algezir, and riden in Belmarye.[1]
At Lyeys was he, and at Satalye,[2]
Whan they were wonne; and in the Grete See
At many a noble aryve hadde he be.
At mortal batailles hadde he been fiftene,
And foughten for our feith at Tramissene[3]
In listes thryes, and ay slayn his fo.
This ilke worthy knight had been also
Somtyme with the lord of Palatye,[4]
Ageyn another hethen in Turkye:
And evermore he hadde a sovereyn prys.
And though that he were worthy, he was wys,
And of his port as meke as is a mayde.
He never yet no vileinye ne sayde
In al his lyf, un-to no maner wight.
He was a verray parfit gentil knight.
But for to tellen yow of his array,
His hors were gode, but he was nat gay.
Of fustian he wered a gipoun
Al bismotered with his habergeoun;
For he was late y-come from his viage,
And wente for to doon his pilgrimage.

THE SQUIRE

With him there was his son, a youthful squire,
A lover and a lusty bachelor,
With locks well curled, as if they'd laid in press.
Some twenty years of age he was, I guess.
In stature he was of an average length,
Wondrously active, aye, and great of strength.
He'd ridden sometime with the cavalry
In Flanders, in Artois, and Picardy,
And borne him well within that little space
In hope to win thereby his lady's grace.
Prinked out he was, as if he were a mead,
All full of fresh-cut flowers white and red.
Singing he was, or fluting, all the day;
He was as fresh as is the month of May.
Short was his gown, with sleeves both long and wide.
Well could he sit on horse, and fairly ride.
He could make songs and words thereto indite,
Joust, and dance too, as well as sketch and write.
So hot he loved that, while night told her tale,
He slept no more than does a nightingale.
Courteous he, and humble, willing and able,
And carved before his father at the table.

With him ther was his sone, a young Squyer,
A lovyere, and a lusty bacheler,
With lokkes crulle, as they were leyd in presse.
Of twenty yeer of age he was, I gesse.
Of his stature he was of evene lengthe,
And wonderly deliver, and greet of strengthe.
And he had been somtyme in chivachye,
In Flaundres, in Artoys, and Picardye,
And born him wel, as of so litel space,
In hope to stonden in his lady grace.
Embrouded was he, as it were a mede
Al ful of fresshe floures, whyte and rede.
Singinge he was, or floytinge, al the day;
He was as fresh as is the month of May.
Short was his goune, with sleves longe and wyde.
Wel coude he sitte on hors, and faire ryde.
He coude songes make and wel endyte,
Juste and eek daunce, and wel purtreye and wryte.
So hote he lovede, that by nightertale
He sleep namore than dooth a nightingale.
Curteys he was, lowly, and servisable,
And carf biforn his fader at the table.

THE YEOMAN

A yeoman had he, nor more servants, no,
At that time, for he chose to travel so;

A Yeman hadde he, and servaunts namo
At that tyme, for him liste ryde so;

[1]Benimarim (the name of a tribe), in Morocco. [2]Modern Adalia, in Asia Minor.
[3]Modern Tlemçen, in Algeria. [4]Modern Balat.

And he was clad in cote and hood of grene;
A sheef of pecok-arwes brighte and kene
Under his belt he bar ful thriftily;
(Wel coude he dresse his takel yemanly:
His arwes drouped noght with fetheres lowe),
And in his hand he bar a mighty bowe.
A not-heed hadde he, with a broun visage.
Of wode-craft wel coude he al the usage.
Upon his arm he bar a gay bracer,
And by his syde a swerd and a bokeler,
And on that other syde a gay daggere,
Harneised wel, and sharp as point of spere;
A Cristofre on his brest of silver shene.
An horn he bar, the bawdrik was of grene;
A forster was he, soothly, as I gesse.

And he was clad in coat and hood of green.
A sheaf of peacock arrows bright and keen
Under his belt he bore right carefully
(Well could he keep his tackle yeomanly:
His arrows had no draggled feathers low),
And in his hand he bore a mighty bow.
A cropped head had he and a sun-browned face.
Of woodcraft knew he all the useful ways.
Upon his arm he bore a bracer gay,
And at one side a sword and buckler, yea,
And at the other side a dagger bright,
Well sheathed and sharp as spear point in the light;
On breast a Christopher of silver sheen.
He bore a horn in baldric all of green;
A forester he truly was, I guess.

THE PRIORESS

Ther was also a Nonne, a Prioress,
That of hir smyling was ful simple and coy;
Hir gretteste ooth was but by sëynt Loy;
And she was cleped madame Eglentyne.
Ful wel she song the service divyne,
Entuned in hir nose ful semely;
And Frensh she spak ful faire and fetisly,
After the scole of Stratford atte Bowe,
For Frensh of Paris was to hir unknowe.
At mete wel y-taught was she with-alle;
She leet no morsel from hir lippes falle,
Ne wette hir fingres in hir sauce depe.
Wel coude she carie a morsel, and wel kepe,
That no drope ne fille up-on hir brest.
In curteisye was set ful muche hir lest.
Hir over lippe wyped she so clene,
That in hir coppe was no ferthing sene
Of grece, whan she dronken hadde hir draughte.
Ful semely after hir mete she raughte,
And sikerly she was of greet disport,
And ful plesaunt, and amiable of port,
And peyned hir to countrefete chere
Of court, and been estatlich of manere,
And to ben holden digne of reverence.
But, for to speken of hir conscience,
She was so charitable and so pitous,
She wolde wepe, if that she sawe a mous
Caught in a trappe, if it were deed or bledde.
Of smale houndes had she, that she fedde
With rosted flesh, or milk and wastel-breed.
But sore weep she if oon of hem were deed,
Or if men smoot it with a yerde smerte:
And al was conscience and tendre herte.
Ful semely hir wimpel pinched was;
Hir nose tretys; hir eyen greye as glas;
Hir mouth ful smal, and ther-to softe and reed;
But sikerly she hadde a fair forheed;
It was almost a spanne brood, I trowe;
For, hardily, she was nat undergrowe.
Ful fetis was hir cloke, as I was war.
Of smal coral aboute hir arm she bar
A peire of bedes, gauded al with grene;
And ther-on heng a broche of gold ful shene,
On which ther was first write a crowned A,
And after, *Amor vincit omnia.*

There was also a nun, a prioress,
Who, in her smiling, modest was and coy;
Her greatest oath was but "By Saint Eloy!"
And she was known as Madam Eglantine.
Full well she sang the services divine,
Intoning through her nose, becomingly;
And fair she spoke her French, and fluently,
After the school of Stratford-at-the-Bow,
For French of Paris was not hers to know.
At table she had been well taught withal,
And never from her lips let morsels fall,
Nor dipped her fingers deep in sauce, but ate
With so much care the food upon her plate
That never driblet fell upon her breast.
In courtesy she had delight and zest.
Her upper lip was always wiped so clean
That in her cup was no iota seen
Of grease, when she had drunk her draught of wine.
Becomingly she reached for meat to dine.
And certainly delighting in good sport,
She was right pleasant, amiable—in short.
She was at pains to counterfeit the look
Of courtliness, and stately manners took,
And would be held worthy of reverence.
But, to say something of her moral sense,
She was so charitable and piteous
That she would weep if she but saw a mouse
Caught in a trap, though it were dead or bled.
She had some little dogs, too, that she fed
On roasted flesh, or milk and fine white bread.
But sore she'd weep if one of them were dead,
Or if men smote it with a rod to smart:
For pity ruled her, and her tender heart.
Right decorous her pleated wimple was;
Her nose was fine; her eyes were blue as glass;
Her mouth was small and therewith soft and red;
But certainly she had a fair forehead;
It was almost a full span broad, I own,
For, truth to tell, she was not undergrown.
Neat was her cloak, as I was well aware.
Of coral small about her arm she'd bear
A string of beads and gauded all with green;
And therefrom hung a brooch of golden sheen
Whereon there was first written a crowned "A,"
And under, *Amor vincit omnia.*

THE NUN, THE THREE PRIESTS, AND THE MONK

Another little nun with her had she,
Who was her chaplain; and of priests she'd three.
A monk there was, one made for mastery,
An outrider,[1] who loved his venery;
A manly man, to be an abbot able.
Full many a blooded horse had he in stable:
And when he rode men might his bridle hear
A-jingling in the whistling wind as clear,
Aye, and as loud as does the chapel bell
Where this brave monk was master of the cell.[2]
The rule of Maurus or Saint Benedict,
By reason it was old and somewhat strict,
This said monk let such old things slowly pace
And followed new-world manners in their place.
He cared not for that text a clean-plucked hen
Which holds that hunters are not holy men;
Nor that a monk, when he is cloisterless,
Is like unto a fish that's waterless;
That is to say, a monk out of his cloister.
But this same text he held not worth an oyster;
And I said his opinion was right good.
What? Should he study as a madman would
Upon a book in cloister cell? Or yet
Go labour with his hands and swink and sweat,
As Austin[3] bids? How shall the world be served?
Let Austin have his toil to him reserved.
Therefore he was a rider day and night;
Greyhounds he had, as swift as bird in flight.
Since riding and the hunting of the hare
Were all his love, for no cost would he spare.
I saw his sleeves were purfled at the hand
With fur of grey, the finest in the land;
Also, to fasten hood beneath his chin,
He had of good wrought gold a curious pin:
A love-knot in the larger end there was.
His head was bald and shone like any glass,
And smooth as one anointed was his face.
Fat was this lord, he stood in goodly case.
His bulging eyes he rolled about, and hot
They gleamed and red, like fire beneath a pot;
His boots were soft; his horse of great estate.
Now certainly he was a fine prelate:
He was not pale as some poor wasted ghost.
A fat swan loved he best of any roast.
His palfrey was as brown as is a berry.

Another Nonne with hir hadde she,
That was hir chapeleyne, and Preestes Three.
A Monk ther was, a fair for the maistrye,
An out-rydere,[1] that lovede venerye;
A manly man, to been an abbot able.
Ful many a deyntee hors hadde he in stable:
And, whan he rood, men mighte his brydel here
Ginglen in a whistling wind as clere,
And eek as loude as dooth the chapel-belle
Ther as this lord was keper of the celle.[2]
The reule of seint Maure or of seint Beneit,
By-cause that it was old and som-del streit,
This ilke monk leet olde thinges pace,
And held after the newe world the space.
He yaf nat of that text a pulled hen,
That seith, that hunters been nat holy men;
Ne that a monk, whan he is cloisterlees,
Is lykned til a fish is waterlees;
This is to seyn, a monk out of his cloistre.
But thilke text held he nat worth an oistre;
And I seyde, his opinioun was good.
What sholde he studie, and make him-selven wood,
Upon a book in cloistre alwey to poure,
Or swinken with his handes, and laboure,
As Austin[3] bit? How shal the world be served?
Lat Austin have his swink to him reserved.
Therfore he was a pricasour aright;
Grehoundes he hadde, as swifte as fowel in flight;
Of priking and of hunting for the hare
Was al his lust, for no cost wolde he spare.
I seigh his sleves purfiled at the hond
With grys, and that the fyneste of a lond;
And, for to festne his hood under his chin,
He hadde of gold y-wroght a curious pin:
A love-knotte in the gretter ende ther was.
His heed was balled, that shoon as any glas,
And eek his face, as he had been anoint.
He was a lord ful fat and in good point;
His eyen stepe, and rollinge in his heed,
That stemed as a forneys of a leed;
His botes souple, his hors in greet estat.
Now certeinly he was a fair prelat;
He was nat pale as a for-pyned goost.
A fat swan loved he best of any roost.
His palfrey was as broun as is a berye.

THE FRIAR

A friar there was, a wanton and a merry,
A limiter,[4] a very festive man.
In all the Orders Four is none that can
Equal his gossip and his fair language.
He had arranged full many a marriage
Of women young, and this at his own cost.
Unto his order he was a noble post.
Well liked by all and intimate was he
With franklins everywhere in his country,
And with the worthy women of the town:

A Frere ther was, a wantown and a merye,
A limitour,[4] a ful solempne man.
In alle the ordres foure is noon that can
So muche of daliaunce and fair langage.
He hadde maad ful many a mariage
Of yonge wommen, at his owne cost.
Un-to his ordre he was a noble post.
Ful wel biloved and famulier was he
With frankeleyns over-al in his contree,
And eek with worthy wommen of the toun:

[1]A monk privileged to ride abroad on the business of his order. [2]A small priory.
[3]Saint Augustine. [4]A friar licensed to beg within a certain district—within limits.

For he had power of confessioun,
As seyde him-self, more than a curat,
For of his ordre he was licentiat.
Ful swetely herde he confessioun,
And plesaunt was his absolucioun;
He was an esy man to yeve penaunce
Ther as he wiste to han a good pitaunce;
For unto a povre ordre for to yive
Is signe that a man is wel y-shrive.
For if he yaf, he dorste make avaunt,
He wiste that a man was repentaunt.
For many a man so hard is of his herte,
He may nat wepe al-thogh him sore smerte.
Therfore, in stede of weping and preyeres,
Men moot yeve silver to the povre freres.
His tipet was ay farsed ful of knyves
And pinnes, for to yeven faire wyves.
And certeinly he hadde a mery note;
Wel coude he singe and pleyen on a rote.
Of yeddinges he bar utterly the prys.
His nekke whyt was as the flour-de-lys;
Ther-to he strong was as a champioun.
He knew the tavernes wel in every toun,
And everich hostiler and tappestere
Bet than a lazar or a beggestere;
For un-to swich a worthy man as he
Acorded nat, as by his facultee,
To have with seke lazars aqueyntaunce.
It is nat honest, it may nat avaunce
For to delen with no swich poraille,
But al with riche and sellers of vitaille.
And over-al, ther as profit sholde aryse,
Curteys he was, and lowly of servyse.
Ther nas no man no-wher so vertuous.
He was the beste beggere in his hous;
And yaf a certeyn ferme for the graunt; [252*b*]
Noon of his bretheren cam ther in his haunt; [*c*]
For thogh a widwe hadde noght a sho,
So plesaunt was his "*In principio*,"
Yet wolde he have a ferthing, er he wente.
His purchas was wel bettre than his rente.
And rage he coude, as it were right a whelpe.
In love-dayes[1] ther coude he muchel helpe.
For there he was nat lyk a cloisterer,
With a thredbar cope, as is a povre scoler,
But he was lyk a maister or a pope.
Of double worsted was his semi-cope,
That rounded as a belle out of the presse.
Somwhat he lipsed, for his wantownesse,
To make his English swete up-on his tonge;
And in his harping, whan that he had songe,
His eyen twinkled in his heed aright,
As doon the sterres in the frosty night.
This worthy limitour was cleped Huberd.

For at confessing he'd more power in gown
(As he himself said) than a good curate,
For of his order he was licentiate.
He heard confession gently, it was said,
Gently absolved too, leaving naught of dread.
He was an easy man to give penance
When knowing he should gain a good pittance;
For to a begging friar, money given
Is sign that any man has been well shriven.
For if one gave (he dared to boast of this),
He took the man's repentance not amiss.
For many a man there is so hard of heart
He cannot weep however pains may smart.
Therefore, instead of weeping and of prayer,
Men should give silver to poor friars all bare.
His tippet was stuck always full of knives
And pins, to give to young and pleasing wives.
And certainly he kept a merry note:
Well could he sing and play upon the rote.
At balladry he bore the prize away.
His throat was white as lily of the May;
Yet strong he was as ever champion.
In towns he knew the taverns, every one,
And every good host and each barmaid too—
Better than begging lepers, these he knew.
For unto no such solid man as he
Accorded it, as far as he could see,
To have sick lepers for acquaintances.
There is no honest advantageousness
In dealing with such poverty-stricken curs;
It's with the rich and with big victuallers.
And so, wherever profit might arise,
Courteous he was and humble in men's eyes.
There was no other man so virtuous.
He was the finest beggar of his house;
A certain district being farmed to him,
None of his brethren dared approach its rim;
For though a widow had no shoes to show,
So pleasant was his *In principio*,
He always got a farthing ere he went.
He lived by pickings, it is evident.
And he could romp as well as any whelp.
On love days[1] could he be of mickle help.
For there he was not like a cloisterer,
With threadbare cope as is the poor scholar,
But he was like a lord or like a pope.
Of double worsted was his semi-cope,
That rounded like a bell, as you may guess.
He lisped a little, out of wantonness,
To make his English soft upon his tongue;
And in his harping, after he had sung,
His two eyes twinkled in his head as bright
As do the stars within the frosty night.
This worthy limiter was named Hubert.

THE MERCHANT

A Marchant was ther with a forked berd,
In mottelee, and hye on horse he sat,
Up-on his heed a Flaundrish bever hat;
His botes clasped faire and fetisly.

There was a merchant with forked beard, and girt
In motley gown, and high on horse he sat,
Upon his head a Flemish beaver hat;
His boots were fastened rather elegantly.

[1]Days appointed for the settling of disputes by arbitration.

His spoke his notions out right pompously,
Stressing the times when he had won, not lost.
He would the sea were held at any cost
Across from Middleburgh to Orwell town.
At money-changing he could make a crown.
This worthy man kept all his wits well set;
There was no one could say he was in debt,
So well he governed all his trade affairs
With bargains and with borrowings and with shares.
Indeed, he was a worthy man withal,
But, sooth to say, his name I can't recall.

His resons he spak ful solempnely,
Souninge alway th'encrees of his winning.
He wolde the see were kept for any thing
Bitwixe Middelburgh and Orewelle.
Wel coude he in eschaunge sheeldes selle.
This worthy man ful wel his wit bisette;
Ther wiste no wight that he was in dette,
So estatly was he of his governaunce,
With his bargaynes, and with his chevisaunce.
For sothe he was a worthy man with-alle,
But sooth to seyn, I noot how men him calle.

THE CLERK

A clerk from Oxford was with us also,
Who'd turned to getting knowledge, long ago.
As meagre was his horse as is a rake,
Nor he himself too fat, I'll undertake,
But he looked hollow and went soberly.
Right threadbare was his overcoat; for he
Had got him yet no churchly benefice,
Nor was so worldly as to gain office.
For he would rather have at his bed's head
Some twenty books, all bound in black and red,
Of Aristotle and his philosophy
Than rich robes, fiddle, or gay psaltery.
Yet, and for all he was philosopher,
He had but little gold within his coffer;
But all that he might borrow from a friend
On books and learning he would swiftly spend,
And then he'd pray right busily for the souls
Of those who gave him wherewithal for schools.
Of study took he utmost care and heed.
Not one word spoke he more than was his need;
And that was said in fullest reverence
And short and quick and full of high good sense.
Pregnant of moral virtue was his speech;
And gladly would he learn and gladly teach.

A Clerk ther was of Oxenford also,
That un-to logik hadde longe y-go.
As lene was his hors as is a rake,
And he nas nat right fat, I undertake;
But loked holwe, and ther-to soberly.
Ful thredbar was his overest courtepy;
For he had geten him yet no benefyce,
Ne was so wordly for to have offyce.
For him was lever have at his beddes heed
Twenty bokes, clad in blak or reed,
Of Aristotle and his philosophye,
Than robes riche, or fithele, or gay sautrye.
But al be that he was a philosophre,
Yet hadde he but litel gold in cofre;
But al that he mighte of his freendes hente,
On bokes and on lerninge he it spente,
And bisily gan for the soules preye
Of hem that yaf him wher-with to scoleye.
Of studie took he most cure and most hede.
Noght o word spak he more than was nede,
And that was seyd in forme and reverence,
And short and quik, and ful of hy sentence.
Souninge in moral vertu was his speche,
And gladly wolde he lerne, and gladly teche.

THE MAN OF LAW

A sergeant of the law, wary and wise,
Who'd often gone to Paul's walk to advise,
There was also, compact of excellence.
Discreet he was, and of great reverence;
At least he seemed so, his words were so wise.
Often he sat as justice in assize,
By patent or commission from the crown;
Because of learning and his high renown,
He took large fees and many robes could own.
So great a purchaser was never known.
All was fee simple to him, in effect,
Wherefore his claims could never be suspect.
Nowhere a man so busy of his class,
And yet he seemed much busier than he was.
All cases and all judgments could he cite
That from King William's time were apposite.
And he could draw a contract so explicit
Not any man could fault therefrom elicit;
And every statute he'd verbatim quote.
He rode but badly in a medley coat,
Belted in a silken sash, with little bars,
But of his dress no more particulars.

A Sergeant of the Lawe, war and wys,
That often hadde been at the parvys,
Ther was also, ful riche of excellence.
Discreet he was, and of greet reverence:
He semed swich, his wordes weren so wyse.
Justyce he was ful often in assyse,
By patente, and by pleyn commissioun;
For his science, and for his heigh renoun
Of fees and robes hadde he many oon.
So greet a purchasour was no-wher noon.
Al was fee simple to him in effect,
His purchasing mighte nat been infect.
No-wher so bisy a man as he ther nas,
And yet he semed bisier than he was.
In termes hadde he caas and domes alle,
That from the tyme of king William were falle.
Therto he coude endyte, and make a thing,
Ther coude no wight pinche at his wryting;
And every statut coude he pleyn by rote.
He rood but hoomly in a medlee cote
Girt with a ceint of silk, with barres smale;
Of his array telle I no lenger tale.

THE FRANKLIN

A Frankeleyn was in his companye;
Whyt was his berd, as is the dayesye.
Of his complexioun he was sangwyn.
Wel loved he by the morwe a sop in wyn.
To liven in delyt was ever his wone,
For he was Epicurus owne sone,
That heeld opinioun, that pleyn delyt
Was verraily felicitee parfyt.
An housholdere, and that a greet, was he;
Seint Julian[1] he was in his contree.
His breed, his ale, was alwey after oon;
A bettre envyned man was no-wher noon.
With-oute bake mete was never his hous,
Of fish and flesh, and that so plentevous,
It snewed in his hous of mete and drinke,
Of alle deyntees that men coude thinke.
After the sondry sesons of the yeer,
So chaunged he his mete and his soper.
Ful many a fat partrich hadde he in mewe,
And many a breem and many a luce in stewe.
Wo was his cook, but-if his sauce were
Poynaunt and sharp, and redy al his gere.
His table dormant in his halle alway
Stood redy covered al the longe day.
At sessiouns ther was he lord and sire;
Ful ofte tyme he was knight of the shire.
An anlas and a gipser al of silk
Heng at his girdel, whyt as morne milk.
A shirreve hadde he been, and a countour;
Was no-wher such a worthy vavasour,[2]

There was a franklin in his company;
White was his beard as is the white daisy.
Of sanguine temperament by every sign,
He loved right well his morning sop in wine.
Delightful living was the goal he'd won,
For he was Epicurus' very son,
That held opinion that a full delight
Was true felicity, perfect and right.
A householder, and that a great, was he;
Saint Julian[1] he was in his own country.
His bread and ale were always right well done;
A man with better cellars there was none.
Baked meat was never wanting in his house,
Of fish and flesh, and that so plenteous
It seemed to snow therein both food and drink
Of every dainty that a man could think.
According to the season of the year
He changed his diet and his means of cheer.
Full many a fattened partridge did he mew,
And many a bream and pike in fish-pond too.
Woe to his cook, except the sauces were
Poignant and sharp, and ready all his gear.
His table, waiting in his hall alway,
Stood ready covered through the livelong day.
At county sessions was he lord and sire,
And often acted as a knight of shire.
A dagger and a trinket-bag of silk
Hung from his girdle, white as morning milk.
He had been sheriff and been auditor;
And nowhere was a worthier vavasor.[2]

THE HABERDASHER, THE CARPENTER, THE WEAVER, THE DYER, AND THE ARRAS-MAKER

An Haberdassher and a Carpenter,
A Webbe, a Dyere, and a Tapicer,
Were with us eek, clothed in o liveree,
Of a solempne and greet fraternitee.
Ful fresh and newe hir gere apyked was;
Hir knyves were y-chaped noght with bras,
But al with silver, wroght ful clene and weel,
Hir girdles and hir pouches every-deel.
Wel semed ech of hem a fair burgeys,
To sitten in a yeldhalle on a deys.
Everich, for the wisdom that he can,
Was shaply for to been an alderman.
For catel hadde they y-nogh and rente,
And eek hir wyves wolde it wel assente;
And elles certein were they to blame.
It is ful fair to been y-clept "*ma dame*,"
And goon to vigilyës al bifore,
And have a mantel royalliche y-bore.

A haberdasher and a carpenter,
An arras-maker, dyer, and weaver
Were with us, clothed in similar livery.
All of one sober, great fraternity.
Their gear was new and well adorned it was;
Their weapons were not cheaply trimmed with brass,
But all with silver; chastely made and well
Their girdles and their pouches too, I tell.
Each man of them appeared a proper burgess
To sit in guildhall on a high dais.
And each of them, for wisdom he could span,
Was fitted to have been an alderman;
For chattels they'd enough, and, too, of rent;
To which their goodwives gave a free assent,
Or else for certain they had been to blame.
It's good to hear "Madam" before one's name,
And go to church when all the world may see,
Having one's mantle borne right royally.

THE COOK

A Cook they hadde with hem for the nones,
To boille the chiknes with the marybones,
And poudre-marchant tart, and galingale.
Wel coude he knowe a draughte of London ale.
He coude roste, and sethe, and broille, and frye,
Maken mortreux, and wel bake a pye.

A cook they had with them, just for the nonce,
To boil the chickens with the marrow-bones,
And flavour tartly and with galingale.
Well could he tell a draught of London ale.
And he could roast and seethe and broil and fry,
And make a good thick soup, and bake a pie.

[1]The patron saint of hospitality. [2]A sub-vassal, next in rank below a baron.

But very ill it was, it seemed to me,
That on his shin a deadly sore had he;
For sweet blanc-mange, he made it with the best.

But greet harm was it, as it thoughte me,
That on his shine a mormal hadde he;
For blankmanger, that made he with the beste.

THE SHIPMAN

There was a sailor, living far out west;
For aught I know, he was of Dartmouth town.
He sadly rode a hackney, in a gown,
Of thick rough cloth falling to the knee.
A dagger hanging on a cord had he
About his neck, and under arm, and down.
The summer's heat had burned his visage brown;
And certainly he was a good fellow.
Full many a draught of wine he'd drawn, I trow,
Of Bordeaux vintage, while the trader slept.
Nice conscience was a thing he never kept.
If that he fought and got the upper hand,
By water he sent them home to every land.
But as for craft, to reckon well his tides,
His currents and the dangerous watersides
His harbours, and his moon, his pilotage,
There was none such from Hull to far Carthage.
Hardy, and wise in all things undertaken,
By many a tempest had his beard been shaken.
He knew well all the havens, as they were,
From Gottland to the Cape of Finisterre,
And every creek in Brittany and Spain;
His vessel had been christened *Madeleine*.

A Shipman was ther, woning fer by weste:
For aught I woot, he was of Dertemouthe.
He rood up-on a rouncy, as he couthe,
In a gowne of falding to the knee.
A daggere hanging on a laas hadde he
Aboute his nekke under his arm adoun.
The hote somer had maad his hewe al broun;
And, certeinly, he was a good felawe.
Ful many a draughte of wyn had he y-drawe
From Burdeux-ward, whyl that the chapman sleep.
Of nyce conscience took he no keep.
If that he faught, and hadde the hyer hond,
By water he sente hem hoom to every lond.
But of his craft to rekene wel his tydes,
His stremes and his daungers him bisydes,
His herberwe and his mone, his lodemenage,
Ther nas noon swich from Hulle to Cartage.
Hardy he was, and wys to undertake;
With many a tempest hadde his berd been shake.
He knew wel alle the havenes, as they were,
From Gootlond to the cape of Finistere,
And every cryke in Britayne and in Spayne;
His barge y-cleped was the Maudelayne.

THE DOCTOR

With us there was a doctor of physic;
In all this world was none like him to pick
For talk of medicine and surgery;
For he was grounded in astronomy.
He often kept a patient from the pall
By horoscopes and magic natural.
Well could he tell the fortune ascendent
Within the houses for his sick patient.
He knew the cause of every malady,
Were it of hot or cold, of moist or dry,
And where engendered, and of what humour;
He was a very good practitioner.
The cause being known, down to the deepest root,
Anon he gave to the sick man his boot.[1]
Ready he was, with his apothecaries,
To send him drugs and all electuaries;
By mutual aid much gold they'd always won—
Their friendship was a thing not new begun.
Well read was he in Esculapius,
And Deiscorides, and in Rufus,
Hippocrates, and Hali, and Galen,
Serapion, Rhazes, and Avicen,
Averrhoës, Gilbert, and Constantine,
Bernard, and Gatisden, and John Damascene.
In diet he was measured as could be,
Including naught of superfluity,
But nourishing and easy. It's no libel
To say he read but little in the Bible.
In blue and scarlet he went clad, withal,
Lined with a taffeta and with sendal;

With us ther was a Doctour of Phisyk,
In al this world ne was ther noon him lyk
To speke of phisik and of surgerye;
For he was grounded in astronomye.
He kepte his pacient a ful greet del
In houres, by his magik naturel.
Wel coude he fortunen the ascendent
Of his images for his pacient.
He knew the cause of everich maladye,
Were it of hoot or cold, or moiste, or drye,
And where engendred, and of what humour;
He was a verrey parfit practisour.
The cause y-knowe, and of his harm the rote,
Anon he yaf the seke man his bote.[1]
Ful redy hadde he his apothecaries,
To sende him drogges and his letuaries,
For ech of hem made other for to winne;
Hir frendschipe nas nat newe to biginne.
Wel knew he th'olde Esculapius,
And Deiscorides, and eek Rufus,
Old Ypocras, Haly, and Galien;
Serapion, Razis, and Avicen;
Averrois, Damascien, and Constantyn;
Bernard, and Gatesden, and Gilbertyn.
Of his diete mesurable was he,
For it was of no superfluitee,
But of greet norissing and digestible.
His studie was but litel on the bible.
In sangwin and in pers he clad was al,
Lyned with taffata and with sendal;

[1] Remedy, relief.

And yet he was but esy of dispence;
He kepte that he wan in pestilence.
For gold in phisik is a cordial,
Therfore he lovede gold in special.

And yet he was right chary of expense;
He kept the gold he gained from pestilence.
For gold in physic is a fine cordial,
And therefore loved he gold exceeding all.

THE WIFE OF BATH

A good Wyf was ther of bisyde Bathe,
But she was som-del deef, and that was scathe.
Of clooth-making she hadde swiche an haunt,
She passed hem of Ypres and of Gaunt.
In al the parisshe wyf ne was ther noon
That to th'offring bifore hir sholde goon;
And if ther dide, certeyn, so wrooth was she,
That she was out of alle charitee.
Hir coverchiefs ful fyne were of ground;
I dorste swere they weyeden ten pound
That on a Sonday were upon hir heed.
Hir hosen weren of fyn scarlet reed,
Ful streite y-teyd, and shoos ful moiste and newe.
Bold was hir face, and fair, and reed of hewe.
She was a worthy womman al hir lyve,
Housbondes at chirche-dore she hadde fyve,
Withouten other companye in youthe;
But therof nedeth nat to speke as nouthe.
And thryes hadde she been at Jerusalem;
She hadde passed many a straunge streem;
At Rome she hadde been, and at Boloigne,
In Galice at seint Jame, and at Coloigne.
She coude muche of wandring by the weye:
Gat-tothed was she, soothly for to seye.
Up-on an amblere esily she sat,
Y-wimpled wel, and on hir heed an hat
As brood as is a bokeler or a targe;
A foot-mantel aboute hir hipes large,
And on hir feet a paire of spores sharpe.
In felawschip wel coude she laughe and carpe.
Of remedyes of love she knew perchaunce,
For she coude of that art the olde daunce.

There was a housewife come from Bath, or near,
Who—sad to say—was deaf in either ear.
At making cloth she had so great a bent
She bettered those of Ypres and even of Ghent.
In all the parish there was no goodwife
Should offering make before her, on my life;
And if one did, indeed, so wroth was she
It put her out of all her charity.
Her kerchiefs were of finest weave and ground;
I dare swear that they weighed a full ten pound
Which, of a Sunday, she wore on her head.
Her hose were of the choicest scarlet red,
Close gartered, and her shoes were soft and new.
Bold was her face, and fair, and red of hue.
She'd been respectable throughout her life,
With five churched husbands bringing joy and strife,
Not counting other company in youth;
But thereof there's no need to speak, in truth.
Three times she'd journeyed to Jerusalem;
And many a foreign stream she'd had to stem;
At Rome she'd been, and she'd been in Boulogne,
In Spain at Santiago, and at Cologne.
She could tell much of wandering by the way:
Gap-toothed was she, it is no lie to say.
Upon an ambler easily she sat,
Well wimpled, aye, and over all a hat
As broad as is a buckler or a targe;
A rug was tucked around her buttocks large,
And on her feet a pair of sharpened spurs.
In company well could she laugh her slurs.
The remedies of love she knew, perchance,
For of that art she'd learned the old, old dance.

THE PARSON

A good man was ther of religioun,
And was a povre Persoun of a toun;
But riche he was of holy thoght and werk.
He was also a lerned man, a clerk,
That Cristes gospel trewely wolde preche;
His parisshens devoutly wolde he teche.
Benigne he was, and wonder diligent,
And in adversitee ful pacient;
And swich he was y-preved ofte sythes.
Ful looth were him to cursen for his tythes,
But rather wolde he yeven, out of doute,
Un-to his povre parisshens aboute
Of his offring, and eek of his substaunce.
He coude in litel thing han suffisaunce.
Wyd was his parisshe, and houses fer a-sonder,
But he ne lafte nat, for reyn ne thonder,
In siknes nor in meschief, to visyte
The ferreste in his parisshe, muche and lyte,
Up-on his feet, and in his hand a staf.
This noble ensample to his sheep he yaf,
That first he wroghte, and afterward he taughte;
Out of the gospel he tho wordes caughte;

There was a good man of religion, too,
A country parson, poor, I warrant you;
But rich he was in holy thought and work.
He was a learned man also, a clerk,
Who Christ's own gospel truly sought to preach;
Devoutly his parishioners would he teach.
Benign he was and wondrous diligent,
Patient in adverse times and well content,
As he was ofttimes proven; always blithe,
He was right loath to curse to get a tithe,
But rather would he give, in case of doubt,
Unto those poor parishioners about,
Part of his income, even of his goods.
Enough with little, coloured all his moods.
Wide was his parish, houses far asunder,
But never did he fail, for rain or thunder,
In sickness, or in sin, or any state,
To visit to the farthest, small and great,
Going afoot, and in his hand a stave.
This fine example to his flock he gave,
That first he wrought and afterwards he taught;
Out of the gospel then that text he caught,

And this figure he added thereunto—
That, if gold rust, what shall poor iron do?
For if the priest be foul, in whom we trust,
What wonder if a layman yield to lust?
And shame it is, if priest take thought for keep,
A shitty shepherd, shepherding clean sheep.
Well ought a priest example good to give,
By his own cleanness, how his flock should live.
He never let his benefice for hire,
Leaving his flock to flounder in the mire,
And ran to London, up to old Saint Paul's
To get himself a chantry there for souls,
Nor in some brotherhood did he withhold;
But dwelt at home and kept so well the fold
That never wolf could make his plans miscarry;
He was a shepherd and not mercenary.
And holy though he was, and virtuous,
To sinners he was not impiteous,
Nor haughty in his speech, nor too divine,
But in all teaching prudent and benign.
To lead folk into Heaven but by stress
Of good example was his busyness.
But if some sinful one proved obstinate,
Be who it might, of high or low estate,
Him he reproved, and sharply, as I know.
There is nowhere a better priest, I trow.
He had no thirst for pomp or reverence,
Nor made himself a special, spiced conscience,
But Christ's own lore, and His apostles' twelve
He taught, but first he followed it himselve.

And this figure he added eek ther-to,
That if gold ruste, what shal iren do?
For if a preest be foul, on whom we truste,
No wonder is a lewed man to ruste;
And shame it is, if a preest take keep,
A shiten shepherde and a clene sheep.
Wel oghte a preest ensample for to yive,
By his clennesse, how that his sheep shold live.
He sette nat his benefice to hyre,
And leet his sheep encombred in the myre,
And ran to London, un-to sëynt Poules,
To seken him a chaunterie for soules,
Or with a bretherhed to been withholde;
But dwelte at hoom, and kepte wel his folde,
So that the wolf ne made it nat miscarie;
He was a shepherde and no mercenarie.
And though he holy were, and vertuous,
He was to sinful man nat despitous,
Ne of his speche daungerous ne digne,
But in his teching discreet and benigne.
To drawen folk to heven by fairnesse
By good ensample, was his bisinesse:
But it were any persone obstinat,
What-so he were, of heigh or lowe estat,
Him wolde he snibben sharply for the nones.
A bettre preest, I trowe that nowher noon is.
He wayted after no pompe and reverence,
Ne maked him a spyced conscience,
But Cristes lore, and his apostles twelve,
He taughte, and first he folwed it him-selve.

THE PLOWMAN

With him there was a plowman, was his brother,
That many a load of dung, and many another
Had scattered, for a good true toiler, he,
Living in peace and perfect charity.
He loved God most, and that with his whole heart
At all times, though he played or plied his art,
And next, his neighbour, even as himself.
He'd thresh and dig, with never thought of pelf,
For Christ's own sake, for every poor wight,
All without pay, if it lay in his might.
He paid his taxes, fully, fairly, well,
Both by his own toil and by stuff he'd sell.
In a tabard he rode upon a mare.
There were also a reeve[1] and miller there;
A summoner, manciple[2] and pardoner,
And these, beside myself, made all there were.

With him ther was a Plowman, was his brother,
That hadde y-lad of dong ful many a fother,
A trewe swinker and a good was he,
Livinge in pees and parfit charitee.
God loved he best with al his hole herte
At alle tymes, thogh him gamed or smerte,
And thanne his neighebour right as him-selve.
He wolde thresshe, and ther-to dyke and delve,
For Cristes sake, for every povre wight,
Withouten hyre, if it lay in his might.
His tythes payed he ful faire and wel,
Bothe of his propre swink and his catel.
In a tabard he rood upon a mere.
Ther was also a Reve[1] and a Millere,
A Somnour and a Pardoner also,
A Maunciple,[2] and my-self; ther were namo.

THE MILLER

The miller was a stout churl, be it known,
Hardy and big of brawn and big of bone;
Which was well proved, for when he went on lam
At wrestling, never failed he of the ram.[3]
He was a chunky fellow, broad of build;
He'd heave a door from hinges if he willed,
Or break it through, by running, with his head.
His beard, as any sow or fox, was red,
And broad it was as if it were a spade.
Upon the coping of his nose he had

The Miller was a stout carl, for the nones,
Ful big he was of braun, and eek of bones;
That proved wel, for over-al ther he cam,
At wrastling he wolde have alwey the ram.[3]
He was short-sholdred, brood, a thikke knarre,
Ther nas no dore that he nolde heve of harre,
Or breke it, at a renning, with his heed.
His berd as any sowe or fox was reed,
And ther-to brood, as though it were a spade.
Up-on the cop right of his nose he hade

[1]A steward or bailiff of an estate.
[2]An officer who purchases victuals for a college. [3]A usual prize in wrestling.

A werte, and ther-on stood a tuft of heres,
Reed as the bristles of a sowes eres;
His nose-thirles blake were and wyde.
A swerd and bokeler bar he by his syde;
His mouth as greet was as a greet forneys.
He was a janglere and a goliardeys,
And that was most of sinne and harlotryes.
Wel coude he stelen corn, and tollen thryes;
And yet he hadde a thombe of gold, pardee.
A whyt cote and a blew hood wered he.
A baggepype wel coude he blowe and sowne,
And ther-with-al he broghte us out of towne.

A wart, and thereon stood a tuft of hairs,
Red as the bristles in an old sow's ears;
His nostrils they were black and very wide.
A sword and buckler bore he by his side.
His mouth was like a furnace door for size.
He was a jester and could poetize,
But mostly all of sin and ribaldries.
He could steal corn and full thrice charge his fees;
And yet he had a thumb of gold, begad.
A white coat and blue hood he wore, this lad.
A bagpipe he could blow well, be it known,
And with that same he brought us out of town.

THE MANCIPLE

A gentil Maunciple was ther of a temple,
Of which achatours mighte take exemple
For to be wyse in bying of vitaille
For whether that he payde, or took by taille,
Algate he wayted so in his achat,
That he was ay biforn and in good stat.
Now is nat that of God a ful fair grace,
That swich a lewed mannes wit shal pace
The wisdom of an heep of lerned men?
Of maistres hadde he mo than thryes ten,
That were of lawe expert and curious;
Of which ther were a doseyn in that hous
Worthy to been stiwardes of rente and lond
Of any lord that is in Engelond,
To make him live by his propre good,
In honour dettelees, but he were wood,
Or live as scarsly as him list desire;
And able for to helpen al a shire
In any cas that mighte falle or happe;
And yit this maunciple sette hir aller cappe.

There was a manciple from an inn of court,
To whom all buyers might quite well resort
To learn the art of buying food and drink;
For whether he paid cash or not, I think
That he so knew the markets, when to buy,
He never found himself left high and dry.
Now is it not of God a full fair grace
That such a vulgar man has wit to pace
The wisdom of a crowd of learned men?
Of masters had he more than three times ten,
Who were in law expert and curious;
Whereof there were a dozen in that house
Fit to be stewards of both rent and land
Of any lord in England who would stand
Upon his own and live in manner good,
In honour, debtless (save his head were wood),
Or live as frugally as he might desire;
These men were able to have helped a shire
In any case that ever might befall;
And yet this manciple outguessed them all.

THE REEVE

The Reve was a sclendre colerik man,
His berd was shave as ny as ever he can.
His heer was by his eres round y-shorn.
His top was dokked lyk a preest biforn.
Ful longe were his legges, and ful lene,
Y-lyk a staf, ther was no calf y-sene.
Wel coude he kepe a gerner and a binne;
Ther was noon auditour coude on him winne.
Wel wiste he, by the droghte, and by the reyn,
The yelding of his seed, and of his greyn.
His lordes sheep, his neet, his dayerye,
His swyn, his hors, his stoor, and his pultrye,
Was hoolly in this reves governing,
And by his covenaunt yaf the rekening,
Sin that his lord was twenty yeer of age;
Ther coude no man bringe him in arrerage.
Ther nas baillif, ne herde, ne other hyne,
That he ne knew his sleighte and his covyne;
They were adrad of him, as of the deeth.
His woning was ful fair up-on an heeth,
With grene treës shadwed was his place.
He coude bettre than his lord purchace.
Ful riche he was astored prively,
His lord wel coude he plesen subtilly,
To yeve and lene him of his owne good,
And have a thank, and yet a cote and hood.

The reeve he was a slender, choleric man,
Who shaved his beard as close as razor can.
His hair was cut round even with his ears;
His top was tonsured like a pulpiteer's.
Long were his legs, and they were very lean,
And like a staff, with no calf to be seen.
Well could he manage granary and bin;
No auditor could ever on him win.
He could foretell, by drought and by the rain,
The yielding of his seed and of his grain.
His lord's sheep and his oxen and his dairy,
His swine and horses, all his stores, his poultry,
Were wholly in this steward's managing;
And, by agreement, he'd made reckoning
Since his young lord of age was twenty years;
Yet no man ever found him in arrears.
There was no agent, hind, or herd who'd cheat
But he knew well his cunning and deceit;
They were afraid of him as of the death.
His cottage was a good one, on a heath;
By green trees shaded with this dwelling-place.
Much better than his lord could he purchase.
Right rich he was in his own private right,
Seeing he'd pleased his lord, by day or night,
By giving him, or lending, of his goods,
And so got thanked—but yet got coats and hoods.

In youth he'd learned a good trade, and had been
A carpenter, as fine as could be seen.
This steward sat a horse that well could trot,
And was all dapple-grey, and was named Scot.
A long surcoat of blue did he parade,
And at his side he bore a rusty blade.
Of Norfolk was this reeve of whom I tell,
From near a town that men call Badeswell.
Bundled he was like friar from chin to croup,
And ever he rode hindmost of our troop.

In youthe he lerned hadde a good mister;
He was a wel good wrighte, a carpenter.
This reve sat up-on a ful good stot,
That was al pomely grey, and highte Scot.
A long surcote of pers up-on he hade,
And by his syde he bar a rusty blade.
Of Northfolk was this reve, of which I telle,
Bisyde a toun men clepen Baldeswelle.
Tukked he was, as is a frere, aboute,
And ever he rood the hindreste of our route.

THE SUMMONER

A summoner was with us in that place,
Who had a fiery-red, cherubic face,
For eczema he had; his eyes were narrow
As hot he was, and lecherous, as a sparrow;
With black and scabby brows and scanty beard;
He had a face that little children feared.
There was no mercury, sulphur, or litharge,
No borax, ceruse, tartar, could discharge,
Nor ointment that could cleanse enough, or bite,
To free him of his boils and pimples white,
Nor of the bosses resting on his cheeks.
Well loved he garlic, onions, aye and leeks,
And drinking of strong wine as red as blood.
Then would he talk and shout as madman would.
And when a deal of wine he'd poured within,
Then would he utter no word save Latin.
Some phrases had he learned, say two or three,
Which he had garnered out of some decree;
No wonder, for he'd heard it all the day;
And all you know right well that even a jay
Can call out "Wat" as well as can the pope.
But when, for aught else, into him you'd grope,
'Twas found he'd spent his whole philosophy;
Just "*Questio quid juris*" would he cry.
He was a noble rascal, and a kind;
A better comrade 'twould be hard to find.
Why, he would suffer, for a quart of wine,
Some good fellow to have his concubine
A twelve-month, and excuse him to the full
(Between ourselves, though, he could pluck a gull).
And if he chanced upon a good fellow,
He would instruct him never to have awe,
In such a case, of the archdeacon's curse,
Except a man's soul lie within his purse;
For in his purse the man should punished be.
"The purse is the archdeacon's Hell," said he.
But well I know he lied in what he said,
A curse ought every guilty man to dread
(For curse can kill, as absolution save),
And 'ware *significavit* to the grave.
In his own power had he, and at ease,
The boys and girls of all the diocese,
And knew their secrets, and by counsel led.
A garland had he set upon his head,
Large as a tavern's wine-bush on a stake;
A buckler had he made of bread they bake.

A Somnour was ther with us in that place,
That hadde a fyr-reed cherubinnes face,
For sawcefleem he was, with eyen narwe.
As hoot he was, and lecherous, as a sparwe;
With scalled browes blake, and piled berd;
Of his visage children were aferd.
Ther nas quik-silver, litarge, ne brimstoon,
Boras, ceruce, ne oille of tartre noon,
Ne oynement that wolde clense and byte,
That him mighte helpen of his whelkes whyte,
Nor of the knobbes sittinge on his chekes.
Wel loved he garleek, oynons, and eek lekes,
And for to drinken strong wyn, reed as blood.
Than wolde he speke, and crye as he were wood.
And whan that he wel dronken hadde the wyn,
Than wolde he speke no word but Latyn.
A fewe termes hadde he, two or three,
That he had lerned out of som decree;
No wonder is, he herde it al the day;
And eek ye knowen wel, how that a jay
Can clepen "Watte," as well as can the pope.
But who-so coude in other thing him grope,
Thanne hadde he spent al his philosophye;
Ay "*Questio quid iuris*" wolde he crye.
He was a gentil harlot and a kinde;
A bettre felawe sholde men noght finde.
He wolde suffre, for a quart of wyn,
A good felawe to have his concubyn
A twelf-month, and excuse him atte fulle:
Ful prively a finch eek coude he pulle.
And if he fond o-wher a good felawe,
He wolde techen him to have non awe,
In swich cas, of the erchedeknes curs,
But-if a mannes soule were in his purs;
For in his purs he sholde y-punisshed be.
"Purs is the erchedeknes helle," seyde he.
But wel I woot he lyed right in dede;
Of cursing oghte ech gilty man him drede—
For curs wol slee, right as assoilling saveth—
And also war him of a *significavit*.
In daunger hadde he at his owne gyse
The yonge girles of the diocyse,
And knew hir counseil, and was al hir reed.
A gerland hadde he set up-on his heed,
As greet as it were for an ale-stake;
A bokeler hadde he maad him of a cake.

THE PARDONER

With him there rode a gentle pardoner
Of Rouncival, his friend and his compeer;

With him ther rood a gentil Pardoner
Of Rouncival, his freend and his compeer,

That streight was comen fro the court of Rome.
Ful loude he song, "Com hider, love, to me."
This somnour bar to him a stif burdoun,
Was never trompe of half so greet a soun.
This pardoner hadde heer as yelow as wex,
But smothe it heng, as dooth a strike of flex;
By ounces henge his lokkes that he hadde,
And ther-with he his shuldres over-spradde;
But thinne it lay, by colpons oon and oon;
But hood, for jolitee, ne wered he noon,
For it was trussed up in his walet.
Him thoughte, he rood al of the newe jet;
Dischevele, save his cappe, he rood al bare.
Swiche glaringe eyen hadde he as an hare.
A vernicle hadde he sowed on his cappe.
His walet lay biforn him in his lappe,
Bret-ful of pardoun come from Rome al hoot.
A voys he hadde as smal as hath a goot.
No berd hadde he, ne never sholde have,
As smothe it was as it were late y-shave;
I trowe he were a gelding or a mare.
But of his craft, fro Berwik into Ware,
Ne was ther swich another pardoner.
For in his male he hadde a pilwe-beer,
Which that, he seyde, was our lady veyl:
He seyde, he hadde a gobet of the seyl
That sëynt Peter hadde, whan that he wente
Up-on the see, til Jesu Crist him hente.
He hadde a croys of latoun, ful of stones,
And in a glas he hadde pigges bones.
But with thise relikes, whan that he fond
A povre person dwelling up-on lond,
Up-on a day he gat him more moneye
Than that the person gat in monthes tweye.
And thus, with feyned flaterye and japes,
He made the person and the peple his apes.
But trewely to tellen, atte laste,
He was in chirche a noble ecclesiaste.
Wel coude he rede a lessoun or a storie,
But alderbest he song an offertorie;
For wel he wiste, whan that song was songe,
He moste preche, and wel affyle his tonge,
To winne silver, as he ful wel coude;
Therefore he song so meriely and loude.

Now have I told you shortly, in a clause,
Th'estat, th'array, the nombre, and eek the cause
Why that assembled was this companye
In Southwerk, at this gentil hostelrye,
That highte the Tabard, faste by the Belle.
But now is tyme to yow for to telle
How that we baren us that ilke night,
Whan we were in that hostelrye alight.
And after wol I telle of our viage,
And al the remenaunt of our pilgrimage.
But first I pray yow, of your curteisye,
That ye n'arette it nat my vileinye,
Thogh that I pleynly speke in this matere,
To telle yow hir wordes and hir chere;
Ne thogh I speke hir wordes properly.
For this ye knowen al-so wel as I,
Who-so shal telle a tale after a man,

Straight from the court of Rome had journeyed he.
Loudly he sang "Come hither, love, to me,"
The summoner joining with a burden round;
Was never horn of half so great a sound.
This pardoner had hair as yellow as wax,
But lank it hung as does a strike of flax;
In wisps hung down such locks as he'd on head,
And with them he his shoulders overspread;
But thin they dropped, and stringy, one by one.
But as to hood, for sport of it, he'd none,
Though it was packed in wallet all the while.
It seemed to him he went in latest style,
Dishevelled, save for cap, his head all bare.
As shiny eyes he had as has a hare.
He had a fine veronica sewed to cap.
His wallet lay before him in his lap,
Stuffed full of pardons brought from Rome all hot.
A voice he had that bleated like a goat.
No beard had he, nor ever should he have,
For smooth his face as he'd just had a shave;
I think he was a gelding or a mare.
But in his craft, from Berwick unto Ware,
Was no such pardoner in any place.
For in his bag he had a pillowcase
The which, he said, was Our True Lady's veil:
He said he had a piece of the very sail
That good Saint Peter had, what time he went
Upon the sea, till Jesus changed his bent.
He had a latten cross set full of stones
And in a bottle had he some pig's bones.
But with these relics, when he came upon
Some simple parson, then this paragon
In that one day more money stood to gain
Than the poor dupe in two months could attain.
And thus, with flattery and suchlike japes,
He made the parson and the rest his apes.
But yet, to tell the whole truth at the last,
He was, in church, a fine ecclesiast.
Well could he read a lesson or a story,
But best of all he sang an offertory;
For well he knew that when that song was sung,
Then might he preach, and all with polished tongue,
To win some silver, as he right well could;
Therefore he sang so merrily and so loud.

Now have I told you briefly, in a clause,
The state, the array, the number, and the cause
Of the assembling of this company
In Southwark, at this noble hostelry
Known as the Tabard Inn, hard by the Bell.
But now the time is come wherein to tell
How all we bore ourselves that very night
When at the hostelry we did alight.
And afterward the story I engage
To tell you of our common pilgrimage.
But first, I pray you, of your courtesy,
You'll not ascribe it to vulgarity
Though I speak plainly of this matter here,
Retailing you their words and means of cheer;
Nor though I use their very terms, nor lie.
For this thing do you know as well as I:
When one repeats a tale told by a man,

He must report, as nearly as he can,
Every least word, if he remember it,
However rude it be, or how unfit;
Or else he may be telling what's untrue,
Embellishing and fictionizing too.
He may not spare, although it were his brother;
He must as well say one word as another.
Christ spoke right broadly out, in holy writ,
And, you know well, there's nothing low in it.
And Plato says, to those able to read:
"The word should be the cousin to the deed."
Also, I pray that you'll forgive it me
If I have not set folk, in their degree
Here in this tale, by rank as they should stand.
My wits are not the best, you'll understand.

Great cheer our host gave to us, every one,
And to the supper set us all anon;
And served us then with victuals of the best.
Strong was the wine and pleasant to each guest.
A seemly man our good host was, withal,
Fit to have been a marshal in some hall;
He was a large man, with protruding eyes,
As fine a burgher as in Cheapside lies;
Bold in his speech, and wise, and right well taught,
And as to manhood, lacking there in naught.
Also, he was a very merry man,
And after meat, at playing he began,
Speaking of mirth among some other things,
When all of us had paid our reckonings;
And saying thus: "Now masters, verily
You are all welcome here, and heartily:
For by my truth, and telling you no lie,
I have not seen, this year, a company
Here in this inn, fitter for sport than now.
Fain would I make you happy, knew I how.
And of a game have I this moment thought
To give you joy, and it shall cost you naught.
"You go to Canterbury; may God speed
And the blest martyr soon requite your meed.
And well I know, as you go on your way,
You'll tell good tales and shape yourselves to play;
For truly there's no mirth nor comfort, none,
Riding the roads as dumb as is a stone;
And therefore will I furnish you a sport,
As I just said, to give you some comfort.
And if you like it, all, by one assent,
And will be ruled by me, of my judgment,
And will so do as I'll proceed to say,
Tomorrow, when you ride upon your way,
Then, by my father's spirit, who is dead,
If you're not gay, I'll give you up my head.
Hold up your hands, nor more about it speak."
Our full assenting was not far to seek;
We thought there was no reason to think twice,
And granted him his way without advice,
And bade him tell his verdict just and wise,
"Masters," quoth he, "here now is my advice;
But take it not, I pray you, in disdain;
This is the point, to put it short and plain,
That each of you, beguiling the long day,

He moot reherce, as ny as ever he can,
Everich a word, if it be in his charge,
Al speke he never so rudeliche and large;
Or elles he moot telle his tale untrewe,
Or feyne thing, or finde wordes newe.
He may nat spare, al-thogh he were his brother;
He moot as wel seye o word as another.
Crist spak him-self ful brode in holy writ,
And wel ye woot, no vileinye is it.
Eek Plato seith, who-so that can him rede,
The wordes mote be cosin to the dede.
Also I prey yow to foryeve it me,
Al have I nat set folk in hir degree
Here in this tale, as that they sholde stonde;
My wit is short, ye may wel understonde.

Greet chere made our hoste us everichon,
And to the soper sette us anon;
And served us with vitaille at the beste.
Strong was the wyn, and wel to drinke us leste.
A semely man our hoste was with-alle
For to han been a marshal in an halle;
A large man he was with eyen stepe,
A fairer burgeys is ther noon in Chepe:
Bold of his speche, and wys, and wel y-taught,
And of manhod him lakkede right naught.
Eek therto he was right a mery man,
And after soper pleyen he bigan,
And spak of mirthe amonges othere thinges,
Whan that we hadde maad our rekeninges;
And seyde thus: "Now, lordinges, trewely,
Ye been to me right welcome hertely:
For by my trouthe, if that I shal nat lye,
I ne saugh this yeer so mery a companye
At ones in this herberwe as is now.
Fayn wolde I doon yow mirthe, wiste I how.
And of a mirthe I am right now bithoght,
To doon yow ese, and it shal coste noght.
Ye goon to Caunterbury; God yow spede,
The blisful martir quyte yow your mede.
And wel I woot, as ye goon by the weye,
Ye shapen yow to talen and to pleye;
For trewely, confort ne mirthe is noon
To ryde by the weye doumb as a stoon;
And therfore wol I make yow disport,
As I seyde erst, and doon yow som confort.
And if yow lyketh alle, by oon assent,
Now for to stonden at my jugement,
And for to werken as I shal yow seye,
To-morwe, whan ye ryden by the weye,
Now, by my fader soule, that is deed,
But ye be merye, I wol yeve yow myn heed.
Hold up your hond, withouten more speche."
Our counseil was nat longe for to seche;
Us thoughte it was noght worth to amke it wys,
And graunted him withouten more avys,
And bad him seye his verdit, as him leste.
"Lordinges," quod he, "now herkneth for the beste;
But tak it not, I prey yow, in desdeyn;
This is the poynt, to speken short and pleyn,
That ech of yow, to shorte with your weye,

In this viage, shal telle tales tweye,
To Caunterbury-ward, I mene it so,
And hom-ward he shal tellen othere two,
Of aventures that whylom han bifalle.
And which of yow that bereth him best of alle,
That is to seyn, that telleth in this cas
Tales of best sentence and most solas,
Shal have a soper at our aller cost
Here in this place, sitting by this post,
Whan that we come agayn fro Caunterbury.
And for to make yow the more mery,
I wol my-selven gladly with yow ryde,
Right at myn owne cost, and be your gyde.
And who-so wol my jugement withseye
Shal paye al that we spenden by the weye.
And if ye vouche-sauf that it be so,
Tel me anon, with-outen wordes mo,
And I wol erly shape me therfore."
This thing was graunted, and our othes swore
With ful glad herte, and preyden him also
That he wold vouche-sauf for to do so,
And that he wolde been our governour,
And of our tales juge and reportour,
And sette a soper at a certeyn prys;
And we wold reuled been at his devys,
In heigh and lowe; and thus, by oon assent,
We been acorded to his jugement.
And ther-up-on the wyn was fet anon;
We dronken, and to reste wente echon,
With-outen any lenger taryinge.
A-morwe, whan that day bigan to springe,
Up roos our host, and was our aller cok.
And gadrede us togidre, alle in a flok,
And forth we riden, a litel more than pas,
Un-to the watering of seint Thomas.
And there our host bigan his hors areste,
And seyde; "Lordinges, herkneth, if yow leste.
Ye woot your forward, and I it yow recorde.
If even-song and morwe-song acorde,
Lat see now who shal telle the firste tale.
As ever mote I drinke wyn or ale,
Who-so be rebel to my jugement
Shal paye for al that by the weye is spent.
Now draweth cut, er that we ferrer twinne;
He which that hath the shortest shal biginne.
Sire knight," quod he, "my maister and my lord,
Now draweth cut, for that is myn acord.
Cometh neer," quod he, "my lady prioresse;
And ye, sir clerk, lat be your shamfastnesse,
Ne studieth noght; ley hond to, every man."
Anon to drawen every wight bigan,
And shortly for to tellen, as it was,
Were it by aventure, or sort, or cas,
The sothe is this, the cut fil to the knight,
Of which ful blythe and glad was every wight;
And telle he moste his tale, as was resoun,
By forward and by composicioun,
As ye han herd; what nedeth wordes mo?
And whan this gode man saugh it was so,
As he that wys was and obedient
To kepe his forward by his free assent,
He seyde: "Sin I shal beginne the game,

Shall tell two stories as you wend your way
To Canterbury town; and each of you
On coming home, shall tell another two,
All of adventures he has known befall.
And he who plays his part the best of all,
That is to say, who tells upon the road
Tales of best sense, in most amusing mode,
Shall have a supper at the others' cost
Here in this room and sitting by this post,
When we come back again from Canterbury.
And now, the more to warrant you'll be merry
I will myself, and gladly, with you ride
At my own cost, and I will be your guide.
But whosoever shall my rule gainsay
Shall pay for all that's bought along the way.
And if you are agreed that it be so,
Tell me at once, or if not, tell me no,
And I will act accordingly. No more."
This thing was granted, and our oaths we swore,
With right glad hearts, and prayed of him, also,
That he would take the office, nor forgo
The place of governor of all of us,
Judging our tales; and by his wisdom thus
Arrange that supper at a certain price,
We to be ruled, each one, by his advice
In things both great and small; by one assent,
We stood committed to his government.
And thereupon, the wine was fetched anon;
We drank, and then to rest went every one,
And that without a longer tarrying.
Next morning, when the day began to spring,
Up rose our host, and acting as our cock,
He gathered us together in a flock,
And forth we rode, a jog-trot being the pace,
Until we reached Saint Thomas' watering-place.
And there our host pulled horse up to a walk,
And said: "Now, masters, listen while I talk.
You know what you agreed at set of sun.
If even-song and morning-song are one,
Let's here decide who first shall tell a tale.
And as I hope to drink more wine and ale,
Whoso proves rebel to my government
Shall pay for all that by the way is spent.
Come now, draw cuts, before we farther win,
And he that draws the shortest shall begin.
Sir knight," said he, "my master and my lord,
You shall draw first as you have pledged your word.
Come near," quoth he, "my lady prioress:
And you sir, clerk, put by your bashfulness,
Nor ponder more; out hands, now, every man!"
At once to draw a cut each one began,
And, to make short the matter, as it was,
Whether by chance or whatsoever cause,
The truth is, that the cut fell to the knight,
At which right happy then was every wight.
Thus that his story first of all he'd tell,
According to the compact, it befell,
As you have heard. Why argue to and fro?
And when this good man saw that it was so,
Being a wise man and obedient
To plighted word, given by free assent,
He said: "Since I must then begin the game,

Why, welcome be the cut, and in God's name!
Now let us ride, and hearken what I say."
  And at that word we rode forth on our way;
And he began to speak, with right good cheer,
His tale anon, as it is written here.

What, welcome be the cut, a Goddes name!
Now lat us ryde, and herkneth what I seye.'
  And with that word we riden forth our weye;
And he bigan with right a mery chere
His tale anon, and seyde in this manere.

HERE ENDETH THE PROLOGUE OF THIS BOOK; AND HERE BEGINNETH THE FIRST TALE, WHICH IS THE KNIGHT'S TALE

THE KNIGHT'S TALE

Iamque domos patrias, Scithice post aspera gentis
Prelia, laurigero, &c. Statius, *Theb.* xii. 519

Once on a time, as old tales tell to us,
There was a duke whose name was Thesëus;
Of Athens he was lord and governor,
And in his time was such a conqueror
That greater was there not beneath the sun.
Full many a rich country had he won;
What with his wisdom and his chivalry
He gained the realm of Femininity,
That was of old time known as Scythia.
There wedded he the queen, Hippolyta,
And brought her home with him to his country.
In glory great and with great pageantry,
And, too, her younger sister, Emily.
And thus, in victory and with melody,
Let I this noble duke to Athens ride
With all his armed host marching at his side.
  And truly, were it not too long to hear,
I would have told you fully how, that year,
Was gained the realm of Femininity
By Thesëus and by his chivalry;
And all of the great battle that was wrought
Where Amazons and the Athenians fought;
And how was wooed and won Hippolyta,
That fair and hardy queen of Scythia;
And of the feast was made at their wedding,
And of the tempest at their home-coming;
But all of that I must for now forbear.
I have, God knows, a large field for my share.
And weak the oxen, and the soil is tough.
The remnant of the tale is long enough.
I will not hinder any, in my turn;
Let each man tell his tale, until we learn
Which of us all the most deserves to win;
So where I stopped, again I'll now begin.
  This duke of whom I speak, of great renown,
When he had drawn almost unto the town,
In all well-being and in utmost pride,
He grew aware, casting his eyes aside,
That right upon the road, as suppliants do,
A company of ladies, two by two,
Knelt, all in black, before his cavalcade;
But such a clamorous cry of woe they made
That in the whole world living man had heard
No such a lamentation, on my word;
Nor would they cease lamenting till at last
They'd clutched his bridle reins and held them fast

Whylom, as olde stories tellen us,
Ther was a duk that highte Theseus;
Of Athenes he was lord and governour,
And in his tyme swich a conquerour,
That gretter was ther noon under the sonne.
Ful many a riche contree hadde he wonne;
What with his wisdom and his chivalrye,
He conquered al the regne of Femenye,
That whylom was y-cleped Scithia;
And weddede the quene Ipolita,
And broghte hir hoom with him in his contree
With muchel glorie and greet solempnitee,
And eek hir yonge suster Emelye.
And thus with victorie and with melodye
Lete I this noble duk to Athenes ryde,
And al his hoost, in armes, him bisyde.
  And certes, if it nere to long to here,
I wolde han told yow fully the manere,
How wonnen was the regne of Femenye
By Theseus, and by his chivalrye;
And of the grete bataille for the nones
Bitwixen Athenës and Amazones;
And how asseged was Ipolita,
The faire hardy quene of Scithia;
And of the feste that was at hir weddinge,
And of the tempest at hir hoom-cominge;
But al that thing I moot as now forbere.
I have, God woot, a large feeld to ere,
And wayke been the oxen in my plough.
The remenant of the tale is long y-nough.
I wol nat letten eek noon of this route;
Lat every felawe telle his tale aboute,
And lat see now who shal the soper winne;
And ther I lefte, I wol ageyn biginne.
  This duk, of whom I make mencioun,
When he was come almost unto the toun,
In al his wele and in his moste pryde,
He was war, as he caste his eye asyde,
Wher that ther kneled in the hye weye
A companye of ladies, tweye and tweye,
Ech after other, clad in clothes blake;
But swich a cry and swich a wo they make,
That in this world nis creature livinge,
That herde swich another weymentinge;
And of this cry they nolde never stenten,
Til they the reynes of his brydel henten.

"What folk ben ye, that at myn hoomcominge
Perturben so my feste with cryinge?"
Quod Theseus, "have ye so greet envye
Of myn honour, that thus compleyne and crye?
Or who hath yow misboden, or offended?
And telleth me if it may been amended;
And why that ye ben clothed thus in blak?"
The eldest lady of hem alle spak,
When she hadde swowned with a deedly chere,
That it was routhe for to seen and here,
And seyde: "Lord, to whom Fortune hath yiven
Victorie, and as a conquerour to liven,
Noght greveth us your glorie and your honour;
But we biseken mercy and socour.
Have mercy on our wo and our distresse.
Som drope of pitee, thurgh thy gentilesse,
Up-on us wrecched wommen lat thou falle,
For certes, lord, ther nis noon of us alle,
That she nath been a duchesse or a quene;
Now be we caitifs, as it is wel sene:
Thanked be Fortune, and hir false wheel,
That noon estat assureth to be weel.
And certes, lord, t'abyden your presence,
Here in the temple of the goddesse Clemence
We han ben waytinge al this fourtenight;
Now help us, lord, sith it is in thy might.
I wrecche, which that wepe and waille thus,
Was whylom wyf to king Capaneus,
That starf at Thebes, cursed be that day!
And alle we, that been in this array,
And maken al this lamentacioun,
We losten alle our housbondes at that toun,
Whyl that the sege ther-aboute lay.
And yet now th'olde Creon, weylaway!
The lord is now of Thebes the citee,
Fulfild of ire and of iniquitee,
He, for despyt, and for his tirannye,
To do the dede bodyes vileinye,
Of alle our lordes, whiche that ben slawe,
Hath alle the bodyes on an heep y-drawe,
And wol nat suffren hem, by noon assent,
Neither to been y-buried nor y-brent,
But maketh houndes ete hem in despyt."
And with that word, with-outen more respyt,
They fillen gruf, and cryden pitously,
"Have on us wrecched wommen som mercy,
And lat our sorwe sinken in thyn herte."
This gentil duk doun from his courser sterte
With herte pitous, whan he herde hem speke.
Him thoughte that his herte wolde breke,
When he saugh hem so pitous and so mat,
That whylom weren of so greet estat.
And in his armes he hem alle up hente,
And hem conforteth in ful good entente;
And swoor his ooth, as he was trewe knight,
He wolde doon so ferforthly his might
Up-on the tyraunt Creon hem to wreke,
That al the peple of Grece sholde speke
How Creon was of Theseus y-served,
As he that hadde his deeth ful wel deserved.
And right anoon, with-outen more abood,
His baner he desplayeth, and forth rood

"What folk are you that at my home-coming
Disturb my triumph with this dolorous thing?"
Cried Theseüs. "Do you so much envy
My honour that you thus complain and cry?
Or who has wronged you now, or who offended?
Come, tell me whether it may be amended;
And tell me, why are you clothed thus, in black?"
The eldest lady of them answered back,
After she'd swooned, with cheek so deathly drear
That it was pitiful to see and hear,
And said: "Lord, to whom Fortune has but given
Victory, and to conquer where you've striven,
Your glory and your honour grieve not us;
But we beseech your aid and pity thus.
Have mercy on our woe and our distress.
Some drop of pity, of your gentleness,
Upon us wretched women, oh, let fall!
For see, lord, there is no one of us all
That has not been a duchess or a queen;
Now we are captives, as may well be seen:
Thanks be to Fortune and her treacherous wheel,
There's none can rest assured of constant weal.
And truly, lord, expecting your return,
In Pity's temple, where the fires yet burn,
We have been waiting through a long fortnight;
Now help us, lord, since it is in your might.
"I, wretched woman, who am weeping thus,
Was once the wife of King Capaneüs,
Who died at Thebes, oh, cursed be the day!
And all we that you see in this array,
And make this lamentation to be known,
All we have lost our husbands at that town
During the siege that round about it lay.
And now the old Creon, ah welaway!
The lord and governor of Thebes city,
Full of his wrath and all iniquity,
He, in despite and out of tyranny,
To do the dead a shame and villainy,
Of all our husbands, lying among the slain,
Has piled the bodies in a heap, amain,
And will not suffer them, nor give consent,
To buried be, or burned, nor will relent,
But sets his dogs to eat them, out of spite."
And on that word, at once, without respite,
They all fell prone and cried out piteously:
"Have on us wretched women some mercy,
And let our sorrows sink into your heart!"
This gentle duke down from his horse did start
With heart of pity, when he'd heard them speak.
It seemed to him his heart must surely break,
Seeing them there so miserable of state,
Who had been proud and happy but so late.
And in his arms he took them tenderly,
Giving them comfort understandingly:
And swore his oath, that as he was true knight,
He would put forth so thoroughly his might
Against the tyrant Creon as to wreak
Vengeance so great that all of Greece should speak
And say how Creon was by Theseüs served,
As one that had his death full well deserved.
This sworn and done, he no more there abode;
His banner he displayed and forth he rode

Toward Thebes, and all his host marched on beside;
Nor nearer Athens would he walk or ride,
Nor take his ease for even half a day,
But onward, and in camp that night he lay;
And thence he sent Hippolyta the queen
And her bright sister Emily, I ween,
Unto the town of Athens, there to dwell
While he went forth. There is no more to tell.
The image of red Mars, with spear and shield,
So shone upon his banner's snow-white field
It made a billowing glitter up and down;
And by the banner borne was his pennon,
On which in beaten gold was worked, complete,
The Minotaur, which he had slain in Crete.
Thus rode this duke, thus rode this conqueror,
And in his host of chivalry the flower,
Until he came to Thebes and did alight
Full in the field where he'd intent to fight.
But to be brief in telling of this thing,
With Creon, who was Thebes' dread lord and king,
He fought and slew him, manfully, like knight,
In open war, and put his host to flight;
And by assault he took the city then,
Levelling wall and rafter with his men;
And to the ladies he restored again
The bones of their poor husbands who were slain,
To do for them the last rites of that day.
But it were far too long a tale to say
The clamour of great grief and sorrowing
Those ladies raised above the bones burning
Upon the pyres, and of the great honour
That Theseüs, the noble conqueror,
Paid to the ladies when from him they went;
To make the story short is my intent.
When, then, this worthy duke, this Theseüs
Had slain Creon and won Thebes city thus,
Still on the field he took that night his rest,
And dealt with all the land as he thought best.
In searching through the heap of enemy dead,
Stripping them of their gear from heel to head,
The busy pillagers could pick and choose,
After the battle, what they best could use;
And so befell that in a heap they found,
Pierced through with many a grievous, bloody wound,
Two young knights lying together, side by side,
Bearing one crest, wrought richly, of their pride,
And of those two Arcita was the one,
The other knight was known as Palamon.
Not fully quick, nor fully dead they were,
But by their coats of arms and by their gear
The heralds readily could tell, withal,
That they were of the Theban blood royal,
And that they had been of two sisters born.
Out of the heap the spoilers had them torn
And carried gently over to the tent
Of Theseüs; who shortly had them sent
To Athens, there in prison cell to lie
For ever, without ransom, till they die.
And when this worthy duke had all this done,
He gathered host and home he rode anon,
With laurel crowned again as conqueror;

To Thebes-ward, and al his host bisyde;
No neer Athenës wolde he go ne ryde,
Ne take his ese fully half a day,
But onward on his wey that night he lay;
And sente anoon Ipolita the quene,
And Emelye hir yonge suster shene,
Un-to the toun of Athenës to dwelle;
And forth he rit; ther nis namore to telle.
The rede statue of Mars, with spere and targe,
So shyneth in his whyte baner large,
That alle the feeldes gliteren up and doun;
And by his baner born is his penoun
Of gold ful riche, in which ther was y-bete
The Minotaur, which that he slough in Crete.
Thus rit this duk, thus rit this conquerour,
And in his host of chivalrye the flour,
Til that he cam to Thebes, and alighte
Faire in a feeld, ther as he thoghte fighte.
But shortly for to speken of this thing,
With Creon, which that was of Thebes king,
He faught, and slough him manly as a knight
In pleyn bataille, and putte the folk to flight;
And by assaut he wan the citee after,
And rente adoun bothe wal, and sparre, and rafter;
And to the ladyes he restored agayn
The bones of hir housbondes that were slayn,
To doon obséquies, as was tho the gyse.
But it were al to long for to devyse
The grete clamour and the waymentinge
That the ladyes made at the brenninge
Of the bodyes, and the grete honour
That Theseus, the noble conquerour,
Doth to the ladyes, whan they from him wente;
But shortly for to telle is myn entente.
Whan that this worthy duk, this Theseus,
Hath Creon slayn, and wonne Thebes thus,
Stille in that feeld he took al night his reste,
And dide with al the contree as him leste.
To ransake in the tas of bodyes dede,
Hem for to strepe of harneys and of wede,
The pilours diden bisinesse and cure,
After the bataille and disconfiture.
And so bifel, that in the tas they founde,
Thurgh-girt with many a grevous blody wounde,
Two yonge knightes ligging by and by,
Bothe in oon armes, wroght ful richely,
Of whiche two, Arcita hight that oon,
And that other knight hight Palamon.
Nat fully quike, ne fully dede they were,
But by hir cote-armures, and by hir gere,
The heraudes knewe hem best in special,
As they that weren of the blood royal
Of Thebes, and of sustren two y-born.
Out of the tas the pilours han hem torn,
And han hem caried softe un-to the tente
Of Theseus, and he ful sone hem sente
To Athenës, to dwellen in prisoun
Perpetuelly, he nolde no raunsoun.
And whan this worthy duk hath thus y-don,
He took his host, and hoom he rood anon
With laurer crowned as a conquerour;

And there he liveth, in joye and in honour,
Terme of his lyf; what nedeth wordes mo?
And in a tour, in angwish and in wo,
Dwellen this Palamoun and eek Arcite,
For evermore, ther may no gold hem quyte.
This passeth yeer by yeer, and day by day,
Til it fil ones, in a morwe of May,
That Emelye, that fairer was to sene
Than is the lilie upon his stalke grene,
And fressher than the May with floures newe—
For with the rose colour stroof hir hewe,
I noot which was the fairer of hem two—
Er it were day, as was hir wone to do,
She was arisen, and al redy dight;
For May wol have no slogardye a-night.
The sesoun priketh every gentil herte,
And maketh him out of his sleep to sterte,
And seith, "Arys, and do thyn observaunce."
This maked Emelye have remembraunce
To doon honour to May, and for to ryse.
Y-clothed was she fresh, for to devyse;
Hir yelow heer was broyded in a tresse,
Bihinde hir bak, a yerde long, I gesse.
And in the gardin, at the sonne up-riste,
She walketh up and doun, and as hir liste
She gadereth floures, party whyte and rede,
To make a sotil gerland for hir hede,
And as an aungel hevenly she song.
The grete tour, that was so thikke and strong,
Which of the castel was the chief dongeoun,
(Ther-as the knightes weren in prisoun,
Of whiche I tolde yow, and tellen shal)
Was evene joynant to the gardin-wal,
Ther as this Emelye hadde hir pleyinge.
Bright was the sonne, and cleer that morweninge,
And Palamon, this woful prisoner,
As was his wone, by leve of his gayler,
Was risen, and romed in a chambre on heigh,
In which he al the noble citee seigh,
And eek the gardin, ful of braunches grene,
Ther-as this fresshe Emelye the shene
Was in hir walk, and romed up and doun.
This sorweful prisoner, this Palamoun,
Goth in the chambre, roming to and fro,
And to him-self compleyning of his wo;
That he was born, ful ofte he seyde, "alas!"
And so bifel, by aventure or cas,
That thurgh a window, thikke of many a barre
Of yren greet, and square as any sparre,
He caste his eye upon Emelya,
And ther-with-al he bleynte, and cryde "a!"
As though he stongen were un-to the herte.
And with that cry Arcite anon up-sterte,
And seyde, "Cosin myn, what eyleth thee,
That art so pale and deedly on to see?
Why crydestow? who hath thee doon offence?
For Goddes love, tak al in pacience
Our prisoun, for it may non other be;
Fortune hath yeven us this adversitee.

There lived he in all joy and all honour
His term of life; what more need words express?
And in a tower, in anguish and distress,
Palamon and Arcita, day and night,
Dwelt whence no gold might help them to take flight.
Thus passed by year by year and day by day,
Till it fell out, upon a morn in May,
That Emily, far fairer to be seen
Than is the lily on its stalk of green,
And fresher than is May with flowers new
(For with the rose's colour strove her hue,
I know not which was fairer of the two),
Before the dawn, as was her wont to do,
She rose and dressed her body for delight;
For May will have no sluggards of the night.
That season rouses every gentle heart
And forces it from winter's sleep to start,
Saying: "Arise and show thy reverence."
So Emily remembered to go thence
In honour of the May, and so she rose.
Clothed, she was sweeter than any flower that blows;
Her yellow hair was braided in one tress
Behind her back, a full yard long, I guess.
And in the garden, as the sun up-rose,
She sauntered back and forth and through each close,
Gathering many a flower, white and red,
To weave a delicate garland for her head;
And like a heavenly angel's was her song.
The tower tall, which was so thick and strong,
And of the castle was the great donjon,
(Wherein the two knights languished in prison,
Of whom I told and shall yet tell, withal),
Was joined, at base, unto the garden wall
Whereunder Emily went dallying.
Bright was the sun and clear that morn in spring,
And Palamon, the woeful prisoner,
As was his wont, by leave of his gaoler,
Was up and pacing round that chamber high,
From which the noble city filled his eye,
And, too, the garden full of branches green,
Wherein bright Emily, fair and serene,
Went walking and went roving up and down.
This sorrowing prisoner, this Palamon,
Being in the chamber, pacing to and fro,
And to himself complaining of his woe,
Cursing his birth, he often cried "Alas!"
And so it was, by chance or other pass,
That through a window, closed by many a bar
Of iron, strong and square as any spar,
He cast his eyes upon Emilia,
And thereupon he blenched and cried out "Ah!"
As if he had been smitten to the heart.
And at that cry Arcita did up-start,
Asking: "My cousin, why what ails you now
That you've so deathly pallor on your brow?
Why did you cry out? Who's offended you?
For God's love, show some patience, as I do,
With prison, for it may not different be;
Fortune has given this adversity.

Some evil disposition or aspect
Of Saturn did our horoscopes affect
To bring us here, though differently 'twere sworn;
But so the stars stood when we two were born;
We must endure it; that, in brief, is plain."
This Palamon replied and said again:
"Cousin, indeed in this opinion now
Your fancy is but vanity, I trow.
It's not our prison that caused me to cry.
But I was wounded lately through the eye
Down to my heart, and that my bane will be.
The beauty of the lady that I see
There in that garden, pacing to and fro,
Is cause of all my crying and my woe.
I know not if she's woman or goddess;
But Venus she is verily, I guess."
And thereupon down on his knees he fell,
And said: "O Venus, if it be thy will
To be transfigured in this garden, thus
Before me, sorrowing wretch, oh now help us
Out of this prison to be soon escaped.
And if it be my destiny is shaped,
By fate, to die in durance, in bondage,
Have pity, then, upon our lineage
That has been brought so low by tyranny."
And on that word Arcita looked to see
This lady who went roving to and fro.
And in that look her beauty struck him so
That, if poor Palamon is wounded sore,
Arcita is as deeply hurt, and more.
And with a sigh he said then, piteously:
"The virgin beauty slays me suddenly
Of her that wanders yonder in that place;
And save I have her pity and her grace,
That I at least may see her day by day,
I am but dead; there is no more to say."
This Palamon, when these words he had heard,
Pitilessly he watched him, and answered:
"Do you say this in earnest or in play?"
"Nay," quoth Arcita, "earnest, now, I say!
God help me, I am in no mood for play!"
Palamon knit his brows and stood at bay.
"It will not prove," he said, "to your honour
After so long a time to turn traitor
To me, who am your cousin and your brother,
Sworn as we are, and each unto the other,
That never, though for death in any pain,
Never, indeed, till death shall part us twain,
Either of us in love shall hinder other,
No, nor in any thing, O my dear brother;
But that, instead, you shall so further me
As I shall you. All this we did agree.
Such was your oath and such was mine also.
You dare not now deny it, well I know.
Thus you are of my party, beyond doubt.
And now you would all falsely go about
To love my lady, whom I love and serve,
And shall while life my heart's blood may preserve.
Nay, false Arcita, it shall not be so.
I loved her first, and told you all my woe,
As to a brother and to one that swore
To further me, as I have said before.

Som wikke aspect or disposicioun
Of Saturne, by sum constellacioun,
Hath yeven us this, al-though we hadde it sworn;
So stood the heven whan that we were born;
We moste endure it: this is the short and pleyn."
This Palamon answerde, and seyde ageyn,
"Cosyn, for sothe, of this opinioun
Thou hast a veyn imaginacioun.
This prison caused me nat for to crye.
But I was hurt right now thurgh-out myn yë
In-to myn herte, that wol my bane be.
The fairnesse of that lady that I see
Yond in the gardin romen to and fro,
Is cause of al my crying and my wo.
I noot wher she be womman or goddesse;
But Venus is it, soothly, as I gesse."
And ther-with-al on kneës doun he fil,
And seyde: "Venus, if it be thy wil
Yow in this gardin thus to transfigure
Bifore me, sorweful wrecche creature,
Out of this prisoun help that we may scapen.
And if so be my destinee be shapen
By eterne word to dyen in prisoun,
Of our linage have som compassioun,
That is so lowe y-broght by tirannye."
And with that word Arcite gan espye
Wher-as this lady romed to and fro.
And with that sighte hir beautee hurte him so,
That, if that Palamon was wounded sore,
Arcite is hurt as muche as he, or more.
And with a sigh he seyde pitously:
"The fresshe beautee sleeth me sodeynly
Of hir that rometh in the yonder place;
And, but I have hir mercy and hir grace,
That I may seen hir atte leeste weye,
I nam but deed; ther nis namore to seye."
This Palamon, whan he tho wordes herde,
Dispitously he loked, and answerde:
"Whether seistow this in ernest or in pley?"
"Nay," quod Arcite, "in ernest, by my fey!
God help me so, me list ful yvele pleye."
This Palamon gan knitte his browes tweye:
"It nere," quod he, "to thee no greet honour
For to be fals, ne for to be traytour
To me, that am thy cosin and thy brother
Y-sworn ful depe, and ech of us til other,
That never, for to dyen in the peyne,
Til that the deeth departe shal us tweyne,
Neither of us in love to hindren other,
Ne in non other cas, my leve brother;
But that thou sholdest trewely forthren me
In every cas, and I shal forthren thee.
This was thyn ooth, and myn also, certeyn;
I wot right wel, thou darst it nat withseyn.
Thus artow of my counseil, out of doute.
And now thou woldest falsly been aboute
To love my lady, whom I love and serve,
And ever shal, til that myn herte sterve.
Now certes, fals Arcite, thou shalt nat so.
I loved hir first, and tolde thee my wo
As to my counseil, and my brother sworn
To forthre me, as I have told biforn.

For which thou art y-bounden as a knight
To helpen me, if it lay in thy might,
Or elles artow fals, I dar wel seyn."
This Arcitë ful proudly spak ageyn,
"Thou shalt," quod he, "be rather fals than I;
But thou art fals, I telle thee utterly;
For *par amour* I loved hir first er thow.
What wiltow seyn? thou wistest nat yet now
Whether she be a womman or goddesse!
Thyn is affeccioun of holinesse,
And myn is love, as to a creature;
For which I tolde thee myn aventure
As to my cosin, and my brother sworn.
I pose, that thou lovedest hir biforn;
Wostow nat wel the olde clerkes sawe,
That 'who shal yeve a lover any lawe?'
Love is a gretter lawe, by my pan,
Than may be yeve to any erthly man.
And therefore positif lawe and swich decree
Is broke al-day for love, in ech degree.
A man moot nedes love, maugree his heed.
He may nat fleen it, thogh he sholde be deed,
Al be she mayde, or widwe, or elles wyf.
And eek it is nat lykly, al thy lyf,
To stonden in hir grace; namore shal I;
For wel thou woost thy-selven, verraily,
That thou and I be dampned to prisoun
Perpetuelly; us gayneth no raunsoun.
We stryve as dide the houndes for the boon,
They foughte al day, and yet hir part was noon;
Ther cam a kyte, whyl that they were wrothe,
And bar awey the boon bitwixe hem bothe.
And therfore, at the kinges court, my brother,
Ech man for him-self, ther is non other.
Love if thee list; for I love and ay shal;
And soothly, leve brother, this is al.
Here in this prisoun mote we endure,
And everich of us take his aventure."
Greet was the stryf and long bitwixe hem tweye,
If that I hadde leyser for to seye;
But to th'effect. It happed on a day,
(To telle it yow as shortly as I may)
A worthy duk that highte Perotheus,
That felawe was un-to duk Theseus
Sin thilke day that they were children lyte,
Was come to Athénës, his felawe to visyte,
And for to pleye, as he was wont to do,
For in this world he loved no man so:
And he loved him as tendrely ageyn.
So wel they loved, as olde bokes seyn,
That whan that oon was deed, sothly to telle,
His felawe wente and soghte him doun in helle;
But of that story list me nat to wryte.
Duk Perotheus loved wel Arcite,
And hadde him knowe at Thebes yeer by yere;
And fynally, at requeste and preyere
Of Perotheus, with-oute any raunsoun,
Duk Theseus him leet out of prisoun,
Freely to goon, wher that him liste over-al,
In swich a gyse, as I you tellen shal.
This was the forward, pleynly for t'endyte,
Bitwixen Theseus and him Arcite:

For which you are in duty bound, as knight,
To help me, if the thing lie in your might,
Or else you're false, I say, and downfallen."
Then this Arcita proudly spoke again:
"You shall," he said, "be rather false than I;
And that you're so, I tell you utterly;
For *par amour* I loved her first, you know.
What can you say? You know not, even now,
Whether she is a woman or goddess!
Yours is a worship as of holiness,
While mine is love, as of a mortal maid;
Wherefore I told you of it, unafraid,
As to my cousin and my brother sworn.
Let us assume you loved her first, this morn;
Know you not well the ancient writer's saw
Of 'Who shall give a lover any law?'
Love is a greater law, aye by my pan,
Than man has ever given to earthly man.
And therefore statute law and such decrees
Are broken daily and in all degrees.
A man must needs have love, maugre his head.
He cannot flee it though he should be dead,
And be she maid, or widow, or a wife.
And yet it is not likely that, in life,
You'll stand within her graces; nor shall I;
For you are well aware, aye verily,
That you and I are doomed to prison drear
Perpetually; we gain no ransom here.
We strive but as those dogs did for the bone;
They fought all day, and yet their gain was none.
Till came a kite while they were still so wroth
And bore the bone away between them both.
And therefore, at the king's court, O my brother,
It's each man for himself and not for other.
Love if you like; for I love and aye shall;
And certainly, dear brother, that is all.
Here in this prison cell must we remain
And each endure whatever fate ordain."
Great was the strife, and long, betwixt the two,
If I had but the time to tell it you,
Save in effect. It happened on a day
(To tell the tale as briefly as I may),
A worthy duke men called Pirithous,
Who had been friend unto Duke Theseüs,
Since each had been a little child, a chit,
Was come to visit Athens and visit
His play-fellow, as he was wont to do,
For in this whole world he loved no man so;
And Theseüs loved him as truly—nay,
So well each loved the other, old books say,
That when one died (it is but truth I tell),
The other went and sought him down in Hell;
But of that tale I have no wish to write.
Pirithous loved Arcita, too, that knight,
Having known him in Thebes full many a year;
And finally, at his request and prayer,
And that without a coin of ransom paid,
Duke Theseüs released him out of shade,
Freely to go where'er he wished, and to
His own devices, as I'll now tell you.
The compact was, to set it plainly down,
As made between those two of great renown:

That if Arcita, any time, were found,
Ever in life, by day or night, on ground
Of any country of this Theseüs,
And he were caught, it was concerted thus,
That by the sword he straight should lose his head.
He had no choice, so taking leave he sped
Homeward to Thebes, lest by the sword's sharp edge
He forfeit life. His neck was under pledge.
How great a sorrow is Arcita's now!
How through his heart he feels death's heavy blow;
He weeps, he wails, he cries out piteously;
He thinks to slay himself all privily.
Said he: "Alas, the day that I was born!
I'm in worse prison, now, and more forlorn;
Now am I doomed eternally to dwell
No more in Purgatory, but in Hell.
Alas, that I have known Pirithous!
For else had I remained with Théseüs,
Fettered within that cell; but even so
Then had I been in bliss and not in woe.
Only the sight of her that I would serve,
Though I might never her dear grace deserve,
Would have sufficed, oh well enough for me!
O my dear cousin Palamon," said he,
"Yours is the victory, and that is sure,
For there, full happily, you may endure.
In prison? Never, but in Paradise!
Oh, well has Fortune turned for you the dice,
Who have the sight of her, I the absence.
For possible it is, in her presence,
You being a knight, a worthy and able,
That by some chance, since Fortune's changeable,
You may to your desire sometime attain.
But I, that am in exile and in pain,
Stripped of all hope and in so deep despair
That there's no earth nor water, fire nor air,
Nor any creature made of them there is
To help or give me comfort, now, in this—
Surely I'll die of sorrow and distress;
Farewell, my life, my love, my joyousness!
"Alas! Why is it men so much complain
Of what great God, or Fortune, may ordain,
When better is the gift, in any guise,
Than men may often for themselves devise?
One man desires only that great wealth
Which may but cause his death or long ill-health.
One who from prison gladly would be free,
At home by his own servants slain might be.
Infinite evils lie therein, 'tis clear;
We know not what it is we pray for here.
We fare as he that's drunken as a mouse;
A drunk man knows right well he has a house,
But he knows not the right way leading thither;
And a drunk man is sure to slip and slither.
And certainly, in this world so fare we;
We furiously pursue felicity,
Yet we go often wrong before we die.
This may we all admit, and specially I,
Who deemed and held, as I were under spell,
That if I might escape from prison cell,
Then would I find again what joy might heal,

That if so were, that Arcite were y-founde
Ever in his lyf, by day or night or stounde
In any contree of this Theseus,
And he were caught, it was acorded thus,
That with a swerd he sholde lese his heed;
Ther nas non other remedye ne reed,
But taketh his leve, and homward he him spedde;
Let him be war, his nekke lyth to wedde!
How greet a sorwe suffreth now Arcite!
The deeth he feleth thurgh his herte smyte;
He wepeth, wayleth, cryeth pitously;
To sleen him-self he wayteth prively.
He seyde, "Allas that day that I was born!
Now is my prison worse than biforn;
Now is me shape eternally to dwelle
Noght in purgatorie, but in helle.
Allas! that ever knew I Perotheus!
For elles hadde I dwelled with Theseus
Y-fetered in his prisoun ever-mo.
Than hadde I been in blisse, and nat in wo.
Only the sighte of hir, whom that I serve,
Though that I never hir grace may deserve,
Wolde han suffised right y-nough for me.
O dere cosin Palamon," quod he,
"Thyn is the victorie of this aventure,
Ful blisfully in prison maistow dure;
In prison? certes nay, but in paradys!
Wel hath fortune y-turned thee the dys,
That hast the sighte of hir, and I th'absence.
For possible is, sin thou hast hir presence,
And art a knight, a worthy and an able,
That by som cas, sin fortune is chaungeable,
Thou mayst to thy desyr som-tyme atteyne.
But I, that am exyled, and bareyne
Of alle grace, and in so greet despeir,
That ther nis erthe, water, fyr, ne eir,
Ne creature, that of hem maked is,
That may me helpe or doon confort in this:
Wel oughte I sterve in wanhope and distresse;
Farwel my lyf, my lust, and my gladnesse!
Allas, why pleynen folk so in commune
Of purveyaunce of God, or of fortune,
That yeveth hem ful ofte in many a gyse
Wel bettre than they can hem-self devyse?
Som man desyreth for to han richesse,
That cause is of his mordre or greet siknesse.
And som man wolde out of his prison fayn,
That in his hous is of his meynee slayn.
Infinite harmes been in this matere;
We witen nat what thing we preyen here.
We faren as he that dronke is as a mous;
A dronke man wot wel he hath an hous,
But he noot which the righte wey is thider;
And to a dronke man the wey is slider.
And certes, in this world so faren we;
We seken faste after felicitee,
But we goon wrong ful often, trewely.
Thus may we seyen alle, and namely I,
That wende and hadde a greet opinioun,
That, if I mighte escapen from prisoun,
Than hadde I been in joye and perfit hele,

Ther now I am exyled from my wele.
Sin that I may nat seen yow, Emelye,
I nam but deed; ther nis no remedye."
Up-on that other syde Palamon,
Whan that he wiste Arcite was agon,
Swich sorwe he maketh, that the grete tour
Resouneth of his youling and clamour.
The pure fettres on his shines grete
Weren of his bittre salte teres wete.
"Allas!" quod he, "Arcita, cosin myn,
Of al our stryf, God woot, the fruyt is thyn
Thow walkest now in Thebes at thy large,
And of my wo thou yevest litel charge.
Thou mayst, sin thou hast wisdom and manhede,
Assemblen alle the folk of our kinrede,
And make a werre so sharp on this citee,
That by som aventure, or som tretee,
Thou mayst have hir to lady and to wyf,
For whom that I mot nedes lese my lyf.
For, as by wey of possibilitee,
Sith thou art at thy large, of prison free,
And art a lord, greet is thyn avauntage,
More than is myn, that sterve here in a cage.
For I mot wepe and wayle, whyl I live,
With al the wo that prison may me yive,
And eek with peyne that love me yiveth also,
That doubleth al my torment and my wo."
Ther-with the fyr of jelousye up-sterte
With-inne his brest, and hente him by the herte
So woodly, that he lyk was to biholde
The box-tree, or the asshen dede and colde.
Tho seyde he; "O cruel goddes, that governe
This world with binding of your word eterne,
And wryten in the table of athamaunt
Your parlement, and your eterne graunt,
What is mankinde more un-to yow holde
Than is the sheep, that rouketh in the folde?
For slayn is man right as another beste,
And dwelleth eek in prison and areste,
And hath siknesse, and greet adversitee,
And ofte tymes gilteless, pardee!
What governaunce is in this prescience,
That gilteless tormenteth innocence?
And yet encreseth this al my penaunce,
That man is bounden to his observaunce,
For Goddes sake, to letten of his wille,
Ther as a beest may al his lust fulfille.
And whan a beest is deed, he hath no peyne;
But man after his deeth moot wepe and pleyne,
Though in this world he have care and wo:
With-outen doute it may stonden so.
Th' answere of this I lete to divynis,
But wel I woot, that in this world gret pyne is.
Allas! I see a serpent or a theef,
That many a trewe man hath doon mescheef,
Goon at his large, and wher him list may turne.
But I mot been in prison thurgh Saturne,
And eek thurgh Juno, jalous and eek wood,
That hath destroyed wel ny al the blood
Of Thebes, with his waste walles wyde.
And Venus sleeth me on that other syde

Who now am only exiled from my weal.
For since I may not see you, Emily,
I am but dead; there is no remedy."
And on the other hand, this Palamon,
When that he found Arcita truly gone,
Such lamentation made he, that the tower
Resounded of his crying, hour by hour.
The very fetters on his legs were yet
Again with all his bitter salt tears wet.
"Alas!" said he, "Arcita, cousin mine,
With all our strife, God knows, you've won the wine.
You're walking, now, in Theban streets, at large,
And all my woe you may from mind discharge.
You may, too, since you've wisdom and manhood,
Assemble all the people of our blood
And wage a war so sharp on this city
That by some fortune, or by some treaty,
You shall yet have that lady to your wife
For whom I now must needs lay down my life.
For surely 'tis in possibility,
Since you are now at large, from prison free,
And are a lord, great is your advantage
Above my own, who die here in a cage.
For I must weep and wail, the while I live,
In all the grief that prison cell may give,
And now with pain that love gives me, also,
Which doubles all my torment and my woe."
Therewith the fires of jealousy up-start
Within his breast and burn him to the heart
So wildly that he seems one, to behold,
Like seared box tree, or ashes, dead and cold.
Then said he: "O you cruel Gods, that sway
This world in bondage of your laws, for aye,
And write upon the tablets adamant
Your counsels and the changeless words you grant,
What better view of mankind do you hold
Than of the sheep that huddle in the fold?
For man must die like any other beast,
Or rot in prison, under foul arrest,
And suffer sickness and misfortune sad,
And still be ofttimes guiltless, too, by gad!
"What management is in this prescience
That, guiltless, yet torments our innocence?
And this increases all my pain, as well,
That man is bound by law, nor may rebel,
For fear of God, but must repress his will,
Whereas a beast may all his lust fulfill.
And when a beast is dead, he feels no pain;
But, after death, man yet must weep amain,
Though in this world he had but care and woe:
There is no doubt that it is even so.
The answer leave I to divines to tell,
But well I know this present world is hell.
Alas! I see a serpent or a thief,
That has brought many a true man unto grief,
Going at large, and where he wills may turn,
But I must lie in gaol, because Saturn,
And Juno too, both envious and mad,
Have spilled out well-nigh all the blood we had
At Thebes, and desolated her wide walls.
And Venus slays me with the bitter galls

Of fear of Arcita, and jealousy."
  Now will I leave this Palamon, for he
Is in his prison, where he still must dwell,
And of Arcita will I forthwith tell.
  Summer being passed away and nights grown long,
Increased now doubly all the anguish strong
Both of the lover and the prisoner.
I know not which one was the woefuller.
For, to be brief about it, Palamon
Is doomed to lie for ever in prison,
In chains and fetters till he shall be dead;
And exiled (on the forfeit of his head)
Arcita must remain abroad, nor see,
For evermore, the face of his lady.
  You lovers, now I ask you this question:
Who has the worse, Arcita or Palamon?
The one may see his lady day by day,
But yet in prison must he dwell for aye.
The other, where he wishes, he may go,
But never see his lady more, ah no.
Now answer as you wish, all you that can,
For I will speak right on as I began.

For jelousye, and fere of him Arcite."
  Now wol I stinte of Palamon a lyte,
And lete him in his prison stille dwelle,
And of Arcita forth I wol yow telle.
  The somer passeth, and the nightes longe
Encresen double wyse the peynes stronge
Bothe of the lovere and the prisoner.
I noot which hath the wofullere mester.
For shortly for to seyn, this Palamoun
Perpetuelly is dampned to prisoun,
In cheynes and in fettres to ben deed;
And Arcite is exyled upon his heed
For ever-mo as out of that contree,
Ne never-mo he shal his lady see.
  Yow loveres axe I now this questioun,
Who hath the worse, Arcite or Palamoun?
That oon may seen his lady day by day,
But in prison he moot dwelle alway.
That other wher him list may ryde or go,
But seen his lady shal he never-mo.
Now demeth as yow liste, ye that can,
For I wol telle forth as I bigan.

HERE ENDETH THE FIRST PART

HERE FOLLOWETH THE SECOND PART

Now when Arcita unto Thebes was come,
He lay and languished all day in his home,
Since he his lady nevermore should see,
But telling of his sorrow brief I'll be.
Had never any man so much torture,
No, nor shall have while this world may endure.
Bereft he was of sleep and meat and drink,
That lean he grew and dry as shaft, I think.
His eyes were hollow and ghastly to behold,
His face was sallow, all pale and ashen-cold,
And solitary kept he and alone,
Wailing the whole night long, making his moan.
And if he heard a song or instrument,
Then he would weep ungoverned and lament;
So feeble were his spirits, and so low,
And so changed was he, that no man could know
Him by his words or voice, whoever heard.
And in this change, for all the world he fared
As if not troubled by malady of love,
But by that humor dark and grim, whereof
Springs melancholy madness in the brain,
And fantasy unbridled holds its reign.
And shortly, all was turned quite upside-down,
Both habits and the temper all had known
Of him, this woeful lover, Dan Arcite.
  Why should I all day of his woe indite?
When he'd endured all this a year or two,
This cruel torment and this pain and woe,
At Thebes, in his own country, as I said,
Upon a night, while sleeping in his bed,
He dreamed of how the winged God Mercury
Before him stood and bade him happier be.
His sleep-bestowing wand he bore upright;
A hat he wore upon his ringlets bright.
Arrayed this god was (noted at a leap)
As he'd been when to Argus he gave sleep.

  Whan that Arcite to Thebes comen was,
Ful ofte a day he swelte and seyde "allas,"
For seen his lady shal he never-mo.
And shortly to concluden al his wo,
So muche sorwe had never creature
That is, or shal, whyl that the world may dure.
His sleep, his mete, his drink is him biraft,
That lene he wex, and drye as is a shaft.
His eyen holwe, and grisly to biholde;
His hewe falwe, and pale as asshen colde,
And solitarie he was, and ever allone,
And wailling al the night, making his mone.
And if he herde song or instrument,
Then wolde he wepe, he mighte nat be stent;
So feble eek were his spirits, and so lowe,
And chaunged so, that no man coude knowe
His speche nor his vois, though men it herde.
And in his gere, for al the world he ferde
Nat oonly lyk the loveres maladye
Of Hereos, but rather lyk manye
Engendred of humour malencolyk,
Biforen, in his celle fantastyk.
And shortly, turned was al up-so-doun
Bothe habit and eek disposicioun
Of him, this woful lovere daun Arcite.
  What sholde I al-day of his wo endyte?
Whan he endured hadde a yeer or two
This cruel torment, and this peyne and wo,
At Thebes, in his contree, as I seyde,
Up-on a night, in sleep as he him leyde,
Him thoughte how that the winged god Mercurie
Biforn him stood and bad him to be murye.
His slepy yerde in hond he bar uprighte;
An hat he werede up-on his heres brighte.
Arrayed was this god (as he took keep)
As he was whan that Argus took his sleep;

And seyde him thus: "T' Athénës shaltou wende;
Ther is thee shapen of thy wo an ende."
And with that word Arcite wook and sterte.
"Now trewely, how sore that me smerte,"
Quod he, "t' Athénës right now wol I fare;
Ne for the drede of deeth shal I nat spare
To see my lady, that I love and serve;
In hir presence I recche nat to sterve."
And with that word he caughte a greet mirour,
And saugh that chaunged was al his colour,
And saugh his visage al in another kinde.
And right anoon it ran him in his minde,
That, sith his face was so disfigured
Of maladye, the which he hadde endured,
He mighte wel, if that he bar him lowe,
Live in Athénes ever-more unknowe,
And seen his lady wel ny day by day.
And right anon he chaunged his array,
And cladde him as a povre laborer,
And al allone, save oonly a squyer,
That knew his privetee and al his cas,
Which was disgysed povrely, as he was,
T' Athénës is he goon the nexte way.
And to the court he wente up-on a day,
And at the gate he profreth his servyse,
To drugge and drawe, what so men wol devyse.
And shortly of this matere for to seyn,
He fil in office with a chamberleyn,
The which that dwelling was with Emelye;
For he was wys, and coude soon aspye
Of every servaunt, which that serveth here.
Wel coude he hewen wode, and water bere,
For he was yong and mighty for the nones,
And ther-to he was strong and big of bones
To doon that any wight can him devyse.
A yeer or two he was in this servyse,
Page of the chambre of Emelye the brighte;
And "Philostrate" he seide that he highte.
But half so wel biloved a man as he
Ne was ther never in court, of his degree;
He was so gentil of condicioun,
That thurghout al the court was his renoun.
They seyden, that it were a charitee
That Theseus wolde enhauncen his degree,
And putten him in worshipful servyse,
Ther as he mighte his vertu excercyse.
And thus, with-inne a whyle, his name is spronge
Bothe of his dedes, and his goode tonge,
That Theseus hath taken him so neer
That of his chambre he made him a squyer,
And yaf him gold to mayntene his degree;
And eek men broghte him out of his contree
From yeer to yeer, ful prively, his rente;
But honestly and slyly he it spente,
That no man wondred how that he it hadde.
And three yeer in this wyse his lyf he ladde,
And bar him so in pees and eek in werre,
Ther nas no man that Theseus hath derre.
And in this blisse lete I now Arcite,
And speke I wol of Palamon a lyte.
In derknesse and horrible and strong prisoun
This seven yeer hath seten Palamoun,

And thus he spoke: "To Athens shall you wend;
For all your woe is destined there to end."
And on that word Arcita woke and started.
"Now truly, howsoever sore I'm smarted,"
Said he, "to Athens right now will I fare;
Nor for the dread of death will I now spare
To see my lady, whom I love and serve;
I will not reck of death, with her, nor swerve."
And with that word he caught a great mirror,
And saw how changed was all his old colour,
And saw his visage altered from its kind.
And right away it ran into his mind
That since his face was now disfigured so,
By suffering endured (as well we know),
He might, if he should bear him low in town,
Live there in Athens evermore, unknown,
Seeing his lady well-nigh every day.
And right anon he altered his array,
Like a poor labourer in mean attire,
And all alone, save only for a squire,
Who knew his secret heart and all his case,
And who was dressed as poorly as he was,
To Athens was he gone the nearest way.
And to the court he went upon a day,
And at the gate he proffered services
To drudge and drag, as any one devises.
And to be brief herein, and to be plain,
He found employment with a chamberlain
Was serving in the house of Emily;
For he was sharp and very soon could see
What every servant did who served her there.
Right well could he hew wood and water bear,
For he was young and mighty, let me own,
And big of muscle, aye and big of bone,
To do what any man asked, in a trice.
A year or two he was in this service,
Page of the chamber of Emily the bright;
He said "Philostrates" would name him right.
But half so well beloved a man as he
Was never in that court, of his degree;
His gentle nature was so clearly shown,
That throughout all the court spread his renown.
They said it were but kindly courtesy
If Theseüs should heighten his degree
And put him in more honourable service
Wherein he might his virtue exercise.
And thus, anon, his name was so up-sprung,
Both for his deeds and sayings of his tongue,
That Theseüs had brought him nigh and nigher
And of the chamber he had made him squire,
And given him gold to maintain dignity.
Besides, men brought him, from his own country,
From year to year, clandestinely, his rent;
But honestly and slyly it was spent,
And no man wondered how he came by it.
And three years thus he lived, with much profit,
And bore him so in peace and so in war
There was no man that Theseüs loved more.
And in such bliss I leave Arcita now,
And upon Palamon some words bestow.
In darksome, horrible, and strong prison
These seven years has now sat Palamon,

Wasted by woe and by his long distress.
Who has a two-fold evil heaviness
But Palamon? whom love yet tortures so
That half out of his wits he is for woe;
And joined thereto he is a prisoner,
Perpetually, not only for a year.
And who could rhyme in English, properly,
His martyrdom? Forsooth, it is not I;
And therefore I pass lightly on my way.
It fell out in the seventh year, in May,
On the third night (as say the books of old
Which have this story much more fully told),
Were it by chance or were it destiny
(Since, when a thing is destined, it must be),
That, shortly after midnight, Palamon,
By helping of a friend, broke from prison,
And fled the city, fast as he might go;
For he had given his guard a drink that so
Was mixed of spice and honey and certain wine
And Theban opiate and anodyne,
That all that night, although a man might shake
This gaoler, he slept on, nor could awake.
And thus he flees as fast as ever he may.
The night was short and it was nearly day,
Wherefore he needs must find a place to hide;
And to a grove that grew hard by, with stride
Of furtive foot, went fearful Palamon.
In brief, he'd formed his plan, as he went on,
That in the grove he would lie fast all day,
And when night came, then would he take his way
Toward Thebes, and there find friends, and of them pray
Their help on Theseüs in war's array;
And briefly either he would lose his life,
Or else win Emily to be his wife;
This is the gist of his intention plain.
Now I'll return to Arcita again,
Who little knew how near to him was care
Till Fortune caught him in her tangling snare.
The busy lark, the herald of the day,
Salutes now in her song the morning grey;
And fiery Phoebus rises up so bright
That all the east is laughing with the light,
And with his streamers dries, among the greves,[1]
The silver droplets hanging on the leaves.
And so Arcita, in the court royal
With Theseüs, and his squire principal,
Is risen, and looks on the merry day.
And now, to do his reverence to May,
Calling to mind the point of his desire,
He on a courser, leaping high like fire,
Is ridden to the fields to muse and play,
Out of the court, a mile or two away;
And to the grove, whereof I lately told,
By accident his way began to hold,
To make him there the garland that one weaves
Of woodbine leaves and of green hawthorn leaves.
And loud he sang within the sunlit sheen:
"O May, with all thy flowers and all thy green,
Welcome be thou, thou fair and freshening May:

Forpyned, what for wo and for distresse;
Who feleth double soor and hevinesse
But Palamon? that love destreyneth so,
That wood out of his wit he gooth for wo;
And eek therto he is a prisoner
Perpetuelly, noght oonly for a yeer.
Who coude ryme in English proprely
His martirdom? for sothe, it am nat I;
Therefore I passe as lightly as I may.
It fel that in the seventhe yeer, in May,
The thridde night, (as olde bokes seyn,
That al this storie tellen more pleyn,)
Were it by aventure or destinee,
(As, whan a thing is shapen, it shal be,)
That, sone after the midnight, Palamoun,
By helping of a freend, brak his prisoun,
And fleeth the citee, faste as he may go;
For he had yive his gayler drinke so
Of a clarree, maad of a certeyn wyn,
With nercotikes and opie of Thebes fyn,
That al that night, thogh that men wolde him shake,
The gayler sleep, he mighte nat awake;
And thus he fleeth as faste as ever he may.
The night was short, and faste by the day,
That nedes-cost he moste him-selven hyde,
And til a grove, faste ther besyde,
With dredful foot than stalketh Palamoun.
For shortly, this was his opinioun,
That in that grove he wolde him hyde al day,
And in the night than wolde he take his way
To Thebes-ward, his freendes for to preye
On Theseus to helpe him to werreye;
And shortly, outher he wolde lese his lyf,
Or winne Emelye un-to his wyf;
This is th'effect and his entente pleyn.
Now wol I torne un-to Arcite ageyn,
That litel wiste how ny that was his care,
Til that fortune had broght him in the snare.
The bisy larke, messager of day,
Saluëth in hir song the morwe gray;
And fyry Phebus ryseth up so brighte,
That al the orient laugheth of the lighte,
And with his stremes dryeth in the greves[1]
The silver dropes, hanging on the leves.
And Arcite, that is in the court royal
With Theseus, his squyer principal,
Is risen, and loketh on the myrie day.
And, for to doon his observaunce to May,
Remembring on the poynt of his desyr,
He on a courser, sterting as the fyr,
Is riden in-to the feeldes, him to pleye,
Out of the court, were it a myle or tweye;
And to the grove, of which that I yow tolde,
By aventure, his wey he gan to holde,
To maken him a gerland of the greves,
Were it of wodebinde or hawethorn-leves,
And loude he song ageyn the sonne shene:
"May, with alle thy floures and thy grene,
Wel-come be thou, faire fresshe May,

[1] Groves.

I hope that I som grene gete may."
And from his courser, with a lusty herte,
In-to the grove ful hastily he sterte,
And in a path he rometh up and doun,
Ther-as, by aventure, this Palamoun
Was in a bush, that no man mighte him see,
For sore afered of his deeth was he.
No-thing ne knew he that it was Arcite:
God wot he wolde have trowed it ful lyte.
But sooth is seyd, gon sithen many yeres,
That "feeld hath eyen, and the wode hath eres."
It is ful fair a man to bere him evene,
For al-day meteth men at unset stevene.
Ful litel woot Arcite of his felawe,
That was so ny to herknen al his sawe,
For in the bush he sitteth now ful stille.
  Whan that Arcite had romed al his fille,
And songen al the roundel lustily,
In-to a studie he fil sodeynly,
As doon thise loveres in hir queynte geres,
Now in the croppe, now doun in the breres,
Now up, now doun, as boket in a welle.
Right as the Friday, soothly for to telle,
Now it shyneth, now it reyneth faste,
Right so can gery Venus overcaste
The hertes of hir folk; right as hir day
Is gerful, right so chaungeth she array.
Selde is the Friday al the wyke y-lyke.
  Whan that Arcite had songe, he gan to syke,
And sette him doun with-outen any more:
"Alas!" quod he, "that day that I was bore!
How longe, Juno, thurgh thy crueltee,
Woltow werreyen Thebes the citee?
Allas! y-broght is to confusioun
The blood royal of Cadme and Amphioun;
Of Cadmus, which that was the firste man
That Thebes bulte, or first the toun bigan,
And of the citee first was crouned king,
Of his linage am I, and his of-spring
By verray ligne, as of the stok royal:
And now I am so caitif and so thral,
That he, that is my mortal enemy,
I serve him as his squyer povrely.
And yet doth Juno me wel more shame,
For I dar noght biknowe myn owne name;
But ther-as I was wont to highte Arcite,
Now highte I Philostrate, noght worth a myte.
Allas! thou felle Mars, allas! Juno,
Thus hath your ire our kinrede al fordo,
Save only me, and wrecched Palamoun,
That Theseus martyreth in prisoun.
And over al this, to sleen me utterly,
Love hath his fyry dart so brenningly
Y-stiked thurgh my trewe careful herte,
That shapen was my deeth erst than my sherte.
Ye sleen me with your eyen, Emelye;
Ye been the cause wherfor that I dye.
Of al the remenant of myn other care
Ne sette I nat the mountaunce of a tare,
So that I coude don aught to your plesaunce!"
And with that word he fil doun in a traunce
A longe tyme; and after he up-sterte.

I hope to pluck some garland green today."
And from his courser, with a lusty heart,
Into the grove right hastily did start,
And on a path he wandered up and down,
Near which, and as it chanced, this Palamon
Lay in the thicket, where no man might see,
For sore afraid of finding death was he.
He knew not that Arcita was so near:
God knows he would have doubted eye and ear,
But it has been a truth these many years
That "Fields have eyes and every wood has ears."
It's well for one to bear himself with poise;
For every day unlooked-for chance annoys.
And little knew Arcita of his friend,
Who was so near and heard him to the end,
Where in the bush he sat now, keeping still.
  Arcita, having roamed and roved his fill,
And having sung his rondel, lustily,
Into a study fell he, suddenly,
As do these lovers in their strange desires,
Now in the trees, now down among the briers,
Now up, now down, like bucket in a well.
Even as on a Friday, truth to tell,
The sun shines now, and now the rain comes fast,
Even so can fickle Venus overcast
The spirits of her people; as her day
Is changeful, so she changes her array.
Seldom is Friday quite like all the week.
  Arcita, having sung, began to speak,
And sat him down, sighing like one forlorn.
"Alas," said he, "the day that I was born!
How long, O Juno, of thy cruelty,
Wilt thou wage bitter war on Thebes city?
Alas! Confounded beyond all reason
The blood of Cadmus and of Amphion;
Of royal Cadmus, who was the first man
To build at Thebes, and first the town began,
And first of all the city to be king;
Of his lineage am I, and his offspring,
By true descent, and of the stock royal:
And now I'm such a wretched serving thrall,
That he who is my mortal enemy,
I serve him as his squire, and all humbly.
And even more does Juno give me shame,
For I dare not acknowledge my own name;
But whereas I was Arcita by right,
Now I'm Philostrates, not worth a mite.
Alas, thou cruel Mars! Alas, Juno!
Thus have your angers all our kin brought low,
Save only me, and wretched Palamon,
Whom Theseüs martyrs yonder in prison.
And above all, to slay me utterly,
Love has his fiery dart so burningly
Struck through my faithful and care-laden heart,
My death was patterned ere my swaddling-shirt.
You slay me with your two eyes, Emily;
You are the cause for which I now must die.
For on the whole of all my other care
I would not set the value of a tare,
So I could do one thing to your pleasance!"
And with that word he fell down in a trance
That lasted long; and then he did up-start.

This Palamon, who thought that through his heart
He felt a cold and sudden sword blade glide,
For rage he shook, no longer would he hide.
But after he had heard Arcita's tale,
As he were mad, with face gone deathly pale,
He started up and sprang out of the thicket,
Crying: "Arcita, oh you traitor wicked,
Now are you caught, that crave my lady so,
For whom I suffer all this pain and woe,
And are my blood, and know my secrets' store,
As I have often told you heretofore,
And have befooled the great Duke Theseus,
And falsely changed your name and station thus:
Either I shall be dead or you shall die.
You shall not love my lady Emily,
But I will love her, and none other, no;
For I am Palamon, your mortal foe.
And though I have no weapon in this place,
Being but out of prison by God's grace,
I say again, that either you shall die
Or else forgo your love for Emily.
Choose which you will, for you shall not depart."
This Arcita, with scornful, angry heart,
When he knew him and all the tale had heard,
Fierce as a lion, out he pulled a sword,
And answered thus: "By God that sits above!
Were it not you are sick and mad for love,
And that you have no weapon in this place,
Out of this grove you'd never move a pace,
But meet your death right now, and at my hand.
For I renounce the bond and its demand
Which you assert that I have made with you.
What, arrant fool, love's free to choose and do,
And I will have her, spite of all your might!
But in as much as you're a worthy knight
And willing to defend your love, in mail,
Hear now this word: tomorrow I'll not fail
(Without the cognizance of any wight)
To come here armed and harnessed as a knight,
And to bring arms for you, too, as you'll see;
And choose the better and leave the worse for me.
And meat and drink this very night I'll bring,
Enough for you, and clothes for your bedding.
And if it be that you my lady win
And slay me in this wood that now I'm in,
Then may you have your lady, for all of me."
This Palamon replied: "I do agree."
And thus they parted till the morrow morn,
When each had pledged his honour to return.
O Cupido, that know'st not charity!
O despot, that no peer will have with thee!
Truly, 'tis said, that love, like all lordship,
Declines, with little thanks, a partnership.
Well learned they that, Arcite and Palamon.
Arcita rode into the town anon,
And on the morrow, ere the dawn, he bore,
Secretly, arms and armour out of store,
Enough for each, and proper to maintain
A battle in the field between the twain.
So on his horse, alone as he was born,
He carried out that harness as he'd sworn;

This Palamoun, that thoughte that thurgh his herte
He felte a cold swerd sodeynliche glyde,
For ire he quook, no lenger wolde he byde.
And whan that he had herd Arcites tale,
As he were wood, with face deed and pale,
He sterte him up out of the buskes thikke,
And seyde: "Arcite, false traitour wikke,
Now artow hent, that lovest my lady so,
For whom that I have al this peyne and wo,
And art my blood, and to my counseil sworn,
As I ful ofte have told thee heer-biforn,
And hast by-japed here duk Theseus,
And falsly chaunged hast thy name thus;
I wol be deed, or elles thou shalt dye.
Thou shalt nat love my lady Emelye,
But I wol love hir only, and namo;
For I am Palamoun, thy mortal fo.
And though that I no wepne have in this place,
But out of prison am astert by grace,
I drede noght that outher thou shalt dye,
Or thou ne shalt nat loven Emelye.
Chees which thou wilt, for thou shalt nat asterte."
This Arcitë, with ful despitous herte,
Whan he him knew, and hadde his tale herd,
As fiers as leoun, pulled out a swerd,
And seyde thus: "by God that sit above,
Nere it that thou art sik, and wood for love,
And eek that thou no wepne hast in this place,
Thou sholdest never out of this grove pace,
That thou ne sholdest dyen of myn hond.
For I defye the seurtee and the bond
Which that thou seyst that I have maad to thee.
What, verray fool, think wel that love is free,
And I wol love hir, maugre al thy might!
But, for as muche thou art a worthy knight,
And wilnest to darreyne hir by batayle,
Have heer my trouthe, to-morwe I wol nat fayle,
With-outen witing of any other wight,
That here I wol be founden as a knight,
And bringen harneys right y-nough for thee;
And chees the beste, and leve the worste for me.
And mete and drinke this night wol I bringe
Y-nough for thee, and clothes for thy beddinge.
And, if so be that thou my lady winne,
And slee me in this wode ther I am inne,
Thou mayst wel have thy lady, as for me."
This Palamon answerde: "I graunte it thee."
And thus they been departed til a-morwe,
When ech of hem had leyd his feith to borwe.
O Cupide, out of alle charitee!
O regne, that wolt no felawe have with thee!
Ful sooth is seyd, that love ne lordshipe
Wol noght, his thankes, have no felaweshipe;
Wel finden that Arcite and Palamoun.
Arcite is riden anon un-to the toun,
And on the morwe, er it were dayes light,
Ful prively two harneys hath he dight,
Bothe suffisaunt and mete to darreyne
The bataille in the feeld bitwix hem tweyne.
And on his hors, allone as he was born,
He carieth al this harneys him biforn;

And in the grove, at tyme and place y-set,
This Arcite and this Palamon ben met.
Tho chaungen gan the colour in hir face;
Right as the hunter in the regne of Trace,
That stondeth at the gappe with a spere,
Whan hunted is the leoun or the bere,
And hereth him come russhing in the greves,
And breketh bothe bowes and the leves,
And thinketh, "heer cometh my mortel enemy,
With-oute faile, he moot be deed, or I;
For outher I mot sleen him at the gappe,
Or he mot sleen me, if that me mishappe:"
So ferden they, in chaunging of hir hewe,
As fer as everich of hem other knewe.
Ther nas no good day, ne no saluing;
But streight, with-outen word or rehersing,
Everich of hem halp for to armen other,
As freendly as he were his owne brother;
And after that, with sharpe speres stronge
They foynen ech at other wonder longe.
Thou mightest wene that this Palamoun
In his fighting were a wood leoun,
And as a cruel tygre was Arcite:
As wilde bores gonne they to smyte,
That frothen whyte as foom for ire wood.
Up to the ancle foghte they in hir blood.
And in this wyse I lete hem fighting dwelle;
And forth I wol of Theseus yow telle
The destinee, ministre general,
That executeth in the world over-al
The purveyaunce, that God hath seyn biforn,
So strong it is, that, though the world had sworn
The contrarie of a thing, by ye or nay,
Yet somtyme it shal fallen on a day
That falleth nat eft with-inne a thousand yere.
For certeinly, our appetytes here,
Be it of werre, or pees, or hate, or love,
Al is this reuled by the sighte above.
This mene I now by mighty Theseus,
That for to honten is so desirous,
And namely at the grete hert in May,
That in his bed ther daweth him no day,
That he nis clad, and redy for to ryde
With hunte and horn, and houndes him bisyde.
For in his hunting hath he swich delyt,
That it is al his joye and appetyt
To been him-self the grete hertes bane:
For after Mars he serveth now Diane.
Cleer was the day, as I have told er this,
And Theseus, with alle joye and blis,
With his Ipolita, the fayre quene,
And Emelye, clothed al in grene,
On hunting be they riden royally.
And to the grove, that stood ful faste by,
In which ther was an hert, as men him tolde,
Duk Theseus the streighte wey hath holde.
And to the launde he rydeth him ful right,
For thider was the hert wont have his flight,
And over a brook, and so forth on his weye.
This duk wol han a cours at him, or tweye,
With houndes, swiche as that him list comaunde.

And in the grove, at time and place they'd set,
Arcita and this Palamon were met.
Each of the two changed colour in the face.
For as the hunter in the realm of Thrace
Stands at the clearing with his ready spear,
When hunted is the lion, or the bear,
And through the forest hears him rushing fast,
Breaking the boughs and leaves, and thinks aghast,
"Here comes apace my mortal enemy!
Now, without fail, he must be slain, or I;
For either I must kill him ere he pass,
Or he will make of me a dead carcass"—
So fared these men, in altering their hue,
So far as each the strength of other knew.
There was no "good-day" given, no saluting,
But without word, rehearsal, or such thing,
Each of them helping, so they armed each other
As dutifully as he were his own brother;
And afterward, with their sharp spears and strong,
They thrust each at the other wondrous long.
You might have fancied that this Palamon,
In battle, was a furious, mad lion,
And that Arcita was a tiger quite:
Like very boars the two began to smite,
Like boars that froth for anger in the wood.
Up to the ankles fought they in their blood.
And leaving them thus fighting fast and fell,
Forthwith of Theseüs I now will tell.
Great destiny, minister-general,
That executes in this world, and for all,
The needs that God foresaw ere we were born,
So strong it is that, though the world had sworn
The contrary of a thing, by yea or nay,
Yet sometime it shall fall upon a day,
Though not again within a thousand years.
For certainly our wishes and our fears,
Whether of war or peace, or hate or love,
All, all are ruled by that Foresight above.
This show I now by mighty Theseüs,
Who to go hunting is so desirous,
And specially of the hart of ten, in May,
That, in his bed, there dawns for him no day
That he's not clothed and soon prepared to ride
With hound and horn and huntsman at his side.
For in his hunting has he such delight,
That it is all his joy and appetite
To be himself the great hart's deadly bane:
For after Mars, he serves Diana's reign.
Clear was the day, as I have told ere this,
When Theseüs, compact of joy and bliss,
With his Hippolyta, the lovely queen,
And fair Emilia, clothed all in green,
A-hunting they went riding royally.
And to the grove of trees that grew hard by,
In which there was a hart, as men had told,
Duke Theseüs the shortest way did hold.
And to the glade he rode on, straight and right,
For there the hart was wont to go in flight,
And over a brook, and so forth on his way.
This duke would have a course at him today,
With such hounds as it pleased him to command.

And when this duke was come upon that land,
Under the slanting sun he looked, anon,
And there saw Arcita and Palamon,
Who furiously fought, as two boars do;
The bright swords went in circles to and fro
So terribly, that even their least stroke
Seemed powerful enough to fell an oak;
But who the two were, nothing did he note.
This duke his courser with the sharp spurs smote,
And in one bound he was between the two,
And lugged his great sword out, and cried out: "Ho!
No more, I say, on pain of losing head!
By mighty Mars, that one shall soon be dead
Who smites another stroke that I may see!
But tell me now what manner of men ye be
That are so hardy as to fight out here
Without a judge or other officer,
As if you rode in lists right royally?"
This Palamon replied, then, hastily,
Saying: "O Sire, what need for more ado?
We have deserved our death at hands of you.
Two woeful wretches are we, two captives
That are encumbered by our own sad lives;
And as you are a righteous lord and judge,
Give us not either mercy or refuge,
But slay me first, for sacred charity;
But slay my fellow here, as well, with me.
Or slay him first; for though you learn it late,
This is your mortal foe, Arcita—wait!—
That from the land was banished, on his head.
And for the which he merits to be dead.
For this is he who came unto your gate,
Calling himself Philostrates—nay, wait!—
Thus has he fooled you well this many a year,
And you have made him your chief squire, I hear:
And this is he that loves fair Emily.
For since the day is come when I must die,
I make confession plainly and say on,
That I am that same woeful Palamon
Who has your prison broken, viciously.
I am your mortal foe, and it is I
Who love so hotly Emily the bright
That I'll die gladly here within her sight.
Therefore do I ask death as penalty;
But slay my fellow with the same mercy,
For both of us deserve but to be slain."
This worthy duke presently spoke again,
Saying: "This judgment needs but a short session:
Your own mouth, aye, and by your own confession,
Has doomed and damned you, as I shall record.
There is no need for torture, on my word.
But you shall die, by mighty Mars the red!"
But then the queen, whose heart for pity bled,
Began to weep, and so did Emily
And all the ladies in the company.
Great pity must it be, so thought they all,
That ever such misfortune should befall:
For these were gentlemen, of great estate,
And for no thing, save love, was their debate.
They saw their bloody wounds, so sore and wide,
And all cried out—greater and less, they cried:
"Have mercy, lord, upon us women all!"

And whan this duk was come un-to the launde,
Under the sonne he loketh, and anon
He was war of Arcite and Palamon,
That foughten breme, as it were bores two;
The brighte swerdes wenten to and fro
So hidously, that with the leeste strook
It seemed as it wolde felle an ook;
But what they were, no-thing he ne woot.
This duk his courser with his spores smoot,
And at a stert he was bitwix hem two,
And pulled out a swerd and cryed, "ho!
Namore, up peyne of lesing of your heed.
By mighty Mars, he shal anon be deed,
That smyteth any strook, that I may seen!
But telleth me what mister men ye been,
That been so hardy for to fighten here
With-outen juge or other officere,
As it were in a listes royally?"
This Palamon answerde hastily
And seyde: "sire, what nedeth wordes mo?
We have the deeth deserved bothe two.
Two woful wrecches been we, two caytyves,
That been encombred of our owne lyves;
And as thou art a rightful lord and juge,
Ne yeve us neither mercy ne refuge,
But slee me first, for seynte charitee;
But slee my felawe eek as wel as me.
Or slee him first; for, though thou knowe it lyte,
This is thy mortal fo, this is Arcite,
That fro thy lond is banished on his heed,
For which he hath deserved to be deed.
For this is he that cam un-to thy gate,
And seyde, that he highte Philostrate.
Thus hath he japed thee ful many a yeer,
And thou has maked him thy chief squyer:
And this is he that loveth Emelye.
For sith the day is come that I shal dye,
I make pleynly my confessioun,
That I am thilke woful Palamoun,
That hath thy prison broken wikkedly.
I am thy mortal fo, and it am I
That loveth so hote Emelye the brighte,
That I wol dye present in hir sighte
Therfore I axe deeth and my juwyse;
But slee my felawe in the same wyse,
For bothe han we deserved to be slayn."
This worthy duk answerde anon agayn,
And seyde, "This is a short conclusioun:
Youre owne mouth, by your confessioun,
Hath dampned you, and I wol it recorde,
It nedeth noght to pyne yow with the corde.
Ye shul be deed, by mighty Mars the rede!"
The quene anon, for verray wommanhede,
Gan for to wepe, and so dide Emelye,
And alle the ladies in the companye.
Gret pitee was it, as it thoughte hem alle,
That ever swich a chaunce sholde falle;
For gentil men they were, of greet estat,
And no-thing but for love was this debat;
And sawe hir blody woundes wyde and sore;
And alle cryden, bothe lasse and more,
"Have mercy, lord, up-on us wommen alle!"

And on hir bare knees adoun they falle,
And wolde have kist his feet ther-as he
stood,
Til at the laste aslaked was his mood;
For pitee renneth sone in gentil herte.
And though he first for ire quook and sterte,
He hath considered shortly, in a clause,
The trespas of hem bothe, and eek the cause:
And al-though that his ire hir gilt accused,
Yet in his reson he hem bothe excused;
As thus: he thoghte wel, that every man
Wol helpe him-self in love, if that he can,
And eek delivere him-self out of prisoun;
And eek his herte had compassioun
Of wommen, for they wepen ever in oon;
And in his gentil herte he thoghte anoon,
And softe un-to himself he seyde: "fy
Up-on a lord that wol have no mercy,
But been a leoun, bothe in word and dede,
To hem that been in repentaunce and drede
As wel as to a proud despitous man
That wol maynteyne that he first bigan!
That lord hath litel of discrecioun,
That in swich cas can no divisioun,
But weyeth pryde and humblesse after oon."
And shortly, whan his ire is thus agoon,
He gan to loken up with eyen lighte,
And spak thise same wordes al on highte:—
"The god of love, a! *benedicite*,
How mighty and how greet a lord is he!
Ayeins his might ther gayneth none obstacles,
He may be cleped a god for his miracles;
For he can maken at his owne gyse
Of everich herte, as that him list devyse.
Lo heer, this Arcite and this Palamoun,
That quitly weren out of my prisoun,
And mighte han lived in Thebes royally,
And witen I am hir mortal enemy,
And that hir deeth lyth in my might also;
And yet hath love, maugree hir eyen two,
Y-broght hem hider bothe for to dye!
Now loketh, is nat that an heigh folye?
Who may been a fool, but-if he love?
Bihold, for Goddes sake that sit above,
Se how they blede! be they noght wel arrayed?
Thus hath hir lord, the god of love, y-payed
Hir wages and hir fees for hir servyse!
And yet they wenen for to been ful wyse
That serven love, for aught that may bifalle!
But this is yet the beste game of alle,
That she, for whom they han this jolitee,
Can hem ther-for as muche thank as me;
She woot namore of al this hote fare,
By God, than woot a cokkow or an hare!
But al mot been assayed, hoot and cold;
A man mot been a fool, or yong or old;
I woot it by my-self ful yore agoon:
For in my tyme a servant was I oon.
And therfore, sin I knowe of loves peyne,
And woot how sore it can a man distreyne,
As he that hath ben caught ofte in his las,
I yow foryeve al hoolly this trespas,

And down upon their bare knees did they fall,
And would have kissed his feet there where he
stood,
Till at the last assuaged was his high mood;
For soon will pity flow through gentle heart.
And though he first for ire did shake and start,
He soon considered, to state the case in brief,
What cause they had for fighting, what for grief;
And though his anger still their guilt accused,
Yet in his reason he held them both excused;
In such wise: he thought well that every man
Will help himself in love, if he but can,
And will himself deliver from prison;
And, too, at heart he had compassion on
Those women, for they cried and wept as one;
And in his gentle heart he thought anon,
And softly to himself he said then: "Fie
Upon a lord that will have no mercy,
But acts the lion, both in word and deed,
To those repentant and in fear and need,
As well as to the proud and pitiless man
That still would do the thing that he began!
That lord must surely in discretion lack
Who, in such case, can no distinction make,
But weighs both proud and humble in one scale."
And shortly, when his ire was thus grown pale,
He looked up to the sky, with eyes alight,
And spoke these words, as he would promise plight:
"The god of love, ah *benedicite!*
How mighty and how great a lord is he!
Against his might may stand no obstacles,
A true god is he by his miracles;
For he can manage, in his own sweet wise,
The heart of anyone as he devise.
Lo, here, Arcita and this Palamon,
That were delivered out of my prison,
And might have lived in Thebes right royally,
Knowing me for their mortal enemy,
And also that their lives lay in my hand;
And yet their love has wiled them to this land,
Against all sense, and brought them here to die!
Look you now, is not that a folly high?
Who can be called a fool, except he love?
And see, for sake of God who sits above,
See how they bleed! Are they not well arrayed?
Thus has their lord, the god of love, repaid
Their wages and their fees for their service!
And yet they are supposed to be full wise
Who serve love well, whatever may befall!
But this is yet the best jest of them all,
That she for whom they have this jollity
Can thank them for it quite as much as me;
She knows no more of all this fervent fare,
By God! than knows a cuckoo or a hare.
But all must be essayed, both hot and cold,
A man must play the fool, when young or old;
I know it of myself from years long gone:
For of love's servants I've been numbered one.
And therefore, since I know well all love's pain,
And know how sorely it can man constrain,
As one that has been taken in the net,
I will forgive your trespass, and forget,

At instance of my sweet queen, kneeling here,
Aye, and of Emily, my sister dear.
And you shall presently consent to swear
That nevermore will you my power dare,
Nor wage war on me, either night or day,
But will be friends to me in all you may;
I do forgive this trespass, full and fair."
And then they swore what he demanded there,
And, of his might, they of his mercy prayed,
And he extended grace, and thus he said:
"To speak for royalty's inheritress,
Although she be a queen or a princess,
Each of you both is worthy, I confess,
When comes the time to wed: but nonetheless,
I speak now of my sister Emily,
The cause of all this strife and jealousy—
You know yourselves she may not marry two,
At once, although you fight or what you do:
One of you, then, and be he loath or lief,
Must pipe his sorrows in an ivy leaf.
That is to say, she cannot have you both,
However jealous one may be, or wroth.
Therefore I put you both in this decree,
That each of you shall learn his destiny
As it is cast; and hear, now, in what wise
The word of fate shall speak through my device.
"My will is this, to draw conclusion flat,
Without reply, or plea, or caveat
(In any case, accept it for the best),
That each of you shall follow his own quest,
Free of all ransom or of fear from me;
And this day, fifty weeks hence, both shall be
Here once again, each with a hundred knights,
Armed for the lists, who stoutly for your rights
Will ready be to battle, to maintain
Your claim to love. I promise you, again,
Upon my word, and as I am a knight,
That whichsoever of you wins the fight,
That is to say, whichever of you two
May with his hundred, whom I spoke of, do
His foe to death, or out of boundary drive,
Then he shall have Emilia to wive
To whom Fortuna gives so fair a grace.
The lists shall be erected in this place.
And God so truly on my soul have ruth
As I shall prove an honest judge, in truth.
You shall no other judgment in me waken
Than that the one shall die or else be taken.
And if you think the sentence is well said,
Speak your opinion, that you're well repaid.
This is the end, and I conclude hereon."
Who looks up lightly now but Palamon?
Who leaps for you but Arcita the knight?
And who could tell, or who could ever write
The jubilation made within that place
Where Theseüs has shown so fair a grace?
But down on knee went each one for delight
And thanked him there with all his heart and
might,
And specially those Thebans did their part.
And thus, with high hopes, being blithe of
heart,

At requeste of the quene that kneleth here,
And eek of Emelye, my suster dere.
And ye shul bothe anon un-to me swere,
That never-mo ye shul my contree dere,
Ne make werre up-on me night ne day,
But been my freendes in al that ye may;
I yow foryeve this trespas every del."
And they him swore his axing fayre and wel,
And him of lordshipe and of mercy preyde,
And he hem graunteth grace, and thus he seyde:
"To speke of royal linage and richesse,
Though that she were a quene or a princesse,
Ech of yow bothe is worthy, doutelees,
To wedden whan tyme is, but nathelees
I speke as for my suster Emelye,
For whom ye have this stryf and jelousye;
Ye woot your-self, she may not wedden two
At ones, though ye fighten ever-mo:
That oon of yow, al be him looth or leef,
He moot go pypen in an ivy-leef;
This is to seyn, she may nat now han bothe,
Al be ye never so jelous, ne so wrothe.
And for-thy I yow putte in this degree,
That ech of yow shal have his destinee
As him is shape; and herkneth in what wyse;
Lo, heer your ende of that I shal devyse.
My wil is this, for plat conclusioun,
With-outen any replicacioun,
If that yow lyketh, tak it for the beste,
That everich of yow shal gon wher him leste
Frely, with-outen raunson or daunger;
And this day fifty wykes, fer ne ner,
Everich of yow shal bringe an hundred knightes,
Armed for listes up at alle rightes,
Al redy to darreyne hir by bataille.
And this bihote I yow, with-outen faille,
Up-on my trouthe, and as I am a knight,
That whether of yow bothe that hath might,
This is to seyn, that whether he or thou
May with his hundred, as I spak of now,
Sleen his contrarie, or out of listes dryve,
Him shal I yeve Emelya to wyve,
To whom that fortune yeveth so fair a grace.
The listes shal I maken in this place,
And God so wisly on my soule rewe,
As I shal even juge been and trewe.
Ye shul non other ende with me maken,
That oon of yow ne shal be deed or taken.
And if yow thinketh this is wel y-sayd,
Seyeth your avys, and holdeth yow apayd.
This is your ende and your conclusioun."
Who loketh lightly now but Palamoun?
Who springeth up for joye but Arcite?
Who couthe telle, or who couthe it endyte,
The joye that is maked in the place
Whan Theseus hath doon so fair a grace?
But doun on knees wente every maner wight,
And thanked him with al her herte and
might,
And namely the Thebans ofte sythe.
And thus with good hope and with herte
blythe

They take hir leve, and hom-ward gonne they ryde
To Thebes, with his olde walles wyde.

They took their leave; and homeward did they ride
To Thebes that sits within her old walls wide.

HERE ENDETH THE SECOND PART

HERE FOLLOWETH THE THIRD PART

I trowe men wolde deme it necligence,
If I foryete to tellen the dispence
Of Theseus, that goth so bisily
To maken up the listes royally;
That swich a noble theatre as it was,
I dar wel seyn that in this world ther nas.
The circuit a myle was aboute,
Walled of stoon, and diched al with-oute.
Round was the shap, in maner of compas,
Ful of degrees, the heighte of sixty pas,
That, whan a man was set on o degree,
He letted nat his felawe for to see.
Est-ward ther stood a gate of marbel whyt,
West-ward, right swich another in the opposit.
And shortly to concluden, swich a place
Was noon in erthe, as in so litel space;
For in the lond ther nas no crafty man,
That geometrie or ars-metrik can,
Ne purtreyour, ne kerver of images,
That Theseus ne yaf him mete and wages
The theatre for to maken and devyse.
And for to doon his ryte and sacrifyse,
He est-ward hath, up-on the gate above,
In worship of Venus, goddesse of love,
Don make an auter and an oratorie;
And west-ward, in the minde and in memorie
Of Mars, he maked hath right swich another,
That coste largely of gold a fother.
And north-ward, in a touret on the wal,
Of alabastre whyt and reed coral
An oratorie riche for to see,
In worship of Dyane of chastitee,
Hath Theseus don wrought in noble wyse.
But yet hadde I foryeten to devyse
The noble kerving, and the portreitures,
The shap, the countenaunce, and the figures,
That weren in thise oratories three.
First in the temple of Venus maystow see
Wroght on the wal, ful pitous to biholde,
The broken slepes, and the sykes colde;
The sacred teres, and the waymenting;
The fyry strokes of the desiring,
That loves servaunts in this lyf enduren;
The othes, that hir covenants assuren;
Plesaunce and hope, desyr, fool-hardinesse,
Beautee and youthe, bauderie, richesse,
Charmes and force, lesinges, flaterye,
Dispense, bisynesse, and jelousye,
That wered of yelwe goldes a gerland,
And a cokkow sitting on hir hand;
Festes, instruments, caroles, daunces,
Lust and array, and alle the circumstaunces
Of love, whiche that I rekne and rekne shal,
By ordre weren peynted on the wal,
And mo than I can make of mencioun.
For soothly, al the mount of Citheroun,

I think that men would deem it negligence
If I forgot to tell of the expense
Of Theseüs, who went so busily
To work upon the lists, right royally;
For such an amphitheatre he made,
Its equal never yet on earth was laid.
The circuit, rising, hemmed a mile about,
Walled all of stone and moated deep without.
Round was the shape as compass ever traces,
And built in tiers, the height of sixty paces,
That those who sat in one tier, or degree,
Should hinder not the folk behind to see.
Eastward there stood a gate of marble white,
And westward such another, opposite.
In brief, no place on earth, and so sublime,
Was ever made in so small space of time;
For in the land there was no craftsman quick
At plane geometry or arithmetic,
No painter and no sculptor of hard stone,
But Theseüs pressed meat and wage upon
To build that amphitheatre and devise.
And to observe all rites and sacrifice,
Over the eastern gate, and high above,
For worship of Queen Venus, god of love,
He built an altar and an oratory;
And westward, being mindful of the glory
Of Mars, he straightway builded such another
As cost a deal of gold and many a bother.
And northward, in a turret on the wall,
Of alabaster white and red coral,
An oratory splendid as could be,
In honour of Diana's chastity,
Duke Theseüs wrought out in noble wise.
But yet have I forgot to advertise
The noble carvings and the portraitures,
The shapes, the countenances, the figures
That all were in these oratories three.
First, in the fane of Venus, one might see,
Wrought on the wall, and piteous to behold,
The broken slumbers and the sighing cold,
The sacred tears and the lamenting dire,
The fiery throbbing of the strong desire,
That all love's servants in this life endure;
The vows that all their promises assure;
Pleasure and hope, desire, foolhardiness,
Beauty, youth, bawdiness, and riches, yes,
Charms, and all force, and lies, and flattery,
Expense, and labour; aye, and Jealousy
That wore of marigolds a great garland
And had a cuckoo sitting on her hand;
Carols and instruments and feasts and dances,
Lust and array, and all the circumstances
Of love that I may reckon or ever shall,
In order they were painted on the wall,
Aye, and more, too, than I have ever known.
For truly, all the Mount of Citheron,

Where Venus has her chief and favoured dwelling,
Was painted on that wall, beyond my telling,
With all the gardens in their loveliness.
Nor was forgot the gate-guard Idleness,
Nor fair Narcissus of the years long gone,
Nor yet the folly of King Solomon,
No, nor the giant strength of Hercules,
Nor Circe's and Medea's sorceries,
Nor Turnus with his hardy, fierce courage,
Nor the rich Croesus, captive in his age.
Thus may be seen that wisdom, nor largess,
Beauty, nor skill, nor strength, nor hardiness,
May with Queen Venus share authority;
For as she wills, so must the whole world be.
Lo, all these folk were so caught in her snare
They cried aloud in sorrow and in care.
Here let suffice examples one or two,
Though I might give a thousand more to you.
  The form of Venus, glorious as could be,
Was naked, floating on the open sea,
And from the navel down all covered was
With green waves, bright as ever any glass.
A citole in her small right hand had she,
And on her head, and beautiful to see,
A garland of red roses, sweet smelling;
Above her swirled her white doves, fluttering.
Before her stood her one son, Cupido,
Whose two white wings upon his shoulders grow;
And blind he was, as it is often seen;
A bow he bore, and arrows bright and keen.
  Why should I not as well, now, tell you all
The portraiture that was upon the wall
Within the fane of mighty Mars the red?
In length and breadth the whole wall was painted
Like the interior of that grisly place,
The mighty temple of great Mars in Thrace,
In that same cold and frosty region where
Mars to his supreme mansion may repair.
  First, on the wall was limned a vast forest
Wherein there dwelt no man nor any beast,
With knotted, gnarled, and leafless trees, so old
The sharpened stumps were dreadful to behold;
Through which there ran a rumbling, even now,
As if a storm were breaking every bough;
And down a hill, beneath a sharp descent,
The temple stood of Mars armipotent,
Wrought all of burnished steel, whereof the gate
Was grim like death to see, and long, and strait.
And therefrom raged a wind that seemed to shake
The very ground, and made the great doors quake.
The northern light in at those same doors shone,
For window in that massive wall was none
Through which a man might any light discern.
The doors were all of adamant eterne,
Rivetted on both sides, and all along,
With toughest iron; and to make it strong,
Each pillar that sustained this temple grim
Was thick as tun, of iron bright and trim.
  There saw I first the dark imagining
Of felony, and all the compassing;
And cruel anger, red as burning coal;
Pickpurses, and the dread that eats the soul;

Ther Venus hath hir principal dwelling,
Was shewed on the wal in portreying,
With al the gardin, and the lustinesse.
Nat was foryeten the porter Ydelnesse,
Ne Narcisus the faire of yore agon,
Ne yet the folye of king Salamon,
Ne yet the grete strengthe of Hercules—
Th'enchauntements of Medea and Circes—
Ne of Turnus, with the hardy fiers corage,
The riche Cresus, caytif in servage.
Thus may ye seen that wisdom ne richesse,
Beautee ne sleighte, strengthe, ne hardinesse,
Ne may with Venus holde champartye;
For as hir list the world than may she gye.
Lo, alle thise folk so caught were in hir las,
Til they for wo ful ofte seyde "allas!"
Suffyceth heer ensamples oon or two,
And though I coude rekne a thousand mo.
  The statue of Venus, glorious for to see,
Was naked fleting in the large see,
And fro the navele doun all covered was
With wawes grene, and brighte as any glas.
A citole in hir right hand hadde she,
And on hir heed, ful semely for to see,
A rose gerland, fresh and wel smellinge;
Above hir heed hir dowves flikeringe.
Biforn hir stood hir sone Cupido,
Up-on his shuldres winges hadde he two;
And blind he was, as it is ofte sene;
A bowe he bar and arwes brighte and kene.
  Why sholde I noght as wel eek telle yow al
The portreiture, that was up-on the wal
With-inne the temple of mighty Mars the rede?
Al peynted was the wal, in lengthe and brede,
Lyk to the estres of the grisly place,
That highte the grete temple of Mars in Trace,
In thilke colde frosty regioun,
Ther-as Mars hath his sovereyn mansioun.
  First on the wal was peynted a foreste,
In which ther dwelleth neither man ne beste,
With knotty knarry bareyn treës olde
Of stubbes sharpe and hidous to biholde;
In which ther ran a rumbel and a swough,
As though a storm sholde bresten every bough:
And downward from an hille, under a bente,
Ther stood the temple of Mars armipotente,
Wroght al of burned steel, of which thentree
Was long and streit, and gastly for to see.
And ther-out cam a rage and such a vese,
That it made al the gates for to rese.
The northren light in at the dores shoon,
For windowe on the wal ne was ther noon,
Thurgh which men mighten any light discerne.
The dores were alle of adamant eterne,
Y-clenched overthwart and endelong
With iren tough; and, for to make it strong,
Every piler, the temple to sustene,
Was tonne-greet, of iren bright and shene.
  Ther saugh I first the derke imagining
Of felonye, and al the compassing;
The cruel ire, reed as any glede;
The pykepurs, and eek the pale drede;

The smyler with the knyf under the cloke;
The shepne brenning with the blake smoke;
The treson of the mordring in the bedde;
The open werre, with woundes al bi-bledde;
Contek, with blody knyf and sharp manace;
Al ful of chirking was that sory place.
The sleere of him-self yet saugh I ther,
His herte-blood hath bathed al his heer;
The nayl y-driven in the shode a-night;
The colde deeth, with mouth gaping upright.
Amiddes of the temple sat meschaunce,
With disconfort and sory contenaunce.
Yet saugh I woodnesse laughing in his rage;
Armed compleint, out-hees, and fiers outrage.
The careyne in the bush, with throte y-corve:
A thousand slayn, and nat of qualm y-storve;
The tiraunt, with the prey by force y-raft;
The toun destroyed, ther was no-thing laft.
Yet saugh I brent the shippes hoppesteres;
The hunte strangled with the wilde beres:
The sowe freten the child right in the cradel;
The cook y-scalded, for al his longe ladel.
Noght was foryeten by th'infortune of Marte;
The carter over-riden with his carte,
Under the wheel ful lowe he lay adoun.
Ther were also, of Martes divisioun,
The barbour, and the bocher, and the smith
That forgeth sharpe swerdes on his stith.
And al above, depeynted in a tour,
Saw I conquest sittinge in greet honour,
With the sharpe swerde over his heed
Hanginge by a sotil twynes threed.
Depeynted was the slaughtre of Julius,
Of grete Nero, and of Antonius;
Al be that thilke tyme they were unborn,
Yet was hir deeth depeynted ther-biforn,
By manasinge of Mars, right by figure;
So was it shewed in that portreiture
As is depeynted in the sterres above,
Who shal be slayn or elles deed for love.
Suffyceth oon ensample in stories olde,
I may not rekne hem alle, thogh I wolde.
The statue of Mars up-on a carte stood,
Armed, and loked grim as he were wood;
And over his heed ther shynen two figures
Of sterres, that been cleped in scriptures,
That oon Puella, that other Rubeus.
This god of armes was arrayed thus:—
A wolf ther stood biforn him at his feet
With eyen rede, and of a man he eet;
With sotil pencel was depeynt this storie,
In redoutinge of Mars and of his glorie.
Now to the temple of Diane the chaste
As shortly as I can I wol me haste,
To telle yow al the descripcioun.
Depeynted been the walles up and doun
Of hunting and of shamfast chastitee.
Ther saugh I how woful Calistopee,
Whan that Diane agreved was with here,
Was turned from a womman til a bere,
And after was she maad the lode-sterre;

The smiling villain, hiding knife in cloak;
The farm barns burning, and the thick black smoke;
The treachery of murder done in bed;
The open battle, with the wounds that bled;
Contest, with bloody knife and sharp menace;
And loud with creaking was that dismal place.
The slayer of himself, too, saw I there,
His very heart's blood matted in his hair;
The nail that's driven in the skull by night;
The cold plague-corpse, with gaping mouth upright.
In middle of the temple sat Mischance,
With gloomy, grimly woeful countenance.
And saw I Madness laughing in his rage;
Armed risings, and outcries, and fierce outrage;
The carrion in the bush, with throat wide carved;
A thousand slain, nor one by plague, nor starved.
The tyrant, with the spoils of violent theft;
The town destroyed, in ruins, nothing left.
And saw I burnt the ships that dance by phares;
The hunter strangled by the fierce wild bears;
The sow chewing the child right in the cradle;
The cook well scalded, spite of his long ladle.
Nothing was lacking of Mars' evil part:
The carter over-driven by his cart,
Under a wheel he lay low in the dust.
There were likewise in Mars' house, as needs must,
The surgeon, and the butcher, and the smith
Who forges sharp swords and great ills therewith.
And over all, depicted in a tower,
Sat Conquest, high in honour and in power,
Yet with a sharp sword hanging o'er his head
But by the tenuous twisting of a thread.
Depicted was the death of Julius,
Of Nero great, and of Antonius;
And though at that same time they were unborn,
There were their deaths depicted to adorn
The menacing of Mars, in likeness sure;
Things were so shown, in all that portraiture,
As are fore-shown among the stars above,
Who shall be slain in war or dead for love.
Suffice one instance from old plenitude,
I could not tell them all, even if I would.
Mars' image stood upon a chariot,
Armed, and so grim that mad he seemed, God wot;
And o'er his head two constellations shone
Of stars that have been named in writings known,
One being Puella, and one Rubeus.
This god of armies was companioned thus:
A wolf there was before him, at his feet,
Red-eyed, and of a dead man he did eat.
A cunning pencil there had limned this story
In reverence of Mars and of his glory.
Now to the temple of Diana chaste,
As briefly as I can, I'll pass in haste,
To lay before you its description well.
In pictures, up and down, the wall could tell
Of hunting and of modest chastity.
There saw I how Callisto fared when she
(Diana being much aggrieved with her)
Was changed from woman into a she-bear,
And after, made into the lone Pole Star;

There was it; I can't tell how such things are.
Her son, too, is a star, as men may see.
There saw I Daphne turned into a tree
(I do not mean Diana, no, but she,
Penëus daughter, who was called Daphne).
I saw Actaeon made a hart all rude
For punishment of seeing Diana nude;
I saw, too, how his fifty hounds had caught
And him were eating, since they knew him not.
And painted farther on, I saw before
How Atalanta hunted the wild boar;
And Meleager, and many another there,
For which Diana wrought him woe and care.
There saw I many another wondrous tale
From which I will not now draw memory's veil.
This goddess on an antlered hart was set,
With little hounds about her feet, and yet
Beneath her perfect feet there was a moon,
Waxing it was, but it should wane full soon.
In robes of yellowish green her statue was,
She'd bow in hand and arrows in a case.
Her eyes were downcast, looking at the ground,
Where Pluto in his dark realm may be found.
Before her was a woman travailing,
Who was so long in giving birth, poor thing,
That pitifully Lucina did she call,
Praying, "Oh help, for thou may'st best of all!"
Well could he paint, who had this picture wrought,
With many a florin he'd his colours bought,
  But now the lists were done, and Thesëus,
Who at so great cost had appointed thus
The temples and the circus, as I tell,
When all was done, he liked it wondrous well.
But hold I will from Thesëus, and on
To speak of Arcita and Palamon.
  The day of their return is forthcoming,
When each of them a hundred knights must bring
The combat to support, as I have told;
And into Athens, covenant to uphold,
Has each one ridden with his hundred knights,
Well armed for war, at all points, in their mights.
And certainly, 'twas thought by many a man
That never, since the day this world began,
Speaking of good knights hardy of their hands,
Wherever God created seas and lands,
Was, of so few, so noble company.
For every man that loved all chivalry,
And eager was to win surpassing fame,
Had prayed to play a part in that great game;
And all was well with him who chosen was.
For if there came tomorrow such a case,
You know right well that every lusty knight
Who loves the ladies fair and keeps his might,
Be it in England, aye or otherwhere,
Would wish of all things to be present there
To fight for some fair lady. *Ben'cite!*
'Twould be a pleasant goodly sight to see!
  And so it was with those with Palamon.
With him there rode of good knights many a one;
Some would be armoured in a habergeon
And in a breastplate, under light jupon;

Thus was it peynt, I can say yow no ferre;
Hir sone is eek a sterre, as men may see.
Ther saugh I Dane, y-turned til a tree,
I mene nat the goddesse Diane,
But Penneus doughter, which that highte Dane.
Ther saugh I Attheon an hert y-maked,
For vengeaunce that he saugh Diane al naked;
I saugh how that his houndes have him caught,
And freten him, for that they knewe him naught.
Yet peynted was a litel forther-moor,
How Atthalante hunted the wilde boor,
And Meleagre, and many another mo,
For which Diane wroghte him care and wo.
Ther saugh I many another wonder storie,
The whiche me list nat drawen to memorie.
This goddessee on an hert ful hye seet,
With smale houndes al aboute hir feet;
And undernethe hir feet she hadde a mone,
Wexing it was, and sholde wanie sone.
In gaude grene hir statue clothed was,
With bowe in honde, and arwes in a cas.
Hir eyen caste she ful lowe adoun,
Ther Pluto hath his derke regioun.
A womman travailinge was hir biforn,
But, for hir child so longe was unborn,
Ful pitously Lucyna gan she calle,
And seyde, "help, for thou mayst best of alle."
Wel couthe he peynten lyfly that it wroghte,
With many a florin he the hewes boghte.
  Now been thise listes maad, and Theseus,
That at his grete cost arrayed thus
The temples and the theatre every del,
Whan it was doon, him lyked wonder wel.
But stinte I wol of Theseus a lyte,
And speke of Palamon and of Arcite.
  The day approcheth of hir retourninge,
That everich sholde an hundred knightes bringe,
The bataille to darreyne, as I yow tolde;
And til Athénës, hir covenant for to holde,
Hath everich of hem broght an hundred knightes
Wel armed for the werre at alle rightes.
And sikerly, ther trowed many a man
That never, sithen that the world bigan,
As for to speke of knighthod of hir hond,
As fer as God hath maked see or lond,
Nas, of so fewe, so noble a companye.
For every wight that lovede chivalrye,
And wolde, his thankes, han a passant name,
Hath preyed that he mighte ben of that game;
And wel was him, that ther-to chosen was.
For if ther fille to-morwe swich a cas,
Ye knowen wel, that every lusty knight,
That loveth paramours, and hath his might,
Were it in Engelond, or elles-where,
They wolde, hir thankes, wilnen to be there.
To fighte for a lady, *ben'cite!*
It were a lusty sighte for to see.
  And right so ferden they with Palamon.
With him ther wenten knightes many oon;
Som wol ben armed in an habergeoun,
In a brest-plat and in a light gipoun;

And somme woln have a peyre plates large;
And somme woln have a Pruce sheld, or a targe;
Somme woln ben armed on hir legges weel,
And have an ax, and somme a mace of steel.
Ther nis no newe gyse, that it nas old.
Armed were they, as I have you told,
Everich after his opinioun.
  Ther maistow seen coming with Palamoun
Ligurge him-self, the grete king of Trace;
Blak was his berd, and manly was his face.
The cercles of his eyen in his heed,
They gloweden bitwixe yelow and reed.
And lyk a griffon loked he aboute,
With kempe heres on his browes stoute;
His limes grete, his braunes harde and stronge,
His shuldres brode, his armes rounde and longe.
And as the gyse was in his contree,
Ful hye up-on a char of gold stood he,
With foure whyte boles in the trays.
In-stede of cote-armure over his harnays,
With nayles yelwe and brighte as any gold,
He hadde a beres skin, col-blak, for-old.
His longe heer was kembd bihinde his bak,
As any ravenes fether it shoon for-blak:
A wrethe of gold arm-greet, of huge wighte,
Upon his heed, set ful of stones brighte,
Of fyne rubies and of dyamaunts.
Aboute his char ther wenten whyte alaunts,
Twenty and mo, as grete as any steer,
To hunten at the leoun or the deer,
And folwed him, with mosel faste y-bounde,
Colers of gold, and torets fyled rounde.
An hundred lordes hadde he in his route
Armed ful wel, with hertes sterne and stoute.
  With Arcita, in stories as men finde,
The grete Emetreus, the king of Inde,
Up-on a stede bay, trapped in steel,
Covered in cloth of gold diapred weel,
Cam ryding lyk the god of armes, Mars.
His cote-armure was of cloth of Tars,
Couched with perles whyte and rounde and grete.
His sadel was of brend gold newe y-bete;
A mantelet upon his shuldre hanginge
Bret-ful of rubies rede, as fyr sparklinge.
His crispe heer lyk ringes was y-ronne,
And that was yelow, and glitered as the sonne.
His nose was heigh, his eyen bright citryn,
His lippes rounde, his colour was sangwyn,
A fewe fraknes in his face y-spreynd,
Betwixen yelow and somdel blak y-meynd,
And as a leoun he his loking caste.
Of fyve and twenty yeer his age I caste.
His berd was wel bigonne for to springe;
His voys was as a trompe thunderinge.
Up-on his heed he wered of laurer grene
A gerland fresh and lusty for to sene.
Up-on his hand he bar, for his deduyt,
An egle tame, as eny lilie whyt.
An hundred lordes hadde he with him there,
Al armed, sauf hir heddes, in al hir gere,

And some wore breast- and back-plates thick and large;
And some would have a Prussian shield, or targe;
Some on their very legs were armoured well,
And carried axe, and some a mace of steel.
There is no new thing, now, that is not old.
And so they all were armed, as I have told,
To his own liking and design, each one.
  There might you see, riding with Palamon,
Lycurgus' self, the mighty king of Thrace;
Black was his beard and manly was his face.
The eyeballs in the sockets of his head,
They glowed between a yellow and a red.
And like a griffon glared he round about
From under bushy eyebrows thick and stout.
His limbs were large, his muscles hard and strong,
His shoulders broad, his arms both big and long,
And, as the fashion was in his country,
High in a chariot of gold stood he,
With four white bulls in traces, to progress.
Instead of coat-of-arms above harness,
With yellow claws preserved and bright as gold,
He wore a bear-skin, black and very old.
His long combed hair was hanging down his back,
As any raven's feather it was black:
A wreath of gold, arm-thick, of heavy weight,
Was on his head, and set with jewels great,
Of rubies fine and perfect diamonds.
About his car there circled huge white hounds,
Twenty or more, as large as any steer,
To hunt the lion or the antlered deer;
And so they followed him, with muzzles bound,
Wearing gold collars with smooth rings and round.
A hundred lords came riding in his rout,
All armed at point, with hearts both stern and stout.
  With Arcita, in tales men call to mind,
The great Emetrëus, a king of Ind,
Upon a bay steed harnessed all in steel,
Covered with cloth of gold, all diapered well,
Came riding like the god of arms, great Mars.
His coat-of-arms was cloth of the Tartars,
Begemmed with pearls, all white and round and great.
Of beaten gold his saddle, burnished late;
A mantle from his shoulders hung, the thing
Close-set with rubies red, like fire blazing.
His crisp hair all in bright ringlets was run,
Yellow as gold and gleaming as the sun.
His nose was high, his eyes a bright citrine,
His lips were full, his colouring sanguine,
And a few freckles on his face were seen,
None either black or yellow, but the mean;
And like a lion he his glances cast.
Not more than five-and twenty years he'd past.
His beard was well beginning, now, to spring;
His voice was as a trumpet thundering.
Upon his brows he wore, of laurel green,
A garland, fresh and pleasing to be seen.
Upon his wrist he bore, for his delight,
An eagle tame, as any lily white.
A hundred lords came riding with him there,
All armed, except their heads, in all their gear,

And wealthily appointed in all things,
For, trust me well, that dukes and earls and kings
Were gathered in this noble company
For love and for increase of chivalry.
About this king there ran, on every side,
Many tame lions and leopards in their pride.
And in such wise these mighty lords, in sum,
Were, of a Sunday, to the city come
About the prime, and in the town did light.
  This Theseüs, this duke, this noble knight,
When he'd conducted them to his city,
And quartered them, according to degree,
He feasted them, and was at so much pains
To give them ease and honour, of his gains,
That men yet hold that never human wit,
Of high or low estate, could better it.
The minstrelsy, the service at the feast,
The great gifts to the highest and the least,
The furnishings of Theseüs' rich palace,
Who highest sat or lowest on the dais,
What ladies fairest were or best dandling,
Or which of them could dance the best, or sing,
Or who could speak most feelingly of love,
Or what hawks sat upon the perch above,
Or what great hounds were lying on the floor—
Of all these I will make no mention more;
But tell my tale, for that, I think, is best;
Now comes the point, and listen if you've zest.
  That Sunday night, ere day began to spring,
When Palamon the earliest lark heard sing,
Although it lacked two hours of being day,
Yet the lark sang, and Palamon sang a lay.
With pious heart and with a high courage
He rose, to go upon a pilgrimage
Unto the blessed Cytherea's shrine
(I mean queen Venus, worthy and benign).
And at her hour he then walked forth apace
Out to the lists wherein her temple was,
And down he knelt in manner to revere,
And from a full heart spoke as you shall hear.
  "Fairest of fair, O lady mine, Venus,
Daughter of Jove and spouse to Vulcanus,
Thou gladdener of the Mount of Citheron,
By that great love thou borest to Adon,
Have pity on my bitter tears that smart
And hear my humble prayer within thy heart.
Alas! I have no words in which to tell
The effect of all the torments of my hell;
My heavy heart its evils can't bewray;
I'm so confused I can find naught to say.
But mercy, lady bright, that knowest well
My heart, and seëst all the ills I feel,
Consider and have ruth upon my sore
As truly as I shall, for evermore,
Well as I may, thy one true servant be,
And wage a war henceforth on chastity.
If thou wilt help, thus do I make my vow,
To boast of knightly skill I care not now,
Nor do I ask tomorrow's victory,
Nor any such renown, nor vain glory
Of prize of arms, blown before lord and churl,
But I would have possession of one girl,

Ful richely in alle maner things.
For trusteth wel, that dukes, erles, kinges,
Were gadered in this noble companye,
For love and for encrees of chivalrye.
Aboute this king ther ran on every part
Ful many a tame leoun and lepart.
And in this wyse thise lordes, alle and some,
Ben on the Sonday to the citee come
Aboute pryme, and in the toun alight.
  This Theseus, this duk, this worthy knight,
Whan he had broght hem in-to his citee,
And inned hem, everich in his degree,
He festeth hem, and dooth so greet labour
To esen hem, and doon hem al honour,
That yet men weneth that no mannes wit
Of noon estat ne coude amenden it.
The minstralcye, the service at the feste,
The grete yiftes to the moste and leste,
The riche array of Theseus paleys,
Ne who sat first ne last up-on the deys,
What ladies fairest been or best daunsinge,
Or which of hem can dauncen best and singe,
Ne who most felingly speketh of love:
What haukes sitten on the perche above,
What houndes liggen on the floor adoun:
Of al this make I now no mencioun;
But al the'effect, that thinketh me the beste;
Now comth the poynt, and herkneth if yow leste.
  The Sonday night, er day began to springe,
When Palamon the larke herde singe,
Although it nere nat day by houres two,
Yet song the larke, and Palamon also.
With holy herte, and with an heigh corage
He roos, to wenden on his pilgrimage
Un-to the blisful Citherea benigne,
I mene Venus, honurable and digne.
And in hir houre he walketh forth a pas
Un-to the listes, ther hir temple was,
And doun he kneleth, and with humble chere
And herte soor, he seyde as ye shul here.
  Faireste of faire, o lady myn, Venus,
Doughter to Jove and spouse of Vulcanus,
Thou glader of the mount of Citheroun,
For thilke love thou haddest to Adoun,
Have pitee of my bittre teres smerte,
And tak myn humble preyer at thyn herte.
Allas! I ne have no langage to telle
Th'effectes ne the torments of myn helle;
Myn herte may myne harmes nat biwreye;
I am so confus, that I can noght seye.
But mercy, lady bright, that knowest weel
My thought, and seest what harmes that I feel,
Considere al this, and rewe up-on my sore,
As wisly as I shal for evermore,
Emforth my might, thy trewe servant be,
And holden werre alwey with chastitee;
That make I myn avow, so ye me helpe.
I kepe noght of armes for to yelpe,
Ne I ne axe nat to-morwe to have victorie,
Ne renoun in this cas, ne veyne glorie
Of pris of armes blowen up and doun,
But I wolde have fully possessioun

Of Emelye, and dye in thy servyse;
Find thou the maner how, and in what wyse.
I reche nat, but it may bettre be,
To have victorie of hem, or they of me,
So that I have my lady in myne armes.
For though so be that Mars is god of armes,
Your vertu is so greet in hevene above,
That, if yow list, I shal wel have my love.
Thy temple wol I worshipe evermo,
And on thyn auter, wher I ryde or go,
I wol don sacrifice, and fyres bete.
And if ye wol nat so, my lady swete,
Than preye I thee, to-morwe with a spere
That Arcita me thurgh the herte bere.
Thanne rekke I noght, whan I have lost my lyf,
Though that Arcita winne hir to his wyf.
This is th'effect and ende of my preyere,
Yif me my love, thou blisful lady dere."
  Whan th'orisoun was doon of Palamon,
His sacrifice he dide, and that anon
Ful pitously, with alle circumstaunces,
Al telle I noght as now his observaunces.
But atte laste the statue of Venus shook,
And made a signe, wher-by that he took
That his preyere accepted was that day.
For thogh the signe shewed a delay,
Yet wiste he wel that graunted was his bone;
And with glad herte he wente him hoom ful sone.
  The thridde houre inequal that Palamon
Bigan to Venus temple for to goon,
Up roos the sonne, and up roos Emelye,
And to the temple of Diane gan hye.
Hir maydens, that she thider with hir ladde,
Ful redily with hem the fyr they hadde,
Th'encens, the clothes, and the remenant al
That to the sacrifyce longen shal;
The hornes fulle of meth, as was the gyse;
Ther lakked noght to doon hir sacrifyse.
Smoking the temple, ful of clothes faire,
This Emelye, with herte debonaire,
Hir body wessh with water of a welle;
But how she dide hir ryte I dar nat telle,
But it be any thing in general;
And yet it were a game to heren al;
To him that meneth wel, it were no charge:
But it is good a man ben at his large.
Hir brighte heer was kempt, untressed al;
A coroune of a grene ook cerial
Up-on hir heed was set ful fair and mete.
Two fyres on the auter gan she bete,
And dide hir thinges, as men may biholde
In Stace of Thebes, and thise bokes olde.
Whan kindled was the fyr, with pitous chere
Un-to Diane she spak, as ye may here.
  "O chaste goddesse of the wodes grene,
To whom bothe heven and erthe and see is sene,
Quene of the regne of Pluto derk and lowe,
Goddesse of maydens, that myn herte hast knowe
Ful many a yeer, and woost what I desire,
As keep me fro thy vengeaunce and thyn ire,
That Attheon aboughte cruelly.
Chaste goddesse, wel wostow that I

Of Emily, and die in thy service;
Find thou the manner how, and in what wise.
For I care not, unless it better be,
Whether I vanquish them or they do me,
So I may have my lady in my arms.
For though Mars is the god of war's alarms,
Thy power is so great in Heaven above,
That, if it be thy will, I'll have my love.
In thy fane will I worship always, so
That on thine altar, where'er I ride or go,
I will lay sacrifice and thy fires feed.
And if thou wilt not so, O lady, cede,
I pray thee, that tomorrow, with a spear,
Arcita bear me through the heart, just here.
For I'll care naught, when I have lost my life,
That Arcita may win her for his wife.
This the effect and end of all my prayer,
Give me my love, thou blissful lady fair."
  Now when he'd finished all the orison,
His sacrifice he made, this Palamon,
Right piously, with all the circumstance,
Albeit I tell not now his observance.
But at the last the form of Venus shook
And gave a sign, and thereupon he took
This as acceptance of his prayer that day.
For though the augury showed some delay,
Yet he knew well that granted was his boon;
And with glad heart he got him home right soon.
  Three hours unequal after Palamon
To Venus' temple at the lists had gone,
Up rose the sun and up rose Emily,
And to Diana's temple did she hie.
Her maidens led she thither, and with them
They carefully took fire and each emblem,
And incense, robes, and the remainder all
Of things for sacrifice ceremonial.
There was not one thing lacking; I'll but add
The horns of mead, as was a way they had.
In smoking temple, full of draperies fair,
This Emily with young heart debonnaire,
Her body washed in water from a well;
But how she did the rite I dare not tell,
Except it be at large, in general;
And yet it was a thing worth hearing all;
When one's well meaning, there is no transgression;
But it is best to speak at one's discretion.
Her bright hair was unbound, but combed withal;
She wore of green oak leaves a coronal
Upon her lovely head. Then she began
Two fires upon the altar stone to fan,
And did her ceremonies as we're told
In Statius' Thebaid and books as old.
When kindled was the fire, with sober face
Unto Diana spoke she in that place.
  "O thou chaste goddess of the wildwood green,
By whom all heaven and earth and sea are seen,
Queen of the realm of Pluto, dark and low,
Goddess of maidens, that my heart dost know
For all my years, and knowest what I desire,
Oh, save me from thy vengeance and thine ire
That on Actaeon fell so cruelly.
Chaste goddess, well indeed thou knowest that I

Desire to be a virgin all my life,
Nor ever wish to be man's love or wife.
I am, thou know'st, yet of thy company,
A maid, who loves the hunt and venery,
And to go rambling in the greenwood wild,
And not to be a wife and be with child.
I do not crave the company of man.
Now help me, lady, since thou may'st and can,
By the three beings who are one in thee.
For Palamon, who bears such love to me,
And for Arcita, loving me so sore,
This grace I pray thee, without one thing more,
To send down love and peace between those two,
And turn their hearts away from me: so do
That all their furious love and their desire,
And all their ceaseless torment and their fire
Be quenched or turned into another place;
And if it be thou wilt not show this grace,
Or if my destiny be moulded so
That I must needs have one of these same two,
Then send me him that most desires me.
Behold, O goddess of utter chastity,
The bitter tears that down my two cheeks fall.
Since thou art maid and keeper of us all,
My maidenhead keep thou, and still preserve,
And while I live a maid, thee will I serve."
  The fires blazed high upon the altar there,
While Emily was saying thus her prayer,
But suddenly she saw a sight most quaint,
For there, before her eyes, one fire went faint,
Then blazed again; and after that, anon,
The other fire was quenched, and so was gone.
And as it died it made a whistling sound,
As do wet branches burning on the ground,
And from the brands' ends there ran out, anon,
What looked like drops of blood, and many a one;
At which so much aghast was Emily
That she was near dazed, and began to cry,
For she knew naught of what it signified;
But only out of terror thus she cried
And wept, till it was pitiful to hear.
But thereupon Diana did appear,
With bow in hand, like any right huntress,
And said: "My daughter, leave this heaviness.
Among the high gods it has been affirmed,
And by eternal written word confirmed,
That you shall be the wife of one of those
Who bear for you so many cares and woes;
But unto which of them I may not tell.
I can no longer tarry, so farewell.
The fires that on my altar burn incense
Should tell you everything, ere you go hence,
Of what must come of love in this your case."
  And with that word the arrows of the chase
The goddess carried clattered and did ring,
And forth she went in mystic vanishing;
At which this Emily astonished was,
And said she then: "Ah, what means this, alas!
I put myself in thy protection here,
Diana, and at thy disposal dear."
  And home she wended, then, the nearest way.
This is the purport; there's no more to say.

Desire to been a mayden al my lyf,
Ne never wol I be no love ne wyf.
I am, thou woost, yet of thy companye,
A mayde, and love hunting and venerye,
And for to walken in the wodes wilde,
And noght to been a wyf, and be with childe.
Noght wol I knowe companye of man.
Now help me, lady, sith ye may and can,
For tho thre formes that thou hast in thee.
And Palamon, that hath swich love to me,
And eek Arcite, that loveth me so sore,
This grace I preye thee with-oute more,
As sende love and pees bitwixe hem two;
And fro me turne awey hir hertes so,
That al hir hote love, and hir desyr,
And al hir bisy torment, and hir fyr
Be queynt, or turned in another place;
And if so be thou wolt not do me grace,
Or if my destinee be shapen so,
That I shal nedes have oon of hem two,
As sende me him that most desireth me.
Bihold, goddesse of clene chastitee,
The bittre teres that on my chekes falle.
Sin thou are mayde, and keper of us alle,
My maydenhede thou kepe and wel conserve,
And whyl I live a mayde, I wol thee serve."
  The fyres brenne up-on the auter clere,
Whyl Emelye was thus in hir preyere;
But sodeinly she saugh a sighte queynte,
For right anon oon of the fyres queynte,
And quiked agayn, and after that anon
That other fyr was queynt, and al agon;
And as it queynte, it made a whistelinge,
As doon thise wete brondes in hir brenninge,
And at the brondes ende out-ran anoon
As it were blody dropes many oon;
For which so sore agast was Emelye,
That she was wel ny mad, and gan to crye,
For she ne wiste what it signifyed;
But only for the fere thus hath she cryed,
And weep, that it was pitee for to here.
And ther-with-al Diane gan appere,
With bowe in hond, right as an hunteresse,
And seyde: "Doghter, stint thyn hevinesse.
Among the goddes hye it is affermed,
And by eterne word write and confermed,
Thou shalt ben wedded un-to oon of tho
That han for thee so muchel care and wo;
But un-to which of hem I may nat telle.
Farwel, for I ne may no lenger dwelle.
The fyres which that on myn auter brenne
Shul thee declaren, er that thou go henne,
Thyn aventure of love, as in this cas."
And with that word, the arwes in the cas
Of the goddesse clateren faste and ringe,
And forth she wente, and made a vanisshinge;
For which this Emelye astoned was,
And seyde, "What amounteth this, allas!
I putte me in thy proteccioun,
Diane, and in thy disposicioun."
  And hoom she gooth anon the nexte weye.
This is th'effect, ther is namore to seye.

The nexte houre of Mars folwinge this,
Arcite un-to the temple walked is
Of fierse Mars, to doon his sacrifyse,
With alle the rytes of his payen wyse.
With pitous herte and heigh devocioun,
Right thus to Mars he seyde his orisoun:
"O stronge god, that in the regnes colde
Of Trace honoured art, and lord y-holde,
And hast in every regne and every lond
Of armes al the brydel in thyn hond,
And hem fortunest as thee list devyse,
Accept of me my pitous sacrifyse.
If so be that my youthe may deserve,
And that my might be worthy for to serve,
Thy godhede, that I may been oon of thyne,
Than preye I thee to rewe up-on my pyne.
For thilke peyne, and thilke hote fyr,
In which thou whylom brendest for desyr,
Whan that thou usedest the grete beautee
Of fayre yonge fresshe Venus free,
And haddest hir in armes at thy wille,
Al-though thee ones on a tyme misfille
Whan Vulcanus had caught thee in his las,
And fond thee ligging by his wyf, allas!
For thilke sorwe that was in thyn herte,
Have routhe as wel up-on my peynes smerte.
I am yong and unkonning, as thou wost,
And, as I trowe, with love offended most,
That ever was any lyves creature;
For she, that dooth me al this wo endure,
Ne reccheth never wher I sinke or flete
And wel I woot, er she me mercy hete,
I moot with strengthe winne hir in the place;
And wel I woot, withouten help or grace
Of thee, ne may my strengthe noght availle.
Than help me, lord, to-morwe in my bataille,
For thilke fyr that whylom brente thee,
As wel as thilke fyr now brenneth me;
And do that I to-morwe have victorie.
Myn be the travaille, and thyn be the glorie!
Thy sovereín temple wol I most honouren
Of any place, and alwey most labouren
In thy pleasunce and in thy craftes stronge,
And in thy temple I wol my baner honge,
And alle the armes of my companye;
And evere-mo, un-to that day I dye,
Eterne fyr I wol biforn thee finde.
And eek to this avow I wol me binde:
My berd, myn heer that hongeth long adoun,
That never yet ne felte offensioun
Of rasour nor of shere, I wol thee yive,
And been thy trewe servant whyl I live.
Now lord, have routhe up-on my sorwes sore,
Yif me victorie, I aske thee namore."
The preyere stinte of Arcita the stronge,
The ringes on the temple-dore that honge,
And eek the dores, clatereden ful faste,
Of which Arcita som-what him agaste.
The fyres brende up-on the auter brighte,
That it gan al the temple for to lighte;
And swete smel the ground anon up-yaf,
And Arcita anon his hand up-haf,

At the next hour of Mars, and following this,
Arcita to the temple walked, that is—
Devoted to fierce Mars, to sacrifice
With all the ceremonies, pagan-wise.
With sobered heart and high devotion, on
This wise, right thus he said his orison.
"O mighty god that in the regions cold
Of Thrace art honoured, where thy lordships hold,
And hast in every realm and every land
The reins of battle in thy guiding hand,
And givest fortune as thou dost devise,
Accept of me my pious sacrifice.
If so it be that my youth may deserve,
And that my strength be worthy found to serve
Thy godhead, and be numbered one of thine,
Then pray I thee for ruth on pain that's mine.
For that same pain and even that hot fire
Wherein thou once did'st burn with deep desire,
When thou did'st use the marvelous beauty
Of fair young wanton Venus, fresh and free,
And had'st her in thine arms and at thy will
(Howbeit with thee, once, all the chance fell ill,
And Vulcan caught thee in his net, whenas
He found thee lying with his wife, alas!)—
For that same sorrow that was in thy heart,
Have pity, now, upon my pains that smart.
I'm young, and little skilled, as knowest thou,
With love more hurt and much more broken now
Than ever living creature was, I'm sure;
For she who makes me all this woe endure,
Whether I float or sink cares not at all,
And ere she'll hear with mercy when I call,
I must by prowess win her in this place;
And well I know, too, without help and grace
Of thee, my human strength shall not avail.
Then help me, lord, tomorrow not to fail,
For sake of that same fire that once burned thee,
The which consuming fire so now burns me;
And grant, tomorrow, I have victory.
Mine be the toil, and thine the whole glory!
Thy sovereign temple will I honour most
Of any spot, and toil and count no cost
To pleasure thee and in thy craft have grace,
And in thy fane my banner will I place,
And all the weapons of my company;
And evermore, until the day I die,
Eternal fire shalt thou before thee find.
Moreover, to this vow myself I bind:
My beard, my hair that ripples down so long,
That never yet has felt the slightest wrong
Of razor or of shears, to thee I'll give,
And be thy loyal servant while I live.
Now, lord, have pity on my sorrows sore;
Give me the victory, I ask no more."
With ended prayer of Arcita the young,
The rings that on the temple door were hung,
And even the doors themselves, rattled so fast
That this Arcita found himself aghast.
The fires blazed high upon the altar bright,
Until the entire temple shone with light;
And a sweet odour rose up from the ground;
And Arcita whirled then his arm around,

And yet more incense on the fire he cast,
And did still further rites; and at the last
The armour of God Mars began to ring,
And with that sound there came a murmuring,
Low and uncertain, saying: "Victory!"
For which he gave Mars honour and glory.
And thus in joy and hope, which all might dare,
Arcita to his lodging then did fare,
Fain of the fight as fowl is of the sun.
  But thereupon such quarrelling was begun,
From this same granting, in the heaven above,
'Twixt lovely Venus, goddess of all love,
And Mars, the iron god armipotent,
That Jove toiled hard to make a settlement;
Until the sallow Saturn, calm and cold,
Who had so many happenings known of old,
Found from his full experience the art
To satisfy each party and each part.
For true it is, age has great advantage;
Experience and wisdom come with age;
Men may the old out-run, but not out-wit.
Thus Saturn, though it scarcely did befit
His nature so to do, devised a plan
To quiet all the strife, and thus began:
  "Now my dear daughter Venus," quoth Saturn,
"My course, which has so wide a way to turn,
Has power more than any man may know.
Mine is the drowning in the sea below;
Mine is the dungeon underneath the moat;
Mine is the hanging and strangling by the throat;
Rebellion, and the base crowd's murmuring,
The groaning and the private poisoning,
And vengeance and amercement —all are mine,
While yet I dwell within the Lion's sign.
Mine is the ruining of all high halls,
And tumbling down of towers and of walls
Upon the miner and the carpenter.
I struck down Samson, that pillar shaker;
And mine are all the maladies so cold,
The treasons dark, the machinations old;
My glance is father of all pestilence.
Now weep no more. I'll see, with diligence,
That Palamon, who is your own true knight,
Shall have his lady, as you hold is right.
Though Mars may help his man, yet none the less
Between you two there must come sometime peace,
And though you be not of one temperament,
Causing each day such violent dissent,
I am your grandsire and obey your will;
Weep then no more, your pleasure I'll fulfill."
  Now will I cease to speak of gods above,
Of Mars and Venus, goddess of all love,
And tell you now, as plainly as I can,
The great result, for which I first began.

And more encens in-to the fyr he caste,
With othere rytes mo; and atte laste
The statue of Mars bigan his hauberk ringe.
And with that soun he herde a murmuringe
Ful lowe and dim, that sayde thus, "Victorie":
For which he yaf to Mars honour and glorie.
And thus with joye, and hope wel to fare,
Arcite anon un-to his inne is fare,
As fayn as fowel is of the brighte sonne.
  And right anon swich stryf ther is bigonne
For thilke graunting, in the hevene above,
Bitwixe Venus, the goddesse of love,
And Mars, the sterne god armipotente,
That Jupiter was bisy it to stente;
Til that the pale Saturnus the colde,
That knew so manye of aventures olde,
Fond in his olde experience an art,
That he ful sone hath plesed every part.
As sooth is sayd, elde hath greet avantage;
In elde is bothe wisdom and usage;
Men may the olde at-renne, and noght at-rede.
Saturne anon, to stinten stryf and drede,
Al be it that it is agayn his kynde,
Of al this stryf he gan remedie fynde.
  "My dere doghter Venus," quod Saturne,
"My cours, that hath so wyde for to turne,
Hath more power than wot any man.
Myn is the drenching in the see so wan;
Myn is the prison in the derke cote;
Myn is the strangling and hanging by the throte;
The murmure, and the cherles rebelling,
The groyning, and the pryvee empoysoning:
I do vengeance and pleyn correccioun
Whyl I dwelle in the signe of the Leoun.
Myn is the ruine of the hye halles,
The falling of the toures and of the walles
Up-on the mynour or the carpenter.
I slow Sampsoun in shaking the piler;
And myne be the maladyes colde,
The derke tresons, and the castes olde;
My loking is the fader of pestilence.
Now weep namore, I shal doon diligence
That Palamon, that is thyn owne knight,
Shal have his lady, as thou hast him hight.
Though Mars shal helpe his knight, yet nathelees
Bitwixe yow ther moot be som tyme pees,
Al be ye noght of o complexioun,
That causeth al day swich divisioun.
I am thin ayel, redy at thy wille;
Weep thou namore, I wol thy lust fulfille."
  Now wol I stinten of the goddes above,
Of Mars, and of Venus, goddesse of love,
And telle yow, as pleynly as I can,
The grete effect, for which that I bigan.

HERE ENDETH THE THIRD PART

HERE FOLLOWETH THE FOURTH PART

  Great was the fête in Athens on that day,
And too, the merry season of the May
Gave everyone such joy and such pleasance
That all that Monday they'd but joust and dance,
Or spend the time in Venus' high service.

  Greet was the feste in Athénës that day,
And eek the lusty seson of that May
Made every wight to been in swich plesaunce,
That al that Monday justen they and daunce,
And spenden it in Venus heigh servyse.

But by the cause that they sholde ryse
Erly, for to seen the grete fight,
Unto hir reste wente they at night.
And on the morwe, whan that day gan springe,
Of hors and harneys, noyse and clateringe
Ther was in hostelryes al aboute;
And to the paleys rood ther many a route
Of lordes, up-on stedes and palfreys.
Ther maystow seen devysing of herneys
So uncouth and so riche, and wroght so weel
Of goldsmithrie, of browding, and of steel;
The sheeldes brighte, testers, and trappures;
Gold-hewen helmes, hauberks, cote-armures;
Lordes in paraments on hir courseres,
Knightes of retenue, and eek squyeres
Nailinge the speres, and helmes bokelinge,
Giggynge of sheeldes, with layneres lacinge;
Ther as need is, they weren no-thing ydel;
The fomy stedes on the golden brydel
Gnawinge, and faste the armurers also
With fyle and hamer prikinge to and fro;
Yemen on fote, and communes many oon
With shorte staves, thikke as they may goon;
Pypes, trompes, nakers, clariounes,
That in the bataille blowen blody sounes;
The paleys ful of peples up and doun,
Heer three, ther ten, holding hir questioun,
Divyninge of thise Theban knightes two.
Somme seyden thus, somme seyde it shal be so;
Somme helden with him with the blake berd,
Somme with the balled, somme with the thikke-
  herd;
Somme sayde, he loked grim and he wolde fighte;
He hath a sparth of twenty pound of wighte.
Thus was the halle ful of divyninge,
Longe after that the sonne gan to springe.
  The grete Theseus, that of his sleep awaked
With minstralcye and noyse that was maked,
Held yet the chambre of his paleys riche,
Til that the Thebane knightes, bothe y-liche
Honoured, were into the paleys fet.
Duk Theseus was at a window set,
Arrayed right as he were a god in trone.
The peple preesseth thider-ward ful sone
Him for to seen, and doon heigh reverence,
And eek to herkne his hest and his sentence.
  An heraud on a scaffold made an ho,
Til al the noyse of peple was y-do;
And whan he saugh the peple of noyse al stille,
Tho showed he the mighty dukes wille.
  "The lord hath of his heigh discrecioun
Considered, that it were destruccioun
To gentil blood, to fighten in the gyse
Of mortal bataille now in this empryse;
Wherfore, to shapen that they shul not dye,
He wol his firste purpos modifye.
No man therfor, up peyne of los of lyf,
No maner shot, ne pollax, ne short knyf
Into the listes sende, or thider bringe;
Ne short swerd for to stoke, with poynt bytinge,
No man ne drawe, ne bere it by his syde.
Ne no man shal un-to his felawe ryde

But for the reason that they must arise
Betimes, to see the heralded great fight,
All they retired to early rest that night.
And on the morrow, when that day did spring,
Of horse and harness, noise and clattering,
There was enough in hostelries about.
And to the palace rode full many a rout
Of lords, bestriding steeds and on palfreys.
There could you see adjusting of harness,
So curious and so rich, and wrought so well
Of goldsmiths' work, embroidery, and of steel;
The shields, the helmets bright, the gay trappings,
The gold-hewn casques, the coats-of-arms, the rings,
The lords in vestments rich, on their coursers,
Knights with their retinues and also squires;
The rivetting of spears, the helm-buckling,
The strapping of the shields, and thong-lacing—
In their great need, not one of them was idle;
The frothing steeds, champing the golden bridle,
And the quick smiths, and armourers also,
With file and hammer spurring to and fro;
Yeoman, and peasants with short staves were out,
Crowding as thick as they could move about;
Pipes, trumpets, kettledrums, and clarions,
That in the battle sound such grim summons;
The palace full of people, up and down,
Here three, there ten, debating the renown
And questioning about these Theban knights,
Some put it thus, some said, "It's so by rights."
Some held with him who had the great black beard,
Some with the bald-heads, some with the thick-
  haired;
Some said, "He looks grim, and he'll fight like hate;
He has an axe of twenty pound in weight."
And thus the hall was full of gossiping
Long after the bright sun began to spring.
  The mighty Theseüs, from sleep awakened
By songs and all the noise that never slackened,
Kept yet the chamber of this rich palace,
Till the two Theban knights, with equal grace
And honour, were ushered in with flourish fitting.
Duke Theseüs was at a window sitting,
Arrayed as he were god upon a throne.
Then pressed the people thitherward full soon,
To see him and to do him reverence,
Aye, and to hear commands of sapience.
  A herald on a scaffold cried out "Ho!"
Till all the people's noise was stilled; and so,
When he observed that all were fallen still,
He then proclaimed the mighty ruler's will.
  "The duke our lord, full wise and full discreet,
Holds that it were but wanton waste to meet
And fight, these gentle folk, all in the guise
Of mortal battle in this enterprise.
Wherefore, in order that no man may die,
He does his earlier purpose modify.
No man, therefore, on pain of loss of life,
Shall any arrow, pole-axe, or short knife
Send into lists in any wise, or bring;
Nor any shortened sword, for point-thrusting,
Shall a man draw, or bear it by his side.
Nor shall a knight against opponent ride,

Save one full course, with any sharp-ground spear;
Unhorsed, a man may thrust with any gear.
And he that's overcome, should this occur,
Shall not be slain, but brought to barrier,
Whereof there shall be one on either side;
Let him be forced to go there and abide.
And if by chance the leader there must go,
Of either side, or slay his equal foe,
No longer, then, shall tourneying endure.
God speed you; go forth now, and lay on sure.
With long sword and with maces fight your fill.
Go now your ways; this is the lord duke's will."
 The voices of the people rent the skies,
Such was the uproar of their merry cries:
"Now God save such a lord, who is so good
He will not have destruction of men's blood!"
Up start the trumpets and make melody.
And to the lists rode forth the company,
In marshalled ranks, throughout the city large,
All hung with cloth of gold, and not with serge.
Full like a lord this noble duke did ride,
With the two Theban knights on either side;
And, following, rode the queen and Emily,
And, after, came another company
Of one and other, each in his degree.
And thus they went throughout the whole city,
And to the lists they came, all in good time.
The day was not yet fully come to prime
When throned was Theseüs full rich and high,
And Queen Hippolyta and Emily,
While other ladies sat in tiers about.
Into the seats then pressed the lesser rout.
And westward, through the gate of Mars, right hearty,
Arcita and the hundred of his party
With banner red is entering anon;
And in that self-same moment, Palamon
Is under Venus, eastward in that place,
With banner white, and resolute of face.
In all the world, searching it up and down,
So equal were they all, from heel to crown,
There were no two such bands in any way.
For there was no man wise enough to say
How either had of other advantage
In high repute, or in estate, or age,
So even were they chosen, as I guess.
And in two goodly ranks they did then dress.
And when the name was called of every one,
That cheating in their number might be none,
Then were the gates closed, and the cry rang loud:
"Now do your devoir, all you young knights proud!"
 The heralds cease their spurring up and down;
Now ring the trumpets as the charge is blown;
And there's no more to say, for east and west
Two hundred spears are firmly laid in rest;
And the sharp spurs are thrust, now, into side.
Now see men who can joust and who can ride!
Now shivered are the shafts on bucklers thick;
One feels through very breast-bone the spear's prick;
Lances are flung full twenty feet in height;
Out flash the swords like silver burnished bright.

But o cours, with a sharp y-grounde spere;
Foyne, if him list, on fote, him-self to were.
And he that is at meschief, shal be take,
And noght slayn, but be broght un-to the stake
That shal ben ordeyned on either syde;
But thider he shal by force, and ther abyde.
And if so falle, the chieftayn be take
On either syde, or elles slee his make,
No lenger shal the turneyinge laste.
God spede yow; goth forth, and ley on faste.
With long swerd and with maces fight your fille.
Goth now your way; this is the lordes wille."
 The voys of peple touchede the hevene,
So loude cryden they with mery stevene:
"God save swich a lord, that is so good,
He wilneth no destruccioun of blood!"
Up goon the trompes and the melodye.
And to the listes rit the companye
By ordinaunce, thurgh-out the citee large,
Hanged with cloth of gold, and nat with sarge.
Ful lyk a lord this noble duk gan ryde,
Thise two Thebanes up-on either syde;
And after rood the quene, and Emelye,
And after that another companye
Of oon and other, after hir degree.
And thus they passen thurgh-out the citee,
And to the listes come they by tyme.
It nas not of the day yet fully pryme,
Whan set was Theseus ful riche and hye,
Ipolita the quene and Emelye,
And other ladies in degrees aboute.
Un-to the seetes preesseth al the route.
And west-ward, thurgh the gates under Marte,
Arcite, and eek the hundred of his parte,
With baner reed is entred right anon;
And in that selve moment Palamon
Is under Venus, est-ward in the place,
With baner whyt, and hardy chere and face.
In al the world, to seken up and doun,
So even with-outen variacioun,
Ther nere swiche companyes tweye.
For ther nas noon so wys that coude seye,
That any hadde of other avauntage
Of worthinesse, ne of estaat, ne age,
So even were they chosen, for to gesse.
And in two renges faire they hem dresse.
Whan that hir names rad were everichoon,
That in hir nombre gyle were ther noon,
Tho were the gates shet, and cryed was loude:
"Do now your devoir, yonge knightes proude!"
 The heraudes lefte hir priking up and doun;
Now ringen trompes loude and clarioun;
Ther is namore to seyn, but west and est
In goon the speres ful sadly in arest;
In goth the sharpe spore in-to the syde.
Ther seen men who can juste, and who can ryde;
Ther shiveren shaftes up-on sheeldes thikke;
He feleth thurgh the herte-spoon the prikke.
Up springen speres twenty foot on highte;
Out goon the swerdes as the silver brighte.

The helmes they to-hewen and to-shrede;
Out brest the blood, with sterne stremes rede.
With mighty maces the bones they to-breste.
He thurgh the thikkeste of the throng gan threste.
Ther stomblen stedes stronge, and doun goth al.
He rolleth under foot as dooth a bal.
He foyneth on his feet with his tronchoun,
And he him hurtleth with his hors adoun.
He thurgh the body is hurt, and sithen y-take,
Maugree his heed, and broght un-to the stake,
As forward was, right ther he moste abyde;
Another lad is on that other syde.
And som tyme dooth hem Theseus to reste,
Hem to refresshe, and drinken if hem leste.
Ful ofte a-day han thise Thebanes two
Togidre y-met, and wroght his felawe wo;
Unhorsed hath ech other of hem tweye.
Ther nas no tygre in the vale of Galgopheye,[1]
Whan that hir whelp is stole, whan it is lyte,
So cruel on the hunte, as is Arcite
For jelous herte upon this Palamoun:
Ne in Belmarye ther nis so fel leoun,
That hunted is, or for his hunger wood,
Ne of his praye desireth so the blood,
As Palamon to sleen his fo Arcite.
The jelous strokes on hir helmes byte;
Out renneth blood on both hir sydes rede.
  Som tyme an ende ther is of every dede;
For er the sonne un-to the reste wente,
The stronge king Emetreus gan hente
This Palamon, as he faught with Arcite,
And made his swerd depe in his flesh to byte;
And by the force of twenty is he take
Unyolden, and y-drawe unto the stake.
And in the rescous of this Palamoun
The stronge king Ligurge is born adoun;
And king Emetreus, for al his strengthe,
Is born out of his sadel a swerdes lengthe,
So hitte him Palamon er he were take;
But al for noght, he was broght to the stake.
His hardy herte mighte him helpe naught;
He moste abyde, whan that he was caught
By force, and eek by composicioun.
  Who sorweth now but woful Palamoun,
That moot namore goon agayn to fighte?
And whan that Theseus had seyn this sighte,
Un-to the folk that foghten thus echoon
He cryde, "Ho! namore, for it is doon!
I wol be trewe juge, and no partye.
Arcite of Thebes shal have Emelye,
That by his fortune hath hir faire y-wonne."
  Anon ther is a noyse of peple bigonne
For joye of this, so loude and heigh withalle,
It semed that the listes sholde falle.
  What can now faire Venus doon above?
What seith she now? what dooth this quene of love?
But wepeth so, for wanting of hir wille,
Til that hir teres in the listes fille;
She seyde: "I am ashamed, doutelees."
Saturnus seyde: "Doghter, hold thy pees.

Helmets are hewed, the lacings ripped and shred;
Out bursts the blood, gushing in stern streams red.
With mighty maces bones are crushed in joust.
One through the thickest throng begins to thrust.
There strong steeds stumble now, and down goes all.
One rolls beneath their feet as rolls a ball.
One flails about with club, being overthrown,
Another, on a mailed horse, rides him down.
One through the body's hurt, and haled, for aid,
Spite of his struggles, to the barricade,
As compact was, and there he must abide;
Another's captured by the other side.
At times Duke Theseüs orders them to rest,
To eat a bite and drink what each likes best.
And many times that day those Thebans two
Met in the fight and wrought each other woe;
Unhorsed each has the other on that day.
No tigress in the vale of Galgophey,[1]
Whose little whelp is stolen in the light,
Is cruel to the hunter as Arcite
For jealousy is cruel to Palamon;
Nor in Belmarie, when the hunt is on
Is there a lion, wild for want of food,
That of his prey desires so much the blood
As Palamon the death of Arcite there.
Their jealous blows fall on their helmets fair;
Out leaps the blood and makes their two sides red.
  But sometime comes the end of every deed;
And ere the sun had sunk to rest in gold,
The mighty King Emetrëus did hold
This Palamon, as he fought with Arcite,
And made his sword deep in the flesh to bite;
And by the force of twenty men he's made,
Unyielded, to withdraw to barricade.
And, trying hard to rescue Palamon,
The mighty King Lycurgus is borne down;
And King Emetrëus, for all his strength,
Is hurled out of the saddle a sword's length,
So hits out Palamon once more, or ere
(But all for naught) he's brought to barrier.
His hardy heart may now avail him naught;
He must abide there now, being fairly caught
By force of arms, as by provision known.
  Who sorrows now but woeful Palamon,
Who may no more advance into the fight?
And when Duke Theseüs had seen this sight,
Unto the warriors fighting, every one,
He cried out: "Hold! No more! For it is done!
Now will I prove true judge, of no party.
Theban Arcita shall have Emily,
Who, by his fortune, has her fairly won."
  And now a noise of people is begun
For joy of this, so loud and shrill withal,
It seems as if the very lists will fall.
  But now, what can fair Venus do above?
What says she now? What does this queen of love
But weep so fast, for thwarting of her will,
Her tears upon the lists begin to spill.
She said: "Now am I shamed and over-flung."
But Saturn said: "My daughter, hold your tongue

[1]Probably the vale of Gargaphie, where Actæon was turned into a stag.

Mars has his will, his knight has all his boon,
And, by my head, you shall be eased, and soon."
The trumpeters and other minstrelsy,
The heralds that did loudly yell and cry,
Were at their best for joy of Arcita.
But hear me further while I tell you—ah!—
The miracle that happened there anon.
This fierce Arcita doffs his helmet soon,
And mounted on a horse, to show his face,
He spurs from end to end of that great place,
Looking aloft to gaze on Emily;
And she cast down on him a friendly eye
(For women, generally speaking, go
Wherever Fortune may her favor show);
And she was fair to see, and held his heart.
But from the ground infernal furies start,
From Pluto sent, at instance of Saturn,
Whereat his horse, for fear, began to turn
And leap aside, all suddenly falling there;
And Arcita before he could beware
Was pitched upon the ground, upon his head,
And lay there, moving not, as he were dead,
His chest crushed in upon the saddle-bow.
And black he lay as ever coal, or crow,
So ran the surging blood into his face.
Anon they carried him from out that place,
With heavy hearts, to Theseus' palace.
There was his harness cut away, each lace,
And swiftly was he laid upon a bed,
For he was yet alive and some words said,
Crying and calling after Emily.
Duke Theseus, with all his company,
Is come again to Athens, his city,
With joyous heart and great festivity.
And though sore grieved for this unhappy fall,
He would not cast a blight upon them all.
Men said, too, that Arcita should not die,
But should be healed of all his injury.
And of another thing they were right fain,
Which was, that of them all no one was slain,
Though each was sore, and hurt, and specially one
Who'd got a lance-head thrust through his breast-
bone.
For other bruises, wounds and broken arms,
Some of them carried salves and some had
charms;
And medicines of many herbs, and sage
They drank, to keep their limbs from hemorrhage.
In all of which this duke, as he well can,
Now comforts and now honours every man,
And makes a revelry the livelong night
For all these foreign lords, as was but right.
Nor was there held any discomfiting,
Save from the jousts and from the tourneying.
For truly, there had been no cause for shame,
Since being thrown is fortune of the game;
Nor is it, to be led to barrier,
Unyielded, and by twenty knights' power,
One man alone, surrounded by the foe,
Driven by arms, and dragged out, heel and toe,
And with his courser driven forth with staves
Of men on foot, yeomen and serving knaves—

Mars hath his wille, his knight hath al his bone,
And, by myn heed, thou shalt ben esed sone."
The trompes, with the loude minstralcye,
The heraudes, that ful loude yolle and crye,
Been in hir wele for joye of daun Arcite.
But herkneth me, and stinteth now a lyte,
Which a miracle ther bifel anon.
This fierse Arcite hath of his helm y-don,
And on a courser, for to shewe his face,
He priketh endelong the large place,
Loking upward up-on this Emelye;
And she agayn him caste a freendlich yë,
(For wommen, as to speken in comune,
They folwen al the favour of fortune);
And she was al his chere, as in his herte.
Out of the ground a furie infernal sterte,
From Pluto sent, at requeste of Saturne,
For which his hors for fere gan to turne,
And leep asyde, and foundred as he leep;
And, er that Arcite may taken keep,
He pighte him on the pomel of his heed,
That in the place he lay as he were deed,
His brest to-brosten with his sadel-bowe.
As blak he lay as any cole or crowe,
So was the blood y-ronnen in his face.
Anon he was y-born out of the place
With herte soor, to Theseus paleys.
Tho was he corven out of his harneys,
And in a bed y-brought ful faire and blyve,
For he was yet in memorie and alyve,
And alway crying after Emelye.
Duk Theseus, with al his companye,
Is comen hoom to Athenes his citee,
With alle blisse and greet solempnitee.
Al be it that this aventure was falle,
He nolde noght disconforten hem alle.
Men seyde eek, that Arcite shal nat dye;
He shal ben heled of his maladye.
And of another thing they were as fayn,
That of hem alle was ther noon y-slayn,
Al were they sore y-hurt, and namely oon,
That with a spere was thirled his brest-
boon.
To othere woundes, and to broken armes,
Some hadden salves, and some hadden
charmes;
Fermacies of herbes, and eek save
They dronken, for they wolde hir limes have.
For which this noble duk, as he wel can,
Conforteth and honoureth every man,
And made revel al the longe night,
Un-to the straunge lordes, as was right.
Ne ther was holden no disconfitinge,
But as a justes or a tourneyinge;
For soothly ther was no disconfiture,
For falling nis nat but an aventure;
Ne to be lad with fors un-to the stake
Unyolden, and with twenty knightes take
O persone allone, with-outen mo,
And haried forth by arme, foot, and to,
And eek his stede driven forth with staves,
With footmen, bothe yemen and eek knaves,

It nas aretted him no vileinye,
Ther may no man clepen it cowardye.
For which anon duk Theseus leet crye,
To stinten alle rancour and envye,
The gree as wel of o syde as of other,
And either syde y-lyk, as otheres brother;
And yaf hem yiftes after hir degree,
And fully heeld a feste dayes three;
And conveyed the kinges worthily
Out of his toun a journee largely.
And hoom wente every man the righte way.
Ther was namore, but "far wel, have good
day!"
Of this bataille I wol namore endyte,
But speke of Palamon and of Arcite.
Swelleth the brest of Arcite, and the sore
Encreesseth at his herte more and more.
The clothered blood, for any lechecraft,
Corrupteth, and is in his bouk y-laft,
That neither veyne-blood, ne ventusinge,
Ne drinke of herbes may ben his helpinge.
The vertu expulsif, or animal,
Fro thilke vertu cleped natural
Ne may the venim voyden, ne expelle.
The pypes of his longes gonne to swelle,
And every lacerte in his brest adoun
Is shent with venim and corrupcioun.
Him gayneth neither, for to gete his lyf,
Vomyt upward, ne dounward laxatif;
Al is to-brosten thilke regioun,
Nature hath now no dominacioun.
And certeinly, ther nature wol nat wirche,
Far-wel, phisyk! go ber the man to chirche!
This al and som, that Arcita mot dye,
For which he sendeth after Emelye,
And Palamon, that was his cosin dere;
Than seyde he thus, as ye shul after here.
"Naught may the woful spirit in myn herte
Declare o poynt of alle my sorwes smerte
To yow, my lady, that I love most;
But I biquethe the service of my gost
To yow aboven every creature,
Sin that my lyf may no lenger dure.
Allas, the wo! allas, the peynes stronge,
That I for yow have suffred, and so longe!
Allas, the deeth! allas, myn Emelye!
Allas, departing of our companye!
Allas, myn hertes quene! allas, my wyf!
Myn hertes lady, endere of my lyf!
What is this world? what asketh men to have?
Now with his love, now in his colde grave
Allone, with-outen any companye.
Far-wel, my swete fo! myn Emelye!
And softe tak me in your armes tweye,
For love of God, and herkneth what I seye.
I have heer with my cosin Palamon
Had stryf and rancour, many a day a-gon,
For love of yow, and for my jelousye.
And Jupiter so wis my soule gye,
To speken of a servant proprely,
With alle circumstaunces trewely,
That is to seyn, trouthe, honour, and knighthede,

All this imputes to one no kind of vice,
And no man may bring charge of cowardice.
For which anon, Duke Theseüs bade cry,
To still all rancour and all keen envy,
The worth, as well of one side as the other,
As equal both, and each the other's brother;
And gave them gifts according to degree,
And held a three days' feast, right royally;
And then convoyed these kings upon their road
For one full day, and to them honour showed.
And home went every man on his right way.
There was naught more but "Farewell" and "Good-
day."
I'll say no more of war, but turn upon
My tale of Arcita and Palamon.
Swells now Arcita's breast until the sore
Increases near his heart yet more and more.
The clotted blood, in spite of all leech-craft,
Rots in his bulk, and there it must be left,
Since no device of skillful blood-letting,
Nor drink of herbs, can help him in this thing.
The power expulsive, or virtue animal
Called from its use the virtue natural,
Could not the poison void, nor yet expel.
The tubes of both his lungs began to swell,
And every tissue in his breast, and down,
Is foul with poison and all rotten grown.
He gains in neither, in his strife to live,
By vomiting or taking laxative;
All is so broken in that part of him,
Nature retains no vigour there, nor vim.
And certainly, where Nature will not work,
It's farewell physic, bear the man to kirk!
The sum of all is, Arcita must die,
And so he sends a word to Emily,
And Palamon, who was his cousin dear;
And then he said to them as you shall hear.
"Naught may the woeful spirit in my heart
Declare one point of how my sorrows smart
To you, my lady, whom I love the most;
But I bequeath the service of my ghost
To you above all others, this being sure
Now that my life may here no more endure.
Alas, the woe! Alas, the pain so strong
That I for you have suffered, and so long!
Alas for death! Alas, my Emily!
Alas, the parting of our company!
Alas, my heart's own queen! Alas, my wife!
My soul's dear lady, ender of my life!
What is this world? What asks a man to have?
Now with his love, now in the cold dark grave
Alone, with never any company.
Farewell, my sweet foe! O my Emily!
Oh, take me in your gentle arms, I pray,
For love of God, and hear what I will say.
"I have here, with my cousin Palamon,
Had strife and rancour many a day that's gone,
For love of you and for my jealousy.
May Jove so surely guide my soul for me,
To speak about a lover properly,
With all the circumstances, faithfully!—
That is to say, truth, honour, and knighthood,

Wisdom, humility and kinship good,
And generous soul and all the lover's art—
So now may Jove have in my soul his part
As in this world, right now, I know of none
So worthy to be loved as Palamon,
Who serves you and will do so all his life.
And if you ever should become a wife,
Forget not Palamon, the noble man."
And with that word his speech to fail began,
For from his feet up to his breast had come
The cold of death, making his body numb.
And furthermore, from his two arms the strength
Was gone out, now, and he was lost, at length.
Only the intellect, and nothing more,
Which dwelt within his heart so sick and sore,
Began to fail now, when the heart felt death,
And his eyes darkened, and he failed of breath.
But on his lady turned he still his eye,
And his last word was, "Mercy, Emily!"
His spirit changed its house and went away.
As I was never there, I cannot say
Where; so I stop, not being a soothsayer;
Of souls here naught shall I enregister;
Nor do I wish their notions, now, to tell
Who write of them, though they say where they dwell.
Arcita's cold; Mars guides his soul on high;
Now will I speak forthwith of Emily.
Shrieked Emily and howled now Palamon,
Till Theseüs his sister took, anon,
And bore her, swooning, from the corpse away.
How shall it help, to dwell the livelong day
In telling how she wept both night and morrow?
For in like cases women have such sorrow,
When their good husband from their side must go,
And, for the greater part, they take on so,
Or else they fall into such malady
That, at the last, and certainly, they die.
Infinite were the sorrows and the tears
Of all old folk and folk of tender years
Throughout the town, at death of this Theban;
For him there wept the child and wept the man;
So great a weeping was not, 'tis certain,
When Hector was brought back, but newly slain,
To Troy. Alas, the sorrow that was there!
Tearing of cheeks and rending out of hair.
"Oh why will you be dead," these women cry,
"Who had of gold enough, and Emily?"
No man might comfort then Duke Theseüs,
Excepting his old father, Ægëus,
Who knew this world's mutations, and men's own.
Since he had seen them changing up and down,
Joy after woe, and woe from happiness:
He showed them, by example, the process.
"Just as there never died a man," quoth he,
"But he had lived on earth in some degree,
Just so there never lived a man," he said,
"In all this world, but must be sometime dead.
This world is but a thoroughfare of woe,
And we are pilgrims passing to and fro;
Death is the end of every worldly sore."
And after this, he told them yet much more

Wisdom, humblesse, estaat, and heigh kinrede,
Fredom, and al that longeth to that art,
So Jupiter have of my soule part,
As in this world right now ne knowe I non
So worthy to ben loved as Palamon,
That serveth yow, and wol don al his lyf.
And if that ever ye shul been a wyf,
Foryet nat Palamon, the gentil man."
And with that word his speche faille gan,
For from his feet up to his brest was come
The cold of deeth, that hadde him overcome.
And yet more-over, in his armes two
The vital strengthe is lost, and al ago.
Only the intellect, with-outen more,
That dwelled in his herte syk and sore,
Gan faillen, when the herte felte deeth,
Dusked his eyen two, and failled breeth,
But on his lady yet caste he his yë;
His laste word was, "mercy, Emelye!"
His spirit chaunged hous, and wente ther,
As I cam never, I can nat tellen where.
Therfor I stinte, I nam no divinistre;
Of soules finde I nat in this registre,
Ne me ne list thilke opiniouns to telle
Of hem, though that they wryten wher they dwelle.
Arcite is cold, ther Mars his soule gye;
Now wol I speken forth of Emelye.
Shrighte Emelye, and howleth Palamon,
And Theseus his suster took anon
Swowninge, and bar hir fro the corps away.
What helpeth it to tarien forth the day,
To tellen how she weep, bothe eve and morwe?
For in swich cas wommen have swich sorwe,
Whan that hir housbonds been from hem ago,
That for the more part they sorwen so,
Or elles fallen in swich maladye,
That at the laste certeinly they dye.
Infinite been the sorwes and the teres
Of olde folk, and folk of tendre yeres,
In al the toun, for deeth of this Theban;
For him ther wepeth bothe child and man;
So greet a weping was ther noon, certayn,
Whan Ector was y-broght, al fresh y-slayn,
To Troye; allas! the pitee that was ther,
Cracching of chekes, rending eek of heer.
"Why woldestow be deed," thise wommen crye,
"And haddest gold y-nough, and Emelye?"
No man mighte gladen Theseus,
Savinge his olde fader Egeus,
That knew this worldes transmutacioun,
As he had seyn it chaungen up and doun,
Joye after wo, and wo after gladnesse:
And shewed hem ensamples and lyknesse.
"Right as ther deyed never man," quod he,
"That he ne livede in erthe in som degree,
Right so ther livede never man," he seyde,
"In al this world, that som tyme he ne deyde.
This world nis but a thurghfare ful of wo,
And we ben pilgrimes, passinge to and fro;
Deeth is an ende of every worldly sore."
And over al this yet seyde he muchel more

To this effect, ful wysly to enhorte
The peple, that they sholde hem reconforte.
  Duk Theseus, with al his bisy cure,
Caste now wher that the sepulture
Of good Arcite may best y-maked be,
And eek most honurable in his degree.
And at the laste he took conclusioun,
That ther as first Arcite and Palamoun
Hadden for love the bataille hem bitwene,
That in that selve grove, swote and grene,
Ther as he hadde his amorous desires,
His compleynt, and for love his hote fires,
He wolde make a fyr, in which th'office
Funeral he mighte al accomplice;
And leet comaunde anon to hakke and hewe
The okes olde, and leye hem on a rewe
In colpons wel arrayed for to brenne;
His officers with swifte feet they renne
And ryde anon at his comaundement.
And after this, Theseus hath y-sent
After a bere, and it al over-spradde
With cloth of gold, the richest that he hadde.
And of the same suyte he cladde Arcite;
Upon his hondes hadde he gloves whyte;
Eek on his heed a croune of laurer grene,
And in his hond a swerd ful bright and kene.
He leyde him bare the visage on the bere,
Therwith he weep that pitee was to here.
And for the peple sholde seen him alle,
Whan it was day, he broghte him to the halle,
That roreth of the crying and the soun.
  Tho cam this woful Theban Palamoun,
With flotery berd, and ruggy asshy heres,
In clothes blake, y-dropped al with teres;
And, passing othere of weping, Emelye,
The rewfulleste of al the companye.
In as muche as the service sholde be
The more noble and riche in his degree,
Duk Theseus leet forth three stedes bringe,
That trapped were in steel al gliteringe,
And covered with the armes of daun Arcite.
Up-on thise stedes, that weren grete and whyte,
Ther seten folk, of which oon bar his sheeld,
Another his spere up in his hondes heeld;
The thridde bar with him his bowe Turkeys,
Of brend gold was the cas, and eek the harneys;
And riden forth a pas with sorweful chere
Toward the grove, as ye shul after here.
  The nobleste of the Grekes that ther were
Upon hir shuldres carieden the bere,
With slakke pas, and eyen rede and wete,
Thurgh-out the citee, by the maister-strete,
That sprad was al with blak, and wonder hye
Right of the same is al the strete y-wrye.
Up-on the right hond wente old Egeus,
And on that other syde duk Theseus,
With vessels in hir hand of gold ful fyn,
Al ful of hony, milk, and blood, and wyn;
Eek Palamon, with ful greet companye;
And after that cam woful Emelye,

To that effect, all wisely to exhort
The people that they should find some comfort.
  Duke Theseüs now considered and with care
What place of burial he should prepare
For good Arcita, as it best might be,
And one most worthy of his high degree.
And at the last concluded, hereupon,
That where at first Arcita and Palamon
Had fought for love, with no man else between,
There, in that very grove, so sweet and green,
Where he mused on his amorous desires
Complaining of love's hot and flaming fires,
He'd make a pyre and have the funeral
Accomplished there, and worthily in all.
And so he gave command to hack and hew
The ancient oaks, and lay them straight and true
In split lengths that would kindle well and burn.
His officers, with sure swift feet, they turn
And ride away to do his whole intent.
And after this Duke Theseüs straightway sent
For a great bier, and had it all o'er-spread
With cloth of gold, the richest that he had.
Arcita clad he, too, in cloth of gold;
White gloves were on his hands where they did fold;
Upon his head a crown of laurel green,
And near his hand a sword both bright and keen.
Then, having bared the dead face on the bier,
The duke so wept, 'twas pitiful to hear.
And, so that folk might see him, one and all,
When it was day he brought them to the hall,
Which echoed of their wailing cries anon.
  Then came this woeful Theban, Palamon,
With fluttery beard and matted, ash-strewn hair,
All in black clothes wet with his tears; and there,
Surpassing all in weeping, Emily,
The most affected of the company.
And so that every several rite should be
Noble and rich, and suiting his degree,
Duke Theseüs commanded that they bring
Three horses, mailed in steel all glittering,
And covered with Arcita's armour bright.
Upon these stallions, which were large and white,
There rode three men, whereof one bore the shield,
And one the spear he'd known so well to wield;
The third man bore his Turkish bow, nor less
Of burnished gold the quiver than harness;
And forth they slowly rode, with mournful cheer,
Toward that grove, as you shall further hear.
  The noblest Greeks did gladly volunteer
To bear upon their shoulders that great bier,
With measured pace and eyes gone red and wet,
Through all the city, by the wide main street,
Which was all spread with black, and, wondrous high.
Covered with this same cloth were houses nigh.
Upon the right hand went old Ægëus,
And on the other side Duke Theseüs,
With vessels in their hands, of gold right fine,
All filled with honey, milk, and blood, and wine;
And Palamon with a great company;
And after that came woeful Emily,

With fire in hands, as use was, to ignite
The sacrifice and set the pyre alight.
Great labour and full great apparelling
Went to the service and the fire-making,
For to the skies that green pyre reached its top,
And twenty fathoms did the arms out-crop,
That is to say, the branches went so wide.
Full many a load of straw they did provide.
But how the fire was made to climb so high;
Or what names all the different trees went by,
As oak, fir, birch, asp, alder, poplar, holm,
Willow, plane, ash, box, chestnut, linden, elm,
Laurel, thorn, maple, beech, yew, dogwood tree,
Or how they were felled, sha'n't be told by me.
Nor how the wood-gods scampered up and down,
Driven from homes that they had called their own,
Wherein they'd lived so long at ease, in peace,
The nymphs, the fauns, the hamadryades;
Nor how the beasts, for fear, and the birds, all
Fled, when that ancient wood began to fall;
Nor how aghast the ground was in the light,
Not being used to seeing the sun so bright;
Nor how the fire was started first with straw,
And then with dry wood, riven thrice by saw,
And then with green wood and with spicery,
And then with cloth of gold and jewellery,
And garlands hanging with full many a flower,
And myrrh, and incense, sweet as rose in bower;
Nor how Arcita lies among all this,
Nor what vast wealth about his body is;
Nor how this Emily, as was their way,
Lighted the sacred funeral fire, that day,
Nor how she swooned when men built up the fire,
Nor what she said, nor what was her desire;
No, nor what gems men on the fire then cast,
When the white flame went high and burned so fast;
Nor how one cast his shield, and one his spear,
And some their vestments, on that burning bier,
With cups of wine, and cups of milk, and blood,
Into that flame, which burned as wild-fire would;
Nor how the Greeks, in one huge wailing rout,
Rode slowly three times all the fire about,
Upon the left hand, with a loud shouting,
And three times more, with weapons clattering,
While thrice the women there raised up a cry;
Nor how was homeward led sad Emily;
Nor how Arcita burned to ashes cold;
Nor aught of how the lichwake they did hold
All that same night, nor how the Greeks did play

Who, naked, wrestled best, with oil anointed,
Nor who best bore himself in deeds appointed.
I will not even tell how they were gone
Home, into Athens, when the play was done;
But briefly to the point, now, will I wend
And make of this, my lengthy tale, an end.
With passing in their length of certain years,
All put by was the mourning and the tears
Of Greeks, as by one general assent;
And then it seems there was a parliament
At Athens, upon certain points in case;
Among the which points spoken of there was

With fyr in honde, as was that tyme the gyse,
To do th'office of funeral servyse.
Heigh labour, and ful greet apparaillinge
Was at the service and the fyr-makinge,
That with his grene top the heven raughte,
And twenty fadme of brede the armes straughte;
This is to seyn, the bowes were so brode.
Of stree first ther was leyd ful many a lode.
But how the fyr was maked up on highte,
And eek the names how the treës highte,
As ook, firre, birch, asp, alder, holm, popler,
Wilow, elm, plane, ash, box, chasteyn, lind, laurer,
Mapul, thorn, beech, hasel, ew, whippel-tree,
How they weren feld, shal nat be told for me;
Ne how the goddes ronnen up and doun,
Disherited of hir habitacioun,
In which they woneden in reste and pees,
Nymphes, Faunes, and Amadrides;
Ne how the bestes and the briddes alle
Fledden for fere, whan the wode was falle;
Ne how the ground agast was of the light,
That was nat wont to seen the sonne bright;
Ne how the fyr was couched first with stree,
And than with drye stokkes cloven a three,
And than with grene wode and spycerye,
And than with cloth of gold and with perrye,
And gerlandes hanging with ful many a flour,
The mirre, th'encens, with al so greet odour;
Ne how Arcite lay among al this,
Ne what richesse aboute his body is;
Ne how that Emelye, as was the gyse,
Putte in the fyr of funeral servyse;
Ne how she swowned whan men made the fyr,
Ne what she spak, ne what was hir desyr;
Ne what jeweles men in the fyr tho caste,
Whan that the fyr was greet and brente faste;
Ne how som caste hir sheeld, and som hir spere,
And of hir vestiments, whiche that they were,
And cuppes ful of wyn, and milk, and blood,
Into the fyr, that brente as it were wood;
Ne how the Grekes with an huge route
Thryës riden al the fyr aboute
Up-on the left hand, with a loud shoutinge,
And thryës with hir speres clateringe;
And thryës how the ladies gonne crye;
Ne how that lad was hom-ward Emelye;
Ne how Arcite is brent to asshen colde;
Ne how that liche-wake was y-holde
Al thilke night, ne how the Grekes pleye
The wake-pleyes, ne kepe I nat to seye;
Who wrastleth best naked, with oille enoynt,
Ne who that bar him best, in no disjoynt.
I wol nat tellen eek how that they goon
Hoom til Athénës, whan the pley is doon;
But shortly to the poynt than wol I wende,
And maken of my longe tale an ende.
By processe and by lengthe of certeyn yeres
Al stinted is the moorning and the teres.
Of Grekes, by oon general assent,
Than semed me ther was a parlement
At Athénës, up-on certeyn poynts and cas;
Among the whiche poynts y-spoken was

To have with certeyn contrees alliaunce,
And have fully of Thebans obeisaunce.
For which this noble Theseus anon
Leet senden after gentil Palamon,
Unwist of him what was the cause and why;
But in his blake clothes sorwefully
He cam at his comaundemente in hye.
Tho sente Theseus for Emelye.
Whan they were set, and hust was al the place,
And Theseus abiden hadde a space
Er any word cam from his wyse brest,
His eyen sette he ther as was his lest,
And with a sad visage he syked stille,
And after that right thus he seyde his wille.
"The firste moevere of the cause above,
Whan he first made the fair cheyne of love,
Greet was th'effect, and heigh was his entente;
Wel wiste he why, and what ther-of he mente;
For with that faire cheyne of love he bond
The fyr, the eyr, the water, and the lond
In certeyn boundes, that they may nat flee;
That same prince and that moevere," quod he,
"Hath stablissed, in this wrecched world adoun,
Certeyne dayes and duracioun
To al that is engendred in this place,
Over the whiche day they may nat pace,
Al mowe they yet tho dayes wel abregge;
Ther needeth non auctoritee allegge,
For it is preved by experience,
But that me list declaren my sentence.
Than may men by this ordre wel discerne,
That thilke moevere stable is and eterne.
Wel may men knowe, but it be a fool,
That every part deryveth from his hool.
For nature hath nat take his beginning
Of no party ne cantel of a thing,
But of a thing that parfit is and stable,
Descending so, til it be corrumpable.
And therfore, of his wyse purveyaunce,
He hath so wel biset his ordinaunce,
That speces of thinges and progressiouns
Shullen enduren by successiouns,
And nat eterne be, with-oute lyë:
This maistow understonde and seen at yë.
"Lo the ook, that hath so long a norisshinge
From tyme that it first biginneth springe,
And hath so long a lyf, as we may see,
Yet at the laste wasted is the tree.
"Considereth eek, how that the harde stoon
Under our feet, on which we trede and goon,
Yit wasteth it, as it lyth by the weye.
The brode river somtyme wexeth dreye.
The grete tounes see we wane and wende.
Than may ye see that al this thing hath ende.
"Of man and womman seen we wel also,
That nedeth, in oon of thise termes two,
This is to seyn, in youthe or elles age,
He moot ben deed, the king as shal a page;
Som in his bed, som in the depe see,
Som in the large feeld, as men may se;
Ther helpeth noght, al goth that ilke weye.
Thanne may I seyn that al this thing moot deye.

The ratifying of alliances
That should hold Thebes from all defiances.
Whereat this noble Theseüs, anon,
Invited there the gentle Palamon,
Not telling him what was the cause and why;
But in his mourning clothes, and sorrowfully,
He came upon that bidding, so say I.
And then Duke Theseüs sent for Emily.
When they were seated and was hushed the place,
And Theseüs had mused a little space,
Ere any word came from his full wise breast,
His two eyes fixed on whoso pleased him best,
Then with a sad face sighed he deep and still,
And after that began to speak his will.
"The Primal Mover and the Cause above,
When first He forged the goodly chain of love,
Great the effect, and high was His intent;
Well knew He why, and what thereof He meant;
For with that goodly chain of love He bound
The fire, the air, the water, and dry ground
In certain bounds, the which they might not flee;
That same First Cause and Mover," then quoth he,
"Has stablished in this base world, up and down,
A certain length of days to call their own
For all that are engendered in this place,
Beyond the which not one day may they pace,
Though yet all may that certain time abridge;
Authority there needs none, I allege,
For it is well proved by experience,
Save that I please to clarify my sense.
Then may men by this order well discern
This Mover to be stable and eterne.
Well may man know, unless he be a fool,
That every part derives but from the whole.
For Nature has not taken his being
From any part and portion of a thing,
But from a substance perfect, stable aye,
And so continuing till changed away.
And therefore, of His Wisdom's Providence,
Has He so well established ordinance
That species of all things and all progressions,
If they'd endure, it must be by successions,
Not being themselves eternal, 'tis no lie:
This may you understand and see by eye.
"Lo now, the oak, that has long nourishing
Even from the time that it begins to spring,
And has so long a life, as we may see,
Yet at the last all wasted is the tree.
"Consider, too, how even the hard stone
Under our feet we tread each day upon
Yet wastes it, as it lies beside the way.
And the broad river will be dry some day.
And great towns wane; we see them vanishing.
Thus may we see the end to everything.
"Of man and woman just the same is true:
Needs must, in either season of the two,
That is to say, in youth or else in age,
All men perish, the king as well as page;
Some in their bed, and some in the deep sea,
And some in the wide field—as it may be;
There's naught will help; all go the same way. Aye,
Then may I say that everything must die.

Who causes this but Jupiter the King?
He is the Prince and Cause of everything,
Converting all back to that primal well
From which it was derived, 'tis sooth to tell.
And against this, for every thing alive,
Of any state, avails it not to strive.
"Then is it wisdom, as it seems to me,
To make a virtue of necessity,
And calmly take what we may not eschew,
And specially that which to all is due.
Whoso would balk at aught, he does folly,
And thus rebels against His potency.
And certainly a man has most honour
In dying in his excellence and flower,
When he is certain of his high good name;
For then he gives to friend, and self, no shame.
And gladder ought a friend be of his death
When, in much honour, he yields up his breath,
Than when his name's grown feeble with old age;
For all forgotten, then, is his courage.
Hence it is best for all of noble name
To die when at the summit of their fame.
The contrary of this is wilfulness.
Why do we grumble? Why have heaviness
That good Arcita, chivalry's fair flower,
Is gone, with honour, in his best-lived hour.
Out of the filthy prison of this life?
Why grumble here his cousin and his wife
About his welfare, who loved them so well?
Can he thank them? Nay, God knows, not! Nor tell
How they his soul and thir own selves offend,
Though yet they may not their desires amend.
"What may I prove by this long argument
Save that we all turn to merriment,
After our grief, and give Jove thanks for grace.
And so, before we go from out this place,
I counsel that we make, of sorrows two,
One perfect joy, lasting for aye, for you;
And look you now, where most woe is herein,
There will we first amend it and begin.
"Sister," quoth he, "you have my full consent,
With the advice of this my Parliament,
That gentle Palamon, your own true knight,
Who serves you well with will and heart and might,
And so has ever, since you knew him first—
That you shall, of your grace, allay his thirst
By taking him for husband and for lord:
Lend me your hand, for this is our accord.
Let now your woman's pity make him glad.
For he is a king's brother's son, by gad;
And though he were a poor knight bachelor,
Since he has served you for so many a year,
And borne for you so great adversity,
This ought to weigh with you, it seems to me,
For mercy ought to dominate mere right."
Then said he thus to Palamon the knight:
"I think there needs but little sermoning
To make you give consent, now, to this thing.
Come near, and take your lady by the hand."
Between them, then, was tied that nuptial band,
Which is called matrimony or marriage,
By all the council and the baronage.

What maketh this but Jupiter the king?
The which is prince and cause of alle thing,
Converting al un-to his propre welle,
From which it is deryved, sooth to telle.
And here-agayns no creature on lyve
Of no degree availleth for to stryve.
"Thanne is it wisdom, as it thinketh me,
To maken vertu of necessitee,
And take it wel, that we may nat eschue,
And namely that to us alle is due.
And who-so gruccheth ought, he dooth folye,
And rebel is to him that al may gye.
And certeinly a man hath most honour
To dyen in his excellence and flour,
Whan he is siker of his gode name;
Than hath he doon his freend, ne him, no shame.
And gladder oghte his freend ben of his deeth,
Whan with honour up-yolden is his breeth,
Than whan his name apalled is for age;
For al forgeten is his vasselage.
Than is it best, as for a worthy fame,
To dyen whan that he is best of name.
The contrarie of al this is wilfulnesse.
Why grucchen we? why have we hevinesse,
That good Arcite, of chivalrye flour
Departed is, with duetee and honour,
Out of this foule prison of this lyf?
Why grucchen heer his cosin and his wyf
Of his wel-fare that loved hem so weel?
Can he hem thank? nay, God wot, never a deel,
That bothe his soule and eek hem-self offende,
And yet they mowe hir lustes nat amende.
"What may I conclude of this longe serie,
But, after wo, I rede us to be merie,
And thanken Jupiter of al his grace?
And, er that we departen from this place,
I rede that we make, of sorwes two,
O parfyt joye, lasting ever-mo;
And loketh now, wher most sorwe is herinne,
Ther wol we first amenden and biginne.
"Suster," quod he, "this is my fulle assent,
With al th'avys heer of my parlement,
That gentil Palamon, your owne knight,
That serveth yow with wille, herte, and might,
And ever hath doon, sin that ye first him knewe,
That ye shul, of your grace, up-on him rewe,
And taken him for housbonde and for lord:
Leen me your hond, for this is our acord.
Lat see now of your wommanly pitee.
He is a kinges brother sone, pardee;
And, though he were a povre bacheler,
Sin he hath served yow so many a yeer,
And had for yow so greet adversitee,
It moste been considered, leveth me;
For gentil mercy oghte to passen right."
Than seyde he thus to Palamon ful right;
"I trowe ther nedeth litel sermoning
To make yow assente to this thing.
Com neer, and tak your lady by the hond."
Bitwixen hem was maad anon the bond,
That highte matrimoine or mariage,
By al the counseil and the baronage.

And thus with alle blisse and melodye
Hath Palamon y-wedded Emelye.
And God, that al this wyde world hath wroght,
Sende him his love, that hath it dere a-boght.
For now is Palamon in alle wele,
Living in blisse, in richesse, and in hele;
And Emelye him loveth so tendrely,
And he hir serveth al-so gentilly,
That never was ther no word hem bitwene
Of jelousye, or any other tene.
Thus endeth Palamon and Emelye;
And God save al this faire companye!
  Amen.

And thus, in all bliss and with melody,
Has Palamon now wedded Emily.
And God, Who all this universe has wrought,
Send him His love, who has it dearly bought.
For now has Palamon, in all things, wealth,
Living in bliss, in riches, and in health;
And Emily loved him so tenderly,
And he served her so well and faithfully,
That never word once marred their happiness,
No jealousy, nor other such distress.
Thus ends now Palamon and Emily;
And may God save all this fair company!
  Amen.

HERE IS ENDED THE KNIGHT'S TALE

THE MILLER'S PROLOGUE

HERE FOLLOWETH THE WORDS BETWEEN THE HOST AND THE MILLER

WHAN that the Knight had thus his tale y-told,
In al the route nas ther yong ne old
That he ne seyde it was a noble storie,
And worthy for to drawen to memorie;
And namely the gentils everichoon.
Our Hoste lough and swoor, "so moot I goon,
This gooth aright; unbokeled is the male;
Lat see now who shal telle another tale:
For trewely, the game is wel bigonne.
Now telleth ye, sir Monk, if that ye conne,
Sumwhat, to quyte with the Knightes tale."
The Miller, that for-dronken was al pale,
So that unnethe up-on his hors he sat,
He nolde avalen neither hood ne hat,
Ne abyde no man for his curteisye,
But in Pilates vois he gan to crye,
And swoor by armes and by blood and bones,
"I can a noble tale for the nones,
With which I wol now quyte the Knightes tale."
  Our Hoste saugh that he was dronke of ale,
And seyde: "abyd, Robin, my leve brother,
Som bettre man shal telle us first another:
Abyd, and lat us werken thriftily."
  "By goddes soul," quod he, "that wol nat I;
For I wol speke, or elles go my wey."
Our Hoste answerde: "tel on, a devel wey!
Thou art a fool, thy wit is overcome."
  "Now herkneth," quod the Miller, "alle and some!
But first I make a protestacioun
That I am dronke, I knowe it by my soun;
And therfore, if that I misspeke or seye,
Wyte it the ale of Southwerk, I yow preye;
For I wol telle a legende and a lyf
Bothe of a Carpenter, and of his wyf,
How that a clerk hath set the wrightes cappe."
  The Reeve answerde and seyde, "stint thy clappe,
Lat be thy lewed dronken harlotrye.
It is a sinne and eek a greet folye
To apeiren any man, or him diffame,

Now when the knight had thus his story told,
In all the rout there was nor young nor old
But said it was a noble story, well
Worthy to be kept in mind to tell;
And specially the gentle folk, each one.
Our host, he laughed and swore, "So may I run,
But this goes well; unbuckled is the mail;
Let's see now who can tell another tale:
For certainly the game is well begun.
Now shall you tell, sir monk, if't can be done,
Something with which to pay for the knight's tale."
  The miller, who with drinking was all pale,
So that unsteadily on his horse he sat,
He would not take off either hood or hat,
Nor wait for any man, in courtesy,
But all in Pilate's voice began to cry,
And by the Arms and Blood and Bones he swore,
"I have a noble story in my store,
With which I will requite the good knight's tale."
  Our host saw, then, that he was drunk with ale,
And said to him: "Wait, Robin, my dear brother,
Some better man shall tell us first another:
Submit and let us work on profitably."
  "Now by God's soul," cried he, "that will not I!
For I will speak, or else I'll go my way."
  Our host replied: "Tell on, then, till doomsday!
You are a fool, your wit is overcome."
  "Now hear me," said the miller, "all and some!
But first I make protestation round
That I'm quite drunk, I know it by my sound:
And therefore, if I slander or mis-say,
Blame it on ale of Southwark, so I pray;
For I will tell a legend and a life
Both of a carpenter and of his wife,
And how a scholar set the good wright's cap."
  The reeve replied and said: "Oh, shut your trap.
Let be your ignorant drunken ribaldry!
It is a sin, and further, great folly
To asperse any man, or him defame,

And, too, to bring upon a man's wife shame.
There are enough of other things to say."
  This drunken miller spoke on in his way,
And said: "Oh, but my dear brother Oswald,
The man who has no wife is no cuckold.
But I say not, thereby, that you are one:
Many good wives there are, as women run,
And ever a thousand good to one that's bad,
As well you know yourself, unless you're mad.
Why are you angry with my story's cue?
I have a wife, begad, as well as you,
Yet I'd not, for the oxen of my plow,
Take on my shoulders more than is enow,
By judging of myself that I am one;
I will believe full well that I am none.
A husband must not be inquisitive
Of God, nor of his wife, while she's alive.
So long as he may find God's plenty there,
For all the rest he need not greatly care."
  What should I say, except this miller rare
He would forgo his talk for no man there,
But told his churlish tale in his own way:
I think I'll here re-tell it, if I may.
And therefore, every gentle soul, I pray
That for God's love you'll hold not what I say
Evilly meant, but that I must rehearse
All of their tales, the better and the worse,
Or else prove false to some of my design.
Therefore, who likes not this, let him, in fine,
Turn over page and choose another tale:
For he shall find enough, both great and small,
Of stories touching on gentility,
And holiness, and on morality;
And blame not me if you do choose amiss.
The miller was a churl, you well know this;
So was the reeve, and many another more,
And ribaldry they told from plenteous store,
Be then advised, and hold me free from blame;
Men should not be too serious at a game.

And eek to bringen wyves in swich fame.
Thou mayst y-nogh of othere thinges seyn."
  This dronken Miller spak ful sone ageyn,
And seyde, "leve brother Osewold,
Who hath no wyf, he is no cokewold.
But I sey nat therfore that thou art oon;
Ther been ful gode wyves many oon,
And ever a thousand gode ayeyns oon badde,
That knowestow wel thy-self, but-if thou madde.
Why artow angry with my tale now?
I have a wyf, pardee, as well as thou,
Yet nolde I, for the oxen in my plogh,
Taken up-on me more than y-nogh,
As demen of my-self that I were oon;
I wol beleve wel that I am noon.
An housbond shal nat been inquisitif
Of goddes privetee, nor of his wyf.
So he may finde goddes foyson there,
Of the remenant nedeth nat enquere.'
  What sholde I more seyn, but this Millere
He nolde his wordes for no man forbere,
But tolde his cherles tales in his manere;
Me thinketh that I shal reherce it here.
And ther-fore every gentil wight I preye,
For goddes love, demeth nat that I seye
Of evel entente, but that I moot reherce
Hir tales alle, be they bettre or werse,
Or elles falsen som of my matere.
And therefore, who-so list it nat y-here,
Turne over the leef, and chese another tale;
For he shal finde y-nowe, grete and smale,
Of storial thing that toucheth gentillesse,
And eek moralitee and holinesse;
Blameth nat me if that ye chese amis.
The Miller is a cherl, ye knowe wel this;
So was the Reeve, and othere many mo,
And harlotrye they tolden bothe two.
Avyseth yow and putte me out of blame;
And eek men shal nat make ernest of game.

HERE ENDETH THE PROLOGUE

THE MILLER'S TALE

HERE BEGINNETH THE MILLER HIS TALE

ONCE on a time was dwelling in Oxford
A wealthy lout who took in guests to board,
And of his craft he was a carpenter.
A poor scholar was lodging with him there,
Who'd learned the arts, but all his phantasy
Was turned to study of astrology;
And knew a certain set of theorems
And could find out by various stratagems,
If men but asked of him in certain hours
When they should have a drought or else have
  showers,
Or if men asked of him what should befall
To anything—I cannot reckon them all.
  This clerk was called the clever Nicholas;
Of secret loves he knew and their solace;

WHYLOM ther was dwellinge at Oxenford
A riche gnof, that gestes heeld to bord,
And of his craft he was a Carpenter.
With him ther was dwellinge a povre scoler,
Had lerned art, but al his fantasye
Was turned for to lerne astrologye,
And coude a certeyn of conclusiouns
To demen by interrogaciouns,
If that men axed him in certein houres,
Whan that men sholde have droghte or elles
  shoures,
Or if men axed him what sholde bifalle
Of everything, I may nat rekene hem alle.
  This clerk was cleped hende Nicholas;
Of derne love he coude and of solas;

And ther-to he was sleigh and ful privee,
And lyk a mayden meke for to see.
A chambre hadde he in that hostelrye
Allone, with-outen any companye,
Ful fetisly y-dight with herbes swote;
And he him-self as swete as is the rote
Of licorys, or any cetewale.
His Almageste and bokes grete and smale,
His astrelabie, longinge for his art,
His augrim-stones[1] layen faire a-part
On shelves couched at his beddes heed:
His presse y-covered with a falding reed.
And al above ther lay a gay sautrye,
On which he made a nightes melodye
So swetely, that al the chambre rong;
And *Angelus ad virginem* he song;
And after that he song the kinges note;
Ful often blessed was his mery throte.
And thus this swete clerk his tyme spente
After his freendes finding and his rente.
  This Carpenter had wedded newe a wyfe
Which that he lovede more than his lyf;
Of eightetene yeer she was of age.
Jalous he was, and heeld hir narwe in cage,
For she was wilde and yong, and he was old,
And demed him-self ben lyk a cokewold.
He knew nat Catoun, for his wit was rude,
That bad man sholde wedde his similitude.
Men sholde wedden after hir estaat,
For youthe and elde is often at debaat.
But sith that he was fallen in the snare,
He moste endure, as other folk, his care.
  Fair was this yonge wyf, and ther-with-al
As any wesele hir body gent and smal.
A ceynt she werede barred al of silk,
A barmclooth eek as whyt as morne milk
Up-on hir lendes, ful of many a gore.
Whyt was hir smok and brouded al bifore
And eek bihinde, on hir coler aboute,
Of col-black silk, with-inne and eek withoute.
The tapes of hir whyte voluper
Were of the same suyte of hir coler;
Hir filet brood of silk, and set ful hye:
And sikerly she hadde a likerous yë.
Ful smale y-pulled were hir browes two,
And tho were bent, and blake as any sloo.
She was ful more blisful on to see
Than is the newe pere-jonette tree;
And softer than the wolle is of a wether.
And by hir girdel heeng a purs of lether
Tasseld with silk, and perled with latoun.
In al this world, to seken up and doun,
There nis no man so wys, that coude thenche
So gay a popelote, or swich a wenche.
Ful brighter was the shyning of hir hewe
Than in the tour the noble y-forged newe.
But of hir song, it was as loude and yerne
As any swalwe sittinge on a berne.
Ther-to she coude skippe and make
  game,
As any kide or calf folwinge his dame.

And he kept counsel, too, for he was sly
And meek as any maiden passing by.
He had a chamber in that hostelry,
And lived alone there, without company,
All garnished with sweet herbs of good repute;
And he himself sweet-smelling as the root
Of licorice, valerian, or setwall.
His *Almagest* and books both great and small,
His astrolabe, belonging to his art,
His algorism stones[1]—all laid apart
On shelves that ranged beside his lone bed's head;
His press was covered with a cloth of red.
And over all there lay a psaltery
Whereon he made an evening's melody,
Playing so sweetly that the chamber rang;
And *Angelus ad virginem* he sang;
And after that he warbled the *King's Note:*
Often in good voice was his merry throat.
And thus this gentle clerk his leisure spends
Supported by some income and his friends.
  This carpenter had lately wed a wife
Whom he loved better than he loved his life;
And she was come to eighteen years of age.
Jealous he was and held her close in cage.
For she was wild and young and he was old,
And deemed himself as like to be cuckold..
He knew not Cato, for his lore was rude:
That vulgar man should wed similitude.
A man should wed according to estate,
For youth and age are often in debate.
But now, since he had fallen in the snare,
He must endure, like other folk, his care,
  Fair was this youthful wife, and therewithal
As weasel's was her body slim and small.
A girdle wore she, barred and striped, of silk.
An apron, too, as white as morning milk
About her loins, and full of many a gore;
White was her smock, embroidered all before
And even behind, her collar round about,
Of coal-black silk, on both sides, in and out;
The strings of the white cap upon her head
Were, like her collar, black silk worked with thread;
Her fillet was of wide silk worn full high:
And certainly she had a lickerish eye.
She'd thinned out carefully her eyebrows two,
And they were arched and black as any sloe.
She was a far more pleasant thing to see
Than is the newly budded young pear-tree;
And softer than the wool is on a wether.
Down from her girdle hung a purse of leather,
Tasselled with silk, with latten beading sown.
In all this world, searching it up and down,
So gay a little doll, I well believe,
Or such a wench, there's no man can conceive.
Far brighter was the brilliance of her hue
Than in the Tower the gold coins minted new.
And songs came shrilling from her pretty head
As from a swallow's sitting on a shed.
Therewith she'd dance too, and could play and
  sham
Like any kid or calf about its dam.

[1]Counting stones.

Her mouth was sweet as bragget or as mead
Or hoard of apples laid in hay or weed.
Skittish she was as is a pretty colt,
Tall as a staff and straight as cross-bow bolt.
A brooch she wore upon her collar low,
As broad as boss of buckler did it show;
Her shoes laced up to where a girl's legs thicken.
She was a primrose, and a tender chicken
For any lord to lay upon his bed,
Or yet for any good yeoman to wed.
Now, sir, and then, sir, so befell the case,
That on a day this clever Nicholas
Fell in with this young wife to toy and play,
The while her husband was down Osney way,
Clerks being as crafty as the best of us;
And unperceived he caught her by the puss,
Saying: "Indeed, unless I have my will,
For secret love of you, sweetheart, I'll spill."
And held her hard about the hips, and how!—
And said: "O darling, love me, love me now,
Or I shall die, and pray you God may save!"
And she leaped as a colt does in the trave,[1]
And with her head she twisted fast away,
And said: "I will not kiss you, by my fay!
Why, let go," cried she, "let go, Nicholas!
Or I will call for help and cry 'alas!'
Do take your hands away, for courtesy!"
This Nicholas for mercy then did cry,
And spoke so well, importuned her so fast
That she her love did grant him at the last,
And swore her oath, by Saint Thomas of Kent,
That she would be at his command, content,
As soon as opportunity she could spy.
"My husband is so full of jealousy,
Unless you will await me secretly,
I know I'm just as good as dead," said she.
"You must keep all quite hidden in this case."
"Nay, thereof worry not," said Nicholas,
"A clerk has lazily employed his while
If he cannot a carpenter beguile."
And thus they were agreed, and then they swore
To wait a while, as I have said before.
When Nicholas had done thus every whit
And patted her about the loins a bit,
He kissed her sweetly, took his psaltery,
And played it fast and made a melody.
Then fell it thus, that to the parish kirk,
The Lord Christ Jesus' own works for to work,
This good wife went, upon a holy day;
Her forehead shone as bright as does the May,
So well she'd washed it when she left off work.
Now there was of that church a parish clerk
Whose name was (as folk called him) Absalom.
Curled was his hair, shining like gold, and from
His head spread fanwise in a thick bright mop;
'Twas parted straight and even on the top;
His cheek was red, his eyes grey as a goose;
With Saint Paul's windows cut upon his shoes,
He stood in red hose fitting famously.
And he was clothed full well and properly
All in a coat of blue, in which were let

Hir mouth was swete as bragot or the meeth,
Or hord of apples leyd in hey or heeth.
Winsinge she was, as is a joly colt,
Long as a mast, and upright as a bolt.
A brooch she baar up-on hir lowe coler,
As brood as is the bos of a bocler.
Hir shoes were laced on hir legges hye;
She was a prymerole, a pigges-nye
For any lord to leggen in his bedde,
Or yet for any good yeman to wedde.
Now sire, and eft sire, so bifel the cas,
That on a day this hende Nicholas
Fil with this yonge wyf to rage and pleye,
Whyl that hir housbond was at Oseneye,
As clerks ben ful subtile and ful queynte;
And prively he caughte hir by the queynte,
And seyde, "y-wis, but if ich have my wille,
For derne love of thee, lemman, I spille."
And heeld hir harde by the haunche-bones,
And seyde, "lemman, love me al at-ones,
Or I wol dyen, also god me save!"
And she sprong as a colt doth in the trave,[1]
And with hir heed she wryed faste awey,
And seyde, "I wol nat kisse thee, by my fey,
Why, lat be," quod she, "lat be, Nicholas,
Or I wol crye out 'harrow' and 'allas.'
Do wey your handes for your curteisye!"
This Nicholas gan mercy for to crye,
And spak so faire, and profred hir so faste,
That she hir love him graunted atte laste,
And swoor hir ooth, by seint Thomas of Kent,
That she wol been at his comandement,
Whan that she may hir leyser wel espye.
"Myn housbond is so ful of jalousye,
That but ye wayte wel and been privee,
I woot right wel I nam but deed," quod she.
"Ye moste been ful derne, as in this cas."
"Nay ther-of care thee noght," quod Nicholas,
"A clerk had litherly biset his whyle,
But-if he coude a carpenter bigyle."
And thus they been acorded and y-sworn
To wayte a tyme, as I have told biforn.
Whan Nicholas had doon thus everydeel,
And thakked hir aboute the lendes weel,
He kist hir swete, and taketh his sautrye,
And pleyeth faste, and maketh melodye.
Than fil it thus, that to the parish-chirche,
Cristes owne werkes for to wirche,
This gode wyf wente on an haliday;
Hir forheed shoon as bright as any day,
So was it wasshen whan she leet hir werk.
Now was ther of that chirche a parish-clerk,
The which that was y-cleped Absolon.
Crul was his heer, and as the gold it shoon,
And strouted as a fanne large and brode;
Ful streight and even lay his joly shode.
His rode was reed, his eyen greye as goos;
With Powles window corven on his shoos,
In hoses rede he wente fetisly.
Y-clad he was ful smal and proprely,
Al in a kirtel of a light wachet;

[1]A frame for confining a horse or colt for shoeing.

Ful faire and thikke been the poyntes set.
And ther-up-on he hadde a gay surplys
As whyt as is the blosme up-on the rys.
A mery child he was, so god me save,
Wel coude he laten blood and clippe and shave,
And make a chartre of lond or acquitaunce.
In twenty manere coude he trippe and daunce
After the scole of Oxenforde tho,
And with his legges casten to and fro,
And pleyen songes on a small rubible;
Ther-to he song som-tyme a loud quinible;
And as wel coude he pleye on his giterne.
In al the toun nas brewhous ne taverne
That he ne visited with his solas,
Ther any galard tappestere was.
But sooth to seyn, he was somdel squaymous
Of farting, and speche daungerous.
This Absolon, that jolif was and gay,
Gooth with a sencer on the haliday,
Sensinge the wyves of the parish faste;
And many a lovely look on hem he caste,
And namely on this carpenteres wyf.
To loke on hir him thoughte a mery lyf,
She was so propre and swete and likerous.
I dar wel seyn, if she had been a mous,
And he a cat, he wolde hir hente anon.
This parish-clerk, this joly Absolon,
Hath in his herte swich a love-longinge,
That of no wyf ne took he noon offringe;
For curteisye, he seyde, he wolde noon.
The mone, whan it was night, ful brighte shoon,
And Absolon his giterne hath y-take,
For paramours, he thoghte for to wake.
And forth he gooth, jolif and amorous,
Til he cam to the carpenteres hous
A litel after cokkes hadde y-crowe;
And dressed him up by a shot-windowe
That was up-on the carpenteres wal.
He singeth in his vois gentil and smal,
"Now, dere lady, if thy wille be,
I preye yow that ye wol rewe on me,"
Ful wel acordaunt to his giterninge.
This carpenter awook, and herde him singe,
And spak un-to his wyf, and seyde anon,
"What! Alison! herestow nat Absolon
That chaunteth thus under our boures wal?"
And she answerde hir housbond therwith-al,
"Yis, god wot, John, I here it every-del."
This passeth forth; what wol ye bet than wel?
Fro day to day this joly Absolon
So woweth hir, that him is wo bigon.
He waketh al the night and al the day;
He kempte his lokkes brode, and made him gay;
He woweth hir by menes and brocage,
And swoor he wolde been hir owne page;
He singeth, brokkinge as a nightingale;
He sente hir piment, meeth, and spyced ale,
And wafres, pyping hote out of the glede;
And for she was of toune, he profred mede.
For some folk wol ben wonnen for richesse,
And som for strokes, and som for gentillesse.
Somtyme, to shewe his lightnesse and maistrye,

Holes for the lacings, which were fairly set.
And over all he wore a fine surplice
As white as ever hawthorn spray, and nice.
A merry lad he was, so God me save,
And well could he let blood, cut hair, and shave,
And draw a deed or quitclaim, as might chance.
In twenty manners could he trip and dance,
After the school that reigned in Oxford, though,
And with his two legs swinging to and fro;
And he could play upon a violin;
Thereto he sang in treble voice and thin;
And as well could he play on his guitar.
In all the town no inn was, and no bar,
That he'd not visited to make good cheer,
Especially were lively barmaids there.
But truth to tell, he was a bit squeamish
Of farting and of language haughtyish.
This Absalom, who was so light and gay,
Went with a censer on the holy day,
Censing the wives like an enthusiast;
And on them many a loving look he cast,
Especially on this carpenter's goodwife.
To look at her he thought a merry life,
She was so pretty, sweet, and lickerous.
I dare well say, if she had been a mouse
And he a cat, he would have mauled her some.
This parish clerk, this lively Absalom
Had in his heart, now, such a love-longing
That from no wife took he an offering,
For courtesy, he said, he would take none.
The moon, when it was night, full brightly shone,
And his guitar did Absalom then take,
For in love-watching he'd intent to wake.
And forth he went, jolly and amorous,
Until he came unto the carpenter's house
A little after cocks began to crow;
And took his stand beneath a shot-window
That was let into the good wood-wright's wall.
He sang then, in his pleasant voice and small,
"Oh now, dear lady, if your will it be,
I pray that you will have some ruth on me,"
The words in harmony with his string-plucking.
This carpenter awoke and heard him sing,
And called unto his wife and said, in sum:
"What, Alison! Do you hear Absalom,
Who plays and sings beneath our bedroom wall?"
And she said to her husband, therewithal:
"Yes, God knows, John, I hear it, truth to tell."
So this went on; what is there better than well?
From day to day this pretty Absalom
So wooed her he was woebegone therefrom.
He lay awake all night and all the day;
He combed his spreading hair and dressed him gay;
By go-betweens and agents, too, wooed he,
And swore her loyal page he'd ever be.
He sang as tremulously as nightingale;
He sent her sweetened wine and well-spiced ale
And waffles piping hot out of the fire,
And, she being town-bred, mead for her desire.
For some are won by means of money spent,
And some by tricks, and some by long descent.
Once, to display his versatility,

He acted Herod on a scaffold high.
But what availed it him in any case?
She was enamoured so of Nicholas
That Absalom might go and blow his horn;
He got naught for his labour but her scorn.
And thus she made of Absalom her ape,
And all his earnestness she made a jape.
For truth is in this proverb, and no lie,
Men say well thus: It's always he that's nigh
That makes the absent lover seem a sloth.
For now, though Absalom be wildly wroth,
Because he is so far out of her sight,
This handy Nicholas stands in his light.
Now bear you well, you clever Nicholas!
For Absalom may wail and sing "Alas!"
And so it chanced that on a Saturday
This carpenter departed to Osney;
And clever Nicholas and Alison
Were well agreed to this effect: anon
This Nicholas should put in play a wile
The simple, jealous husband to beguile;
And if it chanced the game should go a-right,
She was to sleep within his arms all night,
For this was his desire, and hers also.
Presently then, and without more ado,
This Nicholas, no longer did he tarry,
But softly to his chamber did he carry
Both food and drink to last at least a day,
Saying that to her husband she should say—
If he should come to ask for Nicholas—
Why, she should say she knew not where he was,
For all day she'd not seen him, far or nigh;
She thought he must have got some malady,
Because in vain her maid would knock and call;
He'd answer not, whatever might befall.
And so it was that all that Saturday
This Nicholas quietly in chamber lay,
And ate and slept, or did what pleased him best,
Till Sunday when the sun had gone to rest.
This simple man with wonder heard the tale,
And marvelled what their Nicholas might ail,
And said: "I am afraid, by Saint Thomas,
That everything's not well with Nicholas.
God send he be not dead so suddenly!
This world is most unstable, certainly;
I saw, today, the corpse being borne to kirk
Of one who, but last Monday, was at work.
Go up," said he unto his boy anon,
"Call at his door, or knock there with a stone,
Learn how it is and boldly come tell me."
The servant went up, then, right sturdily,
And at the chamber door, the while he stood,
He cried and knocked as any madman would—
"What! How! What do you, Master Nicholay?
How can you sleep through all the livelong day?"
But all for naught, he never heard a word;
A hole he found, low down upon a board,
Through which the house cat had been wont to
creep;
And to that hole he stooped, and through did peep,
And finally he ranged him in his sight.
This Nicholas sat gaping there, upright,

He pleyeth Herodes on a scaffold hye.
But what availleth him as in this cas?
She loveth so this hende Nicholas,
That Absolon may blowe the bukkes horn;
He ne hadde for his labour but a scorn:
And thus she maketh Absolon hir ape,
And al his ernest turneth til a jape.
Ful sooth is this proverbe, it is no lye,
Men seyn right thus, "alwey the nye slye
Maketh the ferre leve to be looth."
For though that Absolon be wood or wrooth,
By-cause that he fer was from hir sighte,
This nye Nicholas stood in his lighte.
Now bere thee wel, thou hende Nicholas!
For Absolon may waille and singe "allas."
Ans so bifel it on a Saterday,
This carpenter was goon til Osenay;
And hende Nicholas and Alisoun
Acorded been to this conclusioun,
That Nicholas shal shapen him a wyle
This sely jalous housbond to bigyle;
And if so be the game wente aright,
She sholde slepen in his arm al night,
For this was his desyr and hir also.
And right anon, with-outen wordes mo,
This Nicholas no lenger wolde tarie,
But doth ful softe un-to his chambre carie
Bothe mete and drinke for a day or tweye,
And to hir housbonde bad hir for to seye,
If that he axed after Nicholas,
She sholde seye she niste where he was,
Of al that day she saugh him nat with yë;
She trowed that he was in maladye,
For, for no cry, hir mayde coude him calle;
He nolde answere, for no-thing that mighte falle.
This passeth forth al thilke Saterday,
That Nicholas stille in his chambre lay,
And eet and sleep, or dide what him leste,
Til Sonday, that the sonne gooth to reste.
This sely carpenter hath greet merveyle
Of Nicholas, or what thing mighte him eyle,
And seyde, "I am adrad, by seint Thomas,
It stondeth nat aright with Nicholas.
God shilde that he deyde sodeynly!
This world is now ful tikel, sikerly;
I saugh to-day a cors y-born to chirche
That now, on Monday last, I saugh him wirche.
Go up," quod he un-to his knave anoon,
"Clepe at his dore, or knokke with a stoon,
Loke how it is, and tel me boldely."
This knave gooth him up ful sturdily,
And at the chambre-dore, whyl that he stood,
He cryde and knokked as that he were wood:—
"What! how! what do ye, maister Nicholay?
How may ye slepen al the longe day?"
But al for noght, he herde nat a word;
An hole he fond, ful lowe up-on a bord,
Ther as the cat was wont in for to
crepe;
And at that hole he looked in ful depe,
And at the laste he hadde of him a sighte.
This Nicholas sat gaping ever up-righte,

As he had kyked on the newe mone.
Adoun he gooth, and tolde his maister sone
In what array he saugh this ilke man.
  This carpenter to blessen him bigan,
And seyde, "help us, seinte Frideswyde!
A man woot litel what him shal bityde.
This man is falle, with his astromye,[1]
In som woodnesse or in some agonye;
I thoghte ay wel how that it sholde be!
Men sholde nat knowe of goddes privetee.
Ye, blessed be alwey a lewed man,
That noght but only his bileve can!
So ferde another clerk with astromye;
He walked in the feeldes for to prye
Up-on the sterres, what ther sholde bifalle,
Til he was in a marle-pit y-falle;
He saugh nat that. But yet, by seint Thomas,
Me reweth sore of hende Nicholas.
He shal be rated of his studying,
If that I may, by Jesus, hevene king!
  Get me a staf, that I may underspore,
Whyl that thou, Robin, hevest up the dore.
He shal out of his studying, as I gesse"—
And to the chambre-dore he gan him dresse.
His knave was a strong carl for the nones,
And by the haspe he haf it up atones;
In-to the floor the dore fil anon.
This Nicholas sat ay as stille as stoon,
And ever gaped upward in-to the eir.
This carpenter wende he were in despeir,
And hente him by the sholdres mightily,
And shook him harde, and cryde spitously,
"What! Nicholay! what, how! what! loke adoun!
Awake, and thenk on Cristes passioun;
I crouche thee from elves and fro wightes!"
Ther-with the night-spel seyde he anon-rightes
On foure halves of the hous aboute,
And on the threshfold of the dore withoute:—
  "Jesu Crist, and sëynt Benedight,
  Blesse this hous from every wikked wight,
  For nightes verye, the white *paternoster!*—
  Where wentestow, seynt Petres soster?"
And atte laste this hende Nicholas
Gan for to syke sore, and seyde, "allas!
Shal al the world be lost eftsones now?"
  This carpenter answerde, "what seystow?
What! thenk on god, as we don, men that swinke."
  This Nicholas answerde, "fecche me drinke;
And after wol I speke in privetee
Of certeyn thing that toucheth me and thee;
I wol telle it non other man, certeyn."
  This carpenter goth doun, and comth ageyn,
And broghte of mighty ale a large quart;
And whan that ech of hem had dronke his part,
This Nicholas his dore faste shette,
And doun the carpenter by him he sette.
  He seyde, "John, myn hoste lief and dere,
Thou shalt up-on thy trouthe swere me here,
That to no wight thou shalt this conseil wreye;
For it is Cristes conseil that I seye,

As if he'd looked too long at the new moon.
Downstairs he went and told his master soon
In what array he'd found this self-same man.
  This carpenter to cross himself began,
And said: "Now help us, holy Frideswide!
Little a man can know what shall betide.
This man is fallen, with his astromy,[1]
Into some madness or some agony;
I always feared that somehow this would be!
Men should not meddle in God's privity.
Aye, blessed always be the ignorant man,
Whose creed is all he ever has to scan!
So fared another clerk with astromy;
He walked into the meadows for to pry
Into the stars, to learn what should befall,
Until into a clay-pit he did fall;
He saw not that. But yet, by Saint Thomas,
I'm sorry for this clever Nicholas.
He shall be scolded for his studying,
If not too late, by Jesus, Heaven's King!
  "Get me a staff, that I may pry before,
The while you, Robin, heave against the door.
We'll take him from this studying, I guess."
  And on the chamber door, then, he did press.
His servant was a stout lad, if a dunce,
And by the hasp he heaved it up at once;
Upon the floor that portal fell anon.
This Nicholas sat there as still as stone,
Gazing with gaping mouth, straight up in air.
This carpenter thought he was in despair,
And took him by the shoulders, mightily,
And shook him hard, and cried out, vehemently:
"What! Nicholay! Why how now! Come, look down!
Awake, and think on Jesus' death and crown!
I cross you from all elves and magic wights!"
  And then the night-spell said he out, by rights,
At the four corners of the house about,
And at the threshold of the door, without:—
  "O Jesus Christ and good Saint Benedict,
Protect this house from all that may afflict,
For the night hag the white Paternoster!—
Where hast thou gone, Saint Peter's sister?"
And at the last this clever Nicholas
Began to sigh full sore, and said: "Alas!
Shall all the world be lost so soon again?"
  This carpenter replied: "What say you, then?
What! Think on God, as we do, men that swink."
  This Nicholas replied: "Go fetch me drink;
And afterward I'll tell you privately
A certain thing concerning you and me;
I'll tell it to no other man or men."
  This carpenter went down and came again,
And brought of potent ale a brimming quart;
And when each one of them had drunk his part,
Nicholas shut the door fast, and with that
He drew a seat and near the carpenter sat.
  He said: "Now, John, my good host, lief and dear,
You must upon your true faith swear, right here,
That to no man will you this word betray;
For it is Christ's own word that I will say,

[1]The carpenter's corruption.

And if you tell a man, you're ruined quite;
This punishment shall come to you, of right,
That if you're traitor you''ll go mad—and should!"
"Nay, Christ forbid it, for His holy blood!"
Said then this simple man: "I am no blab,
Nor, though I say it, am I fond of gab.
Say what you will, I never will it tell
To child or wife, by Him that harried Hell!"
"Now, John," said Nicholas, "I will not lie;
But I've found out, from my astrology,
As I have looked upon the moon so bright,
That now, come Monday next, at nine of night,
Shall fall a rain so wildly mad as would
Have been, by half, greater than Noah's flood.
This world," he said, "in less time than an hour,
Shall all be drowned, so terrible is this shower;
Thus shall all mankind drown and lose all life."
This carpenter replied: "Alas, my wife!
And shall she drown? Alas, my Alison!"
For grief of this he almost fell. Anon
He said: "Is there no remedy in this case?"
"Why yes, good luck," said clever Nicholas,
"If you will work by counsel of the wise;
You must not act on what your wits advise.
For so says Solomon, and it's all true,
'Work by advice and thou shalt never rue.'
And if you'll act as counselled and not fail,
I undertake, without a mast or sail,
To save us all, aye you and her and me.
Haven't you heard of Noah how saved was he,
Because Our Lord had warned him how to keep
Out of the flood that covered earth so deep?"
"Yes," said this carpenter, "long years ago."
"Have you not heard," asked Nicholas, "also
The sorrows of Noah and his fellowship
In getting his wife to go aboard the ship?
He would have rather, I dare undertake,
At that time, and for all the weather black,
That she had one ship fo herself alone.
Therefore, do you know what would best be done?
This thing needs haste, and of a hasty thing
Men must not preach nor do long tarrying.
"Presently go, and fetch here to this inn
A kneading-tub, or brewing vat, and win
One each for us, but see that they are large,
Wherein we may swim out as in a barge,
And have therein sufficient food and drink
For one day only; that's enough, I think.
The water will dry up and flow away
About the prime of the succeeding day.
But Robin must not know of this, your knave,
And even Jill, your maid, I may not save;
Ask me not why, for though you do ask me,
I will not tell you of God's privity.
Suffice you, then, unless your wits are mad,
To have as great a grace as Noah had.
Your wife I shall not lose, there is no doubt,
Go, now your way, and speedily get about,
But when you have, for you and her and me,
Procured these kneading-tubs, or beer-vats, three,
Then you shall hang them near the roof-tree high,
That no man our purveyance may espy.

And if thou telle it man, thou are forlore;
For this vengaunce thou shalt han therfore,
That if thou wreye me, thou shalt be wood!"
"Nay, Crist forbede it, for his holy blood!"
Quod tho this sely man, "I nam no labbe,
Ne, though I seye, I nam nat lief to gabbe.
Sey what thou wolt, I shal it never telle
To child ne wyf, by him that harwed helle!"
"Now John," quod Nicholas, "I wol nat lye;
I have y-founde in myn astrologye,
As I have loked in the mone bright,
That now, a Monday next, at quarter-night,
Shal falle a reyn and that so wilde and wood,
That half so greet was never Noës flood.
This world," he seyde, "in lasse than in an hour
Shal al be dreynt, so hidous is the shour;
Thus shal mankynde drenche and lese hir lyf."
This carpenter answerde, "allas, my wyf!
And shal she drenche? allas! myn Alisoun!"
For sorwe of this he fil almost adoun,
And seyde, "is ther no remedie in this cas?"
"Why, yis, for gode," quod hende Nicholas,
"If thou wolt werken after lore and reed;
Thou mayst nat werken after thyn owene heed.
For thus seith Salomon, that was ful trewe,
"Werk al by conseil, and thou shalt nat rewe."
And if thou werken wolt by good conseil,
I undertake, with-outen mast and seyl,
Yet shal I saven hir and thee and me.
Hastow nat herd how saved was Noë,
Whan that our lord had warned him biforn
That al the world with water sholde be lorn?"
"Yis," quod this carpenter, "ful yore ago."
"Hastow nat herd," quod Nicholas, "also
The sorwe of Noë with his felawshipe,
Er that he mighte gete his wyf to shipe?
Him had be lever, I dar wel undertake,
At thilke tyme, than alle hise wetheres blake,
That she hadde had a ship hir-self allone.
And ther-fore, wostou what is best to done?
This asketh haste, and of an hastif thing
Men may nat preche or maken tarying.
Anon go gete us faste in-to this in
A kneding-trogh, or elles a kimelin,
For ech of us, but loke that they be large,
In which we mowe swimme as in a barge,
And han ther-inne vitaille suffisant
But for a day; fy on the remenant!
The water shal aslake and goon away
Aboute pryme up-on the nexte day.
But Robin may nat wite of this, thy knave,
Ne eek thy mayde Gille I may nat save;
Axe nat why, for though thou aske me,
I wol nat tellen goddes privetee.
Suffiseth thee, but if thy wittes madde,
To han as greet a grace as Noë hadde.
Thy wyf shal I wel saven, out of doute,
Go now thy wey, and speed thee heer-aboute.
But whan thou hast, for hir and thee and me,
Y-geten us thise kneding-tubbes three,
Than shaltow hange hem in the roof ful hye,
That no man of our purveyaunce spye.

And whan thou thus hast doon as I have seyd,
And hast our vitaille faire in hem y-leyd,
And eek an ax, to smyte the corde atwo
When that the water comth, that we may go,
And broke an hole an heigh, up-on the gable,
Unto the gardin-ward, over the stable,
That we may frely passen forth our way
Whan that the grete shour is goon away—
Than shaltow swimme as myrie, I undertake,
As doth the whyte doke after hir drake.
Than wol I clepe, "how! Alisoun! how! John!
Be myrie, for the flood wol passe anon."
And thou wolt seyn, "hayl, maister Nicholay!
Good morwe, I se thee wel, for it is day."
And than shul we be lordes al our lyf
Of al the world, as Noë and his wyf.
  But of o thyng I warne thee ful right,
Be wel avysed, on that ilke night
That we ben entred in-to shippes bord,
That noon of us ne speke nat a word,
Ne clepe, ne crye, but been in his preyere;
For it is goddes owne heste dere.
  Thy wyf and thou mote hange fer a-twinne,
For that bitwixe yow shal be no sinne
No more in looking than ther shal in dede;
This ordinance is seyd, go, god thee spede!
Tomorwe at night, whan men ben alle aslepe,
In-to our kneding-tubbes wol we crepe,
And sitten ther, abyding goddes grace.
Go now thy wey, I have no lenger space
To make of this no lenger sermoning.
Men seyn thus, "send the wyse, and sey
  no-thing":
Thou art so wys, it nedeth thee nat teche;
Go, save our lyf, and that I thee biseche."
  This sely carpenter goth forth his wey.
Ful ofte he seith "allas" and "weylawey,"
And to his wyf he tolde his privetee;
And she was war, and knew it bet than he,
What al this queynte cast was for to seye.
But nathelees she ferde as she wolde deye,
And seyde, "allas! go forth thy wey anon,
Help us to scape, or we ben lost echon;
I am thy trewe verray wedded wyf;
Go, dere spouse, and help to save our lyf."
  Lo! which a greet thyng is affeccioun!
Men may dye of imaginacioun,
So deep may impressioun be take.
This sely carpenter biginneth quake;
Him thinketh verraily that he may see
Noës flood come walwing as the see
To drenchen Alisoun, his hony dere.
He wepeth, weyleth, maketh sory chere,
He syketh with ful many a sory swogh.
He gooth and geteth him a kneding-trogh,
And after that a tubbe and a kimelin,
And prively he sente hem to his in,
And heng hem in the roof in privetee.
His owne hand he made laddres three,
To climben by the ronges and the stalkes
Un-to the tubbes hanginge in the balkes,
And hem vitailled, bothe trogh and tubbe,

And when you thus have done, as I have said,
And have put in our drink and meat and bread,
Also an axe to cut the ropes in two
When the flood comes, that we may float and go,
And cut a hole, high up, upon the gable,
Upon the garden side, over the stable,
That we may freely pass forth on our way
When the great rain and flood are gone that day—
Then shall you float as merrily, I'll stake,
As does the white duck after the white drake.
Then I will call, 'Ho, Alison! Ho John!
Be cheery, for the flood will pass anon.'
And you will say, 'Hail, Master Nicholay!
Good morrow, I see you well, for it is day!'
And then shall we be barons all our life
Of all the world, like Noah and his wife.
  "But of one thing I warn you now, outright.
Be well advised, that on that very night
When we have reached our ships and got aboard,
Not one of us must speak or whisper word,
Nor call, nor cry, but sit in silent prayer;
For this is God's own bidding, hence—don't dare!
  "Your wife and you must hang apart, that in
The night shall come no chance for you to sin
Either in looking or in carnal deed.
These orders I have told you, go, God speed!
Tomorrow night, when all men are asleep,
Into our kneading-tubs will we three creep
And sit there, still, awaiting God's high grace.
Go, now, your way, I have no longer space
Of time to make a longer sermoning.
Men say thus: "Send the wise and say
  nothing."
You are so wise it needs not that I teach;
Go, save our lives, and that I do beseech."
  This silly carpenter went on his way.
Often he cried "Alas!" and "Welaway!"
And to his wife he told all, privately
But she was better taught thereof than he
How all this rigmarole was to apply.
Nevertheless she acted as she'd die,
And said: "Alas! Go on your way anon,
Help us escape, or we are lost, each one;
I am your true and lawfully wedded wife;
Go, my dear spouse, and help to save our life."
  Lo, what a great thing is affection found!
Men die of imagination, I'll be bound,
So deep an imprint may the spirit take.
This hapless carpenter began to quake;
He thought now, verily, that he could see
Old Noah's flood come wallowing like the sea
To drown his Alison, his honey dear.
He wept, he wailed, he made but sorry cheer,
He sighed and made full many a sob and sough.
He went and got himself a kneading-trough
And, after that, two tubs he somewhere found
And to his dwelling privately sent round,
And hung them near the roof, all secretly.
With his own hand, then, made he ladders three,
To climb up by the rungs thereof, it seems
And reach the tubs left hanging to the beams;
And those he victualled, tubs and kneading-trough,

With bread and cheese and good jugged ale, enough
To satisfy the needs of one full day.
But ere he'd put all this in such array,
He sent his servants, boy and maid, right down
Upon some errand into London town.
And on the Monday, when it came on night,
He shut his door, without a candle-light,
And ordered everything as it should be.
And shortly after up they climbed, all three;
They sat while one might plow a furlong-way.
"Now, by Our Father, hush!" said Nicholay,
And "Hush!" said John, and "Hush!" said
Alison.
This carpenter, his loud devotions done,
Sat silent, saying mentally a prayer,
And waiting for the rain, to hear it there.
The deathlike sleep of utter weariness
Fell on this wood-wright even (as I guess)
About the curfew time, or little more;
For travail of his spirit he groaned sore,
And soon he snored, for badly his head lay.
Down by the ladder crept this Nicholay,
And Alison, right softly down she sped.
Without more words they went and got in bed
Even where the carpenter was wont to lie.
There was the revel and the melody!
And thus lie Alison and Nicholas,
In joy that goes by many an alias,
Until the bells for lauds began to ring
And friars to the chancel went to sing.
This parish clerk, this amorous Absalom,
Whom love has made so woebegone and dumb,
Upon the Monday was down Osney way,
With company, to find some sport and play;
And there he chanced to ask a cloisterer,
Privately, after John the carpenter.
This monk drew him apart, out of the kirk,
And said: "I have not seen him here at work
Since Saturday; I think well that he went
For timber, that the abbot has him sent;
For he is wont for timber thus to go,
Remaining at the grange a day or so;
Or else he's surely at his house today;
But which it is I cannot truly say."
This Absalom right happy was and light,
And thought: "Now is the time to wake all night;
For certainly I saw him not stirring
About his door since day began to spring.
So may I thrive, as I shall, at cock's crow,
Knock cautiously upon that window low
Which is so placed upon his bedroom wall.
To Alison then will I tell of all
My love-longing, and thus I shall not miss
That at the least I'll have her lips to kiss.
Some sort of comfort shall I have, I say,
My mouth's been itching all this livelong day;
That is a sign of kissing at the least.
All night I dreamed, too, I was at a feast.
Therefore I'll go and sleep two hours away,
And all this night then will I wake and play."
And so when time of first cock-crow was come,
Up rose this merry lover, Absalom,

With breed and chese, and good ale in a jubbe,
Suffysinge right y-nogh as for a day.
But er that he had maad al this array,
He sente his knave, and eek his wenche also,
Up-on his nede to London for to go.
And on the Monday, whan it drow to night,
He shette his dore with-oute candel-light,
And dressed al thing as it sholde be.
And shortly, up they clomben alle three;
They sitten stille wel a furlong-way.
"Now, *Pater-noster*, clom!" syde Nicholay,
And "clom," quod John, and "clom," seyde
Alisoun.
This carpenter seyde his devocioun,
And stille he sit, and biddeth his preyere,
Awaytinge on the reyn, if he it here.
The dede sleep, for wery bisinesse,
Fil on this carpenter right, as I gesse,
Aboute corfew-tyme, or litel more;
For travail of his goost he groneth sore,
And eft he routeth, for his heed mislay.
Doun of the laddre stalketh Nicholay,
And Alisoun, ful softe adoun she spedde;
With-outen wordes mo, they goon to bedde
Ther-as the carpenter is wont to lye.
Ther was the revel and the melodye;
And thus lyth Alison and Nicholas,
In bisinesse of mirthe and of solas,
Til that the belle of laudes gan to ringe,
And freres in the chauncel gonne singe.
This parish-clerk, this amorous Absolon,
That is for love alwey so wo bigon,
Up-on the Monday was at Oseneye
With companye, him to disporte and pleye,
And axed up-on cas a cloisterer
Ful prively after John the carpenter;
And he drough him a-part out of the chirche,
And seyde, "I noot, I saguh him here nat wirche
Sin Saterday; I trow that he be went
For timber, ther our abbot hath him sent;
For he is wont for timber for to go,
And dwellen at the grange a day or two;
Or elles he is at his hous, certeyn;
Wher that he be, I can nat sothly seyn."
This Absolon ful joly was and light,
And thoghte, "now is tyme wake al night;
For sikirly I saugh him nat stiringe
Aboute his dore sin day bigan to springe.
So moot I thryve, I shal, at cokkes crowe,
Ful prively knokken at his windowe
That stant ful lowe up-on his boures wal.
To Alison now wol I tellen al
My love-longing, for yet I shal nat misse
That at the leste wey I shal hir kisse.
Som maner confort shal I have, parfay,
My mouth hath icched al this longe day;
That is a signe of kissing atte leste.
Al night me mette eek, I was at a feste.
Therfor I wol gon slepe an houre or tweye,
And al the night than wol I wake and pleye."
Whan that the first cok hath crowe, anon
Up rist this joly lover Absolon,

And him arrayeth gay, at point-devys.
But first he cheweth greyn and lycorys,
To smellen swete, er he had kembd his heer.
Under his tonge a trewe love[1] he beer,
For ther-by wende he to ben gracious.
He rometh to the carpenteres hous,
And stille he stant under the shot-windowe;
Un-to his brest it raughte, it was so lowe;
And softe he cogheth with a seim-soun—
"What do ye, hony-comb, swete Alisoun?
My faire brid, my swete cinamome,
Awaketh, lemman myn, and speketh to me!
Wel litel thenken ye up-on my wo,
That for your love I swete ther I go.
No wonder is thogh that I swelte and swete;
I moorne as doth a lamb after the tete.
Y-wis, lemman, I have swich love-longinge,
That lyk a turtel trewe is my moorninge;
I may nat ete na more than a mayde."
"Go fro the window, Jakke fool," she sayde,
"As help me god, it wol nat be 'com ba me,'
I love another, and elles I were to blame,
Wel bet than thee, by Jesu, Absolon!
Go forth thy wey, or I wol caste a ston,
And lat me slepe, a twenty devel wey!"
"Allas," quod Absolon, "and weylawey!
That trewe love was ever so yvel biset!
Than kisse me, sin it may be no bet,
For Jesus love and for the love of me."
"Wiltow than go thy wey ther-with?" quod she.
"Ye, certes, lemman," quod this Absolon.
"Thanne make thee redy," quod she, "I come anon";
And un-to Nicholas she seyde stille, [3720a]
Now hust, and thou shalt laughen al thy fille." [b]
This Absolon doun sette him on his knees,
And seyde, "I am a lord at alle degrees;
For after this I hope ther cometh more!
Lemman, thy grace, and swete brid, thyn ore!"
The window she undoth, and that in haste,
"Have do," quod she, "com of, and speed thee faste,
Lest that our neighebores thee espye."
This Absolon gan wype his mouth ful drye;
Derk was the night as pich, or as the cole,
And at the window out she putte hir hole,
And Absolon, him fil no bet ne wers,
But with his mouth he kiste hir naked ers
Ful savourly, er he was war of this.
Abak he sterte, and thoghte it was amis,
For wel he wiste a womman hath no berd;
He felte a thing al rough and long y-herd,
And seyde, "fy! allas! what have I do?"
"Tehee!" quod she, and clapte the window to;
And Absolon goth forth a sory pas.
"A berd, a berd!" quod hende Nicholas,
"By goddes *corpus*, this goth faire and weel!"
This sely Absolon herde every deel,
And on his lippe he gan for anger byte;
And to him-self he seyde, "I shal thee quyte!"

And dressed him gay and all at point-device,
But first he chewed some licorice and spice
So he'd smell sweet, ere he had combed his hair.
Under his tongue some bits of true-love rare,[1]
For thereby thought he to be more gracious.
He went, then, to the carpenter's dark house.
And silent stood beneath the shot-window;
Unto his breast it reached, it was so low;
And he coughed softly, in a low half tone:
"What do you, honeycomb, sweet Alison?
My cinnamon, my fair bird, my sweetie,
Awake, O darling mine, and speak to me!
It's little thought you give me and my woe,
Who for your love do sweat where'er I go.
Yet it's no wonder that I faint and sweat;
I long as does the lamb for mother's teat.
Truly, sweetheart, I have such love-longing
That like a turtle-dove's my true yearning;
And I can eat no more than can a maid."
"Go from the window, jack-a-napes," she said,
"For, s'help me God it is not 'come kiss me'
I love another, or to blame I'd be,
Better than you, by Jesus, Absalom!
Go on your way, or I'll stone you therefrom,
And let me sleep, the fiends take you away!"
"Alas," quoth Absalom, "and welaway!
That true love ever was so ill beset!
But kiss me, since you'll do no more, my pet,
For Jesus' love and for the love of me."
"And will you go, then, on your way?" asked she.
"Yes truly, darling," said this Absalom.
"Then make you ready," said she, "and I'll come!
And unto Nicholas said she, low and still:
"Be silent now, and you shall laugh your fill."
This Absalom plumped down upon his knees,
And said: "I am a lord in all degrees;
For after this there may be better still!
Darling my sweetest bird, I wait your will."
The window she unbarred, and that in haste.
"Have done," said she, "come on, and do it fast,
Before we're seen by any neighbour's eye."
This Absalom did wipe his mouth all dry;
Dark was the night as pitch, aye dark as coal,
And through the window she put out her hole,
And Absalom no better felt nor worse,
But with his mouth he kissed her naked arse
Right greedily, before he knew of this.
Aback he leapt—it seemed somehow amiss,
For well he knew a woman has no beard;
He'd felt a thing all rough and longish haired,
And said, "Oh fie, alas! What did I do?"
"Teehee!" she laughed, and clapped the window to;
And Absalom went forth a sorry pace.
"A beard! A beard!" cried clever Nicholas,
"Now by God's *corpus* this goes fair and well!"
This hapless Absalom, he heard that yell,
And on his lip, for anger, he did bite;
And to himself he said, "I will requite!"

[1]Probably herb paris.

Who vigorously rubbed and scrubbed his lips
With dust, with sand, with straw, with cloth,
with chips,
But Absalom, and often cried "Alas!
My soul I give now unto Sathanas,
For rather far than own this town," said he,
"For this despite, it's well revenged I'd be.
Alas," said he, "from her I never blenched!"
His hot love was grown cold, aye and all
quenched;
For, from the moment that he'd kissed her arse,
For paramours he didn't care a curse,
For he was healed of all his malady;
Indeed all paramours he did defy,
And wept as does a child that has been beat.
With silent step he went across the street
Unto a smith whom men called Dan Jarvis,
Who in his smithy forged plow parts, that is
He sharpened shares and coulters busily.
This Absalom he knocked all easily,
And said: "Unbar here, Jarvis, for I come."
"What! Who are you?"
"It's I, it's Absalom."
"What! Absalom! For Jesus Christ's sweet tree,
Why are you up so early? *Ben'cite*
What ails you now, man? Some gay girl, God knows,
Has brought you on the jump to my bellows;
By Saint Neot, you know well what I mean."
This Absalom cared not a single bean
For all this play, nor one word back he gave;
He'd more tow on his distaff, had this knave,
Than Jarvis knew, and said he: "Friend so dear,
This red-hot coulter in the fireplace here,
Lend it to me, I have a need for it,
And I'll return it after just a bit."
Jarvis replied: "Certainly, were it gold
Or a purse filled with yellow coins untold,
Yet should you have it, as I am true smith;
But eh, Christ's foe! What will you do therewith?"
"Let that," said Absalom, "be as it may;
I'll tell you all tomorrow, when it's day"—
And caught the coulter then by the cold steel
And softly from the smithy door did steal
And went again up to the wood-wright's wall.
He coughed at first, and then he knocked withal
Upon the window, as before, with care.
This Alison replied: "Now who is there?
And who knocks so? I'll warrant it's a thief."
"Why no," quoth he, "God knows, my sweet
roseleaf,
I am your Absalom, my own darling!
Of gold," quoth he, "I have brought you a ring;
My mother gave it me, as I'll be saved;
Fine gold it is, and it is well engraved;
This will I give you for another kiss."
This Nicholas had risen for a piss,
And thought that it would carry on the jape
To have his arse kissed by this jack-a-nape.
And so he opened window hastily,
And put his arse out thereat, quietly,
Over the buttocks, showing the whole bum;
And thereto said this clerk, this Absalom,

Who rubbeth now, who froteth now his lippes
With dust, with sond, with straw, with clooth,
with chippes,
But Absolon, that seith ful ofte, "allas!
My soule bitake I un-to Sathanas,
But me wer lever than al this toun," quod he,
"Of this despyt awroken for to be!
Allas!" quod he, "allas! I ne hadde y-bleynt!"
His hote love was cold and al
y-queynt;
For fro that tyme that he had kiste hir ers,
Of paramours he sette nat a kers,
For he was heled of his maladye;
Ful ofte paramours he gan deffye,
And weep as dooth a child that is y-bete.
A softe paas he wente over the strete
Un-til a smith men cleped daun Gerveys,
That in his forge smithed plough-harneys;
He sharpeth shaar and culter bisily.
This Absolon knokketh al esily,
And seyde, "undo, Gerveys, and that anon."
"What, who artow?"
"It am I, Absolon."
"What, Absolon! for Cristes swete tree,
Why ryse ye so rathe, ey, *ben'cite!*
What eyleth yow? som gay gerl, god it woot,
Hath broght yow thus up-on the viritoot;
By sëynt Note, ye woot wel what I mene."
This Absolon ne roghte nat a bene
Of al his pley, no word agayn he yaf;
He hadde more tow on his distaf
Than Gerveys knew, and seyde, "freend so dere,
That hote culter in the chimenee here,
As lene it me, I have ther-with to done,
And I wol bringe it thee agayn ful sone."
Gerveys answerde, "certes, were it gold,
Or in a poke nobles alle untold,
Thou sholdest have, as I am trewe smith;
Ey, Cristes foo! what wol ye do ther-with?"
"Ther-of," quod Absolon, "be as be may;
I shal wel telle it thee to-morwe day"—
And caughte the culter by the colde stele.
Ful softe out at the dore he gan to stele,
And wente un-to the carpenteres wal.
He cogheth first, and knokketh ther-with-al
Upon the windowe, right as he dide er.
This Alison answerde, "Who is ther
That knokketh so? I warante it a theef."
"Why, nay," quod he, "god woot, my swete
leef,
I am thyn Absolon, my dereling!
Of gold," quod he, "I have thee broght a ring;
My moder yaf it me, so god me save,
Ful fyn it is, and ther-to wel y-grave;
This wol I yeve thee, if thou me kisse!"
This Nicholas was risen for to pisse,
And thoghte he wolde amenden al the jape,
He sholde kisse his ers er that he scape.
And up the windowe dide he hastily,
And out his ers he putteth prively
Over the buttok, to the haunche-bon;
And ther-with spak this clerk, this Absolon,

"Spek, swete brid, I noot nat wher thou art."
This Nicholas anon leet flee a fart,
As greet as it had been a thonder-dent,
That with the strook he was almost y-blent;
And he was redy with his iren hoot,
And Nicholas amidde the ers he smoot.
Of gooth the skin an hande-brede about,
The hote culter brende so his toute,
And for the smert he wende for to dye.
As he were wood, for wo he gan to crye—
"Help! water! water! help, for goddes herte!"
This carpenter out of his slomber sterte,
And herde oon cryen "water" as he were wood,
And thoghte, "Allas! now comth Nowélis[1] flood!"
He sit him up with-outen wordes mo,
And with his ax he smoot the corde a-two,
And doun goth al; he fond neither to selle,
Ne breed ne ale, til he cam to the selle
Up-on the floor; and ther aswowne he lay.
Up sterte hir Alison, and Nicholay,
And cryden "out" and "harrow" in the strete.
The neighebores, bothe smale and grete,
In ronnen, for to gauren on this man,
That yet aswowne he lay, bothe pale and wan;
For with the fal he brosten hadde his arm;
But stonde he moste un-to his owne harm.
For whan he spake, he was anon bore doun
With hende Nicholas and Alisoun.
They tolden every man that he was wood,
He was agast so of "Nowélis flood"
Thurgh fantasye, that of his vanitee
He hadde y-boght him kneding-tubbes three.
And hadde hem hanged in the roof above;
And that he preyed hem, for goddes love,
To sitten in the roof, *par companye*.
The folk gan laughen at his fantasye;
In-to the roof they kyken and they gape,
And turned al his harm un-to a jape.
For what so that this carpenter answerde,
It was for noght, no man his resen herde;
With othes grete he was so sworn adoun,
That he was holden wood in al the toun;
For every clerk anon-right heeld with other.
They seyde, "the man is wood, my leve brother;"
And every wight gan laughen of this stryf.
Thus swyved was the carpenteres wyf,
For al his keping and his jalousye;
And Absolon hath kist hir nether yë;
And Nicholas is scalded in the toute.
This tale is doon, and god save al the route!

"O speak, sweet bird, I know not where thou art."
This Nicholas just then let fly a fart
As loud as it had been a thunder-clap,
And well-nigh blinded Absalom, poor chap;
But he was ready with his iron hot
And Nicholas right in the arse he got.
Off went the skin a hand's-breadth broad, about,
The coulter burned his bottom so, throughout,
That for the pain he thought that he should die.
And like one mad he started in to cry,
"Help! Water! Water! Help! For God's dear heart!"
This carpenter out of his sleep did start,
Hearing that "Water!" cried as madman would,
And thought, "Alas, now comes down Noel's[1] flood!"
He struggled up without another word
And with his axe he cut in two the cord,
And down went all; he did not stop to trade
In bread or ale till he'd the journey made,
And there upon the floor he swooning lay.
Up started Alison and Nicholay
And shouted "Help!" and "Hello!" down the street
The neighbours, great and small, with hastening feet
Swarmed in the house to stare upon this man,
Who lay yet swooning, and all pale and wan;
For in the falling he had smashed his arm.
He had to suffer, too, another harm,
For when he spoke he was at once borne down
By clever Nicholas and Alison.
For they told everyone that he was odd;
He was so much afraid of "Noel's flood,
Through fantasy, that out of vanity
He'd gone and bought these kneading-tubs, all three,
And that he'd hung them near the roof above;
And that he had prayed them, for God's dear love,
To sit with him and bear him company.
The people laughed at all this fantasy;
Up to the roof they looked, and there did gape,
And so turned all his injury to a jape.
For when this carpenter got in a word,
'Twas all in vain, no man his reasons heard;
With oaths impressive he was so sworn down
That he was held for mad by all the town;
For every clerk did side with every other.
They said: "The man is crazy, my dear brother."
And everyone did laugh at all this strife.
Thus futtered was the carpenter's goodwife,
For all his watching and his jealousy;
And Absalom has kissed her nether eye;
And Nicholas is branded on the butt.
This tale is done, and God save all the rout!

[1] The carpenter's corruption.

HERE ENDETH THE MILLER HIS TALE

THE REEVE'S PROLOGUE

THE PROLOGUE OF THE REEVE'S TALE

When folk had laughed their fill at this nice pass
Of Absalom and clever Nicholas,
Then divers folk diversely had their say;
And most of them were well amused and gay,
Nor at this tale did I see one man grieve,
Save it were only old Oswald the reeve,
Because he was a carpenter by craft.
A little anger in his heart was left,
And he began to grouse and blame a bit.
"S' help me," said he, "full well could I be quit
With blearing of a haughty miller's eye,
If I but chose to speak of ribaldry.
But I am old; I will not play, for age;
Grass time is done, my fodder is rummage,
This white top advertises my old years,
My heart, too, is as mouldy as my hairs,
Unless I fare like medlar, all perverse.
For that fruit's never ripe until it's worse,
And falls among the refuse or in straw.
We ancient men, I fear, obey this law:
Until we're rotten we cannot be ripe;
We dance, indeed, the while the world will pipe.
Desire sticks in our nature like a nail
To have, if hoary head, a verdant tail,
As has the leek; for though our strength be gone,
Our wish is yet for folly till life's done.
For when we may not act, then will we speak;
Yet in our ashes is there fire to reek
"Four embers have we, which I shall confess:
Boasting and lying, anger, covetousness;
These four remaining sparks belong to eld.
Our ancient limbs may well be hard to wield,
But lust will never fail us, that is truth.
And yet I have had always a colt's tooth,
As many years as now are past and done
Since first my tap of life began to run.
For certainly, when I was born, I know
Death turned my tap of life and let it flow;
And ever since that day the tap has run
Till nearly empty now is all the tun.
The stream of life now drips upon the chime;[1]
The silly tongue may well ring out the time
Of wretchedness that passed so long before;
For oldsters, save for dotage, there's no more."
Now when our host had heard this sermoning,
Then did he speak as lordly as a king;
He said: "To what amounts, now, all this wit?
Why should we talk all day of holy writ?
The devil makes a steward for to preach,
And of a cobbler, a sailor or a leech.
Tell forth your tale, and do not waste the time.
Here's Deptford! And it is half way to prime.
There's Greenwich town that many a scoundrel's in;

Whan folk had laughen at this nyce cas
Of Absolon and hende Nicholas,
Diverse folk diversely they seyde;
But, for the more part, they loughe and pleyde,
Ne at this tale I saugh no man him greve,
But it were only Osewold the Reve,
By-cause he was of carpenteres craft.
A litel ire is in his herte y-laft,
He gan to grucche and blamed it a lyte.
"So thee'k," quod he, "ful wel coude I yow quyte
With blering of a proud milleres yë,
If that me liste speke of ribaudye.
But ik am old, me list not pley for age;
Gras-tyme is doon, my fodder is now forage,
This whyte top wryteth myne olde yeres,
Myn herte is al-so mowled as myne heres,
But-if I fare as dooth an open-ers;
That ilke fruit is ever leng the wers,
Til it be roten in mullok or in stree.
We olde men, I drede, so fare we;
Til we be roten, can we nat be rype;
We hoppen ay, whyl that the world wol pype.
For in oure wil ther stiketh ever a nayl,
To have an hoor heed and a grene tayl,
As hath a leek; for thogh our might be goon,
Our wil desireth folie ever in oon.
For whan we may nat doon, than wol we speke;
Yet in our asshen olde is fyr y-reke.
Foure gledes han we, whiche I shal devyse,
Avaunting, lying, anger, coveityse;
Thise foure sparkles longen un-to elde.
Our olde lemes mowe wel been unwelde,
But wil ne shal nat faillen, that is sooth.
And yet ik have alwey a coltes tooth,
As many a yeer as it is passed henne
Sin that my tappe of lyf bigan to renne.
For sikerly, whan I was bore, anon
Deeth drogh the tappe of lyf and leet it gon;
And ever sith hath so the tappe y-ronne,
Til that almost al empty is the tonne.
The streem of lyf now droppeth on the chimbe;[1]
The sely tonge may wel ringe and chimbe
Of wrecchednesse that passed is ful yore;
With olde folk, save dotage, is namore."
Whan that our host hadde herd this sermoning,
He gan to speke as lordly as a king;
He seide, "what amounteth al this wit?
What shul we speke alday of holy writ?
The devel made a reve for to preche,
And of a souter a shipman or a leche.
Sey forth thy tale, and tarie nat the tyme,
Lo, Depeford! and it is half-way pryme.
Lo, Grenewich, ther many a shrewe is inne;

[1]The edge or rim of a cask, formed by the projecting ends of the staves.

It were al tyme thy tale to biginne."
  "Now, sires," quod this Osewold the Reve,
"I pray yow alle that ye nat yow greve,
Thogh I answere and somdel sette his howve;
For leveful is with force force of-showve.
  This dronke millere hath y-told us heer,
How that bigyled was a carpenteer,
Peraventure in scorn, for I am oon.
And, by your leve, I shal him quyte anoon;
Right in his cherles termes wol I speke.
I pray to god his nekke mote breke;
He can wel in myn yë seen a stalke,
But in his owne he can nat seen a balke.

It is high time your story should begin."
  "Now, sirs," then said this Oswald called the reeve,
"I pray you all, now, that you will not grieve
Though I reply and somewhat twitch his cap;
It's lawful to meet force with force, mayhap.
  "This drunken miller has related here
How was beguiled and fooled a carpenter—
Perchance in scorn of me, for I am one.
So, by your leave, I'll him requite anon;
All in his own boor's language will I speak.
I only pray to God his neck may break.
For in my eye he well can see the mote,
But sees not in his own the beam, you'll note."

THE REEVE'S TALE

HERE BEGINNETH THE REEVE'S TALE

AT TRUMPINGTON, nat fer fro Cantebrigge,
Ther goth a brook and over that a brigge,
Up-on the whiche brook ther stant a melle;
And this is verray soth that I yow telle.
A Miller was ther dwelling many a day;
As eny pecok he was proud and gay.
Pypen he coude and fisshe, and nettes bete,
And turne coppes, and wel wrastle and shete;
And by his belt he baar a long panade,
And of a swerd ful trenchant was the blade.
A joly popper baar he in his pouche;
Ther was no man for peril dorste him touche.
A Sheffeld thwitel baar he in his hose;
Round was his face, and camuse was his nose.
As piled as an ape was his skulle.
He was a market-beter atte fulle.
Ther dorste no wight hand up-on him legge,
That he ne swoor he sholde anon abegge.
A theef he was for sothe of corn and mele,
And that a sly, and usaunt for to stele.
His name was hoten dëynous Simkin.
A wyf he hadde, y-comen of noble kin;
The person of the toun hir fader was.
With hir he yaf ful many a panne of bras,
For that Simkin sholde in his blood allye.
She was y-fostred in a nonnerye;
For Simkin wolde no wyf, as he sayde,
But she were wel y-norissed and a mayde,
To saven his estaat of yomanrye.
And she was proud, and pert as is a pye.
A ful fair sighte was it on hem two;
On haly-dayes biforn his wolde he go
With his tipet bouden about his heed,
And she cam after in a gyte of reed;
And Simkin hadde hosen of the same.
Ther dorste no wight clepen hir but "dame."
Was noon so hardy that wente by the weye
That with hir dorste rage or ones pleye,
But-if he wolde be slayn of Simkin
With panade, or with knyf, or boydekin.
For jalous folk ben perilous evermo,

AT Trumpington, not far from Cambridge town,
There is a bridge wherethrough a brook runs down,
Upon the side of which brook stands a mill;
And this is very truth that now I tell.
A miller dwelt there, many and many a day;
As any peacock he was proud and gay.
He could mend nets, and he could fish, and flute,
Drink and turn cups, and wrestle well, and shoot;
And in his leathern belt he did parade
A cutlass with a long and trenchant blade.
A pretty dagger had he in his pouch;
There was no man who durst this man to touch.
A Sheffield whittler bore he in his hose;
Round was his face and turned-up was his nose.
As bald as any ape's head was his skull;
He was a market-swaggerer to the full.
There durst no man a hand on him to lay,
Because he swore he'd make the beggar pay.
A thief he was, forsooth, of corn and meal,
And sly at that, accustomed well to steal.
His name was known as arrogant Simpkin.
A wife he had who came of gentle kin;
The parson of the town her father was.
With her he gave full many a pan of brass,
To insure that Simpkin with his blood ally.
She had been bred up in a nunnery;
For Simpkin would not have a wife, he said,
Save she were educated and a maid
To keep up his estate of yeomanry.
And she was proud and bold as is a pie.
A handsome sight it was to see those two;
On holy days before her he would go
With a broad tippet bound about his head;
And she came after in a skirt of red,
While Simpkin's hose were dyed to match that same
There durst no man to call her aught but dame;
Nor was there one so hardy, in the way,
As durst flirt with her or attempt to play,
Unless he would be slain by this Simpkin
With cutlass or with knife or with bodkin.
For jealous folk are dangerous, you know,

At least they'd have their wives to think them so.
Besides, because she was a dirty bitch,
She was as high as water in a ditch;
And full of scorn and full of back-biting.
She thought a lady should be quite willing
To greet her for her kin and culture, she
Having been brought up in that nunnery.
A daughter had they got between the two,
Of twenty years, and no more children, no,
Save a boy baby that was six months old;
It lay in cradle and was strong and bold.
This girl right stout and well developed was,
With nose tip-tilted and eyes blue as glass,
With buttocks broad, and round breasts full and high,
But golden was her hair, I will not lie.
The parson of the town, since she was fair,
Was purposeful to make of her his heir,
Both of his chattels and of his estate,
But all this hinged upon a proper mate.
He was resolved that he'd bestow her high
Into some blood of worthy ancestry;
For Holy Church's goods must be expended
On Holy Church's blood, as it's descended.
Therefore he'd honour thus his holy blood,
Though Holy Church itself became his food.
Large tolls this miller took, beyond a doubt,
With wheat and malt from all the lands about;
Of which I'd specify among them all
A Cambridge college known as Soler Hall;
He ground their wheat and all their malt he ground.
And on a day it happened, as they found,
The manciple got such a malady
That all men surely thought that he should die.
Whereon this miller stole both flour and wheat
A hundredfold more than he used to cheat;
For theretofore he stole but cautiously,
But now he was a thief outrageously,
At which the warden scolded and raised hell;
The miller snapped his fingers, truth to tell,
And cracked his brags and swore it wasn't so.
There were two poor young clerks, whose names I know,
That dwelt within this Hall whereof I say.
Willful they were and lusty, full of play,
And (all for mirth and to make revelry)
After the warden eagerly did they cry
To give them leave, at least for this one round,
To go to mill and see their produce ground;
And stoutly they proclaimed they's bet their neck
The miller should not steal one half a peck
Of grain, by trick, nor yet by force should thieve;
And at the last the warden gave them leave.
John was the one and Alain was that other;
In one town were they born, and that called Strother,
Far in the north, I cannot tell you where.
This Alain, he made ready all his gear,
And on a horse loaded the sack anon.
Forth went Alain the clerk, and also John,
With good sword and with buckler at their side.
John knew the way and didn't need a guide,

Algate they wolde hir wyves wenden so.
And eek, for she was somdel smoterlich,
She was as digne as water in a dich;
And ful of hoker and of bisemare.
Hir thoughte that a lady sholde hir spare,
What for hir kinrede and hir nortelrye
That she had lerned in the nonnerye.
A doghter hadde they bitwixe hem two
Of twenty yeer, with-outen any mo,
Savinge a child that was of half-yeer age;
In cradel it lay and was a propre page.
This wenche thikke and wel y-growen was,
With camuse nose and yën greye as glas;
With buttokes brode and brestes rounde and hye,
But right fair was hir heer, I wol nat lye.
The person of the toun, for she was feir,
In purpos was to maken hir his heir
Bothe of his catel and his messuage,
And straunge he made it of hir mariage.
His purpos was for to bistowe hir hye
In-to som worthy blood of auncetrye;
For holy chirches good moot been despended
On holy chirches blood, that is descended.
Therfore he wolde his holy blood honoure,
Though that he holy chirche sholde devoure.
Gret soken hath this miller, out of doute,
With whete and malt of al the land aboute;
And nameliche ther was a greet collegge,
Men clepen the Soler-halle at Cantebregge,
Ther was hir whete and eek hir malt y-grounde.
And on a day it happed, in a stounde,
Sik lay the maunciple on a maladye;
Men wenden wisly that he sholde dye.
For which this miller stal bothe mele and corn
An hundred tyme more than biforn;
For ther-biforn he stal but curteisly,
But now he was a theef outrageously,
For which the wardeyn chidde and made fare.
But ther-of sette the miller nat a tare;
He craketh boost, and swoor it was nat so.
Than were ther yonge povre clerkes two,
That dwelten in this halle, of which I seye.
Testif they were, and lusty for to pleye,
And, only for hir mirthe and revelrye,
Up-on the wardeyn bisily they crye,
To yeve hem leve but a litel stounde
To goon to mille and seen hir corn y-grounde;
And hardily, they dorste leye hir nekke,
The miller shold nat stele hem half a pekke
Of corn by sleighte, ne by force hem reve;
And at the laste the wardeyn yaf hem leve.
John hight that oon, and Aleyn hight that other;
Of o toun were they born, that highte Strother,
Fer in the north, I can nat telle where.
This Aleyn maketh redy al his gere,
And on an hors the sak he caste anon.
Forth goth Aleyn the clerk, and also John,
With good swerd and with bokeler by hir syde.
John knew the wey, hem nedede no gyde,

And at the mille the sak adoun he layth.
Aleyn spak first, "al hayl, Symond, y-fayth;
How fares thy faire doghter and thy wyf?"
  "Aleyn! welcome," quod Simkin, "by my lyf,
And John also, how now, what do ye heer?"
  "Symond," quod John, "by god, nede has na peer;
Him boës serve him-selve that has na swayn,
Or elles he is a fool, as clerkes sayn.
Our manciple, I hope he wil be deed,
Swa werkes ay the wanges in his heed.
And forthy is I come, and eek Alayn,
To grinde our corn and carie it ham agayn;
I pray yow spede us hethen that ye may."
  "It shal be doon," quod simkin, "by my fay;
What wol ye doon whyl that it is in hande?"
  "By god, right by the hoper wil I stande,"
Quod John, "and se how that the corn gas in;
Yet saugh I never, by my fader kin,
How that the hoper wagges til and fra."
  Aleyn answerde, "John, and wiltow swa,
Than wil I be bynethe, by my croun,
And se how that the mele falles doun
In-to the trough; that sal be my disport.
For John, in faith, I may been of your sort;
I is as ille a miller as are ye."
  This miller smyled of hir nycetee,
And thoghte, "al this nis doon but for a wyle;
They wene that no man may hem bigyle;
But, by my thrift, yet shal I blere hir yë
For al the sleighte in hir philosophye.
The more queynte crekes that they make,
The more wol I stele whan I take.
In stede of flour, yet wol I yeve hem bren.
'The gretteste clerkes been noght the wysest men,'
As whylom to the wold thus spake the mare;
Of al hir art I counte noght a tare."
  Out at the dore he gooth ful prively,
Whan that he saugh his tyme, softely;
He loketh up and doun til he hath founde
The clerkes hors, ther as it stood y-bounde
Bihinde the mille, under a levesel;
And to the hors he gooth him faire and wel;
He strepeth of the brydel right anon.
And whan the hors was loos, he ginneth gon
Toward the fen, ther wilde mares renne,
Forth with wehee, thurgh thikke and thurgh thenne.
  This miller gooth agayn, no word he seyde,
But dooth his note, and with the clerkes pleyde,
Til that hir corn was faire and wel y-grounde.
And whan the mele is sakked and y-bounde,
This John goth out and fynt his hors away,
And gan to crye "harrow" and "weylaway!
Our hors is lorn! Alayn, for goddes banes,
Step on they feet, com out, man, al at anes!
Allas, our wardeyn has his palfrey lorn."
This Aleyn al forgat, bothe mele and corn,
Al was out of his mynde his housbondrye.
"What? whilk way is he geen?" he gan to crye.
  The wyf cam leping inward with a ren,
She seyde, "allas! your hors goth to the fen

And at the mill he dropped the sack of grain,
"Ah, Simon, hail, good morn," first spoke Alain.
"How fares it with your fair daughter and wife?"
  "Alain! Welcome," said Simpkin, "by my life,
And John also. How now? What do you here?"
  "Simon," said John, "by God, need makes no peer;
He must himself serve who's no servant, eh?
Or else he's but a fool, as all clerks say.
Our manciple—I hope he'll soon be dead,
So aching are the grinders in his head—
And therefore am I come here with Alain
To grind our corn and carry it home again;
I pray you speed us thither, as you may."
  "It shall be done," said Simpkin, "by my fay.
What will you do the while it is in hand?"
  "By God, right by the hopper will I stand,"
Said John, "and see just how the corn goes in;
I never have seen, by my father's kin,
Just how the hopper waggles to and fro."
  Alain replied: "Well, John, and will you so?
Then will I get beneath it, by my crown,
To see there how the meal comes sifting down
Into the trough; and that shall be my sport.
For, John, in faith, I must be of your sort;
I am as bad a miller as you be."
  The miller smiled at this, their delicacy,
And thought: "All this is done but for a wile;
They think there is no man may them beguile;
But, by my thrift, I will yet blear their eyes,
For all the tricks in their philosophies.
The more odd tricks and stratagems they make,
The more I'll steal when I begin to take.
In place of flour I'll give them only bran.
'The greatest clerk is not the wisest man,'
As once unto the grey wolf said the mare.
But all their arts— I rate them not a tare."
  Out of the door he went, then, secretly,
When he had seen his chance, and quietly;
He looked up and looked down, until he found
The clerks' horse where it stood, securely bound,
Behind the mill, under an arbour green;
And to the horse he went, then, all unseen;
He took the bridle off him and anon,
When the said horse was free, why he was gone
Toward the fen, for wild mares ran therein,
And with a neigh he went, through thick and thin.
  This miller straight went back and no word said,
But did his business and with these clerks played,
Until their corn was fairly, fully ground.
But when the flour was sacked and the ears bound,
This John went out, to find his horse away,
And so he cried: "Hello!" and "Weladay!
Our horse is lost! Alain, for Jesus' bones
Get to your feet, come out, man, now, at once!
Alas, our warden's palfrey's lost and lorn!"
  This Alain forgot all, both flour and corn,
Clean out of mind was all his husbandry,
"What? Which way did he go?" began to cry.
  The wife came bounding from the house, and then
She said: "Alas! Your horse went to the fen,

With the wild mares, as fast as he could go.
A curse light on the hand that tied him so,
And him that better should have knotted rein!"
"Alas!" quoth John, "Alain, for Jesus' pain,
Lay off your sword, and I will mine also;
I am as fleet, God knows, as is a roe;
By God's heart, he shall not escape us both!
Why didn't you put him in the barn? My oath!
Bad luck, by God, Alain, you are a fool!"
These foolish clerks began to run and roll
Toward the marshes, both Alain and John.
And when the miller saw that they were gone,
He half a bushel of their flour did take
And bade his wife go knead it and bread make.
He said: "I think those clerks some trickery feared;
Yet can a miller match a clerkling's beard,
For all his learning; let them go their way.
Look where they go, yea, let the children play,
They'll catch him not so readily, by my crown!"
Those simple clerks went running up and down
With "Look out! Halt! Halt! Down here! 'Ware the rear!
Go whistle, you, and I will watch him here!"
But briefly, till it came to utter night,
They could not, though they put forth all their might,
That stallion catch, he always ran so fast,
Till in a ditch they trapped him at the last.
Weary and wet, as beast is in the rain,
Came foolish John and with him came Alain.
"Alas," said John, "the day that I was born!
Now are we bound toward mockery and scorn.
Our corn is stolen, folk will call us fools,
The warden and the fellows at the schools,
And specially this miller. Weladay!"
Thus John complained as he went on his way
Toward the mill, with Bayard[1] once more bound.
The miller sitting by the fire he found,
For it was night, and farther could they not;
But, for the love of God, they him besought
For shelter and for supper, for their penny.
The miller said to them: "If there be any,
Such as it is, why you shall have your part.
My house is small, but you have learned you art;
You can, by metaphysics, make a place
A full mile wide in twenty feet of space.
Let us see now if this place will suffice,
Or make more room with speech, by some device."
"Now, Simon," said John, "by Saint Cuthbert's beard,
You're always merry and have well answered.
As I've heard, man shall take one of two things:
Such as he finds, or take such as he brings.
But specially, I pray you, mine host dear,
Give us some meat and drink and some good cheer,
And we will pay you, truly, to the full.
With empty hand no man takes hawk or gull;
Well, here's our silver, ready to be spent."
This miller to the town his daughter sent
For ale and bread, and roasted them a goose,
And tied their horse, that it might not go loose;

With wilde mares, as faste as he may go.
Unthank come on his hand that bond him so,
And he that bettre sholde han knit the reyne."
"Allas," quod John, "Aleyn, for Cristes peyne,
Lay doun thy swerd, and I wil myn alswa;
I is ful wight, god waat, as is a raa;
By goddes herte he sal nat scape us bathe.
Why nadstow pit the capul ih the lathe?
Il-hayl, by god, Aleyn, thou is a fonne!"
This sely clerkes han ful faste y-ronne
To-ward the fen, bothe Aleyn and eek John.
And whan the miller saugh that they were gon,
He half a busshel if hir flour hath take,
And bad his wyf go knede it in a cake.
He seyde, "I trowe the clerkes were aferd;
Yet can a miller make a clerkes berd
For al his art; now lat hem goon hir weye.
Lo wher they goon, ye, lat the children pleye;
They gete him nat so lightly, by my croun!"
Thise sely clerkes rennen up and doun
With "keep, keep, stand, stand, jossa, warderere,
Ga whistle thou, and I shal kepe him here!"
But shortly, til that it was verray night,
They coude nat, though they do al hir might,
Hir capul cacche, he ran alwey so faste,
Til in a dich they caughte him atte laste.
Wery and weet, as beste is in the reyn,
Comth sely John, and with him comth Aleyn.
"Allas," quod John, "the day that I was born!
Now are we drive til hething and til scorn.
Our corn is stole, men wil us foles calle,
Bathe the wardeyn and our felawes alle,
And namely the miller; weylaway!"
Thus pleyneth John as he goth by the way
Toward the mille, and Bayard[1] in his hond.
The miller sitting by the fyr he fond,
For it was night, and forther mighte they noght;
But, for the love of god, they him bisoght
Of herberwe and of ese, as for hir peny.
The miller seyde agayn, "if ther be eny,
Swich as it is, yet shal ye have your part.
Myn hous is streit, but ye han lerned art;
Ye conne by argumentes make a place
A myle brood of twenty foot of space.
Lat see now if this place may suffyse,
Or make it roum with speche, as is youre gyse."
"Now, Symond," seyde John, "by seint Cutberd,
Ay is thou mery, and this is faire answerd.
I have herd seyd, man sal taa of twa thinges
Slyk he fyndes, or taa slyk as he bringes.
But specially, I pray thee, hoste dere,
Get us som mete and drinke, and make us chere,
And we wil payen trewely atte fulle.
With empty hand men may na haukes tulle;
Lo here our silver, redy for to spende."
This miller in-to toun his doghter sende
For ale and breed, and rosted hem a goos,
And bond hir hors, it sholde nat gon loos;

[1]The horse, any horse.

And in his owne chambre hem made a bed
With shetes and with chalons faire y-spred,
Noght from his owne bed ten foot or twelve.
His doghter hadde a bed, al by hir-selve,
Right in the same chambre, by and by;
It mighte be no bet, and cause why,
Ther was no roumer herberwe in the place.
They soupen and they speke, hem to
  solace,
And drinken ever strong ale atte beste.
Aboute midnight wente they to reste.
  Wel hath this miller vernisshed his heed;
Ful pale he was for-dronken, and nat reed.
He yexeth, and he speketh thurgh the nose
As he were on the quakke, or on the pose.
To bedde he gooth, and with him goth his wyf.
As any jay she light was and jolyf,
So was hir joly whistle wel y-wet.
The cradel at hir beddes feet is set,
To rokken, and to yeve the child to souke.
And whan that dronken al was in the crouke,
To bedde went the doghter right anon;
To bedde gooth Aleyn and also John;
Ther nas na more, hem nedede no dwale.[1]
This miller hath so wisly bibbed ale,
That as an hors he snorteth in his sleep,
Ne of his tayl bihinde he took no keep.
His wyf bar him a burdon, a ful strong,
Men mighte hir routing here two furlong;
The wenche routeth eek *par companye*.
  Aleyn the clerk, that herd this melodye,
He poked John, and seyde, "slepestow?
Herdestow ever slyk a sang er now?
Lo, whilk a compline is y-mel hem alle!
A wilde fyr up-on thair bodyes falle!
Wha herkned ever slyk a ferly thing?
Ye, they sal have the flour of il ending.
This lange night ther tydes me na reste;
But yet, na fors; al sal be for the beste.
For John," seyde he, "als ever moot I thryve,
If that I may, yon wenche wil I swyve.
Som esement has lawe y-shapen us;
For John, ther is a lawe that says thus,
That gif a man in a point be y-greved,
That in another he sal be releved.
Our corn is stoln, shortly, it is na nay,
And we han had an il fit al this day.
And sin I sal have neen amendement,
Agayn my los I wil have esement.
By goddes saule, it sal neen other be!"
  This John answerde, "Alayn, avyse thee,
The miller is a perilous man," he seyde,
"And gif that he out of his sleep abreyde
He mighte doon us bathe a vileinye."
  Aleyn answerde, "count him nat a flye;"
And up he rist, and by the wenche he crepte.
This wenche lay upright, and faste slepte,
Til he so ny was, er she mighte espye,
That it had been to late for to crye,
And shortly for to seyn, they were at on;
Now pley, Aleyn! for I wol speke of John.

And then in his own chamber made a bed,
With sheets and with good blankets fairly spread,
Not from his bed more than twelve feet, or ten.
The daughter made her lone bed near the men,
In the same chamber with them, by and by;
It could not well be bettered, and for why?
There was no larger room in all the place.
They supped and talked, and gained some small
  solace,
And drank strong ale, that evening, of the best.
Then about midnight all they went to rest.
  Well had this miller varnished his bald head,
For pale he was with drinking, and not red.
He hiccoughed and he mumbled through his nose,
As he were chilled, with humours lachrymose.
To bed he went, and with him went his wife.
As any jay she was with laughter rife,
So copiously was her gay whistle wet.
The cradle near her bed's foot-board was set,
Handy for rocking and for giving suck.
And when they'd drunk up all there was in crock,
To bed went miller's daughter, and anon
To bed went Alain and to bed went John.
There was no more; they did not need a dwale.[1]
This miller had so roundly bibbed his ale
That, like a horse, he snorted in his sleep,
While of his tail behind he kept no keep.
His wife joined in his chorus, and so strong,
Men might have heard her snores a full furlong;
And the girl snored, as well, for company.
  Alain the clerk, who heard this melody,
He poked at John and said: "Asleep? But how?
Did you hear ever such a song ere now?
Lo, what a compline is among them all!
Now may the wild-fire on their bodies fall!
Who ever heard so outlandish a thing?
But they shall have the flour of ill ending.
Through this long night there'll be for me no rest;
But never mind, 'twill all be for the best.
For, John," said he, "so may I ever thrive,
As, if I can, that very wench I'll swive.
Some recompense the law allows to us;
For, John, there is a statute which says thus,
That if a man in one point be aggrieved,
Yet in another shall he be relieved.
Our corn is stolen, to that there's no nay,
And we have had an evil time this day.
But since I may not have amending, now,
Against my loss I'll set some fun—and how!
By God's great soul it shan't be otherwise!"
  This John replied: "Alain, let me advise.
The miller is a dangerous man," he said,
"And if he be awakened, I'm afraid
He may well do us both an injury."
  But Alain said: "I count him not a fly."
And up he rose and to the girl he crept.
This wench lay on her back and soundly slept,
Until he'd come so near, ere she might spy,
It was too late to struggle, then or cry;
And, to be brief, these two were soon as one.
Now play, Alain! For I will speak of John.

[1]An opiate, a sleeping potion.

This John lay still a quarter-hour, or so,
Pitied himself and wept for all his woe.
"Alas," said he, "this is a wicked jape!
Now may I say that I am but an ape.
Yet has my friend, there, something for his harm;
He has the miller's daughter on his arm.
He ventured, and his pains are now all fled,
While I lie like a sack of chaff in bed;
And when this jape is told, another day,
I shall be held an ass, a milksop, yea!
I will arise and chance it, by my fay!
'Unhardy is unhappy,' as they say."
And up he rose, and softly then he went
To find the cradle for expedient,
And bore it over to his own foot-board.
Soon after this the wife no longer snored,
But woke and rose and went outside to piss,
And came again and did the cradle miss,
And groped round, here and there, but found it not.
"Alas!" thought she, "my way I have forgot.
I nearly found myself in the clerks' bed.
Eh, *ben'cite*, but that were wrong!" she said.
And on, until by cradle she did stand.
And, groping a bit farther with her hand,
She found the bed, and thought of naught but good,
Because her baby's cradle by it stood,
And knew not where she was, for it was dark;
But calmly then she crept in by the clerk,
And lay right still, and would have gone to sleep.
But presently this John the clerk did leap,
And over on this goodwife did he lie.
No such gay time she'd known in years gone by.
He pricked her hard and deep, like one gone mad.
And so a jolly life these two clerks had
Till the third cock began to crow and sing.
Alain grew weary in the grey dawning,
For he had laboured hard through all the night;
And said: "Farewell, now, Maudy, sweet delight!
The day is come, I may no longer bide;
But evermore, whether I walk or ride,
I am your own clerk, so may I have weal."
"Now, sweetheart," said she, "go and fare you well!
But ere you go, there's one thing I must tell.
When you go walking homeward past the mill,
Right at the entrance, just the door behind,
You shall a loaf of half a bushel find
That was baked up of your own flour, a deal
Of which I helped my father for to steal.
And, darling, may God save you now and keep!"
And with that word she almost had to weep.
Alain arose and thought: "Ere it be dawn,
I will go creep in softly by friend John."
And found the cradle with his hand, anon.
"By God!" thought he, "all wrong I must have gone;
My head is dizzy from my work tonight,
And that's why I have failed to go aright.
I know well, by this cradle, I am wrong,
For here the miller and his wife belong."
And on he went, and on the devil's way,

This John lyth stille a furlong-wey or two,
And to him-self he maketh routhe and wo:
"Allas!" quod he, "this is a wikked jape;
Now may I seyn that I is but an ape.
Yet has my felawe som-what for his harm;
He has the milleris doghter in his arm.
He auntred him, and has his nedes sped,
And I lye as a draf-sek in my bed;
And when this jape is tald another day,
I sal been halde a daf, a cokenay!
I wil aryse, and auntre it, by my fayth!
'Unhardy is unsely,' thus men sayth."
And up he roos and softely he wente
Un-to the cradel, and in his hand it hente,
And baar it softe un-to his beddes feet.
Sone after this the wyf hir routing leet,
And gan awake, and wente hir out to pisse,
And cam agayn, and gan hir cradel misse,
And groped heer and ther, but she fond noon.
"Allas!" quod she, "I hadde almost misgoon;
I hadde almost gon to the clerkes bed.
Ey, *ben'cite!* thanne hadde I foule y-sped":
And forth she gooth til she the cradel fond.
She gropeth alwey forther with hir hond,
And fond the bed, and thoghte noght but good,
By-cause that the cradel by it stood,
And niste wher she was, for it was derk;
But faire and wel she creep in to the clerk,
And lyth ful stille, and wolde han caught a sleep.
With-inne a whyl this John the clerk up leep,
And on this gode wyf he leyth on sore.
So mery a fit ne hadde she nat ful yore;
He priketh harde and depe as he were mad.
This joly lyf han thise two clerkes lad
Til that the thridde cok bigan to singe.
Aleyn wex wery in the daweninge,
For he had swonken al the longe night;
And seyde, "far wel, Malin, swete wight!
The day is come, I may no lenger byde;
But evermo, wher so I go or ryde,
I is thyn awen clerk, swa have I seel!"
"Now dere lemman," quod she, "go, far weel!
But er thou go, o thing I wol thee telle,
Whan that thou wendest homward by the melle,
Right at the entree of the dore bihinde,
Thou shalt a cake of half a busshel finde
That was y-maked of thyn owne mele,
Which that I heelp my fader for to stele.
And, gode lemman, god thee save and kepe!"
And with that word almost she gan to wepe.
Aleyn up-rist and thoughte, "er that it dawe,
I wol go crepen in by my felawe;
And fond the cradel with his hand anon,
"By god," thoghte he, "al wrang I have misgon;
Myn heed is toty of my swink to-night,
That maketh me that I go nat aright.
I woot wel by the cradel, I have misgo,
Heer lyth the miller and his wyf also,"
And forth he goth, a twenty devel way,

Un-to the bed ther-as the miller lay.
He wende have cropen by his felawe John;
And by the miller in he creep anon,
And caughte hym by the nekke, and softe he spak:
He seyde, "thou, John, thou swynes-heed, awak
For Cristes saule, and heer a noble game.
For by that lord that called is seint Jame,
As I have thryes, in this shorte night,
Swyved the milleres doghter bolt-upright,
Whyl thow hast as a coward been agast.
"Ye, false harlot," quod the miller, "hast?
A! false traitour! false clerk!" quod he,
"Thou shalt be deed, by goddes dignitee!
Who dorste be so bold to disparage
My doghter, that is come of swich linage?"
And by the throte-bolle he caughte Alayn.
And he hente hym despitously agayn,
And on the nose he smoot him with his fest.
Doun ran the blody streem up-on his brest;
And in the floor, with nose and mouth to-broke,
They walwe as doon two pigges in a poke.
And up they goon, and doun agayn anon,
Til that the miller sporned at a stoon,
And doun he fil bakward up-on his wyf,
That wiste no-thing of this nyce stryf;
For she was falle aslepe a lyte wight
With John the clerk, that waked hadde al night.
And with the fal, out of hir sleep she breyde—
"Help, holy croys of Bromeholm," she seyde,
"*In manus tuas!* lord, to thee I calle!
Awak, Symond! the feend is on us falle,
Myn herte is broken, help, I nam but deed;
There lyth oon up my wombe and up myn heed;
Help, Simkin, for the false clerkes fighte."
This John sterte up as faste as ever he mighte,
And graspeth by the walles to and fro,
To finde a staf; and she sterte up also,
And knew the estres bet than dide this John,
And by the wal a staf she fond anon,
And saugh a litel shimering of a light,
For at an hole in shoon the mone bright;
And by that light she saugh hem bothe two,
But sikerly she niste who was who,
But as she saugh a whyt thing in hir yë.
And whan she gan the whyte thing espye,
She wende the clerk hadde wered a volupeer.
And with the staf she drough ay neer and neer,
And wende han hit this Aleyn at the fulle,
And smoot the miller on the pyled skulle,
That doun he gooth and cryde, "harrow! I dye!"
Thise clerkes bete him weel and lete him lye;
And greythen hem, and toke hir hors anon,
And eek hir mele, and on hir wey they gon.
And at the mille yet they toke hir cake
Of half a busshel flour, ful wel y-bake.
Thus is the proude miller wel y-bete,
And hath y-lost the grinding of the whete,
And payed for the soper every-deel
Of Aleyn and of John, that bette him weel.

Unto the bed wherein the miller lay.
He thought to have crept in by comrade John,
So, to the miller, in he got anon,
And caught him round the neck, and softly spake,
Saying: "You, John, you old swine's head, awake,
For Christ's own soul, and hear a noble work,
For by Saint James, and as I am a clerk,
I have, three times in this short night, no lack,
Swived that old miller's daughter on her back,
While you, like any coward, were aghast."
"You scoundrel," cried the miller, "you trespassed?
Ah, traitor false and treacherous clerk!" cried he,
"You shall be killed, by God's own dignity!
Who dares be bold enough to bring to shame
My daughter, who is born of such a name?"
And by the gullet, then, he caught Alain.
And pitilessly he handled him amain,
And on the nose he smote him with his fist.
Down ran the bloody stream upon his breast;
And on the floor, with nose and mouth a-soak,
They wallowed as two pigs do in a poke.
And up they came, and down they both went, prone,
Until the miller stumbled on a stone,
And reeled and fell down backwards on his wife,
Who nothing knew of all this silly strife;
For she had fallen into slumber tight
With John the clerk, who's been awake all night.
But at the fall, from sleep she started out.
"Help, holy Cross of Bromholm!" did she shout,
"In *manus tuas*, Lord, to Thee I call!
Simon, awake, the Fiend is on us all!
My heart is broken, help, I am but dead!
There lies one on my womb, one on my head!
Help, Simpkin, for these treacherous clerks do fight!"
John started up, as fast as well he might,
And searched along the wall, and to and fro,
To find a staff; and she arose also,
And knowing the room better than did John,
She found a staff against the wall, anon;
And then she saw a little ray of light,
For through a hole the moon was shining bright;
And by that light she saw the struggling two,
But certainly she knew not who was who,
Except she saw a white thing with her eye.
And when she did this same white thing espy,
She thought the clerk had worn a nightcap here.
And with the staff she nearer drew, and near,
And, thinking to hit Alain on his poll,
She fetched the miller on his bald white skull,
And down he went, crying out, "Help, help, I die!"
The two clerks beat him well and let him lie;
And clothed themselves, and took their horse anon,
And got their flour, and on their way were gone.
And at the mill they found the well-made cake
Which of their meal the miller's wife did bake.
Thus is the haughty miller soundly beat,
And thus he's lost his pay for grinding wheat,
And paid for the two suppers, let me tell,
Of Alain and of John, who've tricked him well.

His wife is taken, also his daughter sweet;
Thus it befalls a miller who's a cheat.
And therefore is this proverb said with truth,
"An evil end to evil man, forsooth."
The cheater shall himself well cheated be.
And God, Who sits on high in majesty,
Save all this company, both strong and frail!
Thus have I paid this miller with my tale.

His wyf is swyved, and his doghter als;
Lo, swich it is a miller to be fals!
And therefore this proverbe is seyd ful sooth,
"Him thar nat wene wel that yvel dooth;
A gylour shal him-self bigyled be."
And God, that sitteth heighe in magestee,
Save al this companye grete and smale!
Thus have I quit the miller in my tale.

HERE IS ENDED THE REEVE'S TALE

THE COOK'S PROLOGUE

THE PROLOGUE OF THE COOK'S TALE

THE cook from London, while the reeve yet spoke,
Patted his back with pleasure at the joke.
"Ha, ha!" laughed he, "by Christ's great suffering,
This miller had a mighty sharp ending
Upon his argument of harbourage!
For well says Solomon, in his language,
'Bring thou not every man into thine house';
For harbouring by night is dangerous.
Well ought a man to know the man that he
Has brought into his own security.
I pray God give me sorrow and much care
If ever, since I have been Hodge[1] of Ware,
Heard I of miller better brought to mark.
A wicked jest was played him in the dark.
But God forbid that we should leave off here;
And therefore, if you'll lend me now an ear,
From what I know, who am but a poor man,
I will relate, as well as ever I can,
A little trick was played in our city."
Our host replied: "I grant it readily.
Now tell on, Roger; see that it be good;
For many a pasty have you robbed of blood,
And many a Jack of Dover[2] have you sold
That has been heated twice and twice grown cold.
From many a pilgrim have you had Christ's curse,
For of your parsley they yet fare the worse,
Which they have eaten with your stubble goose;
For in your shop full many a fly is loose.
Now tell on, gentle Roger, by your name.
But yet, I pray, don't mind if I make game,
A man may tell the truth when it's in play."
"You say the truth," quoth Roger, "by my fay!
But 'true jest, bad jest' as the Fleming saith.
And therefore, Harry Bailey, on your faith,
Be you not angry ere we finish here,
If my tale should concern an inn-keeper.
Nevertheless, I'll tell not that one yet,
But ere we part your jokes will I upset."
And thereon did he laugh, in great good cheer,
And told his tale, as you shall straightway hear.

THE COOK of London, whyl the Reve spak,
For joye, him thoughte, he clawed him on the bak,
"Ha! ha!" quod he, "for Cristes passioun,
This miller hadde a sharp conclusioun
Upon his argument of herbergage!
Wel seyde Salomon in his langage,
'Ne bringe nat every man in-to thyn hous';
For herberwing by nighte is perilous.
Wel oghte a man avysed for to be
Whom that he broghte in-to his privetee.
I pray to god, so yeve me sorwe and care,
If ever, sith I highte Hogge[1] of Ware,
Herde I a miller bettre y-set a-werk.
He hadde a jape of malice in the derk.
But god forbede that we stinten here;
And therfore, if ye vouche-sauf to here
A tale of me, that am a povre man,
I wol yow telle as wel as ever I can
A litel jape that fil in our citee."
Out host answerde, and seide, "I graunte it thee;
Now telle on, Roger, loke that it be good;
For many a pastee hastow laten blood,
And many a Jakke of Dover[2] hastow sold
That hath been twyes hoot and twyes cold.
Of many a pilgrim hastow Cristes curs,
For of thy persly yet they fare the wors,
That they han eten with thy stubbel-goos;
For in thy shoppe is many a flye loos.
Now telle on, gentil Roger, by thy name.
But yet I pray thee, be nat wrooth for game,
A man may seye ful sooth in game and pley."
"Thou seist ful sooth," quod Roger, "by my fey,
But 'sooth pley, quaad pley,' as the Fleming seith;
And ther-fore, Herry Bailly, by thy feith,
Be thou nat wrooth, er we departen heer,
Though that my tale be of an hostileer.
But nathelees I wol nat telle it yit,
But er we parte, y-wis, thou shalt be quit."
And ther-with-al he lough and made chere,
And seyde his tale, as ye shul after here.

[1]A nickname for Roger.
[2]A slang term for a meat pie from which, not being sold the day it was cooked, the gravy was drawn off.

THUS ENDETH THE PROLOGUE OF THE COOK'S TALE

THE COOK'S TALE

HERE BEGINNETH THE COOK'S TALE

A PRENTIS whylom dwelled in our citee,
And of a craft of vitaillers was he;
Gaillard he was as goldfinch in the shawe,
Broun as a berie, a propre short felawe,
With lokkes blake, y-kempt ful fetisly.
Dauncen he coude so wel and jolily,
That he was cleped Perkin Revelour.
He was as ful of love and paramour
As is the hyve ful of hony swete;
Wel was the wenche with him mighte mete.
At every brydale wolde he singe and hoppe,
He loved bet the tavern than the shoppe.
For whan ther any ryding was in Chepe,
Out of the shoppe thider wolde he lepe.
Til that he hadde al the sighte y-seyn,
And daunced wel, he wolde nat come ageyn.
And gadered him a meinee of his sort
To hoppe and singe, and maken swich disport.
And ther they setten steven for to mete
To pleyen at the dys in swich a strete.
For in the toune nas ther no prentys,
That fairer coude caste a paire of dys
Than Perkin coude, and ther-to he was free
Of his dispense, in place of privetee.
That fond his maister wel in his chaffare;
For often tyme he fond his box ful bare.
For sikerly a prentis revelour,
That haunteth dys, riot, or paramour,
His maister shal it in his shoppe abye,
Al have he no part of the minstralcye;
For thefte and riot, they ben convertible,
Al conne he pleye on giterne or ribible.
Revel and trouthe, as in a low degree,
They been ful wrothe al day, as men may see.
This joly prentis with his maister bood,
Til he were ny out of his prentishood,
Al were he snibbed bothe erly and late,
And somtyme lad with revel to Newgate;
But atte laste his maister him bithoghte,
Up-on a day, whan he his paper soghte,
Of a proverbe that seith this same word,
"Wel bet is roten appel out of hord
Than that it rotie al the remenaunt."
So fareth it by a riotous servaunt;
It is wel lasse harm to lete him pace,
Than he shende alle the servants in the place.
Therfore his maister yaf him acquitance,
And bad him go with sorwe and with meschance;
And thus this joly prentis hadde his leve.
Now lat him riote al the night or leve.
And for ther is no theef with-oute a louke,
That helpeth him to wasten and to souke
Of that he brybe can or borwe may,
Anon he sente his bed and his array
Un-to a compeer of his owne sort,

THERE lived a 'prentice, once, in our city,
And of the craft of victuallers was he;
Happy he was as goldfinch in the glade,
Brown as a berry, short, and thickly made,
With black hair that he combed right prettily.
He could dance well, and that so jollily,
That he was nicknamed Perkin Reveller.
He was as full of love, I may aver,
As is a beehive full of honey sweet;
Well for the wench that with him chanced to meet.
At every bridal would he sing and hop,
Loving the tavern better than the shop.
When there was any festival in Cheap,
Out of the shop and thither would he leap,
And, till the whole procession he had seen,
And danced his fill, he'd not return again.
He gathered many fellows of his sort
To dance and sing and make all kinds of sport.
And they would have appointments for to meet
And play at dice in such, or such, a street.
For in the whole town was no apprentice
Who better knew the way to throw the dice
Than Perkin; and therefore he was right free
With money, when in chosen company.
His master found this out in business there;
For often-times he found the till was bare.
For certainly a revelling bond-boy
Who loves dice, wine, dancing, and girls of joy—
His master, in his shop, shall feel the effect,
Though no part have he in this said respect;
For theft and riot always comrades are,
And each alike he played on gay guitar.
Revels and truth, in one of low degree,
Do battle always, as all men may see.
This 'prentice shared his master's fair abode
Till he was nigh out of his 'prenticehood,
Though he was checked and scolded early and late
And sometimes led, for drinking, to Newgate;
But at the last his master did take thought,
Upon a day, when he his ledger sought,
On an old proverb wherein is found this word:
"Better take rotten apple from the hoard
Than let it lie to spoil the good ones there."
So with a drunken servant should it fare;
It is less ill to let him go, apace,
Than ruin all the others in the place.
Therefore he freed and cast him loose to go
His own road unto future care and woe;
And thus this jolly 'prentice had his leave.
Now let him riot all night long, or thieve.
But since there's never thief without a buck
To help him waste his money and to suck
All he can steal or borrow by the way,
Anon he sent his bed and his array
To one he knew, a fellow of his sort,

Who loved the dice and revels and all sport,
And had a wife that kept, for countenance,
A shop, and whored to gain her sustenance.

That lovede dys and revel and disport,
And hadde a wyf that heeld for countenance
A shoppe, and swyved for hir sustenance.

OF THIS COOK'S TALE CHAUCER MADE NO MORE

INTRODUCTION TO THE MAN OF LAW'S PROLOGUE

THE WORDS OF THE HOST TO THE COMPANY

Our good host saw well that the shining sun
The arc of artificial day[1] had run
A quarter part, plus half an hour or more;
And though not deeply expert in such lore,
He reckoned that it was the eighteenth day
Of April, which is harbinger to May;
And saw well that the shadow of each tree
Was, as to length, of even quantity
As was the body upright causing it.
And therefore by the shade he had the wit
To know that Phoebus, shining there so bright,
Had climbed degrees full forty-five in height;
And that, that day, and in that latitude,
It was ten of the clock, he did conclude,
And suddenly he put his horse about.
"Masters," quoth he, "I warn all of this rout,
A quarter of this present day is gone;
Now for the love of God and of Saint John,
Lose no more time, or little as you may;
Masters, the time is wasting night and day,
And steals away from us, what with our sleeping
And with our sloth, when we awake are keeping,
As does the stream, that never turns again,
Descending from the mountain to the plain.
And well may Seneca, and many more,
Bewail lost time far more than gold in store.
'For chattels lost may yet recovered be,
But time lost ruins us for aye,' says he.
It will not come again, once it has fled,
Not any more than will Mag's maidenhead
When she has lost it in her wantonness;
Let's not grow mouldy thus in idleness.
"Sir Lawyer," said he, "as you have hope of bliss,
Tell us a tale, as our agreement is;
You have submitted, by your free assent,
To stand, in this case, to my sole judgment;
Acquit yourself, keep promise with the rest,
And you'll have done your duty, at the least."
"Mine host," said he, "by the gods, I consent;
To break a promise is not my intent.
A promise is a debt, and by my fay
I keep all mine; I can no better say.
For such law as man gives to other wight,
He should himself submit to it, by right;
Thus says our text; nevertheless, 'tis true
I can relate no useful tale to you,

Our Hoste sey wel that the brighte sonne
Th'ark of his artificial day[1] had ronne
The fourthe part, and half an houre, and more;
And though he were not depe expert in lore,
He wiste it was the eightetethe day
Of April, that is messager to May;
And sey wel that the shadwe of every tree
Was as in lengthe the same quantitee
That was the body erect that caused it.
And therfor by the shadwe he took his wit
That Phebus, which that shoon so clere and brighte,
Degrees was fyve and fourty clombe on highte;
And for that day, as in that latitude,
It was ten of the clokke, he gan conclude,
And sodeynly he plighte his hors aboute.
"Lordinges," quod he, "I warne yow, al this route,
The fourthe party of this day is goon;
Now, for the love of god and of seint John,
Leseth no tyme, as ferforth as ye may;
Lordinges, the tyme wasteth night and day,
And steleth from us, what prively slepinge,
And what thurgh necligence in our wakinge,
As dooth the streem, that turneth never agayn,
Descending fro the montaigne in-to playn.
Wel can Senek, and many a philosophre
Biwailen tyme, more than gold in cofre.
'For los of catel may recovered be,
But los of tyme shendeth us,' quod he.
It wol nat come agayn, with-outen drede,
Na more than wol Malkins maydenhede,
Whan she hath lost it in hir wantownesse;
Lat us nat moulen thus in ydelnesse.
"Sir man of lawe," quod he, "so have ye blis,
Tel us a tale anon, as forward is;
Ye been submitted thurgh your free assent
To stonde in this cas at my jugement.
Acquiteth yow, and holdeth your biheste,
Than have ye doon your devoir atte leste."
"Hoste," quod he, "*depardieux* ich assente,
To breke forward is not myn entente.
Biheste is dette, and I wol holde fayn
Al my biheste; I can no better seyn.
For swich lawe as man yeveth another wight,
He sholde him-selven usen it by right;
Thus wol our text; but natheles certeyn
I can right now no thrifty tale seyn,

[1]From sunrise to sunset.

But Chaucer, though he can but lewedly
On metres and on ryming craftily,
Hath seyd hem in swich English as he can
Of olde tyme, as knoweth many a man.
And if he have not seyd hem, leve brother,
In o book, he hath seyd hem in another.
For he hath told of loveres up and doun
Mo than Ovyde made of mencioun
In his Epistelles, that been ful olde.
What sholde I tellen hem, sin they ben tolde?
In youthe he made of Ceys and Alcion,
And sithen hath he spoke of everichon,
Thise noble wyves and thise loveres eke.
Who-so that wol his large volume seke
Cleped the Seintes Legende of Cupyde,
Ther may be seen the large woundes wyde
Of Lucresse, and of Babilan Tisbee;
The swerd of Dido for the false Enee;
The tree of Phillis for hir Demophon;
The pleinte of Dianire and Hermion,
Of Adriane and of Isiphilee;
The bareyne yle stonding in the see;
The dreynte Leander for his Erro;
The teres of Eleyne, and eek the wo
Of Brixseyde, and of thee, Ladomëa;
The crueltee of thee, queen Medëa,
Thy litel children hanging by the hals
For thy Jason, that was of love so fals!
O Ypermistra, Penelopee, Alceste,
Your wyfhod he comendeth with the beste!
  But certeinly no word ne wryteth he
Of thilke wikke ensample of Canacee,
That lovede hir owne brother sinfully;
Of swiche cursed stories I sey 'fy';
Or elles of Tyro Apollonius,
How that the cursed king Antiochus
Birafte his doghter of hir maydenhede,
That is so horrible a tale for to rede,
Whan he hir threw up-on the pavement.
And therfor he, of ful avysement,
Nolde never wryte in none of his sermouns
Of swiche unkinde abhominaciouns,
Ne I wol noon reherse, if that I may.
  But of my tale how shal I doon this day?
Me were looth be lykned, doutelees,
To Muses that men clepe Pierides—
Metamorphoseos wot what I mene:—
But nathelees, I recche noght a bene
Though I come after him with hawe-bake;
I speke in prose, and lat him rymes make."
  And with that word he, with a sobre chere,
Bigan his tale, as ye shal after here.

But Chaucer, though he speaks but vulgarly
In metre and in rhyming dextrously,
Has told them in such English as he can,
In former years, as knows full many a man.
For if he has not told them, my dear brother,
In one book, why he's done so in another.
For he has told of lovers, up and down,
More than old Ovid mentions, of renown,
In his *Epistles*, that are now so old.
Why should I then re-tell what has been told?
In youth he told of Ceyx and Alcyon,
And has since then spoken of everyone—
Of noble wives and lovers did he speak.
And whoso will that weighty volume seek
Called *Legend of Good Women*, need not chide;
There may be ever seen the large wounds wide
Of Lucrece, Babylonian Thisbe;
Dido's for false Aeneas when fled he;
Demophoon and Phyllis and her tree;
The plaint of Deianira and Hermione;
Of Ariadne and Hypsipyle;
The barren island standing in the sea;
The drowned Leander and his fair Hero;
The tears of Helen and the bitter woe
Of Briseis and that of Laodomea;
The cruelty of that fair Queen Medea,
Her little children hanging by the neck
When all her love for Jason came to wreck!
O Hypermnestra, Penelope, Alcestis,
Your wifehood does he honour, since it best is!
  "But certainly no word has written he
Of that so wicked woman, Canace,
Who loved her own blood brother sinfully.
Of suchlike cursed tales, I say 'Let be!'
Nor yet of Tyrian Apollonius;
Nor how the wicked King Antiochus
Bereft his daughter of her maidenhead
(Which is so horrible a tale to read),
When down he flung her on the paving stones.
And therefore he, advisedly, truth owns,
Would never write, in one of his creations,
Of such unnatural abominations.
And I'll refuse to tell them, if I may.
  "But for my tale, what shall I do this day?
Any comparison would me displease
To Muses whom men call Pierides
(The *Metamarphases* show what I mean).
Nevertheless, I do not care a bean
Though I come after him with my plain fare.
I'll stick to prose. Let him his rhymes prepare."
  And thereupon, with sober face and cheer,
He told his tale, as you shall read it here.

THE PROLOGUE OF THE MAN OF LAW'S TALE

O hateful harm! condicion of poverte!
With thurst, with cold, with hunger so
  confounded!
To asken help thee shameth in thyn herte;
If thou noon aske, with nede artow so wounded,
That verray nede unwrappeth al thy wounde hid!
Maugree thyn heed, thou most for indigence
Or stele, or begge, or borwe thy despence!

O HATEFUL evil! State of Poverty!
With thirst, with cold, with hunger so
  confounded!
To ask help shameth thy heart's delicacy;
If none thou ask, by need thou art so wounded
That need itself uncovereth all the wound hid!
Spite of thy will thou must, for indigence,
Go steal, or beg, or borrow thine expense.

Thou blamest Christ, and thou say'st bitterly,
He misdistributes riches temporal;
Thy neighbour dost thou censure, sinfully,
Saying thou hast too little and he hath all.
"My faith," sayest thou, "sometime the reckoning shall
Come on him, when his tail shall burn for greed,
Not having helped the needy in their need."

Hear now what is the judgment of the wise:
"Better to die than live in indigence";
"Thy very pauper neighbours thee despise."
If thou be poor, farewell thy reverence!
Still of the wise man take this full sentence:
"The days of the afflicted are all sin."
Beware, therefore, that thou come not therein!

"If thou be poor, thy brother hateth thee,
And all thy friends will flee from thee, alas!"
O wealthy merchants, full of weal ye be,
O noble, prudent folk in happier case!
Your dice-box doth not tumble out ambsace,[1]
But with *six-cing*[2] ye throw against your chance;
And so, at Christmas, merrily may ye dance!

Ye search all land and sea for your winnings,
And, as wise folk, ye know well the estate
Of all realms; ye are sires of happenings
And tales of peace and tales of war's debate.
But I were now of tales all desolate,
Were't not a merchant, gone this many a year,
Taught me the story which you now shall hear.

Thou blamest Crist, and seyst ful bitterly,
He misdeparteth richesse temporal;
Thy neighebour thou wytest sinfully,
And seyst thou hast to lyte, and he hath al.
"Parfay," seistow, "somtyme he rekne shal,
Whan that his tayl shal brennen in the glede,
For he noght helpeth needfulle in hir nede."

Herkne what is the sentence of the wyse:—
"Bet is to dyën than have indigence";
"Thy selve neighebour wol thee despyse";
If thou be povre, farwel thy reverence!
Yet of the wyse man tak this sentence:—
"Alle the dayes of povre men ben wikke";
Be war therfor, er thou come in that prikke!

"If thou be povre, thy brother hateth thee,
And alle thy freendes fleen fro thee, alas!"
O riche marchaunts, ful of wele ben ye,
O noble, o prudent folk, as in this cas!
Your bagges been nat filled with *ambes as*,[1]
But with *sis cink*,[2] that renneth for your chaunce;
At Cristemasse merie may ye daunce!

Ye seken lond and see for your winninges,
As wyse folk ye knowen al th'estaat
Of regnes; ye ben fadres of tydinges
And tales, bothe of pees and of debat.
I were right now of tales desolat,
Nere that a marchaunt, goon is many a yere,
Me taughte a tale, which that ye shal here.

[1]Double-ace.
[2]Six and five.

THE TALE OF THE MAN OF LAW

HERE BEGINNETH THE MAN OF LAW HIS TALE

In Syria, once, there dwelt a company
Of traders rich, all sober men and true,
That far abroad did send their spicery,
And cloth of gold, and satins rich in hue;
Their wares were all so excellent and new
That everyone was eager to exchange
With them, and sell them divers things and strange

It came to pass, the masters of this sort
Decided that to Rome they all would wend,
Were it for business or for only sport;
No other message would they thither send,
But went themselves to Rome; this is the end.
And there they found an inn and took their rest
As seemed to their advantage suited best.

Sojourned have now these merchants in that town
A certain time, as fell to their pleasance.
And so it happened that the high renown
Of th' emperor's daughter, called the fair Constance
Reported was, with every circumstance,

In Surrie whylom dwelte a companye
Of chapmen riche, and therto sadde and trewe,
That wyde-wher senten her spycerye,
Clothes of gold, and satins riche of hewe;
Her chaffar was so thrifty and so newe,
That every wight hath deyntee to chaffare
With hem, and eek to sellen hem hir ware.

Now fel it, that the maistres of that sort
Han shapen hem to Rome for to wende;
Were it for chapmanhode or for disport,
Non other message wolde they thider sende,
But comen hem-self to Rome, this is the ende;
And in swich place, as thoughte hem avantage
For her entente, they take her herbergage.

Sojourned han thise marchants in that toun
A certein tyme, as fel to hir plesance.
And so bifel, that th'excellent renoun
Of th'emperoures doghter, dame Custance,
Reported was, with every circumstance,

Un-to thise Surrien marchants in swich wyse,
Fro day to day, as I shal yow devyse.

This was the commune vois of every man—
"Our Emperour of Rome, god him see,
A doghter hath that, sin the world bigan,
To rekne as wel hir goodnesse as beautee,
Nas never swich another as is she;
I prey to god in honour hir sustene,
And wolde she were of al Europe the quene.

In hir is heigh beautee, with-oute pryde,
Yowthe, with-oute grenehede or folye;
To alle hir werkes vertu is hir gyde,
Humblesse hath slayn in hir al tirannye.
She is mirour of alle curteisye;
Hir herte is verray chambre of holinesse,
Hir hand, ministre of fredom for almesse."

And al this vois was soth, as god is trewe,
But now to purpos lat us turne agayn;
Thise marchants han doon fraught hir shippes newe,
And, whan they han this blisful mayden seyn,
Hoom to Surryë been they went ful fayn,
And doon her nedes as they han don yore,
And liven in wele; I can sey yow no more.

Now fel it, that thise marchants stode in grace
Of him, that was the sowdan of Surrye;
For whan they came from any strange place,
He wolde, of his benigne curteisye,
Make hem good chere, and bisily espye
Tydings of sondry regnes, for to lere
The wondres that they mighte seen or here.

Amonges othere thinges, specially
Thise marchants han him told of dame Custance,
So gret noblesse in ernest, ceriously,
That this sowdan hath caught so gret plesance
To han hir figure in his remembrance,
That al his lust and al his bisy cure
Was for to love hir whyl his lyf may dure.

Paraventure in thilke large book
Which that men clepe the heven, y-writen was
With sterres, whan that he his birthe took,
That he for love shulde han his deeth, allas!
For in the sterres, clerer than is glas,
Is writen, god wot, who-so coude it rede,
The deeth of every man, withouten drede.

In sterres, many a winter ther-biforn,
Was writen the deeth of Ector, Achilles,
Of Pompey, Julius, er they were born;
The stryf of Thebes; and of Ercules,
Of Sampson, Turnus, and of Socrates
The deeth; but mennes wittes been so dulle,
That no wight can wel rede it atte fulle.

This sowdan for his privee conseil sente,
And, shortly of this mater for to pace,

Unto these Syrian merchants, in such wise,
From day to day, as I will now apprise.

This was the common voice of every man:
"Our emperor of Rome, God save and see,
A daughter has that since the world began,
To reckon as well her goodness as beauty,
Was never such another as is she;
I pray that God her fame will keep, serene,
And would she were of all Europe the queen.

"In her is beauty high, and without pride;
Youth, without crudity or levity;
In all endeavours, virtue is her guide;
Meekness in her has humbled tyranny;
She is the mirror of all courtesy;
Her heart's a very shrine of holiness;
Her hand is freedom's agent for largess."

And all this voice said truth, as God is true.
But to our story let us turn again.
These merchants all have freighted ships anew,
And when they'd seen the lovely maid, they fain
Would seek their Syrian homes with all their train,
To do their business as they'd done of yore,
And live in weal; I cannot tell you more.

Now so it was, these merchants stood in grace
Of Syria's sultan and so wise was he
That when they came from any foreign place
He would, of his benignant courtesy,
Make them good cheer, inquiring earnestly
For news of sundry realms, to learn, by word,
The wonders that they might have seen and heard.

Among some other things, especially
These merchants told him tales of fair Constance;
From such nobility, told of earnestly,
This sultan caught a dream of great pleasance,
And she so figured in his remembrance
That all his wish and all his busy care
Were, throughout life, to love that lady fair.

Now peradventure, in that mighty book
Which men call heaven, it had come to pass,
In stars, when first a living breath he took,
That he for love should get his death, alas!
For in the stars, far clearer than is glass,
Is written, God knows, read it he who can,—
And truth it is—the death of every man.

In stars, full many a winter over-worn,
Was written the death of Hector, Achilles,
Of Pompey, Julius, long ere they were born;
The strife at Thebes; and of great Hercules,
Of Samson, of Turnus, of Socrates,
The death to each; but men's wits are so dull
There is no man may read this to the full.

This sultan for his privy-council sent,
And, but to tell it briefly in this place,

He did to them declare his whole intent,
And said that, surely, save he might have grace
To gain Constance within a little space,
He was but dead; and charged them, speedily
To find out, for his life, some remedy.

By divers men, then, divers things were said;
They reasoned, and they argued up and down;
Full much with subtle logic there they sped;
They spoke of spells, of treachery in Rome town;
But finally, as to an end foreknown,
They were agreed that nothing should gainsay
A marriage, for there was no other way.

Then saw they therein so much difficulty,
When reasoning of it (to make all plain,
Because such conflict and diversity
Between the laws of both lands long had lain)
They held: "No Christian emperor were fain
To have his child wed under our sweet laws,
Given us by Mahomet for God's cause."

But he replied: "Nay, rather then than lose
The Lady Constance, I'll be christened, yes!
I must be hers, I can no other choose.
I pray you let be no rebelliousness;
Save me my life, and do not be careless
In getting her who thus alone may cure
The woe whereof I cannot long endure."

What needs a copious dilation now?
I say: By treaties and by embassy,
And the pope's mediation, high and low,
And all the Church and all the chivalry,
That, to destruction of Mahometry
And to augmenting Christian faith so dear,
They were agreed, at last, as you shall hear.

The sultan and his entire baronage
And all his vassals, they must christened be,
And he shall have Constance in true marriage,
And gold (I know not in what quantity),
For which was found enough security;
This, being agreed, was sworn by either side.
Now, Constance fair, may great God be your guide!

Now would some men expect, as I may guess,
That I should tell of all the purveyance
The emperor, of his great nobleness,
Has destined for his daughter, fair Constance.
But men must known that so great ordinance
May no one tell within a little clause
As was arrayed there for so high a cause.

Bishops were named who were with her to wend,
Ladies and lords and knights of high renown,
And other folk—but I will make an end,
Except that it was ordered through the town
That everyone, with great devotion shown,
Should pray to Christ that He this marriage lead
To happy end, and the long voyage speed.

He hath to hem declared his entente,
And seyde hem certein, "but he mighte have grace
To han Custance with-inne a litel space,
He nas but deed"; and charged hem, in hye,
To shapen for his lyf som remedye.

Diverse men diverse thinges seyden;
They argumenten, casten up and doun
Many a subtil resoun forth they leyden,
They speken of magik and abusioun;
But finally, as in conclusioun,
They can not seen in that non avantage,
Ne in non other wey, save mariage.

Than sawe they ther-in swich difficultee
By wey of resoun, for to speke al playn,
By-cause that ther was swich diversitee
Bitwene hir bothe lawes, that they sayn,
They trowe "that no cristen prince wolde fayn
Wedden his child under oure lawes swete
That us were taught by Mahoun our prophete."

And he answerde, "rather than I lese
Custance, I wol be cristned doutelees;
I mot ben hires, I may non other chese.
I prey yow holde your arguments in pees;
Saveth my lyf, and beeth noght recchelees
To geten hir that hath my lyf in cure;
For in this wo I may not longe endure."

What nedeth gretter dilatacioun?
I seye, by tretis and embassadrye,
And by the popes mediacioun,
And al the chirche, and al the chivalrye,
That, in destrucccioun of Maumetrye,
And in encrees of Cristes lawe dere,
They ben acorded, so as ye shal here;

How that the sowdan and his baronage
And alle his liges shulde y-cristned be,
And he shal han Custance in mariage,
And certein gold, I noot what quantitee,
And her-to founden suffisant seurtee;
This same acord was sworn on eyther syde;
Now, faire Custance, almighty god thee gyde!

Now wolde som men waiten, as I gesse,
That I shulde tellen al the purveyance
That th'emperour, of his grete noblesse,
Hath shapen for his doghter dame Custance.
Wel may men knowe that so gret ordinance
May no man tellen in a litel clause
As was arrayed for so heigh a cause.

Bisshopes ben shapen with hir for to wende,
Lordes, ladyes, knightes of renoun,
And other folk y-nowe, this is the ende;
And notifyed is thurgh-out the toun
That every wight, with gret devocioun,
Shulde preyen Crist that he this mariage
Receyve in gree, and spede this viage.

The day is comen of hir departinge,
I sey, the woful day fatal is come,
That ther may be no lenger taryinge,
But forthward they hem dressen, alle and some;
Custance, that was with sorwe al overcome,
Ful pale arist, and dresseth hir to wende;
For wel she seeth ther is non other ende.

Allas! what wonder is it though she wepte,
That shal be sent to strange nacioun
Fro freendes, that so tendrely hir kepte,
And to be bounden under subieccioun
Of oon, she knoweth not his condicioun.
Housbondes been alle gode, and han ben yore,
That knowen wyves, I dar say yow no more.

"Fader," she sayde, "thy wrecched child
  Custance
Thy yonge doghter, fostred up so softe,
And ye, my moder, my soverayn plesance
Over alle thing, out-taken Crist on-lofte,
Custance, your child, hir recomandeth ofte
Un-to your grace, for I shal to Surryë,
Ne shal I never seen yow more with yë.

Allas! un-to the Barbre nacioun
I moste anon, sin that it is your wille;
But Crist, that starf for our redempcioun,
So yeve me grace, his hestes to fulfille;
I, wrecche womman, no fors though I spille.
Wommen are born to thraldom and penance,
And to ben under mannes governance."

I trowe, at Troye, whan Pirrus brak the wal
Or Ylion brende, at Thebes the citee,
N'at Rome, for the harm thurgh Hanibal
That Romayns hath venquisshed tymes three,
Nas herd swich tendre weping for pitee
As in the chambre was for hir departinge;
Bot forth she moot, wher-so she wepe or singe.

O firste moeving cruel firmament,
With thy diurnal sweigh that crowdest ay
And hurlest al from Est til Occident,
That naturelly wolde holde another way,
Thy crowding set the heven in swich array
At the beginning of this fiers viage,
That cruel Mars hath slayn this mariage.

Infortunat ascendent tortuous,
Of which the lord is helples falle, allas!
Out of his angle in-to the derkest hous.
O Mars, O Atazir,[1] as in this cas!
O feble mone, unhappy been thy pas!
Thou knittest thee ther thou art nat receyved,
Ther thou were weel, fro thennes artow
  weyved.

Imprudent emperour of Rome, allas!
Was ther no philosophre in al thy toun?
Is no tyme bet than other in swich cas?

The day is come, at last, for leave-taking
I say, the woeful, fatal day is come,
When there may be no longer tarrying,
But to go forth make ready all and some;
Constance, who was with sorrow overcome,
Rose, sad and pale, and dressed herself to wend;
For well she saw there was no other end.

Alas! What wonder is it that she wept?
She shall be sent to a strange country, far
From friends that her so tenderly have kept,
And bound to one her joy to make or mar
Whom she knows not, nor what his people are.
Husbands are all good, and have been of yore,
That know their wives, but I dare say no more.

"Father," she said, "your wretched child,
  Constance,
Your daughter reared in luxury so soft,
And you, my mother, and my chief pleasance,
Above all things, save Christ Who rules aloft,
Constance your child would be remembered oft
Within your prayers, for I to Syria go,
Nor shall I ever see you more, ah no!

"Unto the land of Barbary my fate
Compels me now, because it is your will;
But Christ, Who died to save our sad estate,
So give me grace, His mandates I'll fulfill;
I, wretched woman, though I die, 'tis nil.
Women are born to slave and to repent,
And to be subject to man's government."

I think , at Troy, when Pyrrhus broke the wall;
When Ilium burned; when Thebes fell, that city;
At Rome, for all the harm from Hannibal,
Who vanquished Roman arms in campaigns three—
I think was heard no weeping for pity
As in the chamber at her leave-taking;
Yet go she must, whether she weep or sing.

O primal-moving, cruel Firmament,
With thy diurnal pressure, that doth sway
And hurl all things from East to Occident,
Which otherwise would hold another way,
Thy pressure set the heavens in such array,
At the beginning of this wild voyage,
That cruel Mars hath murdered this marriage.

Unfortunate ascendant tortuous,
Of which the lord has helpless fall'n, alas,
Out of his angle to the darkest house!
O Mars! O Atazir in present case![1]
O feeble Moon, unhappy is thy pace!
Thou'rt in conjunction where thou'rt not received,
And where thou should'st go, thou hast not
  achieved.

Imprudent emperor of Rome, alas!
Was no philosopher in all thy town?
Is one time like another in such case?

[1]The influence of a star on other stars or on men.

Indeed, can there be no election shown,
Especially to folk of high renown,
And when their dates of birth may all men know?
Alas! We are too ignorant or too slow.

To ship is brought this fair and woeful maid,
Full decorously, with every circumstance.
"Now Jesus Christ be with you all," she said;
And there's no more, save "Farewell, fair
  Constance!"
She strove to keep a cheerful countenance,
And forth I let her sail in this manner,
And turn again to matters far from her.

The mother of the sultan, well of vices,
Has heard the news of her son's full intent,
How he will leave the ancient sacrifices;
And she at once for her own council sent;
And so they came to learn what thing she meant.
And when they were assembled, each compeer,
She took her seat and spoke as you shall hear.

"My lords," said she, "you know well, every
  man,
My son intends to forgo and forget
The holy precepts of our Alkoran.
Given by God's own prophet, Mahomet.
But I will make one vow to great God yet:
The life shall rather from my body start
Than Islam's laws out of my faithful heart!

"What should we get from taking this new creed
But thralldom for our bodies and penance?
And afterward, be drawn to Hell, indeed,
For thus denying our faith's inheritance?
But, lords, if you will give your sustenance,
And join me for the wisdom I've in store,
I swear to save us all for evermore."

They swore and they assented, every man,
To live by her and die, and by her stand;
And each of them, in what best wise he can,
Shall gather friends and followers into band;
And she shall take the enterprise in hand,
The form of which I soon will you apprise,
And to them all she spoke, then, in this wise.

"We will first feign the Christian faith to take;
Cold water will not harm us from the rite;
And I will such a feast and revel make
As will, I trust, to lull be requisite.
For though his wife be christened ever so white,
She shall have need to wash away the red,
Though a full font of water be there sped."

O sultana, root of iniquity!
Virago, you Semiramis second!
O serpent hid in femininity,
Just as the Serpent deep in Hell is bound!
O pseudo-woman, all that may confound
Virtue and innocence, through your malice,
Is bred in you, the nest of every vice!

Of viage is ther noon eleccioun,
Namely to folk of heigh condicioun,
Nat whan a rote is of a birthe y-knowe?
Allas! we ben to lewed or to slowe.

To shippe is brought this woful faire mayde
Solempnely, with every circumstance.
"Now Jesu Crist be with yow alle," she sayde;
Ther nis namore but "farewel! faire
  Custance!"
She peyneth hirto make good countenance,
And forth I lete hir sayle in this manere,
And turne I wol agayn to my matere.

The moder of the sowdan, welle of vyces,
Espyëd hath hir sones pleyn entente,
How he wol lete his olde sacrifyces,
And right anon she for hir conseil sente;
And they ben come, to knowe what she mente.
And when assembled was this folk in-fere,
She sette hir doun, and sayde as ye shal here.

"Lordes," quod she, "ye knowen
  everichon,
How that my sone in point is for to lete
The holy lawes of our Alkaron,
Yeven by goddes message Makomete.
But oon avow to grete god I hete,
The lyf shal rather out of my body sterte
Than Makometes lawe out of myn herte!

What shulde us tyden of this newe lawe
But thraldom to our bodies and penance?
And afterward in helle to be drawe
For we reneyed Mahoun our creance?
But, lordes, wol ye maken assurance,
As I shal seyn, assenting to my lore,
And I shal make us sauf for evermore?"

They sworen and assenten, every man,
To live with hir and dye, and by hir stonde;
And everich, in the beste wyse he can,
To strengthen hir shal alle his freendes fonde;
And she hath this empryse y-take on honde,
Which ye shal heren that I shal devyse,
And to hem alle she spak right in this wyse.

"We shul first feyne us cristendom to take,
Cold water shal not greve us but a lyte;
And I shal swich a feste and revel make,
That, as I trowe, I shal the sowdan quyte.
For though his wyf be cristned never so whyte,
She shal have nede to wasshe awey the rede,
Thogh she a font-ful water with hir lede."

O sowdanesse, rote of iniquitee,
Virago, thou Semyram the secounde,
O serpent under femininitee,
Lyk to the serpent depe in helle y-bounde,
O feyned womman, al that may confounde
Vertu and innocence, thurgh thy malyce,
Is bred in thee, as nest of every vyce!

O Satan, envious sin thilke day
That thou were chased from our heritage,
Wel knowestow to wommen the olde way!
Thou madest Eva bringe us in servage.
Thou wolt fordoon this cristen mariage.
Thyn instrument so, weylawey the whyle!
Makestow of wommen, whan thou wolt begyle.

This sowdanesse, whom I thus blame and warie,
Leet prively hir conseil goon hir way.
What sholde I in this tale lenger tarie?
She rydeth to the sowdan on a day,
And seyde him, that she wolde reneye hir lay,
And cristendom of preestes handes fonge,
Repenting hir she hethen was so longe,

Biseching him to doon hir that honour,
That she moste han the cristen men to feste;
"To plesen hem I wol do my labour."
The sowdan seith, "I wol don at your heste."
And kneling thanketh hir of that requeste.
So glad he was, he niste what to seye;
She kiste hir sone, and hoom she gooth hir weye.

O Satan, envious since that same day
When thou wert banished from our heritage,
Well know'st thou unto woman thine old way!
Thou made'st Eve bring us into long bondage.
Thou wilt destroy this Christian marriage.
Thine instrument—ah welaway the while!—
Make'st thou of woman when thou wilt beguile!

Now this sultana whom I blame and harry,
Let, secretly, her council go their way.
Why should I longer in my story tarry?
She rode unto the sultan, on a day,
And told him she'd renounce her old faith, yea,
Be christened at priests' hands, with all the throng.
Repentant she'd been heathen for so long.

Beseeching him to do her the honour
To let her have the Christian men to feast:
"To entertain them will be my labour."
The sultan said: "I'll be at your behest."
And, kneeling, thanked her for that fair request,
So glad he was he knew not what to say;
She kissed her son, and homeward went her way.

HERE ENDETH THE FIRST PART

HERE FOLLOWETH THE SECOND PART

Arryved ben this Cristen folk to londe,
In Surrie, with a greet solempne route,
And hastily this sowdan sente his sonde,
First to his moder, and al the regne aboute,
And seyde, his wyf was comen, out of doute,
And preyde hir for to ryde agayn the quene,
The honour of his regne to sustene.

Gret was the prees, and riche was th'array
Of Surriens and Romayns met y-fere;
The moder of the sowdan, riche and gay,
Receyveth hir with al-so glad a chere
As any moder mighte hir doghter dere,
And to the nexte citee ther bisyde
A softe pas solempnely they ryde.

Noght trowe I the triumphe of Julius,
Of which that Lucan maketh swich a bost,
Was royaller, ne more curious
Than was th'assemblee of this blisful host.
But this scorpioun, this wikked gost,
The sowdanesse, for al hir flateringe,
Caste under this ful mortally to stinge.

The sowdan comth him-self sone after this
So royally, that wonder is to telle,
And welcometh hir with alle joye and blis.
And thus in merthe and joye I lete hem dwelle.
The fruyt of this matere is that I telle.
Whan tyme cam, men thoughte it for the beste
That revel stinte, and men goon to hir reste.

The tyme cam, this olde sowdanesse
Ordeyned hath this feste of which I tolde,
And to the feste Cristen folk hem dresse
In general, ye! bothe yonge and olde.

Arrived now are these Christian folk at land,
In Syria, with a great stately rout,
And hastily this sultan gave command,
First to his mother and all the realm about,
Saying his wife was come, beyond a doubt,
And prayed her that she ride to meet the queen,
That all due honour might be shown and seen.

Great was the crush and rich was the array
Of Syrians and Romans, meeting here;
The mother of the sultan, rich and gay,
Received her open-armed, with smiling cheer,
As any mother might a daughter dear;
And to the nearest city, with the bride,
At gentle pace, right festively they ride.

I think the triumph of great Julius,
Whereof old Lucan make so long a boast,
Was not more royal nor more curious
Than was the assembling of this happy host.
But this same Scorpion, this wicked ghost—
The old sultana, for all her flattering,
Chose in that sign full mortally to sting.

The sultan came himself, soon after this,
So regally 'twere wonderful to tell,
And welcomed her into all joy and bliss.
And thus in such delight I let them dwell.
The fruit of all is what I now shall tell.
When came the time, men thought it for the best
Their revels cease, and got them home to rest.

The time came when this old sultana there
Has ordered up the feast of which I told,
Whereto the Christian folk did them prepare,
The company together, young and old.

There men might feast and royalty behold,
With dainties more than I can e'en surmise;
But all too dear they've bought it, ere they rise.

O sudden woe! that ever will succeed
On worldly bliss, infused with bitterness;
That ends the joy of earthly toil, indeed;
Woe holds at last the place of our gladness.
Hear, now, this counsel for your certainness:
Upon your most glad day, bear then in mind
The unknown harm and woe that come behind.

For, but to tell you briefly, in one word—
The sultan and the Christians, every one,
Were all hewed down and thrust through, at the
  board,
Save the fair Lady Constance, she alone.
This old sultana, aye, this cursed crone
Has, with her followers, done this wicked deed,
For she herself would all the nation lead.

There was no Syrian that had been converted,
Being of the sultan's council resolute,
But was struck down, ere from the board he'd
  started.
And Constance have they taken now, hot-foot,
And on a ship, of rudder destitute,
They her have placed, bidding her learn to sail
From Syria to Italy—or fail.

A certain treasure that she'd brought, they add,
And, truth to tell, of food great quantity
They have her given, and clothing too she had;
And forth she sails upon the wide salt sea.
O Constance mine, full of benignity,
O emperor's young daughter, from afar
He that is Lord of fortune be your star!

She crossed herself, and in a pious voice
Unto the Cross of Jesus thus said she:
"O bright, O blessed Altar of my choice,
Red with the Lamb's blood full of all pity,
That washed the world from old iniquity,
Me from the Fiend and from his claws, oh keep
That day when I shall drown within the deep!

"Victorious Tree, Protection of the true,
The only thing that worthy was to bear
The King of Heaven with His wounds so new,
The White Lamb Who was pierced through with
  the spear,
Driver of devils out of him and her
Who on Thine arms do lay themselves in faith,
Keep me and give me grace before my death!"

For years and days drifted this maiden pure,
Through all the seas of Greece and to the strait
Of dark Gibraltar did she adventure;
On many a sorry meal now may she bait;
Upon her death full often may she wait
Before the wild waves and the winds shall drive
Her vessel where it shall some day arrive.

Here may men feste and royaltee biholde,
And deyntees mo than I can yow devyse,
But al to dere they boughte it er they ryse.

O sodeyn wo! that ever art successour
To worldly blisse, spreynd with bitternesse;
Th'ende of the joye of our worldly labour;
Wo occupieth the fyn of our gladnesse.
Herke this conseil for thy sikernesse,
Up-on thy glade day have in thy minde
The unwar wo or harm that comth bihinde.

For shortly for to tellen at o word,
The sowdan and the Cristen everichone
Ben al to-hewe and stiked at the
  bord,
But it were only dame Custance allone.
This olde sowdanesse, cursed crone,
Hath with hir frendes doon this cursed dede,
For she hir-self wolde al the contree lede.

Ne ther was Surrien noon that was converted
That of the conseil of the sowdan woot,
That he nas al to-hewe er he
  asterted.
And Custance han they take anon, foot-hoot,
And in a shippe al sterelees, god woot,
They han hir set, and bidde hir lerne sayle
Out of Surrye agaynward to Itayle.

A certein tresor that she thider ladde,
And, sooth to sayn, vitaille gret plentee
They han hir yeven, and clothes eek she hadde,
And forth she sayleth in the salte see.
O my Custance, ful of benignitee,
O emperoures yonge doghter dere,
He that is lord of fortune be thy stere!

She blesseth hir, and with ful pitous voys
Un-to the croys of Crist thus seyde she,
"O clere, o welful auter, holy croys,
Reed of the lambes blood full of pitee,
That wesh the world fro the olde iniquitee,
Me fro the feend, and fro his clawes kepe,
That day that I shal drenchen in the depe.

Victorious tree, proteccioun of trewe,
That only worthy were for to bere
The king of heven with his woundes newe,
The whyte lamb, that hurt was with the
  spere,
Flemer of feendes out of him and here
On which thy limes feithfully extenden,
Me keep, and yif me might my lyf t'amenden."

Yeres and dayes fleet this creature
Thurghout the see of Grece un-to the strayte
Of Marrok, as it was hir aventure;
On many a sory meel now may she bayte;
After her deeth ful often may she wayte,
Er that the wilde wawes wol hir dryve
Un-to the placë, ther she shal arryve.

Men mighten asken why she was not slayn?
Eek at the feste who mighte hir body save?
And I answere to that demaunde agayn,
Who saved Daniel in the horrible cave,
Ther every wight save he, maister and knave,
Was with the leoun frete er he asterte?
No wight but god, that he bar in his herte.

God liste to shewe his wonderful miracle
In hir, for we sholde seen his mighty werkes;
Crist, which that is to every harm triacle,
By certein menes ofte, as knowen clerkes,
Doth thing for certein ende that ful derk is
To mannes wit, that for our ignorance
Ne conne not knowe his prudent purveyance.

Now, sith she was not at the feste y-slawe,
Who kepte hir fro the drenching in the see?
Who kepte Jonas in the fisshes mawe
Til he was spouted up at Ninivee?
Wel may men knowe it was no wight but he
That kepte peple Ebraik fro hir drenchinge,
With drye feet thurgh-out the see passinge.

Who bad the foure spirits of tempest,
That power han t'anoyen land and see,
"Bothe north and south, and also west and est,
Anoyeth neither see, ne land, ne tree?"
Sothly, the comaundour of that was he,
That fro the tempest ay this womman kepte
As wel whan [that] she wook as whan she slepte.

Wher mighte this womman mete and drinke have?
Three yeer and more how lasteth hir vitaille?
Who fedde the Egipcien Marie in the cave,
Or in desert? no wight but Crist, sans faille.
Fyve thousand folk it was as gret mervaille
With loves fyve and fisshes two to fede.
God sente his foison at hir grete nede.

She dryveth forth in-to our occean
Thurgh-out our wilde see, til, atte laste,
Under an hold that nempnen I ne can,
Fer in Northumberlond the wawe hir caste,
And in the sond hir ship stiked so faste,
That thennes wolde it noght of al a tyde,
The wille of Crist was that she shulde abyde.

The constable of the castel doun is fare
To seen this wrak, and al the ship he soghte,
And fond this wery womman ful of care;
He fond also the tresor that she broghte.
In hir langage mercy she bisoghte
The lyf out of hir body for to twinne,
Hir to delivere of wo that she was inne.

A maner Latin corrupt was hir speche,
But algates ther-by was she understonde;
The constable, whan him list no lenger seche,
This woful womman broghte he to the londe;
She kneleth doun, and thanketh goddes
  sonde.

Men might well ask: But why was she not slain?
And at that feast who could her body save?
And I reply to that demand, again:
Who saved young Daniel in the dreadful cave
Where every other man, master and knave,
Was killed by lions ere he might up-start?
No one, save God, Whom he bore in his heart.

God willed to show this wondrous miracle
Through her, that we should see His mighty works;
And Christ Who every evil can dispel,
By certain means does oft, as know all clerks,
Do that whereof the end in darkness lurks
For man's poor wit, which of its ignorance
Cannot conceive His careful purveyance.

Now, since she was not slain at feast we saw,
Who kept her that she drowned not in the sea?
But who kept Jonah in the fish's maw
Till he was spewed forth there at Nineveh?
Well may men know it was no one but He
Who saved the Hebrew people from drowning
When, dry-shod, through the sea they went walking

Who bade the four great spirits of tempest,
That power have to harry land and sea,
"Not north, nor south, nor yet to east, nor west
Shall ye molest the ocean, land, or tree?"
Truly, the Captain of all this was He
Who from the storm has aye this woman kept,
As well when waking as in hours she slept.

Where might this woman get her drink and meat?
Three years and more, how lasted her supply?
Who gave Egyptian Mary food to eat
In cave or desert? None but Christ, say I.
Five thousand folk, the gospels testify,
On five loaves and two fishes once did feed.
And thus God sent abundance for her need.

Forth into our own ocean then she came,
Through all our wild white seas, until at last,
Under a keep, whose name I cannot name,
Far up Northumberland, her ship was cast,
And on the sands drove hard and stuck so fast
That thence it moved not, no, for all the tide,
It being Christ's will that she should there abide.

The warden of the castle down did fare
To view this wreck, and through the ship he sought
And found this weary woman, full of care;
He found, also, the treasure she had brought.
In her own language mercy she besought
That he would help her soul from body win
To free her from the plight that she was in.

A kind of bastard Latin did she speak,
But, nevertheless, these folk could understand;
The constable no longer thought to seek,
But led the sorrowing woman to the land;
There she knelt down and thanked God, on the
  sand,

But who or what she was, she would not say,
For threat or promise, though she died that day.

She said she'd been bewildered by the sea,
And had lost recollection, by her truth;
The warden had for her so great pity,
As had his wife, that both they wept for ruth.
She was so diligent to toil, in sooth,
To serve and please all folk within that place,
That all loved her who looked upon her face.

This warden and Dame Hermengild, his wife,
Were pagans, and that country, everywhere;
But Hermengild now loved her as her life,
And Constance has so long abided there,
And prayed so oft, with many a tearful prayer,
That Jesus has converted, through His grace,
Dame Hermengild, the lady of that place.

In all that land no Christian dared speak out
All Christians having fled from the country,
For pagan men had conquered all about
The regions of the north, by land and sea;
To Wales was fled the Christianity
Of the old Britons dwelling in this isle;
That was their refuge in the wild meanwhile.

Yet ne'er were Christian Britons so exiled
But some of them assembled, privately,
To honour Christ, and heathen folk beguiled;
And near the castle dwelt of such men three.
But one of them was blind and could not see,
Save with the inner optics of his mind,
Wherewith all men see after they go blind.

Bright was the sun upon that summer's day
When went the warden and his wife also,
And Constance, down the hill, along the way
Toward the sea, a furlong off, or so,
To frolic and to wander to and fro;
And in their walk on this blind man they came,
With eyes fast shut, a creature old and lame.

"In name of Christ!" this blind old Briton cried,
"Dame Hermengild, give me my sight again."
But she was frightened of the words, and sighed,
Lest that her husband, briefly to be plain,
Should have her, for her love of Jesus, slain;
Till Constance strengthened her and bade her work
The will of God, as daughter of His kirk.

The warden was confounded by that sight,
And asked: "What mean these words and this affair?"
Constance replied: "Sir, it is Jesus' might
That helps all poor folk from the foul Fiend's snare."
And so far did she our sweet faith declare
That she the constable, before 'twas eve,
Converted, and in Christ made him believe.

This constable, though not lord of that place

But what she was, she wolde no man seye,
For foul ne fair, thogh that she shulde deye.

She seyde, she was so mased in the see
That she forgat hir minde, by hir trouthe;
The constable hath of hir so greet pitee,
And eek his wyf, that they wepen for routhe,
She was so diligent, with-outen slouthe,
To serve and plesen everich in that place,
That alle hir loven that loken on hir face.

This constable and dame Hermengild his wyf
Were payens, and that contree everywhere;
But Hermengild lovede hir right as hir lyf,
And Custance hath so longe sojourned there,
In orisons, with many a bitter tere,
Til Jesu hath converted thurgh his grace
Dame Hermengild, constablesse of that place.

In al that lond no Cristen durste route,
Alle Cristen folk ben fled fro that contree
Thurgh payens, that conquereden al aboute
The plages of the North, by land and see;
To Walis fled the Cristianitee
Of olde Britons, dwellinge in this yle;
Ther was hir refut for the mene whyle.

But yet nere Cristen Britons so exyled
That ther nere somme that in hir privetee
Honoured Crist, and hethen folk bigyled;
And ny the castel swiche ther dwelten three.
That oon of hem was blind, and mighte nat see
But it were with thilke yën of his minde,
With whiche men seen, after that they ben blinde.

Bright was the sonne as in that someres day,
For which the constable and his wyf also
And Custance han y-take the righte way
Toward the see, a furlong wey or two,
To pleyen and to romen to and fro;
And in hir walk this blinde man they mette
Croked and old, with yën faste y-shette.

"In name of Crist," cryde this blinde Britoun
"Dame Hermengild, yif me my sighte agayn."
This lady wex affrayed of the soun,
Lest that hir housbond, shortly for to sayn,
Wolde hir for Jesu Cristes love han slayn,
Til Custance made hir bold, and bad hir werche
The wil of Crist, as doghter of his chirche.

The constable wex abasshed of that sight,
And seyde, "what amounteth al this fare?"
Custance answerde, "sire, it is Cristes might,
That helpeth folk out of the feendes snare."
And so ferforth she gan our lay declare,
That she the constable, er that it were eve,
Converted, and on Crist made him bileve.

This constable was no-thing lord of this place

Of which I speke, ther he Custance
 fond,
But kept it strongly, many wintres space,
Under Alla, king of al Northumberlond,
That was ful wys, and worthy of his hond
Agayn the Scottes, as men may wel here,
But turne I wol agayn to my matere.

Sathan, that ever us waiteth to bigyle,
Saugh of Custance al hir perfeccioun,
And caste anon how he mighte quyte hir whyle,
And made a yong knight, that dwelte in that toun,
Love hir so hote, of foul affeccioun,
That verraily him thoughte he shulde spille
But he of hir mighte ones have his wille.

He woweth hir, but it availleth noght,
She wolde do no sinne, by no weye;
And, for despyt, he compassed in his thoght
To maken hir on shamful deth to deye.
He wayteth whan the constable was aweye,
And prively, up-on a night, he crepte
In Hermengildes chambre whyl she slepte.

Wery, for-waked in her orisouns,
Slepeth Custance, and Hermengild also.
This knight, thurgh Sathanas temptaciouns,
Al softely is to the bed y-go,
And kitte the throte of Hermengild a-two,
And leyde the blody knyf by dame Custance,
And wente his wey, ther god yeve him
 meschance!

Sone after comth this constable hoom agayn,
And eek Alla, that king was of that lond,
And saugh his wyf despitously y-slayn,
For which ful ofte he weep and wrong his hond,
And in the bed the blody knyf he fond
By dame Custance; allas! what mighte she seye?
For verray wo hir wit was al aweye.

To king Alla was told al this meschance,
And eek the tyme, and where, and in what wyse
That in a ship was founden dame Custance,
As heer-biforn that ye han herd devyse.
The kinges herte of pitee gan agryse,
Whan he saugh so benigne a creature
Falle in disese and in misaventure.

For as the lomb toward his deeth is broght,
So stant this innocent bifore the king;
This false knight that hath this tresoun wroght
Berth hir on hond that she hath doon this thing.
But nathelees, ther was greet moorning
Among the peple, and seyn, "they can not gesse
That she hat doon so greet a wikkednesse.

For they han seyn hir ever so vertuous,
And loving Hermengild right as her lyf."
Of this bar witnesse everich in that hous
Save he that Hermengild slow with his knyf.
This gentil king hath caught a gret motyf

Where he'd found Constance, wrecked upon the
 sand,
Had held it well for many a winter's space,
For Alla, king of all Northumberland,
Who was full wise and hardy of his hand
Against the Scots, as men may read and hear,
But I will to my tale again—give ear.

Satan, that ever waits, men to beguile,
Saw now, in Constance, all perfection grown,
And wondering how to be revenged the while,
He made a young knight, living in the town,
Love her so madly, with foul passion flown,
That verily he thought his life should spill,
Save that, of her, he once might have his will.

He wooed her, but it all availed him naught;
She would not sin in any wise or way;
And, for despite, he plotted in his thought
To make her die a death of shame some day.
He waited till the warden was away,
And, stealthily by night, he went and crept
To Hermengild's bed-chamber, while she slept.

Weary with waking for her orisons,
Slept Constance, and Dame Hermengild also.
This knight, by Satan's tempting, came at once
And softly to the bedside he did go.
And cut the throat of Hermengild, and so
Laid the hot reeking knife by fair Constance,
And went his way—where God give him
 mischance!

Soon after came the warden home again,
And with him Alla, king of all that land,
And saw his wife so pitilessly slain,
For which he wept and cried and wrung his hand;
And in the bed the bloody dagger, and
The Lady Constance. Ah! What could she say?
For very woe her wits went all away.

King Alla was apprised of this sad chance,
And told the time, and where, and in what wise
Was found in a wrecked ship the fair Constance,
As heretofore you've heard my tale apprise.
But in the king's heart pity did arise
When he saw so benignant a creature
Fallen in distress of such misadventure.

For as the lamb unto his death is brought,
So stood this innocent before the king;
And the false knight that had this treason wrought,
He swore that it was she had done this thing.
Nevertheless, there was much sorrowing
Among the people, saying, "We cannot guess
That she has done so great a wickedness.

"For we have seen her always virtuous,
And loving Hermengild as she loved life."
To this bore witness each one in that house,
Save he that slew the victim with his knife.
The gentle king suspected motive rife

In that man's heart; and thought he would inquire
Deeper therein, the truth to learn entire.

Alas, Constance! You have no champion,
And since you cannot fight, it's welaway!
But He Who died for us the cross upon,
And Satan bound (who lies yet where he lay),
So be your doughty Champion this day!
For, except Christ a miracle make known,
You shall be slain, though guiltless, and right soon.

She dropped upon her knees and thus she prayed:
"Immortal God, Who saved the fair Susanna
From lying blame, and Thou, O gracious Maid
(Mary, I mean, the daughter of Saint Anna),
Before whose Child the angels sing hosanna,
If I be guiltless of this felony,
My succour be, for otherwise I die!"

Have you not sometimes seen a pallid face
Among the crowd, of one that's being led
Toward his death—one who had got no grace?
And such a pallor on his face was spread
All men must mark it, full of horrid dread,
Among the other faces in the rout.
So stood fair Constance there and looked about.

O queens that live in all prosperity,
Duchesses, and you ladies, every one,
Have pity, now, on her adversity;
An emperor's young daughter stands alone;
She has no one to whom to make her moan.
O royal blood that stands there in such dread,
Far are your friends away in your great need!

This King Alla has such compassion shown
(Since gentle heart is full of all pity),
That from his two eyes ran the tears right down.
"Now hastily go fetch a book," quoth he,
"And if this knight will swear that it was she
Who slew the woman, then will we make clear
The judge we shall appoint the case to hear."

A book of Gospels writ in British tongue
Was brought, and on this Book he swore anon
Her guilt; but then the people all among
A clenched hand smote him on the shoulder-bone,
And down he fell, as stunned as by a stone,
And both his eyes burst forth out of his face
In sight of everybody in that place.

A voice was heard by all that audience,
Saying: "You have here slandered the guiltless
Daughter of Holy Church, in high Presence;
Thus have you done, and further I'll not press."
Whereat were all the folk aghast, no less;
As men amazed they stand there, every one,
For dread of vengeance, save Constance alone.

Great was the fear and, too, the repentance
Of those that held a wrong suspicion there
Against this simple innocent Constance;

Of this witnesse, and thoghte he wolde enquere
Depper in this, a trouthe for to lere.

Allas! Custance! thou hast no champioun,
Ne fighte canstow nought, so weylawey!
But he, that starf for our redempcioun
And bond Sathan (and yit lyth ther he lay)
So be thy stronge champioun this day!
For, but-if Crist open miracle kythe,
Withouten gilt thou shalt be slayn as swythe.

She sette her doun on knees, and thus she sayde,
"Immortal god, that savedest Susanne
Fro false blame, and thou, merciful mayde,
Mary I mene, doghter to Seint Anne,
Bifore whos child aungeles singe Osanne,
If I be giltlees of this felonye,
My socour be, for elles I shal dye!"

Have ye nat seyn som tyme a pale face,
Among a prees, of him that hath be lad
Toward his deeth, wher-as him gat no grace,
And swich a colour in his face hath had,
Men mighte knowe his face, that was bistad,
Amonges alle the faces in that route:
So stant Custance, and loketh hir aboute.

O quenes, livinge in prosperitee,
Duchesses, and ye ladies everichone,
Haveth som routhe on hir adversitee;
An emperoures doghter stant allone;
She hath no wight to whom to make hir mone.
O blood royal, that stondes in this drede,
Fer ben thy freendes at thy grete nede!

This Alla king hath swich compassioun,
As gentil herte is fulfild of pitee,
That from his yën ran the water doun.
"Now hastily do fecche a book," quod he,
"And if this knight wol sweren how that she
This womman slow, yet wole we us avyse
Whom that we wole that shal ben our justyse."

A Briton book, writen with Evangyles,
Was fet, and on this book he swoor anoon
She gilty was, and in the mene whyles
A hand him smoot upon the nekke-boon,
That doun he fil atones as a stoon,
And bothe his yën broste out of his face
In sight of every body in that place.

A vois was herd in general audience,
And seyde, "thou hast desclaundred giltelees
The doghter of holy chirche in hey presence:
Thus hastou doon, and yet holde I my pees."
Of this mervaille agast was al the prees;
As mased folk they stoden everichone,
For drede of wreche, save Custance allone.

Greet was the drede and eek the repentance
Of hem that hadden wrong suspeccioun
Upon this sely innocent Custance;

And, for this miracle, in conclusioun,
And by Custances mediacioun,
The king, and many another in that place,
Converted was, thanked be Cristes grace!

This false knight was slayn for his untrouthe
By jugement of Alla hastifly;
And yet Custance hadde of his deeth gret routhe.
And after this Jesus, of his mercy,
Made Alla wedden ful solempnely
This holy mayden, that is so bright and shene,
And thus hath Crist y-maad Custance a quene.

But who was woful, if I shal nat lye,
Of this wedding but Donegild, and na mo,
The kinges moder, ful of tirannye?
Hir thoughte hir cursed herte brast a-two;
She wolde noght hir sone had do so;
Hir thoughte a despit, that he sholde take
So strange a creature un-to his make.

Me list nat of the chaf nor of the stree
Maken so long a tale, as of the corn.
What sholde I tellen of the royaltee
At mariage, or which cours gooth biforn,
Who bloweth in a trompe or in an horn?
The fruit of every tale is for to seye;
They ete, and drinke, and daunce, and singe, and pleye.

They goon to bedde, as it was skile and right;
For, thogh that wyves been ful holy thinges,
They moste take in pacience at night
Swich maner necessaries as been plesinges
To folk that han y-wedded hem with ringes,
And leye a lyte hir holinesse asyde
As for the tyme; it may no bet bityde.

On hir he gat a knave-child anoon,
And to a bishop and his constable eke
He took his wyf to kepe, whan he is goon
To Scotland-ward, his fo-men for to seke;
Now faire Custance, that is so humble and meke,
So longe is goon with childe, til that stille
She halt hir chambre, abyding Cristes wille.

The tyme is come, a knave-child she ber;
Mauricius at the font-stoon they him calle;
This constable dooth forth come a messager,
And wroot un-to his king, that cleped was Alle,
How that this blisful tyding is bifalle,
And othere tydings speedful for to seye;
He tak'th the lettre, and forth he gooth his weye.

This messager, to doon his avantage,
Un-to the kinges moder rydeth swythe,
And salueth hir ful faire in his langage,
"Madame," quod he, "ye may be glad and blythe,
And thanke god an hundred thousand sythe;
My lady quene hath child, with-outen doute,
To joye and blisse of al this regne aboute.

And by this miracle so wondrous fair,
And by her mediation and her prayer,
The king, with many another in that place,
Was there converted, thanks to Christ His grace!

This lying knight was slain for his untruth,
By sentence of King Alla, hastily;
Yet Constance had upon his death great ruth.
And after this, Jesus, of His mercy,
Caused Alla take in marriage, solemnly,
This holy maiden, so bright and serene,
And thus has Christ made fair Constance a queen.

But who was sad, if I am not to lie,
At this but Lady Donegild, she who
Was the king's mother, full of tyranny?
She thought her wicked heart must burst in two;
She would he'd never thought this thing to do;
And so she hugged her anger that he'd take
So strange a wife as this creature must make.

Neither with chaff nor straw it pleases me
To make a long tale, here, but with the corn.
Why should I tell of all the royalty
At that wedding, or who went first, well-born,
Or who blew out a trumpet or a horn?
The fruit of every tale is but to say,
They eat and drink and dance and sing and play.

They went to bed, as was but just and right,
For though some wives are pure and saintly things,
They must endure, in patience, in the night,
Such necessaries as make pleasurings
To men whom they have wedded well with rings,
And lay their holiness a while aside;
There may no better destiny betide.

On her he got a man-child right anon;
And to a bishop and the warden eke
He gave his wife to guard, while he was gone
To Scotland, there his enemies to seek;
Now Constance, who so humble is, and meek,
So long is gone with child that, hushed and still,
She keeps her chamber, waiting on Christ's will.

The time was come, a baby boy she bore;
Mauritius they did name him at the font;
This constable sent forth a messenger
And wrote unto King Alla at the front
Of all this glad event, a full account,
And other pressing matters did he say.
He took the letter and went on his way.

This messenger, to forward his own ends,
To the king's mother rode with swiftest speed,
Humbly saluting her as down he bends:
"Madam," quoth he, "be joyful now indeed!
To God a hundred thousand thanks proceed.
The queen has borne a child, beyond all doubt,
To joy and bliss of all this land about.

"Lo, here are letters sealed that say this thing,
Which I must bear with all the speed I may;
If you will send aught to your son, the king,
I am your humble servant, night and day."
Donegild answered: "As for this time, nay:
But here tonight I'd have you take your rest;
Tomorrow I will say what I think best."

This messenger drank deep of ale and wine,
And stolen were his letters, stealthily,
Out of his box, while slept he like a swine;
And counterfeited was, right cleverly,
Another letter, wrought full sinfully,
Unto the king, of this event so near,
All from the constable, as you shall hear.

The letter said, "the queen delivered was
Of such a fiendish, horrible creature,
That in the castle none so hardy as
Durst, for a lengthy time, there to endure.
The mother was an elf or fairy, sure,
Come there by chance of charm, or sorcery,
And all good men hated her company."

Sad was the king when this letter he'd seen;
But to no man he told his sorrows sore,
But with his own hand he wrote back again:
"Welcome what's sent from Christ, for evermore,
To me, who now am learned in His lore;
Lord, welcome be Thy wish, though hidden
still,
My own desire is but to do Thy will.

"Guard well this child, though foul it be or fair,
And guard my wife until my home-coming;
Christ, when He wills it, may send me an heir
More consonant than this with my liking."
This letter sealed, and inwardly weeping,
To the same messenger 'twas taken soon,
And forth he went; there's no more to be done.

O messenger, possessed of drunkenness,
Strong is your breath, your limbs do falter aye,
And you betray all secrets, great and less;
Your mind is gone, you jangle like a jay;
Your face is mottled in a new array!
Where drunkenness can reign, in any rout,
There is no counsel kept, beyond a doubt.

O Donegild, there is no English mine
Fit for your malice and your tyranny!
Therefore you to the Fiend I do resign,
Let him go write of your foul treachery!
Fie, mannish women! Nay, by God, I lie!
Fie, *fiendish spirit*, for I dare well tell,
Though you walk here, your spirit is in Hell!

This messenger came from the king again,
And at the king's old mother's court did light,
And she was of this messenger full fain
To please him in whatever way she might.
He drank until his girdle was too tight,

Lo, heer the lettres seled of this thing,
That I mot bere with al the haste I may;
If ye wol aught un-to your sone the king,
I am your servant, bothe night and day."
Donegild answerde, "as now at this tyme, nay;
But heer al night I wol thou take thy reste,
Tomorwe wol I seye thee what me leste."

This messager drank sadly ale and wyn,
And stolen were his lettres prively
Out of his box, whyl he sleep as a swyn:
And countrefeted was ful subtilly
Another lettre, wroght ful sinfully,
Un-to the king direct of this matere
Fro his constable, as ye shul after here.

The lettre spak, "the queen delivered was
Of so horrible a feendly creature,
That in the castel noon so hardy was
That any whyle dorste ther endure.
The moder was an elf, by aventure
Y-come, by charmes or by sorcerye,
And every wight hateth hir companye."

Wo was this king whan he this lettre had seyn,
But to no wighte he tolde his sorwes sore,
But of his owene honde he wroot ageyn,
"Welcome the sonde of Crist for evermore
To me, that am now lerned in his lore;
Lord, welcome be thy lust and thy
plesaunce,
My lust I putte al in thyn ordinaunce!

Kepeth this child, al be it foul or fair,
And eek my wyf, un-to myn hoom-cominge;
Crist, whan him list, may sende me an heir
More agreable than this to my lykinge."
This lettre he seleth, prively wepinge,
Which to the messager was take sone,
And forth he gooth; ther is na more to done.

O messager, fulfild of dronkenesse,
Strong is thy breeth, thy limes faltren ay,
And thou biwreyest alle secreenesse.
Thy mind is lorn, thou janglest as a jay,
Thy face is turned in a newe array!
Ther dronkenesse regneth in any route,
Ther is no conseil hid, with-outen doute.

O Donegild, I ne have noon English digne
Un-to thy malice and thy tirannye!
And therfor to the feend I thee resigne,
Let him endyten of thy traitorye!
Fy, mannish, fy! o nay, by god, I lye,
Fy, *feendly* spirit, for I dar wel telle,
Though thou heer walke, they spirit is in helle!

This messager comth fro the king agayn,
And at the kinges modres court he lighte,
And she was of this messager ful fayn,
And plesed him in al that ever she mighte.
He drank, and wel his girdel underpighte.

He slepeth, and he snoreth in his gyse
Al night, un-til the sonne gan aryse.

Eft were his lettres stolen everichon
And countrefeted lettres in this wyse;
“The king comandeth his constable anon,
Up peyne of hanging, and on heigh juÿse,
That he ne sholde suffren in no wyse
Custance in-with his regne for t'abyde
Thre dayes and a quarter of a tyde;

But in the same ship as he hir fond,
Hir and hir yonge sonne, and al hir gere,
He sholde putte, and croude hir fro the lond,
And charge hir that she never eft come there.”
O my Custance, wel may thy goost have fere
And sleping in thy dreem been in penance,
When Donegild caste al this ordinance!

This messager on morwe, whan he wook,
Un-to the castel halt the nexte wey,
And to the constable he the letre took;
And whan that he this pitous lettre sey,
Ful ofte he seyde “allas!” and “weylawey!”
“Lord Crist,” quod he, “how may this world endure?
So ful of sinne is many a creature!

O mighty god, if that it be thy wille,
Sith thou art rightful juge, how may it be
That thou wolt suffren innocents to spille,
And wikked folk regne in prosperitee?
O good Custance, allas! so wo is me
That I mot be thy tormentour, or deye
On shames deeth; ther is noon other weye!”

Wepen bothe yonge and olde in al that place,
Whan that the king this cursed lettre sente,
And Custance, with a deedly pale face,
The ferthe day toward hir ship she wente.
But natheles she taketh in good entente
The wille of Crist, and, kneling on the stronde,
She seyde, “lord! ay wel-com be thy sonde!

He that me kepte fro the false blame
Whyl I was on the londe amonges yow,
He can me kepe from harme and eek fro shame
In salte see, al-thogh I see nat how.
As strong as ever he was, he is yet now.
In him triste I, and in his moder dere,
That is to me my seyl and eek my stere.”

Hir litel child lay weping in hir arm,
And kneling, pitously to him she seyde,
“Pees, litel sone, I wol do thee non harm.”
With that hir kerchef of hir heed she breyde,
And over his litel yën she it leyde;
And in hir arm she lulleth it ful faste,
And in-to heven hir yën up she caste.

“Moder,” quod she, “and mayde bright, Marye,
Sooth is that thurgh wommannes eggement

He slept and snored and mumbled, drunken-wise,
All night, until the sun began to rise.

Again were his letters stolen, every one,
And others counterfeited, in this wise:
“The king commands his constable, anon,
On pain of hanging by the high justice,
That he shall suffer not, in any guise,
Constance within the kingdom to abide
Beyond three days and quarter of a tide.

“But in the ship wherein she came to strand
She and her infant son and all her gear
Shall be embarked and pushed out from the land,
And charge her that she never again come here.”
O Constance mine, well might your spirit fear,
And, sleeping, in your dream have great grievance
When Donegild arranged this ordinance.

This messenger, the morrow, when he woke,
Unto the castle held the nearest way,
And to the constable the letter took;
And when he'd read and learned what it did say,
Often he cried “Alas!” and “Welaway!
Lord Christ,” quoth he, “how may this world endure?
So full of sin is many a bad creature.

“O mighty God, and is it then Thy will?
Since Thou art righteous Judge, how can it be
That innocence may suffer so much ill
And wicked folk reign in prosperity?
O good Constance, alas! Ah, woe is me
That I must be your torturer, or die
A shameful death! There is no other way.”

Wept both the young and old of all that place
Because the king this cursed letter sent,
And Constance, with a deathly pallid face,
Upon the fourth day to the ship she went.
Nevertheless, she took as good intent
The will of Christ, and kneeling on the strand,
She said: “Lord, always welcome Thy command!

“He that did keep me from all lying blame
The while I lived among you, sun and snow,
He can still guard me from all harm and shame
Upon salt seas, albeit I see not how.
As strong as ever He was, so is He now.
In Him I trust and in His Mother dear,
He is my sail, the star by which I steer.”

Her little child lay crying in her arm,
And kneeling, piteously to him she said:
“Peace, little son, I will do you no harm.”
With that the kerchief took she from her braid,
And binding it across his eyes, she laid
Again her arm about and lulled him fast
Asleep, and then to Heaven her eyes up-cast.

“Mother,” she said, “O Thou bright Maid, Mary,
True is it that through woman's incitement

Mankind was banished and is doomed to die,
For which Thy Son upon the cross was rent;
Thy blessed eyes saw all of His torment;
Wherefore there's no comparison between
Thy woe and any woe of man, though keen.

"Thou sawest them slay Thy Son before Thine eyes;
And yet lives now my little child, I say!
O Lady bright, to Whom affliction cries,
Thou glory of womanhood, O Thou fair May,
Haven of refuge, bright star of the day,
Pity my child, Who of Thy gentleness
Hast pity on mankind in all distress!

"O little child, alas! What is your guilt,
Who never wrought the smallest sin? Ah me,
Why will your too hard father have you killed?
Have mercy, O dear constable!" cried she,
"And let my little child bide, safe from sea;
And if you dare not save him, lest they blame,
Then kiss him once in his dear father's name!"

Therewith she gazed long backward at the land,
And said: "Farewell, my husband merciless!"
And up she rose and walked right down the strand
Toward the ship; followed her all the press;
And ever she prayed her child to cry the less;
And took her leave; and with a high intent
She crossed herself; and aboard ship she went.

Victualled had been the ship, 'tis true—indeed
Abundantly—for her, and for long space;
Of many other things that she should need
She had great plenty, thanks be to God's grace!
Through wind and weather may God find her place
And bring her home! I can no better say;
But out to sea she stood upon her way.

Mankind was lorn and damned ay to dye,
For which thy child was on a croys y-rent;
Thy blisful yën sawe al his torment;
Than is ther no comparisoun bitwene
Thy wo and any wo man may sustene.

Thou sawe thy child y-slayn bifor thyn yën,
And yet now liveth my litel child, parfay!
Now, lady bright, to whom alle woful cryën,
Thou glorie of wommanhede, thou faire may,
Thou haven of refut, brighte sterre of day,
Rewe on my child, that of thy gentillesse
Rewest on every rewful in distresse!

O litel child, allas! what is thy gilt,
That never wroughtest sinne as yet, pardee,
Why wil thyn harde fader han thee spilt?
O mercy, dere constable!" quod she;
"As lat my litel child dwelle heer with thee;
And if thou darst not saven him, for blame,
So kis him ones in his fadres name!"

Ther-with she loketh bakward to the londe,
And seyde, "far-wel, housbond routhelees!"
And up she rist, and walketh doun the stronde
Toward the ship; hir folweth al the prees,
And ever she preyeth hir child to holde his pees;
And taketh hir leve, and with an holy entente
She blesseth hir; and in-to ship she wente.

Vitailled was the ship, it is no drede,
Habundantly for hir, ful longe space,
And other necessaries that sholde nede
She hadde y-nogh, heried be goddes grace!
For wind and weder almighty god purchace,
And bringe hir hoom! I can no bettre seye;
But in the see she dryveth forth hir weye.

HERE ENDETH THE SECOND PART

HERE FOLLOWETH THE THIRD PART

Alla the king came home soon after this
Unto his castle, of the which I've told,
And asked for wife and child, whom he did miss.
The constable about his heart grew cold,
And plainly all the story he then told,
As you have heard, I cannot tell it better,
And showed the king his seal and the false letter.

And said: "My lord, as you commanded me,
On pain of death, so have I done—in vain!"
The messenger was tortured until he
Made known the facts to all men, full and plain,
From night to night, in what beds he had lain.
And thus, by dint of subtle questioning,
'Twas reasoned out from whom this harm did
spring.

The hand was known, now, that the letter wrote,
And all the venom of this cursed deed,
But in what wise I certainly know not,
The effect is this, that Alla, for her meed,
His mother slew, as men may plainly read,

Alla the king comth hoom, sone after this,
Unto his castel of the which I tolde,
And axeth wher his wyf and his child is.
The constable gan aboute his herte colde,
And pleynly al the maner he him tolde
As ye han herd, I can telle it no bettre,
And sheweth the king his seel and [eek] his lettre,

And seyde, "lord, as ye comaunded me
Up peyne of deeth, so have I doon, certein."
This messager tormented was til he
Moste biknowe and tellen, plat and plein,
Fro night to night, in what place he had leyn.
And thus, by wit and subtil enqueringe,
Ymagined was by whom this harm gan
springe.

The hand was knowe that the lettre wroot,
And al the venim of this cursed dede,
But in what wyse, certeinly I noot.
Th'effect is this, that Alla, out of drede,
His moder slow, that men may pleinly rede,

For that she traitour was to hir ligeaunce.
Thus endeth olde Donegild with meschaunce.

The sorwe that this Alla, noght and day,
Maketh for his wyf and for his child also,
Ther is no tonge that it telle may.
But now wol I un-to Custance go,
That fleteth in the see, in peyne and wo,
Fyve yeer and more, as lyked Cristes sonde,
Er that hir ship approched un-to londe.

Under an hethen castel, atte laste,
Of which the name in my text noght I finde,
Custance and eek hir child the see up-caste.
Almighty god, that saveth al mankinde,
Have on Custance and on hir child som minde,
That fallen is in hethen land eft-sone,
In point to spille, as I shal telle yow sone.

Doun from the castel comth ther many a wight
To gauren on this ship and on Custance.
But shortly, from the castel, on a night,
The lordes styward—god yeve him meschaunce!—
A theef, that had reneyed our creaunce,
Com in-to ship allone, and seyde he sholde
Hir lemman be, wher-so she wolde or nolde.

Wo was this wrecched womman tho bigon,
Hir child cryde, and she cryde pitously;
But blisful Marie heelp hir right anon;
For with hir strugling wel and mightily
The theef fil over bord al sodeinly,
And in the see he dreynte for vengeance;
And thus hath Crist unwemmed kept Custance.

AUTHOR

O foule lust of luxurie! lo, thyn ende!
Nat only that thou feyntest mannes minde,
But verraily thou wolt his body shende;
Th'ende of thy werk or of thy lustes blinde
Is compleyning, how many-oon may men finde
That noght for werk som-tyme, bur for th'entente
To doon this sinne, ben outher sleyn or shente!

How may this wayke womman han this strengthe
Hir to defende agayn this renegat?
O Golias, unmesurable of lengthe,
How mighte David make thee so mat,
So yong and of armure so desolat?
How dorste he loke up-on thy dredful face?
Wel may men seen, it nas but goddes grace!

Who yaf Judith corage or hardinesse
To sleen him, Olofernus, in his tente,
And to deliveren out of wrecchednesse
The peple of god? I seye, for this ententе,
That, right as god spirit of vigour sente
To hem, and saved hem out of meschance,
So sente he might and vigour to Custance.

Forth goth hir ship thurgh-out the narwe mouth
Of Jubaltar and Septe, dryving ay,

She being false to her sworn allegiance,
And thus old Donegild ended with mischance.

The sorrow that this Alla, night and day,
Felt for his wife, and for his child also,
There is no human tongue on earth to say.
But now will I back to fair Constance go,
Who drifted on the seas, in pain and woe,
Five years and more, as was Lord Christ's command
Before her ship approached to any land.

Under a heathen castle, at the last,
Whereof the name not in my text I find,
Constance and her young son the sea did cast.
Almighty God, Redeemer of mankind,
Have Constance and her little child in mind!
Who must fall into heathen hands and soon
Be near to death, as I shall tell anon.

Down from the castle came full many a wight
To stare upon the ship and on Constance.
But briefly, from the castle, on a night,
The warden's steward—God give him mischance!—
A thief who had renounced allegiance
To Christ, came to the ship and said he should
Possess her body, whether or not she would.

Woe for this wretched woman then began,
Her child cried out and she cried, piteously;
But blessed Mary helped her soon; the man
With whom she struggled well and mightily,
This thief fell overboard all suddenly,
And in the sea was drowned by God's vengeance;
And thus has Christ unsullied kept Constance.

O foul desire of lechery, lo thine end!
Not only dost thou cripple a man's mind,
But verily dost thou his body rend;
The end of all thy work and thy lusts blind
Is bitterness; how many may we find
That not for actions but for mere intent
To do this sin, to shame or death are sent.

How could this poor weak woman have the strength
To keep herself against that renegade?
Goliath of immeasurable length,
How could young David such a death have made,
So slight and without armour? How arrayed
Himself to look upon that dreadful face?
Men may well see, it was but God's own grace!

Who gave to Judith courage all reckless
To slay him, Holofernes, in his tent,
And to deliver out of wretchedness
The folk of God? I say, for this intent
That just as God a soul of vigour sent
To them, and saved them out of their mischance,
So sent He might and vigour to Constance.

Forth went her ship and through the narrow mouth
Of Ceuta and Gibraltar, on its way,

Sometimes to west, and sometimes north or south,
Aye and sometimes east, many a weary day,
Until Christ's Mother (blest be She for aye!)
Did destine, out of good that is endless,
To make an end of Constance' heaviness.

But let us leave this Constance now, and turn
To speak of that same Roman emperor
Who does, from Syria, by letters, learn
The slaughter of Christians and the dishonour
Done to his daughter by a vile traitor—
I mean that old sultana, years ago,
Who, at the feast, slew all men, high and low.

For which this emperor did send anon
A senator, with royal ordinance,
And other lords, God knows, and many a one,
On Syrians to take full high vengeance.
They burn, they slay, they give them all
mischance
Through many a day; but, briefly to make end,
Homeward to Rome, at last, the victors wend.

This senator returned with victory
To Rome again, sailing right royally,
And spoke the ship (so goes the old story)
In which our Constance sat so piteously,
Nothing he knew of who she was, or why
She was in such a plight; nor would she say
Aught of herself, though she might die that day.

He took her into Rome, and to his wife
Gave her in charge, and her young son also;
And in his house she lived awhile her life.
Thus can Our Lady bring from deepest woe
Most woeful Constance, aye and more, we know.
And for a long time dwelt she in that place,
Engaged in God's good works, such was her grace.

The senator's good wife her own aunt was,
Yet for all that she knew her never the more;
I will no longer tarry in this case,
But to King Alla, whom we left, of yore,
Weeping for his lost wife and sighing sore,
I will return, and I will leave Constance
Under the senator's roof and governance.

King Alla, who had had his mother slain,
Upon a day fell to such repentance,
That, but to tell it briefly and be plain,
To Rome he came to pay his just penance
And put himself in the pope's ordinance,
In high and low; and Jesus Christ he sought
To pardon all the wicked deeds he'd wrought.

The news anon through all Rome town was borne,
How King Alla would come on pilgrimage,
By harbingers that unto him were sworn;
Whereat the senator, as was usage,
Rode out to him, with many of his lineage,
As well to show his own magnificence
As do to any king a reverence.

Som-tyme West, som-tyme North and South,
And som-tyme Est, ful many a wery day,
Til Cristes moder (blessed be she ay!)
Hath shapen, thurgh hir endelees goodnesse,
To make an ende of al hir hevinesse.

Now lat us stinte of Custance but a throwe,
And speke we of the Romain Emperour,
That out of Surrie hath by lettres knowe
The slaughtre of Cristen folk, and dishonour
Don to his doghter by a fals traitour,
I mene the cursed wikked sowdanesse,
That at the feste leet sleen both more and lesse.

For which this emperour hath sent anoon
His senatour, with royal ordinance,
And othere lordes, got wot, many oon,
On Surriens to taken heigh vengeance.
They brennen, sleen, and bringe hem to mes-
chance
Ful many a day; but shortly, this is the ende,
Homward to Rome they shapen hem to wende.

This senatour repaireth with victorie
To Rome-ward, sayling ful royally,
And mette the ship dryving, as seith the storie,
In which Custance sit ful pitously.
No-thing ne knew he what she was, ne why
She was in swich array; ne she nil seye
Of hir estaat, althogh she sholde deye.

He bringeth hir to Rome, and to his wyf
He yaf hir, and hir yonge sone also;
And with the senatour she ladde her lyf.
Thus can our lady bringen out of wo
Woful Custance, and many another mo.
And longe tyme dwelled she in that place,
In holy werkes ever, as was hir grace.

The senatoures wyf hir aunte was,
But for al that she knew hir never the more;
I wol no lenger tarien in this cas,
But to king Alla, which I spak of yore,
That for his wyf wepeth and syketh sore,
I wol retourne, and lete I wol Custance
Under the senatoures governance.

King Alla, which that hadde his moder slayn,
Upon a day fil in swich repentance,
That, if I shortly tellen shal and plain,
To Rome he comth, to receyven his penance;
And putte him in the popes ordinance
In heigh and low, and Jesu Crist bisoghte
Foryeve his wikked werkes that he wroghte.

The fame anon thurgh Rome toun is born,
How Alla king shal come in pilgrimage,
By herbergeours that wenten him biforn;
For which the senatour, as was usage,
Rood him ageyn, and many of his linage,
As wel to shewen his heighe magnificence
As to don any king a reverence.

Greet chere dooth this noble senatour
To king Alla, and he to him also;
Everich of hem doth other greet honour;
And so bifel that, in a day or two,
This senatour is to king Alla go
To feste, and shortly, if I shal nat lye,
Custances sone wente in his companye.

Som men wolde seyn, at requeste of Custance,
This senatour hath lad this child to feste;
I may nat tellen every circumstance,
Be as be may, ther was he at the leste.
But soth is this, that, at his modres heste,
Biforn Alla, during the metes space,
The child stood, loking in the kinges face.

This Alla king hath of this child greet wonder,
And to the senatour he seyde anon,
"Whos is that faire child that stondeth yonder?"
"I noot," quod he, "by god, and by seint John!
A moder he hath, but fader hath he non
That I of woot"—but shortly, in a stounde,
He tolde Alla how that this child was founde.

"But god wot," quod this senatour also,
"So vertuous a livere in my lyf,
Ne saugh I never as she, ne herde of mo
Of worldly wommen, mayden, nor of wyf;
I dar wel seyn hir hadde lever a knyf
Thurgh-out her breste, than been a womman wikke;
Ther is no man coude bringe hir to that prikke."

Now was this child lyk un-to Custance
As possible is a creature to be.
This Alla hath the face in remembrance
Of dame Custance, and ther-on mused he
If that the childes moder were aught she
That was his wyf, and prively he sighte,
And spedde him fro the table that he mighte.

"Parfay," thoghte he, "fantome is in myn heed!
I oghte deme, of skilful jugement,
That in the salte see my wyf is deed."
And afterward he made his argument—
"What woot I, if that Crist have hider y-sent
My wyf by see, as wel as he hir sente
To my contree fro thennes that she wente?"

And, after noon, hoom with the senatour
Goth Alla, for to seen this wonder chaunce.
This senatour dooth Alla greet honour,
And hastifly he sente after Custaunce.
But trusteth weel, hir liste nat to daunce
Whan that she wiste wherefor was that sonde.
Unnethe up-on hir feet she mighte stonde.

When Alla saugh his wyf, faire he hir grette,
And weep, that it was routhe for to see.
For at the firste look he on hir sette
He knew wel verraily that it was she.
And she for sorwe as domb stant as a tree;

Great welcome gave this noble senator
To King Alla, and he to him also;
Each of them showed the other much honour;
And so befell that, in a day or so,
This senator to King Alla did go
To feast, and briefly, if I may not lie,
Constance' young son went in his company.

Some men would say, 'twas instance of Constance
That sent him with the senator to feast;
I cannot tell you every circumstance,
Be it as may be, he was there, at least.
But truth is that, at his mother's behest,
Before the king, during the banquet's space,
The child stood, looking in King Alla's face.

This child aroused within the king great wonder,
And to the senator he said, anon:
"Whose is the fair child that is standing yonder?"
"I know not," quoth he, "by God and Saint John!
A mother he has, but father has he none
That I know of"—and briefly, at a bound,
He told King Alla how this child was found.

"But God knows," said this senator, as well,
"So virtuous a liver, in my life
I never saw, as she is, nor heard tell
Of earthly woman, maiden, no nor wife.
I dare say, she would rather have a knife
Thrust through her breast than play a female trick;
There is no man could bring her to the prick."

Now this boy was as like unto Constance
As it was possible for one to be.
Alla had kept the face in remembrance
Of Dame Constance, and thereon now mused he:
Mayhap the mother of the child was she
Who was his wife. And inwardly he sighed,
And left the table with a hasty stride.

"In faith," thought he, "a phantom's in my head!
I ought to hold, by any right judgment,
That in the wide salt sea my wife is dead."
And afterward he made this argument:
"How know I but that Christ has hither sent
My wife by sea, as surely as she went
To my own land, the which was evident?"

And, after noon, home with the senator
Went Alla, all to test this wondrous chance.
The senator did Alla great honour,
And hastily he sent for fair Constance.
But, trust me, she was little fain to dance
When she had heard the cause of that command.
Scarcely upon her two feet could she stand.

When Alla saw his wife, he greeted her,
Then wept till it was a sad thing to see.
For, at the first glance, when she entered there,
He knew full verily that it was she.
And she for grief stood dumb as ever tree;

So was her heart shut up in her distress
When she remembered his unkindliness.

Twice did she swoon away there, in his sight;
He wept and he protested piteously.
"Now God," quoth he, "and all His angels bright
So truly on my spirit have mercy
As of your ills all innocent am I,
As is Maurice, my son, so like your face,
Or may the foul Fiend take me from this place!"

Long was the sobbing and the bitter pain
Before their woeful hearts could find surcease;
Great was the pity to hear them complain,
Whereof their sorrows surely did increase.
I pray you all my labour to release;
I cannot tell their grief until tomorrow,
I am so weary, speaking long of sorrow.

But, truth being known and all doubt now dismissed,
And Alla proven guiltless of her woe,
I think a hundred times they must have kissed,
And such great bliss there was between the two
That, save the joy that nevermore shall go,
There was naught like it, present time or past,
Nor shall be, ever, while the world shall last.

Then prayed she of her husband, all meekly,
As for her pain a splendid anodyne,
That he would pray her father, specially,
That, of his majesty, he would incline
And that, some day, would come with him to dine;
She prayed him, also, he should in no way
Unto her father one word of her say.

Some men would say, it was the child Maurice
Did bear this message to the emperor;
But, as I guess, King Alla was too nice
In etiquette to one of such honour
As he that was of Christendom the flower,
To send a child; and it is best to deem
He went himself, and so it well may seem.

This emperor has granted, graciously,
To come to dinner, as he's been besought,
And, well I think, he pondered busily
Upon the child, and on his daughter thought.
Alla went to his inn, and, as he ought,
Made ready for the feast in every wise
As far as his experience could devise.

The morrow came, and Alla rose to dress,
And, too, his wife, the emperor to meet;
And forth they rode in joy and happiness.
And when she saw her father in the street,
She lighted down, and falling at his feet,
"Father," quoth she, "your young child, your Constance,
Is now gone clean out of your remembrance.

"I am your daughter Constance," then said she,
"That once you sent to Syria. 'Tis I.

So was hir herte shet in hir distresse
Whan she remembred his unkindenesse.

Twyës she swowned in his owne sighte;
He weep, and him excuseth pitously:—
"Now god," quod he, "and alle his halwes brighte
So wisly on my soule as have mercy,
That of your harm as giltelees am I
As is Maurice my sone so lyk your face;
Elles the feend me fecche out of this place!"

Long was the sobbing and the bitter peyne
Er that hir woful hertes mighte cesse;
Greet was the pitee for to here hem pleyne,
Thurgh whiche pleintes gan hir wo encresse.
I prey yow al my labour to relese;
I may nat telle hir wo un-til tomorwe,
I am so wery for to speke of sorwe.

But fynally, when that the sooth is wist
That Alla giltelees was of hir wo,
I trowe an hundred tymes been they kist,
And swich a blisse is ther bitwix hem two
That, save the joye that lasteth evermo,
Ther is non lyk, that any creature
Hath seyn or shal, whyl that the world may dure.

Tho preyde she hir housbond mekely,
In relief of hir longe pitous pyne,
That he wold preye hir fader specially
That, of his magestee, he wolde enclyne
To vouche-sauf som day with him to dyne;
She preyde him eek, he sholde by no weye
Un-to hir fader no word of hir seye.

Som men wold seyn, how that the child Maurice
Doth this message un-to this emperour;
But, as I gesse, Alla was nat so nyce
To him, that was of so sovereyn honour
As he that is of Cristen folk the flour,
Sente any child, but it is bet to deme
He wente him-self, and so it may wel seme.

This emperour hath graunted gentilly
To come to diner, as he him bisoghte;
And wel rede I, he loked bisily
Up-on this child, and on his doghter thoghte.
Alla goth to his in, and, as him oghte,
Arrayed for this feste in every wyse
As ferforth as his conning may suffyse.

The morwe cam, and Alla gan him dresse,
And eek his wyf, this emperour to mete;
And forth they ryde in joye and in gladnesse.
And whan she saugh hir fader in the strete,
She lighte doun, and falleth him to fete.
"Fader," quod she, "your yonge child Custance
Is now ful clene out of your remembrance.

I am your doghter Cústancë," quod she,
"That whylom ye han sent un-to Surrye.

It am I, fader, that in the salte see
Was put allone and dampned for to dye.
Now, gode fader, mercy I yow crye,
Send me namore un-to non hethenesse,
But thonketh my lord heer of his kindenesse."

Who can the pitous joye tellen al
Bitwix hem three, sin they ben thus y-mette?
But of my tale make an ende I shal;
The day goth faste, I wol no lenger lette.
This glade folk to diner they hem sette;
In joye and blisse at mete I lete hem dwelle
A thousand fold wel more than I can telle.

This child Maurice was sithen emperour
Maad by the pope, and lived Cristenly.
To Cristes chirche he dide greet honour;
But I lete al his storie passen by,
Of Custance is my tale specially.
In olde Romayn gestes may men finde
Maurices lyf; I bere it noght in minde.

This king Alla, whan he his tyme sey,
With his Custance, his holy wyf so swete,
To Engelond been they come the righte wey,
Wher-as they live in joye and in quiete.
But litel whyl it lasteth, I yow hete,
Joye of this world, for tyme wol nat abyde;
Fro day to night it changeth as the tyde.

Who lived ever in swich delyt o day
That him ne moeved outher conscience,
Or ire, or talent, or som kin affray,
Envye, or pryde, or passion, or offence?
I ne seye but for this ende this sentence,
That litel whyl in joye or in plesance
Lasteth the blisse of Alla with Custance.

For deeth, that taketh of heigh and low his rente,
When passed was a yeer, even as I gesse,
Out of this world this king Alla he hente,
For whom Custance hath ful gret hevinesse.
Now lat us preyen god his soule blesse!
And dame Custance, fynally to seye,
Towards the toun of Rome gooth hir weye.

To Rome is come this holy creature,
And fyndeth ther hir frendes hole and sounde:
Now is she scaped al hir aventure;
And whan that she hir fader hath y-founde,
Doun on hir kneës falleth she to grounde;
Weping for tendrenesse in herte blythe,
She herieth god an hundred thousand sythe.

In vertu and in holy almes-dede
They liven alle, and never a-sonder wende;
Til deeth departed hem, this lyf they lede.
And fareth now weel, my tale is at an ende.
Now Jesu Crist, that of his might may sende
Joye after wo, governe us in his grace,
And kepe us alle that ben in this place! Amen.

It is I, father, who, on the salt sea,
Was sent, alone to drift and doomed to die.
But now, good father, mercy must I cry:
Send me no more to heathendom, godless,
But thank my lord, here, for his kindliness."

But all the tender joy, who'll tell it all
That was between the three who thus are met?
But of my tale, now, make an end I shall;
The day goes fast, I will no longer fret.
These happy folk at dinner are all set,
And there, in joy and bliss, I let them dwell;
Happier a thousand fold than I can tell.

This child Maurice was, since then, emperor
Made by the pope, and lived right christianly.
Unto Christ's Church he did a great honour;
But I let all his story pass me by.
Of Constance is my tale, especially.
In ancient Roman histories men may find
The life of Maurice; I've it not in mind.

This King Alla, when came the proper day,
With his Constance, his saintly wife so sweet,
To England went again, by the straight way,
Where they did live in joy and quiet meet.
But little while it lasts us, thus complete,
Joy of this world, for time will not abide;
From day to day it changes as the tide.

Who ever lived in such delight one day
That was not stirred therefrom by his conscience,
Desire, or anger, or some kindred fray,
Envy, or pride, or passion, or offense?
I say but to one ending this sentence:
That but a little while in joy's pleasance
Lasted the bliss of Alla and Constance.

For death, that takes from high and low his rent,
When but a year had passed, as I should guess,
Out of the world King Alla quickly sent,
For whom Constance felt heavy wretchedness.
Now let us pray that God his soul will bless!
And of Dame Constance, finally to say,
Towards the town of Rome she took her way.

To Rome is come this holy one and pure,
And finds that all her friends are safe and sound;
For now she's done with all her adventure;
And when she'd come there, and her father found,
Down on her two knees fell she to the ground,
Weeping but joyful gave she God her praise
A hundred thousand times for all His ways.

In virtue, and with alms and holy deed,
They all live there, nor ever asunder wend;
Till death does part them, such a life they lead.
And fare now well, my tale is at an end.
And Jesus Christ, Who of His might may send
Joy after woe, govern us by His grace
And keep us all that now are in this place! Amen.

HERE ENDETH THE TALE OF THE MAN OF LAW

THE WIFE OF BATH'S PROLOGUE

THE PROLOGUE OF THE WIFE OF BATH'S TALE

Experience, though no authority
Were in this world, were good enough for me,
To speak of woe that is in all marriage;
For, masters, since I was twelve years of age,
Thanks be to God Who is for aye alive,
Of husbands at church door have I had five;
For men so many times have wedded me;
And all were worthy men in their degree.
But someone told me not so long ago
That since Our Lord, save once, would never go
To wedding (that at Cana in Galilee),
Thus, by this same example, showed He me
I never should have married more than once.
Lo and behold! What sharp words, for the nonce,
Beside a well Lord Jesus, God and man,
Spoke in reproving the Samaritan:
'For thou hast had five husbands,' "thus said He,
'And he whom thou hast now to be with thee
Is not thine husband." Thus He said that day,
But what He meant thereby I cannot say;
And I would ask now why that same fifth man
Was not husband to the Samaritan?
How many might she have, then, in marriage?
For I have never heard, in all my age,
Clear exposition of this number shown,
Though men may guess and argue up and down.
But well I know and say, and do not lie,
God bade us to increase and multiply;
That worthy text can I well understand.
And well I know He said, too, my husband
Should father leave, and mother, and cleave to me;
But no specific number mentioned He,
Whether of bigamy or octogamy;
Why should men speak of it reproachfully?
   Lo, there's the wise old king Dan Solomon;
I understand he had more wives than one;
And now would God it were permitted me
To be refreshed one half as oft as he!
Which gift of God he had for all his wives!
No man has such that in this world now lives.
God knows, this noble king, it strikes my wit,
The first night he had many a merry fit
With each of them, so much he was alive!
Praise be to God that I have wedded five![1]
Welcome the sixth whenever come he shall.
Forsooth, I'll not keep chaste for good and all;
When my good husband from the world is gone,
Some Christian man shall marry me anon;

"Experience, though noon auctoritee
Were in this world, were right y-nough to me
To speke of wo that is in mariage;
For, lordinges, sith I twelf yeer was of age,
Thonked be god that is eterne on lyve,
Housbondes at chirche-dore I have had fyve;
For I so ofte have y-wedded be;
And alle were worthy men in hir degree.
But me was told certeyn, nat longe agon is,
That sith that Crist ne wente never but onis
To wedding in the Cane of Galilee,
That by the same ensample taughte he me
That I ne sholde wedded be but ones.
Herke eek, lo! which a sharp word for the nones
Besyde a welle Jesus, god and man,
Spake in repreve of the Samaritan:
"Thou hast y-had fyve housbondes," quod he,
"And thilke man, the which that hath now thee,
Is noght thyn housbond"; thus seyde he certeyn;
What that he mente ther-by, I can nat seyn;
But that I axe, why that the fifthe man
Was noon housbond to the Samaritan?
How manye mighte she have in mariage?
Yet herde I never tellen in myn age
Upon this nombre diffinicioun;
Men may devyne and glosen up and doun.
But wel I woot expres, with-oute lye,
God bad us for to wexe and multiplye;
That gentil text can I wel understonde.
Eek wel I woot he seyde, myn housbonde
Sholde lete fader and moder, and take me;
But of no nombre mencioun made he,
Of bigamye or of octogamye;
Why sholde men speke of it vileinye?
   Lo, here the wyse king, dan Salomon;
I trowe he hadde wyves mo than oon;
As, wolde god, it leveful were to me
To be refresshed half so ofte as he!
Which yifte of god hadde he for alle his wyvis!
No man hath swich, that in this world alyve is.
God woot, this noble king, as to my wit,
The firste night had many a mery fit
With ech of hem, so wel was him on lyve!
Blessed be god that I have wedded fyve![1]
Welcome the sixte, whan that ever he shal.
For sothe, I wol nat kepe me chast in al;
Whan myn housbond is fro the world y-gon,
Som Cristen man shal wedde me anon;

[1]Here some MSS. insert the following genuine (but rejected) lines:

Of whom I did pick out and choose the best
Both for their nether purse and for their chest.
Different schools make divers perfect clerks,
Different methods learned in sundry works
Make the good workman perfect, certainly.
Of full five husbands tutoring am I.

Of whiche I have y-piked out the beste
Bothe of hir nether purs and of hir cheste.
Diverse scoles maken parfit clerkes,
Divers praktik, in many sondry werkes,
Maketh the werkman parfit sekirly.
Of fyve husbondes scolering am I.

For thanne th'apostle seith, that I am free
To wedde, a godd's half, wher it lyketh me.
He seith that to be wedded is no sinne;
Bet is to be wedded than to brinne.
What rekketh me, thogh folk seye vileinye
Of shrewed Lameth and his bigamye?
I woot wel Abraham was an holy man,
And Jacob eek, as forferth as I can;
And ech of hem hadde wyves mo than two;
And many another holy man also.
Whan saugh ye ever, in any maner age,
That hye god defended mariage
By expres word? I pray you, telleth me;
Or wher comanded he virginitee?
I woot as wel as ye, it is no drede,
Th'apostel, whan he speketh of maydenhede;
He seyde, that precept ther-of hadde he noon.
Men may conseille a womman to been oon,
But conseilling is no comandement;
He putte it in our owene jugement
For hadde god comanded maydenhede,
Thanne hadde he dampned wedding with the dede;
And certes, if ther were no seed y-sowe,
Virginitee, wher-of than sholde it growe?
Poul dorste nat comanden atte leste
A thing of which his maister yaf noon heste.
The dart is set up for virginitee;
Cacche who so may, who renneth best lat see.
But this word is nat take of every wight,
But ther as god list give it of his might.
I woot wel, that th'apostel was a mayde;
But natheless, thogh that he wroot and sayde,
He wolde that every wight were swich as he,
Al nis but conseil to virginitee;
And for to been a wyf, he yaf me leve
Of indulgence; so it is no repreve
To wedde me, if that my make dye,
With-oute excepcioun of bigamye.
Al were it good no womman for to touche,
He mente as in his bed or in his couche;
For peril is bothe fyr and tow t'assemble;
Ye knowe what this ensample may resemble.
This is al and som, he heeld virginitee
More parfit than wedding in freletee.
Freeltee clepe I, but-if that he and she
Wolde leden al hir lyf in chastitee.
I graunte it wel, I have noon envye,
Thogh maydenhede preferre bigamye;
Hem lyketh to be clene, body and goost,
Of myn estaat I nil nat make no boost.
For wel ye knowe, a lord in his houshold,
He hath nat every vessel al of gold;
Somme been of tree, and doon hir lord servyse.
God clepeth folk to him in sondry wyse,
And everich hath of god a propre yifte,
Som this, som that,—as him lyketh shifte.
Virginitee is greet perfeccioun,
And continence eek with devocioun.
But Crist, that of perfeccioun is welle,
Bad nat every wight he sholde go selle
All that he hadde, and give it to the pore,

For then, the apostle says that I am free
To wed, in God's name, where it pleases me.
He says that to be wedded is no sin;
Better to marry than to burn within.
What care I though folk speak reproachfully
Of wicked Lamech and his bigamy?
I know well Abraham was holy man,
And Jacob, too, as far as know I can;
And each of them had spouses more than two;
And many another holy man also.
Or can you say that you have ever heard
That God has ever by His express word
Marriage forbidden? Pray you, now, tell me;
Or where commanded He virginity?
I read as well as you no doubt have read
The apostle when he speaks of maidenhead;
He said, commandment of the Lord he'd none.
Men may advise a woman to be one,
But such advice is not commandment, no;
He left the thing to our own judgment so.
For had Lord God commanded maidenhood,
He'd have condemned all marriage as not good;
And certainly, if there were no seed sown,
Virginity—where then should it be grown?
Paul dared not to forbid us, at the least,
A thing whereof his Master'd no behest.
The dart is set up for virginity;
Catch it who can; who runs best let us see.
"But this word is not meant for every wight,
But where God wills to give it, of His might.
I know well that the apostle was a maid;
Nevertheless, and though he wrote and said
He would that everyone were such as he,
All is not counsel to virginity;
And so to be a wife he gave me leave
Out of permission; there's no shame should grieve
In marrying me, if that my mate should die,
Without exception, too, of bigamy.
And though 'twere good no woman's flesh to touch,
He meant, in his own bed or on his couch;
For peril 'tis fire and tow to assemble;
You know what this example may resemble.
This is the sum: he held virginity
Nearer perfection than marriage for frailty.
And frailty's all, I say, save he and she
Would lead their lives throughout in chastity.
"I grant this well, I have no great envy
Though maidenhood's preferred to bigamy;
Let those who will be clean, body and ghost,
Of my condition I will make no boast.
For well you know, a lord in his household,
He has not every vessel all of gold;
Some are of wood and serve well all their days.
God calls folk unto Him in sundry ways,
And each one has from God a proper gift,
Some this, some that, as pleases Him to shift.
"Virginity is great perfection known,
And continence e'en with devotion shown.
But Christ, Who of perfection is the well,
Bade not each separate man he should go sell
All that he had and give it to the poor

And follow Him in such wise going before.
He spoke to those that would live perfectly;
And, masters, by your leave, such am not I.
I will devote the flower of all my age
To all the acts and harvests of marriage.
"Tell me also, to what purpose or end
The genitals were made, that I defend,
And for what benefit was man first wrought?
Trust you right well, they were not made for naught
Explain who will and argue up and down
That they were made for passing out, as known,
Of urine, and our two belongings small
Were just to tell a female from a male,
And for no other cause—ah, say you no?
Experience knows well it is not so;
And, so the clerics be not with me wroth,
I say now that they have been made for both,
That is to say, for duty and for ease
In getting, when we do not God displease.
Why should men otherwise in their books set
That man shall pay unto his wife his debt?
Now wherewith should he ever make payment,
Except he used his blessed instrument?
Then on a creature were devised these things
For urination and engenderings.
"But I say not that every one is bound,
Who's fitted out and furnished as I've found,
To go and use it to beget an heir;
Then men would have for chastity no care.
Christ was a maid, and yet shaped like a man,
And many a saint, since this old world began,
Yet has lived ever in perfect chastity.
I bear no malice to virginity;
Let such be bread of purest white wheat-seed,
And let us wives be called but barley bread;
And yet with barley bread (if Mark you scan)
Jesus Our Lord refreshed full many a man.
In such condition as God places us
I'll persevere, I'm not fastidious.
In wifehood I will use my instrument
As freely as my Maker has it sent.
If I be niggardly, God give me sorrow!
My husband he shall have it, eve and morrow,'
When he's pleased to come forth and pay his debt.
I'll not delay, a husband I will get
Who shall be both my debtor and my thrall
And have his tribulations therewithal
Upon his flesh, the while I am his wife.
I have the power during all my life
Over his own good body, and not he.
For thus the apostle told it unto me;
And bade our husbands that they love us well.
And all this pleases me whereof I tell."
Up rose the pardoner, and that anon.
"Now dame," said he, "by God and by Saint John,
You are a noble preacher in this case!
I was about to wed a wife, alas!
Why should I buy this on my flesh so dear?
No, I would rather wed no wife this year."
"But wait, "said she, "my tale is not begun;
Nay, you shall drink from out another tun

And in swich wyse folwe him and his fore.
He spak to hem that wolde live parfitly;
And lordinges, by your leve, that am nat I.
I wol bistowe the flour of al myn age
In th' actes and in fruit of mariage.
Telle me also, to what conclusioun
Were membres maad of generacioun,
And for what profit was a wight y-wroght?
Trusteth right wel, they wer nat maad for noght.
Glose who-so wole, and seye bothe up and doun,
That they were maked for purgacioun
Of urine, and our bothe thinges smale
Were eek to knowe a femele from a male,
And for noon other cause: sey ye no?
The experience woot wel it is noght so;
So that the clerkes be nat with me wrothe,
I sey this, that they maked been for bothe,
This is to seye, for office, and for ese
Of engendrure, ther we nat god displese.
Why sholde men elles in hir bokes sette,
That man shal yelde to his wyf hir dette?
Now wher-with sholde he make his payement,
If he ne used his sely instrument?
Than were they maad up-on a creature,
To purge uryne, and eek for engendrure.
But I seye noght that every wight is holde,
That hath swich harneys as I to yow tolde,
To goon and usen hem in engendrure;
Than sholde men take of chastitee no cure.
Crist was a mayde, and shapen as a man,
And many a seint, sith that the world bigan,
Yet lived they ever in parfit chastitee.
I nil envye no virginitee;
Lat hem be breed of pured whete-seed,
And lat us wyves hoten barly-breed;
And yet with barly-breed, Mark telle can,
Our lord Jesu refresshed many a man.
In swich estaat as god hath cleped us
I wol persevere, I nam nat precious.
In wyfhode I wol use myn instrument
As frely as my maker hath it sent.
If I be daungerous, god yeve me sorwe!
Myn housbond shal it have bothe eve and morwe,
Whan that him list com forth and paye his dette.
An housbonde I wol have, I nil nat lette,
Which shal be bothe my dettour and my thral,
And have his tribulacioun with-al
Up-on his flessh, whyl that I am his wyf.
I have the power duringe al my lyf
Up-on his propre body, and noght he.
Right thus th'apostel tolde it un-to me;
And bad our housbondes for to love us weel.
Al this sentence me lyketh every-deel"—
Up sterte the Pardoner, and that anon,
"Now dame," quod he, "by god and by seint John,
Ye been a noble prechour in this cas!
I was aboute to wedde a wyf; allas!
What sholde I bye it on my flesh so dere?
Yet hadde I lever wedde no wyf to-yere!"
"Abyde!" quod she, "my tale is nat bigonne;
Nay, thou shalt drinken of another tonne

Er that I go, shal savoure wors than ale.
And whan that I have told thee forth my tale
Of tribulacioun in mariage,
Of which I am expert in al myn age,
This to seyn, my-self have been the whippe;—
Than maystow chese whether thou wolt sippe
Of thilke tonne that I shal abroche.
Be war of it, er thou to ny approche;
For I shal telle ensamples mo than ten.
Who-so that nil be war by othere men,
By him shul othere men corrected be.
The same wordes wryteth Ptholomee;
Rede in his Almageste, and take it there."
"Dame, I wolde praye yow, if your wil it were,"
Seyde this Pardoner, "as ye bigan,
Telle forth your tale, spareth for no man,
And teche us yonge men of your praktike."
"Gladly," quod she, "sith it may yow
lyké.
But yet I praye to al this companye,
If that I speke after my fantasye,
As taketh not a-grief of that I seye;
For myn entente nis but for to pleye.
"Now sires, now wol I telle forth my tale.—
As ever mote I drinken wyn or ale,
I shal seye sooth, tho housbondes that I hadde,
As three of hem were gode and two were badde.
The three men were gode, and riche, and olde;
Unnethe mighte they the statut holde
In which that they were bounden un-to me.
Ye woot wel what I mene of this, pardee!
As help me god, I laughe whan I thinke
How pitously a-night I made hem swinke;
And by my fey, I tolde of it no stoor.
They had me yeven hir gold and hir tresoor;
Me neded nat do lenger diligence
To winne hir love, or doon hem reverence.
They loved me so wel, by god above,
That I ne tolde no deyntee of hir love!
A wys womman wol sette hir ever in oon
To gete hir love, ther as she hath noon.
But sith I hadde hem hoolly in myn hond,
And sith they hadde me yeven all hir lond,
What sholde I taken hede hem for to plese,
But it were for my profit and myn ese?
I sette hem so a-werke, by my fey,
That many a night they songen 'weilawey!'
The bacoun was nat fet for hem, I trowe,
That som men han in Essex at Dunmowe.
I governed hem so wel, after my lawe,
That ech of hem ful blisful was and fawe
To bringe me gaye thinges fro the fayre.
They were ful glad whan I spak to hem fayre;
For god it woot, I chidde hem spitously.
Now herkneth, how I bar me proprely,
Ye wyse wyves, that can understonde.
Thus shul ye speke and bere hem wrong on
honde;
For half so boldely can ther no man
Swere and lyen as a womman can.
I sey nat this by wyves that ben wyse,
But-if it be whan they hem misavyse

Before I cease, and savour worse than ale.
And when I shall have told you all my tale
Of tribulation that is in marriage,
Whereof I've been an expert all my age,
That is to say, myself have been the whip,
Then may you choose whether you will so sip
Out of that very tun which I shall broach.
Beware of it ere you too near approach;
For I shall give examples more than ten.
Whoso will not be warned by other men
By him shall other men corrected be.
The self-same words has written Ptolemy;
Read in his Almagest and find it there."
"Lady, I pray you, if your will it were,"
Spoke up this pardoner, "as you began,
Tell forth your tale, nor spare for any man,
And teach us younger men of your technique.
"Gladly," said she, "since it may please, not
pique.
But yet I pray of all this company
That if I speak from my own phantasy,
They will not take amiss the things I say;
For my intention's only but to play.
"Now, sirs, now will I tell you forth my tale.
And as I may drink ever wine and ale,
I will tell truth of husbands that I've had,
For three of them were good and two were bad.
The three were good men and were rich and old.
Not easily could they the promise hold
Whereby they had been bound to cherish me.
You know well what I mean by that, pardie!
So help me God, I laugh now when I think
How pitifully by night I made them swink;
And by my faith I set by it no store.
They'd given me their gold, and treasure more;
I needed not do longer diligence
To win their love, or show them reverence.
They all loved me so well, by God above,
I never did set value on their love!
A woman wise will strive continually
To get herself loved, when she's not, you see.
But since I had them wholly in my hand,
And since to me they'd given all their land,
Why should I take heed, then, that I should please,
Save it were for my profit or my ease?
I set them so to work, that, by my fay,
Full many a night they sighed out 'Welaway!'
The bacon was not brought them home, I trow,
That some men have in Essex at Dunmowe.
I governed them so well, by my own law,
That each of them was happy as a daw,
And fain to bring me fine things from the fair.
And they were right glad when I spoke them fair;
For God knows that I nagged them mercilessly.
"Now hearken how I bore me properly,
All you wise wives that well can understand.
"Thus shall you speak and wrongfully
demand;
For half so brazenfacedly can no man
Swear to his lying as a woman can.
I say not this to wives who may be wise,
Except when they themselves do misadvise.

A wise wife, if she knows what's for her good,
Will swear the crow is mad, and in this mood
Call up for witness to it her own maid;
But hear me now, for this is what I said.
" 'Sir Dotard, is it thus you stand today?
Why is my neighbour's wife so fine and gay?
She's honoured over all where'er she goes;
I sit at home, I have no decent clo'es.
What do you do there at my neighbour's house?
Is she so fair? Are you so amorous?
Why whisper to our maid? *Benedicite!*
Sir Lecher old, let your seductions be!
And if I have a gossip or a friend,
Innocently, you blame me like a fiend
If I but walk, for company, to his house!
You come home here as drunken as a mouse,
And preach there on your bench, a curse on you!
You tell me it's a great misfortune, too,
To wed a girl who costs more than she's worth;
And if she's rich and of a higher birth,
You say it's torment to abide her folly
And put up with her pride and melancholy.
And if she be right fair, you utter knave,
You say that every lecher will her have;
She may no while in chastity abide
That is assailed by all and on each side.
" 'You say, some men desire us for our gold,
Some for our shape and some for fairness told;
And some, that she can either sing or dance,
And some, for courtesy and dalliance;
Some for her hands and for her arms so small;
Thus all goes to the devil in your tale.
You say men cannot keep a castle wall
That's long assailed on all sides, and by all.
" 'And if that she be foul, you say that she
Hankers for every man that she may see;
For like a spaniel will she leap on him
Until she finds a man to be victim;
And not a grey goose swims there in the lake
But finds a gander willing her to take.
You say, it is a hard thing to enfold
Her whom no man will in his own arms hold.
This say you, worthless, when you go to bed;
And that no wise man needs thus to be wed,
No, nor a man that hearkens unto Heaven.
With furious thunder-claps and fiery levin
May your thin, withered, wrinkled neck be broke;
" 'You say that dripping eaves, and also
smoke,
And wives contentious, will make men to flee
Out of their houses; ah, *benedicite!*
What ails such an old fellow so to chide?
" 'You say that all we wives our vices hide
Till we are married, then we show them well;
That is a scoundrel's proverb, let me tell!
" 'You say that oxen, asses, horses,
hounds
Are tried out variously, and on good grounds;
Basins and bowls, before men will them buy,
And spoons and stools and all such goods you try,
And so with pots and clothes and all array;
But of their wives men get no trial, you say,

A wys wyf, if that she can hir good,
Shal beren him on hond the cow is wood,
And take witnesse of hir owene mayde
Of hir assent; but herkneth how I sayde.
" 'Sir olde kaynard, is this thyn array?
Why is my neighebores wyf so gay?
She is honoured over-al ther she goth;
I sitte at hoom, I have no thrifty cloth.
What dostow at my neighebores hous?
Is she so fair? artow so amorous?
What rowne ye with our mayde? *ben'cite!*
Sir olde lechour, lat thy japes be!
And if I have a gossib or a freend,
With-outen gilt, thou chydest as a feend,
If that I walke or pleye un-to his hous!
Thou comest hoom as dronken as a mous,
And prechest on thy bench, with yvel preef!
Thou seist to me, it is a greet meschief
To wedde a povre womman, for costage;
And if that she be riche, of heigh parage,
Than seistow that it is a tormentrye
To suffre hir pryde and hir malencolye.
And if that she be fair, thou verray knave,
Thou seyst that every holour wol hir have;
She may no whyle in chastitee abyde,
That is assailled up-on ech a syde.
Thou seyst, som folk desyre us for richesse,
Som for our shap, and som for our fairnesse;
And som, for she can outher singe or daunce,
And som, for gentillesse and daliaunce;
Som, for hir handes and hir armes smale;
Thus goth al to the devel by thy tale.
Thou seyst, men may nat kepe a castelwal;
It may so longe assailled been over-al.
And if that she be foul, thou seist that she
Coveiteth every man that she may see;
For as a spaynel she wol on him lepe,
Til that she finde som man hir to chepe;
Ne noon so grey goos goth ther in the lake,
As, seistow, that wol been with-oute make.
And seyst, it is an hard thing for to welde
A thing that no man wol, his thankes, helde.
Thus seistow, lorel, whan thow goost to bedde;
And that no wys man nedeth for to wedde,
Ne no man that entendeth un-to hevene.
With wilde thonder-dint and firy levene
Mote thy welked nekke be to-broke!
Thow seyst that dropping houses, and eek
smoke,
And chyding wyves, maken men to flee
Out of hir owene hous; a! *ben'cite!*
What eyleth swich an old man for to chyde?
Thow seyst, we wyves wol our vyces hyde
Til we be fast, and than we wol hem shewe;
Wel may that be a proverbe of a shrewe!
Thou seist, that oxen, asses, hors, and
houndes,
They been assayed at diverse stoundes;
Bacins, lavours, er that men hem bye,
Spones and stoles, and al swich housbondrye,
And so been pottes, clothes, and array;
But folk of wyves maken noon assay

Til they be wedded; olde dotard shrewe!
And than, seistow, we wol oure vices shewe.
Thou seist also, that it displeseth me
But-if that thou wolt preyse my beautee,
And but thou poure alwey up-on my face,
And clepe me "faire dame" in every place;
And but thou make a feste on thilke day
That I was born, and make me fresh and gay,
And but thou do to my norice honour,
And to my chamberere with-inne my bour,
And to my fadres folk and his allyes;—
Thus seistow, olde barel ful of lyes!
And yet of our apprentice Janekyn.
For his crisp heer, shyninge as gold so fyn,
And for he squiereth me both up and doun,
Yet hastow caught a fals suspecioun;
I wol hym noght, thogh thou were deed
to-morwe.
But tel me this, why hydestow, with sorwe,
The keyes of thy cheste awey fro me?
It is my good as wel as thyn, pardee.
What wenestow make an idiot of our dame?
Now by that lord, that called is seint Jame,
Thou shalt nat bothe, thogh that thou were wood,
Be maister of my body and of my good;
That oon thou shalt forgo, maugree thyne yën;
What nedeth thee of me to enquere or spyën?
I trowe, thou woldest loke me in thy cheste!
Thou sholdest seye, "wyf, go wher thee leste,
Tak your disport, I wol nat leve no talis;
I knowe yow for a trewe wyf, dame Alis."
We love no man that taketh kepe or charge
Wher that we goon, we wol ben at our large.
Of alle men y-blessed moot he be,
The wyse astrologien Dan Ptholome,
That seith this proverbe in his Almageste,
"Of alle men his wisdom is the hyeste,
That rekketh never who hath the world in honde."
By this proverbe thou shalt understonde,
Have thou y-nogh, what that thee recche or care
How merily that othere folkes fare?
For certeyn, olde dotard, by your leve,
Ye shul have queynte right y-nough at eve.
He is to greet a nigard that wol werne
A man to lighte his candle at his lanterne;
He shal have never the lasse light, pardee;
Have thou y-nough, thee thar nat pleyne thee
Thou seyst also, that if we make us gay
With clothing and with precious array.
That it is peril of our chastitee;
And yet, with sorwe, thou most enforce thee,
And seye thise wordes in the apostles name,
"In habit, maad with chastitee and shame,
Ye wommen shul apparaille yow," quod he,
"And noght in tressed heer and gay perree,
As perles, ne with gold, ne clothes riche";
After thy text, ne after thy rubriche
I wol nat wirche as muchel as a gnat.
Thou seydest this, that I was lyk a cat;
For who-so wolde senge a cattes skin,
Thanne wolde the cat wel dwellen in his in;
And if the cattes skin be slyk and gay,

Till they are married, base old dotard you!
And then we show what evil we can do.
" 'You say also that it displeases me
Unless you praise and flatter my beauty,
And save you gaze always upon my face
And call me "lovely lady" every place;
And save you make a feast upon that day
When I was born, and give me garments gay;
And save due honour to my nurse is paid
As well as to my faithful chambermaid,
And to my father's folk and his allies—
Thus you go on, old barrel full of lies!
" 'And yet of our apprentice, young Jenkin,
For his crisp hair, showing like gold so fine,
Because he squires me walking up and down,
A false suspicion in your mind is sown;
I'd give him naught, though you were dead
tomorrow.
" 'But tell me this, why do you hide, with sorrow,
The keys to your strong box away from me?
It is my gold as well as yours, pardie.
Why would you make an idiot of your dame?
Now by Saint James, but you shall miss your aim,
You shall not be, although like mad you scold,
Master of both my body and my gold;
One you'll forgo in spite of both your eyes;
Why need you seek me out or set on spies?
I think you'd like to lock me in your chest!
You should say: "Dear wife, go where you like best,
Amuse yourself, I will believe no tales;
You're my wife Alis true, and truth prevails."
We love no man that guards us or gives charge
Of where we go, for we will be at large.
" 'Of all men the most blessed may he be,
That wise astrologer, Dan Ptolemy,
Who says this proverb in his Almagest:
"Of all men he's in wisdom the highest
That nothing cares who has the world in hand."
And by this proverb shall you understand:
Since you've enough, why do you reck or care
How merrily all other folks may fare?
For certainly, old dotard, by your leave,
You shall have cunt all right enough at eve.
He is too much a niggard who's so tight
That from his lantern he'll give none a light.
For he'll have never the less light, by gad;
Since you've enough, you need not be so sad.
" 'You say, also, that if we make us gay
With clothing, all in costliest array,
That it's a danger to our chastity;
And you must back the saying up, pardie!
Repeating these words in the apostle's name:
"In habits meet for chastity, not shame,
Your women shall be garmented," said he,
"And not with broidered hair, or jewellery,
Or pearls, or gold, or costly gowns and chic";
After your text and after your rubric
I will not follow more than would a gnat.
You said this, too, that I was like a cat;
For if one care to singe a cat's furred skin,
Then would the cat remain the house within;
And if the cat's coat be all sleek and gay,

She will not keep in house a half a day,
But out she'll go, ere dawn of any day,
To show her skin and caterwaul and play.
This is to say, if I'm a little gay,
To show my rags I'll gad about all day.
"'Sir Ancient Fool, what ails you with your spies?
Though you pray Argus, with his hundred eyes,
To be my body-guard and do his best,
Faith, he sha'n't hold me, save I am modest;
I could delude him easily—trust me!
"'You said, also, that there are three things—
three—
The which things are a trouble on this earth,
And that no man may ever endure the fourth:
O dear Sir Rogue, may Christ cut short your life!
Yet do you preach and say a hateful wife
Is to be reckoned one of these mischances.
Are there no other kinds of resemblances
That you may liken thus your parables to,
But must a hapless wife be made to do?
"'You liken woman's love to very Hell,
To desert land where waters do not well.
You liken it, also, unto wildfire;
The more it burns, the more it has desire
To consume everything that burned may be.
You say that just as worms destroy a tree,
Just so a wife destroys her own husband;
Men know this who are bound in marriage band.'
"Masters, like this, as you must understand,
Did I my old men charge and censure, and
Claim that they said these things in drunkenness;
And all was false, but yet I took witness
Of Jenkin and of my dear niece also.
O Lord, the pain I gave them and the woe,
All guiltless, too, by God's grief exquisite!
For like a stallion could I neigh and bite.
I could complain, though mine was all the guilt,
Or else, full many a time, I'd lost the tilt.
Whoso comes first to mill first gets meal ground;
I whimpered first and so did them confound.
They were right glad to hasten to excuse
Things they had never done, save in my ruse,
"With wenches would I charge him, by this hand,
When, for some illness, he could hardly stand.
Yet tickled this the heart of him, for he
Deemed it was love produced such jealousy.
I swore that all my walking out at night
Was but to spy on girls he kept outright;
And under cover of that I had much mirth.
For all such wit is given us at birth;
Deceit, weeping, and spinning, does God give
To women, naturally, the while they live.
And thus of one thing I speak boastfully,
I got the best of each one, finally,
By trick, or force, or by some kind of thing,
As by continual growls or murmuring;
Especially in bed had they mischance,
There would I chide and give them no pleasance;
I would no longer in the bed abide
If I but felt his arm across my side,
Till he had paid his ransom unto me;
Then would I let him do his nicety.

She wol nat dwelle in house half a day,
But forth she wole, er any day be dawed,
To shewe hir skin, and goon a-caterwawed;
This is to seye, if I be gay, sir shrewe,
I wol renne out, my borel for to shewe.
Sire olde fool, what eyleth thee to spyën?
Thogh thou preye Argus, with his hundred yën,
To be my warde-cors, as he can best,
In feith, he shal nat kepe me but me lest;
Yet coude I make his berd, so moot I thee.
Thou seydest eek, that ther ben thinges
three,
The whiche thinges troublen al this erthe,
And that no wight ne may endure the ferthe:
O leve sir shrewe, Jesu shorte thy lyf!
Yet prechestow, and seyst, an hateful wyf
Y-rekened is for oon of thise meschances.
Been ther none othere maner resemblances
That ye may lykne your parables to,
But-if a sely wyf be oon of tho?
Thou lykenest wommanes love to helle,
To bareyne lond, ther water may not dwelle.
Thou lyknest it also to wilde fyr;
The more it brenneth, the more it hath desyr
To consume every thing that brent wol be.
Thou seyst, that right as wormes shende a tree,
Right so a wyf destroyeth hir housbonde;
This knowe they that been to wyves bonde.'
Lordinges, right thus, as ye have understonde,
Bar I stifly myne olde housbondes on honde,
That thus they seyden in hir dronkenesse;
And al was fals, but that I took witnesse
On Janekin and on my nece also.
O lord, the peyne I dide hem and the wo,
Ful giltelees, by goddes swete pyne!
For as an hors I coude byte and whyne.
I coude pleyne, thogh I were in the gilt,
Or elles often tyme hadde I ben spilt.
Who-so that first to mille comth, first grint;
I pleyned first, so was our werre y-stint.
They were ful glad t'excusen hem ful blyve
Of thing of which they never agilte hir lyve.
Of wenches wolde I beren him on honde,
Whan that for syk unnethes mighte he stonde.
Yet tikled it his herte, for that he
Wende that I hadde of him so greet chiertee.
I swoor that al my walkinge out by nighte
Was for t'espye wenches that he dighte;
Under that colour hadde I many a mirthe.
For al swich wit is yeven us in our birthe;
Deceite, weping, spinning god hath yive
To wommen kindely, whyl they may live.
And thus of o thing I avaunte me,
Atte ende I hadde the bettre in ech degree,
By sleighte, or force, or by som maner thing,
As by continuel murmur or grucching;
Namely a-bedde hadden they meschaunce,
Ther wolde I chyde and do hem no plesaunce;
I wolde no lenger in the bed abyde,
If that I felte his arm over my syde,
Til he had maad his raunson un-to me;
Than wolde I suffre him do his nycetee.

And ther-fore every man this tale I telle,
Winne who-so may, for al is for to selle.
With empty hand men may none haukes lure;
For winning wolde I al his lust endure,
And make me a feyned appetyt;
And yet in bacon hadde I never delyt;
That made me that ever I wolde hem chyde.
For thogh the pope had seten hem bisyde,
I wolde nat spare hem at hir owene bord.
For by my trouthe, I quitte hem word for word.
As help me verray god omnipotent,
Thogh I right now sholde make my testament,
I ne owe hem nat a word that it nis quit
I broghte it so aboute by my wit,
That they moste yeve it up, as for the beste;
Or elles hadde we never been in reste.
For thogh he loked as a wood leoun,
Yet sholde he faille of his conclusioun.
  Thanne wolde I seye, 'gode lief, tak keep
How mekely loketh Wilkin oure sheep;
Com neer, my spouse, lat me ba thy cheke!
Ye sholde been al pacient and meke,
And han a swete spyced conscience,
Sith ye so preche of Jobes pacience.
Suffreth alwey, sin ye so wel can preche;
And but ye do, certein we shal yow teche
That it is fair to have a wyf in pees.
Oon of us two moste bowen, doutelees;
And sith a man is more resonable
Than womman is, ye moste been suffrable.
What eyleth yow to grucche thus and grone?
Is it for ye wolde have my queynte allone?
Why taak it al, lo, have it every-deel;
Peter! I shrewe yow but ye love it weel!
For if I wolde selle my *bele chose*,
I coude walke as fresh as is a rose;
But I wol kepe it for your owene tooth.
Ye be to blame, by god, I sey yow sooth.'
  Swiche maner wordes hadde we on honde.
Now wol I speken of my fourthe housbonde.
  My fourthe housbonde was a revelour,
This is to seyn, he hadde a paramour;
And I was yong and ful of ragerye,
Stiborn and strong, and joly as a pye.
Wel coude I daunce to an harpe smale,
And singe, y-wis, as any nightingale,
Whan I had dronke a draughte of swete wyn.
Metellius, the foule cherl, the swyn,
That with a staf birafte his wyf hir lyf,
For she drank wyn, thogh I hadde been his wyf,
He sholde nat han daunted me fro drinke;
And, after wyn, on Venus moste I thinke:
For al so siker as cold engendreth hayl,
A likerous mouth moote han a likerous tayl.
In womman vinolent is no defence,
This knowen lechours by experience.
  But, lord Crist! whan that it remembreth me
Up-on my yowthe, and on my jolitee,
It tikleth me aboute myn herte rote.
Unto this day it dooth myn herte bote
That I have had my world as in my tyme.
But age, allas! that al wol envenyme,

And therefore to all men this tale I tell,
Let gain who may, for everything's to sell.
With empty hand men may no falcons lure;
For profit would I all his lust endure,
And make for him a well-feigned appetite;
Yet I in bacon never had delight;
And that is why I used so much to chide.
For if the pope were seated there beside
I'd not have spared them, no, at their own board.
For by my truth, I paid them, word for word.
So help me the True God Omnipotent,
Though I right now should make my testament,
I owe them not a word that was not quit.
I brought it so about, and by my wit,
That they must give it up, as for the best,
Or otherwise we'd never have had rest.
For though he glared and scowled like lion mad,
Yet failed he of the end he wished he had.
  "Then would I say: 'Good dearie, see you keep
In mind how meek is Wilkin, our old sheep;
Come near, my spouse, come let me kiss your cheek!
You should be always patient, aye, and meek,
And have a sweetly scrupulous tenderness,
Since you so preach of old Job's patience, yes.
Suffer always, since you so well can preach;
And, save you do, be sure that we will teach
That it is well to leave a wife in peace.
One of us two must bow, to be at ease;
And since a man's more reasonable, they say,
Than woman is, you must have patience aye.
What ails you that you grumble thus and groan?
Is it because you'd have my cunt alone?
Why take it all, lo, have it every bit;
Peter! Beshrew you but you're fond of it!
For if I would go peddle my *belle chose*,
I could walk out as fresh as is a rose;
But I will keep it for your own sweet tooth.
You are to blame, by God I tell the truth.'
  "Such were the words I had at my command.
Now will I tell you of my fourth husband.
  "My fourth husband, he was a reveller,
That is to say, he kept a paramour;
And young and full of passion then was I,
Stubborn and strong and jolly as a pie.
Well could I dance to tune of harp, nor fail
To sing as well as any nightingale
When I had drunk a good draught of sweet wine.
Metellius, the foul churl and the swine,
Did with a staff deprive his wife of life
Because she drank wine; had I been his wife
He never should have frightened me from drink;
For after wine, of Venus must I think:
For just as surely as cold produces hail,
A liquorish mouth must have a lickerish tail.
In women wine's no bar of impotence,
This know all lechers by experience.
  "But Lord Christ! When I do remember me
Upon my youth and on my jollity,
It tickles me about my heart's deep root.
To this day does my heart sing in salute
That I have had my world in my own time.
But age, alas! that poisons every prime,

Has taken away my beauty and my pith;
Let go, farewell, the devil go therewith!
The flour is gone, there is no more to tell,
The bran, as best I may, must I now sell;
But yet to be right merry I'll try, and
Now will I tell you of my fourth husband.
"I say that in my heart I'd great despite
When he of any other had delight.
But he was quit, by God and by Saint Joce!
I made, of the same wood, a staff most gross;
Not with my body and in manner foul,
But certainly I showed so gay a soul
That in his own thick grease I made him fry
For anger and for utter jealousy.
By God, on earth I was his purgatory,
For which I hope his soul lives now in glory.
For God knows, many a time he sat and sung
When the shoe bitterly his foot had wrung
There was no one, save God and he, that knew
How, in so many ways, I'd twist the screw.
He died when I came from Jerusalem,
And lies entombed beneath the great rood-beam,
Although his tomb is not so glorious
As was the sepulchre of Darius,
The which Apelles wrought full cleverly;
'Twas waste to bury him expensively.
Let him fare well. God give his soul good rest,
He now is in the grave and in his chest.
"And now of my fifth husband will I tell.
God grant his soul may never get to Hell!
And yet he was to me most brutal, too;
My ribs yet feel as they were black and blue,
And ever shall, until my dying day.
But in our bed he was so fresh and gay,
And therewithal he could so well impose,
What time he wanted use of my *belle chose*,
That though he'd beaten me on every bone,
He could re-win my love, and that full soon.
I guess I loved him best of all, for he
Gave of his love most sparingly to me.
We women have, if I am not to lie,
In this love matter, a quaint fantasy;
Look out a thing we may not lightly have,
And after that we'll cry all day and crave.
Forbid a thing, and that thing covet we;
Press hard upon us, then we turn and flee.
Sparingly offer we our goods, when fair;
Great crowds at market make for dearer ware,
And what's too common brings but little price;
All this knows every woman who is wise.
"My fifth husband, may God his spirit bless!
Whom I took all for love, and not riches,
Had been sometime a student at Oxford,
And had left school and had come home to board
With my best gossip, dwelling in our town,
God save her soul! Her name was Alison.
She knew my heart and all my privity
Better than did our parish priest, s'help me!
To her confided I my secrets all.
For had my husband pissed against a wall,
Or done a thing that might have cost his life,
To her and to another worthy wife,

Hath me biraft my beautee and my pith;
Lat go, fare-wel, the devel go therwith!
The flour is goon, ther is na-more to telle,
The bren, as I best can, now moste I selle;
But yet to be right mery wol I fonde.
Now wol I tellen of my fourthe housbonde.
I seye, I hadde in herte greet despyt
That he of any other had delyt.
But he was quit, by god and by seint Joce!
I made him of the same wode a croce;
Nat of my body in no foul manere,
But certeinly, I made folk swich chere,
That in his owene grece I made him frye
For angre, and for verray jalousye.
By god, in erthe I was his purgatorie,
For which I hope his soule be in glorie.
For god it woot, he sat ful ofte and song
Whan that his shoo ful bitterly him wrong.
Ther was no wight, save god and he, that wiste,
In many wyse, how sore I him twiste.
He deyde whan I cam fro Jerusalem,
And lyth y-grave under the rode-beem,
Al is his tombe noght so curious
As was the sepulcre of him, Darius,
Which that Appelles wroghte subtilly;
It nis but wast to burie him preciously.
Lat him fare-wel, god yeve his soule reste,
He is now in the grave and in his cheste.
Now of my fifthe housbond wol I telle.
God lete his soule never come in helle!
And yet was he to me the moste shrewe;
That fele I on my ribbes al by rewe,
And ever shal, un-to myn ending-day.
But in our bed he was so fresh and gay,
And ther-with-al so wel coude he me glose,
Whan that he wolde han my *bele chose*,
That thogh he hadde me bet on every boon,
He coude winne agayn my love anoon.
I trowe I loved him beste, for that he
Was of his love daungerous to me.
We wommen han, if that I shal nat lye,
In this matere a queynte fantasye;
Wayte what thing we may nat lightly have,
Ther-after wol we crye al-day and crave.
Forbede us thing, and that desyren we;
Prees on us faste, and thanne wol we flee.
With daunger oute we al our chaffare;
Greet prees at market maketh dere ware,
And to greet cheep is holde at litel prys;
This knoweth every womman that is wys.
My fifthe housbonde, god his soule blesse!
Which that I took for love and no richesse,
He som-tyme was a clerk of Oxenford,
And had left scole, and wente at hoom to bord
With my gossib, dwellinge in oure toun,
God have hir soule! hir name was Alisoun.
She knew myn herte and eek my privetee
Bet than our parisshe-preest, so moot I thee!
To hir biwreyed I my conseil al.
For had myn housbonde pissed on a wal,
Or doon a thing that sholde han cost his lyf,
To hir, and to another worthy wyf,

And to my nece, which that I loved weel,
I wolde han told his conseil every-deel.
And so I dide ful often, god it woot,
That made his face ful often reed and hoot
For verray shame, and blamed him-self for he
Had told to me so greet a privetee

And so bifel that ones, in a Lente,
(So often tymes I to my gossib wente,
For ever yet I lovede to be gay,
And for to walke, in March, Averille, and May,
Fro hous to hous, to here sondry talis,
That Jankin clerk, and my gossib dame Alis,
And I my-self, in-to the feldes wente.
Myn housbond was at London al that Lente;
I hadde the bettre leyser for to pleye,
And for to see, and eek for to be seye
Of lusty folk; what wiste I wher my grace
Was shapen for to be, or in what place?
Therefore I made my visitaciouns,
To vigilies and to processiouns,
To preching eek and to thise pilgrimages,
To pleyes of miracles and mariages,
And wered upon my gaye scarlet gytes.
Thise wormes, ne thise motthes, ne thise mytes,
Upon my peril, frete hem never a deel;
And wostow why? for they were used weel.

Now wol I tellen forth what happed me.
I seye, that in the feeldes walked we,
Til trewely we hadde swich daliance,
This clerk and I; that of my purveyance
I spak to him, and seyde him, how that he,
If I were widwe, sholde wedde me.
For certeinly, I sey for no bobance,
Yet was I never with-outen purveyance
Of mariage, n'of othere thinges eek.
I holde a mouses herte nat worth a leek,
That hath but oon hole for to sterte to,
And if that faille, thanne is al y-do.

I bar him on honde, he hadde enchanted me;
My dame taughte me that soutiltee.
And eek I seyde, I mette of him al night;
He wolde han slayn me as I lay up-right,
And al my bed was ful of verray blood,
But yet I hope that he shal do me good;
For blood bitokeneth gold, as me was taught.
And al was fals, I dremed of it right naught,
But as I folwed ay my dames lore,
As wel of this as of other thinges more.

But now sir, lat me see, what I shal seyn?
A! ha! by god, I have my tale ageyn.

Whan that my fourthe housbond was on bere,
I weep algate, and made sory chere,
As wyves moten, for it is usage,
And with my coverchief covered my visage;
But for that I was purveyed of a make,
I weep but smal, and that I undertake.

To chirche was myn housbond born a-morwe
With neighebores, that for him maden sorwe;
And Jankin oure clerk was oon of tho.
As help me god, whan that I saugh him go
After the bere, me thoughte he hadde a paire
Of legges and of feet so clene and faire,

And to my niece whom I loved always well,
I would have told it—every bit I'd tell,
And did so, many and many a time, God wot,
Which made his face full often red and hot
For utter shame; he blamed himself that he
Had told me of so deep a privity.

"So it befell that on a time, in Lent
(For oftentimes I to my gossip went,
Since I loved always to be glad and gay
And to walk out, in March, April, and May,
From house to house, to hear the latest malice),
Jenkin the clerk, and my gossip Dame Alis,
And I myself into the meadows went.
My husband was in London all that Lent;
I had the greater leisure, then, to play,
And to observe, and to be seen, I say,
By pleasant folk; what knew I where my face
Was destined to be loved, or in what place?
Therefore I made my visits round about
To vigils and processions of devout,
To preaching too, and shrines of pilgrimage,
To miracle plays, and always to each marriage,
And wore my scarlet skirt before all wights.
These worms and all these moths and all these mites,
I say it at my peril, never ate;
And know you why? I wore it early and late.

"Now will I tell you what befell to me.
I say that in the meadows walked we three
Till, truly, we had come to such dalliance,
This clerk and I, that, of my vigilance,
I spoke to him and told him how that he,
Were I a widow, might well marry me.
For certainly I say it not to brag,
But I was never quite without a bag
Full of the needs of marriage that I seek.
I hold a mouse's heart not worth a leek
That has but one hole into which to run,
And if it fail of that, then all is done.

"I made him think he had enchanted me;
My mother taught me all that subtlety.
And then I said I'd dreamed of him all night,
He would have slain me as I lay upright,
And all my bed was full of very blood;
But yet I hoped that he would do me good,
For blood betokens gold, as I was taught.
And all was false, I dreamed of him just—naught,
Save as I acted on my mother's lore,
As well in this thing as in many more.

"But now, let's see, what was I going to say?
Aha, by God, I know! It goes this way.

"When my fourth husband lay upon his bier,
I wept enough and made but sorry cheer,
As wives must always, for it's custom's grace,
And with my kerchief covered up my face;
But since I was provided with a mate,
I really wept but little, I may state.

"To church my man was borne upon the morrow
By neighbours, who for him made signs of sorrow;
And Jenkin, our good clerk, was one of them.
So help me God, when rang the requiem
After the bier, I thought he had a pair
Of legs and feet so clean-cut and so fair

That all my heart I gave to him to hold.
He was, I think, but twenty winters old,
And I was forty, if I tell the truth;
But then I always had a young colt's tooth.
Gap-toothed I was, and that became me well;
I had the print of holy Venus' seal.
So help me God, I was a healthy one,
And fair and rich and young and full of fun;
And truly, as my husbands all told me,
I had the silkiest *quoniam* that could be.
For truly, I am all Venusian
In feeling, and my brain is Martian.
Venus gave me my lust, my lickerishness,
And Mars gave me my sturdy hardiness.
Taurus was my ascendant, with Mars therein.
Alas, alas, that ever love was sin!
I followed always my own inclination
By vitue of my natal constellation;
Which wrought me so I never could withdraw
My Venus-chamber from a good fellow.
Yet have I Mars's mark upon my face,
And also in another private place.
For God so truly my salvation be
As I have never loved for policy,
But ever followed my own appetite,
Though he were short or tall, or black or white;
I took no heed, so that he cared for me,
How poor he was nor even of what degree.
"What should I say now, save, at the month's end,
This jolly, gentle, Jenkin clerk, my friend,
Had wedded me full ceremoniously,
And to him gave I all the land in fee
That ever had been given me before;
But later I repented me full sore.
He never suffered me to have my way.
By God, he smote me on the ear, one day,
Because I tore out of his book a leaf,
So that from this my ear is grown quite deaf.
Stubborn I was as is a lioness,
And with my tongue a very jay, I guess,
And walk I would, as I had done before,
From house to house, though I should not, he swore.
For which he oftentimes would sit and preach
And read old Roman tales to me and teach
How one Sulpicius Gallus left his wife
And her forsook for term of all his life
Because he saw her with bared head, I say,
Looking out from his door, upon a day.
"Another Roman told he of by name
Who, since his wife was at a summer-game
Without his knowing, he forsook her eke.
And then would he within his Bible seek
That proverb of the old Ecclesiast
Where he commands so freely and so fast
That man forbid his wife to gad about;
Then would he thus repeat, with never doubt:
'Whoso would build his whole house out of sallows,
And spur his blind horse to run over fallows,
And let his wife alone go seeking hallows,
Is worthy to be hanged upon the gallows.'
But all for naught, I didn't care a haw

That al myn herte I yaf un-to his hold.
He was, I trowe, a twenty winter old,
And I was fourty, if I shal seye sooth;
But yet I hadde alwey a coltes tooth.
Gat-tothed I was, and that bicam me weel;
I hadde the prente of sëynt Venus seel.
As help me god, I was a lusty oon,
And faire and riche, and yong, and wel bigoon;
And trewely, as myne housbondes tolde me,
I had the beste *quoniam* mighte be.
For certes, I am al Venerien
In felinge, and myn herte is Marcien.
Venus me yaf my lust, my likerousnesse,
And Mars yaf me my sturdy hardinesse.
Myn ascendent was Taur, and Mars therinne.
Allas! allas! that ever love was sinne!
I folwed ay myn inclinacioun
By vertu of my constellacioun;
That made me I coude noght withdrawe
My chambre of Venus from a good felawe.
Yet have I Martes mark up-on my face,
And also in another privee place.
For, god so wis be my savacioun,
I ne loved never by no discrecioun,
But ever folwede myn appetyt,
Al were he short or long, or blak or whyt;
I took no kepe, so that he lyked me,
How pore he was, ne eek of what degree.
What sholde I seye, but, at the monthes ende,
This joly clerk Jankin, that was so hende,
Hath wedded me with greet solempnitee,
And to him yaf I al the lond and fee
That ever was me yeven ther-bifore;
But afterward repented me ful sore.
He nolde suffre nothing of my list.
By god, he smoot me ones on the list,
For that I rente out of his book a leef,
That of the strook myn ere wex al deef.
Stiborn I was as is a leonesse,
And of my tonge a verray jangleresse,
And walke I wolde, as I had doon biforn,
From hous to hous, al-though he had it sworn.
For which he often tymes wolde preche,
And me of olde Romayn gestes teche,
How he, Simplicius Gallus, lefte his wyf,
And hir forsook for terme of al his lyf,
Noght but for open-heeded he hir say
Lokinge out at his dore upon a day.
Another Romayne tolde he me by name,
That, for his wyf was at a someres game
With-oute his witing, he forsook hir eke.
And than wolde he up-on his Bible seke
That ilke proverbe of Ecclesiaste,
Wher he comandeth and forbedeth faste
Man shal nat suffre his wyf go roule aboute;
Than wolde he seye right thus, withouten doute,
'Who-so that buildeth his hous al of salwes,
And priketh his blinde hors over the falwes,
And suffreth his wyf to go seken halwes,
Is worthy to been hanged on the galwes!'
But al for noght, I sette noght an hawe

Of his proverbes n'of his olde sawe,
Ne I wolde nat of him corrected be.
I hate him that my vices telleth me,
And so do mo, god woot! of us than I.
This made him with me wood al outrely;
I nolde noght forbere him in no cas.
Now wol I seye yow sooth by seint Thomas,
Why that I rente out of his book a leef,
For which he smoot me so that I was deef.
He hadde a book that gladly, night and day,
For his desport he wolde rede alway.
He cleped in Valerie and Theofraste,
At whiche book he lough alwey ful faste.
And eek ther was som-tyme a clerk at Rome,
A cardinal, that highte Seint Jerome,
That made a book agayn Jovinian;
In whiche book eek ther was Tertulan,
Crisippus, Trotula, and Helowys,
That was abbesse nat fer fro Parys;
And eek the Parables of Salomon,
Ovydes Art, and bokes many on,
And alle thise wer bounden in o volume.
And every night and day was his custume,
Whan he had leyser and vacacioun
From other worldly occupacioun,
To reden on this book of wikked wyves.
He knew of hem mo legendes and lyves
Than been of gode wyves in the Bible.
For trusteth wel, it is an impossible
That any clerk wol speke good of wyves,
But-if it be of holy seintes lyves,
Ne of noon other womman never the mo.
Who peyntede the leoun, tel me who?[1]
By god, if wommen hadde writen stories,
As clerkes han with-inne hir oratories.
They wolde han writen of men more wikkednesse
Than all the mark of Adam may redresse.
The children of Mercurie and of Venus
Been in hir wirking ful contrarious;
Mercurie loveth wisdom and science,
And Venus loveth ryot and dispence.
And, for hir diverse disposicioun,
Ech falleth in otheres exaltacioun;
And thus, god woot! Mercurie is desolat
In Pisces, wher Venus is exaltat;
And Venus falleth ther Mercurie is reysed;
Therfore no womman of no clerk is preysed.
The clerk, whan he is old, and may noght do
Of Venus werkes worth his olde sho,
Than sit he doun, and writ in his dotage
That wommen can nat kepe hir mariage!
But now to purpos, why I tolde thee
That I was beten for a book, pardee.
Up-on a night Jankin, that was our syre,
Redde on his book, as he sat by the fyre,
Of Eva first, that, for hir wikkednesse,
Was al mankinde broght to wrecchednesse,
For which that Jesu Crist him-self was slayn,
That boghte us with his herte-blood agayn.
Lo, here expres of womman may ye finde,
That womman was the los of al mankinde.

For all his proverbs, nor for his old saw,
Nor yet would I by him corrected be.
I hate one that my vices tells to me,
And so do more of us—God knows!—than I.
This made him mad with me, and furiously,
That I'd not yield to him in any case.
"Now will I tell you truth, by Saint Thomas,
Of why I tore from out his book a leaf,
For which he struck me so it made me deaf.
"He had a book that gladly, night and day,
For his amusement he would read alway.
He called it 'Theophrastus' and 'Valerius,'
At which book would he laugh, uproarious.
And, too, there sometime was a clerk at Rome,
A cardinal, that men called Saint Jerome,
Who made a book against Jovinian;
In which book, too, there was Tertullian,
Chrysippus, Trotula, and Heloïse
Who was abbess near Paris' diocese;
And too, the *Proverbs* of King Solomon,
And Ovid's *Art*, and books full many a one.
And all of these were bound in one volume.
And every night and day 'twas his custom,
When he had leisure and took some vacation
From all his other worldly occupation,
To read, within this book, of wicked wives.
He knew of them more legends and more lives
Than are of good wives written in the Bible.
For trust me, it's impossible, no libel,
That any cleric shall speak well of wives,
Unless it be of saints and holy lives,
But naught for other women will they do.
Who painted first the lion, tell me who?[1]
By God, if women had but written stories,
As have these clerks within their oratories,
They would have written of men more wickedness
Than all the race of Adam could redress.
The children of Mercury and of Venus
Are in their lives antagonistic thus;
For Mercury loves wisdom and science,
And Venus loves but pleasure and expense.
Because they different dispositions own,
Each falls when other's in ascendant shown.
And God knows Mercury is desolate
In Pisces, wherein Venus rules in state;
And Venus falls when Mercury is raised;
Therefore no woman by a clerk is praised.
A clerk, when he is old and can naught do
Of Venus' labours worth his worn-out shoe,
Then sits he down and writes, in his dotage,
That women cannot keep vow of marriage!
"But now to tell you, as I started to,
Why I was beaten for a book, *pardieu*.
Upon a night Jenkin, who was our sire,
Read in his book, as he sat by the fire,
Of Mother Eve who, by her wickedness,
First brought mankind to all his wretchedness,
For which Lord Jesus Christ Himself was slain,
Who, with His heart's blood, saved us thus again.
Lo here, expressly of woman, may you find
That woman was the ruin of mankind.

[1]Referring to one of Æsop's fables.

"Then read he out how Samson lost his hairs,
Sleeping, his leman cut them with her shears;
And through this treason lost he either eye.
"Then read he out, if I am not to lie,
Of Hercules, and Deianira's desire
That caused him to go set himself on fire.
"Nothing escaped him of the pain and woe
That Socrates had with his spouses two;
How Xantippe threw piss upon his head;
This hapless man sat still, as he were dead;
He wiped his head, no more durst he complain
Than 'Ere the thunder ceases comes the rain.'
"Then of Pasiphaë, the queen of Crete,
For cursedness he thought the story sweet;
Fie! Say no more—it is an awful thing—
Of her so horrible lust and love-liking.
"Of Clytemnestra, for her lechery,
Who caused her husband's death by treachery,
He read all this with greatest zest, I vow.
"He told me, too, just when it was and how
Amphiaraus at Thebes lost his life;
My husband had a legend of his wife
Eriphyle who, for a brooch of gold,
In secrecy to hostile Greeks had told
Whereat her husband had his hiding place,
For which he found at Thebes but sorry grace.
"Of Livia and Lucia told he me,
For both of them their husbands killed, you see,
The one for love, the other killed for hate;
Livia her husband, on an evening late,
Made drink some poison, for she was his foe.
Lucia, lecherous, loved her husband so
That, to the end he'd always of her think,
She gave him such a philtre, for love-drink,
That he was dead or ever it was morrow;
And husbands thus, by same means, came to sorrow.
"Then did he tell how one Latumius
Complained unto his comrade Arrius
That in his garden grew a baleful tree
Whereon, he said, his wives, and they were three,
Had hanged themselves for wretchedness and woe.
'O brother,' Arrius said, 'and did they so?
Give me a graft of that same blessed tree
And in my garden planted it shall be!'
"Of wives of later date he also read,
How some had slain their husbands in their bed
And let their lovers shag them all the night
While corpses lay upon the floor upright.
And some had driven nails into the brain
While husbands slept and in such wise were slain.
And some had given them poison in their drink.
He told more evil than the mind can think.
And therewithal he knew of more proverbs
Than in this world there grows of grass or herbs.
'Better,' he said, 'your habitation be
With lion wild or dragon foul,' said he,
'Than with a woman who will nag and chide.'
'Better,' he said, 'on the housetop abide
Than with a brawling wife down in the house;
Such are so wicked and contrarious
They hate the thing their husband loves, for aye.'
He said, 'a woman throws her shame away

Tho redde he me how Sampson loste his heres,
Slepinge, his lemman kitte hem with hir sheres;
Thurgh whiche tresoun loste he bothe his yën.
Tho redde he me, if that I shal nat lyen,
Of Hercules and of his Dianyre,
That caused him to sette himself a-fyre.
No-thing forgat he the penaunce and wo
That Socrates had with hise wyves two;
How Xantippa caste pisse up-on his heed;
This sely man sat stille, as he were deed;
He wyped his heed, namore dorste he seyn
But 'er that thonder stinte, comth a reyn.'
Of Phasipha, that was the quene of Crete,
For shrewednesse, him thoughte the tale swete;
Fy! spek na-more—it is a grisly thing—
Of hir horrible lust and hir lyking.
Of Clitemistra, for hir lecherye,
That falsly made hir housbond for to dye,
He redde it with ful good devocioun.
He tolde me eek for what occasioun
Amphiorax at Thebes loste his lyf;
Myn housbond hadde a legende of his wyf,
Eriphilem, that for an ouche of gold
Hath prively un-to the Grekes told
Wher that hir housbonde hidde him in a place,
For which he hadde at Thebes sory grace.
Of Lyma tolde he me, and of Lucye,
They bothe made hir housbondes for to dye;
That oon for love, that other was for hate;
Lyma hir housbond, on an even late,
Empoysoned hath, for that she was his fo.
Lucya, likerous, loved hir housbond so,
That, for he sholde alwey up-on hir thinke,
She yaf him swich a maner love-drinke,
That he was deed, er it were by the morwe;
And thus algates housbondes han sorwe.
Than tolde he me, how oon Latumius
Compleyned to his felawe Arrius,
That in his gardin growed swich a tree,
On which, he seyde, how that his wyves three
Hanged hem-self for herte despitous.
'O leve brother,' quod this Arrius,
'Yif me a plante of thilke blissed tree,
And in my gardin planted shal it be!'
Of later date, of wyves hath he red,
That somme han slayn hir housbondes in hir bed,
And lete hir lechour dighte hir al the night
Whyl that the corps lay in the floor up-right.
And somme han drive nayles in hir brayn
Whyl that they slepte, and thus they han hem slayn.
Somme han hem yeve poysoun in hir drinke.
He spak more harm than herte may bithinke.
And ther-with-al, he knew of mo proverbes
Than in this world ther growen gras or herbes.
'Bet is,' quod he, 'thyn habitacioun
Be with a leoun or a foul dragoun,
Than with a womman usinge for to chyde.
Bet is,' quod he, 'hye in the roof abyde
Than with an angry wyf doun in the hous;
They been so wikked and contrarious;
They haten that hir housbondes loveth ay.'
He seyde, 'a womman cast hir shame away,

Whan she cast of hir smok'; and forthermo,
'A fair womman, but she be chaast also,
Is lyk a gold ring in a sowes nose.'
Who wolde wenen, or who wolde suppose
The wo that in myn herte was, and pyne?
And whan I saugh he wolde never fyne
To reden on this cursed book al night,
Al sodeynly three leves have I plight
Out of his book, right as he radde, and eke,
I with my fist so took him on the cheke,
That in our fyr he fil bakward adoun.
And he up-stirte as dooth a wood leoun,
And with his fist he smoot me on the heed,
That in the floor I lay as I were deed.
And when he saugh how stille that I lay,
He was agast, and wolde han fled his way,
Til atte laste out of my swogh I breyde:
'O! hastow slayn me, false theef?' I seyde,
'And for my land thus hastow mordred me?
Er I be deed, yet wol I kisse thee.'
And neer he cam, and kneled faire adoun,
And seyde, 'dere suster Alisoun,
As help me god, I shal thee never smyte;
That I have doon, it is thy-self to wyte.
Foryeve it me, and that I thee biseke'—
And yet eft-sones I hitte him on the cheke,
And seyde, 'theef, thus muchel am I wreke;
Now wol I dye, I may ne lenger speke.'
But atte laste, with muchel care and wo,
We fille acorded, by us selven two.
He yaf me al the brydel in myn hond
To han the governance of hous and lond,
And of his tonge and of his hond also,
And made him brenne his book anon right tho.
And whan that I hadde geten un-to me,
By maistrie, al the soveraynetee,
And that he seyde, 'myn owene trewe wyf,
Do as thee lust the terme of al thy lyf,
Keep thyn honour, and keep eek myn estaat'—
After that day we hadden never debaat.
God help me so, I was to him as kinde
As any wyf from Denmark un-to Inde,
And also trewe, and so was he to me.
I prey to god that sit in magestee,
So blesse his soule, for his mercy dere!
Now wol I seye my tale, if ye wol here."

When she throws off her smock,' and further, too:
'A woman fair, save she be chaste also,
Is like a ring of gold in a sow's nose.'
Who would imagine or who would suppose
What grief and pain were in this heart of mine?
"And when I saw he'd never cease, in fine,
His reading in this cursed book at night,
Three leaves of it I snatched and tore outright
Out of his book, as he read on; and eke
I with my fist so took him on the cheek
That in our fire he reeled and fell right down.
Then he got up as does a wild lion,
And with his fist he struck me on the head,
And on the floor I lay as I were dead.
And when he saw how limp and still I lay,
He was afraid and would have run away,
Until at last out of my swoon I made:
'Oh, have you slain me, you false thief?' I said,
'And for my land have you thus murdered me?
Kiss me before I die, and let me be.'
"He came to me and near me he knelt down,
And said: 'O my dear sister Alison,
So help me God, I'll never strike you more;
What I have done, you are to blame therefor.
But all the same forgiveness now I seek!'
And thereupon I hit him on the cheek,
And said: 'Thief, so much vengeance do I wreak!
Now will I die, I can no longer speak!'
But at the last, and with much care and woe,
We made it up between ourselves. And so
He put the bridle reins within my hand
To have the governing of house and land;
And of his tongue and of his hand, also;
And made him burn his book, right then, oho!
And when I had thus gathered unto me
Masterfully, the entire sovereignty,
And he had said: 'My own true wedded wife,
Do as you please the term of all your life,
Guard your own honour and keep fair my state'—
After that day we never had debate.
God help me now, I was to him as kind
As any wife from Denmark unto Ind,
And also true, and so was he to me.
I pray to God, Who sits in majesty,
To bless his soul, out of His mercy dear!
Now will I tell my tale, if you will hear."

BEHOLD THE WORDS BETWEEN THE SUMMONER AND THE FRIAR

The Frere lough, whan he hadde herd al this,
"Now, dame," quod he, "so have I joye or blis,
This is a long preamble of a tale!"
And whan the Somnour herde the Frere gale,
"Lo!" quod the Somnour, "goddes armes two!
A frere wol entremette him ever-mo.
Lo, gode men, a flye and eek a frere
Wol falle in every dish and eek matere.
What spekestow of preambulacioun?
What! amble, or trotte, or pees, or go sit doun;
Thou lettest our disport in this manere."
"Ye, woltow so, sir Somnour?" qoud the Frere,
"Now, by my feith, I shal, er that I go,

The friar laughed when he had heard all this.
"Now dame," said he, "so have I joy or bliss
This is a long preamble to a tale!"
And when the summoner heard this friar's hail,
"Lo," said the summoner, "by God's arms two!
A friar will always interfere, mark you.
Behold, good men, a housefly and a friar
Will fall in every dish and matters higher.
Why speak of preambling, you in your gown?
What! Amble, trot, hold peace, or go sit down;
You hinder our diversion thus to inquire."
"Aye, say you so, sir summoner?" said the friar,
"Now by my faith I will, before I go,

Tell of a summoner such a tale, or so,
That all the folk shall laugh who're in this place."
"Otherwise, friar, I beshrew your face,"
Replied this summoner, "and beshrew me
If I do not tell tales here, two or three,
Of friars ere I come to Sittingbourne,
That certainly will give you cause to mourn,
For well I know your patience will be gone."
Our host cried out, "Now peace, and that anon!"
And said he: "Let the woman tell her tale.
You act like people who are drunk with ale.
Do, lady, tell your tale, and that is best."
"All ready, sir," said she, "as you request,
If I have license of this worthy friar."
"Yes, dame," said he, "to hear you's my
desire."

Telle of a Somnour swich a tale or two,
That alle the folk shal laughen in this place."
"Now elles, Frere, I bishrewe thy face,"
Quod this Somnour, "and I bishrewe me,
But-if I telle tales two or three
Of freres er I come to Sidingborne,
That I shal make thyn herte for to morne;
For wel I woot thy pacience is goon."
Our hoste cryde "pees! and that anoon!"
And seyde, "lat the womman telle hir tale.
Ye fare as folk that dronken been of ale.
Do, dame, tel forth your tale, and that is best."
"Al redy, sir," quod she, "right as yow lest,
If I have licence of this worthy Frere."
"Yis, dame," quod he, "tel forth, and I wol
here."

HERE ENDETH THE WIFE OF BATH HER PROLOGUE

THE TALE OF THE WIFE OF BATH

HERE BEGINNETH THE TALE OF THE WIFE OF BATH

Now in the olden days of King Arthur,
Of whom the Britons speak with great honour,
All this wide land was land of faëry
The elf-queen, with her jolly company,
Danced oftentimes on many a green mead;
This was the old opinion, as I read.
I speak of many hundred years ago;
But now no man can see the elves, you know.
For now the so-great charity and prayers
Of limiters and other holy friars
That do infest each land and every stream
As thick as motes are in a bright sunbeam,
Blessing halls, chambers, kitchens, ladies' bowers,
Cities and towns and castles and high towers,
Manors and barns and stables, aye and dairies—
This causes it that there are now no fairies.
For where was wont to walk full many an elf,
Right there walks now the limiter himself
In noons and afternoons and in mornings,
Saying his matins and such holy things,
As he goes round his district in his gown.
Women may now go safely up and down,
In every copse or under every tree;
There is no other incubus than he,
And would do them nothing but dishonour.
And so befell it that this King Arthur
Had at his court a lusty bachelor
Who, on a day, came riding from river;[1]
And happened that, alone as she was born,
He saw a maiden walking through the corn,
From whom, in spite of all she did and said,
Straightway by force he took her maidenhead;
For which violation was there such clamour,
And such appealing unto King Arthur,
That soon condemned was this knight to be dead
By course of law, and should have lost his head,
Peradventure, such being the statute then;

In th'olde dayes of the king Arthour,
Of which that Britons speken greet honour,
Al was this land fulfild of fayerye.
The elf-queen, with hir joly companye,
Daunced ful ofte in many a grene mede;
This was the olde opinion, as I rede.
I speke of manye hundred yeres ago;
But now can no man see none elves mo.
For now the grete charitee and prayeres
Of limitours and othere holy freres,
That serchen every lond and every streem,
As thikke as motes in the sonne-beem,
Blessinge halles, chambres, kichenes, boures,
Citees, burghes, castels, hye toures,
Thropes, bernes, shipnes, dayeryes,
This maketh that ther been no fayeryes.
For ther as wont to walken was an elf,
Ther walketh now the limitour himself
In undermeles and in morweninges,
And seyth his matins and his holy thinges
As he goth in his limitacioun.
Wommen may go saufly up and doun,
In every bush, or under every tree;
Ther is noon other incubus but he,
And he ne wol doon hem but dishonour.
And so bifel it, that this king Arthour
Hadde in his hous a lusty bacheler,
That on a day cam rydinge fro river;[1]
And happed that, allone as she was born,
He saugh a mayde walkinge him biforn,
Of which mayde anon, maugree hir heed,
By verray force he refte hir maydenheed,
For which oppressioun was swich clamour
And swich pursute un-to the king Arthour,
That dampned was this knight for to be deed
By cours of lawe, and sholde han lost his heed
Paraventure, swich was the statut tho;

[1]That is, from hawking for waterfowl beside a stream or mere.

But that the quene and othere ladies mo
So longe preyeden the king of grace,
Til he his lyf him graunted in the place,
And yaf him to the quene al at hir wille,
To chese, whether she wolde him save or spille.
The quene thanketh the king with al hir might,
And after this thus spak she to the knight,
Whan that she saugh hir tyme, up-on a day:
"Thou standest yet," quod she, "in swich array,
That of thy lyf yet hastow no suretee.
I grante thee lyf, if thou canst tellen me
What thing is it that wommen most desyren?
Be war, and keep thy nekke-boon from yren.
And if thou canst nat tellen it anon,
Yet wol I yeve thee leve for to gon
A twelf-month and a day, to seche and lere
An answere suffisant in this matere.
And suretee wol I han, er that thou pace,
Thy body for to yelden in this place."
Wo was this knight and sorwefully he syketh;
But what! he may nat do al as him lyketh.
And at the laste, he chees him for to wende,
And come agayn, right at the yeres ende,
With swich answere as god wolde him purveye;
And taketh his leve, and wendeth forth his weye.
He seketh every hous and every place,
Wher-as he hopeth for to finde grace,
To lerne, what thing wommen loven most;
But he ne coude arryven in no cost,
Wher-as he mighte finde in this matere
Two creatures accordinge in-fere.
Somme seyde, wommen loven best richesse,
Somme seyde, honour, somme seyde, jolynesse;
Somme, riche array, somme seyden, lust abedde,
And ofte tyme to be widwe and wedde.
Somme seyde, that our hertes been most esed,
Whan that we been y-flatered any y-plesed.
He gooth ful ny the sothe, I wol nat lye;
A man shal winne us best with flaterye;
And with attendance, and with bisinesse,
Been we y-lymed, bothe more and lesse.
And somme seyn, how that we loven best
For to be free, and do right as us lest,
And that no man repreve us of our vyce,
But seye that we be wyse, and no-thing nyce.
For trewely, ther is noon of us alle,
If any wight wol clawe us on the galle,
That we nil kike, for he seith us sooth;
Assay, and he shal finde it that so dooth.
For be we never so vicious with-inne,
We wol been holden wyse, and clene of sinne.
And somme seyn, that greet delyt han we
For to ben holden stable and eek secree,
And in o purpos stedefastly to dwelle,
And nat biwreye thing that men us telle.
But that tale is nat worth a rake-stele;
Pardee, we wommen conne no-thing hele;
Witnesse on Myda; wol ye here the tale?
Ovyde, amonges othere thinges smale,

But that the other ladies and the queen
So long prayed of the king to show him grace,
He granted life, at last, in the law's place,
And gave him to the queen, as she should will,
Whether she'd save him, or his blood should spill.
The queen she thanked the king with all her might,
And after this, thus spoke she to the knight,
When she'd an opportunity, one day:
"You stand yet," said she, "in such poor a way
That for your life you've no security.
I'll grant you life if you can tell to me
What thing it is that women most desire.
Be wise, and keep your neck from iron dire!
And if you cannot tell it me anon,
Then will I give you license to be gone
A twelvemonth and a day, to search and learn
Sufficient answer in this grave concern.
And your knight's word I'll have, ere forth you pace,
To yield your body to me in this place."
Grieved was this knight, and sorrowfully he sighed;
But there! he could not do as pleased his pride.
And at the last he chose that he would wend,
And come again upon the twelvemonth's end,
With such an answer as God might purvey;
And so he took his leave and went his way.
He sought out every house and every place
Wherein he hoped to find that he had grace
To learn what women love the most of all;
But nowhere ever did it him befall
To find, upon the question stated here,
Two persons who agreed with statement clear.
Some said that women all loved best riches,
Some said, fair fame, and some said, prettiness;
Some, rich array, some said 'twas lust abed
And often to be widowed and re-wed.
Some said that our poor hearts are aye most eased
When we have been most flattered and thus pleased
And he went near the truth, I will not lie;
A man may win us best with flattery;
And with attentions and with busyness
We're often limed, the greater and the less.
And some say, too, that we do love the best
To be quite free to do our own behest,
And that no man reprove us for our vice,
But saying we are wise, take our advice.
For truly there is no one of us all,
If anyone shall rub us on a gall,
That will not kick because he tells the truth.
Try, and he'll find who does so, I say sooth.
No matter how much vice we have within,
We would be held for wise and clean of sin.
And some folk say that great delight have we
To be held constant, also trustworthy,
And on one purpose steadfastly to dwell,
And not betray a thing that men may tell.
But that tale is not worth a rake's handle;
By God, we women can no thing conceal,
As witness Midas. Would you hear the tale?
Ovid, among some other matters small,

Said Midas had beneath his long curled hair,
Two ass's ears that grew in secret there,
The which defect he hid, as best he might,
Full cunningly from every person's sight,
And, save his wife, no one knew of it, no.
He loved her most, and trusted her also;
And he prayed of her that to no creature
She'd tell of his disfigurement impure.
She swore him: Nay, for all this world to win
She would do no such villainy or sin
And cause her husband have so foul a name;
Nor would she tell it for her own deep shame.
Nevertheless, she thought she would have died
Because so long the secret must she hide;
It seemed to swell so big about her heart
That some word from her mouth must surely start;
And since she dared to tell it to no man,
Down to a marsh, that lay hard by, she ran;
Till she came there her heart was all afire,
And as a bittern booms in the quagmire,
She laid her mouth low to the water down:
"Betray me not, you sounding water blown,"
Said she, "I tell it to none else but you:
Long ears like asses' has my husband two!
Now is my heart at ease, since that is out;
I could no longer keep it, there's no doubt."
Here may you see, though for a while we bide,
Yet out it must; no secret can we hide.
The rest of all this tale, if you would hear,
Read Ovid: in his book does it appear.
This knight my tale is chiefly told about
When what he went for he could not find out,
That is, the thing that women love the best,
Most saddened was the spirit in his breast;
But home he goes, he could no more delay.
The day was come when home he turned his way;
And on his way it chanced that he should ride
In all his care, beneath a forest's side,
And there he saw, a-dancing him before,
Full four and twenty ladies, maybe more;
Toward which dance eagerly did he turn
In hope that there some wisdom he should learn.
But truly, ere he came upon them there,
The dancers vanished all, he knew not where.
No creature saw he that gave sign of life,
Save, on the greensward sitting, an old wife;
A fouler person could no man devise.
Before the knight this old wife did arise,
And said: "Sir knight, hence lies no travelled way.
Tell me what thing you seek, and by your fay.
Perchance you'll find it may the better be;
These ancient folk know many things," said she.
"Dear mother," said this knight assuredly,
"I am but dead, save I can tell, truly,
What thing it is that women most desire;
Could you inform me, I'd pay well your hire."
"Plight me your troth here, hand in hand," said she,
"That you will do, whatever it may be,
The thing I ask if it lie in your might;
And I'll give you your answer ere the night."

Seyde, Myda hadde, under his longe heres,
Growing up-on his heed two asses eres,
The whiche vyce he hidde, as he best mighte,
Ful subtilly from every mannes sighte,
That, save his wyf, ther wiste of it na-mo.
He loved hir most, and trusted hir also;
He preyede hir, that to no creature
She sholde tellen of his disfigure.
She swoor him "nay, for al this world to winne,
She nolde do that vileinye or sinne,
To make hir housbond han so foul a name;
She nolde nat telle it for hir owene shame."
But nathelees, hir thoughte that she dyde,
That she so longe sholde a conseil hyde;
Hir thoughte it swal so sore aboute hir herte,
That nedely som word hir moste asterte;
And sith she dorste telle it to no man,
Doun to a mareys faste by she ran;
Til she came there, hir herte was a-fyre,
And, as a bitore bombleth in the myre,
She leyde hir mouth un-to the water doun:
"Biwreye me nat, thou water, with thy soun,"
Quod she, "to thee I telle it, and namo;
Myn housbond hath longe asses eres two!
Now is myn herte all hool, now is it oute;
I mighte no lenger kepe it, out of doute,"
Heer may ye se, thogh we a tyme abyde,
Yet out it moot, we can no conseil hyde;
The remenant of the tale if ye wol here,
Redeth Ovyde, and ther ye may it lere.
This knight, of which my tale is specially,
Whan that he saugh he mighte nat come therby,
This is to seye, what wommen loven moost,
With-inne his brest ful sorweful was the goost;
But hoom he gooth, he mighte nat sojourne.
The day was come, that hoomward moste he tourne,
And in his wey it happed him to ryde,
In al this care, under a forest-syde,
Wher-as he saugh up-on a daunce go
Of ladies foure and twenty, and yet mo;
Toward the whiche daunce he drow ful yerne,
In hope that som wisdom sholde he lerne.
But certeinly, er he came fully there,
Vanisshed was this daunce, he niste where.
No creature saugh he that bar lyf,
Save on the grene he saugh sittinge a wyf;
A fouler wight ther may no man devyse.
Agayn the knight this olde wyf gan ryse,
And seyde, "sir knight, heer-forth ne lyth no wey.
Tel me, what that ye seken, by your fey?
Paraventure it may the bettre be;
Thise olde folk can muchel thing," quod she.
"My leve mooder," quod this knight certyen,
"I nam but deed, but-if that I can seyn
What thing it is that wommen most desyre;
Coude ye me wisse, I wolde wel quyte your hyre."
"Plight me thy trouthe, heer in myn hand," quod she,
"The nexte thing that I requere thee,
Thou shalt it do, if it lye in thy might;
And I wol telle it yow er it be night."

“Have heer my trouthe,” quod the knight, “I grante.”
“Thanne,” quod she, “I dar me wel avante,
Thy lyf is sauf, for I wol stonde therby,
Up-on my lyf, the queen wol seye as I.
Lat see which is the proudeste of hem alle,
That wereth on a coverchief or a calle,
That dar seye nay, of that I shal thee teche;
Lat us go forth with-outen lenger speche.”
Tho rouned she a pistel in his ere,
And bad him to be glad, and have no fere.
When they be comen to the court, this knight
Seyde, “he had holde his day, as he hadde hight,
And redy was his answere,” as he sayde.
Ful many a noble wyf, and many a mayde,
And many a widwe, for that they ben wyse,
The quene hir-self sittinge as a justyse,
Assembled been, his answere for to here;
And afterward this knight was bode appere.
To every wight comanded was silence,
And that the knight sholde telle in audience,
What thing that worldly wommen loven best.
This knight ne stood nat stille as doth a best,
But to his questioun anon answerde
With manly voys, that al the court it herde:
“My lige lady, generally,” quod he,
“Wommen desyren to have sovereyntee
As wel over hir housbond as hir love,
And for to been in maistrie him above;
This is your moste desyr, thogh ye me kille,
Doth as yow list, I am heer at your wille.”
In al the court ne was ther wyf ne mayde,
Ne widwe, that contraried that he sayde,
But seyden, “he was worthy han his lyf.”
And with that word up stirte the olde wyf,
Which that the knight saugh sittinge in the grene:
“Mercy,” quod she, “my sovereyn lady quene!
Er that your court departe, do me right.
I taughte this answere un-to the knight;
For which he plighte me his trouthe there,
The firste thing I wolde of him requere,
He wolde it do, if it lay in his might.
Bifore the court than preye I thee, sir knight,”
Quod she, “that thou me take un-to thy wyf;
For wel thou wost that I have kept thy lyf.
If I sey fals, sey nay, up-on thy fey!”
This knight answerde, “allas! and weylawey!
I woot right wel that swich was my biheste.
For goddes love, as chees a newe requeste;
Tak al my good, and lat my body go.”
“Nay than,” quod she, “I shrewe us bothe two!
For thogh that I be foul, and old, and pore,
I nolde for al the metal, ne for ore,
That under erthe is grave, or lyth above,
But-if thy wyf I were, and eek thy love.”
“My love?” quod he; “nay, my dampnacioun!
Allas! that any of my nacioun
Sholde ever so foule disparaged be!”
But al for noght, the ende is this, that he
Constreyned was, he nedes moste hir wedde;
And taketh his olde wyf, and gooth to bedde.

“Have here my word,” said he. “That thing I grant.”
“Then,” said the crone, “of this I make my vaunt
Your life is safe; and I will stand thereby,
Upon my life, the queen will say as I.
Let's see which is the proudest of them all
That wears upon her hair kerchief or caul,
Shall dare say no to that which I shall teach;
Let us go now and without longer speech.”
Then whispered she a sentence in his ear,
And bade him to be glad and have no fear.
When they were come unto the court, this knight
Said he had kept his promise as was right,
And ready was his answer, as he said.
Full many a noble wife, and many a maid,
And many a widow, since they are so wise,
The queen herself sitting as high justice,
Assembled were, his answer there to hear;
And then the knight was bidden to appear.
Command was given for silence in the hall,
And that the knight should tell before them all
What thing all worldly women love the best.
This knight did not stand dumb, as does a beast,
But to this question presently answered
With manly voice, so that the whole court heard:
“My liege lady, generally,” said he,
“Woman desire to have the sovereignty
As well upon their husband as their love,
And to have mastery their man above;
This thing you most desire, though me you kill
Do as you please, I am here at your will.”
In all the court there was no wife or maid
Or widow that denied the thing he said,
But all held, he was worthy to have life.
And with that word up started the old wife
Whom he had seen a-sitting on the green.
“Mercy, ”cried she, “my sovereign lady queen!
Before the court's dismissed, give me my right.
'Twas I who taught the answer to this knight;
For which he did plight troth to me, out there,
That the first thing I should of him require
He would do that, if it lay in his might.
Before the court, now, pray I you sir knight,”
Said she, “that you will take me for your wife;
For well you know that I have saved your life.
If this be false, say nay, upon your fay!”
This knight replied: “Alas and welaway!
That I so promised I will not protest.
But for God's love pray make a new request,
Take all my wealth and let my body go.”
“Nay then,” said she, “beshrew us if I do!
For though I may be foul and old and poor,
I will not, for all metal and all ore
That from the earth is dug or lies above,
Be aught except your wife and your true love.”
“My love?” cried he, “nay, rather my damnation!
Alas! that any of my race and station
Should ever so dishonoured foully be!”
But all for naught; the end was this, that he
Was so constrained he needs must go and wed,
And take his ancient wife and go to bed.

Now, peradventure, would some men say here,
That, of my negligence, I take no care
To tell you of the joy and all the array
That at the wedding feast were seen that day.
Make a brief answer to this thing I shall;
I say, there was no joy or feast at all;
There was but heaviness and grievous sorrow;
For privately he wedded on the morrow,
And all day, then, he hid him like an owl;
So sad he was, his old wife looked so foul.

Great was the woe the knight had in his thought
When he, with her, to marriage bed was brought;
He rolled about and turned him to and fro.
His old wife lay there, always smiling so
And said: "O my dear husband, *ben'cite!*
Fares every knight with wife as you with me?
Is this the custom in King Arthur's house?
Are knights of his all so fastidious?
I am your own true love and, more, your wife;
And I am she who saved your very life;
And truly, since I've never done you wrong,
Why do you treat me so, this first night long?
You act as does a man who's lost his wit;
What is my fault? For God's love tell me it,
And it shall be amended, if I may."

"Amended!" cried this knight, "Alas, nay, nay!
It will not be amended ever, no!
Your are so loathsome, and so old also,
And therewith of so low a race were born,
It's little wonder that I toss and turn.
Would God my heart would break within my breast!"

"Is this," asked she, "the cause of your unrest?"

"Yes, truly," said he, "and no wonder 'tis."

"Now, sir," said she, "I could amend all this,
If I but would, and that within days three,
If you would bear yourself well towards me.

"But since you speak of such gentility
As is descended from old wealth, till ye
Claim that for that you should be gentlemen,
I hold such arrogance not worth a hen.
Find him who is most virtuous alway,
Alone or publicly, and most tries aye
To do whatever noble deeds he can,
And take him for the greatest gentleman.
Christ wills we claim from Him gentility,
Not from ancestors of landocracy.
For though they give us all their heritage,
For which we claim to be of high lineage,
Yet can they not bequeath, in anything,
To any of us, their virtuous living,
That made men say they had gentility,
And bade us follow them in like degree.

"Well does that poet wise of great Florence,
Called Dante, speak his mind in this sentence;
Somewhat like this may it translated be:
'Rarely unto the branches of the tree
Doth human worth mount up: and so ordains
He Who bestows it; to Him it pertains.'[1]

Now wolden som men seye, paraventure,
That, for my necligence, I do no cure
To tellen yow the joye and al th'array
That at the feste was that ilke day.
To whiche thing shortly answere I shal;
I seye, ther nas no joye ne feste at al,
Ther nas but hevinesse and muche sorwe;
For prively he wedded hir on a morwe,
And al day after hidde him as an oule;
So wo was him, his wyf looked so foule.

Greet was the wo the knight hadde in his thoght,
Whan he was with his wyf a-bedde y-broght;
He walweth, and he turneth to and fro.
His olde wyf lay smylinge evermo,
And seyde, "o dere housbond, *ben'cite!*
Fareth every knight thus with his wyf as ye?
Is this the lawe of king Arthures hous?
Is every knight of his so dangerous?
I am your owene love and eek your wyf;
I am she, which that saved hath your lyf;
And certes, yet dide I yow never unright;
Why fare ye thus with me this firste night?
Ye faren lyk a man had lost his wit;
What is my gilt? for godd's love, tel me it,
And it shal been amended, if I may."

"Amended?" quod this knight, "allas! nay, nay!
It wol nat been amended never mo!
Thou art so loothly, and so old also,
And ther-to comen of so lowe a kinde,
That litel wonder is, thogh I walwe and winde.
So wolde god myn herte wolde breste!"

"Is this," quod she, "the cause of your unreste?"

"Ye, certainly," quod he, "no wonder is."

"Now, sire," quod she, "I coude amende al this,
If that me liste, er it were dayes three,
So wel ye mighte bere yow un-to me.

But for ye speken of swich gentillesse
As is descended out of old richesse,
That therfore sholden ye be gentil men,
Swich arrogance is nat worth an hen.
Loke who that is most vertuous alway,
Privee and apert, and most entendeth ay
To do the gentil dedes that he can,
And tak him for the grettest gentil man.
Crist wol, we clayme of him our gentillesse,
Nat of our eldres for hir old richesse.
For thogh they yeve us al hir heritage,
For which we clayme to been of heigh parage,
Yet may they nat biquethe, for no-thing,
To noon of us hir vertuous living,
That made hem gentil men y-called be;
And bad us folwen hem in swich degree.

Wel can the wyse poete of Florence,
That highte Dant, speken in this sentence;
Lo in swich maner rym is Dantes tale:
'Ful selde up ryseth by his branches smale
Prowesse of man; for god, of his goodnesse,
Wol that of him we clayme our gentillesse';[1]

[1] Dante, *Divine Comedy*, *Purgat.*, VII, 122, 123.

For of our eldres may we no-thing clayme
But temporel thing, that man may hurte and mayme,
  Eek every wight wot this as wel as I,
If gentillesse were planted naturelly
Un-to a certeyn linage, doun the lyne,
Privee ne apert, than wolde they never fyne
To doon of gentillesse the faire offyce;
They mighte do no vileinye or vyce.
  Tak fyr, and ber it in the derkeste hous
Bitwix this and the mount of Caucasus,
And lat men shette the dores and go thenne;
Yet wol the fyr as faire lye and brenne,
As twenty thousand men mighte it biholde;
His office naturel ay wol it holde,
Up peril of my lyf, til that it dye.
  Heer may ye see wel, how that genterye
Is nat annexed to possessioun,
Sith folk ne doon hir operacioun
Alwey, as dooth the fyr, lo! in his kinde.
For, god it woot, men may wel often finde
A lordes sone do shame and vileinye;
And he that wol han prys of his gentrye
For he was boren of a gentil hous,
And hadde hise eldres noble and vertuous,
And nil him-selven do no gentil dedis,
Ne folwe his gentil auncestre that deed is,
He nis nat gentil, be he duk or erl;
For vileyns sinful dedes make a cherl.
For gentillesse nis but renomee
Of thyne auncestres, for hir heigh bountee,
Which is a strange thing to thy persone.
Thy gentillesse cometh fro god allone;
Than comth our verray gentillesse of grace,
It was no-thing biquethe us with our place.
  Thenketh how noble, as seith Valerius,
Was thilke Tullius Hostilius,
That out of povert roos to heigh noblesse.
Redeth Senek, and redeth eek Boëce,
Ther shul ye seen expres that it no drede is,
That he is gentil that doth gentil dedis;
And therfore, leve housbond, I thus conclude,
Al were it that myne auncestres were rude,
Yet may the hye god, and so hope I,
Grante me grace to liven vertuously.
Thanne am I gentil, whan that I beginne
To liven vertuously and weyve sinne.
  And ther-as ye of povert me repreve,
The hye god, on whom that we bileve.
In wilful povert chees to live his lyf.
And certes every man, mayden, or wyf,
May understonde that Jesus, hevene king,
Ne wolde nat chese a vicious living.
Glad povert is an honest thing, certeyn;
This wol Senek and othere clerkes seyn.
Who-so that halt him payd of his poverte,
I holde him riche, al hadde he nat a sherte.
He that coveyteth is a povre wight,
For he wolde han that is nat in his might.
But he that noght hath, ne coveyteth have,
Is riche, al-though ye holde him but a knave.
  Verray povert, it singeth proprely;

For of our fathers may we nothing claim
But temporal things, that man may hurt and maim.
  "And everyone knows this as well as I,
If nobleness were implanted naturally
Within a certain lineage, down the line,
In private and in public, I opine,
The ways of gentleness they'd alway show
And never fall to vice and conduct low.
  "Take fire and carry it in the darkest house
Between here and the Mount of Caucasus,
And let men shut the doors and from them turn;
Yet will the fire as fairly blaze and burn
As twenty thousand men did it behold;
Its nature and its office it will hold,
On peril of my life, until it die.
  "From this you see that true gentility
Is not allied to wealth a man may own,
Since folk do not their deeds, as may be shown,
As does the fire, according to its kind.
For God knows that men may full often find
A lord's son doing shame and villainy;
And he that prizes his gentility
In being born of some old noble house,
With ancestors both noble and virtuous,
But will himself do naught of noble deeds
Nor follow him to whose name he succeeds,
He is not gentle, be he duke or earl;
For acting churlish makes a man a churl.
Gentility is not just the renown
Of ancestors who have some greatness shown,
In which you have no portion of your own.
Your own gentility comes from God alone;
Thence comes our true nobility by grace,
It was not willed us with our rank and place
  "Think how noble, as says Valerius,
Was that same Tullius Hostilius,
Who out of poverty rose to high estate.
Seneca and Boethius inculcate,
Expressly (and no doubt it thus proceeds),
That he is noble who does noble deeds;
And therefore, husband dear, I thus conclude:
Although my ancestors mayhap were rude,
Yet may the High Lord, and so hope I,
Grant me the grace to live right virtuously.
Then I'll be gentle when I do begin
To live in virtue and to do no sin.
  "And when you me reproach for poverty,
The High God, in Whom we believe, say I,
In voluntary poverty lived His life.
And surely every man, or maid, or wife
May understand that Jesus, Heaven's King,
Would not have chosen vileness of living.
Glad poverty's an honest thing, that's plain,
Which Seneca and other clerks maintain.
Whoso will be content with poverty,
I hold him rich, though not a shirt has he.
And he that covets much is a poor wight,
For he would gain what's all beyond his might
But he that has not, nor desires to have,
Is rich, although you hold him but a knave.
  "True poverty, it sings right naturally;

Juvenal gaily says of poverty:
'The poor man, when he walks along the way,
Before the robbers he may sing and play.
Poverty's odious good, and, as I guess,
It is a stimulant to busyness;
A great improver, too, of sapience
In him that takes it all with due patience.
Poverty's this, though it seem misery—
Its quality may none dispute, say I.
Poverty often, when a man is low,
Makes him his God and even himself to know.
And poverty's an eye-glass, seems to me,
Through which a man his loyal friends may see.
Since you've received no injury from me,
Then why reproach me for my poverty.
"Now, sir, with age you have upbraided me;
And truly, sir, though no authority
Were in a book, you gentles of honour
Say that men should the aged show favour,
And call him father, of your gentleness;
And authors could I find for this, I guess.
"Now since you say that I am foul and old,
Then fear you not to be made a cuckold;
For dirt and age, as prosperous I may be,
Are mighty wardens over chastity.
Nevertheless, since I know your delight,
I'll satisfy your worldly appetite.
"Choose, now," said she, "one of these two things, aye,
To have me foul and old until I die,
And be to you a true and humble wife,
And never anger you in all my life;
Or else to have me young and very fair
And take your chance with those who will repair
Unto your house, and all because of me,
Or in some other place, as well may be.
Now choose which you like better and reply."
This knight considered, and did sorely sigh,
But at the last replied as you shall hear:
"My lady and my love, and wife so dear,
I put myself in your wise governing;
Do you choose which may be the more pleasing,
And bring most honour to you, and me also.
I care not which it be of these things two;
For if you like it, that suffices me."
"Then have I got of you the mastery,
Since I may choose and govern, in earnest?"
"Yes, truly, wife," said he, "I hold that best."
"Kiss me," said she, "we'll be no longer wroth,
For by my truth, to you I will be both;
That is to say, I'll be both good and fair.
I pray God I go mad, and so declare,
If I be not to you as good and true
As ever wife was since the world was new.
And, save I be, at dawn, as fairly seen
As any lady, empress, or great queen
That is between the east and the far west,
Do with my life and death as you like best.
Throw back the curtain and see how it is."
And when the knight saw verily all this,
That she so very fair was, and young too,

Juvenal seith of povert merily:
'The povre man, whan he goth by the weye,
Bifore the theves he may singe and pleye.'
Povert is hateful good, and, as I gesse,
A ful greet bringer out of bisinesse;
A greet amender eek of sapience
To him that taketh it in pacience.
Povert is this, al-though it seme elenge:
Possessioun, that no wight wol chalenge.
Povert ful ofte, whan a man is lowe,
Maketh his god and eek him-self to knowe.
Povert a spectacle is, as thinketh me,
Thurgh which he may his verray frendes see.
And therfore, sire, sin that I noght yow greve,
Of my povert na-more ye me repreve.
Now, sire, of elde ye repreve me;
And certes, sire, thogh noon auctoritee
Were in no book, ye gentils of honour
Seyn that men sholde an old wight doon favour,
And clepe him fader, for your gentillesse;
And auctours shal I finden, as I gesse.
Now ther y seye, that I am foul and old,
Than drede you noght to been a cokewold;
For filthe and elde, al-so mote I thee,
Been grete wardeyns up-on chastitee.
But nathelees, sin I knowe your delyt,
I shal fulfille your worldly appetyt.
Chees now," quod she, "oon of thise thinges tweye,
To han me foul and old til that I deye,
And be to yow a trewe humble wyf,
And never yow displese in al my lyf,
Or elles ye wol han me yong and fair,
And take your aventure of the repair
That shal be to your hous, by-cause of me,
Or in som other place, may wel be.
Now chees your-selven, whether that yow lyketh."
This knight avyseth him and sore syketh,
But atte laste he seyde in this manere,
"My lady and my love, and wyf so dere,
I put me in your wyse governance;
Cheseth your-self, which may be most plesance,
And most honour to yow and me also.
I do no fors the whether of the two;
For as yow lyketh, it suffiseth me."
"Thanne have I gete of yow maistrye," quod she,
"Sin I may chese, and governe as me lest?"
"Ye, certes, wyf," quod he, "I holde it best."
"Kis me," quod she, "we be no lenger wrothe;
For, by my trouthe, I wol be to yow bothe,
This is to seyn, ye, bothe fair and good.
I prey to god that I mot sterven wood,
But I to yow be al-so good and trewe
As ever was wyf, sin that the world was newe.
And, but I be to-morn as fair to sene
As any lady, emperyce, or quene,
That is bitwixe the est and eke the west,
Doth with my lyf and deeth right as yow lest.
Cast up the curtin, loke how that it is."
And whan the knight saugh verrailly al this,
That she so fair was, and so yong ther-to,

For joye he hente hir in his armes two,
His herte bathed in a bath of blisse;
A thousand tyme a-rewe he gan hir kisse.
And she obeyed him in every thing
That mighte doon him plesance or lyking.
And thus they live, un-to hir lyves ende,
In parfit joye; and Jesu Crist us sende
Housbondes meke, yonge, and fresshe a-bedde,
And grace t'overbyde hem that we wedde.
And eek I preye Jesu shorte hir lyves
That wol nat be governed by hir wyves;
And olde and angry nigardes of dispence,
God sende hem sone verray pestilence.

For joy he clasped her in his strong arms two,
His heart bathed in a bath of utter bliss;
A thousand times, all in a row, he'd kiss.
And she obeyed his wish in everything
That might give pleasure to his love-liking.
And thus they lived unto their lives' fair end,
In perfect joy; and Jesus to us send
Meek husbands, and young ones, and fresh in bed,
And good luck to outlive them that we wed.
And I pray Jesus to cut short the lives
Of those who'll not be governed by their wives;
And old and querulous niggards with their pence,
And send them soon a mortal pestilence!

HERE ENDETH THE WIFE OF BATH'S TALE

THE FRIAR'S PROLOGUE

THE PROLOGUE OF THE FRIAR'S TALE

THIS worthy limitour, this noble Frere,
He made alwey a maner louring chere
Upon the Somnour, but for honestee
No vileyns word as yet to him spak he.
But atte laste he seyde un-to the Wyf,
"Dame," quod he, "god yeve yow right good lyf!
Ye han heer touched, al-so mote I thee,
In scole-matere greet difficultee;
Ye han seyd muchel thing right wel, I seye;
But dame, here as we ryden by the weye,
Us nedeth nat to speken but of game,
And lete auctoritees, on goddes name,
To preching and to scole eek of clergye.
But if it lyke to this companye,
I wol yow of a somnour telle a game.
Pardee, ye may wel knowe by the name,
That of a somnour may no good be sayd;
I praye that noon of you be yvel apayd.
A somnour is a renner up and doun
With mandements for fornicacioun,
And is y-bet at every tounes ende."
Our host tho spak, "a! sire, ye sholde be hende
And curteys, as a man of your estaat;
In companye we wol have no debaat.
Telleth your tale, and lat the Somnour be."
"Nay," quod the Somnour, "lat him seye to me
What so him list; whan it comth to my lot,
By god, I shal him quyten every grot.
I shal him tellen which a greet honour
It is to be a flateringe limitour;[1]
And his offyce I shal him telle, y-wis."
Our host answerde, "pees, na-more of this."
And after this he seyde un-to the Frere,
"Tel forth your tale, leve maister deere."

THIS worthy limiter, this noble friar,
He turned always a lowering face, and dire,
Upon the summoner, but for courtesy
No rude and insolent word as yet spoke he.
But at the last he said unto the wife:
"Lady," said he, "God grant you a good life!
You have here touched, as I may prosperous be,
Upon school matters of great difficulty;
You have said many things right well, I say;
But, lady, as we ride along our way,
We need but talk to carry on our game,
And leave authorities, in good God's name,
To preachers and to schools for clergymen.
But if it pleases all this company, then,
I'll tell you of a summoner, to make game.
By God, you could surmise it by the name
That of a summoner may no good be said;
I pray that no one will be angry made.
A summoner is a runner up and down
With summonses for fornication known,
And he is beaten well at each town's end."
Our host then spoke: "O sir, you should attend
To courtesy, like man of your estate;
In company here we will have no debate.
Tell forth your tale and let the summoner be."
"Nay," said the summoner, "let him say to me
What pleases him; when it falls to my lot,
By God I'll then repay him, every jot.
I'll then make plain to him what great honour
It is to be a flattering limiter;[1]
I'll certainly tell him what his business is."
Our host replied: "Oh peace, no more of this!"
And after that he said unto the friar:
"Tell now your tale to us, good master dear."

HERE ENDETH THE PROLOGUE OF THE FRIAR

[1]Skeat omits Tyrwhitt's Il. 6377-8.

THE FRIAR'S TALE

HERE BEGINNETH THE FRIAR'S TALE

Once on a time there dwelt in my country
An archdeacon, a man of high degree,
Who boldly executed the Church's frown
In punishment of fornication known,
And of witchcraft and of all known bawdry,
And defamation and adultery
Of church-wardens, and of fake testaments
And contracts, and the lack of sacraments,
And still of many another kind of crime
Which need not be recounted at this time,
And usury and simony also.
But unto lechers gave he greatest woe;
They should lament if they were apprehended;
And payers of short tithes to shame descended.
If anyone informed of such, 'twas plain
He'd not escape pecuniary pain.
For all short tithes and for small-offering
He made folk pitifully to howl and sing.
For ere the bishop caught them with his crook,
They were already in the archdeacon's book.
Then had he, by his competent jurisdiction,
Power to punish them by such infliction.
He had a summoner ready to his hand,
A slyer rogue was not in all England;
For cunningly he'd espionage to trail
And bring reports of all that might avail.
He could protect of lechers one or two
To learn of four and twenty more, mark you.
For though this man were wild as is a hare,
To tell his evil deeds I will not spare;
For we are out of his reach of infliction;
They have of us no competent jurisdiction,
Nor ever shall for term of all their lives.
"Peter! So are the women of the dives,"
The summoner said, "likewise beyond my cure!"
"Peace, with mischance and with misadventure!"
Thus spoke our host, "and let him tell his tale.
Now tell it on, despite the summoner's wail,
Nor spare in anything, my master dear."
This false thief, then, this summoner (said the friar)
Had always panders ready to his hand,
For any hawk to lure in all England,
Who told him all the scandal that they knew;
For their acquaintances were nothing new.
They were all his informers privily;
And he took to himself great gain thereby;
His master knew not how his profits ran.
Without an order, and an ignorant man,
Yet would he summon, on pain of Christ's curse,
Those who were glad enough to fill his purse
And feast him greatly at the taverns all.
And just as Judas had his purses small
And was a thief, just such a thief was he.
His master got but half of every fee.

Whilom ther was dwellinge in my contree
An erchedeken, a man of heigh degree,
That boldely dide execucioun
In punisshinge of fornicacioun,
Of wicchecraft, and eek of bauderye,
Of diffamacioun, and avoutrye,
Of chirche-reves, and of testaments,
Of contractes, and of lakke of sacraments,
And eek of many another maner cryme
Which nedeth nat rehercen at this tyme;
Of usure, and of symonye also.
But certes, lechours dide he grettest wo;
They sholde singen, if that they were hent;
And smale tytheres weren foule y-shent.
If any persone wolde up-on hem pleyne,
Ther mighte asterte him no pecunial peyne.
For smale tythes and for smal offringe
He made the peple pitously to singe.
For er the bisshop caughte hem with his hook,
They weren in the erchedeknes book.
Thanne hadde he, thurgh his jurisdiccioun,
Power to doon on hem correccioun.
He hadde a Somnour redy to his hond,
A slyer boy was noon in Engelond;
For subtilly he hadde his espiaille,
That taughte him, wher that him mighte availle.
He coude spare of lechours oon or two,
To techen him to foure and twenty mo.
For thogh this Somnour wood were as an hare,
To telle his harlotrye I wol nat spare;
For we been out of his correccioun;
They han of us no jurisdiccioun,
Ne never shullen, terme of alle hir lyves.
"Peter! so been the wommen of the styves,"
Quod the Somnour, "y-put out of my cure!"
"Pees, with mischance and with misaventure,"
Thus seyde our host, "and lat him telle his tale.
Now telleth forth, thogh that the Somnour gale,
Ne spareth nat, myn owene maister dere."
This false theef, this Somnour, quod the Frere,
Hadde alwey baudes redy to his hond,
As any hauk to lure in Engelond,
That tolde him al the secree that they knewe;
For hir acqueyntance was nat come of newe.
They weren hise approwours prively;
He took him-self a greet profit therby;
His maister knew nat alwey what he wan.
With-outen mandement, a lewed man
He coude somne, on peyne of Cristes curs,
And they were gladde for to fille his purs,
And make him grete festes atte nale.
And right as Judas hadde purses smale,
And was a theef, right swich a theef was he;
His maister hadde but half his duëtee.

He was, if I shal yeven him his laude,
A theef, and eek a Somnour, and a baude.
He hadde eek wenches at his retenue,
That, whether that sir Robert or sir Huwe,
Or Jakke, or Rauf, or who-so that it were,
That lay by hem, they tolde it in his ere;
Thus was the wenche and he of oon assent.
And he wolde fecche a feyned mandement,
And somne hem to the chapitre bothe two,
And pile the man, and lete the wenche go.
Thanne wolde he seye, "frend, I shal for thy sake
Do stryken hir out of our lettres blake;
Thee thar na-more as in this cas travaille;
I am thy freend, ther I thee may availle."
Certeyn he knew of bryberyes mo
Than possible is to telle in yeres two.
For in this world nis dogge for the bowe,
That can an hurt deer from an hool y-knowe,
Bet than this Somnour knew a sly lechour,
Or an avouter, or a paramour.
And, for that was the fruit of al his rente,
Therefore on it he sette al his entente.
And so bifel, that ones on a day
This Somnour, ever waiting on his pray,
Rood for to somne a widwe, an old ribybe,
Feyninge a cause, for he wolde brybe.
And happed that he saugh bifore him ryde
A gay yeman, under a forest-syde.
A bowe he bar, and arwes brighte and kene;
He hadde up-on a courtepy of grene;
An hat up-on his heed with frenges blake.
"Sir," quod this Somnour, "hayl! and wel a-take!"
"Wel-come," quod he, "and every good felawe!
Wher rydestow under this grene shawe?"
Seyde this yeman, "wiltow fer to day?"
This Somnour him answerde, and seyde, "nay;
Heer faste by," quod he, "is myn entente
To ryden, for to reysen up a rente
That longeth to my lordes duëtee."
"Artow thanne a bailly?"
"Ye!" quod he.
He dorste nat, for verray filthe and shame,
Seye that he was a somnour, for the name.
"*Depardieux*," quod this yeman, "dere brother,
Thou art a bailly, and I am another.
I am unknowen as in this contree;
Of thyn aqueyntance I wolde praye thee,
And eek of brotherhede, if that yow leste.
I have gold and silver in my cheste;
If that thee happe to comen in our shyre,
Al shal be thyn, right as thou wolt desyre."
"Grantmercy," quod this Somnour, "by my feith!"
Everich in otheres hand his trouthe leith,
For to be sworne bretheren til they deye.
In daliance they ryden forth hir weye.
This Somnour, which that was as ful of jangles,
As ful of venim been thise wariangles,
And ever enquering up-on every thing,

He was, if I'm to give him proper laud,
A thief, and more, a summoner, and a bawd.
He'd even wenches in his retinue,
And whether 'twere Sir Robert, or Sir Hugh,
Or Jack, or Ralph, or whosoever 'twere
That lay with them, they told it in his ear;
Thus were the wench and he in partnership.
And he would forge a summons from his scrip,
And summon to the chapter-house those two
And fleece the man and let the harlot go.
Then would he say: "My friend, and for your sake,
Her name from our blacklist will I now take;
Trouble no more for what this may entail;
I am your friend in all where 'twill avail."
He knew more ways to fleece and blackmail you
Than could be told in one year or in two.
For in this world's no dog trained to the bow
That can a hurt deer from a sound one know
Better than this man knew a sly lecher,
Or fornicator, or adulterer.
And since this was the fruit of all his rent,
Therefore on it he fixed his whole intent.
And so befell that once upon a day
This summoner, ever lurking for his prey,
Rode out to summon a widow, an old rip,
Feigning a cause, for her he planned to strip.
It happened that he saw before him ride
A yeoman gay along a forest's side.
A bow he bore, and arrows bright and keen;
He wore a short coat of the Lincoln green,
And hat upon his head, with fringes black.
"Sir," said the summoner, "hail and well met, Jack!"
"Welcome," said he, "and every comrade good!
Whither do you ride under this greenwood?"
Said this yeoman, "Will you go far today?"
This summoner replied to him with: "Nay,
Hard by this place," said he, "'tis my intent
To ride, sir, to collect a bit of rent
Pertaining to my lord's temporality."
"And are you then a bailiff?"
"Aye," said he.
He dared not, no, for very filth and shame,
Say that he was a summoner, for the name.
"In God's name," said this yeoman then, "dear brother,
You are a bailiff and I am another.
I am a stranger in these parts, you see;
Of your acquaintance I'd be glad," said he,
"And of your brotherhood, if 'tis welcome.
I've gold and silver in my chest at home,
And if you chance to come into our shire,
All shall be yours, just as you may desire."
"Many thanks," said this summoner, "by my faith!"
And they struck hands and made their solemn oath
To be sworn brothers till their dying day.
Gossiping then they rode upon their way.
This summoner, who was as full of words
As full of malice are these butcher birds,
And ever enquiring after everything,

"Brother," asked he, "where now is your dwelling
If some day I should wish your side to reach?"
This yeoman answered him in gentle speech,
"Brother," said he, "far in the north country,
Where, as I hope, some day you'll come to me.
Before we part I will direct you so
You'll never miss it when that way you go."
"Now, brother," said this summoner, "I pray
You'll teach me, while we ride along our way,
Since that you are a bailiff, as am I,
A trick or two, and tell me faithfully
How, in my office, I may most coin win;
And spare not for nice conscience, nor for sin,
But as my brother tell your arts to me."
"Now by my truth, dear brother," then said he,
If I am to relate a faithful tale,
My wages are right scanty, and but small.
My lord is harsh to me and niggardly,
My job is most laborious, you see;
And therefore by extortion do I live.
Forsooth, I take all that these men will give;
By any means, by trick or violence,
From year to year I win me my expense.
I can no better tell you faithfully,"
"Now truly," said this summoner, "so do I.
I never spare to take a thing, God wot,
Unless it be too heavy or too hot.
What I get for myself, and privately,
No kind of conscience for such things have I.
But for extortion, I could not well live,
Nor of such japes will I confession give.
Stomach nor any conscience have I, none;
A curse on father-confessors, every one.
Well are we met, by God and by Saint James!
But, my dear brother, tell your name or names."
Thus said the summoner, and in meanwhile
The yeoman just a little began to smile.
"Brother," said he, "and will you that I tell?
I am a fiend, my dwelling is in Hell.
But here I ride about in hope of gain
And that some little gift I may obtain.
My only income is what so is sent.
I see you ride with much the same intent
To win some wealth, you never care just how;
Even so do I, for I would ride, right now,
Unto the world's end, all to get my prey."
"Ah," cried he, "*ben'cite!* What do you say?
I took you for a yeoman certainly.
You have a human shape as well as I;
Have you a figure then determinate
In Hell, where you are in your proper state?"
"Nay," said he, "there of figure we have none;
But when it pleases us we can take one,
Or else we make you think we have a shape,
Sometimes like man, or sometimes like an ape;
Or like an angel can I seem, you know.
It is no wondrous thing that this is so;
A lousy juggler can deceive, you see,
And by gad, I have yet more craft than he."
"Why," asked the summoner, "ride you then, or go,

"Brother," quod he, "where is now your dwelling,
Another day if that I sholde yow seche?"
This yeman him answerde in softe speche,
"Brother," quod he, "fer in the north contree,
Wher, as I hope, som-tyme I shal thee see.
Er we departe, I shal thee so wel wisse,
That of myn hous ne shaltow never misse."
"Now, brother," quod this Somnour, "I yow preye,
Teche me, whyl that we ryden by the weye,
Sin that ye been a baillif as am I,
Som subtiltee, and tel me feithfully
In myn offyce how I may most winne;
And spareth nat for conscience ne sinne,
But as my brother tel me, how do ye?"
"Now, by my trouthe, brother dere," seyde he,
"As I shal tellen thee a feithful tale,
My wages been ful streite and ful smale.
My lord is hard to me and daungerous,
And myn offyce is ful laborous;
And therfore by extorcions I live.
For sothe, I take al that men wol me yive;
Algate, by sleyghte or by violence,
Fro yeer to yeer I winne al my dispence.
I can no bettre telle feithfully."
"Now, certes," quod this Somnour, "so fare I;
I spare nat to taken, god it woot,
But-if it be to hevy or to hoot.
What I may gete in conseil prively,
No maner conscience of that have I;
Nere myn extorcioun, I mighte nat liven,
Ne of swiche japes wol I nat be shriven.
Stomak ne conscience ne knowe I noon;
I shrewe thise shrifte-fadres everichoon.
Wel be we met, by god and by seint Jame!
But, leve brother, tel me than thy name,"
Quod this Somnour; and in this mene whyle,
This yeman gan a litel for to smyle.
"Brother," quod he, "wiltow that I thee telle?
I am a feend, my dwelling is in helle.
And here I ryde about my purchasing,
To wite where men wolde yeve me any thing.
My purchas is th'effect of al my rente.
Loke how thou rydest for the same entente,
To winne good, thou rekkest never how;
Right so fare I, for ryde wolde I now
Un-to the worldes ende for a preye."
"A," quod this Somnour, "*ben'cite*, what sey ye?
I wende ye were a yeman trewely.
Ye han a mannes shap as wel as I;
Han ye figure than determinat
In helle, ther ye been in your estat?"
"Nay, certeinly," quod he, "ther have we noon;
But whan us lyketh, we can take us oon,
Or elles make yow seme we ben shape
Som-tyme lyk a man, or lyk an ape;
Or lyk an angel can I ryde or go.
It is no wonder thing thogh it be so;
A lousy jogelour can deceyve thee,
And pardee, yet can I more craft than he."
"Why," quod the Somnour, "ryde ye thanne or goon

In sondry shap, and nat alwey in oon?"
"For we," quod he, "wol us swich formes make
As most able is our preyes for to take."
"What maketh yow to han al this labour?"
"Ful many a cause, leve sir Somnour,"
Seyde this feend, "but alle thing hath tyme.
The day is short, and it is passed pryme,
And yet ne wan I no-thing in this day.
I wol entende to winnen, if I may,
And nat entende our wittes to declare.
For, brother myn, thy wit is al to bare
To understonde, al-thogh I tolde hem thee.
But, for thou axest why labouren we;
For, som-tyme, we ben goddes instruments,
And menes to don his comandements,
Whan that him list, up-on his creatures,
In divers art and in divers figures.
With-outen him we have no might, certayn,
If that him list to stonden ther-agayn.
And som-tyme, at our prayere, han we leve
Only the body and nat the soule greve;
Witnesse on Job, whom that we diden wo.
And som-tyme han we might of bothe two,
This is to seyn, of soule and body eke.
And somtyme be we suffred for to seke
Up-on a man, and doon his soule unreste,
And nat his body, and al is for the beste.
Whan he withstandeth our temptacioun,
It is a cause of his savacioun;
Al-be-it that it was nat our entente
He sholde be sauf, but that we wolde him hente.
And som-tyme be we servant un-to man,
As to the erchebisshop Seint Dunstan
And to the apostles servant eek was I."
"Yet tel me," quod the Somnour, "feithfully,
Make ye yow newe bodies thus alway
Of elements?"
the feend answerde, "nay;
Som-tyme we feyne, and som-tyme we aryse
With dede bodies in ful sondry wyse,
And speke as renably and faire and wel
As to the Phitonissa dide Samuel.
And yet wol som men seye it was nat he;
I do no fors of your divinitee.
But o thing warne I thee, I wol nat jape,
Thou wolt algates wite how we ben shape;
Thou shalt her-afterward, my brother dere,
Com ther thee nedeth nat of me to lere.
For thou shalt by thyn owene experience
Conne in a chayer rede of this sentence
Bet than Virgyle, whyl he was on lyve,
Or Dant also; now lat us ryde blyve.
For I wol holde companye with thee
Til it be so, that thou forsake me."
"Nay," quod this Somnour, "that shal nat bi-
tyde;
I am a yeman, knowen is ful wyde;
My trouthe wol I holde as in this cas.
For though thou were the devel Sathanas,
My trouthe wol I holde to my brother,
As I am sworn, and ech of us til other
For to be trewe brother in this cas;

In sundry shapes, and not in one, you know?"
"Because," said he, "we will such figures make
As render likely that our prey we'll take."
"What causes you to have all this labour?"
"Full many a cause, my dear sir summoner,"
Replied the fiend, "but each thing has its time.
The day is short, and it is now past prime,
And yet have I won not a thing this day.
I will attend to winning, if I may,
And not our different notions to declare.
For, brother mine, your wits are all too bare
To understand, though I told mine fully.
But since you ask me why thus labour we—
Well, sometimes we are God's own instruments
And means to do His orders and intents,
When so He pleases, upon all His creatures,
In divers ways and shapes, and divers features.
Without Him we've no power, 'tis certain,
If He be pleased to stand against our train.
And sometimes, at our instance, have we leave
Only the body, not the soul, to grieve;
As witness Job, to whom we gave such woe.
And sometimes have we power of both, you know,
That is to say, of soul and body too.
And sometimes we're allowed to search and do
That to a man which gives his soul unrest,
And not his body, and all is for the best.
And when one does withstand all our temptation,
It is the thing that gives his soul salvation;
Albeit that it was not our intent
He should be saved; we'd have him impotent.
And sometimes we are servants unto man,
As to that old archbishop, Saint Dunstan,
And to the apostles servant once was I."
"Yet tell me," said the summoner, "faithfully,
Make you yourselves new bodies thus alway
Of elements?"
The fiend replied thus: "Nay.
Sometimes we feign them, sometimes we arise
In bodies that are dead, in sundry wise,
And speak as reasonably and fair and well
As to the witch at En-dor Samuel.
And yet some men maintain it was not he;
I do not care for your theology.
But of one thing I warn, nor will I jape,
You shall in all ways learn our proper shape;
You shall hereafter come, my brother dear,
Where you'll not need to ask of me, as here.
For you shall, of your own experience,
In a red chair have much more evidence
Than Virgil ever did while yet alive,
Or ever Dante; now let's swiftly drive.
For I will hold with you my company
Till it shall come to pass you part from me."
"Nay," said the other, "that shall not
betide;
"I am a bailiff, known both far and wide;
My promise will I keep in this one case.
For though you were the devil Sathanas,
My troth will I preserve to my dear brother,
As I have sworn, and each of us to other,
That we will be true brothers in this case;

And let us both about our business pace.
Take your own part, of what men will you give,
And I will mine; and thus may we both live.
And if that either of us gets more than other,
Let him be true and share it with his brother."
"Agreed, then," said the devil, "by my fay,"
And with that word they rode upon their way.
As they drew near the town—it happened so—
To which this summoner had planned to go,
They saw a cart that loaded was with hay,
The which a carter drove along the way.
Deep was the mire, for which the cart now stood.
The carter whipped and cried as madman would,
"Hi, Badger, Scot! What care you for the stones?
The Fiend," he cried, "take body of you and bones,
As utterly as ever you were foaled!
More trouble you've caused me than can be told!
Devil take all, the horses, cart, and hay!"
This summoner thought, "Here shall be played a play."
And near the fiend he drew, as naught were there,
And unobserved he whispered in his ear:
"Listen, my brother, listen, by your faith;
Hear you not what the carter says in wrath?
Take all, at once, for he has given you
Both hay and cart, and his three horses too."
"Nay," said the devil, "God knows, never a bit.
It is not his intention, trust to it.
Ask him yourself, if you believe not me,
Or else withhold a while, and you shall see."
This carter stroked his nags upon the croup,
And they began in collars low to stoop.
"Hi now!" cried he, "May Jesus Christ you bless
And all His creatures, greater, aye and less!
That was well pulled, old horse, my own grey boy!
I pray God save you, and good Saint Eloy!
Now is my cart out of the slough, by gad!"
"Lo, brother," said the fiend, "what said I, lad?
Here may you see, my very own dear brother,
The peasant said one thing, but thought another.
Let us go forth upon our travellers' way;
Here win I nothing I can take today."
When they had come a little out of town,
This summoner whispered, to his brother drawn,
"Brother," said he, "here lives an ancient crone
Who'd quite as gladly lose her neck as own
She must give up a penny, good or bad.
But I'll have twelvepence, though it drive her mad
Or I will summon her to our office;
And yet God knows I know of her no vice.
But since you cannot, in this strange country,
Make your expenses, here take note of me."
This summoner knocked on the widow's gate.
"Come out," cried he, "you old she-reprobate!
I think you've got some friar or priest there, eh?"
"Who knocks then?" said the widow. "*Ben'cite!*
God save you, master, what is your sweet will?"
"I have," said he, "a summons here, a bill;

And bothe we goon abouten our purchas.
Tak thou thy part, what that men wol thee yive,
And I shal myn; thus may we bothe live.
And if that any of us have more than other,
Lat him be trewe, and parte it with his brother."
"I graunte," quod the devel, "by my fey."
And with that word they ryden forth hir wey.
And right at the entring of the tounes ende,
To which this Somnour shoop him for to wende,
They saugh a cart, that charged was with hey,
Which that a carter droof forth in his wey.
Deep was the wey, for which the carte stood.
The carter smoot, and cryde, as he were wood,
"Hayt, Brok! hayt, Scot! what spare ye for the stones?
The feend," quod he, "yow fecche body and bones,
As ferforthly as ever were ye foled!
So muche wo as I have with yow tholed!
The devel have al, bothe hors and cart and hey!"
This Somnour seyde, "heer shal we have a pley;"
And neer the feend he drough, as noght ne were,
Ful prively, and rouned in his ere:
"Herkne, my brother, herkne, by thy feith;
Herestow nat how that the carter seith?
Hent it anon, for he hath yeve it thee,
Bothe hey and cart, and eek hise caples three."
"Nay," quod the devel, "god wot, never a deel;
It is nat his entente, trust me weel.
Axe him thy-self, if thou nat trowest me,
Or elles stint a while, and thou shalt see."
This carter thakketh his hors upon the croupe,
And they bigonne drawen and to-stoupe;
"Heyt, now!" quod he, "ther Jesu Crist yow blesse,
And al his handwerk, bothe more and lesse!
That was wel twight, myn owene lyard boy!
I pray god save thee and sëynt Loy!
Now is my cart out of the slow, pardee!"
"Lo! brother," quod the feend, "what tolde I thee?
Heer may ye see, myn owene dere brother,
The carl spak oo thing, but he thoghte another.
Lat us go forth abouten our viage;
Heer winne I no-thing up-on cariage."
Whan that they comen som-what out of toune,
This Somnour to his brother gan to roune,
"Brother," quod he, "heer woneth an old rebekke,
That hadde almost as lief to lese hir nekke
As for to yeve a peny of hir good.
I wol han twelf pens, though that she be wood,
Or I wol sompne hir un-to our offyce;
And yet, god woot, of hir knowe I no vyce.
But for thou canst nat, as in this contree,
Winne thy cost, tak heer ensample of me."
This Somnour clappeth at the widwes gate.
"Com out," quod he, "thou olde viritrate!
I trowe thou hast som frere or preest with thee!"
"Who clappeth?" seyde this widwe, "*ben'cite!*
God save you, sire, what is your swete wille?"
"I have," quod he, "of somonce here a bille;

Up peyne of cursing, loke that thou be
To-morn bifore the erchedeknes knee
T'answere to the court of certeyn thinges."
"Now, lord," quod she, "Crist Jesu, king of kinges,
So wisly helpe me, as I ne may.
I have been syk, and that ful many a day.
I may nat go so fer," quod she, "ne ryde,
But I be deed, so priketh it in my syde.
May I nat axe a libel, sir Somnour,
And answere there, by my procutour,
To swich thing as men wol opposen me?"
"Yis," quod this Somnour, "pay anon, lat se,
Twelf pens to me, and I wol thee acquyte.
I shall no profit han ther-by but lyte;
My maister hath the profit, and nat I.
Com of, and lat me ryden hastily;
Yif me twelf pens, I may no lenger tarie."
"Twelf pens," quod she, "now lady Seinte Marie
So wisly help me out of care and sinne,
This wyde world thogh that I sholde winne,
Ne have I nat twelf pens with-inne myn hold.
Ye knowen wel that I am povre and old;
Kythe your almesse on me povre wrecche."
"Nay than," quod he, "the foule feend me fecche
If I th'excuse, though thou shul be spilt!"
"Alas," quod she, "god woot, I have no gilt."
"Pay me," quod he, "or by the swete seinte Anne,
As I wol bere awey thy newe panne
For dette, which that thou owest me of old,
Whan that thou madest thyn housbond cokewold,
I payde at hoom for thy correccioun."
"Thou lixt," quod she, "by my savacioun!
Ne was I never er now, widwe ne wyf,
Somoned un-to your court in al my lyf;
Ne never I nas but of my body trewe!
Un-to the devel blak and rough of hewe
Yeve I thy body and my panne also!"
And whan the devel herde hir cursen so
Up-on hir knees, he seyde in this manere,
"Now Mabely, myn owene moder dere,
Is this your wil in ernest, that ye seye?"
"The devel," quod she, "so fecche him er he deye,
And panne and al, but he wol him repente!"
"Nay, olde stot, that is nat myn entente,"
Quod this Somnour, "for to repente me,
For any thing that I have had of thee;
I wolde I hadde thy smok and every clooth!"
"Now, brother," quod the devel, "be nat wrooth;
Thy body and this panne ben myne by right.
Thou shalt with me to helle yet to-night,
Where thou shalt knowen of our privetee
More than a maister of divinitee":
And with that word this foule feend him hente;
Body and soule, he with the devel wente
Wher-as that somnours han hir heritage.
And god, that maked after his image

On pain of excommunication be
Tomorrow morn at the archdeacon's knee
To answer to the court for certain things."
"Now, lord," said she, "Christ Jesus, King of kings,
So truly keep me as I cannot; nay,
I have been sick, and that for many a day.
I cannot walk so far," said she, "nor ride,
Save I were dead, such aches are in my side.
Will you not give a writ, sir summoner,
And let my proctor for me there appear
To meet this charge, whatever it may be?"
"Yes," said this summoner, "pay anon—let's see—
Twelvepence to me, and I'll have you acquitted.
Small profit there for me, be it admitted;
My master gets the profit, and not I.
Come then, and let me ride on, speedily;
Give me twelvepence, I may no longer tarry."
"Twelvepence!" cried she, "Our Lady Holy Mary
So truly keep me out of care and sin,
And though thereby I should the wide world win,
I have not twelvepence in my house all told.
You know right well that I am poor and old;
Show mercy unto me, a poor old wretch!"
"Nay, then," said he, "the foul Fiend may me fetch
If I excuse you, though your life be spilt!"
"Alas!" cried she, "God knows I have no guilt!"
"Pay me," he cried, "or by the sweet Saint Anne
I'll take away with me your brand-new pan
For debt that you have owed to me of old,
When you did make your husband a cuckold;
I paid at home that fine to save citation."
"You lie," she cried then, "by my own salvation!
Never was I, till now, widow or wife,
Summoned unto your court in all my life;
Nor ever of my body was I untrue!
Unto the Devil rough and black of hue
Give I your body and my pan also!"
And when the devil heard her cursing so
Upon her knees, he said to her just here:
"Now, Mabely, my own old mother dear,
Is this your will, in earnest, that you say?"
"The Devil," said she, "take him alive today,
And pan and all, unless he will repent!"
"Nay, you old heifer, it's not my intent,"
The summoner said, "for pardon now to sue
Because of aught that I have had from you;
I would I had your smock and all your clo'es."
"Nay, brother," said the devil, "easy goes;
Your body and this pan are mine by right.
And you shall come to Hell with me tonight,
Where you shall learn more of our privity
Than any doctor of divinity."
And with that word this foul fiend to him bent;
Body and soul he with the devil went
Where summoners have their rightful heritage.
And God, Who made after His own image

Mankind, now save and guide us, all and some;
And grant that summoners good men become!

Masters, I could have told you, said this friar,
Were I not pestered by this summoner dire,
After the texts of Christ and Paul and John,
And of our other doctors, many a one,
Such torments that your hearts would shake with dread,
Albeit by no tongue can half be said,
Although I might a thousand winters tell,
Of pains in that same cursed house of Hell.
But all to keep us from that horrid place,
Watch, and pray Jesus for His holy grace,
And so reject the tempter Sathanas.
Hearken this word, be warned by this one case;
The lion lies in wait by night and day
To slay the innocent, if he but may.
Dispose your hearts in grace, that you withstand
The Fiend, who'd make you thrall among his band
He cannot tempt more than beyond your might;
For Christ will be your champion and knight.
And pray that all these summoners repent
Of their misdeeds, before the Fiend torment.

Mankinde, save and gyde us alle and some;
And leve this Somnour good man to bicome!

Lordinges, I coude han told yow, quod this Frere,
Hadde I had leyser for this Somnour here,
After the text of Crist [and] Poul and John,
And of our othere doctours many oon,
Swiche peynes, that your hertes mighte agryse,
Al-be-it so, no tonge may devyse,
Thogh that I mighte a thousand winter telle,
The peyne of thilke cursed hous of helle.
But, for to kepe us fro that cursed place,
Waketh, and preyeth Jesu for his grace
So kepe us fro the temptour Sathanas.
Herketh this word, beth war as in this cas;
The leoun sit in his await alway
To slee the innocent, if that he may.
Disposeth ay your hertes to withstonde
The feend, that yow wolde make thral and bonde.
He may nat tempten yow over your might;
For Crist wol be your champion and knight.
And prayeth that thise Somnours hem repente
Of hir misdedes, er that the feend hem hente.

HERE ENDETH THE FRIAR'S TALE

THE SUMMONER'S PROLOGUE

THE PROLOGUE OF THE SUMMONER'S TALE

HIGH in his stirrups, then, the summoner stood;
Against the friar his heart, as madman's would,
Shook like a very aspen leaf, for ire.
"Masters," said he, "but one thing I desire;
I beg of you that, of your courtesy,
Since you have heard this treacherous friar lie,
You suffer it that I my tale may tell!
This friar he boasts he knows somewhat of Hell,
And God He knows that it is little wonder;
Friars and fiends are never far asunder.
For, by gad, you have oftentimes heard tell
How such a friar was snatched down into Hell
In spirit, once, and by a vision blown;
And as an angel led him up and down
To show the pains and torments that there were,
In all the place he saw no friar there.
Of other folk he saw enough in woe;
And to the angel then he questioned so:
" 'Now, sir,' said he, 'have friars such a grace
That none of them shall come into this place? '
" 'Nay,' said the angel, 'millions here are thrown!'
And unto Sathanas he led him down.
" 'And now has Sathanas,' said he, 'a tail
Broader than of a galleon is the sail.
Hold up thy tail, thou Sathanas!' said he,
" 'Show forth thine arse and let the friar see
Where is the nest of friars in this place!'
And ere one might go half a furlong's space,
Just as the bees come swarming from a hive,

THIS Somnour in his stiropes hye stood;
Up-on this Frere his herte was so wood,
That lyk an aspen leef he quook for yre.
"Lordinges," quod he, "but o thing I desyre;
I yow biseke that, of your curteisye,
Sin ye han herd this false Frere lye,
As suffereth me I may my tale telle!
This Frere bosteth that he knoweth helle,
And god it woot, that it is litel wonder;
Freres and feendes been but lyte a-sonder.
For pardee, ye han ofte tyme herd telle,
How that a frere ravisshed was to helle
In spirit ones by a visioun;
And as an angel ladde him up and doun,
To shewen him the peynes that ther were,
In al the place saugh he nat a frere;
Of other folk he saugh y-nowe in wo.
Un-to this angel spak the frere tho:
'Now, sir,' quod he, 'han freres swich a grace
That noon of hem shal come to this place?'
'Yis,' quod this angel, 'many a millioun!"
And un-to Sathanas he ladde him doun.
'And now hath Sathanas,' seith he, 'a tayl
Brodder than of a carrik is the sayl.
Hold up thy tayl, thou Sathanas!' quod he,
'Shewe forth thyn ers, and lat the frere see
Wher is the nest of freres in this place!'
And, er that half a furlong-wey of space,
Right so as bees out swarmen from an hyve,

Out of the develes ers ther gonne dryve
Twenty thousand freres in a route,
And thurgh-out helle swarmeden aboute
And comen agayn, as faste as they may gon,
And in his ers they crepten everichon.
He clapte his tayl agayn, and layful stille.
This frere, whan he loked hadde his fille
Upon the torments of this sory place,
His spirit god restored of his grace
Un-to his body agayn, and he awook;
But natheles, for fere yet he quook,
So was the develes ers ay in his minde,
That is his heritage of verray kinde.
God save yow alle, save this cursed Frere;
My prologe wol I ende in this manere."

Out of the Devil's arse-hole there did drive
Full twenty thousand friars in a rout,
And through all Hell they swarmed and ran about,
And came again, as fast as they could run,
And in his arse they crept back, every one.
He clapped his tail to and then lay right still.
This friar, when he'd looked at length his fill
Upon the torments of that sorry place,
His spirit God restored, of His high grace,
Into his body, and he did awake;
Nevertheless for terror did he quake
So was the Devil's arse-hole in his mind,
Which is his future home, and like in kind.
God save all but this cursed friar here;
My prologue ends thus; to my tale give ear."

HERE ENDETH THE PROLOGUE OF THE SUMMONER'S TALE

THE SUMMONER'S TALE

HERE BEGINNETH THE SUMMONER HIS TALE

LORDINGES, ther is in Yorkshire, as I gesse,
A mersshy contree called Holdernesse,
In which ther wente a limitour aboute,
To preche, and eek to begge, it is no doute.
And so bifel, that on a day this frere
Had preched at a chirche in his manere,
And specially, aboven every thing,
Excited he the peple in his preching
To trentals,[1] and to yeve, for goddes sake,
Wher-with men mighten holy houses make,
Ther as divyne service is honoured,
Nat ther as it is wasted and devoured,
Ne ther it nedeth nat for to be yive,
As to possessioners, that mowen live,
Thanked be god, in wele and habundaunce.
"Trentals," seyde he, "deliveren fro penaunce
Hir freendes soules, as wel olde as yonge,
Ye, whan that they been hastily y-songe;
Nat for to holde a preest joly and gay,
He singeth nat but o masse in a day;
Delivereth out," quod he, "anon the soules;
Ful hard it is with fleshhook or with oules
To been y-clawed, or to brenne or bake;
Now spede yow hastily, for Cristes sake."
And whan this frere had seyd al his entente,
With *qui cum patre* forth his wey he wente.
When folk in chirche had yeve him what hem leste,
He wente his wey, no lenger wolde he reste,
With scrippe and tipped staf, y-tukked hye;
In every hous he gan to poure and prye,
And beggeth mele, and chese, or elles corn.
His felawe hadde a staf tipped with horn,
A peyre of tables al of yvory,
And a poyntel polisshed fetisly,
And wroot the names alwey, as he stood,
Of alle folk that yaf him any good,

MASTERS, there is in Yorkshire, as I guess,
A marshy region that's called Holderness,
Wherein there went a limiter about
To preach, and to beg too, beyond a doubt.
And so befell that on a day this friar
Had preached in church in his own manner dire,
And specially, and above everything,
Incited he the people, by preaching,
To trentals,[1] and to give, for God's own sake,
The means wherewith men might new churches make,
That there the services of God might flower,
And not to them who waste and wealth devour,
Nor where there's no necessity to give,
As to the monks, who easily may live—
Thanks be to God!—and need no wealth to gain.
"Trentals," said he, "deliver from their pain
The souls of friends who're dead, the old and young,
Yea, even when they have been hastily sung;
Not that I hold as frivolous and gay,
A priest who only sings one mass a day.
Act quickly now," said he, "their souls redeem,
For hard it is, with spikes and hooks, I deem,
To be so torn, aye, or to burn or bake;
Now speed you all to this, for Christ's own sake!"
And when this friar had said all that he meant,
With *cui cum patre* on his way he went,
When folk in church had given at his behest,
He went his way, no longer would he rest,
With scrip and ferruled staff and skirts tucked high;
In every house he went to peer and pry,
And beg for flour and cheese, or else for corn.
His fellow had a staff was tipped with horn,
A set of tablets all of ivory,
And stylus that was polished elegantly,
And wrote the names down always as he stood,
Of those that gave him anything of good,

[1]Series of thirty Masses for the dead.

As if for them he later meant to pray.
"Give us of wheat or malt or rye," he'd say,
"A bushel; or a God's cake; or some cheese;
We may not choose, so give us what you please;
Give us God's halfpenny or a mass-penny,
Or give us of your brawn, if you have any;
A small piece of your blanket, my dear dame.
Our sister dear, lo, here I write your name;
Bacon or beef, or such thing as you find."
A sturdy menial went these two behind—
The servant of their host—and bore a sack,
And what men gave them, laid it on his back.
And when they'd left the house, why, then anon
He planed away the names of folk, each one,
That he before had written on his tables;
And thus he served them mockeries and fables.
("Nay, there you lie, you summoner!" cried the friar.
"Peace, for Christ's Mother's sake, call no one liar!"
Our host said. "Tell your tale, nor spare at all."
"So thrive I," said this summoner, "that I shall.")
Along he went from house to house, till he
Came to a house where he was wont to be
Refreshed more than in hundred places round.
And sick the goodman of the place he found;
Bedridden on a couch he prostrate lay.
"*Deus hic*," said he. "Thomas, my friend, good day,"
Said he, this friar, courteously and soft.
"Thomas," said he, "may God repay you! Oft
Have I sat on this bench and fared right well.
Here have I eaten many a merry meal."
And from the bench he drove away the cat,
And laid down there his steel-tipped staff and hat
And his scrip, too, and sat him softly down.
His fellow had gone walking into town,
With the said menial, to a hostelry
Wherein he thought that very night to lie.
"O my dear master," whispered this sick man,
"How have you fared since this month March began?
"I've seen you not this fortnight, aye or more."
"God knows," said he, "that I have toiled full sore;
And very specially for your salvation
Have I said precious prayers, and at each station,
And for our other friends, whom may God bless!
I have today been to your church, at Mass,
And preached a sermon after my poor wit,
Not wholly from the text of holy writ,
For that is hard and baffling in the main;
And therefore all its meaning I'll explain.
Glosing's a glorious thing, and that's certain,
For letters kill, as scholars say with pain.
Thus have I taught them to be charitable,
And spend their money reasonably, as well.
And there I saw your dame—ah, where is she?"
"Yonder within the yard I think she'll be,"
Said this sick man, "and she will come anon."
"Eh, master! Welcome be you, by Saint John!"
Exclaimed the wife. "How fare you, heartily?"

Ascaunces that he wolde for hem preye.
"Yeve us a busshel whete, malt, or reye,
A goddes kechil, or a trip of chese,
Or elles what yow list, we may nat chese;
A goddes halfpeny or a masse-peny,
Or yeve us of your brawn, if ye have eny;
A dagon of your blanket, leve dame,
Our suster dere, lo! here I write your name;
Bacon or beef, or swich thing as ye finde."
A sturdy harlot wente ay hem bihinde,
That was hir hostes man, and bar a sak,
And what men yaf hem, leyde it on his bak.
And whan that he was out at dore anon,
He planed awey the names everichon
That he biforn had writen in his tables;
He served hem with nyfles and with fables.
"Nay, ther thou lixt, thou Somnour," quod the Frere.
"Pees," quod our Host, "for Cristes moder dere;
Tel forth thy tale and spare it nat at al."
So thryve I, quod this Somnour, so I shal.—
So longe he wente hous by hous, til he
Cam til an hous ther he was wont to be
Refresshed more than in an hundred placis.
Sik lay the gode man, whos that the place is;
Bedrede up-on a couche lowe he lay.
"*Deus hic*," quod he, "O Thomas, freend, good day,"
Seyde this frere curteisly and softe.
"Thomas," quod he, "god yelde yow! ful ofte
Have I up-on this bench faren ful weel.
Here have I eten many a mery meel";
And fro the bench he droof awey the cat,
And leyde adoun his potente and his hat,
And eek his scrippe, and sette him softe adoun.
His felawe was go walked in-to toun,
Forth with his knave, in-to that hostelrye
Wher-as he shoop him thilke night to lye.
"O dere maister," quod this syke man,
"How han ye fare sith that March bigan?
I saugh yow noght this fourtenight or more."
"God woot," quod he, "laboured have I ful sore;
And specially, for thy savacioun
Have I seyd many a precious orisoun,
And for our othere frendes, god hem blesse!
I have to-day been at your chirche at messe,
And seyd a sermon after my simple wit,
Nat al after the text of holy writ;
For it is hard to yow, as I suppose,
And therfore wol I teche yow al the glose.
Glosinge is a glorious thing, certeyn,
For lettre sleeth, so as we clerkes seyn.
Ther have I taught hem to be charitable,
And spende hir good ther it is resonable,
And ther I saugh our dame; a! wher is she?"
"Yond in the yerd I trowe that she be,"
Seyde this man, "and she wol come anon."
"Ey, maister! wel-come be ye, by seint John!"
Seyde this wyf, "how fare ye hertely?"

The frere aryseth up ful curteisly,
And hir embraceth in his armes narwe,
And kiste hir swete, and chirketh as a sparwe
With his lippes: "dame," quod he, "right weel,
As he that is your servant every deel.
Thanked be god, that yow yaf soule and lyf,
Yet saugh I nat this day so fair a wyf
In al the chirche, god so save me!"
"Ye, god amende defautes, sir," quod she,
"Algates wel-come be ye, by my fey!"
"Graunt mercy, dame, this have I founde alwey.
But of your grete goodnesse, by your leve,
I wolde prey yow that ye nat yow greve,
I wol with Thomas speke a litel throwe.
Thise curats been ful necligent and slowe
To grope tendrely a conscience.
In shrift, in preching is my diligence,
And studie in Petres wordes, and in Poules.
I walke, and fisshe Cristen mennes soules,
To yelden Jesu Crist his propre rente;
To sprede his word is set al myn entente."
"Now, by your leve, o dere sir," quod she,
"Chydeth him weel, for seinte Trinitee.
He is as angry as a pissemyre,
Though that he have al that he can desyre.
Though I him wrye a-night and make him warm,
And on hym leye my leg outher myn arm,
He groneth lyk our boor, lyth in our sty.
Other desport right noon of him have I;
I may nat plese him in no maner cas."
"O Thomas! *Je vous dy*, Thomas! Thomas!
This maketh the feend, this moste ben amended.
Ire is a thing that hye god defended,
And ther-of wol I speke a word or two."
"Now maister," quod the wyf, "er that I go,
What wol ye dyne? I wol go ther-aboute."
"Now dame," quod he, "*Je vous dy sanz doute*,
Have I nat of a capon but the livere,
And of your softe breed nat but a shivere,
And after that a rosted pigges heed,
(But that I nolde no beest for me were deed),
Thanne hadde I with yow hoomly suffisaunce.
I am a man of litel sustenaunce.
My spirit hath his fostring in the Bible.
The body is ay so redy and penyble
To wake, that my stomak is destroyed.
I prey yow, dame, ye be nat anoyed,
Though I so freendly yow my conseil shewe;
By god, I wolde nat telle it but a fewe."
"Now, sir," quod she, "but o word er I go;
My child is deed with-inne thise wykes two,
Sone after that ye wente out of this toun."
"His deeth saugh I by revelacioun,"
Seith this frere, "at hoom in our dortour.
I dar wel seyn that, er that half an hour
After his deeth, I saugh him born to blisse
In myn avisioun, so god me wisse!
So dide our sexteyn and our fermerer,
That han been trewe freres fifty yeer;
They may now, god be thanked of his lone,
Maken hir jubilee and walke allone.

The friar arose, and that full courteously,
And her embraced within his two arms narrow,
And kissed her sweetly, chirping like a sparrow
With his two lips. "Ah, dame," said he, "right well,
As one that is your servant, let me tell,
Thanks be to God Who gave you soul and life,
For saw I not this day so fair a wife
In all the congregation, God save me!"
"Yea, God correct all faults, sir," answered she,
"But you are always welcome, by my fay!"
"Many thanks, dame, this have I found alway.
But of your innate goodness, by your leave,
I'd beg of you you won't be cross or grieve
If I with Thomas speak a little now.
These curates are right negligent and slow
In searching tenderly into conscience.
To preach confession is my diligence,
And I do study Peter's words and Paul's.
I walk and fish for Christian persons' souls
To yield to Jesus Christ His increment;
To spread His gospel is my whole intent."
"Now, by your leave, O my dear sir," said she,
"Berate him well, for Holy Trinity.
He is as crabbed as an old pismire,
Though he has everything he can desire.
Though him I cover at night, and make him warm,
And lay my leg across him, or my arm,
He grunts and groans like our old boar in sty
And other sport—just none from him have I.
I cannot please him, no, in any case."
"O Thomas, "*je vous dis*, Thomas, Thomas!
This is the Fiend's work, this must be amended,
Anger's a thing that makes High God offended,
And thereof will I speak a word or two."
"Now, master," said the wife, "before I go,
What will you eat? I will about it scoot."
"Now, dame," said he then, "*je vous dis, sans doute*,
Had I of a fat capon but the liver,
And of your soft white bread naught but a sliver,
And after that a pig's head well roasted
(Save that I would no beast for me were dead),
Then had I with you plain sufficiency.
I am a man of little gluttony.
My spirit has its nourishment in the Bible.
My body is so inured and so pliable
To watching, that my appetite's destroyed.
I pray you, lady, be you not annoyed
Though I so intimately my secret show;
By God, I would reveal it to but few."
"Now, sir," said she, "but one word ere I go;
My child has died within this fortnight—oh,
Soon after you left town last, it did die."
"His death saw I by revelation, aye,"
Replied this friar, "at home in dormitory
Less than an hour, I dare say, ere to glory,
After his death, I saw him borne in bliss
In vision mine, may God me guide in this!
So did our sexton and infirmarian,
Who have been true friars fifty years, each man;
And may now, God be thanked for mercy shown,
Observe their jubilee and walk alone.

And I rose up and did my brothers seek,
With many a tear down trickling on my cheek,
And without noise or clashing of the bells;
Te deum was our song and nothing else,
Save that to Christ I said an orison,
And thanked Him for the vision he had shown.
For, sir and dame, trust me full well in all,
Our orisons are more effectual,
And more we see of Christ's own secret things
Than folk of the laity, though they were kings.
We live in poverty and abstinence,
And laymen live in riches and expense
Of meat and drink, and in their gross delight.
This world's desires we hold in great despite.
Dives and Lazarus lived differently,
And different recompense they had thereby.
Whoso would pray, he must fast and be clean,
Fatten his soul and keep his body lean.
We fare as says the apostle; clothes and food
Suffice us, though they be not over-good.
The cleanness and the fasting of us friars
Result in Christ's accepting all our prayers.
"Lo, Moses forty days and forty nights
Fasted before the mightiest God of mights
Spoke with him on the Mountain of Sinai.
With empty belly, fasting long, say I,
Received he there the law that had been writ
By God's hand; and Elias (you know of it)
On Mount Horeb, ere he had any speech
With the High God, Who is our spirits' leech,
He fasted long and deep his contemplation.
"Aaron, who ruled the temple of his nation,
And all the other great priests, every one,
When they into the temple would be gone
To pray there for the folk and do their rites.
They would not drink of that which man excites
And makes him drunk or stirs in any way,
But there in abstinence they'd watch and pray
Lest they should die—to what I say take heed!—
Were they not sober when they prayed, indeed.
Beware my words. No more! for it suffices.
Our Lord Christ, as the holy writ apprises,
Gave us example of fasting and of prayers.
Therefore we mendicants, we simple friars,
Are sworn to poverty and continence,
To charity, meekness, and abstinence,
To persecution for our righteousness,
To weeping, pity, and to cleanliness.
And therefore may you see that all our prayers—
I speak of us, we mendicants, we friars—
Are to the High God far more acceptable
Than yours, with all the feasts you make at table.
From Paradise, if I am not to lie,
Was man chased out because of gluttony;
And chaste was man in Paradise, that's plain.
"But hear now, Thomas, lest I speak in vain.
I have no text for it, I must admit,
But by analogy the words will fit,
That specially our sweet Lord Christ Jesus
Spoke of the begging friars when He said thus:
'Blest are the poor in spirit.' So said He,
And so through all the gospel may you see

And up I roos, and al our covent eke,
With many a tere trikling on my cheke,
Withouten noyse or claterynge of belles;
Te deum was our song and no-thing elles,
Save that to Crist I seyde an orisoun,
Thankinge him of his revelacioun.
For sir and dame, trusteth me right weel,
Our orisons been more effectueel,
And more we seen of Cristes secree thinges
Than burel folk, al-though they weren kinges.
We live in povert and in abstinence,
And burel folk in richesse and despence
Of mete and drinke, and in hir foul delyt.
We han this worldes lust al in despyt.
Lazar and Dives liveden diversly,
And diverse guerdon hadden they ther-by.
Who-so wol preye, he moot faste and be clene,
And fatte his soule and make his body lene.
We fare as seith th'apostle; cloth and fode
Suffysen us, though they be nat ful gode.
The clennesse and the fastinge of us freres
Maketh that Crist accepteth our preyeres.
Lo, Moyses fourty dayes and fourty night
Fasted, er that the heighe god of might
Spak with him in the mountain of Sinay.
With empty wombe, fastinge many a day,
Receyved he the lawe that was writen
With goddes finger; and Elie, wel ye witen,
In mount Oreb, er he hadde any speche
With hye god, that is our lyves leche,
He fasted longe and was in contemplaunce.
Aaron, that hadde the temple in governaunce,
And eek the othere preestes everichon,
In-to the temple whan they sholde gon
To preye for the peple, and do servyse,
They nolden drinken, in no maner wyse,
No drinke, which that mighte hem dronke make,
But there in abstinence preye and wake,
Lest that they deyden; tak heed what I seye.
But they be sobre that for the peple preye,
War that I seye; namore! for it suffyseth.
Our lord Jesu, as holy writ devyseth,
Yaf us ensample of fastinge, and preyeres.
Therfor we mendinants, we sely freres,
Been wedded to poverte and continence,
To charitee, humblesse, and abstinence,
To persecucion for rightwisnesse,
To wepinge, misericorde, and clennesse.
And therfor may ye see that our preyeres—
I speke of us, we mendinants, we freres—
Ben to the hye god more acceptable
Than youres, with your festes at the table.
Fro Paradys first, if I shal nat lye,
Was man out chaced for his glotonye;
And chaast was man in Paradys, certeyn.
But herkne now, Thomas, what I shal seyn.
I ne have no text of it, as I suppose,
But I shall finde it in a maner glose,
That specially our swete lord Jesus
Spak this by freres, whan he seyde thus:
"Blessed be they that povre in spirit been."
And so forth al the gospel may ye seen,

Wher it be lyker our professioun,
Or hirs that swimmen in possessioun.
Fy on hir pompe and on hir glotonye!
And for hir lewednesse I hem diffye.
Me thinketh they ben lyk Jovinian,
Fat as a whale, and walkinge as a swan;
Al vinolent as botel in the spence.
Hir preyer is of ful gret reverence;
Whan they for soules seye the psalm of Davit,
Lo, 'buf!' they seye, '*cor meum eructavit!*'
Who folweth Cristes gospel and his fore,
But we that humble been and chast and pore,
Werkers of goddes word, not auditours?
Therfore, right as an hauk up, at a sours,
Up springeth in-to their, right so prayeres
Of charitable and chaste bisy freres
Maken hir sours to goddes eres two.
Thomas! Thomas! so mote I ryde or go,
And by that lord that clepid is seint Yve,
Nere thou our brother, sholdestou nat thryve!
In our chapitre praye we day and night
To Crist, that he thee sende hele and might,
Thy body for to welden hastily."
"God woot," quod he, "no-thing ther-of fele I;
As help me Crist, as I, in fewe yeres,
Han spended, up-on dyvers maner freres,
Ful many a pound; yet fare I never the bet.
Certeyn, my good have I almost biset.
Farwel, my gold! for it is al ago!"
The frere answerde, "O Thomas, dostow so?
What nedeth yow diverse freres seche?
What nedeth him that hath a parfit leche
To sechen othere leches in the toun?
Your inconstance is your confusioun.
Holde ye than me, or elles our covent,
To praye for yow ben insufficient?
Thomas, that jape his nat worth a myte;
Your maladye is for we han to lyte.
'A! yif that covent half a quarter otes!'
'A! yif that covent four and twenty grotes!'
'A! yif that frere a peny, and lat him go!'
Nay, nay, Thomas! it may no-thing be so.
What is a ferthing worth parted in twelve?
Lo, ech thing that is oned in him-selve
Is more strong than whan it is toscatered.
Thomas, of me thou shalt nat been y flatered;
Thou woldest han our labour al for noght.
The hye god, that al this world hath wroght,
Seith that the werkman worthy is his hyre.
Thomas! noght of your tresor I desyre
As for my-self, but that al our covent
To preye for yow is ay so diligent,
And for to builden Cristes owene chirche.
Thomas! if ye wol lernen for to wirche,
Of buildinge up of chirches may ye finde
If it be good, in Thomas lyf of Inde.
Ye lye heer, ful of anger and of yre,
With which the devel set your herte a-fyre,
And chyden heer this sely innocent,
Your wyf, that is so meke and pacient.
And therfor, Thomas, trowe me if thee leste,
Ne stryve nat with thy wyf, as for thy beste;

Whether the Word fit better our profession
Or theirs, the monks', who swim in rich possession
Fie on their pomp and on their gluttony!
And for their lewdness do I them defy.
"It seems to me they're like Jovinian,
Fat as a whale and waddling as a swan;
As full of wine as bottle in the spence.
Their prayers are always of great reverence,
When they for souls that psalm of David say:
'*Cor meum eructavit*—bouf!'—that way!
Who follow Christ's Word going on before
But we who are so humble, chaste, and poor,
And doers of God's Word, not hearers, merely?
As falcons rise to heaven, just so clearly
Spring up into the air the holy prayers
Of charitable and chaste and toiling friars
Make their way upward into God's ears two.
Thomas, O Thomas! As I ride or go,
And by that lord whom all we call Saint Yve,
Were you not brother to us, you'd not thrive!
In our chapter we pray both day and night
To Christ, that He will send you health and might
To move about again, and speedily."
"God knows," said he, "nothing thereof feel I;
So help me Christ as I, these last few years,
Have spent on divers friars, it appears,
Full many a pound; and I'm no better yet.
Truly my wealth have I almost upset.
Farewell my gold! for it has slipped away."
The friar replied: "Ah, Thomas, so you say!
But why need you to different friars reach?
Why should he need, who has a perfect leech,
To call in other leeches from the town?
Your trouble from your fickleness has grown.
Think you that I, or at least our convent,
Could not suffice to pray? That's what I meant.
Thomas, your feeble joke's not worth a tittle;
Your illness lasts because you've given too little.
" 'Ah, give that convent bushels four of oats!'
'Ah, give that convent four and twenty groats!'
'Ah, give that friar a penny and let him go!'
"Nay, nay, Thomas, the thing should not be so!
What is a farthing worth, when split twelve ways?
A thing in its integrity displays
Far greater strength than does a unit scattered.
Thomas, by me you shall not here be flattered;
You would you had our labour all for naught.
But the High God, Who all this world has wrought,
Says that the workman's worthy of his hire.
Thomas! Naught of your treasure I desire
As for myself, but that all our convent
To pray for you is always diligent,
And also to build up Christ's holy kirk.
Thomas! If you will learn the way to work,
Of building up of churches you may find
(If it be good) in Thomas' life, of Inde.
You lie here, full of anger and of ire,
Wherewith the Devil set your heart afire,
And you chide here this hapless innocent,
Your wife, who is so meek and so patient.
And therefore, Thomas, trust me if you please,
Scold not your wife, who tries to give you ease;

And bear this word away now, by your faith,
Touching this thing, lo what the wise man saith:
'Within thy house do not the lion play,
Oppress thy subjects in no kind of way,
Nor cause thine equals and thy friends to flee'
And Thomas, yet again I charge you, be
Wary of her that in your bosom sleeps;
Beware the serpent that so slyly creeps
Under the grass and stings so treacherously.
Beware, my son, and hear this patiently,
That twenty thousand men have lost their lives
For quarrelling with their sweet ones, and their wives.
Now, since you have so holy and meek a wife,
Why need you, Thomas, so to stir up strife?
There is, indeed, no serpent so cruel,
When man treads on his tail, nor half so fell,
As woman is when she is filled with ire;
Vengeance is then the whole of her desire.
Anger's a sin, one of the deadly seven,
Abominable unto the God of Heaven;
And it is sure destruction unto one.
This every vulgar vicar or parson
Can say, how anger leads to homicide.
Truth, anger's the executant of pride
I could of anger tell you so much sorrow
My tale should last until it were tomorrow.
And therefore I pray God both day and night,
An ireful man, God send him little might!
It is great harm and truly great pity
To set an ireful man in high degree.
"For once there was an ireful potentate,
(As Seneca says) and while he ruled the state,
Upon a day out riding went knights two,
And as Dame Fortune willed it, it was so
That one of them came home, and one did not.
Anon that knight before the judge was brought,
Who said thus: 'Sir, you have your fellow slain,
For which I doom you to the death, amain.'
And to another knight commanded he,
'Go lead him to his death, so I charge ye'
It happened, as they went along their way,
Toward the place where he must die that day,
They met the knight that men had thought was dead
Then thought they, it were best not go ahead,
And so led both unto the judge again.
They said: 'O lord, this knight, he has not slain
His fellow; for he stands here sound, alive.'
'You shall die then,' he cried, 'so may I thrive!
That is to say, you shall all die, all three!'
And then to the first knight 'twas thus said he:
'I doomed you, and therefore you must be dead.
And you, also, must needs now lose your head,
Since you're the causing of your fellow's end.'
And then on the third knight did he descend:
'You have not done what I ordained should be!'
And thus he did away with all the three.
"Ireful Cambyses was a drunkard too,
And much delighted dirty deeds to do.
And so befell, a lord of his household,
Who loved all moral virtue, we are told,
Said on a day, when they were talking, thus:

And ber this word awey now, by thy feith,
Touchinge this thing, lo, what the wyse seith:
'With-in thyn hous ne be thou no leoun;
To thy subgits do noon oppressioun;
Ne make thyne aqueyntances nat to flee.'
And Thomas, yet eft-sones I charge thee,
Be war from hir that in thy bosom slepeth;
War fro the serpent that so slyly crepeth
Under the gras, and stingeth subtilly.
Be war, my sone, and herkne paciently,
That twenty thousand men han lost hir lyves,
For stryving with hir lemmans and hir wyves.
Now sith ye han so holy and meke a wyf,
What nedeth yow, Thomas, to maken stryf?
Ther nis, y-wis, no serpent so cruel,
Whan man tret on his tayl, ne half so fel,
As womman is, whan she hath caught an ire;
Vengeance is thanne al that they desyre.
Ire is a sinne, oon of the grete of sevene,
Abhominable un-to the god of hevene;
And to him-self it is destruccion.
This every lewed viker or person
Can seye, how Ire engendreth homicyde.
Ire is, in sooth, executour of pryde.
I coude of Ire seye so muche sorwe,
My tale sholde laste til to-morwe.
And therfor preye I god bothe day and night,
An irous man, god sende him litel might!
It is greet harm and, certes, gret pitee,
To sette an irous man in heigh degree.
Whilom ther was an irous potestat,
As seith Senek, that, duringe his estaat,
Up-on a day out riden knightes two,
And as fortune wolde that were so,
That oon of hem cam hoom, that other noght.
Anon the knight bifore the juge is broght,
That seyde thus, 'thou hast thy felawe slayn.
For which I deme thee to the deeth, certayn.'
And to another knight comanded he,
'Go lede him to the deeth, I charge thee.'
And happed, as they wente by the weye
Toward the place ther he sholde deye,
The knight cam, which men wenden had be deed.
Thanne thoughte they, it was the beste reed,
To lede hem bothe to the juge agayn.
They seiden, 'lord, the knight ne hath nat slayn
His felawe; here he standeth hool alyve.'
'Ye shul be deed,' quod he, 'so moot I thryve!
That is to seyn, bothe oon, and two, and three!'
And to the firste knight right thus spak he,
'I dampned thee, thou most algate be deed.
And thou also most nedes lese thyn heed,
For thou art cause why thy felawe deyth.'
And to the thridde knight right thus he seyth,
'Thou hast nat doon that I comanded thee.'
And thus he dide don sleen hem alle three.
Irous Cambyses was eek dronkelewe,
And ay delyted him to been a shrewe.
And so bifel, a lord of his meynee,
That lovede vertuous moralitee,
Seyde on a day bitwix hem two right thus:

'A lord is lost, if he be vicious;
And dronkenesse is eek a foul record
Of any man, and namely in a lord.
Ther is ful many an eye and many an ere
Awaiting on a lord, and he noot where.
For goddes love, drink more attemprely;
Wyn maketh man to lesen wrecchedly
His minde, and eek his limes everichon.'
'The revers shaltouse,' quod he, 'anon;
And preve it, by thyn owene experience,
That wyn ne dooth to folk no swich offence.
Ther is no wyn bireveth me my might
Of hand ne foot, ne of myn eyen sight'—
And, for despyt, he drank ful muchel more
An hondred part than he had doon bifore;
And right anon, this irous cursed wrecche
Leet this knightes sone bifore him fecche,
Comandinge him he sholde bifore him stonde.
And sodeynly he took his bowe in honde,
And up the streng he pulled to his ere,
And with an arwe he slow the child right there:
'Now whether have I a siker hand or noon?'
Quod he, 'is al my might and minde agoon?
Hath wyn bireved me myn eyen sight?'
What sholde I telle th'answere of the knight?
His sone was slayn, ther is na-more to seye.
Beth war therfor with lordes how ye pleye.
Singeth *Placebo*, and I shal, if I can,
But-if it be un-to a povre man.
To a povre man men sholde hise vyces telle,
But nat to a lord, thogh he sholde go to helle.
Lo irous Cirus, thilke Percien,
How he destroyed the river of Gysen,
For that an hors of his was dreynt therinne,
Whan that he wente Babiloigne to winne.
He made that the river was so smal,
That wommen mighte wade it over-al.
Lo, what seyde he, that so wel teche can?
'Ne be no felawe to an irous man,
Ne with no wood man walke by the weye,
Lest thee repente'; ther is na-more to seye.
Now Thomas, leve brother, lef thyn ire;
Thou shalt me finde as just as is a squire.
Hold nat the develes knyf ay at thyn herte;
Thyn angre dooth thee al to sore smerte;
But shewe to me al thy confessioun."
"Nay," quod the syke man, "by Seint Simoun!
I have be shriven this day at my curat;
I have him told al hoolly myn estat;
Nedeth na-more to speke of it," seith he,
"But if me list of myn humilitee."
"Yif me thanne of thy gold, to make our
cloistre,"
Quod he, "for many a muscle and many an oistre,
Whan other men han ben ful wel at eyse,
Hath been our fode, our cloistre for to reyse.
And yet, god woot, unnethe the fundement
Parfourned is, ne of our pavement
Nis nat a tyle yet with-inne our wones;
By god, we owen fourty pound for stones!
Now help, Thomas, for him that harwed helle!
For elles moste we our bokes selle.

'A lord is lost if he be too vicious;
And drunkenness is foul thing to record
Of any man, and specially of a lord.
There is full many an eye and many an ear
Waiting upon a lord, nor knows he where.
For God's dear love, sir, drink more moderately;
Wine causes man to lose, and wretchedly,
His mind, and his limbs' usage, every one.'
" 'The opposite you'll see,' said he, 'anon;
And you'll prove, by your own experience,
That wine does not to men such foul offence.
There is no wine can rob me of my might
Of hand or foot, nor yet of my eyesight!'
And for despite he drank much wine the more,
A hundred times, than he had drunk before;
And then anon this ireful wicked wretch
Sent one this knight's young son to go and fetch,
And ordered that before him he should stand.
And suddenly he took his bow in hand,
And drew the string thereof up to his ear,
And with an arrow slew the child right there.
'Now tell me whether I've sure hand, or none!'
He said, 'And are my might and mind all gone?
Has wine deprived me of my good eyesight?'
"How shall I tell the answer of the knight?
His son was slain, there is no more to say.
Beware, therefore, with lords look how you play.
But sing *placebo* and 'I shall, if I can,'
Unless it be unto a helpless man.
To a poor man men should his vices tell,
But to a lord, no, though he go to Hell.
"Lo, ireful Cyrus, that great Persian king,
Destroyed the river Gyndes at its spring,
Because a horse of his was drowned therein
When he went forth old Babylon to win.
He caused the river to become so small
That women could go wading through it all.
"Lo, what said he whose teaching all commend?
'An angry man take never for a friend,
Nor with a madman walk along the way,
Lest you repent.' There is no more to say.
"Now, Thomas, my dear brother, leave your ire;
You shall find me as just as is a squire.
Hold not the Devil's knife against your heart;
Your anger does too sorely burn and smart;
But show me all, now, in confession, son."
"Nay," said the sick man, "by Saint Simeon!
I have been shriven today by my curate;
I have him told the whole truth of my state;
There's no more need to speak of it," said he,
"Save as I please, of my humility."
"Then give me of your gold to build our
cloister,"
Said he, "for many a mussel and an oyster,
When other men have been well at their ease,
Have been our food, that building should not cease,
And yet, God knows, is finished nothing more
Than the foundation, while of all the floor
There's not a tile yet laid to call our own;
By God, we owe full forty pounds for stone!
Now help, Thomas, for Him that harried Hell!
Else must we turn about and our books sell.

And if you laymen lack our high instruction,
Then will the world go all to its destruction.
For whoso shall deny us right to live,
So may God save me, Thomas, by your leave,
He'll have deprived the whole world of the sun.
For who can teach and work as we have done?
And that's not been for little time," said he;
"Elias and Elisha used to be
Friars, you'll find the scriptures do record,
And beggars too, thanks be to the good Lord!
Now, Thomas, help for holy charity!"
And down he went then, kneeling on one knee.
This sick man, he went well-nigh mad for ire;
He would have had that friar set afire
For the hypocrisy that he had shown.
"Such things as I possess and are my own,"
Said he, "those may I give you and no other.
You tell me that I am as your own brother?"
"Yea, truly," said the friar, "trust me well;
I gave your wife a letter with our seal."
"That's well," said he, "and something will I give
Unto your holy convent while I live,
And right anon you'll have it in your hand,
On this condition only, understand,
That you divide it so, my own dear brother,
That every friar shall have as much as other.
This shall you swear upon the faith you own,
And without fraud or cavil, be it known."
"I swear it," said this friar, "on my faith!"
And on the sick man's laid his hand therewith.
"Lo, hear my oath! In me shall truth not lack."
"Now then, come put your hand right down my back,"
Replied this man, "and grope you well behind;
For underneath my buttocks shall you find
A thing that I have hid in privity."
"Ah," thought the friar, "this shall go with me!"
And down he thrust his hand right to the cleft,
In hope that he should find there some good gift.
And when the sick man felt the friar here
Groping about his hole and all his rear,
Into his hand he let the friar a fart.
There is no stallion drawing loaded cart
That might have let a fart of such a sound.
The friar leaped up as with wild lion's bound:
"Ah, treacherous churl," he cried, "by God's own bones,
I'll see that he who scorns me thus atones;
You'll suffer for this fart—I'll find a way!"
The servants, who had heard all this affray,
Came leaping in and chased the friar out;
And forth he scowling went, with angry shout,
And found his fellow, where he'd left his store.
He glared about as he were some wild boar;
He ground and gnashed his teeth, so wroth was he.
He quickly sought the manor, there to see
The lord thereof, whose honour was the best,
And always to the friar he confessed;
This worthy man was lord of that village.
The friar came, as he were in a rage,
Where sat the lord at dinner at his board.

And if ye lakke our predicacioun,
Than gooth the world al to destruccioun.
For who-so wolde us fro this world bireve,
So god me save, Thomas, by your leve,
He wolde bireve out of this world the sonne.
For who can teche and werchen as we conne?
And that is nat of litel tyme," quod he;
"But sith that Elie was, or Elisee,
Han freres been, that finde I of record,
In charitee, y-thanked be our lord.
Now Thomas, help, for seinte Charitee!"
And doun anon he sette him on his knee.
This syke man wex wel ny wood for ire;
He wolde that the frere had been on-fire
With his false dissimulacioun.
"Swich thing as is in my possessioun,"
Quod he, "that may I yeven, and non other.
Ye sey me thus, how that I am your brother?"
"Ye, certes," quod the frere, "trusteth weel;
I took our dame our lettre with our seel."
"Now wel," quod he, "and som-what shal I yive
Un-to your holy covent whyl I live,
And in thyn hand thou shalt it have anoon;
On this condicioun, and other noon,
That thou departe it so, my dere brother,
That every frere have also muche as other.
This shaltou swere on thy professioun,
With-outen fraude or cavillacioun."
"I swere it," quod this frere, "upon my feith!"
And ther-with-al his hand in his he leith:
"Lo, heer my feith! in me shal be no lak."
"Now thanne, put thyn hand doun by my bak,"
Seyde this man, "and grope wel bihinde;
Bynethe my buttok ther shaltow finde
A thing that I have hid in privetee."
"A!" thoghte this frere, "this shal go with me!"
And doun his hand he launcheth to the clifte,
In hope for to finde ther a yifte.
And whan this syke man felte this frere
Aboute his tuwel grope there and here,
Amidde his hand he leet the frere a fart.
Ther nis no capul, drawinge in a cart,
That mighte have lete a fart of swich a soun.
The frere up stirte as doth a wood leoun:
"A! false cherl," quod he, "for goddes bones,
This hastow for despyt doon, for the nones!
Thou shalt abye this fart, if that I may!"
His meynee, whiche that herden this affray,
Cam lepinge in, and chaced out the frere;
And forth he gooth, with a ful angry chere,
And fette his felawe, ther-as lay his stoor.
He looked as it were a wilde boor;
He grinte with his teeth, so was he wrooth.
A sturdy pas doun to the court he gooth,
Wher-as ther woned a man of greet honour,
To whom that he was alwey confessour;
This worthy man was lord of that village.
This frere cam, as he were in a rage,
Wher-as this lord sat eting at his bord.

Unnethes mighte the frere speke a word,
Til atte laste he seyde: "god yow see!"
This lord gan loke, and seide, "*ben'cite!*
What, frere John, what maner world is this?
I see wel that som thing ther is amis.
Ye loken as the wode were ful of thevis,
Sit doun anon, and tel me what your greef is,
And it shal been amended, if I may."
"I have," quod he, "had a despyt this day,
God yelde yow! adoun in your village,
That in this world is noon so povre a page,
That he nolde have abhominacioun
Of that I have receyved in your toun.
And yet ne greveth me no-thing so sore,
As that this olde cherl, with lokkes hore,
Blasphemed hath our holy covent eke."
"Now, maister," quod this lord, "I yow biseke."
"No maister, sire," quod he, "but servitour,
Thogh I have had in scole swich honour.
God lyketh nat that 'Raby' men us calle,
Neither in market ne in your large halle."
"No fors," quod he, "but tel me al your grief."
"Sire," quod this frere, "an odious meschief
This day bitid is to myn ordre and me,
And so *per consequens* to ech degree
Of holy chirche, god amende it sone!"
"Sir," quod the lord, "ye woot what is to done.
Distempre yow noght, ye be my confessour;
Ye been the salt of the erthe and the savour.
For goddes love your pacience ye holde;
Tel me your grief":
and he anon him tolde,
As ye han herd biforn, ye woot wel what.
The lady of the hous ay stille sat,
Til she had herd al what the frere sayde:
"Ey, goddes moder," quod she, "blisful mayde!
Is ther oght elles? telle me feithfully."
"Madame," quod he, "how thinketh yow her-by?"
"How that me thinketh?" quod she; "so god me speede,
I seye, a cherl hath doon a cherles dede.
What shold I seye? god lat him never thee!
His syke heed is ful of vanitee,
I hold him in a maner frenesye."
"Madame," quod he, "by god I shal nat lye;
But I on other weyes may be wreke,
I shal diffame him over-al ther I speke,
This false blasphemour, that charged me
To parte that wol nat departed be,
To every man y-liche, with meschaunce!"
The lord sat stille as he were in a traunce,
And in his herte he rolled up and doun,
"How hadde this cherl imaginacioun
To shewe swich a probleme to the frere?
Never erst er now herde I of swich matere;
I trowe the devel putte it in his minde.
In ars-metryke shal ther no man finde,
Biforn this day, of swich a questioun.
Who sholde make a demonstracioun,
That every man sholde have y-liche his part
As of the soun or savour of a fart?

And hardly could the friar speak a word,
Till at the last he said, "God be with ye!"
This lord looked up and said then, "*Ben'cite!*
What, Friar John! What kind of world is this?
I see right well that something is amiss.
You look as if the wood were full of thieves,
Sit down, and tell me what it is that grieves,
And it shall be amended, if I may."
"I have," said he, "insulted been today—
May God reward you!—down in your village.
And in this world is not so poor a page
As would not feel the insult, if 'twere thrown
At him, that I have suffered in your town.
Yet nothing grieves me in this matter more
Than that this peasant, with his long locks hoar,
Has thus blasphemed our holy convent too."
"Now, master," said his lordship, "I pray you—"
"No master, sir," said he, "but servitor,
Though true, I had in school such honour, sir.
But rabbi—God's not pleased that men so call
Us, in the public square or your wide hall."
"No matter," said he, "tell me all your grief."
"Sir," said this friar, "an odious mischeif
Was this day done to my order and me,
And so, *per consequens*, to each degree
Of Holy Church, may God it soon amend!"
"Sir," said the lord, "the story I attend.
As my confessor, pray your wrath control;
Salt of the earth are you—the savour whole.
For love of God, I beg you patience hold;
Tell me your grievance."
And anon he told
As you have heard before, you know well what.
The lady of the house right silent sat
Till she had heard all that the friar said:
"Eh, by God's Mother," cried she, "Blessed Maid!
Is there aught else? A point that we did miss?"
"Madam," asked he, "what do you think of this?"
"What do I think?" she asked, "So God me speed
I say, a churl has done a churlish deed.
What should I say? May God desert him! See—
Why his sick head is full of vanity.
The man, no doubt, is more or less insane."
"Madam," said he, "I will not lie or feign:
If otherwise I cannot vengeance wreak,
I will defame him wheresoe'er I speak,
This false blasphemer who has dared charge me
Thus to divide what won't divided be,
To every man alike, and with mischance!"
The lord sat still as he were in a trance,
And in his mind he rolled it up and down:
"How had this churl imagination grown
To pose so fine a problem to the friar?
I never heard the like, or I'm a liar;
I think the devil stuck it in his mind.
And in arithmetic did no man find,
Before this day, such puzzling question shown.
Who could be able, now, to make it known
How every man should have an equal part
Of both the sound and savour of a fart?

O scrupulous proud churl, beshrew his face!
Lo, sirs," this lord said then, with hard grimace,
"Who ever heard of such a thing ere now?
To every man alike? But tell me how!
Why it's impossible, it cannot be!
Exacting churl, God give him never glee!
The rumbling of a fart, and every sound,
Is but the air's reverberation round,
And ever it wastes, by little and little, away.
There is no man can judge, aye, by my fay,
Whether it were divided equally.
Behold, my churl! And yet how cursedly
To my confessor has he made this crack!
I hold him surely a demoniac!
Now eat your meat and let the churl go play,
Let him go hang himself, the devil's way!"
  Now the lord's squire stood ready near the board
To carve his meat, and he heard, word for word,
All of the things that I to you have said.
"My lord," said he, "be not ill pleased indeed;
For I could tell, for cloth to make a gown,
To you, sir friar, so you do not frown,
How this said fart evenly doled could be
Among your fellows, if the thing pleased me."
  "Tell," said the lord, "and you shall have anon
Cloth for a gown, by God and by Saint John!"
  "My lord," said he, "when next the weather's fair,
And there's no wind to stir the quiet air,
Let someone bring a cartwheel to this hall,
But see there are no missing spokes at all.
Twelve spokes a cartwheel has, sir, commonly.
And bring me then twelve friars, and know you why?
Because a convent's thirteen, as I guess.
The present confessor, for his worthiness,
He shall complete the tale of this convent.
Then shall they all kneel down, by one assent,
And at each spoke's end, in this manner, sire,
Let the nose be laid firmly of a friar.
Your noble sir confessor, whom God save,
Shall hold his nose upright beneath the nave.
Then shall this churl, with belly stiff and taut
As any tabour—let him here be brought;
And set him on the wheel of this same cart,
Upon the hub, and make him let a fart.
And you shall see, on peril of my life,
With proof so clear that there shall be no strife,
That equally the sound of it will wend,
And the stink too, to each spoke's utter end;
Save that this worthy man, your confessor,
Because he is a man of great honour,
Shall have first fruits, as reasonable it is;
The noble custom of all friars is this,
The worthy men of them shall be first served;
And certainly this has he well deserved.
He has today taught us so much of good,
With preaching in the pulpit where he stood,
That for my part I gladly should agree,
He might well have the first smell of farts three,
And so would all his convent, generously,
He bears himself so well and holily."

O nyce proude cherl, I shrewe his face!
Lo, sires," quod the lord, with harde grace,
"Who ever herde of swich a thing er now?
To every man y-lyke? tel me how.
It is an inpossible, it may nat be!
Ey, nyce cherl, god lete him never thee!
The rumblinge of a fart, and every soun,
Nis but of eir reverberacioun,
And ever it wasteth lyte and lyte awey.
Ther is no man can demen, by my fey,
If that it were departed equally.
What, lo, my cherl, lo, yet how shrewedly
Un-to my confessour to-day he spak!
I holde him certeyn a demoniak!
Now ete your mete, and lat the cherl go pleye,
Lat him go honge himself, a devel weye!"
  Now stood the lordes squyer at the bord,
That carf his mete, and herde, word by word,
Of alle thinges of which I have yow sayd.
"My lord," quod he, "be ye nat yvel apayd;
I coude telle, for a goune-clooth,
To yow, sir frere, so ye be nat wrooth,
How that this fart sholde even deled be
Among your covent, if it lyked me."
  "Tel," quod the lord, "and thou shalt have anon
A goune-cloth, by god and by Seint John!"
  "My lord," quod he, "whan that the weder is fair,
With-outen wind or perturbinge of air,
Lat bringe a cartwheel here in-to this halle,
But loke that it have his spokes alle.
Twelf spokes hath a cartwheel comunly.
And bring me than twelf freres, woot ye why?
For thrittene is a covent, as I gesse.
The confessour heer, for his worthinesse,
Shal parfourne up the nombre of his covent.
Than shal they knele doun, by oon assent,
And to every spokes ende, in this manere,
Ful sadly leye his nose shal a frere.
Your noble confessour, ther god him save,
Shal holde his nose upright, under the nave.
Than shal this cherl, with bely stif and toght
As any tabour, hider been y-broght;
And sette him on the wheel right of this cart,
Upon the nave, and make him lete a fart.
And ye shul seen, up peril of my lyf,
By preve which that is demonstratif,
That equally the soun of it wol wende,
And eek the stink, un-to the spokes ende;
Save that this worthy man, your confessour,
By-cause he is a man of greet honour,
Shal have the firste fruit, as reson is;
The noble usage of freres yet is this,
The worthy men of hem shul first be served;
And certeinly, he hath it weel deserved.
He hath to-day taught us so muchel good
With preching in the pulpit ther he stood,
That I may vouche-sauf, I sey for me,
He hadde the firste smel of fartes three,
And so wolde al his covent hardily;
He bereth him so faire and holily."

The lord, the lady, and ech man, save the frere,
Seyde that Jankin spak, in this matere,
As wel as Euclide or [as] Ptholomee.
Touchinge this cherl, they seyde, subtiltee
And heigh wit made him speken as he spak;
He nis no fool, ne no demoniak.
And Jankin hath y-wonne a newe goune.—
My tale is doon we been almost at toune.

The lord, the lady, and each man, save the friar,
Agreed that Jenkin spoke, as classifier,
As well as Euclid or as Ptolemy.
Touching the churl, they said that subtlety
And great wit taught him how to make his crack.
He was no fool, nor a demoniac.
And Jenkin by this means has won a gown.
My tale is done, we're almost into town.

HERE ENDETH THE SUMMONER'S TALE

THE CLERK'S PROLOGUE

HERE FOLLOWETH THE PROLOGUE OF THE CLERK OF OXFORD'S TALE

"Sir clerk of Oxenford," our hoste sayde,
"Ye ryde as coy and stille as dooth a mayde,
Were newe spoused, sitting at the bord;
This day ne herde I of your tonge a word.
I trowe ye studie aboute som sophyme,
But Salomon seith, "every thing hath tyme."
For goddes sake, as beth of bettre chere,
It is no tyme for to studien here.
Telle us som mery tale, by your fey;
For what man that is entred in a pley,
He nedes moot unto the pley assente.
But precheth nat, as freres doon in Lente,
To make us for our olde sinnes wepe,
Ne that thy tale make us nat to slepe.
Telle us som mery thing of aventures;—
Your termes, your colours, and your figures,
Kepe hem in stoor til so be ye endyte
Heigh style, as whan that men to kinges wryte.
Speketh so pleyn at this tyme, I yow preye,
That we may understonde what ye seye."
This worthy clerk benignely answerde,
"Hoste," quod he, "I am under your yerde;
Ye han of us as now the governaunce,
And therfor wol I do yow obeisaunce,
As fer as reson axeth, hardily.
I wol yow telle a tale which that I
Lerned at Padowe of a worthy clerk,
As preved by his wordes and his werk.
He is now deed and nayled in his cheste,
I prey to god so yeve his soule reste!
Fraunceys Petrark, the laureat poete,
Highte this clerk, whos rethoryke sweete
Enlumined al Itaille of poetrye,
As Linian dide of philosophye
Or lawe, or other art particuler;
But deeth, that wol nat suffre us dwellen heer
But as it were a twinkling of an yë,
Hem bothe hath slayn, and alle shul we dyë.
But forth to tellen of this worthy man,
That taughte me this tale, as I bigan,
I seye that first with heigh style he endyteth,
Er he the body of his tale wryteth,
A proheme, in the which discryveth he
Pemond, and of Saluces the contree,
And speketh of Apennyn, the hilles hye,
That been the boundes of West Lumbardye,

Sir clerk of Oxford," our good host then said,
"You ride as quiet and still as is a maid
But newly wedded, sitting at the board;
This day I've heard not from your tongue a word.
Perhaps you mull a sophism that's prime.
But Solomon says, each thing to its own time.
"For God's sake, smile and be of better cheer,
It is no time to think and study here.
Tell us some merry story, if you may;
For whatsoever man will join in play,
He needs must to the play give his consent.
But do not preach, as friars do in Lent,
To make us, for our old sins, wail and weep,
And see your tale shall put us not to sleep.
"Tell us some merry thing of adventures.
Your terms, your colours, and your speech-figures,
Keep them in store till so be you indite
High style, as when men unto kings do write.
Speak you so plainly, for this time, I pray,
That we can understand what things you say."
This worthy clerk, benignly he answered.
"Good host," said he, "I am under your yard;
You have of us, for now, the governance,
And therefore do I make you obeisance
As far as reason asks it, readily.
I will relate to you a tale that I
Learned once, at Padua, of a worthy clerk,
As he proved by his words and by his work.
He's dead, now, and nailed down within his chest,
And I pray God to give his soul good rest!
"Francis Petrarch, the laureate poet,
Was this clerk's name, whose rhetoric so sweet
Illumed all Italy with poetry,
As did Lignano with philosophy,
Or law, or other art particular;
But Death, that suffers us not very far,
Nor more, as 'twere, than twinkling of an eye,
Has slain them both, as all of us shall die.
"But forth, to tell you of this worthy man,
Who taught this tale to me, as I began,
I say that first, with high style he indites,
Before the body of his tale he writes,
A proem to describe those lands renowned,
Saluzzo, Piedmont, and the region round,
And speaks of Apennines, those hills so high
That form the boundary of West Lombardy,

And of Mount Viso, specially, the tall,
Whereat the Po, out of a fountain small,
Takes its first springing and its tiny source
That eastward ever increases in its course
Toward Emilia, Ferrara, and Venice;
The which is a long story to devise.
And truly, in my judgment reluctant
It is a thing not wholly relevant,
Save that he introduces thus his gear:
But this is his tale, which you now may hear."

And of Mount Vesulus in special,
Where as the Poo, out of a welle smal,
Taketh his firste springing and his sours,
That estward ay encresseth in his cours
To Emelward, to Ferrare, and Venyse:
The which a long thing were to devyse.
And trewely, as to my jugement,
Me thinketh it a thing impertinent,
Save that he wol conveyen his matere:
But this his tale, which that ye may here."

THE CLERK'S TALE

HERE BEGINNETH THE TALE OF THE CLERK OF OXFORD

There is, in the west side of Italy,
Down at the foot of Mount Viso the cold,
A pleasant plain that yields abundantly,
Where many a tower and town one may behold,
That were there founded in the times of old.
With many another fair delightful sight;
Saluzzo is this noble region bright.

A marquis once was lord of all that land,
As were his noble ancestors before;
Obedient and ready to his hand
Were all his lieges, both the less and more.
Thus in delight he lived, and had of yore,
Beloved and feared, through favour of Fortune,
Both by his lords and by the common run.

Therewith he was, to speak of lineage,
Born of the noblest blood of Lombardy,
With person fair, and strong, and young of age,
And full of honour and of courtesy;
Discreet enough to lead his nation, he,
Save in some things wherein he was to blame,
And Walter was this young lord's Christian name.

I blame him thus, that he considered naught
Of what in coming time might him betide,
But on his present wish was all his thought,
As, he would hunt and hawk on every side;
Well-nigh all other cares would he let slide,
And would not, and this was the worst of all,
Marry a wife, for aught that might befall.

That point alone his people felt so sore
That in a flock one day to him they went,
And one of them, the wisest in all lore,
Or else because the lord would best consent
That he should tell him what the people meant,
Or else that he could make the matter clear,
He to the marquis spoke as you shall hear.

"O noble marquis, your humanity
Assures us, aye, and gives us hardiness
As often as there is necessity
That we to you may tell our heaviness.
Accept, lord, now of your great nobleness

Ther is, at the west syde of Itaille,
Doun at the rote of Vesulus the colde,
A lusty playne, habundant of vitaille,
Wher many a tour and toun thou mayst biholde,
That founded were in tyme of fadres olde,
And many another delitable sighte,
And Saluces this noble contree highte.

A markis whylom lord was of that londe,
As were his worthy eldres him bifore;
And obeisant and redy to his honde
Were alle his liges, bothe lasse and more.
Thus in delyt he liveth, and hath don yore,
Biloved and drad, thurgh favour of fortune,
Bothe of his lordes and of his commune.

Therwith he was, to speke as of linage,
The gentilleste y-born of Lumbardye,
A fair persone, and strong, and yong of age,
And ful of honour and of curteisye;
Discreet y-nogh his contree for to gye,
Save in somme thinges that he was to blame,
And Walter was this yonge lordes name.

I blame him thus, that he considereth noght
In tyme cominge what mighte him bityde,
But on his lust present was al his thoght,
As for to hauke and hunte on every syde;
Wel ny alle othere cures leet he slyde,
And eek he nolde, and that was worst of alle,
Wedde no wyf, for noght that may bifalle.

Only that point his peple bar so sore,
That flokmele on a day they to him wente,
And oon of hem, that wysest was of lore,
Or elles that the lord best wolde assente
That he sholde telle him what his peple mente,
Or elles coude he shewe wel swich matere,
He to the markis seyde as ye shul here.

"O noble markis, your humanitee
Assureth us and yeveth us hardinesse,
As ofte as tyme is of necessitee
That we to yow mowe telle our hevinesse
Accepteth, lord, now for your gentillesse.

That we with pitous herte un-to yow pleyne,
And lete your eres nat my voys disdeyne.

Al have I noght to done in this matere
More than another man hath in this place,
Yet for as muche as ye, my lord so dere,
Han alwey shewed me favour and grace,
I dar the better aske of yow a space
Of audience, to shewen our requeste,
And ye, my lord, to doon right as yow leste.

For certes, lord, so wel us lyketh yow
And al your werk and ever han doon, that we
Ne coude nat us self devysen how
We mighte liven in more felicitee,
Save o thing, lord, if it your wille be,
That for to been a wedded man yow leste,
Than were your peple in sovereyn hertes reste.

Boweth your nekke under that blisful yok
Of soveraynetee, noght of servyse,
Which that men clepeth spousaille or wedlok;
And thenketh, lord, among your thoghtes wyse,
How that our dayes passe in sondry wyse;
For though we slepe or wake, or rome, or ryde,
Ay fleeth the tyme, it nil no man abyde.

And though your grene youthe floure as yit,
In crepeth age alwey, as stille as stoon,
And deeth manaceth every age, and smit
In ech estaat, for ther escapeth noon:
And al so certein as we knowe echoon
That we shul deye, as uncerteyn we alle
Been of that day whan deeth shal on us falle.

Accepteth than of us the trewe entente,
That never yet refuseden your heste,
And we wol, lord, if that ye wol assente,
Chese yow a wyf in short tyme, atte leste,
Born of the gentilleste and of the meste
Of al this lond, so that it oghte seme
Honour to god and yow, as we can deme.

Deliver us out of al this bisy drede,
And tak a wyf, for hye goddes sake;
For if it so bifelle, as god forbede.
That thurgh your deeth your linage sholde slake,
And that a straunge successour sholde take
Your heritage, o! wo were us alyve!
Wherfor we pray you hastily to wyve."

Hir meke preyere and hir pitous chere
Made the markis herte han pitee.
"Ye wol," quod he, "myn owene peple dere,
To that I never erst thoghte streyne me.
I me rejoysed of my libertee,
That selde tyme is founde in mariage;
Ther I was free, I moot been in servage.

But nathelees I see your trewe entente,
And truste upon your wit, and have don ay;

That we with sincere hearts may here complain,
Nor let your ears my humble voice disdain.

"Though I have naught to do in this matter
More than another man has in this place,
Yet for as much as you, most honoured sir,
Have always showed me favour and much grace,
I dare the more to ask of you a space
Of audience, to set forth our request,
And you, my lord, will do as you like best.

"For truly, lord, so well do we like you
And all your works (and ever have), that we—
We could not, of ourselves, think what to do
To make us live in more felicity,
Save one thing, lord, and if your will it be,
That to be wedded man you hold it best,
Then were your people's hearts at utter rest.

"But bow your neck beneath that blessed yoke
Of sovereignty and not of hard service,
The which men call espousal or wedlock;
And pray think, lord, among your thoughts so wise,
How our days pass and each in different guise;
For though we sleep or wake or roam or ride,
Time flies, and for no man will it abide.

"And though your time of green youth flower as yet,
Age creeps in always, silent as a stone;
Death threatens every age, nor will forget
For any state, and there escapes him none:
And just as surely as we know, each one,
That we shall die, uncertain are we all
What day it is when death shall on us fall.

"Accept then of us, lord, the true intent,
That never yet refused you your behest,
And we will, lord, if you will give consent,
Choose you a wife without delay, at least,
Born of the noblest blood and the greatest
Of all this land, so that it ought to seem
Honour to God and you, as we shall deem.

"Deliver us from all our constant dread
And take yourself a wife, for High God 's sake;
For if it so befell, which God forbid,
That by your death your noble line should break
And that a strange successor should come take
Your heritage, woe that we were alive!
Wherefore we pray you speedily to wive."

Their humble prayer and their so earnest cheer
Roused in the marquis' heart great sympathy.
"You'd have me," he replied, "my people dear,
Do what I've never yet thought necessary.
I have rejoiced in my fond liberty,
That men so seldom find in their marriage;
Where I was free, I must be in bondage.

"Nevertheless, I see your true intent,
And know there's always sense in what you say;

Wherefore of my free will will I consent
To wed a wife, as soon as ever I may.
But whereas you have offered here today
To choose a wife for me, I you release
From that, and pray that you thereof will cease.

"For God knows well that children oft retain
Naught of their worthy elders gone before;
Goodness comes all from God, not of the strain
Whereof they were engendered; furthermore
I trust in God's great goodness, and therefore
My marriage and my state and all my ease
I leave to Him to do with as He please.

"Let me alone in choosing of my wife,
That burden on my own back I'll endure;
But I pray you, and charge you on your life,
That what wife I may take, me you'll assure
You'll honour her throughout her life's tenure,
In word and deed, both here and everywhere,
As if she were an emperor's daughter fair.

"And furthermore, this shall you swear, that you
Against my choice shall neither grouse nor strive;
Since I'm forgoing liberty, and woo
At your request, so may I ever thrive
As, where my heart is set, there will I wive;
And save you give consent in such manner,
I pray you speak no more of this matter."

With hearty will they swore and gave assent
To all this, and no one of them said nay;
Praying him, of his grace, before they went,
That he would set for them a certain day
For his espousal, soon as might be; yea,
For still the people had a little dread
Lest that the marquis would no woman wed.

He granted them the day that pleased him best
Whereon he would be married, certainly,
And said he did all this at their request;
And they with humble hearts, obediently,
Kneeling upon their knees full reverently,
All thanked him there, and thus they made an
end
Of their design and homeward did they wend.

And thereupon he to his officers
Ordered that for the fête they should provide,
And to his household gentlemen and squires,
Such charges gave as pleased him to decide;
And all obeyed him: let him praise or chide,
And each of them did all his diligence
To show unto the fête his reverence.

Wherfor of my free wil I wol assente
To wedde me, as sone as ever I may.
But ther-as ye han profred me to-day
To chese me a wyf, I yow relesse
That choys, and prey yow of that profre cesse.

For god it woot, that children ofte been
Unlyk her worthy eldres hem bifore;
Bountee comth al of god, nat of the streen
Of which they been engendred and y-bore;
I truste in goddes bountee, and therfore
My mariage and myn estaat and reste
I him bitake; he may don as him leste.

Lat me alone in chesinge of my wyf,
That charge up-on my bak I wol endure;
But I yow preye, and charge up-on your lyf,
That what wyf that I take, ye me assure
To worshipe hir, whyl that hir lyf may dure,
In word and werk, bothe here and everywhere,
As she an emperoures doghter were.

And forthermore, this shal ye swere, that ye
Agayn my choys shul neither grucche ne stryve;
For sith I shal forgoon my libertee
At your requeste, as ever moot I thryve,
Ther as myn herte is set, ther wol I wyve;
And but ye wole assente in swich manere,
I prey yow, speketh na-more of this matere."

With hertly wil they sworen, and assenten
To al this thing, ther seyde no wight nay;
Bisekinge him of grace, er that they wenten,
That he wolde graunten hem a certein day
Of his spousaille, as sone as ever he may;
For yet alwey the peple som-what dredde
Lest that this markis no wyf wolde wedde.

He graunted hem a day, swich as him leste,
On which he wolde be wedded sikerly,
And seyde, he dide al this at hir requeste;
And they, with humble entente, buxomly,
Knelinge up-on her knees ful reverently
Him thanken alle, and thus they han an
ende
Of hir entente, and hoom agayn they wende.

And heer-up-on he to his officeres
Comaundeth for the feste to purveye,
And to his privee knightes and squyeres
Swich charge yaf, as him liste on hem leye;
And they to his comandement obeye,
And ech of hem doth al his diligence
To doon un-to the feste reverence.

HERE ENDETH THE FIRST PART

HERE BEGINNETH THE SECOND PART

Not far from that same honoured palace where
This marquis planned his marriage, at this tide,
There stood a hamlet, on a site most fair,
Wherein the poor folk of the countryside
Stabled their cattle and did all abide,

Noght fer fro thilke paleys honurable
Ther-as this markis shoop his mariage,
Ther stood a throp, of site delitable,
In which that povre folk of that village
Hadden hir bestes and hir herbergage,

And of hir labour took hir sustenance
After that th'erthe yaf hem habundance.

Amonges thise povre folk ther dwelte a man
Which that was holden povrest of hem alle;
But hye god som tyme senden can
His grace in-to a litel oxes stalle:
Janicula men of that throp him calle.
A doghter hadde he, fair y-nogh to sighte,
And Grisildis this yonge mayden highte.

But for to speke of vertuous beautee,
Than was she oon the faireste under sonne;
For povreliche y-fostred up was she,
No likerous lust was thurgh hir herte y-ronne;
Wel ofter of the welle than of the tonne
She drank, and for she wolde vertu plese,
She knew wel labour, but non ydel ese.

But thogh this mayde tendre were of age,
Yet in the brest of hir virginitee
Ther was enclosed rype and sad corage;
And in greet reverence and charitee
Hir olde povre fader fostred she;
A fewe sheep spinning on feeld she kepte,
She wolde noght been ydel til she slepte.

And whan she hoomward cam, she wolde bringe
Wortes or othere herbes tymes ofte,
The whiche she shredde and seeth for hir livinge,
And made hir bed ful harde and no-thing softe;
And ay she kepte hir fadres lyf on-lofte
With everich obeisaunce and diligence
That child may doon to fadres reverence.

Up-on Grisilde, this povre creature,
Ful ofte sythe this markis sette his yë
As he on hunting rood paraventure;
And whan it fil that he mighte hir espye,
He noght with wantoun loking of folye
His yën caste on hir, but in sad wyse
Up-on hir chere he wolde him ofte avyse,

Commending in his herte hir wommanhede,
And eek hir vertu, passing any wight
Of so yong age, as wel in chere as dede.
For thogh the peple have no greet insight
In vertu, he considered ful right
Hir bountee, and disposed that he wolde
Wedde hir only, if ever he wedde sholde.

The day of wedding cam, but no wight can
Telle what womman that it sholde be;
For which merveille wondred many a man,
And seyden, what they were in privetee,
"Wol nat our lord yet leve his vanitee?
Wol he nat wedde? allas, allas the whyle!
Why wol he thus him-self and us bigyle?"

But natheles this markis hath don make

And where their labour gave them sustenance
After the earth had yielded abundance.

Amongst these humble folk there dwelt a man
Who was considered poorest of them all;
But the High God of Heaven sometimes can
Send His grace to a little ox's stall;
Janicula men did this poor man call.
A daughter had he, fair enough to sight;
Griselda was this young maid's name, the bright.

If one should speak of virtuous beauty,
Then was she of the fairest under sun;
Since fostered in dire poverty was she,
No lust luxurious in her heart had run;
More often from the well than from the tun
She drank, and since she would chaste virtue please,
She knew work well, but knew not idle ease.

But though this maiden tender was of age,
Yet in the breast of her virginity
There was enclosed a ripe and grave courage;
And in great reverence and charity
Her poor old father fed and fostered she;
A few sheep grazing in a field she kept,
For she would not be idle till she slept.

And when she homeward came, why she would bring
Roots and green herbs, full many times and oft,
The which she'd shred and boil for her living,
And made her bed a hard one and not soft;
Her father kept she in their humble croft
With what obedience and diligence
A child may do for father's reverence.

Upon Griselda, humble daughter pure,
The marquis oft had looked in passing by,
As he a-hunting rode at adventure;
And when it chanced that her he did espy,
Not with the glances of a wanton eye
He gazed at her, but all in sober guise,
And pondered on her deeply in this wise:

Commending to his heart her womanhood,
And virtue passing that of any wight,
Of so young age in face and habitude.
For though the people have no deep insight
In virtue, he considered all aright
Her goodness, and decided that he would
Wed only her, if ever wed he should.

The day of wedding came, but no one can
Tell who the woman is that bride shall be;
At which strange thing they wondered, many a man,
And they said, marvelling, in privacy:
"Will not our lord yet leave his vanity?
Will he not wed? Alas, alas, the while!
Why will he thus himself and us beguile?"

Nevertheless, this marquis has bade make,

Of jewels set in gold and in rich azure,
Brooches and rings, all for Griselda's sake,
And for her garments took he then the measure
By a young maiden of her form and stature,
And found all other ornaments as well
That for such wedding would be meet to tell.

The time of mid-morn of that very day
Approached when this lord's marriage was to be;
And all the palace was bedecked and gay,
Both hall and chambers, each in its degree;
With kitchens stuffed with food in great plenty,
There might one see the last and least dainty
That could be found in all of Italy.

This regal marquis, splendidly arrayed,
With lords and ladies in his company
(Who to attend the feasting had been prayed),
And of his retinue the bachelory,
With many a sound of sundry melody,
Unto the village whereof I have told,
In this array the nearest way did hold.

Griselda who, God knows, was innocent
That for her sake was all this fine array,
To fetch some water, to a fountain went,
Yet she returned soon, did this lovely may,
For she had heard it said that on this day
The marquis was to wed, and if she might,
She was full fain to see the glorious sight.

She thought: "With other maidens I will stand
(Who are my friends) within our door, and see
The marchioness, and therefore I'll turn hand
To do at home, as soon as it may be,
The household work that's waiting there for me;
And then I'll be at leisure to behold
Her, if they this way to the castle hold."

And as across her threshold she'd have gone,
The marquis came, and for her did he call;
And she set down her water jar anon
Beside the threshold, in an ox's stall,
And down upon her two knees did she fall
And, kneeling, with grave countenance, was still
Till she had heard what was his lordship's will.

This thoughtful marquis spoke unto this maid
Full soberly, and said in this manner:
"Griselda, where's your father?" so he said.
And she, with reverence and with humble cheer,
Answered: "My lord, he is but inside here."
And in she went without more tarrying
And to the marquis did her father bring.

He by the hand then took this ancient man
And said, when he had led him well aside:
"Janicula, I neither will nor can
Conceal my love, nor my heart's longing hide,
If you but acquiesce, whate'er betide,
Your daughter will I take, before I wend,
To be my wife until her life's dear end.

Of gemmes, set in gold and in asure,
Broches and ringes, for Grisildis sake,
And of hir clothing took he the mesure
By a mayde, lyk to hir stature,
And eek of othere ornamentes alle
That un-to swich a wedding sholde falle.

The tyme of undern of the same day
Approcheth, that this wedding sholde be;
And al the paleys put was in array,
Bothe halle and chambres, ech in his degree;
Houses of office stuffed with plentee
Ther maystow seen of deyntevous vitaille,
That may be founde, as fer as last Itaille.

This royal markis, richely arrayed,
Lordes and ladyes in his companye,
The whiche unto the feste were y-prayed,
And of his retenue the bachelrye,
With many a soun of sondry melodye,
Un-to the village, of the which I tolde,
In this array the righte wey han holde.

Grisilde of this, god woot, ful innocent,
That for hir shapen was al this array,
To fecchen water at a welle is went,
And cometh hoom as sone as ever she may.
For wel she hadde herd seyd, that thilke day
The markis sholde wedde, and, if she mighte,
She wolde fayn han seyn som of that sighte.

She thoghte, "I wol with othere maydens stonde,
That been my felawes, in our dore, and see
The markisesse, and therfor wol I fonde
To doon at hoom, as sone as it may be,
The labour which that longeth un-to me;
And than I may at leyser hir biholde,
If she this wey un-to the castel holde."

And as she wolde over hir threshfold goon,
The markis cam and gan hir for to calle;
And she set doun hir water-pot anoon
Bisyde the threshfold, in an oxes stalle,
And doun up-on hir knees she gan to falle,
And with sad contenance kneleth stille
Til she had herd what was the lordes wille.

This thoghtful markis spak un-to this mayde
Ful sobrely, and seyde in this manere,
"Wher is your fader, Grisildis?" he sayde,
And she with reverence, in humble chere,
Answerde, "lord, he is al redy here."
And in she gooth with-outen lenger lette,
And to the markis she hir fader fette.

He by the hond than took this olde man,
And seyde thus, whan he him hadde asyde,
"Janicula, I neither may ne can
Lenger the plesance of myn herte hyde.
If that thou vouche-sauf, what-so bityde,
Thy doghter wol I take, er that I wende,
As for my wyf, un-to hir lyves ende.

Thou lovest me, I woot it wel, certeyn,
And art my feithful lige man y-bore;
And al that lyketh me, I dar wel seyn
It lyketh thee, and specially therfore
Tel me that poynt that I have seyd bifore,
If that thou wolt un-to that purpos drawe,
To take me as for thy sone-in-lawe?"

"You love me, and I know it well today,
And are my faithful liege, and were of yore;
And all that pleases me, I dare well say,
Pleases you too; especially therefore
Assure me on the point I made before—
Can we together in this compact draw,
And will you take me as your son-in-law?"

This sodeyn cas this man astoned so,
That reed he wex, abayst, and al quaking
He stood; unnethes seyde he wordes mo,
But only thus: "lord," quod he, "my willing
Is as ye wole, ne ayeines your lyking
I wol no-thing; ye be my lord so dere;
Right as yow lust governeth this matere."

This sudden word the man astonished so
That red he grew, abashed, and all quaking
He stood; nor could he answer further, no,
Than but to say: "O Lord, I am willing
To do your will; but against your liking
I'll do no thing; you are my lord so dear
That what you wish governs this matter here."

"Yet wol I," quod this markis softely,
"That in thy chambre I and thou and she
Have a collacion, and wostow why?
For I wol axe if it hir wille be
To be my wyf, and reule hir after me;
And al this shal be doon in thy presence,
I wol noght speke out of thyn audience."

"Then I will," said this marquis, quietly,
"That in your chamber you and I and she
Have consultation, and do you know why?
Because I'd ask her if her will it be
To be my wife and so be ruled by me;
And all this shall be done in your presence,
I will not speak without your audience."

And in the chambre whyl they were aboute
Hir tretis, which as ye shal after here,
The peple cam un-to the hous with-oute,
And wondred hem in how honest manere
And tentifly she kepte hir fader dere.
But outerly Grisildis wondre mighte,
For never erst ne saugh she swich a sighte.

And while in chamber they three were about
Their business, whereof you'll hereafter hear,
The people crowded through the house without
And wondered by what honest method there
So carefully she'd kept her father dear.
But more Griselda wondered, as she might,
For never before that saw she such a sight.

No wonder is thogh that she were astoned
To seen so greet a gest come in that place;
She never was to swiche gestes woned,
For which she loked with ful pale face.
But shortly forth this tale for to chace,
Thise arn the wordes that the markis sayde
To this benigne verray feithful mayde.

No wonder, though, astonishment she felt
At seeing so great a guest within that place;
With people of his sort she'd never dealt,
Wherefore she looked on with a pallid face.
But briefly through the matter now to race,
These are the very words the marquis said
To this most modest, truly constant maid.

"Grisilde," he seyde, "ye shul wel understonde
It lyketh to your fader and to me
That I yow wedde, and eek it may so stonde,
As I suppose, ye wol that it so be.
But thise demandes axe I first," qoud he,
"That, sith it shal be doon in hastif wyse,
Wol ye assente, or elles yow avyse?

"Griselda," said he, "you shall understand
It's pleasing to your father and to me
That I wed you, and even it may stand,
As I suppose, that you would have it be.
But these demands must I first make," said he,
"And since it shall be done in hasty wise,
Will you consent, or will you more advise?

I seye this, be ye redy with good herte
To al my lust, and that I frely may,
As me best thinketh, do yow laughe or smerte,
And never ye to grucche it, night ne day?
And eek whan I sey 'ye,' ne sey nat 'nay,'
Neither by word ne frowning contenance;
Swer this, and here I swere our alliance."

"I say this: Are you ready with good heart
To grant my wish, and that I freely may,
As I shall think best, make you laugh or smart,
And you to grumble never, night or day?
And too, when I say 'yea' you say not 'nay'
By word or frown to what I have designed.
Swear this, and here I will our contract bind."

Wondring upon this word, quaking for drede,
She seyde, "lord, undigne and unworthy
Am I to thilke honour that ye me bede;
But as ye wol your-self, right so wol I.
And heer I swere that never willingly

Wondering upon this word, quaking for fear,
She said: "My lord, unsuited, unworthy
Am I to take the honour you give me here;
But what you'd have, that very thing would I.
And here I swear that never willingly,

In deed or thought, will I you disobey,
To save my life, and I love life, I say."

"This is enough, Griselda mine," cried he.
And forth he went then with full sober cheer
Out at the door, and after him came she,
And to the people who were waiting near,
"This is my wife," he said, "who's standing here.
Honour her, all, and love her, all, I pray,
Who love me; and there is no more to say."

And so that nothing of her former gear
She should take with her to his house, he bade
That women strip her naked then and there;
Whereat these ladies were not over-glad
To handle clothes wherein she had been clad.
Nevertheless, this maiden bright of hue
From head to foot they clothed her all anew.

Her hair they combed and brushed, which fell
  untressed
All artlessly, and placed a coronal
With their small fingers on her head, and dressed
Her robes with many jewels great and small;
Of her array how shall I tell withal?
Scarcely the people knew her for fairness,
So transformed was she in her splendid dress.

This marquis her has married with a ring
Brought for the purpose there; and then has set
Upon a horse, snow-white and well ambling,
And to his palace, without longer let,
With happy following folk and more they met,
Conveyed her home, and thus the day they spent
In revelry until the sun's descent.

And briefly forth throughout this tale to chase,
I say that unto this new marchioness
God has such favour sent her, of His grace,
It seemed in no way true, by likeliness,
That she was born and bred in humbleness,
As in a hovel or an ox's stall,
But rather nurtured in an emperor's hall.

To everyone she soon became so dear
And worshipful, that folk where she had dwelt
And from her birth had known her, year by year,
Although they could have sworn it, scarcely felt
That to Janicula, with whom I've dealt,
She really was a daughter, for she seemed
Another creature now, or so they deemed.

For though she ever had been virtuous,
She was augmented by such excellence
Of manners based on noble goodness thus,
And so discreet and wise of eloquence,
So gentle and so worthy reverence,
And she could so the people's hearts embrace,
That each her loved that looked upon her face.

Not only in Saluzzo, in the town,
Was published wide the goodness of her name,

In werk ne thoght I nil yow disobeye,
For to be deed, though me were looth to deye."

"This is y-nogh, Grisilde myn!" quod he.
And forth he gooth with a ful sobre chere
Out at the dore, and after that cam she,
And to the peple he seyde in this manere,
"This is my wyf," quod he, "that standeth here.
Honoureth hir, and loveth hir, I preye,
Who-so me loveth; ther is na-more to seye."

And for that no-thing of hir olde gere
She sholde bringe in-to his hous, he bad
That wommen sholde dispoilen hir right there;
Of which thise ladyes were nat right glad
To handle hir clothes wher-in she was clad.
But natheles this mayde bright of hewe
Fro foot to heed they clothed han al newe.

Hir heres han they kembd, that lay
  untressed
Ful rudely, and with hir fingers smale
A corone on hir heed they han y-dressed,
And sette hir ful of nowches grete and smale;
Of hir array what sholde I make a tale?
Unnethe the peple hir knew for hir fairnesse,
Whan she translated was in swich richesse.

This markis hath hir spoused with a ring
Broght for the same cause, and than hir sette
Up-on an hors, snow-whyt and wel ambling,
And to his paleys, er he lenger lette,
With joyful people that hir ladde and mette,
Conveyed hir, and thus the day they spende
In revel, til the sonne gan descende.

And shortly forth this tale for to chace,
I seye that to this newe markisesse
God hath swich favour sent hir of his grace,
That it ne semed nat by lyklinesse
That she was born and fed in rudenesse,
As in a cote or in an oxe-stalle,
But norished in an emperoures halle.

To every wight she woxen is so dere
And worshipful, that folk ther she was bore
And from hir birthe knewe hir yeer by yere,
Unnethe trowed they, but dorste han swore
That to Janicle, of which I spak bifore,
She doghter nas, for, as by conjecture,
Hem thoughte she was another creature.

For thogh that ever vertuous was she,
She was encressed in swich excellence
Of thewes gode, y-set in heigh bountee,
And so discreet and fair of eloquence,
So benigne and so digne of reverence,
And coude so the peples herte embrace,
That ech hir lovede that loked on hir face.

Noght only of Saluces in the toun
Publiced was the bountee of hir name,

But eek bisyde in many a regioun,
If oon seyde wel, another seyde the same;
So spradde of hir heigh bountee the fame,
That men and wommen, as wel yonge as olde,
Gon to Saluce, upon hir to biholde.

Thus Walter lowly, nay but royally,
Wedded with fortunat honestetee,
In goddes pees lived ful esily
At hoom, and outward grace y-nogh had he;
And for he saugh that under low degree
Was ofte vertu hid, the peple him helde
A prudent man, and that is seyn ful selde.

Nat only this Grisildis thurgh hir wit
Coude al the feet of wyfly hoomlinesse,
But eek, whan that the cas requyred it,
The commune profit coude she redresse.
Ther nas discord, rancour, ne hevinesse
In al that lond, that she ne coude apese,
And wysly bringe hem alle in reste and ese.

Though that hir housbonde absent were anoon,
If gentil men, or othere of hir contree
Were wrothe, she wolde bringen hem atoon;
So wyse and rype wordes hadde she,
And jugements of so greet equitee,
That she from heven sent was, as men wende,
Peple to save and every wrong t'amende.

Nat longe tyme after that this Grisild
Was wedded, she a doughter hath y-bore,
Al had hir lever have born a knave child.
Glad was this markis and the folk therfore;
For though a mayde child come al bifore,
She may unto a knave child atteyene
By lyklihed, sin she nis nat bareyne.

But throughout many a land where she'd renown
If one said well, another said the same;
So widespread of her goodness was the fame
That men and women came; the young and old
Went to Saluzzo, her but to behold.

Thus Walter lowly, nay, but royally,
Wedded, by Fortune's grace, right honourably,
In the good peace of God lived easily
At home, and outward grace enough had he;
And since he saw that under low degree
Is virtue often hid, the people fairly
Held him a prudent man, and that's done rarely.

Not only this Griselda through her wit
Knew how with wifely arts her home to bless,
But also, when there was need for it,
The people's wrongs she knew how to redress.
There was no discord, rancour, heaviness
In all that land that she could not appease,
And wisely bring them all to rest and ease.

Although her husband from the court were gone,
If gentlemen, or less, of her country
Were angered, she would bring them all at one;
So wise and so mature of speech was she,
And judgments gave of so great equity,
Men felt that God from Heaven her did send
People to save and every wrong to amend.

Not long Griselda had, it seems, been wed
Before a daughter to her lord she bore,
Though of a son she'd rather have gone to bed.
Glad were the marquis and the folk therefor;
For though a girl-child came thus all before,
She might well to a boy-child yet attain,
Since barren she was not, it now was plain.

HERE ENDETH THE SECOND PART

HERE BEGINNETH THE THIRD PART

Ther fil, as it bifalleth tymes mo,
Whan that this child had souked but a throwe,
This markis in his herte longeth so
To tempte his wyf, hir sadnesse for to knowe,
That he ne mighte out of his herte throwe
This merveillous desyr, his wyf t'assaye,
Needless, god woot, he thoughte hir for t'affraye.

He hadde assayed hir y-nogh bifore,
And fond hir ever good; what neded it
Hir for to tempte and alwey more and more?
Though som men preise it for a subtil wit,
But as for me, I seye that yvel it sit
T'assaye a wyf whan that it is no nede,
And putten her in anguish and in drede.

For which this markis wroghte in this manere;
He cam alone a-night, ther as she lay,
With sterne face and with ful trouble chere,
And seyde thus, "Grisild," quod he, "that day
That I yow took out of your povre array,

It happened, as it has sometimes before,
That when this child had sucked a month or so,
This marquis in his heart such longing bore
To test his wife, her patience thus to know,
He could not in his heart the chance forgo
This marvelous desire his wife to try;
'Twas needless, God knows, thus to peek and pry.

He had sufficiently tried her before
And found her ever good; what needed it
That he should test her ever more and more?
Though some men praise it for a subtle wit,
Yet I say that to him 'twas no credit
To try his wife when there was never need,
Putting her heart to anguish and to dread.

In doing which the marquis took his turn:
He came alone by night to where she lay
And with a troubled look and features stern
He said to her: "Griselda mine, that day
When I removed you from your poor array

And placed you in a state of nobleness—
You have not all forgotten that, I guess.

"I say, Griselda, this your dignity
Wherein I have so placed you, as I trow,
Has not made you forgetful now to be
That I raised you from poor estate and low
For any good you might then have or know.
Take heed of every word that now I say,
There's no one else shall hear it, by my fay.

"You know and well enough how you came here
Into this house, it is not long ago,
And though to me you are both lief and dear,
Unto my nobles you are not; and so
They say that unto them 'tis shame and woe
To be your subjects and compelled to serve
You who are village-born and naught deserve.

"And specially, since that girl-child you bore,
These things they've said—of this there is no doubt;
But I desire, as I have done before,
To live at peace with all the folk about;
I cannot in this matter leave them out.
I must do with your daughter what is best,
Not as I would, but under men's behest.

"And yet, God knows, the act is hard for me;
And only with your knowledge would I bring
The deed to pass, but this I would," said he,
"That you assent with me to this one thing.
Show now that patience in your life's dealing
You told me of and swore to in your village
The day that marked the making of our marriage."

When she had heard all this, this she received
With never a word or change of countenance;
For, as it seemed, she was in no way grieved.
She said: "Lord, all lies at your own pleasance;
My child and I, with hearty obeisance,
Are all yours, and you may save us or kill
That which is yours; do you what thing you will.

"There is no thing, and so God my soul save,
That you may like displeasing unto me;
I do not wish a single thing to have,
Nor dread a thing to lose, save only ye;
This will is in my heart and aye shall be,
Nor length of time nor death may this deface,
Nor turn my passion to another place."

Glad was this marquis of her answering,
And yet he feigned as if he were not so;
All dreary were his face and his bearing
When it came time from chamber he should go.
Soon after this, a quarter-hour or so,
He privily told all of his intent
Unto a man, whom to his wife he sent.

A kind of sergeant was this serving man,
Who had proved often faithful, as he'd found,
In matters great, and such men often can

And putte yow in estaat of heigh noblesse,
Ye have nat that forgeten, as I gesse.

I seye, Grisild, this present dignitee,
In which that I have put yow, as I trowe,
Maketh yow nat foryetful for to be
That I yow took in povre estaat ful lowe
For any wele ye moot your-selven knowe.
Tak hede of every word that I yow seye,
Ther is no wight that hereth it but we tweye.

Ye woot your-self wel, how that ye cam here
In-to this hous, it is nat longe ago,
And though to me that ye be lief and dere,
Un-to my gentils ye be no-thing so;
They seyn, to hem it is greet shame and wo
For to be subgets and ben in servage
To thee, that born art of a smal village.

And namely, sith thy doghter was y-bore,
Thise wordes han they spoken doutelees;
But I desyre, as I have doon bifore,
To live my lyf with hem in reste and pees;
I may nat in this caas be recchelees.
I moot don with thy doghter for the beste,
Nat as I wolde, but as my peple leste.

And yet, god wot, this is ful looth to me;
But nathelees with-oute your witing
I wol nat doon, but this wol I," quod he,
"That ye to me assente as in this thing.
Shewe now your pacience in your werking
That ye me highte and swore in your village
That day that maked was our mariage."

Whan she had herd al this, she noght ameved
Neither in word, or chere, or countenaunce;
For, as it semed, she was nat agreved:
She seyde, "lord, al lyth in your plesaunce,
My child and I with hertly obeisaunce
Ben youres al, and ye mowe save or spille
Your owene thing; werketh after your wille.

Ther may no-thing, god so my soule save,
Lyken to yow that may displese me;
Ne I desyre no-thing for to have,
Ne drede for to lese, save only ye;
This wil is in myn herte and ay shal be.
No lengthe of tyme or deeth may this deface,
Ne chaunge my corage to another place."

Glad was this markis of hir answering,
But yet he feyned as he were nat so;
Al drery was his chere and his loking
Whan that he sholde out of the chambre go.
Sone after this, a furlong wey or two,
He prively hath told al his entente
Un-to a man, and to his wyf him sente.

A maner sergeant was this privee man,
The which that feithful ofte he founden hadde
In thinges grete, and eek swich folk wel can

Don execucioun on thinges badde.
The lord knew wel that he him loved and dradde;
And whom this sergeant wiste his lordes wille,
In-to the chambre he stalked him ful stille.

"Madame," he seyde, "ye mote foryeve it me,
Thogh I do thing to which I am constreyned;
Ye ben so wys that ful wel knowe ye
That lordes hestes mowe nat been y-feyned;
They mowe wel been biwailled or compleyned,
But men mot nede un-to her lust obeye,
And so wol I; ther is na-more to seye.

This child I am comanded for to take"—
And spak na-more, but out the child he hente
Despitously, and gan a chere make
As though he wolde han slayn it er he wente.
Grisildis mot al suffren and consente;
And as a lamb she sitteth meke and stille,
And leet this cruel sergeant doon his wille.

Suspecious was the diffame of this man,
Suspect his face, suspect his word also;
Suspect the tyme in which he this bigan.
Allas! hir doghter that she lovede so
She wende he wolde han slawen it right tho.
But natheles she neither weep ne syked,
Consenting hir to that the markis lyked.

But atte laste speken she bigan,
And mekely she to the sergeant preyde,
So as he was a worthy gentil man,
That she moste kisse hir child er that it deyde;
And in her barm this litel child she leyde
With ful sad face, and gan the child to kisse
And lulled it, and after gan it blisse.

And thus she seyde in hir benigne voys,
"Far weel, my child; I shal thee never see;
But, sith I thee have marked with the croys,
Of thilke fader blessed mote thou be,
That for us deyde up-on a croys of tree.
Thy soule, litel child, I him bitake,
For this night shaltow dyen for my sake."

I trowe that to a norice in this cas
It had ben hard this rewthe for to se;
Wel mighte a mooder than han cryed "allas!"
But nathelees so sad stedfast was she,
That she endured all adversitee,
And to the sergeant mekely she sayde,
"Have heer agayn your litel yonge mayde.

Goth now," quod she, "and dooth my lordes heste,
But o thing wol I preye yow of your grace,
That, but my lord forbad yow, atte leste
Burieth this litel body in som place
That bestes ne no briddes it to-race."
But he no word wol to that purpos seye,
But took the child and wente upon his weye.

This sergeant cam un-to his lord ageyn,

Do evil faithfully, as can a hound.
The lord knew this man loved him and was bound;
And when this sergeant learned his lordship's will
He stalked into the chamber, grim and still.

"Madam," said he, "you must forgive it me,
Though I do that to which I am constrained;
You are so wise you know well, it may be,
That a lord's orders may not well be feigned;
They may be much lamented or complained,
But men must needs their every wish obey,
And thus will I; there is no more to say.

"This child I am commanded now to take"—
And spoke no more, but seized that innocent
Pitilessly, and did a gesture make
As if he would have slain it ere he went,
Griselda, she must suffer and consent;
And so, meek as a lamb, she sat there, still,
And let this cruel sergeant do his will.

Suspicious of repute was this same man,
Suspect his face, suspect his word also,
Suspect the time when this thing he began,
Alas! Her daughter that she had loved so,
She thought he'd slay it right there, whether or no.
Nevertheless, she neither wept nor sighed,
Doing the marquis' liking though she died.

At last she found her voice and thus began
And meekly to the sergeant then she prayed
That, as he was a worthy, gentle man,
She might kiss her child once before his blade;
And on her breast this child she laid,
With sad face, and so kissed it and did press
And lulled it and at last began to bless.

And thus she said in her benignant voice:
"Farewell, my child that I no more shall see;
But now I've crossed you thus, I will rejoice
That of the Father blessed may you be,
Who died for us upon the bitter tree.
Your soul, my little child, to Him I give;
This night you die for my sake—though I live."

I think that to a nurse in such a case
It had been hard this pitiful thing to see;
Well might a mother then have cried "Alas!"
But so steadfastly serious was she
That she endured all her adversity,
And to the sergeant she but meekly said:
"I give you now again your little maid.

"Go now," said she, "and do my lord's behest,
But one thing will I pray you, of your grace,
That, save my lord forbade you, at the least
Bury this little body in some place
Where beasts nor birds will tear its limbs and face."
But no word to that purpose would he say,
But took the child and went upon his way.

This sergeant went unto his lord again

And of Griselda's words and of her cheer
He told him point by point, all short and plain,
And so presented him his daughter dear.
A little pity felt the marquis here;
Nevertheless, he held his purpose still,
As great lords do when they will have their will;

And bade the sergeant that he privily
Should softly swaddle the young child and wrap
With all the necessaries, tenderly,
And in a coffer or some garment lap;
But upon pain his head should meet mishap
No man should know the least of his intent,
Nor whence he came, nor whither that he went;

But to Bologna, to his sister dear
Who then was of Panago the countess,
He should take it, and tell of matters here,
Asking of her she do her busyness
This child to foster in all nobleness;
And whose the child was, that he bade her hide
From everyone, for aught that might betide.

The sergeant goes and has fulfilled this thing;
But to this marquis now return must we;
For soon he went to see her, wondering
If by his wife's demeanour he might see,
Or by her conversation learn that she
Were changed in aught; but her he could not find
Other than ever serious and kind.

As glad, as humble, as busy in service,
And even in love, as she was wont to be,
Was she to him at all times in each wise;
And of her daughter not a word spoke she.
No strange nor odd look of adversity
Was seen in her, and her dear daughter's name
She never named in earnest nor in game.

And of Grisildis wordes and hir chere
He tolde him point for point, in short and playn,
And him presenteth with his doghter dere.
Somwhat this lord hath rewthe in his manere;
But nathelees his purpos heeld he stille,
As lordes doon, whan they wol han hir wille;

And bad his sergeant that he privily
Sholde this child ful softe winde and wrappe
With alle circumstances tendrely,
And carie it in a cofre or in a lappe;
But, up-on peyne his heed of for to swappe,
That no man sholde knowe of his entente,
Ne whenne he cam, ne whider that he wente;

But at Boloigne to his suster dere,
That thilke tyme of Panik was countesse,
He sholde it take, and shewe hir this matere,
Bisekinge hir to don hir bisinesse
This child to fostre in alle gentilesse;
And whos child that it was he bad hir hyde
From every wight, for oght that may bityde.

The sergeant gooth, and hath fulfild this thing;
But to this markis now retourne we;
For now goth he ful faste imagining
If by his wyves chere he mighte see,
Or by hir word aperceyve that she
Were chaunged; but he never hir coude finde
But ever in oon y-lyke sad and kinde.

As glad, as humble, as bisy in servyse,
And eek in love as she was wont to be,
Was she to him in every maner wyse;
Ne of hir doghter noght a word spak she.
Non accident for noon adversitee
Was seyn in hir, ne never hir doghter name
Ne nempned she, in ernest nor in game.

HERE ENDETH THE THIRD PART

HERE FOLLOWETH THE FOURTH PART

In this way over them there passed four years
Ere she with child was; but as High God would,
A boy-child then she bore, as it appears,
By Walter, fair and pleasing to behold.
And when folk this word to the father told,
Not only he but all the people raised
Their joyous hymns to God and His grace praised.

When he was two years old and from the breast
Weaned by his nurse, it chanced upon a day
This marquis had another wish to test
And try his wife yet further, so they say.
Oh, needless her temptation in this way!
But wedded men no measure can observe
When they've a wife who's patient and will serve.

"Wife," said this marquis, "you have heard before,
My people bear our marriage with ill-will;
Particularly since my son you bore
Now it is worse than ever, all this ill.
Their murmurs all my heart and courage kill,

In this estaat ther passed been foure yeer
Er she with childe was; but, as god wolde,
A knave child she bar by this Walter,
Ful gracious and fair for to biholde.
And whan that folk it to his fader tolde,
Nat only he, but al his contree, merie
Was for this child, and god they thanke and herie.

Whan it was two yeer old, and fro the brest
Departed of his norice, on a day
This markis caughte yet another lest
To tempte his wyf yet ofter, if he may.
O needles was she tempted in assay!
But wedded men ne knowe no mesure,
Whan that they finde a pacient creature.

"Wyf," quod this markis, "ye han herd er this,
My peple sikly berth our mariage,
And namely, sith my sone y-boren is,
Now is it worse than ever in al our age.
The murmur sleeth myn herte and my corage;

For to myne eres comth the voys so smerte,
That it wel ny destroyed hath myn herte.

Now sey they thus, 'whan Walter is agoon,
Then shal the blood of Janicle succede
And been our lord, for other have we noon';
Swiche wordes seith my peple, out of drede.
Wel oughte I of swich murmur taken hede;
For certeinly I drede swich sentence,
Though they nat pleyn speke in myn audience.

I wolde live in pees, if that I mighte;
Wherfor I am disposed outerly,
As I his suster servede by nighte,
Right so thenke I to serve him prively;
This warne I yow, that ye nat sodeynly
Out of your-self for no wo sholde outraye;
Beth pacient, and ther-of I yow preye."

"I have," quod she, "seyd thus, and ever shal,
I wol no thing, ne nil no thing, certayn,
But as yow list; noght greveth me at al,
Thogh that my doghter and my sone be slayn,
At your comandement, this is to sayn.
I have noght had no part of children tweyne
But first siknesse, and after wo and peyne.

Ye been our lord, doth with your owene thing
Right as yow list; axeth no reed at me.
For, as I lefte at hoom al my clothing,
Whan I first cam to yow, right so," quod she,
"Lefte I my wil and al my libertee,
And took your clothing; wherfor I yow preye,
Doth your plesaunce, I wol your lust obeye.

And certes, if I hadde prescience
Your wil to knowe er ye your lust me tolde,
I wolde it doon with-outen necligence;
But now I woot your lust and what ye wolde,
Al your plesaunce ferme and stable I holde;
For wiste I that my deeth wolde do yow ese,
Right gladly wolde I dyen, yow to plese.

Deth may noght make no comparisoun
Un-to your love": and, whan this markis sey
The constance of his wyf, he caste adoun
His yën two, and wondreth that she may
In pacience suffre al this array.
And forth he gooth with drery contenaunce.
But to his herte it was ful greet plesaunce.

This ugly sergeant, in the same wyse
That he hir doghter caughte, right so he,
Or worse, if men worse can devyse,
Hath hent hir sone, that ful was of beautee.
And ever in oon so pacient was she,
That she no chere made of hevinesse,
But kiste hir sone, and after gan it blesse;

Save this; she preyed him that, if he mighte,
Hir litel sone he wolde in erthe grave,
His tendre limes, delicat to sighte,

For to my ears come words so aimed to smart
That they have well-nigh broken all my heart.

"Now they say this: 'When Walter's dead and gone,
Then shall Janicula's base blood succeed
And be our lord, for other have we none!'
Such words my people say, 'tis true, indeed!
Well ought I of such murmurs to take heed;
For truly do I fear the populace,
Though they say nothing plainly to my face.

I would exist in peace, if that I might;
Wherefore I am determined utterly
That as his sister served I, and by night,
Just so will I serve him full secretly;
And thus I warn you, that not suddenly
Out of yourself for woe you start or stray;
Be patient in this sorrow, so I pray."

"I have," said she, "said thus, and ever shall:
I'll have no thing, or not have, that's certain,
Save as you wish; nothing grieves me at all,
Even though my daughter and my son are slain
At your command, and that, I think, is plain.
I have had no part in my children twain
But sickness first, and after, woe and pain.

"You are our master; do with your own thing
Just as you like; no counsel ask of me.
For, as I left at home all my clothing
When first I came to you, just so," said she,
"Left I my will and all my liberty,
And took your clothing; wherefore do I pray
You'll do your pleasure, I'll your wish obey.

"For certainly, if I had prescience
Your will to know ere you your wish had told,
I would perform it without negligence;
But now I know the wish that you unfold,
To do your pleasure firmly will I hold;
For knew I that my death would give you ease,
Right gladly would I die, lord, you to please.

"For death can offer no loss that is known
Compared to your love's loss." And when, I say,
He saw his wife's great constancy, then down
He cast his eyes, and wondered at the way
She would in patience all his will obey;
And forth he went with dreary countenance,
But in his heart he knew a great pleasance.

This ugly sergeant in the very wise
That he her daughter took away, so he
(Or worse, if worse than this men could devise)
Has taken her son, the child of such beauty.
And always yet so all-patient was she
That she no sign gave forth of heaviness,
But kissed her son and so began to bless;

Save this: She prayed him that, and if he might,
Her son he'd bury in an earthen grave,
His tender limbs, so delicate to sight,

From ravenous birds and from all beasts to save.
But she no answer out of him could have.
He went his way as if he cared nor thought,
But to Bologna tenderly 'twas brought.

This marquis wondered ever more and more
Upon her patience; and indeed if he
Had not known truly in her years before
That she had loved her children perfectly,
He would have thought that out of subtlety
And malice, or from some urge more savage
She suffered this with calm face and courage.

But well he knew that, next himself, 'twas plain
She loved her children best in every wise.
But now to ask of women I am fain,
Whether these trials should not the man suffice?
What could an obdurate husband more devise
To prove her wifehood and her faithfulness,
And he continuing in his stubbornness?

But there are folk to such condition grown
That, when they do a certain purpose take,
They cannot quit the intent they thus own,
But just as they were bound unto a stake
They will not from that first hard purpose shake.
Just so this marquis fully was purposed
To test his wife, as he was first disposed.

He watched her, if by word or countenance
She show a change toward him, or in courage;
But never could he find a variance.
She was aye one in heart and in visage;
And aye the farther that she went in age,
The more true, if such thing were possible,
She was in love, and painstaking, as well.

From which it seemed that, as between those
two,
There was but one will, for, to Walter's quest,
The same thing was her sole desire also,
And—God be thanked!—all fell out for the best.
She showed well that, in all this world's unrest,
A wife, of her volition, nothing should
Will to be done, save as her husband would.

The scandal of this Walter widely spread,
That, of his cruel heart, he'd wickedly
(Because a humble woman he had wed)
Murdered his two young children secretly.
Such murmurs went among them commonly.
No wonder, either, for to people's ear
There came no word but they'd been murdered
there.

For which, whereas the people theretofore
Had loved him, now the scandal of such shame
Caused them to hate where they had loved before;
To be a murderer brings a hateful name.
Nevertheless, in earnest nor in game
Would he from this his cruel plan be bent;
To test his wife was all his fixed intent.

Fro foules and fro bestes for to save.
But she non answer of him mighte have.
He wente his wey, as him no-thing ne roghte;
But to Boloigne he tendrely it broghte.

This markis wondreth ever lenger the more
Up-on hir pacience, and if that he
Ne hadde soothly knowen ther-bifore,
That parfitly hir children lovede she,
He wolde have wend that of som subtiltee,
And of malice or for cruel corage,
That she had suffred this with sad visage.

But wel he knew that next him-self, certayn,
She loved hir children best in every wyse.
But now of wommen wolde I axen fayn,
If thise assayes mighte nat suffyse?
What coude a sturdy housbond more devyse
To preve hir wyfhod and hir stedfastnesse,
And he continuing ever in sturdinesse?

But ther ben folk of swich condicioun,
That, whan they have a certein purpos take,
They can nat stinte of hir entencioun,
But, right as they were bounden to a stake,
They wol nat of that firste purpos slake.
Right so this markis fulliche hath purposed
To tempte his wyf, as he was first disposed.

He waiteth, if by word or contenance
That she to him was changed of corage;
But never coude he finde variance;
She was ay oon in herte and in visage;
And ay the forther that she was in age,
The more trewe, if that it were possible,
She was to him in love, and more penible.

For which it semed thus, that of hem
two
Ther nas but o wil; for, as Walter leste,
The same lust was hir plesance also,
And, god be thanked, al fil for the beste.
She shewed wel, for no worldly unreste
A wyf, as of hir-self, no-thing ne sholde
Wille in effect, but as hir housbond wolde.

The sclaundre of Walter ofte and wyde spradde,
That of a cruel herte he wikkedly,
For he a povre womman wedded hadde,
Hath mordred bothe his children prively.
Swich murmur was among hem comunly.
No wonder is, for to the peples ere
Ther cam no word but that they mordred
were.

For which, wher-as his peple ther-bifore
Had loved him wel, the sclaundre of his diffame
Made hem that they him hatede therfore;
To been a mordrer is an hateful name.
But natheles, for ernest ne for game
He of his cruel purpos nolde stente;
To tempte his wyf was set al his entente.

Whan that his doghter twelf yeer was of age,
He to the court of Rome, in subtil wyse
Enformed of his wil, sente his message,
Comaunding hem swiche bulles to devyse
As to his cruel purpos may suffyse,
How that the pope, as for his peples reste,
Bad him to wedde another, if him leste.

Now when his daughter was twelve years of age,
He to the court of Rome (in sublte wise
Informed of his design) sent his message,
Commanding them such bulls they should devise
As for his cruel purpose would suffice,
How that the pope, for Walter's people's rest,
Bade him to wed another, and the best.

I seye, he bad they sholde countrefete
The popes bulles, making mencioun
That he hath leve his firste wyf to lete,
As by the popes dispensacioun,
To stinte rancour and dissencioun
Bitwixe his peple and him; thus seyde the bulle,
The which they han publiced atte fulle.

I say, he ordered they should counterfeit
A papal bull and set it forth therein
That he had leave his first wife now to quit,
By papal dispensation, with no sin,
To stop all such dissension as did win
Between his folk and him; thus said the bull,
The which thing they did publish to the full.

The rude peple, as it no wonder is,
Wenden ful wel that it had been right so;
But whan thise tydinges cam to Grisildis,
I deme that hir herte was ful wo.
But she, y-lyke sad for evermo,
Disposed was, this humble creature,
Th'adversitee of fortune al t'endure.

The ignorant people, as no wonder is,
Supposed of course that things were even so;
But when Griselda's ears caught word of this,
I judge that then her heart was filled with woe.
But she, for ever steadfast, still did show
Herself disposed, this humble meek creature,
The adversity of Fortune to endure.

Abyding ever his lust and his plesaunce,
To whom that she was yeven, herte and al,
As to hir verray worldly suffisaunce;
But shortly if this storie I tellen shal,
This markis writen hath in special
A lettre in which he sheweth his entente,
And secrely he to Boloigne it sente.

Abiding ever his wish and pleasure still,
To whom she had been given, heart and all,
He was her worldly hope, for good or ill;
But to tell all this briefly, if I shall,
This marquis wrote, in letter personal,
The devious working of his whole intent
And secretly 'twas to Bologna sent.

To th'erl of Panik, which that hadde tho
Wedded his suster, preyde he specially
To bringen hoom agayn his children two
In honurable estaat al openly.
But o thing he him preyede outerly,
That he to no wight, though men wolde enquere,
Sholde nat telle, whos children that they were,

Unto Panago's count, who had, we know,
Wedded his sister, prayed he specially
To bring him home again his children two,
In honourable estate, all openly.
But one more thing he prayed him, utterly,
That he to no one, whoso should inquire,
Would tell who was their mother or their sire,

But seye, the mayden sholde y-wedded be
Un-to the markis of Saluce anon.
And as this erl was preyed, so dide he;
For at day set he on his wey is goon
Toward Saluce, and lordes many oon,
In riche array, this mayden for to gyde;
Hir yonge brother ryding hir bisyde.

But say: The maiden married was to be
Unto Saluzzo's marquis and anon.
And as this count was asked, so then did he;
For on day set he on his way was gone
Toward Saluzzo, with lords many a one,
In rich array, this maiden there to guide,
With her young brother riding at her side.

Arrayed was toward hir mariage
This fresshe mayde, ful of gemmes clere;
Hir brother, which that seven yeer was of age,
Arrayed eek ful fresh in his manere.
And thus in greet noblesse and with glad chere,
Toward Saluces shaping hir journey,
Fro day to day they ryden in hir wey.

So toward her marriage went this fresh young maid
Clad richly and bedecked with jewels clear;
Her brother with her, boyishly arrayed,
And all anew, was now in his eighth year.
And thus in great pomp and with merry cheer,
Toward Saluzzo went they on their way,
And rode along together day by day.

HERE ENDETH THE FOURTH PART

HERE FOLLOWETH THE FIFTH PART

Among al this, after his wikke usage,
This markis, yet his wyf to tempte more
To the uttereste preve of hir corage,
Fully to han experience and lore

Meanwhile, according to his wicked way,
This marquis still to test his wife once more,
Even to the final proof of her, I say,
Fully to have experience to the core

If she were yet as steadfast as before,
He on a day in open audience
Loudly said unto her this rude sentence:

"Truly, Griselda, I'd much joy, perchance,
When you I took for wife, for your goodness
And for your truth and your obedience,
Not for your lineage nor your wealth, I guess:
But now I know, in utter certainness,
That in great lordship, if I well advise,
There is great servitude in sundry wise.

"I may not act as every plowman may;
My people have constrained me that I take
Another wife, and this they ask each day;
And now the pope, hot rancour thus to slake,
Consents, I dare the thing to undertake;
And truly now this much to you I'll say,
My new wife journeys hither on her way.

"Be strong of heart and leave at once her place,
And that same dower that you brought to me,
Take it again, I grant it of my grace;
Return you to your father's house," said he;
"No man may always have prosperity;
With a calm heart I urge you to endure
The stroke of Fortune or of adventure."

And she replied again, of her patience:
"My lord," said she, "I know, and knew alway,
How that between your own magnificence
And my poor state, no person can or may
Make a comparison in an equal way.
I never held me worthy or of grade
To be your wife, no, nor your chambermaid.

"And in this house, where lady you made me
(The High God do I take now to witness,
And as He truly may my soul's joy be),
I never held me lady nor mistress,
But only servant to your worthiness;
And ever shall, while my life may endure,
Beyond all worldly beings, that is sure,

"That you so long, of your benignity,
Have held me here in honour in this way,
Where I was never worthy, once, to be,
For that, thank God and you—to God I pray
He will reward you. There's no more to say.
Unto my father gladly will I wend
And dwell with him until my life shall end.

"Where I was fostered when an infant small,
There will I lead my life till I be dead,
A widow, clean in body, heart, and all.
For, since I gave to you my maidenhead,
And am your true and lawful wife, wedded,
May God forbid such a lord's wife to take
Another man for husband or love's sake.

"And of your new wife, may God of His grace
Grant you but joy and all prosperity:

If that she were as stedfast as bifore,
He on a day in open audience
Ful boistously hath seyd hir this sentence:

"Certes, Grisilde, I hadde y-nough plesaunce
To han yow to my wyf for your goodnesse.
As for your trouthe and for your obeisaunce,
Nought for your linage ne for your richesse;
But now knowe I in verray soothfastnesse
That in gret lordshipe, if I wel avyse,
Ther is gret servitute in sondry wyse.

I may nat don as every plowman may;
My peple me constreyneth for to take
Another wyf, and cryen day by day;
And eek the pope, rancour for to slake,
Consenteth it, that dar I undertake;
And treweliche thus muche I wol yow seye,
Ny newe wyf is coming by the weye.

Be strong of herte, and voyde anon hir place,
And thilke dower that ye broghten me
Tak it agayn, I graunte it of my grace;
Retourneth to your fadres hous," quod he;
"No man may alwey han prosperitee;
With evene herte I rede yow t'endure
The strook of fortune or of aventure."

And she answerde agayn in pacience,
"My lord," quod she, "I woot, and wiste alway
How that bitwixen your magnificence
And my poverte no wight can ne may
Maken comparison; it is no nay.
I ne heeld me never digne in no manere
To be your wyf, no, ne your chamberere.

And in this hous, ther ye me lady made—
The heighe god take I for my witnesse,
And also wisly he my soule glade—
I never heeld me lady ne maistresse,
But humble servant to your worthinesse,
And ever shal, whyl that my lyf may dure,
Aboven every worldly creature.

That ye so longe of your benignitee
Han holden me in honour and nobleye,
Wher-as I was noght worthy for to be,
That thonke I god and yow, to whom I preye
Foryelde it yow; there is na-more to seye.
Un-to my fader gladly wol I wende,
And with him dwelle un-to my lyves ende.

Ther I was fostred of a child ful smal,
Til I be deed, my lyf ther wol I lede
A widwe clene, in body, herte, and al.
For sith I yaf to yow my maydenhede,
And am your trewe wyf, it is no drede,
God shilde swich a lordes wyf to take
Another man to housbonde or to make.

And of your newe wyf, god of his grace
So graunte yow wele and prosperitee;

For I wol gladly yelden hir my place,
In which that I was blisful wont to be,
For sith it lyketh yow, my lord," quod she,
"That whylom weren al myn hertes reste,
That I shal goon, I wol gon whan yow leste.

But ther-as ye me profre swich dowaire
As I first broghte, it is wel in my minde
It were my wrecched clothes, no-thing faire,
The which to me were hard now for to finde.
O gode god! how gentil and how kinde
Ye semed by your speche and your visage
The day that maked was our mariage!

But sooth is seyd, algate I finde it trewe—
For in effect it preved is on me—
Love is noght old as whan that it is newe.
But certes, lord, for noon adversitee,
To dyen in the cas, it shal nat be
That ever in word or werk I shal repente
That I yow yaf myn herte in hool entente.

My lord, ye woot that, in my fadres place,
Ye dede me strepe out of my povre wede,
And richely me cladden, of your grace.
To yow broghte I noght elles, out of drede,
But feyth and nakednesse and maydenhede.
And here agayn my clothing I restore,
And eek my wedding-ring, for evermore.

The remenant of your jewels redy be
In-with your chambre, dar I saufly sayn;
Naked out of my fadres hous," quod she,
"I cam, and naked moot I turne agayn.
Al your plesaunce wol I folwen fayn;
But yet I hope it be nat your entente
That I smoklees out of your paleys wente.

Ye coude nat doon so dishoneste a thing,
That thilke wombe in which your children leye
Sholde, biforn the peple, in my walking,
Be seyn al bare; wherfor I yow preye,
Lat me nat lyk a worm go by the weye.
Remembre yow, myn owene lord so dere,
I was your wyf, thogh I unworthy were.

Wherfor, in guerdon of my maydenhede,
Which that I broghte, and noght agayn I bere,
As voucheth sauf to yeve me, to my mede,
But swich a smok as I was wont to were,
That I therwith may wrye the wombe of here
That was your wyf; and heer take I my leve
Of yow, myn owene lord, lest I yow greve."

"The smok," quod he, "that thou hast on thy
bak,
Lat it be stille, and ber it forth with thee."
But wel unnethes thilke word he spak,
But wente his wey for rewthe and for pitee.
Biforn the folk hir-selven strepeth she,
And in hir smok, with heed and foot al bare,
Toward hir fader hous forth is she fare.

For I will gladly yield to her my place,
Wherein so happy I was wont to be,
For since it pleases you, my lord," said she,
Who have been all my heart's ease and its rest,
That I shall go, I'll go when you request.

"But whereas now you proffer me such dower
As first I brought to you, it's in my mind
That 'twas my wretched clothes and nothing fair.
The which to me were hard now for to find.
O my good God! How noble and how kind
You seemed then, in your speech and in your face.
The day we married in that humble place.

"But truth is said—at least I find it true
For actually its proof is seen in me—
Old love is not the same as when it's new.
But truly, lord, for no adversity,
Though I should die of all this, shall it be
That ever in word or deed I shall repent
That I gave you my heart in whole intent.

"My lord, you know that, in my father's place,
You stripped from me my poor and humble weed
And clothed me richly, of your noble grace.
I brought you nothing else at all indeed,
Than faith and nakedness and maidenhead.
And here again my clothing I restore,
And, too, my wedding-ring, for evermore.

"The rest of all your jewels, they will be
Within your chamber, as I dare maintain;
Naked out of my father's house," said she,
"I came, and naked I return again.
To follow aye your pleasure I am fain,
But yet I hope it is not your intent
That smockless from your palace I be sent.

"You could not do so base and shameful thing
That the same womb in which your children lay
Should, before all the folk, in my walking,
Be seen all bare; and therefore do I pray
Let me not like a worm go on my way.
Remember that, my own lord, always dear,
I was your wife, though I unworthy were.

Wherefore, as guerdon for my maidenhead,
The which I brought, but shall not with me bear,
Let them but give me, for my only meed,
Such a poor smock as I was wont to wear,
That I therewith may hide the womb of her
Who was your wife; and here I take my leave
Of you, my own dear lord, lest you should grieve."

"The smock, "said he, "that you have on your
back,
Let it stay there and wear it forth," said he.
But firmness in so saying the man did lack;
But went his way for ruth and for pity.
Before the folk her body then stripped she
And in her smock, with head and feet all bare,
Toward her father's hovel did she fare.

The folk they followed, weeping and with cries,
And Fortune did they curse as they passed on;
But she with weeping did not wet her eyes,
And all this while of words she said not one.
Her father, who had heard this news anon,
Cursed then the day and hour when from the earth,
A living creature, nature gave him birth.

The folk hir folwe wepinge in hir weye,
And fortune ay they cursen as they goon;
But she fro weping kepte hir yën dreye,
Ne in this tyme word ne spak she noon.
Hir fader, that this tyding herde anoon,
Curseth the day and tyme that nature
Shoop him to been a lyves creature.

For, beyond any doubt, this poor old man
Had always feared the marquis soon would tire,
And doubted since the marriage first began,
If when the lord had satisfied desire,
He would not think a wife of station higher,
For one of his degree, had been more right,
And send her thence as soon as ever he might.

For out of doute this olde povre man
Was ever in suspect of hir mariage;
For ever he demed, sith that it bigan,
That whan the lord fulfild had his corage,
Him wolde thinke it were a disparage
To his estaat so lowe for t'alighte,
And voyden hir as sone as ever he mighte.

To meet his daughter hastily went he,
For he, by noise of folk, knew her coming;
And with her old coat, such as it might be,
He covered her, full sorrowfully weeping;
But the coat over her he could not bring,
For poor the cloth, and many days had passed
Since on her marriage day she wore it last.

Agayns his doghter hastilich goth he,
For he by noyse of folk knew hir cominge,
And with hir olde cote, as it mighte be,
He covered hir, ful sorwefully wepinge;
But on hir body mighte he it nat bringe.
For rude was the cloth, and more of age
By dayes fele than at hir mariage.

Thus with her father, for a certain space,
Did dwell this flower of wifely meek patience,
Who neither by her words nor in her face,
Before the people nor in their absence,
Showed that she thought to her was done offense;
Nor of her high estate a remembrance
Had she, to judge by her calm countenance.

Thus with hir fader, for a certeyn space,
Dwelleth this flour of wyfly pacience,
That neither by hir wordes ne hir face
Biforn the folk, ne eek in hir absence,
Ne shewed she that hir was doon offence;
Ne of hir heigh estaat no remembraunce
Ne hadde she, as by hir countenaunce.

No wonder, though, for while in high estate,
Her soul kept ever full humility;
No mouth complaining, no heart delicate,
No pomp, no look of haughty royalty,
But full of patience and benignity,
Discreet and prideless, always honourable,
And to her husband meek and firm as well.

No wonder is, for in hir grete estaat
Hir goost was ever in pleyn humylitee;
No tendre mouth, non herte delicaat,
No pompe, no semblant of royaltee,
But ful of pacient benignitee,
Discreet and prydeles, ay honurable,
And to hir housbonde ever meke and stable.

Men speak of Job and of his humbleness,
As clerks, when they so please, right well can write
Concerning men, but truth is, nevertheless,
Though clerks' praise of all women is but slight,
No man acquits himself in meekness quite
As women can, nor can be half so true
As women are, save this be something new.

Men speke of Job and most for his humblesse,
As clerkes, whan hem list, can wel endyte,
Namely of men, but as in soothfastnesse,
Thogh clerkes preyse wommen but a lyte,
Ther can no man in humblesse him acquyte
As womman can, ne can ben half so trewe
As wommen been, but it be falle of-newe.

[*SIXTH PART*]

Now from Bologna is Panago come,
Whereof the word spread unto great and less,
And in the ears of people, all and some,
It was told, too, that a new marchioness
Came with him, in such pomp and such richness
That never had been seen with human eye
So noble array in all West Lombardy.

Fro Boloigne is this erl of Panik come,
Of which the fame up-sprang to more and lesse,
And in the peples eres alle and some
Was couth eek, that a newe markisesse
He with him broghte, in swich pompe and richesse,
That never was ther seyn with mannes yë
So noble array in al West Lumbardye.

The marquis, who had planned and knew all this
Before this count was come, a message sent
To poor Griselda, who had lost her bliss;
With humble heart and features glad she went

The markis, which that shoop and knew al this,
Er that this erl was come, sente his message
For thilke sely povre Grisildis;
And she with humble herte and glad visage,

Nat with no swollen thoght in hir corage,
Cam at his heste, and on hir knees hir sette,
And reverently and wysly she him grette.

And on her knees before her lord she bent.
No pride of thought did her devotion dim;
She wisely and with reverence greeted him.

"Grisild," quod he, "my wille is outerly,
This mayden, that shal wedded been to me,
Receyved be to-morwe as royally
As it possible is in myn hous to be.
And eek that every wight in his degree
Have his estaat in sitting and servyse
And heigh plesaunce, as I can best devyse.

He said, "Griselda, hear what I shall say:
This maiden, who'll be wedded unto me,
Shall be received with splendour of array
As royally as in my house may be,
And, too, that everyone in his degree
Have his due rank in seating and service,
And high pleasance, as I can best devise.

I have no wommen suffisaunt certayn
The chambres for t'arraye in ordinaunce
After my lust, and therfor wolde I fayn
That thyn were al swich maner governaunce;
Thou knowest eek of old al my plesaunce;
Though thyn array be badde and yvel biseye,
Do thou thy devoir at the leeste weye."

"I have not serving women adequate
To set the rooms in order as I would.
And so I wish you here to regulate
All matters of the sort as mistress should.
You know of old the ways I think are good,
And though you're clothed in such a slattern's way,
Go do at least your duty as you may."

"Nat only, lord, that I am glad," quod she,
"To doon your lust, but I desyre also
Yow for to serve and plese in my degree
With-outen feynting, and shal evermo.
Ne never, for no wele ne no wo,
Ne shal the gost with-in myn herte stente
To love yow best with al my trewe entente."

"Not only am I glad, my lord," said she,
"To do your wish, but I desire also
To serve you and to please in my degree;
This without wearying I'll always do.
And ever, lord, in happiness or woe,
The soul within my heart shall not forgo
To love you best with true intent, I know."

And with that word she gan the hous to dighte,
And tables for to sette and beddes make;
And peyned hir to doon al that she mighte,
Preying the chambereres, for goddes sake,
To hasten hem, and faste swepe and shake;
And she, the moste servisable of alle,
Hath every chambre arrayed and his halle.

Then she began to put the house aright,
To set the tables and the beds to make;
And was at pains to do all that she might,
Praying the chambermaids, for good God's sake,
To make all haste and sweep hard and to shake;
And she, who was most serviceable of all,
Did every room array, and his wide hall.

Abouten undern gan this erl alighte,
That with him broghte thise noble children tweye,
For which the peple ran to seen the sighte
Of hir array, so richely biseye;
And than at erst amonges hem they seye,
That Walter was no fool, thogh that him leste
To chaunge his wyf, for it was for the beste.

About mid-morning did this count alight,
Who brought with him these noble children twain,
Whereat the people ran to see the sight
Of their array, so rich was all the train;
And for the first time did they not complain,
But said that Walter was no fool, at least,
To change his wife, for it was for the best.

For she is fairer, as they demen alle,
Than is Grisild, and more tendre of age,
And fairer fruit bitwene hem sholde falle,
And more plesant, for hir heigh linage;
Hir brother eek so fair was of visage,
That hem to seen the peple hath caught plesaunce,
Commending now the markis governaunce.—

For she was fairer far, so thought they all,
Than was Griselda, and of younger age,
And fairer fruit betwixt the two should fall,
And pleasing more, for her high lineage;
Her brother, too, so fair was of visage,
That, seeing them, the people all were glad,
Commending now the sense the marquis had.

AUTHOR

"O stormy peple! unsad and ever untrewe!
Ay undiscreet and chaunging as a vane,
Delyting ever in rumbel that is newe,
For lyk the mone ay wexe ye and wane;
Ay ful of clapping, dere y-nogh a jane;
Your doom is fals, your constance yvel preveth,
A ful greet fool is he that on yow leveth!"

"O storm-torn people! Unstable and untrue!
Aye indiscreet, and changing as a vane,
Delighting ever in rumour that is new,
For like the moon aye do you wax and wane;
Full of all chatter, dear at even a jane;
Your judgment's false, your constancy deceives,
A full great fool is he that you believes!"

Thus seyden sadde folk in that citee,

Thus said the sober folk of that city,

Seeing the people staring up and down,
For they were glad, just for the novelty,
To have a young new lady of their town.
No more of this I'll mention or make known;
But to Griselda I'll myself address
To tell her constancy and busyness.

Full busy Griselda was in everything
That to the marquis' feast was pertinent;
Nothing was she confused by her clothing,
Though rude it was and somewhat badly
 rent.
But with a glad face to the gate she went,
With other folk, to greet the marchioness,
And afterward she did her busyness.

With so glad face his guests she did receive,
And with such tact, each one in his degree,
That no fault in it could a man perceive;
But all they wondered much who she might be
That in so poor array, as they could see,
Yet knew so much of rank and reverence;
And worthily they praised her high prudence.

In all this while she never once did cease
The maiden and her brother to commend
With kindness of a heart that was at peace,
So well that no man could her praise amend.
But at the last, when all these lords did wend
To seat themselves to dine, then did he call
Griselda, who was busy in his hall.

"Griselda," said he, as it were in play,
"How like you my new wife and her beauty?"
"Right well," said she, "my lord, for by my
 fay
A fairer saw I never than is she.
I pray that God give her prosperity;
And so I hope that to you both He'll send
Great happiness until your lives shall end.

"One thing I beg my lord, and warn also,
That you prick not, with any tormenting,
This tender maid, as you've hurt others so;
For she's been nurtured in her up-bringing
More tenderly, and, to my own thinking,
She could not such adversity endure
As could one reared in circumstances poor."

And when this Walter thought of her patience,
Her glad face, with no malice there at all,
And how so oft he'd done to her offence,
And she aye firm and constant as a wall,
Remaining ever blameless through it all,
This cruel marquis did his heart address
To pity for her wifely steadfastness.

"This is enough, Griselda mine!"
 cried he,
"Be now no more ill pleased nor more afraid;
I have your faith and your benignity,
As straitly as ever woman's was, assayed

Whan that the peple gazed up and doun,
For they were glad, right for the noveltee,
To han a newe lady of hir toun.
Na-more of this make I now mencioun;
But to Grisilde agayn wol I me dresse,
And telle hir constance and hir bisinesse.—

Ful bisy was Grisilde in every thing
That to the feste was apertinent;
Right noght was she abayst of hir clothing
Though it were rude and somdel eek
 torent.
But with glad chere to the yate is went,
With other folk, to grete the markisesse,
And after that doth forth hir bisinesse.

With so glad chere his gestes she receyveth,
And conningly, everich in his degree,
That no defaute no man aperceyveth;
But ay they wondren what she mighte be
That in so povre array was for to see,
And coude swich honour and reverence;
And worthily they preisen hir prudence.

In al this mene whyle she ne stente
This mayde and eek hir brother to commende
With al hir herte, in ful benigne entente,
So wel, that no man coude hir prys amende.
But atte laste, whan that thise lordes wende
To sitten doun to mete, he gan to calle
Grisilde, as she was bisy in his halle.

"Grisilde," quod he, as it were in his pley,
"How lyketh thee my wyf and hir beautee?"
"Right wel," quod she, "my lord; for, in good
 fey,
A fairer say I never noon than she.
I prey to god yeve hir prosperitee;
And so hope I that he wol to yow sende
Plesance y-nogh un-to your lyves ende.

O thing biseke I yow and warne also,
That ye ne prikke with no tormentinge
This tendre mayden, as ye han don mo;
For she is fostred in hir norishinge
More tendrely, and, to my supposinge,
She coude nat adversitee endure
As coude a povre fostred creature."

And whan this Walter say hir pacience,
Hir glade chere and no malice at al,
And he so ofte had doon to hir offence,
And she ay sad and constant as a wal,
Continuing ever hir innocence overal,
This sturdy markis gan his herte dresse
To rewen up-on hir wyfly stedfastnesse.

"This is y-nogh, Grisilde myn,"
 quod he,
"Be now na-more agast ne yvel apayed;
I have thy feith and thy benignitee,
As wel as ever womman was, assayed,

In greet estaat, and povreliche arrayed.
Now knowe I, dere wyf, thy stedfastnesse,"—
And hir in armes took and gan hir kesse.

And she for wonder took of it no keep;
She herde nat what thing he to hir seyde;
She ferde as she had stert out of a sleep,
Til she out of hir masednesse abreyde.
"Grisilde," quod he, "by god that for us deyde,
Thou art my wyf, ne noon other I have,
Ne never hadde, as god my soule save!

This is thy doghter which thou hast supposed
To be my wyf; that other feithfully
Shal be myn heir, as I have ay purposed;
Thou bare him in thy body trewely.
At Bologne have I kept hem prively;
Tak hem agayn, for now maystow nat seye
That thou hast lorn non of thy children
tweye.

And folk that otherweyes han seyd of me,
I warne hem wel that I have doon this dede
For no malice ne for no crueltee,
But for t'assaye in thee thy wommanhede,
And nat to sleen my children, god forbede!
But for to kepe hem prively and stille,
Til I thy purpos knewe and al thy wille."

Whan she this herde, aswowne doun she
falleth
For pitous joye, and after hir swowninge
She bothe hir yonge children un-to hir calleth,
And in hir armes, pitously wepinge,
Embraceth hem, and tendrely kissinge
Ful lyk a mooder, with hir salte teres
She batheth bothe hir visage and hir heres.

O, which a pitous thing it was to see
Hir swowning, and hir humble voys to here!
"Grauntmercy, lord, that thanke I yow," quod
she,
"That ye han saved me my children dere!
Now rekke I never to ben deed right here;
Sith I stonde in your love and in your grace,
No fors of deeth, ne whan my spirit pace!

O tendre, o dere, o yonge children myne,
Your woful mooder wende stedfastly
That cruel houndes or som foul vermyne
Hadde eten yow; but god, of his mercy,
And your benigne fader tendrely
Hath doon yow kept"; and in that same stounde
Al sodeynly she swapte adoun to grounde.

And in her swough so sadly holdeth she
Hir children two, whan she gan hem t'embrace,
That with greet sleighte and greet difficultee
The children from hir arm they gonne arace.
O many a teer on many a pitous face
Doun ran of hem that stoden hir bisyde;
Unnethe abouten hir mighte they abyde.

In high place and in poverty arrayed.
Now know I well ,dear wife, your steadfastness."
And he began to kiss her and to press.

And she, for wonder, took of this no keep;
She heard not what the thing was he had cried;
She fared as if she'd started out of sleep,
Till from bewilderment she roused her pride.
"Griselda," said he, "by our God Who died,
You are my wife, no other one I have,
Nor ever had, as God my soul may save!

"This is your daughter, whom you have supposed
Should be my wife; the other child truly
Shall be my heir, as I have aye purposed;
You bore him in your body faithfully.
I've kept them at Bologna secretly;
Take them again, for now you cannot say
That you have lost your children twain for
aye.

"And folk that otherwise have said of me,
I warn them well that I have done this deed
Neither for malice nor for cruelty,
But to make trial in you of virtue hid,
And not to slay my children, God forbid!
But just to keep them privily and still
Till I your purpose knew and all your will."

When she heard this, she swooned and down did
fall
For pitiful joy, and after her swooning
Both her young children to her did she call,
And in her arms, full piteously weeping,
Embraced them, and all tenderly kissing,
As any mother would, with many a tear
She bathed their faces and their sunny hair.

Oh, what a pitiful thing it was to see
Her swooning, and her humble voice to hear!
"Thanks, lord, that I may thank you now," said
she
"That you have saved to me my children dear!
Now I am ready for my death right here;
Since I stand in your love and in your grace,
Death matters not, nor what my soul may face!

"O young, O dear, O tender children mine,
Your woeful mother thought for long, truly,
That cruel hounds, or birds, or foul vermin
Had eaten you; but God, of His mercy,
And your good father, all so tenderly,
Have kept you safely." And in swoon profound
Suddenly there she fell upon the ground.

And in her swoon so forcefully held she
Her children two, whom she'd had in embrace,
That it was hard from her to set them free,
Her arms about them gently to unlace.
Oh, many a tear on many a pitying face
Ran down, of those were standing there beside;
Scarcely, for sympathy, could they abide.

But Walter cheered her till her sorrow fled;
And she rose up, abashed, out of her trance;
All praised her now, and joyous words they said,
Till she regained her wonted countenance.
Walter so honoured her by word and glance
That it was pleasing to observe the cheer
Between them, now again together here.

These ladies, when they found a tactful way,
Withdrew her and to her own room were gone,
And stripped her out of her so rude array,
And in a cloth of gold that brightly shone,
Crowned with a crown of many a precious stone
Upon her head, once more to hall they brought
Her, where they honoured her as all they ought.

Thus had this heavy day a happy end,
For everyone did everything he might
The day in mirth and revelry to spend
Till in the heavens shone the stars' fair light.
For far more grand in every person's sight
This feast was, and of greater cost, 'twas said,
Than were the revels when they two were wed.

Full many a year in high prosperity
They lived, these two, in harmony and rest,
And splendidly his daughter married he
Unto a lord, one of the worthiest
In Italy; and then in peace, as best
His wife's old father at his court he kept
Until the soul out of his body crept.

His son succeeded to his heritage
In rest and peace, after the marquis' day,
And wedded happily at proper age,
Albeit he tried his wife not, so they say.
This world is not so harsh, deny who may,
As in old times that now are long since gone,
And hearken what this author says thereon.

This story's told here, not that all wives should
Follow Griselda in humility,
For this would be unbearable, though they
would,
But just that everyone, in his degree,
Should be as constant in adversity
As was Griselda; for that Petrarch wrote
This tale, and in a high style, as you'll note.

For since a woman once was so patient
Before a mortal man, well more we ought
Receive in good part that which God has sent;
For cause he has to prove what He has wrought.
But He tempts no man that His blood has bought,
As James says, if you his epistle read;
Yet does He prove folk at all times, indeed,

And suffers us, for our good exercise,
With the sharp scourges of adversity
To be well beaten oft, in sundry wise;
Not just to learn our will; for truly He,
Ere we were born, did all our frailty see;

Walter hir gladeth, and hir sorwe slaketh;
She ryseth up, abaysed, from hir traunce,
And every wight hir joye and feste maketh,
Til she hath caught agayn hir contenaunce.
Walter hir dooth so feithfully plesaunce,
That it was deyntee for to seen the chere
Bitwixe hem two, now they ben met y-fere.

Thise ladyes, whan that they hir tyme say,
Han taken hir, and in-to chambre goon,
And strepen hir out of hir rude array,
And in a cloth of gold that brighte shoon,
With a coroune of many a riche stoon
Up-on hir heed, they in-to halle hir broghte,
And ther she was honoured as hir oghte.

Thus hath this pitous day a blisful ende,
For every man and womman dooth his might
This day in murthe and revel to dispende
Til on the welkne shoon the sterres light.
For more solempne in every mannes sight
This feste was, and gretter of costage,
Than was the revel of hir mariage.

Ful many a yeer in heigh prosperitee
Liven thise two in concord and in reste,
And richely his doghter maried he
Un-to a lord, oon of the worthieste
Of al Itaille; and than in pees and reste
His wyves fader in his court he kepeth,
Til that the soule out of his body crepeth.

His sone succedeth in his heritage
In reste and pees, after his fader day;
And fortunat was eek in mariage,
Al putte he nat his wyf in greet assay.
This world is nat so strong, it is no nay,
As it hath been in olde tymes yore,
And herkneth what this auctour seith therfore.

This storie is seyd, nat for that wyves sholde
Folwen Grisilde as in humilitee,
For it were importable, though they
wolde;
But for that every wight, in his degree,
Sholde be constant in adversitee
As was Grisilde; therfor Petrark wryteth
This storie, which with heigh style he endyteth.

For, sith a womman was so pacient
Un-to a mortal man, wel more us oghte
Receyven al in gree that god us sent;
For greet skile is, he preve that he wroghte.
But he ne tempteth no man that he boghte,
As seith seint Jame, if ye his pistel rede;
He preveth folk al day, it is no drede,

And suffreth us, as for our excercyse,
With sharpe scourges of adversitee
Ful ofte to be bete in sondry wyse;
Nat for to knowe our wil, for certes he,
Er we were born, knew al our freletee;

And for our beste is al his governaunce;
Lat us than live in vertuous suffraunce.[1]

But o word, lordinges, herkneth er I go:—
It were ful hard to finde now a dayes
In al a toun Grisildes three or two;
For, if that they were put to swiche assayes,
The gold of hem hath now so badde alayes
With bras, that thogh the coyne be fair at yë,
It wolde rather breste a-two than plye.

For which heer, for the wyves love of Bathe,
Whos lyf and al hir secte god mayntene
In heigh maistrye, and elles were it scathe,
I wol with lusty herte fresshe and grene
Seyn yow a song to glade yow, I wene,
And lat us stinte of ernestful matere:—
Herkneth my song, that seith in this manere.

But for our good is all that He doth give.
So then in virtuous patience let us live.[1]

But one word, masters, hearken ere I go:
One hardly can discover nowadays,
In all a town, Griseldas three or two;
For, if they should be put to such assays,
Their gold's so badly alloyed, in such ways,
With brass, that though the coin delight the eye,
'Twill rather break in two than bend, say I.

But now, for love of the good wife of Bath,
Whose life and all whose sex may God maintain
In mastery high, or else it were but scathe,
I will with joyous spirit fresh and green
Sing you a song to gladden you, I ween;
From all such serious matters let's be gone;
Hearken my song, which runs in this way on:

THE ENVOY OF CHAUCER

Grisilde is deed, and eek hir pacience,
And bothe atones buried in Itaille;
For which I crye in open audience,
No wedded man so hardy be t'assaille
His wyves pacience, in hope to finde
Grisildes, for in certein he shall faille!

O noble wyves, ful of heigh prudence,
Lat noon humilitee your tonge naille,
Ne lat no clerk have cause or diligence
To wryte of yow a storie of swich mervaille
As of Grisildis pacient and kinde;
Lest Chichevache[2] yow swelwe in hir entraille!

Folweth Ekko, that holdeth no silence,
But evere answereth at the countretaille;
Beth nat bidaffed for your innocence,
But sharply tak on yow the governaille.
Emprinteth wel this lesson in your minde
For commune profit, sith it may availle.

Ye archewyves, stondeth at defence,
Sin ye be stronge as is a greet camaille;
Ne suffreth nat that men yow doon offence.
And sclendre wyves, feble as in bataille,
Beth egre as is a tygre yond in Inde;
Ay clappeth as a mille, I yow consaille.

No dreed hem nat, do hem no reverence;

GRISELDA's dead, and dead is her patience,
In Italy both lie buried, says the tale;
For which I cry in open audience,
That no man be so hardy as to assail
His own wife's patience, in a hope to find
Griselda, for 'tis certain he shall fail!

O noble wives, full of a high prudence,
Let not humility your free tongue nail,
Nor let some clerk have cause for diligence
To write of you so marvelous detail
As of Griselda, patient and so kind;
Lest *Chichevache*[2] swallow you in her entrail!

Nay, follow Echo, that holds no silence,
But answers always like a countervail;
Be not befooled, for all your innocence,
But take the upper hand and you'll prevail.
And well impress this lesson on your mind,
For common profit, since it may avail.

Strong-minded women, stand at your defence,
Since you are strong as camel and don't ail,
Suffer no man to do to you offence;
And slender women in a contest frail,
Be savage as a tiger there in Ind;
Clatter like mill, say I, to beat the male.

Nay, fear them not, nor do them reverence;

[1]It seems to have been Chaucer's intention, in the first instance, to end this Tale here. Hence, we find, in MSS E. Hn. Cm. Dd., the following genuine, but rejected stanza, suitable for insertion at this point:

Behold the merry words of the Host

This worthy Clerk, whan ended was his tale,
Our hoste seyde, and swoor by goddes bones,
"Me were lever than a barel ale
My wyf at hoom had herd this legende ones;
This is a gentil tale for the nones,
As to my purpos, wiste ye my wille;
But thing that wol nat be, lat it be stille."

Now when this worthy clerk had told his tale,
Our host remarked, and swore by God's own bones:
"I'd rather than receive a keg of ale
My wife at home had heard this legend once;
This is a noble story, for the nonce,
And to my purpose, if you knew my will;
But that which cannot be, let it lie still."

Here endeth the Tale of the Clerk of Oxford

[2]A fabulous monster, in medieval satires, that fed on patient wives, and was therefore very lean.

For though your husband be all armed in mail,
The arrows of your shrewish eloquence
Shall pierce his breast and pierce his aventail.
In jealousy I counsel that you bind,
And you shall make him cower as does a
quail.

If you are fair to see, in folks' presence,
Show them your face and with your clothes regale;
If you are foul, be lavish of expense,
To gain friends never cease to do travail;
Be lightsome as a linden leaf in wind,
And let him worry, weep and wring and
wail!

For though thyn housbonde armed be in maille,
The arwes of thy crabbed eloquence
Shal perce his brest, and eek his aventaille;
In jalousye I rede eek thou him binde,
And thou shalt make him couche as dooth a
quaille.

If thou be fair, ther folk ben in presence
Shew thou thy visage and thyn apparaille;
If thou be foul, be free of thy dispence,
To gete thee freendes ay do thy travaille;
Be ay of chere as light as leef on linde,
And lat him care, and wepe, and wringe, and
waille!

HERE ENDETH THE CLERK OF OXENFORD HIS TALE

THE MERCHANT'S PROLOGUE

THE PROLOGUE OF THE MERCHANT'S TALE

Of weeping and wailing, care and other sorrow
I know enough, at eventide and morrow,"
The merchant said, "and so do many more
Of married folk, I think, who this deplore,
For well I know that it is so with me.
I have a wife, the worst one that can be;
For though the foul Fiend to her wedded were,
She'd overmatch him, this I dare to swear.
How could I tell you anything special
Of her great malice? She is shrew in all.
There is a long and a large difference
Between Griselda's good and great patience
And my wife's more than common cruelty.
Were I unbound, as may I prosperous be!
I'd never another time fall in the snare.
We wedded men in sorrow live, and care;
Try it who will, and he shall truly find
I tell the truth, by Saint Thomas of Ind,
As for the greater part, I say not all.
Nay, God forbid that it should so befall!
"Ah, good sir host! I have been married, lad,
These past two months, and no day more, by gad;
And yet I think that he whose days alive
Have been all wifeless, although men should
rive
Him to the heart, he could in no wise clear
Tell you so much of sorrow as I here
Could tell you of my spouse's cursedness."
"Now," said our host, "merchant, so God you
bless,
Since you're so very learned in that art,
Full heartily, I pray you, tell us part."
"Gladly," said he, "but of my own fresh sore,
For grief of heart I may not tell you more."

"Weping and wayling, care, and other sorwe
I know y-nogh, on even and a-morwe,"
Quod the Marchaunt, "and so don othere mo
That wedded been, I trowe that it be so.
For, wel I woot, if fareth so with me.
I have a wyf, the worste that may be;
For thogh the feend to hir y-coupled were,
She wolde him overmacche, I dar wel swere.
What sholde I yow reherce in special
Hir hye malice? she is a shrewe at al.
Ther is a long and large difference
Bitwix Grisildis grete pacience
And of my wyf the passing crueltee.
Were I unbounden, al-so moot I thee!
I wolde never eft comen in the snare.
We wedded men live in sorwe and care;
Assaye who-so wol, and he shal finde
I seye sooth, by seint Thomas of Inde,
As for the more part, I sey nat alle.
God shilde that it sholde so bifalle!
A! good sir hoost! I have y-wedded be
Thise monthes two, and more nat, pardee;
And yet, I trowe, he that all his lyve
Wyflees hath been, though that men wolde him
ryve
Un-to the herte, ne coude in no manere
Tellen so muchel sorwe, as I now here
Coude tellen of my wyves cursednesse!"
"Now," quod our hoost, "Marchaunt, so god
yow blesse,
Sin ye so muchel knowen of that art,
Ful hertely I pray yow telle us part."
"Gladly," quod he, "but of myn owene sore,
For sory herte, I telle may na-more."

THE MERCHANT'S TALE

HERE BEGINNETH THE MERCHANT'S TALE

Whylom ther was dwellinge in Lumbardye
A worthy knight, that born was of Pavye,
In which he lived in greet prosperitee;
And sixty yeer a wyflees man was he,
And folwed ay his bodily delyt
On wommen, ther-as was his appetyt,
As doon thise foles that ben seculeer.
And whan that he was passed sixty yeer,
Were it for holinesse or for dotage,
I can nat seye, but swich a greet corage,
Hadde this knight to been a wedded man,
That day and night he dooth al that he can
T'espyen where he mighte wedded be;
Preyinge our lord to granten him, that he
Mighte ones knowe of thilke blisful lyf
That is bitwixe an housbond and his wyf;
And for to live under that holy bond
With which that first god man and womman bond.
"Non other lyf," seyde he, "is worth a bene;
For wedlok is so esy and so clene,
That in this world it is a paradys."
Thus seyde this olde knight, that was so wys.
  And certeinly, as sooth as god is king,
To take a wyf, it is a glorious thing,
And namely whan a man is old and hoor;
Thanne is a wyf the fruit of his tresor.
Than sholde he take a yong wyf and a feir,
On which he mighte engendren him an heir,
And lede his lyf in joye and in solas,
Wher-as thise bacheleres singe "allas,"
Whan that they finden any adversitee
In love, which nis but childish vanitee.
And trewely it sit wel to be so,
That bacheleres have often peyne and wo;
On brotel ground they builde, and brotelnesse
They finde, whan they wene sikernesse.
They live but as a brid or as a beste,
In libertee, and under non areste,
Ther-as a wedded man in his estaat
Liveth a lyf blisful and ordinaat,
Under the yok of mariage y-bounde;
Wel may his herte in joye and blisse habounde.
For who can be so buxom as a wyf?
Who is so trewe, and eek so ententyf
To kepe him, syk and hool, as is his make?
For wele or wo, she wol him nat forsake.
She nis nat wery him to love and serve,
Thogh that he lye bedrede til he sterve.
And yet somme clerkes seyn, it nis nat so,
Of whiche he, Theofraste, is oon of tho.
What force though Theofraste liste lye?
"Ne take no wyf," quod he, "for housbondrye,
As for to spare in houshold thy dispence;
A trewe servant dooth more diligence,
Thy good to kepe, than thyn owene wyf.

Once on a time there dwelt in Lombardy
One born in Pavia, a knight worthy,
And there he lived in great prosperity;
And sixty years a wifeless man was he,
And followed ever his bodily delight
In women, whereof was his appetite,
As these fool laymen will, so it appears.
And when he had so passed his sixty years,
Were it for piety or for dotage
I cannot say, but such a rapturous rage
Had this knight to become a wedded man
That day and night he did his best to scan
And spy a place where he might wedded be;
Praying Our Lord to grant to him that he
Might once know something of that blissful life
That is between a husband and his wife;
And so to live within that holy band
Wherein God first made man and woman stand.
"No other life," said he, "is worth a bean;
For wedlock is so easy and so clean
That in this world it is a paradise."
Thus said this ancient knight, who was so wise.
  And certainly, as sure as God is King,
To take a wife, it is a glorious thing,
Especially when a man is old and hoary;
Then is a wife the fruit of wealth and glory.
Then should he take a young wife and a fair,
On whom he may beget himself an heir,
And lead his life in joy and in solace,
Whereas these bachelors do but sing "Alas!"
When they fall into some adversity
In love, which is but childish vanity.
And truly, it is well that it is so
That bachelors have often pain and woe;
On shifting ground they build, and shiftiness
They find when they suppose they've certainness.
They live but as a bird does, or a beast,
In liberty and under no arrest,
Whereas a wedded man in his high state
Lives a life blissful, ordered, moderate,
Under the yoke of happy marriage bound;
Well may his heart in joy and bliss abound.
For who can be so docile as a wife?
Who is so true as she whose aim in life
Is comfort for him, sick or well, to make?
For weal or woe she will not him forsake.
She's ne'er too tired to love and serve, say I,
Though he may lie bedridden till he die.
And yet some writers say it is not so,
And Theophrastus is one such, I know.
What odds though Theophrastus chose to lie?
"Take not a wife," said he, "for husbandry,
If you would spare in household your expense;
A faithful servant does more diligence
To keep your goods than your own wedded wife.

For she will claim a half part all her life;
And if you should be sick, so God me save,
Your true friends or an honest serving knave
Will keep you better than she that waits, I say,
After your wealth, and has done, many a day.
And if you take a wife to have and hold,
Right easily may you become cuckold."
This judgment and a hundred such things worse
Did this man write, may God his dead bones curse!
But take no heed of all such vanity.
Defy old Theophrastus and hear me.
A wife is God's own gift, aye verily;
All other kinds of gifts, most certainly,
As lands, rents, pasture, rights in common land,
Or moveables, in gift of Fortune stand,
And pass away like shadows on the wall.
But, without doubt, if plainly speak I shall,
A wife will last, and in your house endure
Longer than you would like, peradventure.
But marriage is a solemn sacrament;
Who has no wife I hold on ruin bent;
He lives in helplessness, all desolate,
I speak of folk in secular estate.
And hearken why, I say not this for naught:
It's because woman was for man's help wrought.
The High God, when He'd Adam made, all rude,
And saw him so alone and belly-nude,
God of His goodness thus to speak began:
"Let us now make a help meet for this man,
Like to himself." And then he made him Eve.
Here may you see, and here prove, I believe,
A wife is a man's help and his comfort,
His earthly paradise and means of sport;
So docile and so virtuous is she
That they must needs live in all harmony.
One flesh they are, and one flesh, as I guess,
Has but one heart in weal and in distress.
A wife! Ah, Holy Mary, *ben'cite!*
How may a man have any adversity
Who has a wife? Truly, I cannot say.
The bliss that is between such two, for aye,
No tongue can tell, nor any heart can think.
If he be poor, why, she helps him to swink;
She keeps his money and never wastes a deal;
All that her husband wishes she likes well;
She never once says "nay" when he says "yea."
"Do this," says he; "All ready, sir," she'll say.
O blissful state of wedlock, prized and dear,
So pleasant and so full of virtue clear,
So much approved and praised as fortune's peak,
That every man who holds him worth a leek
Upon his bare knees ought, through all his life,
To give God thanks, Who's sent to him a wife;
Or else he should pray God that He will send
A wife to him, to last till his life's end.
For then his life is set in certainness;
He cannot be deceived, as I may guess,
So that he act according as she's said;
Then may he boldly carry high his head,
They are so true and therwithal so wise;
Wherefore, if you will do as do the wise,
Then aye as women counsel be your deed.

For she wol clayme half part al hir lyf;
And if that thou be syk, so god me save,
Thy verray frendes or a trewe knave
Wol kepe thee bet than she that waiteth ay
After thy good, and hath don many a day."
And if thou take a wyf un-to thyn hold, [9180*a*]
Ful lightly maystow been a cokewold. [*b*]
This sentence, and an hundred thinges worse,
Wryteth this man, ther god his bones corse!
But take no kepe of al swich vanitee;
Deffye Theofraste and herke me.
A wyf is goddes yifte verraily;
Alle other maner yiftes hardily,
As londes, rentes, pasture, or commune,
Or moebles, alle ben yiftes of fortune,
That passen as a shadwe upon a wal.
But dredelees, if pleynly speke I shal,
A wyf wol laste, and in thyn hous endure,
Wel lenger than thee list, paraventure.
Mariage is a ful gret sacrement;
He which that hath no wyf, I holde him shent;
He liveth helplees and al desolat,
I speke of folk in seculer estaat.
And herke why, I sey nat this for noght,
That womman is for mannes help y-wroght.
The hye god, whan he hadde Adam maked,
And saugh him al allone, bely-naked,
God of his grete goodnesse seyde than,
"Lat us now make an help un-to this man
Lyk to him-self"; and thanne he made him Eve.
Heer may ye se, and heer-by may ye preve,
That wyf is mannes help and his confort,
His paradys terrestre and his disport
So buxom and so vertuous is she,
They moste nedes live in unitee.
O flesh they been, and o flesh, as I gesse,
Hath but on herte, in wele and in distresse.
A wyf! a! Seinte Marie, *ben'cite!*
How mighte a man han any adversitee
That hath a wyf? certes, I can nat seye.
The blisse which that is bitwixe hem tweye
Ther may no tonge telle, or herte thinke.
If he be povre, she helpeth him to swinke;
She kepeth his good, and wasteth never a deel;
Al that hir housbonde lust, hir lyketh weel;
She seith not ones "nay," when he seith "ye."
"Do this," seith he; "al redy, sir" seith she.
O blisful ordre of wedlok precious,
Thou art so mery, and eek so vertuous,
And so commended and appreved eek,
That every man that halt him worth a leek,
Up-on his bare knees oghte al his lyf
Thanken his god that him hath sent a wyf;
Or elles preye to god him for to sende
A wyf, to laste un-to his lyves ende.
For thanne his lyf is set in sikernesse;
He may nat be deceyved, as I gesse,
So that he werke after his wyves reed;
Than may he boldly beren up his heed,
They been so trewe and ther-with-al so wyse;
For which, if thou wolt werken as the wyse,
Do alwey so as wommen wol thee rede.

Lo, how that Jacob, as thise clerkes rede,
By good conseil of his moder Rebekke,
Bond the kides skin aboute his nekke;
Thrugh which his fadres benisoun he wan.
Lo, Judith, as the storie eek telle can,
By wys conseil she goddes peple kepte,
And slow him, Olofernus, whyl he slepte.
Lo Abigayl, by good conseil how she
Saved hir housbond Nabal, whan that he
Sholde han be slayn; and loke, Ester also
By good conseil delivered out of wo
The peple of god, and made him, Mardochee,
Of Assuere enhaunced for to be.
Ther nis no-thing in gree superlatyf,
As seith Senek, above an humble wyf.
Suffre thy wyves tonge, as Caton bit;
She shal comande, and thou shalt suffren it;
And yet she wol obeye of curteisye.
A wyf is keper of thyn housbondrye;
Wel may the syke man biwaille and wepe,
Ther-as ther nis no wyf the hous to kepe.
I warne thee, if wysly thou wolt wirche,
Love wel thy wyf, as Crist loveth his chirche.
If thou lovest thy-self, thou lovest thy wyf;
No man hateth his flesh, but in his lyf
He fostreth it, and therfore bidde I thee,
Cherisse thy wyf, or thou shalt never thee.
Housbond and wyf, what so men jape or pleye,
Of worldly folk holden the siker weye;
They been so knit, ther may noon harm bityde:
And namely, up-on the wyves syde.
For which this Januarie, of whom I tolde,
Considered hath, in with his dayes olde,
The lusty lyf, the vertuous quiete,
That is in mariage hony-swete;
And for his freendes on a day he sente,
To tellen hem th'effect of his entente.
With face sad, his tale he hath hem told;
He seyde, "freendes, I am hoor and old,
And almost, god wot, on my pittes brinke;
Up-on my soule somwhat moste I thinke.
I have my body folily despended;
Blessed be god, that it shal been amended!
For I wol be, certeyn, a wedded man,
And that anoon in al the haste I can,
Un-to som mayde fair and tendre of age.
I prey yow, shapeth for my mariage
Al sodeynly, for I wol nat abyde;
And I wol fonde t'espyen, on my syde,
To whom I may be wedded hastily.
But for-as-muche as ye ben mo than I,
Ye shullen rather swich a thing espyen
Than I, and wher me best were to allyen.
But o thing warne I yow, my freendes dere,
I wol non old wyf han in no manere.
She shal nat passe twenty yeer, certayn;
Old fish and yong flesh wolde I have ful fayn.
Bet is," quod he, "a pyk than a pikerel;
And bet than old boef is the tendre veel.
I wol no womman thritty yeer of age,
It is but bene-straw and greet forage.

Lo, how young Jacob, as these clerics read,
About his hairless neck a kid's skin bound,
A trick that Dame Rebecca for him found,
By which his father's benison he won.
Lo, Judith, as the ancient stories run,
By her wise counsel she God's people kept.
And Holofernes slew, while yet he slept.
Lo, Abigail, by good advice how she
Did save her husband, Nabal, when that he
Should have been slain; and lo, Esther also
By good advice delivered out of woe.
The people of God and got him, Mordecai,
By King Ahasuerus lifted high.
There is no pleasure so superlative
(Says Seneca) as a humble wife can give.
Suffer your wife's tongue, Cato bids, as fit;
She shall command, and you shall suffer it;
And yet she will obey, of courtesy.
A wife is keeper of your husbandry:
Well may the sick man wail and even weep
Who has no wife the house to clean and keep.
I warn you now, if wisely you would work,
Love well your wife, as Jesus loves His Kirk.
For if you love yourself, you love your wife;
No man hates his own flesh, but through his life
He fosters it, and so I bid you strive
To cherish her, or you shall never thrive.
Husband and wife, despite men's jape or play,
Of all the world's folk hold the safest way;
They are so knit there may no harm betide.
Especially upon the good wife's side.
For which this January, of whom I told,
Did well consider, in his days grown old,
The pleasant life, the virtuous rest complete
That are in marriage, always honey-sweet;
And for his friends upon a day he sent
To tell them the effect of his intent.
With sober face his tale to them he's told;
He said to them: "My friends, I'm hoar and old,
And almost, God knows, come to my grave's brink;
About my soul, now, somewhat must I think.
I have my body foolishly expended;
Blessed be God, that thing shall be amended!
For I will be, truly, a wedded man,
And that anon, in all the haste I can,
Unto some maiden young in age and fair.
I pray you for my marriage all prepare,
And do so now, for I will not abide;
And I will try to find one, on my side,
To whom I may be wedded speedily.
But for as much as you are more than I,
It's better that you have the thing in mind
And try a proper mate for me to find.
"But of one thing I warn you, my friends dear,
I will not have an old wife coming here.
She shan't have more than twenty years, that's plain;
Of old fish and young flesh I am full fain.
Better," said he, "a pike than pickerel;
And better than old beef is tender veal.
I'll have no woman thirty years of age,
It is but bean-straw and such rough forage.

And these old widows, God knows that, afloat,
They know so much of spells when on Wade's[1] boat,
And do such petty harm, when they think best,
That with one should I never live at rest.
For several schools can make men clever clerks;
Woman in many schools learns clever works.
But certainly a young thing men may guide,
Just as warm wax may with one's hands be plied.
Wherefore I tell you plainly, in a clause,
I will not have an old wife, for that cause.
For if it chanced I made that sad mistake
And never in her could my pleasure take,
My life I'd lead then in adultery
And go straight to the devil when I die.
No children should I then on her beget;
Yet would I rather hounds my flesh should fret
Than that my heritage descend and fall
Into strange hands, and this I tell you all.
I dote not, and I know the reason why
A man should marry, and furthermore know I
There speaks full many a man of all marriage
Who knows no more of it than knows my page,
Nor for what reasons man should take a wife.
If one may not live chastely all his life,
Let him take wife whose quality he's known
For lawful procreation of his own
Blood children, to the honour of God above,
And not alone for passion or for love;
And because lechery they should eschew
And do their family duty when it's due;
Or because each of them should help the other
In trouble, as a sister shall a brother;
And live in chastity full decently.
But, sirs, and by your leave, that is not I.
For, God be thanked, I dare to make a vaunt,
I feel my limbs are strong and fit to jaunt
In doing all man's are expected to;
I know myself and know what I can do.
Though I am hoar, I fare as does a tree
That blossoms ere the fruit be grown; you see
A blooming tree is neither dry nor dead.
And I feel nowhere hoary but on head;
My heart and all my limbs are still as green
As laurel through the year is to be seen.
And now that you have heard all my intent,
I pray that to my wish you will assent."
Then divers men to him diversely told,
Of marriage, many an instance known of old.
Some blamed it and some praised it, that's certain,
But at the last, and briefly to make plain,
Since altercation follows soon or late
When friends begin such matters to debate,
There fell a strife between his brothers two,
Whereof the name of one was Placebo
And verily Justinus was that other.
Placebo said: "O January, brother,
Full little need had you, my lord so dear,
Counsel to ask of anyone that's here;
Save that you are so full of sapience
That you like not, what of your high prudence,

And eek thise olde widwes, god it woot,
They conne so muchel craft on Wade's[1] boot,
So muchel broken harm, whan that hem leste,
That with hen sholde I never live in reste.
For sondry scoles maken sotil clerkis;
Womman of manye scoles half a clerk is.
But certeynly, a yong thing may men gye,
Right as men may warm wex with handes plye.
Wherfore I sey yow pleynly, in a clause,
I wol non old wyf han right for this cause.
For if so were, I hadde swich mischaunce,
That I in hir ne coude han no plesaunce,
Thanne sholde I lede my lyf in avoutrye,
And go streight to the devel, whan I dye.
Ne children sholde I none up-on hir geten;
Yet were me lever houndes had me eten,
Than that myn heritage sholde falle
In straunge hand, and this I tell yow alle.
I dote nat, I woot the cause why
Men sholde wedde, and forthermore wot I,
Ther speketh many a man of mariage,
That woot na-more of it than woot my page,
For whiche causes man sholde take a wyf.
If he ne may nat liven chast his lyf,
Take him a wyf with greet devocioun,
By-cause of leveful procreacioun
Of children, to th'onour of god above,
And nat only for paramour or love;
And for they sholde lecherye eschue,
And yelde hir dettes whan that they ben due;
Or for that ech of hem sholde helpen other
In meschief, as a suster shal the brother;
And live in chastitee ful holily.
But sires, by your leve, that am nat I.
For god be thanked, I dar make avaunt,
I fele my limes stark and suffisaunt
To do al that a man bilongeth to;
I woot my-selven best what I may do.
Though I be hoor, I fare as dooth a tree
That blosmeth er that fruyt y-woxen be;
A blosmy tree nis neither drye ne deed.
I fele me nowher hoor but on myn heed;
Myn herte and alle my limes been as grene
As laurer thurgh the yeer is for to sene.
And sin that ye han herd al myn entente,
I prey yow to my wil ye wole assente."
Diverse men diversely him tolde
Of mariage manye ensamples olde.
Somme blamed it, somme preysed it, certeyn;
But atte laste, shortly for to seyn,
As al day falleth altercacioun
Bitwixen freendes in disputisoun,
Ther fil a stryf bitwixe his bretheren two,
Of whiche that oon was cleped Placebo,
Justinus soothly called was that other.
Placebo seyde, "o Januarie, brother,
Ful litel nede had ye, my lord so dere,
Conseil to axe of any that is here;
But that ye been so ful of sapience,
That yow ne lyketh, for your heighe prudence,

[1]In Teutonic mythology, a giant, regarded as a storm or sea demon. On his ship he could pass from place to place instantaneously.

To weyven fro the word of Salomon.
This word seyde he un-to us everichon:
'Wirk alle thing by conseil,' thus seyde he,
'And thanne shaltow nat repente thee.'
But though that Salomon spak swich a word,
Myn owene dere brother and my lord,
So wisly god my soule bringe at reste,
I hold your owene conseil is the beste.
For brother myn, of me tak this motyf,
I have now been a court-man al my lyf.
And god it woot, though I unworthy be,
I have stonden in ful greet degree
Abouten lordes of ful heigh estaat;
Yet hadde I never with noon of hem debaat.
I never hem contraried, trewely;
I woot wel that my lord can more than I.
What that he seith, I holde it ferme and stable;
I seye the same, or elles thing semblable.
A ful gret fool is any conseillour,
That serveth any lord of heigh honour,
That dar presume, or elles thenken it,
That his conseil sholde passe his lordes wit.
Nay, lordes been no foles, by my fay;
Ye han your-selven shewed heer to-day
So heigh sentence, so holily and weel,
That I consente and conferme every-deel
Your wordes alle, and your opinioun.
By god, ther nis no man in al this toun
N'in al Itaille, that coude bet han sayd;
Crist halt him of this conseil wel apayd.
And trewely, it is an heigh corage
Of any man, that stapen is in age,
To take a yong wyf; by my fader kin,
Your herte hangeth on a joly pin.
Doth now in this matere right as yow leste,
For finally I holde it for the beste."
Justinus, that ay stille sat and herde,
Right in this wyse to Placebo answerde:
"Now brother myn, be pacient, I preye,
Sin ye han seyd, and herkneth what I seye.
Senek among his othere wordes wyse
Seith, that a man oghte him right wel avyse,
To whom he yeveth his lond or his catel.
And sin I oghte avyse me right wel
To whom I yeve my good awey fro me,
Wel muchel more I oghte avysed be
To whom I yeve my body; for alwey
I warne yow wel, it is no childes pley
To take a wyf with-oute avysement.
Men moste enquere, this is myn assent,
Wher she by wys, or sobre, or dronkelewe,
Or proud, or elles other-weys a shrewe;
A chydester, or wastour of thy good,
Or riche, or poore, or elles mannish wood.
Al-be-it so that no man finden shal
Noon in this world that trotteth hool in al,
Ne man ne beest, swich as men coude devyse;
But nathelees, it oghte y-nough suffise
With any wyf, if so were that she hadde
Mo gode thewes than hir vyces badde;
And al this axeth leyser for t'enquere.

To vary from the word of Solomon.
This word said he to each and every one:
'Do everything by counsel,' thus said he,
'And then thou hast no cause to repent thee.'
But although Solomon spoke such a word,
My own dear brother and my proper lord,
So truly may God bring my soul to rest
As I hold your own counsel is the best.
For, brother mine, of me take this one word,
I've been a courtier all my days, my lord.
And God knows well, though I unworthy be,
I have stood well, and in full great degree,
With many lords of very high estate;
Yet ne'er with one of them had I debate.
I never contradicted, certainly;
I know well that my lord knows more than I.
Whate'er he says, I hold it firm and stable;
I say the same, or nearly as I'm able.
A full great fool is any councillor
That serves a lord of any high honour
And dares presume to say, or else think it,
His counsel can surpass his lordship's wit.
Nay, lords are never fools, nay, by my fay;
You have yourself, sir, showed, and here today,
With such good sense and piety withal
That I assent to and confirm it all,
The words and the opinions you have shown.
By God, there is no man in all this town,
Or Italy, it better could have phrased;
And Christ Himself your counsel would have praised.
And truthfully, it argues high courage
In any man that is advanced in age
To take a young wife; by my father's kin,
A merry heart you've got beneath your skin!
Do in this matter at your behest,
For, finally, I hold that for the best."
Justinus, who sat still and calm, and heard,
Right in this wise Placebo he answered:
"Now, brother mine, be patient, so I pray;
Since you have spoken, hear what I shall say.
For Seneca, among his words so wise,
Says that a man ought well himself advise
To whom he'll give his chattels or his land.
And since I ought to know just where I stand
Before I give my wealth away from me,
How much more well advised I ought to be
To whom I give my body; for alway
I warn you well, that it is not child's play
To take a wife without much advisement.
Men must inquire, and this is my intent,
Whether she's wise, or sober, or drunkard,
Or proud, or else in other things froward,
Or shrewish, or a waster of what's had,
Or rich, or poor, or whether she's man-mad.
And be it true that no man finds, or shall,
One in this world that perfect is in all,
Of man or beast, such as men could devise;
Nevertheless, it ought enough suffice
With any wife, if so were that she had
More traits of virtue that her vices bad;
And all this leisure asks to see and hear.

For God knows I have wept full many a tear
In privity, since I have had a wife.
Praise whoso will a wedded man's good life,
Truly I find in it but cost and care
And many duties, of all blisses bare.
And yet, God knows, my neighbours round about,
Especially the women, many a rout,
Say that I've married the most steadfast wife,
Aye, and the meekest one there is in life.
But I know best where pinches me my shoe.
You may, for me, do as you please to do;
But take good heed, since you're a man of age,
How you shall enter into a marriage,
Especially with a young wife and a fair.
By Him Who made the water, earth, and air,
The youngest man there is in all this rout
Is busy enough to bring the thing about
That he alone shall have his wife, trust me.
You'll not be able to please her through years three,
That is to say, to give all she desires.
A wife attention all the while requires.
I pray you that you be not offended."
"Well?" asked this January, "And have you said?
A straw for Seneca and your proverbs!
I value not a basketful of herbs
Your schoolmen's terms; for wiser men than you,
As you have heard, assent and bid me do
My purpose now. Placebo, what say ye?"
"I say it is a wicked man," said he,
"That hinders matrimony, certainly."
And with that word they rose up, suddenly,
Having assented fully that he should
Be wedded when he pleased and where he would.
Imagination and his eagerness
Did in the soul of January press
As he considered marriage for a space.
Many fair shapes and many a lovely face
Passed through his amorous fancy, night by night.
As who might take a mirror polished bright
And set it in the common market-place
And then should see full many a figure pace
Within the mirror; just in that same wise
Did January within his thought surmise
Of maidens whom he dwelt in town beside.
He knew not where his fancy might abide.
For if the one have beauty of her face,
Another stands so in the people's grace
For soberness and for benignity,
That all the people's choice she seems to be;
And some were rich and had an evil name.
Nevertheless, half earnest, half in game,
He fixed at last upon a certain one
And let all others from his heart be gone,
And chose her on his own authority;
For love is always blind and cannot see.
And when in bed at night, why then he wrought
To portray, in his heart and in his thought,
Her beauty fresh and her young age, so tender,
Her middle small, her two arms long and slender,
Her management full wise, her gentleness,
Her womanly bearing, and her seriousness.
And when to her at last his choice descended,

For god it woot, I have wept many a tere
Ful prively, sin I have had a wyf.
Preyse who-so wole a wedded mannes lyf,
Certein, I finde in it but cost and care,
And observances, of alle blisses bare.
And yet, god woot, my neighebores aboute,
And namely of wommen many a route,
Seyn that I have the moste stedefast wyf,
And eek the mekeste oon that bereth lyf.
But I wot best wher wringeth me my sho.
Ye mowe, for me, right as yow lyketh do;
Avyseth yow, ye been a man of age,
How that ye entren in-to mariage,
And namely with a yong wyf and a fair.
By him that made water, erthe, and air,
The yongest man that is in al this route
Is bisy y-nogh to bringen it aboute
To han his wyf allone, trusteth me.
Ye shul nat plese hir fully yeres three,
This is to seyn, to doon hir ful plesaunce.
A wyf axeth ful many an observaunce.
I prey yow that ye be nat yvel apayd."
"Wel," quod this Januarie, "and hastow sayd?
Straw for thy Senek, and for thy proverbes,
I counte nat a panier ful of herbes
Of scole-termes; wyser men than thow,
As thou hast herd, assenteden right now
To my purpos; Placebo, what sey ye?"
"I seye, it is a cursed man," quod he,
"That letteth matrimoine, sikerly,"
And with that word they rysen sodeynly,
And been assented fully, that he sholde
Be wedded whanne him list and wher he wolde.
Heigh fantasye and curious bisinesse
Fro day to day gan in the soule impresse
Of Januarie aboute his mariage.
Many fair shap, and many a fair visage
Ther passeth thurgh his herte, night by night.
As who-so toke a mirour polished bright,
And sette it in a commune market-place,
Than sholde he see many a figure pace
By his mirour; and, in the same wyse,
Gan Januarie in with his thoght devyse
Of maydens, whiche that dwelten him bisyde.
He wiste nat wher that he mighte abyde.
For if that oon have beautee in hir face,
Another stant so in the peples grace
For hir sadnesse, and hir benignitee,
That of the peple grettest voys hath she.
And somme were riche, and hadden badde name.
But nathelees, bitwixe ernest and game,
He atte laste apoynted him on oon,
And leet alle othere from his herte goon,
And chees hir of his owene auctoritee;
For love is blind al day, and may nat see.
And whan that he was in his bed y-broght,
He purtreyed, in his herte and in his thoght,
Hir fresshe beautee and hir age tendre,
Hir myddel smal, hir armes longe and sclendre,
Hir wyse governaunce, hir gentillesse,
Hir wommanly beringe and hir sadnesse.
And whan that he on hir was condescended,

Him thoughte his chois mighte nat ben amended.
For whan that he him-self concluded hadde,
Him thoughte ech other mannes wit so badde,
That inpossible it were to replye
Agayn his chois, this was his fantasye.
His freendes sente he to at his instaunce,
And preyed hem to doon him that plesaunce,
That hastily they wolden to him come;
He wolde abregge hir labour, alle and some.
Nedeth na-more for him to go ne ryde,
He was apoynted ther he wolde abyde.
Placebo cam, and eek his freendes sone,
And alderfirst he bad hem alle a bone,
That noon of hem none argumentes make
Agayn the purpos which that he hath take;
"Which purpos was plesant to god," seyde he,
"And verray ground of his prosperitee."
He seyde, ther was a mayden in the toun,
Which that of beautee hadde greet renoun,
Al were it so she were of smal degree;
Suffyseth him hir youthe and hir beautee.
Which mayde, he seyde, he wolde han to his wyf,
To lede in ese and holinesse his lyf.
And thanked god, that he mighte han hire al,
That no wight of his blisse parten shal.
And preyde hem to labouren in this nede,
And shapen that he faille nat to spede;
For thanne, he seyde, his spirit was at ese.
"Thanne is," quod he, "no-thing may me displese,
Save o thing priketh in my conscience,
The which I wol reherce in your presence.
I have," quod he, "herd seyd, ful yore ago,
Ther may no man han parfite blisses two,
This is to seye, in erthe and eek in hevene.
For though he kepe him fro the sinnes sevene,
And eek from every branche of thilke tree,
Yet is ther so parfit felicitee,
And so greet ese and lust in mariage,
That ever I am agast, now in myn age,
That I shal lede now so mery a lyf,
So delicat, with-outen wo and stryf,
That I shal have myn hevene in erthe here.
For sith that verray hevene is boght so dere,
With tribulacioun and greet penaunce,
How sholde I thanne, that live in swich plesaunce
As alle wedded men don with hir wyvis,
Come to the blisse ther Crist eterne on lyve is?
This is my drede, and ye, my bretheren tweye,
Assoilleth me this questioun, I preye."
Justinus, which that hated his folye,
Answerde anon, right in his japerye;
And for he wolde his longe tale abregge,
He wolde noon auctoritee allegge,
But seyde, "sire, so ther be noon obstacle
Other than this, god of his hye miracle
And of his mercy may so for yow wirche,
That, er ye have your right of holy chirche,
Ye may repente of wedded mannes lyf,
In which ye seyn ther is no wo ne stryf.
And elles, god forbede but he sente
A wedded man him grace to repente

He thought that choice might never be amended.
For when he had concluded thus, egad,
He thought that other men had wits so bad
It were impossible to make reply
Against his choice, this was his fantasy.
His friends he sent to, at his own instance,
And prayed them give him, in this wise, pleasance,
That speedily they would set forth and come:
He would abridge their labour, all and some.
He need not more to walk about or ride,
For he'd determined where he would abide.
Placebo came, and all his friends came soon,
And first of all he asked of them the boon
That none of them an argument should make
Against the course he fully meant to take;
"Which purpose pleasing is to God," said he,
"And the true ground of my felicity."
He said there was a maiden in the town
Who had for beauty come to great renown,
Despite the fact she was of small degree;
Sufficed him well her youth and her beauty.
Which maid, he said, he wanted for his wife,
To lead in ease and decency his life.
And he thanked God that he might have her, all,
That none partook of his bliss now, nor shall.
And prayed them all to labour in this need
And so arrange that he'd fail not, indeed;
For then, he said, his soul should be at ease.
"And then," said he, "there's naught can me displease,
Save one lone thing that sticks in my conscience,
The which I will recite in your presence.
"I have," said he, "heard said, and long ago,
There may no man have perfect blisses two,
That is to say, on earth and then in Heaven.
For though he keep from sins the deadly seven,
And too, from every branch of that same tree,
Yet is there so complete felicity
And such great pleasure in the married state
That I am fearful, since it comes so late,
That I shall lead so merry and fine a life,
And so delicious, without woe and strife,
That I shall have my heaven on earth here.
For since that other Heaven is bought so dear,
With tribulation and with great penance,
How should I then, who live in such pleasance,
As all these wedded men do with their wives,
Come to the bliss where Christ Eternal lives?
This is my fear, and you, my brothers, pray
Resolve for me this problem now, I say."
Justinus, who so hated this folly,
Answered anon in jesting wise and free;
And since he would his longish tale abridge,
He would no old authority allege,
But said: "Sir, so there is no obstacle
Other than this, God, of high miracle
And of His mercy, may so for you work
That, ere you have your right of Holy Kirk,
You'll change your mind on wedded husband's life,
Wherein you say there is no woe or strife.
And otherwise, God grant that there be sent
To wedded man the fair grace to repent

Often, and sooner than a single man!
And therefore, sir, this is the best I can:
Despair not, but retain in memory,
Perhaps she may your purgatory be!
She may be God's tool, she may be God's whip;
Then shall your spirit up to Heaven skip
Swifter than does an arrow from the bow!
I hope to God, hereafter you shall know
That there is none so great felicity
In marriage, no nor ever shall there be,
To keep you from salvation that's your own,
So that you use, with reason that's well known,
The charms of your wife's body temperately,
And that you please her not too amorously,
And that you keep as well from other sin.
My tale is done now, for my wit is thin.
Be not deterred hereby, my brother dear"—
(But let us pass quite over what's said here.
The wife of Bath, if you have understood,
Has treated marriage, in its likelihood,
And spoken well of it in little space)—
"Fare you well now, God have you in His grace."
And with that word this Justin and his brother
Did take their leave, and each of them from other.
For when they all saw that it must needs be,
They so arranged, by sly and wise treaty,
That she, this maiden, who was Maia hight,
As speedily indeed as ever she might,
Should wedded be unto this January.
I think it were too long a time to tarry
To tell of deed and bond between them, and
The way she was enfeoffed of all his land;
Or to hear tell of all her rich array.
But finally was come the happy day
When to the church together they two went,
There to receive the holy sacrament.
Forth came the priest with stole about his neck,
Saying of Rebecca and Sarah she should reck
For wisdom and for truth in her marriage;
And said his orisons, as is usage,
And crossed them, praying God that He should bless,
And made all tight enough with holiness.
Thus are they wedded with solemnity,
And at the feast are sitting, he and she,
With other worthy folk upon the dais.
All full of joy and bliss the palace gay is,
And full of instruments and viandry,
The daintiest in all of Italy.
Before them played such instruments anon
That Orpheus or Theban Amphion
Never in life made such a melody.
With every course there rose loud minstrelsy,
And never Joab sounded trump, to hear,
Nor did Theodomas, one half so clear
At Thebes, while yet the city hung in doubt.
Bacchus the wine poured out for all about,
And Venus gaily laughed for every wight.
For January had become her knight,
And would make trial of his amorous power
In liberty and in the bridal bower;

Wel ofte rather than a sengle man!
And therfore, sire, the beste reed I can,
Dispeire yow noght, but have in your memorie,
Paraunter she may be your purgatorie!
She may be goddes mene, and goddes whippe;
Than shal your soule up to hevene skippe
Swifter than dooth an arwe out of the bowe!
I hope to god, her-after shul ye knowe,
That their nis no so greet felicitee
In mariage, ne never-mo shal be,
That yow shal lette of your savacioun,
So that ye use, as skile is and resoun,
The lustes of your wyf attemprely,
And that ye plese hir nat to amorously,
And that ye kepe yow eek from other sinne.
My tale is doon:—for my wit is thinne.
Beth nat agast her-of, my brother dere."—
(But lat us waden out of this matere.
The Wyf of Bathe, if ye han understonde,
Of mariage, which we have on honde,
Declared hath ful wel in litel space).—
"Fareth now wel, god have yow in his grace."
And with this word this Justin and his brother
Han take hir leve, and ech of hem of other.
For whan they sawe it moste nedes be,
They wroghten so, by sly and wys tretee,
That she, this mayden, which that Maius highte,
As hastily as ever that she mighte,
Shal wedded be un-to this Januarie.
I trowe it were to longe yow to tarie,
If I yow tolde of every scrit and bond,
By which that she was feffed in his lond;
Or for to herknen of hir riche array.
But finally y-comen is the day
That to the chirche bothe be they went
For to receyve the holy sacrement.
Forth comth the preest, with stole aboute his nekke,
And bad hir be lyk Sarra and Rebekke,
In wisdom and in trouthe of mariage;
And seyde his orisons, as is usage,
And crouched hem, and bad god sholde hem blesse,
And made al siker y-nogh with holinesse.
Thus been they wedded with solempnitee,
And at the feste sitteth he and she
With other worthy folk up-on the deys.
Al ful of joye and blisse is the paleys,
And ful of instruments and of vitaille,
The moste deyntevous of al Itaille.
Biforn hem stoode swiche instruments of soun,
That Orpheus, ne of Thebes Amphioun,
Ne maden never swich a melodye.
At every cours than cam loud minstralcye,
That never tromped Joab, for to here,
Nor he, Theodomas, yet half so clere,
At Thebes, whan the citee was in doute.
Bacus the wyn hem skinketh al aboute,
And Venus laugheth up-on every wight.
For Januarie was bicome hir knight,
And wolde bothe assayen his corage
In libertee, and eek in mariage;

And with hir fyrbrond in hir hand aboute
Daunceth biforn the bryde and al the route.
And certeinly, I dar right wel seyn this,
Ymenëus, that god of wedding is,
Saugh never his lyf so mery a wedded man.
Hold thou thy pees, thou poete Marcian,
That wrytest us that ilke wedding murie
Of hir, Philologye, and him, Mercurie,
And of the songes that the Muses songe.
To smal is bothe thy penne, and eek thy tonge,
For to descryven of this mariage.
Whan tendre youthe hath wedded stouping age,
Ther is swich mirthe that it may nat be writen;
Assayeth it your-self, than may ye witen
If that I lye or noon in this matere.
  Maius, that sit with so benigne a chere,
Hir to biholde it semed fayërye;
Quene Ester loked never with swich an yë
On Assuer, so meke a look hath she.
I may yow nat devyse al hir beautee;
But thus muche of hir beautee telle I may,
That she was lyk the brighte morwe of May,
Fulfild of alle beautee and plesaunce.
  This Januarie is ravisshed in a traunce
At every time he loked on hir face;
But in his herte he gan hir to manace,
That he that night in armes wolde hir streyne
Harder than ever Paris dide Eleyne.
But nathelees, yet hadde he greet pitee,
That thilke night offenden hir moste he;
And thoughte, "allas! o tendre creature!
Now wolde god ye mighte wel endure
Al my corage, it is so sharp and kene;
I am agast ye shul it nat sustene.
But god forbede that I dide al my might!
Now wolde god that it were woxen night,
And that the night wolde lasten evermo.
I wolde that al this peple were ago."
And finally, he doth al his labour,
As he best mighte, savinge his honour,
To haste hem fro the mete in subtil wyse.
  The tyme cam that reson was to
    ryse;
And after that, men daunce and drinken faste,
And spyces al aboute the hous they caste;
And ful of joye and blisse is every man;
All but a squyer, highte Damian,
Which carf biforn the knight ful many a day.
He was so ravisshed on his lady May,
That for the verray peyne he was ny wood;
Almost he swelte and swowned ther he stood.
So sore hath Venus hurt him with hir brond,
As that she bar it daunsinge in hir hond.
And to his bed he wente him hastily;
Na-more of him as at this tyme speke I.
But ther I lete him wepe y-nough and pleyne,
Til fresshe May wol rewen on his peyne.

And with her firebrand in her hand, about
Danced she before the bride and all the rout.
And certainly I dare right well say this,
That Hymenaeus, god of wedded bliss,
Ne'er saw in life so merry a married man.
Hold thou thy peace, thou poet Marcian
Who tellest how Philology was wed
And how with Mercury she went to bed,
And of the sweet songs by the Muses sung.
Too slight are both thy pen and thy thin tongue
To show aright this wedding on thy page.
When tender youth has wedded stooping age,
There is such mirth that no one may it show;
Try it yourself, and then you well will know
Whether I lie or not in matters here.
  Maia, she sat there with so gentle cheer,
To look at her it seemed like faëry;
Queen Esther never looked with such an eye
Upon Ahasuerus, so meek was she.
I can't describe to you all her beauty;
But thus much of her beauty I can say,
That she was like the brightening morn of May,
Fulfilled of beauty and of all pleasance.
  January was rapt into a trance
With each time that he looked upon her face;
And in his heart her beauty he'd embrace,
And threatened in his arms to hold her tight,
Harder than Paris Helen did, that night.
But nonetheless great pity, too, had he
Because that night she must deflowered be;
And thought: "Alas! O tender young creature!
Now would God you may easily endure
All my desire, it is so sharp and keen.
I fear you can't sustain it long, my queen.
But God forbid that I do all I might!
And now would God that it were come to night,
And that the night would last for ever—oh,
I wish these people would arise and go."
And at the last he laboured all in all,
As best he might for manners there in hall,
To haste them from the feast in subtle wise.
  Time came when it was right that they should
    rise;
And after that men danced and drank right fast,
And spices all about the house they cast;
And full of bliss and joy was every man,
All but a squire, a youth called Damian,
Who'd carved before the knight full many a day.
He was so ravished by his Lady May
That for the very pain, as madman would,
Almost he fell down fainting where he stood.
So sore had Venus hurt him with her brand,
When she went dancing, bearing it in hand.
And to his bed he took him speedily;
No more of him just at this time say I.
I'll let him weep his fill, with woe complain,
Until fresh May have ruth upon his pain.

AUTHOR

  O perilous fyr, that in the bedstraw bredeth!
O famulier foo, that his servyce bedeth!
O servant traitour, false hoomly hewe,

  O parlous fire that in the bedstraw breeds!
O foe familiar that his service speeds!
O treacherous servant, false domestic who

Is most like adder in bosom, sly, untrue,
God shield us all from knowing aught of you!
O January, drunk of pleasure's brew
In marriage, see how now your Damian,
Your own trained personal squire, born your man
Wishes and means to do you villainy.
God grant that on this household foe you'll spy!
For in this world no pestilence is worse
Than foe domestic, constantly a curse.
When traversed has the sun his arc of day,
No longer may the body of him stay
On the horizon, in that latitude.
Night with his mantle, which is dark and rude,
Did overspread the hemisphere about;
And so departed had this joyous rout
From January, with thanks on every side.
Home to their houses happily they ride,
Whereat they do what things may please them best,
And when they see the time come, go to rest.
Soon after that this hasty January
Would go to bed, he would no longer tarry.
He drank of claret, hippocras, vernage,
All spiced and hot to heighten his love's rage;
And many an aphrodisiac, full and fine,
Such as the wicked monk, Dan Constantine,
Has written in his book *De Coitu;*
Not one of all of them he did eschew.
And to his friends most intimate, said he:
"For God's love, and as soon as it may be,
Let all now leave this house in courteous wise."
And all they rose, just as he bade them rise.
They drank good-night, and curtains drew anon;
The bride was brought to bed, as still as stone;
And when the bed had been by priest well blessed,
Out of the chamber everyone progressed.
And January lay down close beside
His fresh young May, his paradise, his bride.
He soothed her, and he kissed her much and oft,
With the thick bristles of his beard, not soft,
But sharp as briars, like a dogfish skin,
For he'd been badly shaved ere he came in.
He stroked and rubbed her on her tender face,
And said: "Alas! I fear I'll do trespass
Against you here, my spouse, and much offend
Before the time when I will down descend.
But nonetheless, consider this," said he,
"There is no workman, whosoe'er he be,
That may work well, if he works hastily;
This will be done at leisure, perfectly.
It makes no difference how long we two play;
For in true wedlock were we tied today;
And blessed be the yoke that we are in,
For in our acts, now, we can do no sin.
A man can do no sin with his own wife,
Nor can he hurt himself with his own knife;
For we have leave most lawfully to play."
Thus laboured he till came the dawn of day;
And then he took in wine a sop of bread,
And upright sat within the marriage bed,
And after that he sang full loud and clear
And kissed his wife and made much wanton cheer.
He was all coltish, full of venery,

Lyk to the naddre in bosom sly untrewe,
God shilde us alle from your aqueyntaunce!
O Januarie, dronken in plesaunce
Of mariage, see how thy Damian,
Thyn owene squyer and thy borne man,
Entendeth for to do thee vileinye.
God graunte thee thyn hoomly fo t'espye.
For in this world nis worse pestilence
Than hoomly foo al day in thy presence.
Parfourned hath the sonne his ark diurne,
No lenger may the body of him sojurne
On th'orisonte, as in that latitude.
Night with his mantel, that is derk and rude,
Gan oversprede the hemisperie aboute;
For which departed is this lusty route
Fro Januarie, with thank on every syde.
Hom to hir houses lustily they ryde,
Wher-as they doon hir thinges as hem leste,
And whan they sye hir tyme, goon to reste.
Sone after that, this hastif Januarie
Wolde go to bedde, he wolde no lenger tarie.
He drinketh ipocras, clarree, and vernage
Of spyces hote, t'encresen his corage;
And many a letuarie hadde he ful fyn,
Swiche as the cursed monk dan Constantyn
Hath writen in his book *de Coitu;*
To eten hem alle, he nas no-thing eschu.
And to his privee freendes thus seyde he:
"For goddes love, as sone as it may be,
Lat voyden al this hous in curteys wyse."
And they han doon right as he wol devyse.
Men drinken, and the travers drawe anon;
The bryde was broght a-bedde as stille as stoon;
And whan the bed was with the preest y-blessed,
Out of the chambre hath every wight him dressed.
And Januarie hath faste in armes take
His fresshe May, his paradys, his make.
He lulleth hir, he kisseth hir ful ofte
With thikke bristles of his berd unsofte,
Lyk to the skin of houndfish, sharp as brere,
For he was shave al newe in his manere.
He rubbeth hir aboute hir tendre face,
And seyde thus, "allas! I moot trespace
To yow, my spouse, and yow gretly offende,
Er tyme come that I wil doun descende.
But nathelees, considereth this," quod he,
"Ther nis no werkman, what-so-ever he be,
That may bothe werke wel and hastily;
This wol be doon at leyser parfitly.
It is no fors how longe that we pleye;
In trewe wedlok wedded be we tweye;
And blessed bye the yok that we been inne,
For in our actes we mowe do no sinne.
A man may do no sinne with his wyf,
Ne hurte him-selven with his owene knyf;
For we han leve to pleye us by the lawe."
Thus laboureth he til that the day gan dawe;
And than he taketh a sop in fyn clarree,
And upright in his bed than sitteth he,
And after that he sang ful loude and clere,
And kiste his wyf, and made wantoun chere.
He was al coltish, ful of ragerye,

And ful of jargon as a flekked pye.
The slakke skin aboute his nekke shaketh,
Whyl that he sang; so chaunteth he and craketh.
But god wot what that May thoughte in hir herte,
Whan she him saugh up sittinge in his shorte,
In his night-cappe, and with his nekke lene;
She preyseth nat his pleying worth a bene.
Than seide he thus, "my reste wol I take;
Now day is come, I may no lenger wake."
And doun he leyde his heed, and sleep til pryme.
And afterward, whan that he saugh his tyme,
Up ryseth Januarie; but fresshe May
Holdeth hir chambre un-to the fourthe day,
As usage is of wyves for the beste.
For every labour som-tyme moot han reste,
Or elles longe may he nat endure;
This is to seyn, no lyves creature,
Be it of fish, or brid, or beest, or man.

And full of chatter as a speckled pie.
The slackened skin about his neck did shake
The while he sang and chanted like a crake.
But God knows what thing May thought in her heart
When up she saw him sitting in his shirt,
In his nightcap, and with his neck so lean;
She valued not his playing worth a bean.
Then said he thus: "My rest now will I take;
Now day is come, I can no longer wake."
And down he laid his head and slept till prime.
And afterward, when saw he it was time,
Up rose this January; but fresh May,
She kept her chamber untill the fourth day,
As custom is of wives, and for the best.
For every worker sometime must have rest,
Or else for long he'll certainly not thrive,
That is to say, no creature that's alive,
Be it of fish or bird, or beast, or man.

AUTHOR

Now wol I speke of woful Damian,
That languissheth for love, as ye shul here;
Therfore I speke to him in this manere:
I seye, "O sely Damian, allas!
Answere to my demaunde, as in this cas,
How shaltow to thy lady fresshe May
Telle thy wo? She wole alwey seye 'nay';
Eek if thou speke, she wol thy wo biwreye;
God be thyn help, I can no bettre seye."
This syke Damian in Venus fyr
So brenneth, that he dyeth for desyr;
For which he putte his lyf in aventure,
No lenger mighte he in this wyse endure;
But prively a penner gan he borwe,
And in a lettre wroot he al his sorwe,
In manere of a compleynt or a lay,
Un-to his faire fresshe lady May.
And in a purs of silk, heng on his sherte,
He hath it put, and leyde it at his herte.
The mone that, at noon, was, thilke day
That Januarie hath wedded fresshe May,
In two of Taur, was in-to Cancre gliden;
So longe hath Maius in hir chambre biden,
As custume is un-to thise nobles alle.
A bryde shal nat eten in the halle,
Til dayes foure or three dayes atte leste
Y-passed been; than lat hir go to feste.
The fourthe day compleet fro noon to noon,
Whan that the heighe masse was y-doon,
In halle sit this Januarie, and May
As fresh as is the brighte someres day.
And so bifel, how that this gode man
Remembred him upon this Damian,
And seyde, "Seinte Marie! how may this be,
That Damian entendeth nat to me?
Is he ay syk, or how may this bityde?"
His squyeres, whiche that stoden ther bisyde,
Excused him by-cause of his siknesse,
Which letted him to doon his bisinesse;
Noon other cause mighte make him tarie.

Now will I speak of woeful Damian,
Who languished for his love, as you shall hear;
I thus address him in this fashion here.
I say: "O hapless Damian, alas!
Answer to my demand in this your case,
How shall you to your lady, lovely May,
Tell all your woe? She would of course say 'Nay.'
And if you speak, she will your state betray;
God be your help! I can no better say."
This lovesick Damian in Venus' fire
So burned, he almost perished for desire;
Which put his life in danger, I am sure;
Longer in this wise could he not endure;
But privily a pen-case did he borrow
And in a letter wrote he all his sorrow,
In form of a complaint or of a lay,
Unto his fair and blooming Lady May.
And in a purse of silk hung in his shirt,
He put the poem and laid it next his heart.
The moon, which was at noon of that same day
Whereon this January wedded May
Half way through Taurus, had to Cancer glided,
So long had Maia in her chamber bided,
As is the custom among nobles all.
A bride shall not eat in the common hall
Until four days, or three days at the least,
Have fully passed; then let her go to feast.
On the fourth day, complete from noon to noon,
After the high Mass had been said and done,
In hall did January sit with May
As fresh as is the fair bright summer day.
And so befell it there that this good man
Recalled to mind his squire, this Damian,
And said: "Why holy Mary! How can it be
That Damian attends not here on me?
Is he sick always? How may this betide?"
His other squires, who waited there beside,
Made the excuse that he indeed was ill,
Which kept him from his proper duties still;
There was no other cause could make him tarry.

"That is a pity," said this January,
"He is a gentle squire, aye, by my truth!
If he should die, it were great harm and ruth;
As wise and secret, and discreet is he
As any man I know of his degree;
Therewith he's manly and he's serviceable,
And to become a useful man right able.
But after meat, as soon as ever I may,
I will myself go visit him, with May,
To give him all the comfort that I can,"
And for that word they blessed him, every man,
Because, for goodness and his gentleness,
He would so go to comfort, in sickness,
His suffering squire, for 'twas a gentle deed.
"Dame," said this January, "take good heed
That after meat, you, with your women all,
When you have gone to chamber from this hall,—
That all you go to see this Damian;
Cheer him a bit, for he's a gentleman;
And tell him that I'll come to visit him
After I've rested—a short interim;
And get this over quickly, for I'll bide
Awake until you sleep there at my side."
And with that word he raised his voice to call
A squire, who served as marshal of his hall,
And certain things he wished arranged were told.
This lovely May then did her straight way hold,
With all her women, unto Damian.
Down by his bed she sat, and so began
To comfort him with kindly word and glance.
This Damian, when once he'd found his chance,
In secret wise his purse and letter, too,
Wherein he'd said what he aspired to,
He put into her hand, with nothing more,
Save that he heaved a sigh both deep and sore,
And softly to her in this wise said he:
"Oh, mercy! Don't, I beg you, tell on me;
For I'm but dead if this thing be made known,"
This purse she hid in bosom of her gown
And went her way; you get no more of me.
But unto January then came she,
Who on his bedside sat in mood full soft.
He took her in his arms and kissed her oft,
And laid him down to sleep, and that anon.
And she pretended that she must be gone
Where you know well that everyone has need.
And when she of this note had taken heed,
She tore it all to fragments at the last
And down the privy quietly it cast.
Who's in brown study now but fair fresh May?
Down by old January's side she lay,
Who slept, until the cough awakened him;
He prayed her strip all naked for his whim;
He would have pleasure of her, so he said,
And clothes were an encumbrance when in bed,
And she obeyed him, whether lief or loath.
But lest these precious folk be with me wroth,
How there he worked, I dare not to you tell;
Nor whether she thought it paradise or hell;
But there I leave them working in their wise
Till vespers rang and they must needs arise.
Were it by destiny or merely chance,

"That me forthinketh," quod this Januarie,
"He is a gentil squyer, by my trouthe!
If that he deyde, it were harm and routhe;
He is as wys, discreet, and as secree
As any man I woot of his degree;
And ther-to manly and eek servisable,
And for to been a thrifty man right able.
But after mete, as sone as ever I may,
I wol my-self visyte him and eek May,
To doon him al the confort that I can."
And for that word him blessed every man,
That, of his bountee and his gentillesse,
He wolde so conforten in siknesse
His squyer, for it was a gentil dede.
"Dame," quod this Januarie, "tak good hede,
At-after mete ye, with your wommen alle,
Whan ye han been in chambre out of this halle,
That alle ye go see this Damian;
Doth him disport, he is a gentil man;
And telleth him that I wol him visyte,
Have I no-thing but rested me a lyte;
And spede yow faste, for I wole abyde
Til that ye slepe faste by my syde."
And with that word he gan to him to calle
A squyer, that was marchal of his halle,
And tolde him certeyn thinges, what he wolde.
This fresshe May hath streight hir wey y-holde,
With alle hir wommen, un-to Damian.
Doun by his beddes syde sit she than,
Confortinge him as goodly as she may.
This Damian, whan that his tyme he say,
In secree wise his purs, and eek his bille,
In which that he y-writen hadde his wille,
Hath put in-to hir hand, with-outen more,
Save that he syketh wonder depe and sore,
And softely to hir right thus seyde he:
"Mercy! and that ye nat discovere me;
For I am deed, if that this thing be kid."
This purs hath she inwith hir bosom hid,
And wente hir wey; ye gete namore of me.
But un-to Januarie y-comen is she,
That on his beddes syde sit ful softe.
He taketh hir, and kisseth hir ful ofte,
And leyde him doun to slepe, and that anon.
She feyned hir as that she moste gon
Ther-as ye woot that every wight mot nede.
And whan she of this bille hath taken hede,
She rente it al to cloutes atte laste,
And in the privee softely it caste.
Who studieth now but faire fresshe May?
Adoun by olde Januarie she lay,
That sleep, til that the coughe hath him awaked;
Anon he preyde hir strepen hir al naked;
He wolde of hir, he seyde, han som plesaunce,
And seyde, hir clothes dide him encombrance,
And she obeyeth, be hir lief or looth.
But lest that precious folk be with me wrooth,
How that he wroghte, I dar nat to yow telle;
Or whether hir thoughte it paradys or helle;
But here I lete hem werken in hir wyse
Til evensong rong, and that they moste aryse.
Were it by destinee or aventure,

Were it by influence or by nature,
Or constellacion, that in swich estat
The hevene stood, that tyme fortunat
Was for to putte a bille of Venus werkes
(For alle thing hath tyme, as seyn thise clerkes)
To any womman, for to gete hir love,
I can nat seye; but grete god above,
That knoweth that non act is causelees,
He deme of al, for I wol holde my pees.
But sooth is this, how that this fresshe May
Hath take swich impression that day,
For pitee of this syke Damian,
That from hir herte she ne dryve can
The remembraunce for to doon him ese.
"Certeyn," thoghte she, "whom that this thing displese,
I rekke noght, for here I him assure,
To love him best of any creature,
Though he na-more hadde than his sherte."
Lo, pitee renneth sone in gentil herte.

Heer may ye se how excellent franchyse
In wommen is, whan they hem narwe avyse.
Som tyrant is, as ther be many oon,
That hath an herte as hard as any stoon,
Which wolde han lete him sterven in the place
Wel rather than han graunted him hir grace;
And hem rejoysen in hir cruel pryde,
And rekke nat to been an homicyde.

This gentil May, fulfilled of pitee,
Right of hir hande a lettre made she,
In which she graunteth him hir verray grace;
Ther lakketh noght but only day and place,
Wher that she mighte un-to his lust suffyse:
For it shal be right as he wol devyse.
And whan she saugh hir time, up-on a day,
To visite this Damian goth May,
And sotilly this lettre doun she threste
Under his pilwe, rede it if him leste.
She taketh him by the hand, and harde him twiste
So secrely, that no wight of it wiste,
And bad him been al hool, and forth she wente
To Januarie, whan that he for hir sente.

Up ryseth Damian the nexte morwe,
Al passed was his siknesse and his sorwe.
He kembeth him, he proyneth him and pyketh,
He dooth al that his lady lust and lyketh;
And eek to Januarie he gooth as lowe
As ever dide a dogge for the bowe.
He is so plesant un-to every man,
(For craft is al, who-so that do it can)
That every wight is fayn to speke him good;
And fully in his lady grace he stood.
Thus lete I Damian aboute his nede,
And in my tale forth I wol procede.

Somme clerkes holden that felicitee
Stant in delyt, and therefor certeyn he,
This noble Januarie, with al his might,
In honest wyse, as longeth to a knight,
Shoop him to live ful deliciously.
His housinge, his array, as honestly
To his degree was maked as a kinges.
Amonges othere of his honest thinges,

By nature or some other circumstance,
Or constellation's sign, that in such state
The heavens stood, the time was fortunate
To make request concerning Venus' works
(For there's a time for all things, say these clerks)
To any woman, to procure her love,
I cannot say; but the great God above,
Who knows there's no effect without a cause,
He may judge all, for here my voice withdraws.
But true it is that this fair blooming May
Was so affected and impressed that day
For pity of this lovesick Damian,
That from her heart she could not drive or ban
Remembrance of her wish to give him ease.
"Certainly," thought she, "whom this may displease
I do not care, for I'd assure him now
Him with my love I'd willingly endow,
Though he'd no more of riches than his shirt."
Lo, pity soon wells up in gentle heart.

Here may you see what generosity
In women is when they advise closely.
Perhaps some tyrant (for there's many a one)
Who has a heart as hard as any stone,
Would well have let him die within that place
Much rather than have granted him her grace;
And such would have rejoiced in cruel pride,
Nor cared that she were thus a homicide.

This gentle May, fulfilled of all pity,
With her own hand a letter then wrote she
In which she granted him her utmost grace;
There was naught lacking now, save time and place
Wherein she might suffice to ease his lust:
For all should be as he would have it, just.
And when she'd opportunity on a day,
To visit Damian went this lovely May,
And cleverly this letter she thrust close
Under his pillow, read it if he chose.
She took him by the hand and hard did press,
So secretly that no one else could guess,
And bade him gain his health, and forth she went
To January, when for her he sent.

Up rose this Damian upon the morrow,
For gone was all his sickness and his sorrow.
He combed himself and preened his feathers smooth
He did all that his lady liked, in sooth;
And then to January went as low
As ever did a hound trained to the bow.
He was so pleasant unto every man
(For craft is everything for those who can),
That everyone was fain to speak his good;
And fully in his lady's grace he stood.
Thus Damian I leave about his need
And forward in my tale I will proceed.

Some writers hold that all felicity
Stands in delight, and therefor, certainly,
This noble January, with all his might,
Honourably, as does befit a knight,
Arranged affairs to live deliciously.
His housing, his array, as splendidly
Befitted his condition as a king's.
Among the rest of his luxurious things

He built a garden walled about with stone;
So fair a garden do I know of none.
For, without doubt, I verily suppose
That he who wrote *The Romance of the Rose*
Could not its beauty say in singing wise;
Nor could Priapus' power quite suffice,
Though he is god of gardens all, to tell
The beauty of that garden, and the well
Which was beneath the laurel always green.
For oftentimes God Pluto and his queen,
Fair Proserpine and all her faëry
Disported there and made sweet melody
About that well, and danced there, as men told.
  This noble knight, this January old,
Such pleasure had therein to walk and play,
That none he'd suffer bear the key, they say,
Save he himself; for of the little wicket
He carried always the small silver clicket
With which, as pleased him, he'd unlock the gate.
And when he chose to pay court to his mate
In summer season, thither would he go
With May, his wife, and no one but they two;
And divers things that were not done abed,
Within that garden there were done, 'tis said.
And in this manner many a merry day
Lived this old January and young May.
But worldly pleasure cannot always stay,
And January's joy must pass away.

He made a gardin, walled al with stoon;
So fair a gardin woot I nowher noon.
For out of doute, I verraily suppose,
That he that wroot the Romance of the Rose
Ne coude of it the beautee wel devyse;
Ne Priapus ne mighte nat suffyse,
Though he be god of gardins, for to telle
The beautee of the gardin and the welle,
That stood under a laurer alwey grene.
Ful ofte tyme he, Pluto, and his quene,
Proserpina, and al hir fayërye
Disporten hem and maken melodye
Aboute that welle, and daunced, as men tolde.
  This noble knight, this Januarie the olde,
Swich deintee hath in it to walke and pleye,
That he wol no wight suffren bere the keye
Save he him-self; for of the smale wiket
He bar alwey of silver a smal cliket,
With which, whan that him leste, he it unshette.
And whan he wolde paye his wyf hir dette
In somer seson, thider wolde he go,
And May his wyf, and no wight but they two;
And thinges whiche that were nat doon a-bedde,
He in the gardin parfourned hem and spedde.
And in this wyse, many a mery day,
Lived this Januarie and fresshe May.
But worldly joye may nat alwey dure
To Januarie, ne to no creature.

AUTHOR

  O sudden chance, O Fortune, thou unstable,
Like to the scorpion so deceptive, able
To flatter with thy mouth when thou wilt
  sting;
Thy tail is death, through thine envenoming.
O fragile joy! O poison sweetly taint!
O monster that so cleverly canst paint
Thy gifts in all the hues of steadfastness
That thou deceivest both the great and less!
Why hast thou January thus deceived,
That had'st him for thine own full friend received?
And now thou hast bereft him of his eyes,
For sorrow of which in love he daily dies.
  Alas! This noble January free,
In all his pleasure and prosperity,
Is fallen blind, and that all suddenly.
He wept and he lamented, pitifully;
And therewithal the fire of jealousy
Lest that his wife should fall to some folly,
So burned within his heart that he would fain
Both him and her some man had swiftly slain.
For neither after death nor in his life
Would he that she were other's love or wife,
But dress in black and live in widow's state,
Lone as the turtle-dove that's lost her mate.
But finally, after a month or twain,
His grief somewhat abated, to speak plain;
For when he knew it might not elsewise be,
He took in patience his adversity,
Save, doubtless, he could not renounce, as done,
His jealousy, from which he never won.
For this his passion was so outrageous

  O sedeyn hap, o thou fortune instable,
Lyk to the scorpioun so deceivable,
That flaterest with thyn heed when thou wolt
  stinge;
Thy tayl is deeth, thurgh thyn enveniminge.
O brotil joye! o swete venim queynte!
O monstre, that so subtilly canst peynte
Thy yiftes, under hewe of stedfastnesse,
That thou deceyvest bothe more and lesse!
Why hastow Januarie thus deceyved,
That haddest him for thy ful frend receyved?
And now thou hast biraft him bothe hise yën,
For sorwe of which desyreth he to dyen.
  Allas! this noble Januarie free,
Amidde his lust and his prosperitee,
Is woxen blind, and that al sodeynly.
He wepeth and he wayleth pitously;
And ther-with-al the fyr of jalousye,
Lest that his wyf sholde falle in som folye,
So brente his herte, that he wolde fayn
That som man bothe him and hir had slayn.
For neither after his deeth, nor in his lyf,
Ne wolde he that she were love ne wyf,
But ever live as widwe in clothes blake,
Soul as the turtle that lost hath hir make.
But atte laste, after a monthe or tweye,
His sorwe gan aswage, sooth to seye;
For whan he wiste it may noon other be,
He paciently took his adversitee;
Save, out of doute, he may nat forgoon
That he nas jalous evermore in oon;
Which jalousye it was so outrageous,

That neither in halle, n'in noon other hous,
Ne in noon other place, never-the-mo,
He nolde suffre hir for to ryde or go,
But-if that he had hand on hir alway;
For which ful ofte wepeth fresshe May,
That loveth Damian so benignely,
That she mot outher dyen sodeynly,
Or elles she mot han him as hir leste;
She wayteth whan hir herte wolde breste.
Up-on that other syde Damian
Bicomen is the sorwefulleste man
That ever was; for neither night ne day
Ne mighte he speke a word to fresshe May,
As to his purpos, of no swich matere,
But-if that Januarie moste it here,
That hadde an hand up-on hir evermo.
But nathelees, by wryting to and fro
And privee signes, wiste he what she mente;
And she knew eek the fyn of his entente.

That neither in his hall nor other house
Nor any other place, not ever, no,
He suffered her to ride or walking go,
Unless he had his hand on her alway;
For which did often weep this fresh young May,
Who loved her Damian so tenderly
That she must either swiftly die or she
Must have him as she willed, her thirst to slake;
Biding her time, she thought her heart would break.
And on the other side this Damian
Was now become the most disconsolate man
That ever was; for neither night nor day
Might he so much as speak a word to May
Of his desire, as I am telling here,
Save it were said to January's ear,
Who never took his blind hand off her, no.
Nevertheless, by writing to and fro
And secret signals, he knew what she meant;
And she too knew the aim of his intent.

AUTHOR

O Januarie, what mighte it thee availle,
Thou mightest see as fer as shippes saille?
For also good is blind deceyved be,
As be deceyved whan a man may see.
Lo, Argus, which that hadde an hondred yën,
For al that ever he coude poure or pryen,
Yet was he blent; and, god wot, so ben mo,
That wenen wisly that it be nat so.
Passe over is an ese, I sey na-more.
This fresshe May, that I spak of so yore,
In warme wex hath emprented the cliket,
That Januarie bar of the smale wiket,
By which in-to his gardin ofte he wente.
And Damian, that knew al hir entente,
The cliket countrefeted prively;
Ther nis na-more to seye, but hastily
Som wonder by this cliket shal bityde,
Which ye shul heren, if ye wole abyde.

O January, what might it now avail
Could your eyes see as far as ships can sail?
For it's as pleasant, blind, deceived to be
As be deceived while yet a man may see.
Lo, Argus, who was called the hundred-eyed,
No matter how he peered and watched and pried,
He was deceived; and God knows others too
Who think, and firmly, that it is not so.
Oblivion is peace; I say no more.
This lovely May, of whom I spoke before,
In warm wax made impression of the key
Her husband carried, to the gate where he
In entering his garden often went.
And Damian, who knew all her intent,
The key did counterfeit, and privately;
There is no more to say, but speedily
Some mischief of this latch-key shall betide,
Which you shall hear, if you but time will bide.

AUTHOR

O noble Ovyde, ful sooth seystou, god woot!
What sleighte is it, thogh it be long and hoot,
That he nil finde it out in som manere?
By Piramus and Tesbee may men lere;
Thogh they were kept ful longe streite overal,
They been accorded, rouninge thurgh a wal,
Ther no wight coude han founde out swich a sleighte.
But now to purpos; er that dayes eighte
Were passed, er the monthe of Juil, bifil
That Januarie hath caught so greet a wil,
Thurgh egging of his wyf, him for to pleye
In his gardin, and no wight but they tweye,
That in a morwe un-to this May seith he:
"Rys up, my wyf, my love, my lady free;
The turtles vois is herd, my douve swete;
The winter is goon, with alle his reynes wete:
Com forth now, with thyn eyën columbyn!
How fairer been thy brestes than is wyn!
The gardin is enclosed al aboute;

O noble Ovid, truth you say, God wot!
What art is there, though it be long and hot,
But Love will find it somehow suits his turn?
By Pyramus and Thisbe may men learn;
Though they were strictly kept apart in all,
They soon accorded, whispering through a wall,
Where none could have suspected any gate.
But now to purpose: ere had passed days eight,
And ere the first day of July, befell
That January was under such a spell,
Through egging of his wife, to go and play
Within his garden, and no one but they,
That on a morning to this May said he:
"Rise up, my wife, my love, my lady free;
The turtle's voice is heard, my dove so sweet;
The winter's past, the rain's gone, and the sleet;
Come forth now with your two eyes columbine!
How sweeter are your breasts than is sweet wine!
The garden is enclosed and walled about;

Come forth, my white spouse, for beyond all doubt
You have me ravished in my heart, O wife!
No fault have I found in you in my life.
Come forth, come forth, and let us take our sport;
I chose you for my wife and my comfort."
Such were the lewd old words that then used he;
To Damian a secret sign made she
That he should go before them with his clicket;
This Damian then opened up the wicket,
And in he slipped, and that in manner such
That none could see nor hear; and he did crouch
And still he sat beneath a bush anon.
This January, blind as is a stone,
With Maia's hand in his, and none else there,
Into his garden went, so fresh and fair,
And then clapped to the wicket suddenly.
"Now, wife," said he, "here's none but you and I,
And you're the one of all that I best love.
For by that Lord Who sits in Heaven above,
Far rather would I die upon a knife
Than do offence to you, my true, dear wife!
For God's sake think how I did choose you out,
And for no love of money, beyond doubt,
But only for the love you roused in me.
And though I am grown old and cannot see,
Be true to me, and I will tell you why.
Three things, it's certain, shall you gain thereby;
First, Christ's dear love, and honour of your own,
And all my heritage of tower and town;
I give it you, draw deeds to please you, pet;
This shall be done tomorrow ere sunset.
So truly may God bring my soul to bliss,
I pray you first, in covenant, that we kiss.
And though I'm jealous, yet reproach me not.
You are so deeply printed in my thought
That, when I do consider your beauty
And therewith all the unlovely age of me,
I cannot, truly, nay, though I should die,
Abstain from being in your company,
For utter love; of this there is no doubt.
Now kiss me, wife, and let us walk about."
This blooming May, when these words she had heard,
Graciously January she answered,
But first and foremost she began to weep.
"I have also," said she, "a soul to keep,
As well as you, and also honour mine,
And of my wifehood that sweet flower divine
Which I assured you of, both safe and sound,
When unto you that priest my body bound;
Wherefore I'll answer you in this manner,
If I may by your leave, my lord so dear.
I pray to God that never dawns the day
That I'll not die, foully as woman may,
If ever I do unto my kin such shame,
And likewise damage so my own fair name,
As to be false; and if I grow so slack,
Strip me and put me naked in a sack
And in the nearest river let me drown.
I am a lady, not a wench of town.
Why speak you thus? Men ever are untrue,
And woman have reproaches always new.

Com forth, my whyte spouse; out of doute,
Thou hast me wounded in myn herte, o wyf!
No spot of thee ne knew I al my lyf.
Com forth, and lat us taken our disport;
I chees thee for my wyf and my confort."
Swiche olde lewed wordes used he;
On Damian a signe made she,
That he sholde go biforen with his cliket:
This Damian thanne hat opened the wiket,
And in he stirte, and that in swich manere,
That no wight mighte it see neither y-here;
And stille he sit under a bush anoon.
This Januarie, as blind as is a stoon,
With Maius in his hand, and no wight mo,
In-to his fresshe gardin is ago,
And clapte to the wiket sodeynly.
"Now, wyf," quod he, "heer nis but thou and I,
That art the creature that I best love.
For, by that lord that sit in heven above,
Lever ich hadde dyen on a knyf,
Than thee offende, trewe dere wyf!
For goddes sake, thenk how I thee chees,
Noght for no coveityse, douteless,
But only for the love I had to thee.
And though that I be old, and may nat see,
Beth to me trewe, and I shal telle yow why.
Three thinges, certes, shul ye winne therby;
First, love of Crist, and to your-self honour,
And al myn heritage, toun and tour;
I yeve it yow, maketh chartres as yow leste;
This shal be doon to-morwe er sonne reste.
So wisly god my soule bringe in blisse,
I prey yow first, in covenant ye me kisse.
And thogh that I be jalous, wyte me noght.
Ye been so depe enprented in my thoght,
That, whan that I considere your beautee,
And ther-with-al the unlykly elde of me
I may nat, certes, thogh I sholde dye,
Forbere to been out of your companye
For verray love; this is with-outen doute.
Now kis me, wyf, and lat us rome aboute."
This fresshe May, whan she thise wordes herde,
Benignely to Januarie answerde,
But first and forward she bigan to wepe.
"I have," quod she, "a soule for to kepe
As wel as ye, and also myn honour,
And of my wyfhod thilke tendre flour,
Which that I have assured in your hond,
Whan that the preest to yow my body bond;
Wherfore I wole answere in this manere
By the leve of yow, my lord so dere:
I prey to god, that never dawe the day
That I ne sterve, as foule as womman may,
If ever I do un-to my kin that shame,
Or elles I empeyre so my name,
That I be fals; and if I do that lakke,
Do strepe me and put me in a sakke,
And in the nexte river do me drenche.
I am a gentil womman and no wenche.
Why speke ye thus? but men ben ever untrewe,
And wommen have repreve of yow ay newe.

Ye han non other contenance, I leve,
But speke to us of untrust and repreve."
And with that word she saugh wher Damian
Sat in the bush, and coughen she bigan,
And with hir finger signes made she,
That Damian sholde climbe up-on a tree,
That charged was with fruit, and up he wente;
For verraily he knew al hir entente,
And every signe that she coude make
Wel bet than Januarie, hir owene make.
For in a lettre she had told him al
Of this matere, how he werchen shal.
And thus I lete him sitte up-on the pyrie,
And Januarie and May rominge myrie.
Bright was the day, and blew the firmament,
Phebus of gold his stremes doun hath sent.
To gladen every flour with his warmnesse.
He was that tyme *in Geminis*, as I gesse,
But litel fro his declinacioun
Of Cancer, Jovis exaltacioun.
And so bifel, that brighte morwe-tyde,
That in that gardin, in the ferther syde,
Pluto, that is the king of fayërye,
And many a lady in his companye,
Folwinge his wyf, the quene Proserpyne,
Ech after other, right as any lyne—
Whyl that she gadered floures in the mede,
In Claudian ye may the story rede,
How in his grisly carte he hir fette:—
This king of fairye thanne adoun him sette
Up-on a bench of turves, fresh and grene,
And right anon thus seyde he to his quene.
"My wyf," quod he, "ther may no wight sey
nay;
Th'experience so preveth every day
The treson whiche that wommen doon to man.
Ten hondred thousand [stories] telle I can
Notable of your untrouthe and brotilnesse.
O Salomon, wys, richest of richesse,
Fulfild of sapience and of worldly glorie,
Ful worthy been thy wordes to memorie
To every wight that wit and reson can.
Thus preiseth he yet the bountee of man:
'Amonges a thousand men yet fond I oon,
But of wommen alle fond I noon.'
Thus seith the king that knoweth your wikked-
nesse;
And Jesus *filius Syrak*, as I gesse,
Ne speketh of yow but selde reverence.
A wilde fyr and corrupt pestilence
So falle up-on your bodies yet to-night!
Ne see ye nat this honurable knight,
By-cause, allas! that he is blind and old,
His owene man shal make him cokewold;
Lo heer he sit, the lechour, in the tree.
Now wol I graunten, of my magestee,
Un-to this olde blinde worthy knight
That he shal have ayeyn his eyen sight,
Whan that his wyf wold doon him vileinye;
Than shal he knowen al hir harlotrye
Both in repreve of hir and othere mo."
"Ye shal," quod Proserpyne, "wol ye so;

No reason or excuse have you, I think,
And so you harp on women who hoodwink."
And with that word she saw where Damian
Sat under bush; to cough then she began,
And with her slender finger signs made she
That Damian should climb into a tree
That burdened was with fruit, and up he went;
For verily he knew her full intent,
And understood each sign that she could make,
Better than January, her old rake.
For in a letter she had told him all
Of how he should proceed when time should fall.
And thus I leave him in the pear-tree still
While May and January roam at will.
Bright was the day and blue the firmament,
Phoebus his golden streamers down has sent
To gladden every flower with his warmness.
He was that time in Gemini, I guess,
And but a little from his declination
Of Cancer, which is great Jove's exaltation.
And so befell, in that bright morning-tide,
That in this garden, on the farther side,
Pluto, who is the king of Faëry,
With many a lady in his company,
Following his wife, the fair Queen Proserpine,
Each after other, straight as any line
(While she was gathering flowers on a mead,
In Claudian you may the story read
How in his grim car he had stolen her)—
This king of Faëry sat down yonder
Upon a turfen bank all fresh and green,
And right anon thus said he to his queen.
"My wife," said he, "there may no one say
nay;
Experience proves fully every day
The treason that these women do to man.
Ten hundred thousand stories tell I can
To show your fickleness and lies. Of which,
O Solomon wise, and richest of the rich,
Fulfilled of sapience and worldly glory,
Well worth remembrance are thy words and story
By everyone who's wit, and reason can.
Thus goodness he expounds with praise of man:
'Among a thousand men yet found I one,
But of all women living found I none.'
"Thus spoke the king that knew your
wickedness;
And Jesus son of Sirach, as I guess,
Spoke of you seldom with much reverence.
A wild-fire and a rotten pestilence
Fall on your bodies all before tonight!
Do you not see this honourable knight,
Because, alas! he is both blind and old,
His own sworn man shall make him a cuckold;
Lo, there he sits, the lecher, in that tree.
Now will I grant, of my high majesty,
Unto this old and blind and worthy knight,
That he shall have again his two eyes' sight,
Just when his wife shall do him villainy;
Then shall he know of all her harlotry,
Both in reproach to her and others too."
"You shall," said Proserpine, "if will you so;

Now by my mother's father's soul, I swear
That I will give her adequate answer,
And all such women after, for her sake;
That, though in any guilt caught, they'll not quake,
But with a bold face they'll themselves excuse,
And bear him down who would them thus accuse.
For lack of answer none of them shall die.
Nay, though a man see things with either eye,
Yet shall we women brazen shamelessly
And weep and swear and wrangle cleverly,
So that you men shall stupid be as geese.
What do I care for your authorities?
"I know well that this Jew, this Solomon
Found fools among us women, many a one,
But though he never found a good woman,
Yet has there found full many another man
Women right true, right good, and virtuous.
Witness all those that dwell in Jesus' house;
With martyrdom they proved their constancy.
The *Gesta Romanorum* speak kindly
Of many wives both good and true also.
But be not angry, sir, though it be so
That he said he had found no good woman,
I pray you take the meaning of the man;
He meant that sovereign goodness cannot be
Except in God, Who is the Trinity.
"Ah, since of very God there is but one,
Why do you make so much of Solomon?
What though he built a temple for God's house?
What though he were both rich and glorious?
So built he, too, a temple to false gods,
How could he with the Law be more at odds?
By gad, clean as his name you whitewash, sir,
He was a lecher and idolater;
And in old age the True God he forsook.
And if that God had not, as says the Book,
Spared him for father David's sake, he should
Have lost his kingdom sooner than he would.
I value not, of all the villainy
That you of women write, a butterfly.
I am a woman, and needs must I speak,
Or else swell up until my heart shall break.
For since he said we gossip, rail, and scold,
As ever may I my fair tresses hold,
I will not spare, for any courtesy,
To speak him ill who'd wish us villainy."
"Dame," said this Pluto, "be no longer wroth;
I give it up; but since I swore my oath
That I would give to him his sight again,
My word shall stand, I warn you that's certain.
I am a king, it suits me not to lie."
"And I," said she, "am queen of Faëry.
Her answer shall she have, I undertake;
No further talk hereof let us two make
Forsooth, I will not longer be contrary."
Now let us turn again to January,
Who in the garden with his lovely May
Sang, and that merrier than the popinjay,
"I love you best, and ever shall, I know."
And so about the alleys did he go
Till he had come at last to that pear-tree

Now, by my modres sires soule I swere,
That I shal yeven hir suffisant answere,
And alle wommen after, for hir sake;
That, though they be in any gilt y-take,
With face bold they shulle hem-self excuse,
And bere hem doun that wolden hem accuse.
For lakke of answer, noon of hem shal dyen.
Al hadde man seyn a thing with bothe his yën,
Yit shul we wommen visage it hardily,
And wepe, and swere, and chyde subtilly,
So that ye men shul been as lewed as gees.
What rekketh me of your auctoritees?
I woot wel that this Jew, this Salomon,
Fond of us wommen foles many oon.
But though that he ne fond no good womman,
Yet hath ther founde many another man
Wommen ful trewe, ful gode, and vertuous.
Witnesse on hem that dwelle in Cristes hous,
With martirdom they preved hir constance.
The Romayn gestes maken remembrance
Of many a verray trewe wyf also.
But sire, ne be nat wrooth, al-be-it so,
Though that he seyde he fond no good womman,
I prey yow take the sentence of the man;
He mente thus, that in sovereyn bontee
Nis noon but god, that sit in Trinitee.
Ey! for verray god, that nis but oon,
What make ye so muche of Salomon?
What though he made a temple, goddes hous?
What though he were riche and glorious?
So made he eek a temple of false goddis,
How mighte he do a thing that more forbode is?
Pardee, as faire as ye his name emplastre,
He was a lechour and an ydolastre;
And in his elde he verray god forsook.
And if that god ne hadde, as seith the book,
Y-spared him for his fadres sake, he sholde
Have lost his regne rather than he wolde.
I sette noght of al the vileinye,
That ye of wommen wryte, a boterflye.
I am a womman, nedes moot I speke,
Or elles swelle til myn herte breke.
For sithen he seyde that we ben jangleresses,
As ever hool I mote brouke my tresses,
I shal nat spare, for no curteisye,
To speke him harm that wolde us vileinye."
"Dame," quod this Pluto, "be no lenger wrooth;
I yeve it up; but sith I swoor myn ooth
That I wolde graunten him his sighte ageyn,
My word shal stonde, I warne yow, certeyn.
I am a king, it sit me noght to lye."
"And I," quod she, "a queene of fayërye.
Hir answere shal she have, I undertake;
Lat us na-more wordes heer-of make.
For sothe, I wol no lenger yow contrarie."
Now lat us turne agayn to Januarie,
That in the gardin with his faire May
Singeth, ful merier than the papejay,
"Yow love I best, and shal, and other noon."
So longe aboute the aleyes is he goon,
Til he was come agaynes thilke pyrie,

Wher-as this Damian sitteth ful myrie
An heigh, among the fresshe leves grene.
This fresshe May, that is so bright and shene,
Gan for to syke, and seyde, "allas, my syde!
Now sir," quod she, "for aught that may bityde,
I moste han of the peres that I see,
Or I mot dye, so sore longeth me
To eten of the smale peres grene.
Help, for hir love that is of hevene quene!
I telle yow wel, a womman in my plyt
May han to fruit so greet an appetyt,
That she may dyen, but she of it have."
"Allas!" quod he, "that I ne had heer a knave
That coude climbe; allas! allas!" quod he,
"That I am blind."
"Ye, sir, no fors," quod she:
"But wolde ye vouche-sauf, for goddes sake,
The pyrie in with your armes for to take,
(For wel I woot that ye mistruste me)
Thanne sholde I climbe wel y-nogh," quod she,
"So I my foot mighte sette upon your bak."
"Certes," quod he, "ther-on shal be no lak,
Mighte I yow helpen with myn herte blood."
He stoupeth doun, and on his bak she stood,
And caughte hir by a twiste, and up she gooth.
Ladies, I prey yow that ye be nat wrooth;
I can nat glose, I am a rude man.
And sodeynly anon this Damian
Gan pullen up the smok, and in he throng.
And whan that Pluto saugh this grete wrong,
To Januarie he gaf agayn his sighte,
And made him see, as wel as ever he mighte.
And whan that he hadde caught his sighte agayn,
Ne was ther never man of thing so fayn.
But on his wyf his thoght was evermo;
Up to the tree he caste his eyen two,
And saugh that Damian his wyf had dressed
In swich manere, it may nat ben expressed
But if I wolde speke uncurteisly:
And up he yaf a roring and a cry
As doth the moder whan the child shal dye:
"Out! help! allas! harrow!" he gan to crye,
"O stronge lady store, what dostow?"
And she answerde, "sir, what eyleth yow?
Have pacience, and reson in your minde,
I have yow holpe on bothe your eyen blinde.
Up peril of my soule, I shal nat lyen,
As me was taught, to hele with your yën,
Was no-thing bet to make yow to see
Than strugle with a man up-on a tree.
God woot, I dide it in ful good entente."
"Strugle!" quod he, "ye, algate in it wente!
God yeve yow bothe on shames deeth to dyen!
He swyved thee, I saugh it with myne yën,
And elles be I hanged by the hals!"
"Thanne is," quod she, "my medicyne al fals;
For certeinly, if that ye mighte see,
Ye wolde nat seyn thise wordes un-to me;
Ye han som glimsing and no parfit sighte."
"I see," quod he, "as wel as ever I mighte,
Thonked be god! with bothe myne eyen two,
And by my trouthe, me thoughte he dide thee so."

Wherein this Damian sat right merrily
On high, among the young leaves fresh and green.
This blooming May, who was so bright of sheen,
Began to sigh, and said: "Alas, my side!
Now, sir," said she, "no matter what betide,
I must have some of these pears that I see,
Or I may die, so much I long," said she,
"To eat some of those little pears so green.
Help, for Her love Who is of Heaven Queen!
I tell you well, a woman in my plight
May have for fruit so great an appetite
That she may die if none of it she have."
"Alas!" said he, "that I had here a knave
That could climb up, alas, alas!" said he,
"That I am blind."
"Yea, sir, no odds," said she,
"If you'd but grant me, and for God's dear sake,
That this pear-tree within your arms you'd take
(For well I know that you do not trust me),
Then I could climb up well enough," said she,
"So I my foot might set upon your back."
"Surely," said he, "thereof should be no lack,
Might I so help you with my own heart's blood."
So he stooped down, and on his back she stood,
And gave herself a twist and up went she.
Ladies, I pray you be not wroth with me;
I cannot gloze, I'm an uncultured man.
For of a sudden this said Damian
Pulled up her smock and thrust both deep and long.
And when King Pluto saw this awful wrong,
To January he gave again his sight,
And made him see as well as ever he might.
And when he thus had got his sight again,
Never was man of anything so fain.
But since his wife he thought of first and last,
Up to the tree his eyes he quickly cast,
And saw how Damian his wife had dressed
In such a way as cannot be expressed,
Save I should rudely speak and vulgarly:
And such a bellowing clamour then raised he
As does a mother when her child must die:
"Out! Help! Alas! Oh, help me!" he did cry,
"Outlandish, brazen woman, what do you do?"
And she replied: "Why, sir, and what ails you?
Have patience, and do reason in your mind
That I have helped you for your two eyes blind.
On peril of my soul, I tell no lies,
But I was taught that to recover eyes
Was nothing better, so to make you see,
Than struggle with a man up in a tree.
God knows I did it with a good intent."
"Struggle!" cried he, "but damme, in it went!
God give you both a shameful death to die!
He banged you, for I saw it with my eye,
Or may they hang me by the neck up, else!"
"Then is," said she, "my medicine all false;
For certainly, if you could really see.
You would not say these cruel words to me;
You catch but glimpses and no perfect sight."
"I see," said he, "as well as ever I might—
Thanks be to God!—and with my two eyes, too,
And truth, I thought he did that thing to you."

"You are bewildered still, good sir," said she,
"Such thanks I have for causing you to see;
Alas!" she cried, "that ever I was so kind!"
"Now, dame," said he, "put all this out of mind
Come down, my dear, and if I have missaid,
God help me if I'm not put out indeed.
But by my father's soul, I thought to have seen
How Damian right over you did lean
And that your smock was pulled up to his breast."
"Yes, sir," said she, "you may think as seems best:
But, sir, a man that wakens out of sleep,
He cannot suddenly take note and keep
Of any thing, or see it perfectly,
Until he has recovered verily;
Just so a man that blinded long has been,
He cannot say that suddenly he's seen
So well, at first, when sight is new to him,
As later, when his sight's no longer dim.
Until your sight be settled for a while,
There may full many a thing your mind beguile.
Beware, I pray you, for, by Heaven's King,
Full many a man thinks that he sees a thing,
And it is other quite than what it seems.
And he that misconstrues, why, he misdeems."
And with that word she leaped down from the tree.
This January, who is glad but he?
He kissed her and he hugged her much and oft,
And on her belly stroked and rubbed her soft,
And home to palace led her, let me add.
And now, good men, I pray you to be glad.
For here I end my tale of January;
God bless us, and His Mother, Holy Mary!

"Ye maze, maze, gode sire," quod she,
"This thank have I for I have maad yow see;
Allas!" quod she, "that ever I was so kinde!"
"Now, dame," quod he, "lat al passe out of minde.
Com doun, my lief, and if I have missayd,
God help me so, as I am yvel apayd.
But, by my fader soule, I wende han seyn,
How that this Damian had by thee leyn,
And that thy smok had leyn up-on his brest."
"Ye, sire," quod she, "ye may wene as yow lest;
But, sire, a man that waketh out of his sleep,
He may nat sodeynly wel taken keep
Up-on a thing, ne seen it parfitly,
Til that he be adawed verraily;
Right so a man, that longe hath blind y-be,
Ne may nat sodeynly so wel y-see,
First whan his sighte is newe come ageyn,
As he that hath a day or two y-seyn.
Til that your sighte y-satled be a whyle,
Ther may ful many a sighte yow bigyle.
Beth war, I prey yow; for, by hevene king,
Ful many a man weneth to seen a thing,
And it is al another than it semeth.
He that misconceyveth, he misdemeth."
And with that word she leep doun fro the tree.
This Januarie, who is glad but he?
He kisseth hir, and clippeth hir ful ofte,
And on hir wombe he stroketh hir ful softe,
And to his palays hoom he hath hir lad.
Now, gode men, I pray yow to be glad.
Thus endeth heer my tale of Januarie;
God blesse us and his moder Seinte Marie!

HERE IS ENDED THE MERCHANT'S TALE OF JANUARY

EPILOGUE TO THE MERCHANT'S TALE

"Eh! By God's mercy!" cried our host. Said he:
"Now such a wife I pray God keep from me!
Behold what tricks, and lo, what subtleties
In women are. For always busy as bees
Are they, us simple men thus to deceive,
And from the truth they turn aside and leave;
By this same merchant's tale it's proved, I feel,
But, beyond doubt, as true as any steel
I have a wife, though poor enough she be;
But of her tongue a babbling shrew is she,
And she's a lot of other vices too.
No matter, though, with this we've naught to do.
But know you what? In secret, be it said,
I am sore sorry that to her I'm wed.
For if I should up-reckon every vice
The woman has, I'd be a fool too nice,
And why? Because it should reported be
And told her by some of this company;
Who'd be the ones, I need not now declare,
Since women know the traffic in such ware;
Besides, my wit suffices not thereto
To tell it all; wherefore my tale is through."

"Ey! goddes mercy!" seyde our Hoste tho,
"Now swich a wyf I pray god kepe me fro!
Lo, whiche sleightes and subtilitees
In wommen been! for ay as bisy as bees
Ben they, us sely men for to deceyve,
And from a sothe ever wol they weyve;
By this Marchauntes Tale it preveth weel.
But doutelees, as trewe as any steel
I have a wyf, though that she povre be;
But of hir tonge a labbing shrewe is she,
And yet she hath an heep of vyces mo;
Ther-of no fors, lat alle swiche thinges go.
But, wite ye what? in conseil be it seyd,
Me reweth sore I am un-to hir teyd.
For, and I sholde rekenen every vyce
Which that she hath, y-wis, I were to nyce,
And cause why; it sholde reported be
And told to hir of somme of this meynee;
Of whom, it nedeth nat for to declare,
Sin wommen connen outen swich chaffare;
And eek my wit suffyseth nat ther-to
To tellen al; wherfor my tale is do."

THE SQUIRE'S TALE

THE SQUIRE'S PROLOGUE

"Squier, com neer, if it your wille be,
And sey somwhat of love; for, certes, ye
Connen ther-on as muche as any man."
"Nay, sir," quod he, "but I wol seye as I can
With hertly wille; for I wol nat rebelle
Agayn your lust; a tale wol I telle.
Have me excused if I speke amis,
My wil is good; and lo, my tale is this."

"Squire, come nearer, if your will it be,
And speak to us of love; for certainly
You know thereof as much as any man."
"Nay, sir," said he, "but I'll do what I can
With hearty will; for I will not rebel
Against your wishes, but a tale will tell.
Hold me excused if I say aught amiss,
My aim is good, and lo, my tale is this."

HERE BEGINNETH THE SQUIRE'S TALE

At Sarray, in the land of Tartarye,
Ther dwelte a king, that werreyed Russye,
Thurgh which ther deyde many a doughty man.
This noble king was cleped Cambinskan,
Which in his tyme was of so greet renoun
That ther nas no-wher in no regioun
So excellent a lord in alle thing;
Him lakked noght that longeth to a king.
As of the secte of which that he was born
He kepte his lay, to which that he was sworn;
And ther-to he was hardy, wys, and riche,
And pitëous and just, alwey y-liche;
Sooth of his word, benigne and honurable,
Of his corage as any centre stable;
Yong, fresh, and strong, in armes desirous
As any bacheler of al his hous.
A fair persone he was and fortunat,
And kepte alwey so wel royal estat,
That ther was nowher swich another man.
This noble king, this Tartre Cambinskan
Hadde two sones on Elpheta his wyf,
Of whiche th'eldeste highte Algarsyf,
That other sone was cleped Cambalo.
A doghter hadde this worthy king also,
That yongest was, and highte Canacee.
But for to telle yow al hir beautee,
It lyth nat in my tonge, n'in my conning;
I dar nat undertake so heigh a thing.
Myn English eek is insufficient;
It moste been a rethor excellent,
That coude his colours longing for that art,
If he sholde hir discryven every part.
I am non swich, I moot speeke as I can.
And so bifel that, whan this Cambinskan
Hath twenty winter born his diademe,
As he was wont fro yeer to yeer, I deme,
He leet the feste of his nativitee
Don cryen thurghout Sarray his citee,
The last Idus of March, after the yeer.
Phebus the sonne ful joly was and cleer;
For he was neigh his exaltacioun
In Martes face, and in his mansioun
In Aries, the colerik hote signe.
Ful lusty was the weder and benigne,
For which the foules, agayn the sonne shene,

At Sarai, in the land of Tartary,
There dwelt a king who warred on Russia, he,
Whereby there died full many a doughty man.
This noble king was known as Cambinskan,
Who in his time was of so great renown
That there was nowhere in the wide world known
So excellent a lord in everything;
He lacked in naught belonging to a king.
As for the faith to which he had been born,
He kept its law to which he had been sworn;
And therewith he was hardy, rich, and wise,
And merciful and just in all men's eyes,
True to his word, benign and honourable,
And in his heart like any center stable;
Young, fresh, and strong, in warfare ambitious
As any bachelor knight of all his house.
Of handsome person, he was fortunate,
And kept always so well his royal state
That there was nowhere such another man.
This noble king, this Tartar Cambinskan
Had got two sons on Elpheta, his wife,
Of whom the elder's name was Algarsyf,
And that same second son was Cambalo.
A daughter had this worthy king, also,
Who was the youngest, and called Canace.
But to describe to you all her beauty,
It lies not in my tongue nor my knowing;
I dare not undertake so high a thing.
My English is quite insufficient for
What must require a finished orator
Who knew the colours needful to that art
If he were to describe her every part.
I am none such, I must speak as I can.
And so befell that, when this Cambinskan
Had twenty winters worn his diadem,
As he was wont from year to year, I deem,
He let the feast of his nativity
Be cried throughout all Sarai, his city,
The last *Idus* of March, as 'twas that year.
Phoebus the sun right festive was, and clear;
For he was near his exaltation grown
In face of Mars, and in his mansion known
In Aries, the choleric hot sign.
Right pleasant was the weather, and benign,
For which the wild birds in the sun's gold sheen,

What of the season and the springing green,
Full loudly sang their love and their affection;
It seemed that they had got themselves protection
Against the sword of winter keen and cold.
This Cambinskan, of whom I have you told,
High in the palace, mounted on his throne
With crown and royal vestments sat alone,
And held his feast, so splendid and so rich
That in this world its like was not, of which,
If I should tell you all of the array,
Then would it occupy a summer's day.
Besides, it needs not here that I apprise
Of every course the order of service.
I will not tell you of their each strange sauce,
Nor of their swans, nor of their heronshaws.
Moreover, in that land, as tell knights old,
There are some foods which they for dainties hold,
Of which in this land the esteem is small;
There is no man that can report them all.
I will not so delay you, for it's prime,
And all the fruit of this were loss of time;
Unto my first theme I will have recourse.
And so befell that, after the third course,
While this great king sat in his state that day,
Hearing his minstrels on their instruments play
Before him at the board, deliciously,
In at the hall door, and all suddenly,
There came a knight upon a steed of brass,
Holding in hand a mirror broad of glass.
Upon his thumb he had a golden ring,
And by his side a naked sword hanging;
And up he rode right to the highest board.
In all the hall there was not spoken word
For marvel of this knight; him to behold,
They stared and stretched and craned, both young and old.
This stranger knight, who came thus suddenly,
Armed at all points, except his head, richly,
Saluted king and queen and those lords all,
In order of rank, as they sat there in hall,
Showing such humble courtesy to each
In manner of behaviour and in speech,
That Gawain, with his old-time courtesy,
Though he were come again from Faëry,
Could not have bettered him in any word.
And after this, before the king's high board,
He with a manly voice said his message,
After the form in use in his language,
Without mistake in syllable or letter;
And, that his tale should seem to all the better,
According to his language was his cheer,
As men teach art of speech both there and here;
Albeit that I cannot ape his style,
Nor can I climb across so high a stile,
Yet say I this, as to his broad intent,
To this amounts the whole of what he meant,
If so be that I have it yet in mind.
He said: "The king of Araby and Ind,
My liege-lord, on this great and festive day
Salutes you as he now best can and may,
And sends to you, in honour of your feast,
By me, that am prepared for your behest,

What for the seson and the yonge grene,
Ful loude songen hir affeccioun;
Hem semed han geten hem protecciouns
Agayn the swerd of winter kene and cold.
This Cambinskan, of which I have yow told,
In royal vestiment sit on his deys,
With diademe, ful heighe in his paleys,
And halt his feste, so solempne and so riche
That in this world ne was ther noon it liche.
Of which if I shal tellen al th'array,
Than wolde it occupye a someres day;
And eek it nedeth nat for to devyse
At every cours the ordre of hir servyse.
I wol nat tellen of hir strange sewes,
Ne of hir swannes, ne of hir heronsewes.
Eek in that lond, as tellen knightes olde,
Ther is som mete that is ful deyntee holde,
That in this lond men recche of it but smal;
Ther nis no man that may reporten al.
I wol nat tarien yow, for it is pryme,
And for it is no fruit but los of tyme;
Un-to my firste I wol have my recours.
And so bifel that, after the thridde cours,
Whyl that this king sit thus in his nobleye,
Herkninge his minstralles hir thinges pleye
Biforn him at the bord deliciously,
In at the halle-dore al sodeynly
Ther cam a knight up-on a stede of bras,
And in his hand a brood mirour of glas.
Upon his thombe he hadde of gold a ring,
And by his syde a naked swerd hanging;
And up he rydeth to the heighe bord.
In al the halle ne was ther spoke a word
For merveille of this knight; him to biholde
Ful bisily ther wayten yonge and olde.
This strange knight, that cam thus sodeynly,
Al armed save his heed ful richely,
Saluëth king and queen, and lordes alle,
By ordre, as they seten in the halle,
With so heigh reverence and obeisaunce
As wel in speche as in contenaunce,
That Gawain, with his olde curteisye,
Though he were come ageyn out of Fairye,
Ne coude him nat amende with a word.
And after this, biforn the heighe bord,
He with a manly voys seith his message,
After the forme used in his langage,
With-outen vyce of sillable or of lettre;
And, for his tale sholde seme the bettre,
Accordant to his wordes was his chere,
As techeth art of speche hem that it lere;
Al-be-it that I can nat soune his style,
Ne can nat climben over so heigh a style,
Yet seye I this, as to commune entente,
Thus muche amounteth al that ever he mente,
If it so be that I have it in minde.
He seyde, "the king of Arabie and of Inde,
My lige lord, on this solempne day
Saluëth yow as he best can and may,
And sendeth yow, in honour of your feste,
By me, that am al redy at your heste,

This stede of bras, that esily and wel
Can, in the space of o day naturel,
This is to seyn, in foure and twenty houres,
Wher-so yow list, in droghte or elles shoures,
Beren your body in-to every place
To which your herte wilneth for to pace
With-outen wem of yow, thurgh foul or fair;
Or, if yow list to fleen as hye in the air
As doth an egle, whan him list to sore,
This same stede shal bere yow ever-more
With-outen harm, til ye be ther yow
  leste,
Though that ye slepen on his bak or reste;
And turne ayeyn, with wrything of a pin.
He that it wroghte coude ful many a gin;
He wayted many a constellacioun
Er he had doon this operacioun;
And knew ful many a seel and many a bond.
  This mirour eek, that I have in myn hond,
Hath swich a might, that men may in it see
Whan ther shal fallen any adversitee
Un-to your regne or to your-self also;
And openly who is your freend or foo.
And over al this, if any lady bright
Hath set hir herte on any maner wight,
If he be fals, she shal his treson see,
His newe love and al his subtiltee
So openly, that ther shal no-thing hyde.
Wherfor, ageyn this lusty someres tyde,
This mirour and this ring, that ye may see,
He hath sent to my lady Canacee,
Your excellente doghter that is here.
  The vertu of the ring, if ye wol here,
Is this; that, if hir lust it for to were
Up-on hir thombe, or in hir purs it bere,
Ther is no foul that fleeth under the hevene
That she ne shal wel understonde his stevene,
And knowe his mening openly and pleyn,
And answere him in his langage ageyn.
And every gras that groweth up-on rote
She shal eek knowe, and whom it wol do bote,
Al be his woundes never so depe and wyde.
  This naked swerd, that hangeth by my syde,
Swich vertu hath, that what man so ye smyte,
Thurgh-out his armure it wol kerve and byte,
Were it as thikke as is a branched ook;
And what man that is wounded with the strook
Shal never be hool til that yow list, of grace,
To stroke him with the platte in thilke place
Ther he is hurt: this is as muche to seyn
Ye mote with the platte swerd ageyn
Stroke him in the wounde, and it wol close;
This is a verray sooth, with-outen glose,
It failleth nat whyl it is in your hold."
  And whan this knight hath thus his tale told,
He rydeth out of halle, and doun he lighte.
His stede, which that shoon as sonne brighte,
Stant in the court, as stille as any stoon.
This knight is to his chambre lad anon,
And is unarmed and to mete y-set.
  The presents been ful royally y-fet,
This is to seyn, the swerd and the mirour,

This steed of brass, that easily and well
Can, in one natural day ('tis truth I tell),
That is to say, in four and twenty hours,
Where'er you please, in drought or else in showers,
Bear you in body unto every place
To which your heart wills that you go apace,
Without least hurt to you, through foul or fair;
Or, if you please to fly as high in air
As does an eagle when he wills to soar,
This self-same steed will bear you evermore
Without least harm, till you have gained your
  quest,
Although you sleep upon his back, or rest;
And he'll return, by twisting of a pin.
He that made this could make full many a gin;
He waited, watching many a constellation
Before he did contrive this operation;
And he knew many a magic seal and band.
  "This mirror, too, which I have in my hand,
Has power such that in it men may see
When there shall happen any adversity
Unto your realm, and to yourself also;
And openly who is your friend or foe.
More than all this, if any lady bright
Has set her heart on any kind of wight,
If he be false she shall his treason see,
His newer love and all his subtlety
So openly that nothing can he hide.
Wherefore, upon this pleasant summertide,
This mirror and this ring, which you may see,
He has sent to my Lady Canace,
Your most surpassing daughter, who is here.
  "The virtue of the ring, if you will hear,
Is this: that if she pleases it to wear
Upon her thumb, or in her purse to bear,
There is no bird that flies beneath the heaven
But she shall understand his language, even
To know his meaning openly and plain,
And answer him in his own words again.
And every herb that grows upon a root
She shall know, too, and whom 'twill heal, to boot,
Although his wounds be never so deep and wide.
  "This naked sword that's hanging by my side
Such virtue has that any man you smite,
Right through his armour will it carve and bite,
Were it as thick as is a branching oak;
And that man who is wounded by its stroke
Shall never be whole until you please, of grace,
To strike him with the flat in that same place
Where he is hurt; which is to say, 'tis plain,
That you may with the flat sword blade again
Strike him upon the wound and it will close;
This is the truth, I seek not to impose,
For it shall fail not while it's in your hold."
  And when this knight had thus his message told,
He rode out of the hall and did alight.
His steed, which shone as sun does, and as bright,
Stood in the courtyard, still as any stone.
This knight was to a chamber led anon,
And was unarmed, and there at meat sat down.
  The gifts were brought and royally were shown
That is to say, the sword and glass of power,

And borne anon into the donjon tower
By certain officers detailed thereto;
The ring to Canace was borne also
With ceremony, where she sat at table.
But certainly, it is no lie or fable,
The horse of brass could no way be removed;
It stood as it were glued to ground. 'Twas proved
There was no man could lead it out or drive
With any windlass that he might contrive.
And why? Because they hadn't craft to heave it.
And therefore in that place they had to leave it
Until the knight had taught them the manner
Of moving it, as you'll hereafter hear.

Great was the press of people to and fro
Swarming to see this horse that stood there so;
For it so high was, and so broad and long,
So well proportioned as to be most strong,
Just as it were a steed of Lombardy;
Therewith as horselike and as quick of eye
As if a gentle Apulian courser 'twere.
For truly, from his tail unto his ear
Nature nor art could better nor amend
In any wise, as people did contend.
But evermore their greatest wonder was,
How it could go, being made all of brass;
It was of Faëry, as to people seemed.
And divers folk diversely of it deemed;
So many heads, so many wits, one sees.
They buzzed and murmured like a swarm of bees,
And played about it with their fantasy,
Recalling what they'd learned from poetry;
Like Pegasus it was that mounted high,
That horse which had great wings and so could fly;
Or else it was the horse of Greek Sinon
Who brought Troy to destruction, years agone,
As men in these old histories may read.
"My heart," said one, "is evermore in dread;
I think some men-at-arms are hid therein
Who have in mind this capital to win.
It were right well that of such things we know."
Another whispered to his fellow, low,
And said: "He lies, for it is rather like
Some conjured up appearance of magic,
Which jugglers practise at these banquets great."
Of sundry doubts like these they all did treat,
As vulgar people chatter commonly
Of all things that are made more cunningly
Than they can in their ignorance comprehend;
They gladly judge they're made for some base end.

And some much wondered on the mirror's power,
That had been borne up to the donjon tower,
And how men in it such strange things could see.
Another answered, saying it might be
Quite natural, by angles oddly spaced
And sly reflections thus within it placed,
And said, at Rome was such a one, men know.
They spoke of Alhazen and Vitello
And Aristotle, who wrote, in their lives,
On mirrors strange and on perspectives,
As all they know who've read their published word.

And other folk did wonder on the sword
That had the power to pierce through anything;

And born anon in-to the heighe tour
With certeine officers ordeyned therfore;
And un-to Canacee this ring was bore
Solempnely, ther she sit at the table.
But sikerly, with-outen any fable,
The hors of bras, that may nat be remewed,
It stant as it were to the ground y-glewed.
Ther may no man out of the place it dryve
For noon engyn of windas or polyve;
And cause why, for they can nat the craft.
And therefore in the place they han it laft
Til that the knight hath taught hem the manere
To voyden him, as ye shal after here.

Greet was the prees, that swarmeth to and fro,
To gauren on this hors that stondeth so;
For it so heigh was, and so brood and long,
So wel proporcioned for to ben strong,
Right as it were a stede of Lumbardye;
Ther-with so horsly, and so quik of yë
As it a gentil Poileys courser were.
For certes, fro his tayl un-to his ere,
Nature ne art ne coude him nat amende
In no degree, as al the peple wende.
But evermore hir moste wonder was,
How that it coude goon, and was of bras;
It was of Fairye, as the peple semed.
Diverse folk diversely they demed;
As many hedes, as many wittes ther been.
They murmureden as dooth a swarm of been,
And maden skiles after hir fantasyes,
Rehersinge of thise olde poetryes,
And seyden, it was lyk the Pegasee,
The hors that hadde winges for to flee;
Or elles it was the Grekes hors Synon,
That broghte Troye to destruccion,
As men may in thise olde gestes rede.
"Myn herte," quod oon, "is evermore in drede;
I trowe som men of armes been ther-inne,
That shapen hem this citee for to winne.
It were right good that al swich thing were knowe."
Another rowned to his felawe lowe,
And seyde, "he lyeth, it is rather lyk
An apparence y-maad by som magyk,
As jogelours pleyen at thise festes grete."
Of sondry doutes thus they jangle and trete,
As lewed peple demeth comunly
Of thinges that ben maad more subtilly
Than they can in her lewednes comprehende;
They demen gladly to the badder ende.

And somme of hem wondred on the mirour,
That born was up in-to the maister-tour,
How men mighte in it swiche thinges see.
Another answerde, and seyde it mighte wel be
Naturelly, by composicious
Of angles and of slye reflexiouns,
And seyden, that in Rome was swich oon.
They speken of Alocen and Vitulon,
And Aristotle, that writen in hir lyves
Of queynte mirours and of prospectyves,
As knowen they that han hir bokes herd.

And othere folk han wondred on the swerd
That wolde percen thurgh-out every-thing;

And fille in speche of Thelophus the king,
And of Achilles with his queynte spere,
For he coude with it bothe hele and dere,
Right in swich wyse as men may with the swerd
Of which right now ye han your-selven herd.
They speken of sondry harding of metal,
And speke of medicynes ther-with-al,
And how, and whanne, it sholde y-harded be;
Which is unknowe algates unto me.
  Tho speke they of Canaceës ring,
And seyden alle, that swich a wonder thing
Of craft of ringes herde they never non,
Save that he, Moyses, and king Salomon
Hadde a name of konning in swich art.
Thus seyn the peple, and drawen hem apart.
But nathelees, somme seyden that it was
Wonder to maken of fern-asshen glas,
And yet nis glas nat lyk asshen of fern;
But for they han y-knowen it so fern,
Therefore cesseth her jangling and her wonder.
As sore wondren somme on cause of thonder,
On ebbe, on flood, on gossomer, and on mist,
And alle thing, til that the cause is wist.
Thus jangle they and demen and devyse,
Til that the king gan fro the bord aryse.
  Phebus hath laft the angle meridional,
And yet ascending was the beest royal,
The gentil Leon, with his Aldiran,
Whan that this Tartre king, this Cambinskan,
Roos fro his bord, ther that he sat ful hye.
Toforn him gooth the loude minstralcye,
Til he cam to his chambre of parements,
Ther as they sownen diverse instruments,
That it is lyk an heven for to here.
Now duncen lusty Venus children dere,
For in the Fish hir lady sat ful hye,
And loketh on hem with a freendly yë.
  This noble king is set up in his trone.
This strange knight is fet to him ful sone,
And on the daunce he gooth with Canacee.
Heer is the revel and the jolitee
That is nat able a dul man to devyse.
He moste han knowen love and his servyse,
And been a festlich man as fresh as May,
That sholde yow devysen swich array.
  Who coude telle yow the forme of daunces,
So uncouthe and so fresshe contenaunces,
Swich subtil loking and dissimulinges
For drede of jalouse mennes aperceyvinges?
No man but Launcelot, and he is deed.
Therefor I passe of al this lustiheed;
I seye na-more, but in this jolynesse
I lete hem, til men to the soper dresse.
  The styward bit the spyces for to hye,
And eek the wyn, in al this melodye.
The usshers and the squyers ben y-goon;
The spyces and the wyn is come anoon.
They ete and drinke; and whan this hadde an ende,
Un-to the temple, as reson was, they wende.

And so they spoke of Telephus the king,
And of Achilles with his magic spear,
Wherewith he healed and hurt too, 'twould appear,
Even as a man might do with this new sword
Of which, but now, I've told and you have heard.
They spoke of tempering metal sundry wise,
And medicines therewith, which men devise,
And how and when such steel should hardened be;
Which, nevertheless, is all unknown to me.
  Then spoke they of fair Canace's gold ring,
And all men said that such a wondrous thing
They'd ne'er heard of as being in ring-craft done,
Except that Moses and King Solomon
Had each a name for cunning in such art.
Thus spoke the people and then drew apart,
But notwithstanding, some said that it was
Wondrous to make fern-ashes into glass,
Since glass is nothing like the ash of fern;
But since long since of this thing men did learn,
Therefore they ceased their gabble and their wonder,
As sorely wonder some on cause of thunder,
Of ebb, of flood, of gossamer, of mist,
And each thing, till they know what cause exist.
Thus did they chatter and judge and thus surmise
Until the king did from the board arise.
  Phoebus had left the angle meridional,
And yet ascending was that beast royal,
The noble Lion, with his Aldiran,
When that this Tartar king, this Cambinskan
Rose from his board where he had sat full high.
Before him went the sounding minstrelsy,
Into a room hung with rich ornaments,
Wherein they sounded divers instruments
Till it was like a heavenly thing to hear.
And now danced merry Venus' children dear,
For in the Fish their lady sat on high
And looked upon them with a friendly eye.
  This noble king sat high upon his throne.
And this strange knight was brought to him anon,
And then to dance he went with Canace.
Here was such revel and such jollity
As no dull man is able to surmise;
He must have known and served love's high emprise,
And be a festive man as fresh as May
Who could for you describe such an array.
  Who could tell you the figures of the dances,
So odd and strange and the blithe countenances,
The subtle glances and dissimulation
For fear of jealous persons' observation?
No man but Launcelot, and he is dead!
I therefore pass the joyous life they led
And saw no more, but in this jolliness
I leave them till to supper all did press.
  The steward bade them serve the spices, aye.
And the rich wine through all this melody.
The ushers and the squires got them gone;
The spices and the wine were come anon.
They ate and drank, and when this had an end,
Unto the temple, as was right, did wend.

The service done, they supped while yet 'twas day.
What needs it that I tell all their array?
Each man knows well that at a kingly feast
There's plenty for the greatest and the least,
And dainties more than are in my knowing.
Then, after supper, went this noble king
To see the horse of brass, with all the rout
Of lords and ladies thronging him about.
Such wondering was there on this horse of brass
That, since the siege of Troy did overpass,
When once a horse seemed marvellous to men.
Was there such wondering as happened then.
But finally the king asked of this knight
The virtue of this courser, and the might,
And prayed him tell the means of governance.
This horse anon began to trip and dance
When this strange knight laid hand upon the rein
And said: "Sire, there's no more I need explain
Than, when you wish to journey anywhere,
You must but twirl a peg within his ear,
Which I will show you when alone with you.
You must direct him to what place also,
Or to what country you may please to ride.
And when you come to where you would abide,
Bid him descend, and twirl another pin,
For therein lies the secret of the gin,
And he will then descend and do your will;
And there he'll stand, obedient and still.
Though all the world the contrary had sworn,
He shall not thence be drawn nor thence be borne.
Or, if you wish to bid him thence be gone,
Twirl but this pin and he'll depart anon
And vanish utterly from all men's sight,
And then return to you, by day or night,
When you shall please to call him back again
In such a fashion as I will explain
When we two are alone, and that full soon.
Ride when you choose, there's no more to be done."
Instructed when the king was by that knight,
And when he'd stablished in his mind aright
The method and the form of all this thing,
Then glad and blithe this noble doughty king
Repaired unto his revels as before.
The bridle to the donjon tower they bore,
And placed among his jewels rich and dear.
How I know not, the horse did disappear
Out of their sight; you get no more of me.
But thus I leave, in joy and jollity,
This Cambinskan with all his lords feasting
Well nigh until the day began to spring.

The service doon, they soupen al by day.
What nedeth yow rehercen hir array?
Ech man wot wel, that at a kinges feeste
Hath plentee, to the moste and to the leeste,
And deyntees mo than been in my knowing.
At-after soper gooth this noble king
To seen this hors of bras, with al the route
Of lordes and of ladyes him aboute.
Swich wondring was ther on this hors of bras
That, sin the grete sege of Troye was,
Ther-as men wondreden on an hors also,
Ne was ther swich a wondring as was tho.
But fynally the king axeth this knight
The vertu of this courser and the might,
And preyede him to telle his governaunce.
This hors anoon bigan to trippe and daunce,
Whan that this knight leyde hand up-on his reyne,
And seyde, "sir, ther is na-more to seyne,
But, whan yow list to ryden any-where,
Ye moten trille a pin, stant in his ere,
Which I shall telle yow bitwix vs two.
Ye mote nempne him to what place also
Or to what contree that yow list to ryde.
And whan ye come ther as yow list abyde,
Bidde him descende, and trille another pin,
For ther-in lyth the effect of al the gin,
And he wol doun descende and doon your wille;
And in that place he wol abyde stille,
Though al the world the contrarie hadde y-swore;
He shal nat thennes ben y-drawe n'y-bore.
Or, if yow liste bidde him thennes goon,
Trille this pin, and he wol vanishe anoon
Out of the sighte of every maner wight,
And come agayn, be it by day or night,
When that yow list to clepen him ageyn
In swich a gyse as I shal to yow seyn
Bitwixe yow and me, and that ful sone.
Ryde whan yow list, ther is na-more to done."
Enformed whan the king was of that knight,
And hath conceyved in his wit aright
The maner and the forme of al this thing,
Thus glad and blythe, this noble doughty king
Repeireth to his revel as biforn.
The brydel is un-to the tour y-born,
And kept among his jewels leve and dere.
The hors vanisshed, I noot in what manere,
Out of hir sighte; ye gete na-more of me.
But thus I lete in lust and Iolitee
This Cambynskan his lordes festeyinge,
Til wel ny the day bigan to springe.

HERE ENDETH THE FIRST PART

HERE FOLLOWETH THE SECOND PART

The nurse of good digestion, natural sleep,
Caused them to nod, and bade them they take keep
That labour and much drinking must have rest;
And with a gaping mouth all these he pressed,
And said that it was time they laid them down,
For blood was in the ascendant, as was shown,
And nature's friend, the blood, must honoured be.

The norice of digestioun, the slepe,
Gan on hem winke, and bad hem taken kepe,
That muchel drink and labour wolde han reste;
And with a galping mouth hem alle he keste,
And seyde, "it was tyme to lye adoun,
For blood was in his dominacioun;
Cherissheth blood, natures freend," quod he.

They thanken him galpinge, by two, by three,
And every wight gan drawe him to his reste,
As slepe hem bad; they toke it for the beste.
Hir dremes shul nat been y-told for me;
Ful were hir hedes of fumositee,
That causeth dreem, of which ther nis no charge.
They slepen til that it was pryme large,
The moste part, but it were Canacee;
She was ful mesurable, as wommen be.
For of hir fader hadde she take leve
To gon to reste, sone after it was eve;
Hir liste nat appalled for to be,
Nor on the morwe unfestlich for to see;
And slepte hir firste sleep, and thanne awook.
For swich a joye she in hir herte took
Both of hir queynte ring and hir mirour,
That twenty tyme she changed hir colour;
And in hir slepe, right for impressioun
Of hir mirour, she hadde a visioun.
Wherfore, er that the sonne gan up glyde,
She cleped on hir maistresse hir bisyde,
And seyde, that hir liste for to ryse.
Thise olde wommen that been gladly wyse,
As is hir maistresse, answerde hir anoon,
And seyde, "madame, whider wil ye goon
Thus erly? for the folk ben alle on reste."
"I wol," quod she, "aryse, for me leste
No lenger for to slepe, and walke aboute."
Hir maistresse clepeth wommen a gret route,
And up they rysen, wel a ten or twelve;
Up ryseth fresshe Canacee hir-selve,
As rody and bright as dooth the yonge sonne,
That in the Ram is four degrees up-ronne;
Noon hyer was he, whan she redy was;
And forth she walketh esily a pas,
Arrayed after the lusty seson sote
Lightly, for to pleye and walke on fote;
Nat but with fyve or six of hir meynee;
And in a trench, forth in the park, goth she.
The vapour, which that fro the erthe glood,
Made the sonne to seme rody and brood;
But nathelees, it was so fair a sighte
That it made alle hir hertes for to lighte,
What for the seson and the morweninge,
And for the foules that she herde singe:
For right anon she wiste what they mente
Right by hir song, and knew al hir entente.
The knotte, why that every tale is told,
If it be taried til that lust be cold
Of hem that han it after herkned yore,
The savour passeth ever lenger the more,
For fulsomnesse of his prolixitee.
And by the same reson thinketh me,
I sholde to the knotte condescende,
And maken of hir walking sone an ende.
Amidde a tree fordrye, as whyt as chalk,
As Canacee was pleying in hir walk,
Ther sat a faucon over hir heed ful hye,
That with a pitous voys so gan to crye
That all the wode resouned of hir cry.

They thanked him, gaping all, by two, by three,
And every one began to go to rest,
As sleep them bade; they took it for the best.
But here their dreams shall not by me be said;
The fumes of wine had filled each person's head,
Which cause senseless dreams at any time.
They slept next morning till the hour of prime,
That is, the others, but not Canace;
She was right temperate, as women be.
For of her father had she taken leave,
To go to rest, soon after it was eve;
For neither pale nor languid would she be,
Nor wear a weary look for men to see;
But slept her first deep sleep and then awoke.
For so much joy upon her heart there broke
When she looked on the mirror and the ring
That twenty times she flushed, and sleep did bring—
So strong an impress had the mirror made—
A vision of it to the slumbering maid.
Wherefore, ere up the sun began to glide,
She called her mistress, sleeping there beside,
And said to her that she was pleased to rise.
Old women like this governess are wise,
Or often so, and she replied anon,
And said: "My lady, where will you be gone
Thus early? For the folk are all at rest."
"I will," said she, "arise, for I've no zest
For longer sleep, and I will walk about."
Her mistress called of women a great rout,
And they rose up, a dozen more or less,
And up rose lovely Canace to dress,
As ruddy and bright as is the warm young sun
That in the Ram now four degrees has run;
He was no higher when she all ready was;
And forth she sauntered at an easy pace,
Arrayed according to the season sweet,
Lightly, to play and walk on maiden feet;
With five or six girls of her company
All down an alley, through the park, went she.
The morning mists that rose from the damp earth
Reddened the sun and broadened it in girth;
Nevertheless it was so fair a sight
That it made all their hearts dance for delight,
What of the season and the fair morning,
And all the myriad birds that she heard sing;
For when she heard, she knew well what they meant,
Just by their songs, and learned all their intent.
The point of every story, why it's told,
If it's delayed till interest grow cold
In those who have, perchance, heard it before,
The savour passes from it more and more,
For fulsomeness of its prolixity.
And for this reason, as it seems to me,
I should to my tale's major point descend
And make of these girls' walking a swift end.
Amidst a dry, dead tree, as white as chalk,
As Canace was playing in her walk,
There sat a falcon overhead full high,
That in a pitiful voice began to cry,
Till all the wood resounded mournfully.

For she had beaten herself so pitiably
With both her wings that the red glistening blood
Ran down the tree trunk whereupon she stood.
And ever in one same way she cried and shrieked,
And with her beak her body she so pricked
That there's no tiger, nor a cruel beast
That dwells in open wood or deep forest,
Would not have wept, if ever weep he could,
For pity of her, she shrieked alway so loud.
For never yet has been a man alive—
If but description I could well contrive—
That heard of such a falcon for fairness,
As well of plumage as of nobleness
Of shape, and all that reckoned up might be.
A falcon peregrine she was, and she
Seemed from a foreign land; and as she stood
She fainted now and then for loss of blood,
Till almost she had fallen from the tree.

This king's fair daughter, Princess Canace,
Who on her finger bore the magic ring
Whereby she understood well everything
That any bird might in his language say,
And in such language could reply straightway,
She understood well what this falcon said,
And of her pity well-nigh was she dead.
So to the tree she went right hastily,
And on this falcon looked she pitifully,
And held her lap up wide, for she knew now
The falcon must come falling from the bough
When next it swooned away from loss of blood.
A long while waiting there the princess stood,
Till at the last she spoke, in her voice clear,
Unto the hawk, as you'll hereafter hear.

"What is the cause, if it be one to tell,
That you are in this furious pain of hell?"
Said Canace unto this hawk above.
"Is this for sorrow of death or loss of love?
For, as I think, these are the causes two
That torture gentle heart with greatest woe;
Of other ills there is no need to speak,
Because such harm upon yourself you wreak;
Which proves right well that either love or dread
Must be the reason for your cruel deed,
Since I can see no one that gives you chase.
For love of God, come, do yourself some grace,
Or say what thing may help; for west nor east
Have I before now seen a bird or beast
That ever treated self so wretchedly.
You slay me with your sorrow, verily,
Such great compassion in my heart has grown.
For God's dear love, come from the dry tree down;
And, as I am a monarch's daughter true,
If I but verily the real cause knew
Of your distress, if it lay in my might,
I would make you amends before the night,
As truly help me God of human kind!
And even now will I look out and find
Some herbs to heal your hurts with, speedily."

Then shrieked this falcon the more piteously
Than ever, and to ground fell down anon,
And lay there, swooning, deathlike as a stone,
Till Canace within her lap did take

Y-beten hath she hir-self so pitously
With bothe hir winges, til the rede blood
Ran endelong the tree ther-as she stood.
And ever in oon she cryde alwey and shrighte,
And with hir beek hir-selven so she prighte,
That ther nis tygre, ne noon so cruel beste,
That dwelleth either in wode or in foreste
That nolde han wept, if that he wepe coude,
For sorwe of hir, she shrighte alwey so loude.
For ther nas never yet no man on lyve—
If that I coude a faucon wel discryve—
That herde of swich another of fairnesse,
As wel of plumage as of gentillesse
Of shap, and al that mighte y-rekened be.
A faucon peregryn than semed she
Of fremde land; and evermore, as she stood,
She swowneth now and now for lakke of blood,
Til wel neigh is she fallen fro the tree.

This faire kinges doghter, Canacee,
That on hir finger bar the queynte ring,
Thurgh which she understood wel every thing
That any foul may in his ledene seyn,
And coude answere him in his ledene ageyn,
Hath understonde what this faucon seyde,
And wel neigh for the rewthe almost she deyde.
And to the tree she gooth ful hastily,
And on this faucon loketh pitously,
And heeld hir lappe abrood, for wel she wiste
The faucon moste fallen fro the twiste,
When that it swowned next, for lakke of blood.
A longe while to wayten hir she stood
Till atte laste she spak in this manere
Un-to the hauk, as ye shul after here.

"What is the cause, if it be for to telle,
That ye be in this furial pyne of helle?"
Quod Canacee un-to this hauk above.
"Is this for sorwe of deeth or los of love?
For, as I trowe, thise ben causes two
That causen moost a gentil herte wo;
Of other harm it nedeth nat to speke.
For ye your-self upon your-self yow wreke,
Which proveth wel, that either love or drede
Mot been encheson of your cruel dede,
Sin that I see non other wight yow chace.
For love of god, as dooth your-selven grace
Or what may ben your help; for west nor eest
Ne sey I never er now no brid ne beest
That ferde with him-self so pitously.
Ye slee me with your sorwe, verraily;
I have of yow so gret compassioun.
For goddes love, com fro the tree adoun;
And, as I am a kinges doghter trewe,
If that I verraily the cause knewe
Of your disese, if it lay in my might,
I wolde amende it, er that it were night,
As wisly helpe me gret god of kinde!
And herbes shal I right y-nowe y-finde
To hele with your hurtes hastily."

Tho shrighte this faucon more pitously
Than ever she dide, and fil to grounde anoon,
And lyth aswowne, deed, and lyk a stoon,
Til Canacee hath in hir lappe hir take

Un-to the tyme she gan of swough awake.
And, after that she of hir swough gan breyde,
Right in hir haukes ledene thus she seyde:—
"That pitee renneth sone in gentil herte,
Feling his similitude in peynes smerte,
Is preved al-day, as men may it see,
As wel by werk as by auctoritee;
For gentil herte kytheth gentillesse.
I see wel, that ye han of my distresse
Compassioun, my faire Canacee,
Of verray wommanly benignitee
That nature in your principles hath set.
But for non hope for to fare the bet,
But for to obeye un-to your herte free,
And for to maken other be war by me,
As by the whelp chasted is the leoun,
Right for that cause and that conclusioun,
Whyl that I have a leyser and a space,
Myn harm I wol confessen, er I pace."
And ever, whyl that oon hir sorwe tolde,
That other weep, as she to water wolde,
Til that the faucon bad hir to be stille;
And, with a syk, right thus she seyde hir wille.
"Ther I was bred (allas! that harde day!)
And fostred in a roche of marbul gray
So tendrely, that nothing eyled me,
I niste nat what was adversitee,
Til I coude flee ful hye under the sky.
Tho dwelte a tercelet[1] me faste by,
That semed welle of alle gentillesse;
Al were he ful of treson and falsnesse,
It was so wrapped under humble chere,
And under hewe of trouthe in swich manere,
Under plesance, and under bisy peyne,
That no wight coude han wend he coude feyne
So depe in greyn he dyed his coloures.
Right as a serpent hit him under floures
Til he may seen his tyme for to byte,
Right so this god of love, this ypocryte,
Doth so his cerimonies and obeisaunces,
And kepeth in semblant alle his observances
That sowneth in-to gentillesse of love.
As in a toumbe is al the faire above,
And under is the corps, swich as ye woot,
Swich was this ypocryte, bothe cold and hoot,
And in this wyse he served his entente,
That (save the feend) non wiste what he mente.
Til he so longe had wopen and compleyned,
And many a yeer his service to me feyned,
Til that myn herte, to pitous and to nyce,
Al innocent of his crouned malice,
For-fered of his deeth, as thoughte me,
Upon his othes and his seuretee,
Graunted him love, on this condicioun,
That evermore myn honour and renoun
Were saved, bothe privee and apert;
This is to seyn, that, after his desert,
I yaf him al myn herte and al my thoght—
God woot and he, that otherwyse noght—
And took his herte in chaunge for myn for ay.
But sooth is seyd, gon sithen many a day,

And hold the bird till she began to wake.
And when from out her fainting fit she made,
All in her own hawk's language thus she said:
"That pity wells up soon in gentle heart,
Feeling its likeness in all pains that smart,
Is proved, and day by day, as men may see,
As well by deeds as by authority;
For gentle heart can spy out gentleness.
I see well that you have on my distress
Compassion, my fair Princess Canace,
Of truly womanly benignity
That nature in your character has set.
Not that I hope much good therefrom to get,
But to obey the word of your heart free,
And so that others may be warned by me,
As by the whelp instructed is the lion,
Just for that cause and reason shall I fly on,
While yet I have the leisure and the space,
The story of my wrongs to you I'll trace."
And ever, while the one her sorrow said,
The other wept, as she to water'd fled,
Until the falcon bade her to be still;
And with a sigh, right thus she said her will.
"Where I was born (alas, that cruel day!)
And fostered on a rock of marble grey
So tenderly that nothing troubled me,
I knew not what it was, adversity,
Till I could soar on high under the sky.
There dwelt a handsome tercelet[1] there, hard by,
Who seemed the well of every nobleness;
Though he was full of treason and falseness,
It was so hidden under humble bearing,
And under hues of truth which he was wearing,
And under kindness, never used in vain,
That no one could have dreamed that he could feign,
So deeply ingrained were his colours dyed.
But just as serpent under flower will hide
Until he sees the time has come to bite,
Just so this god of love, this hypocrite
With false humility for ever served
And seemed a wooer who the rites observed
That so become the gentleness of love.
As of a tomb the fairness is above,
While under is the corpse, such as you know,
So was this hypocrite, cold and hot also;
And in this wise he served his foul intent
That (save the Fiend) no one knew what he meant,
Till he so long had wept and had complained,
And many a year his service to me feigned,
That my poor heart, a pitiful sacrifice,
All ignorant of his supreme malice,
Fearing he'd die, as it then seemed to me,
Because of his great oaths and surety,
Granted him love, on this condition known,
That evermore my honour and renown
Were saved, both private fame and fame overt;
That is to say, that, after his desert
I gave him all my heart and all my thought—
God knows, and he, that more I gave him naught—
And took his heart in change for mine, for aye.
But true it is, and has been many a day,

[1]The male of the peregrine falcon.

A true man and a thief think not at one.
And when he saw the thing so far was gone
That I had fully granted him my love,
In such a way as I've explained above,
And given him my faithful heart, as free
As he swore he had given his to me,
Anon this tiger, full of doubleness,
Fell on his knees, devout in humbleness,
With so high reverence, and, by his face,
So like a lover in his gentle grace,
So ravished, as it seemed, for very joy,
That never Jason nor Paris of Troy—
Jason? Nay, truly, nor another man
Since Lamech lived, who was the first began
To love two women (those that write have sworn),
Not ever, since the primal man was born,
Could any man, by twenty-thousandth part,
Enact the tricks of this deceiver's art;
Nor were he worthy to unlace his shoe,
Where double-dealing or deceit were due,
Nor could so thank a person as he me!
His manner was most heavenly to see,
For any woman, were she ever so wise;
So painted he, and combed, at point-device,
His manner, all in all, and every word.
And so much by his bearing was I stirred
And for the truth I thought was in his heart,
That, if aught troubled him and made him smart,
Though ever so little bit, and I knew this,
It seemed to me I felt death's cruel kiss.
And briefly, so far all these matters went,
My will became his own will's instrument;
That is to say, my will obeyed his will
In everything in reason, good or ill,
Keeping within the bounds of honour ever.
Never had I a thing so dear—ah, never!—
As him, God knows! nor ever shall anew.
"This lasted longer than a year or two
While I supposed of him no thing but good.
But finally, thus at the last it stood,
That Fortune did decree that he must win
Out of that place, that home, that I was in.
Whether I felt woe, there's no question, none;
I can't describe my feelings, no, not one;
But one thing dare I tell, and that boldly,
I came to know the pain of death thereby;
Such grief I felt for him, none might believe.
So on a day of me he took his leave,
So sorrowfully, too, I thought truly
That he felt even as deep a woe as I,
When I had heard him speak and saw his hue.
Nevertheless, I thought he was so true,
And that to me he would come back again
Within a little while, let me explain;
And 'twas quite reasonable that he must go
For honour's sake, for oft it happens so,
That I made virtue of necessity,
And took it well, because it had to be.
A look of cheer I felt not I put on,
And took his hand, I swear it by Saint John,
And said to him: 'Behold, I'm yours in all;
Be you to me as I have been, and shall.'

'A trew wight and a theef thenken nat oon.'
And, whan he saugh the thing so fer y-goon,
That I had graunted him fully my love,
In swich a gyse as I have seyd above,
And yeven him my trewe herte, as free
As he swoor he his herte yaf to me;
Anon this tygre, ful of doublenesse,
Fil on his knees with so devout humblesse,
With so heigh reverence, and, as by his chere,
So lyk a gentil lovere of manere,
So ravisshed, as it semed, for the joye,
That never Jason, ne Parys of Troye,
Jason? certes, ne non other man,
Sin Lameth was, that alderfirst bigan
To loven two, as writen folk biforn,
Ne never, sin the firste man was born,
Ne coude man, by twenty thousand part,
Countrefete the sophimes of his art;
Ne were worthy unbokele his galoche,
Ther doublenesse or feyning sholde approche,
Ne so coude thanke a wight as he did me!
His maner was an heven for to see
Til any womman, were she never so wys;
So peynted he and kembde at point-devys
As wel his wordes as his contenaunce.
And I so lovede him for his obeisaunce,
And for the trouthe I demed in his herte,
That, if so were that any thing him smerte,
Al were it never so lyte, and I it wiste,
Me thoughte, I felte deeth myn herte twiste.
And shortly, so ferforth this thing is went,
That my wil was his willes instrument;
This is to seyn, my wil obeyed his wil
In alle thing, as fer as reson fil,
Keping the boundes of my worship ever.
Ne never hadde I thing so leef, ne lever,
As him, god woot! ne never shal na-mo.
This lasteth lenger than a yeer or two,
That I supposed of him noght but good.
But fynally, thus atte laste it stood,
That fortune wolde that he moste twinne
Out of that place which that I was inne.
Wher me was wo, that is no questioun;
I can nat make of it discripcioun;
For o thing dar I tellen boldely,
I knowe what is the peyne of deth ther-by;
Swich harm I felte for he ne mighte bileve.
So on a day of me he took his leve,
So sorwefully eek, that I wende verraily
That he had felt as muche harm as I,
Whan that I herde him speke, and saugh his hewe.
But nathelees, I thoughte he was so trewe,
And eek that he repaire sholde ageyn
With-inne a litel whyle, sooth to seyn;
And reson wolde eek that he moste go
For his honour, as ofte it happeth so,
That I made vertu of necessitee,
And took it wel, sin that it moste be.
As I best mighte, I hidde fro him my sorwe,
And took him by the hond, seint John to borwe,
And seyde him thus: 'lo, I am youres al;
Beth swich as I to yow have been, and shal.'

What he answerde, it nedeth noght reherce,
Who can sey bet than he, who can do werse?
Whan he hath al wel seyd, thanne hath he doon.
'Therfor bihoveth him a ful long spoon
That shal ete with a feend,' thus herde I seye.
So atte laste he moste forth his weye,
And forth he fleeth, til he cam ther him leste.
Whan it cam him to purpos for to reste,
I trowe he hadde thilke text in minde,
That 'alle thing, repeiring to his kinde,
Gladeth him-self'; thus seyn men, as I gesse;
Men loven of propre kinde newfangelnesse,
As briddes doon that men in cages fede.
For though thou night and day take of hem hede,
And strawe hir cage faire and softe as silk,
And yeve hem sugre, hony, breed and milk,
Yet right anon, as that his dore is uppe,
He with his feet wol spurne adoun his cuppe,
And to the wode he wol and wormes ete;
So newefangel been they of hir mete,
And loven novelryes of propre kinde;
No gentillesse of blood [ne] may hem binde.
So ferde this tercelet, allas the day!
Though he were gentil born, and fresh and gay,
And goodly for to seen, and humble and free,
He saugh up-on a tyme a kyte flee,
And sodeynly he loved this kyte so,
That al his love is clene fro me ago,
And hath his trouthe falsed in this wyse;
Thus hath the kyte my love in hir servyse,
And I am lorn with-outen remedye!"
And with that word this faucon gan to crye,
And swowned eft in Canaceës barme.
  Greet was the sorwe, for the haukes harme,
That Canacee and alle hir wommen made;
They niste how they mighte the faucon glade.
But Canacee hom bereth hir in hir lappe,
And softely in plastres gan hir wrappe,
Ther as she with hir beek had hurt hirselve.
Now can nat Canacee but herbes delve
Out of the grounde, and make salves newe
Of herbes precious, and fyne of hewe,
To helen with this hauk; fro day to night
She dooth hir bisinesse and al hir might.
And by hir beddes heed she made a mewe,
And covered it with veluëttes blewe,
In signe of trouthe that is in wommen sene.
And al with-oute, the mewe is peynted grene,
In which were peynted alle thise false foules,
As beth thise tidifs, tercelets, and oules,
Right for despyt were peynted hem bisyde,
And pyes, on hem for to crye and chyde.
  Thus lete I Canacee hir hauk keping;
I wol na-more as now speke of hir ring,
Til it come eft to purpos for to seyn
How that this faucon gat hir love ageyn
Repentant, as the storie telleth us,
By mediacioun of Cambalus,
The kinges sone, of whiche I yow tolde.
But hennes-forth I wol my proces holde
To speke of aventures and of batailles,
That never yet was herd so grete mervailles.

What he replied it needs not I rehearse,
Who can say better than he, who can do worse?
When he had well said, all his good was done.
'It well behooves him take a lengthy spoon
Who eats with devils,' so I've heard folk say.
So at the last he must be on his way,
And forth he flew to where it pleased him best.
When it became his purpose he should rest,
I think he must have had this text in mind,
That 'Everything, returning to its kind,
Gladdens itself'; thus men say, as I guess;
Men love, and naturally, newfangledness,
As do these birds that men in cages feed.
For though you night and day take of them heed,
And fairly strew their cage as soft as silk,
And give them sugar, honey, bread, and milk,
Yet on the instant when the door is up,
They with their feet will spurn their feeding cup,
And to the wood will fly and worms will eat;
So are they all newfangled of their meat,
And love all novelties of their own kind;
Nor nobleness of blood may ever bind.
So fared this tercelet, oh, alas the day!
Though he was gently born, and fresh and gay,
And handsome, and well-mannered, aye and free,
He saw a kite fly, and it proved a she,
And suddenly he loved this she-kite so
That all his love for me did quickly go,
And all his truth turned falsehood in this wise;
Thus has this kite my love in her service,
And I am love-lorn without remedy."
And with that word the hawk began to cry,
And after, swooned on Canace's fair arm.
  Great was the sorrow for the falcon's harm
That Canace and all her women made;
They knew not how they might this falcon aid.
But Canace home bore her in her lap,
And softly her in poultices did wrap
Where she with her own beak had hurt herself.
Now Canace dug herbs more rich than pelf
Out of the ground, and made up ointments new
Of precious herbs, all beautiful of hue,
Wherewith to heal this hawk; from day to night
She nursed her carefully with all her might.
And by her bed's head she contrived a mew
And lined the cage with velvets all of blue,
Symbol of truth that is in women seen.
And all without, the mew was painted green,
And there were painted all these treacherous fowls
As are these titmice, tercelets, and these owls,
While for despite were painted there beside
Magpies, that they might cry at them and chide.
  Thus leave I Canace her hawk keeping,
I will no more, just now, speak of her ring,
Till I come back with purpose to explain
How this poor falcon got her love again
Repentant, as the story tells to us,
By mediation of that Cambalus,
The king's son, of whom I've already told.
But henceforth I a straightened course will hold
Great battles and adventures to relate,
Whereof were never heard such marvels great.

First will I tell you of King Cambinskan
Who won so many a town and many a man;
And after will I speak of Algarsyf,
How he won Theodora for his wife,
For whom full oft in peril great he was,
Had he been helped not by the steed of brass;
And after that I'll speak of Cambalo,
Who in the lists fought with the brothers two
For Canace, before he could her win.
And where I left off, I'll again begin.

First wol I telle yow of Cambinskan,
That in his tyme many a citee wan;
And after wol I speke of Algarsyf,
How that he wan Theodora to his wyf,
For whom ful ofte in greet peril he was,
Ne hadde he ben holpen by the stede of bras;
And after wol I speke of Cambalo,
That faught in listes with the bretheren two
For Canacee, er that he mighte hir winne.
And ther I lefte I wol ageyn biginne.

HERE ENDETH THE SECOND PART

HERE BEGINNETH THE THIRD PART

Apollo in his chariot whirled so high
That in the God Mercurius' house, the sly—

Appollo whirleth up his char so hye, [11,019*a*]
Til that the god Mercurius hous the slye—[*b*]

(*Unfinished*)

HERE FOLLOWETH THE WORDS OF THE FRANKLIN TO THE SQUIRE, AND THE WORDS OF THE HOST TO THE FRANKLIN

In faith, sir squire, you have done well with it,
And openly I praise you for your wit,"
The franklin said, "Considering your youth,
So feelingly you speak, sir, in good truth!
In my opinion, there is none that's here
In eloquence shall ever be your peer,
If you but live; may God give you good chance
And in all virtue send continuance!
For, sir, your speech was great delight to me.
I have a son, and by the Trinity
I'd rather have, than twenty pounds in land,
Though it were right now fallen to my hand,
He were a man of such discretion shown
As you, sir; fie on what a man may own,
Unless the man have virtue therewithal.
I've checked my son, and yet again I shall,
For he toward virtue chooses not to wend;
But just to play at dice, and gold to spend,
And lose all that he has, is his usage,
And he would rather talk with any page
Than to commune with any gentle wight
From whom he might learn courtesy aright."
"A straw for courtesy!" exclaimed our host;
"What, franklin? God, sir, well you know, I trust,
That each of you must tell us, at the least,
A tale or two, or break his sworn behest."
"I know it, " said the franklin; "I am fain,
And pray you all, you do not me disdain,
Though to this man I speak a word or two"
"Come, tell your tale, sir, without more ado."
"Gladly, sir host," said he, "I will obey
Your will, good host; now hearken what I say.
For I'll not be contrary in any wise,
At least so far as my wit shall suffice;
I pray to God that it may please you; rough
Though it may be, I'll know 'tis good enough."

"In feith, Squier, thou hast thee wel y-quit,
And gentilly I preise wel thy wit,"
Quod the Frankeleyn, "considering thy youthe,
So feelingly thou spekest, sir, I allow the!
As to my doom, there is non that is here
Of eloquence that shal be thy pere,
If that thou live; god yeve thee good chaunce,
And in vertu sende thee continuaunce!
For of thy speche I have greet deyntee.
I have a sone, and, by the Trinitee,
I hadde lever than twenty pound worth lond,
Though it right now were fallen in myn hond,
He were a man of swich discrecioun
As that ye been! fy on possessioun
But-if a man be vertuous with-al.
I have my sone snibbed, and yet shal,
For he to vertu listeth nat entende;
But for to pleye at dees, and to despende,
And lese al that he hath, is his usage.
And he hath lever talken with a page
Than to comune with any gentil wight
Ther he mighte lerne gentillesse aright.'
"Straw for your gentillesse," quod our host;
"What, frankeleyn? pardee, sir, wel thou wost
That eche of yow mot tellen atte leste
A tale or two, or breken his biheste."
"That knowe I wel, sir," quod the frankeleyn;
"I prey yow, haveth me nat in desdeyn
Though to this man I speke a word or two."
"Telle on thy tale with-outen wordes mo."
"Gladly, sir host," quod he, "I wol obeye
Un-to your wil; now herkneth what I seye.
I wol yow nat contrarien in no wyse
As fer as that my wittes wol suffyse;
I prey to god that it may plesen yow,
Than woot I wel that it is good y-now."

THE FRANKLIN'S PROLOGUE

THE PROLOGUE OF THE FRANKLIN'S TALE

THISE olde gentil Britons in hir dayes
Of diverse aventures maden layes,
Rymeyed in hir firste Briton tonge;
Which layes with hir instruments they songe,
Or elles redden hem for hir plesaunce;
And oon of hem have I in remembraunce,
Which I shal seyn with good wil as I can.
　But, sires, by-cause I am a burel man,
At my biginning first I yow biseche
Have me excused of my rude speche;
I lerned never rethoryk certeyn;
Thing that I speke, it moot be bare and pleyn.
I sleep never on the mount of Pernaso,
Ne lerned Marcus Tullius Cithero.
Colours ne knowe I none, with-outen drede,
But swiche colours as growen in the mede,
Or elles swiche as men dye or peynte.
Colours of rethoryk ben me to queynte;
My spirit feleth noght of swich matere.
But if yow list, my tale shul ye here.

"THESE ancient gentle Bretons, in their days.
Of divers high adventures made great lays
And rhymed them in their primal Breton tongue;
The which lays to their instruments they sung,
Or else recited them where joy might be;
And one of them have I in memory,
Which I shall gladly tell you, as I can.
　But, sirs, because I am an ignorant man,
At my beginning must I first beseech
You will excuse me for my vulgar speech;
I never studied rhetoric, that's certain;
That which I say, it must be bare and plain.
I never slept on Mount Parnassus, no,
Nor studied Marcus Tullius Cicero.
Colours I know not, there's no doubt indeed,
Save colours such as grow within the mead,
Or such as men achieve with dye or paint.
Colours of rhetoric I find but quaint;
My spirit doesn't feel the beauty there.
But if you wish, my story you shall hear."

THE FRANKLIN'S TALE

HERE BEGINNETH THE FRANKLIN'S TALE

IN Armorik, that called is Britayne,
Ther was a knight that loved and dide his payne
To serve a lady in his beste wyse;
And many a labour, many a greet empryse
He for his lady wroghte, er she were wonne.
For she was oon, the faireste under sonne,
And eek therto come of so heigh kinrede,
That wel unnethes dorste this knight, for drede,
Telle hir his wo, his peyne, and his distresse.
But atte laste, she, for his worthinesse,
And namely for his meke obeysaunce,
Hath swich a pitee caught of his penunce,
That prively she fil of his accord
To take him for hir housbonde and hir lord,
Of swich lordshipe as men han over hir wyves;
And for to lede the more in blisse hir lyves,
Of his free wil he swoor hir as a knight,
That never in al his lyf he, day ne night,
Ne sholde up-on him take no maistrye
Agayn hir wil, ne kythe hir jalousye,
But hir obeye, and folwe hir wil in al
As any lovere to his lady shal;
Save that the name of soveraynetee,
That wolde he have for shame of his degree.
　She thanked him, and with ful greet humblesse
She seyde, "sire, sith of your gentillesse
Ye profre me to have so large a reyne,
Ne wolde never god bitwixe us tweyne,

IN old Armorica, now Brittany,
There was a knight that loved and strove, did he
To serve a lady in the highest wise;
And many a labour, many a great emprise
He wrought for her, or ever she was won.
For she was of the fairest under sun,
And therewithal come of so high kindred
That scarcely could this noble knight, for dread,
Tell her his woe, his pain, and his distress.
But at the last she, for his worthiness,
And specially for his meek obedience,
Had so much pity that, in consequence,
She secretly was come to his accord
To take him for her husband and her lord,
Of such lordship as men have over wives;
And that they might be happier in their lives,
Of his free will he swore to her, as knight,
That never in his life, by day or night,
Would he assume a right of mastery
Against her will, nor show her jealousy,
But would obey and do her will in all
As any lover of his lady shall;
Save that the name and show of sovereignty,
Those would he have, lest he shame his degree
　She thanked him, and with a great humbleness
She said: "Since, sir, of your own nobleness
You proffer me to have so loose a rein
Would God there never come between us twain,

For any guilt of mine, a war or strife.
Sir, I will be your humble, faithful wife,
Take this as truth till heart break in my breast."
Thus were they both in quiet and in rest.
For one thing, sirs, I safely dare to say,
That friends each one the other must obey
If they'd be friends and long keep company.
Love will not be constrained by mastery;
When mastery comes, the god of love anon
Beats his fair wings, and farewell! He is gone!
Love is a thing as any spirit free;
Women by nature love their liberty,
And not to be constrained like any thrall,
And so do men, if say the truth I shall.
Observe who is most patient in his love,
He is advantaged others all above.
Patience is virtue high, and that's certain;
For it does vanquish, as these clerks make plain,
Things that oppression never could attain.
One must not chide for trifles nor complain.
Learn to endure, or else, so may I go,
You'll have to learn it, whether you will or no.
For in this world, it's certain, no one is
Who never does or says sometimes amiss.
Sickness, or woe, or what the stars have sent,
Anger, or wine, or change of temperament
Causes one oft to do amiss or speak.
For every wrong one may not vengeance wreak;
Conditions must determine temperance
In all who understand good governance.
And therefore did this wise and worthy knight,
To live in quiet, patience to her plight,
And unto him full truly did she swear
That never should he find great fault in her.
Here may men see an humble wise accord;
Thus did she take her servant and her lord,
Servant in love and lord in their marriage;
So was he both in lordship and bondage;
In bondage? Nay, but in lordship above,
Since he had both his lady and his love;
His lady truly, and his wife also,
To which the law of love accords, we know.
And when he was in this prosperity,
Home with his wife he went to his country,
Not far from Penmarch, where his dwelling was.
And there he lived in bliss and all solace.
Who could relate, save those that wedded be,
The joy, the ease, and the prosperity
That are between a husband and a wife?
A year and more endured this blissful life,
Until the knight, of whom I've spoken thus,
Who at Kayrrud[1] was called Arviragus,
Arranged to go and dwell a year or twain
In England, which was then known as Britain,
To seek in arms renown and great honour;
For his desire was fixed in such labour;
And there he lived two years (the book says thus).
Now will I hold from this Arviragus,
And I will speak of Dorigen his wife,
Who loved her husband as her heart's own life.
For all his absence wept she and she sighed,

As in my gilt, were outher werre or stryf.
Sir, I wol be your humble trewe wyf,
Have heer my trouthe, til that myn herte breste."
Thus been they bothe in quiete and in reste.
For o thing, sires, saufly dar I seye,
That frendes everich other moot obeye,
If they wol longe holden companye.
Love wol nat ben constreyned by maistrye;
Whan maistrie comth, the god of love anon
Beteth hise winges, and farewel! he is gon!
Love is a thing as any spirit free;
Wommen of kinde desiren libertee,
And nat to ben constreyned as a thral;
And so don men, if I soth seyen shal.
Loke who that is most pacient in love,
He is at his avantage al above.
Pacience is an heigh vertu certeyn;
For it venquisseth, as thise clerkes seyn,
Thinges that rigour sholde never atteyne.
For every word men may nat chyde or pleyne.
Lerneth to suffre, or elles, so moot I goon,
Ye shul it lerne, wher-so ye wole or noon.
For in this world, certein, ther no wight is,
That he ne dooth or seith som-tyme amis.
Ire, siknesse, or constellacioun,
Wyn, wo, or chaunginge of complexioun
Causeth ful ofte to doon amis or speken.
On every wrong a man may nat be wreken;
After the tyme, moste be temperaunce
To every wight that can on governaunce.
And therfore hath this wyse worthy knight,
To live in ese, suffrance hir bihight,
And she to him ful wisly gan to swere
That never sholde ther be defaute in here.
Heer may men seen an humble wys accord;
Thus hath she take hir servant and hir lord,
Servant in love, and lord in mariage;
Than was he bothe in lordship and servage;
Servage? nay, but in lordshipe above,
Sith he hath bothe his lady and his love;
His lady, certes, and his wyf also,
The which that lawe of love acordeth to.
And whan he was in this prosperitee,
Hoom with his wyf he gooth to his contree,
Nat fer fro Penmark, ther his dwelling was,
Wher-as he liveth in blisse and in solas.
Who coude telle, but he had wedded be,
The joye, the ese, and the prosperitee
That is bitwixe an housbonde and his wyf?
A yeer and more lasted this blisful lyf,
Til that the knight of which I speke of thus,
That of Kayrrud[1] was cleped Arveragus,
Shoop him to goon, and dwelle a yeer or tweyne
In Engelond, that cleped was eek Briteyne,
To seke in armes worship and honour;
For al his lust he sette in swich labour;
And dwelled ther two yeer, the book seith thus.
Now wol I stinte of this Arveragus,
And speken I wole of Dorigene his wyf,
That loveth hir housbonde as hir hertes lyf.
For his absence wepeth she and syketh,

[1]Probably modern Karru.

As doon thise noble wyves whan hem lyketh.
She moorneth, waketh, wayleth, fasteth, pleyneth;
Desyr of his presence hir so distreyneth,
That al this wyde world she sette at noght.
Hir frendes, whiche that knewe hir hevy thoght,
Conforten hir in al that ever they may;
They prechen hir, they telle hir night and day,
That causelees she sleeth hir-self, allas!
And every confort possible in this cas
They doon to hir with al hir bisinesse,
Al for to make hir leve hir hevinesse.
By proces, as ye knowen everichoon,
Men may so longe graven in a stoon,
Til som figure ther-inne emprented be.
So longe han they conforted hir, til she
Receyved hath, by hope and by resoun,
Th'emprenting of hir consolacioun,
Thurgh which hir grete sorwe gan aswage;
She may nat alwey duren in swich rage.
And eek Arveragus, in al this care,
Hath sent hir lettres hoom of his welfare,
And that he wol come hastily agayn;
Or elles hadde this sorwe hir herte slayn.
Hir freendes sawe hir sorwe gan to slake,
And preyede hir on knees, for goddes sake,
To come and romen hir in companye,
Awey to dryve hir derke fantasye.
And finally, she graunted that requeste;
For wel she saugh that it was for the beste.
Now stood hir castel faste by the see,
And often with hir freendes walketh she
Hir to disporte up-on the bank an heigh,
Wher-as she many a ship and barge seigh
Seilinge hir cours, wher-as hem liste go;
But than was that a parcel of hir wo.
For to hir-self ful ofte "allas!" seith she,
"Is ther no ship, of so manye as I see,
Wol bringen hom my lord? than were myn herte
Al warisshed of his bittre peynes smerte."
Another tyme ther wolde she sitte and thinke,
And caste hir eyen dounward fro the brinke.
But whan she saugh the grisly rokkes blake,
For verray fere so wolde hir herte quake,
That on hir feet she mighte hir noght sustene.
Than wolde she sitte adoun upon the grene,
And pitously in-to the see biholde,
And seyn right thus, with sorweful sykes colde:
"Eterne god, that thurgh thy purveyaunce
Ledest the world by certein governaunce,
In ydel, as men seyn, ye no-thing make;
But, lord, thise grisly feendly rokkes blake,
That semen rather a foul confusioun
Of werk than any fair creacioun
Of swich a parfit wys god and a stable,
Why han ye wroght this werk unresonable?
For by this werk, south, north, ne west, ne eest,
Ther nis y-fostred man, ne brid, ne beest;
It dooth no good, to my wit, but anoyeth.
See ye nat, lord, how mankinde it destroyeth?
An hundred thousand bodies of mankinde
Han rokkes slayn, al be they nat in minde,

As noble wifes do at a lone fireside.
She mourned, watched, wailed, she fasted and complained;
Desire for him so bound her and constrained.
That all this wide world did she set at naught.
Her friends, who knew her grief and heavy thought,
Comforted her as they might do or say;
They preached to her, they told her night and day
That for no cause she killed herself, alas!
And every comfort possible in this pass
They gave to her, in all their busyness,
To make her thus put by her heaviness.
With passing time, as you know, every one,
Men may so long with tools engrave a stone
That thereon will some figure printed be.
And so long did they comfort her that she
Received at last, by hope and reason grown,
Imprinted consolations as her own,
Whereby her sorrow did somewhat assuage;
She could not always live in such a rage.
And, then, Arviragus, through all her care,
Had sent her letters home, of his welfare,
And that he would come speedily again;
Otherwise had this sorrow her heart slain.
Her friends saw that her grief began to slake,
And prayed her on their knees, for dear God's sake,
To come and wander in their company
And drive away her gloomy fantasy.
And finally she granted that request;
For well she saw that it was for the best.
Now stood her castle very near the sea,
And often with her good friends wandered she
For pleasure on the cliffs that reared so high,
Whence she saw many a ship and barge go by,
Sailing their courses where they wished to go;
But that was part and parcel of her woe.
For to herself full oft, "Alas!" said she,
"Is there no ship, of many that I see,
Will bring me home my lord? Then were my heart
Recovered of its bitter pains that smart."
At other times there would she sit and think,
And cast her two eyes downward from the brink.
But when she saw the grisly rocks all black,
For very fear her heart would start aback
And quake so that her feet would not sustain
Her weight. Then on the grass she'd sit again
And piteously upon the sea she'd stare,
And say, with dull sighs on the empty air:
"Eternal God, Who by Thy providence
Leadest the world with a true governance,
Idly, as men say, dost Thou nothing make;
But, Lord, these grisly, fiendish rocks, so black,
That seem but rather foul confusion thrown
Awry than any fair world of Thine own,
Aye of a perfect wise God and stable,
Why hast Thou wrought this insane work, pray tell?
For by this work, north, south, and west and east,
There is none nurtured, man, nor bird, nor beast;
It does no good, to my mind, but annoys.
See'st Thou not, Lord, how mankind it destroys?
A hundred thousand bodies of mankind
Have died on rocks, whose names are not in mind,

And man's a creature made by Thee most fair,
After Thine image, as Thou didst declare.
Then seemed it that Thou had'st great charity
Toward mankind; but how then may it be
That Thou hast wrought such means man to destroy,
Which means do never good, but ever annoy?
I know well, clerics gladly do attest,
By arguments, that all is for the best,
Though I can never the real causes know.
But O Thou God Who made'st the wind to blow,
Keep Thou my lord! This is my argument;
To clerks I leave disputing on what's meant.
But O would God that all these rocks so black
Were sunken down to Hell for my lord's sake!
These rocks, they slay my very heart with fear."
Thus would she say, with many a piteous tear.
Her friends saw that to her it was no sport
To wander by the sea, but discomfort;
And so arranged to revel somewhere else.
They led her along rivers and to wells,
And such delightful places; and told fables,
And danced, and played at chess, and played at
tables.[1]
So on a day, all in the morningtide,
Unto a garden which was there beside,
Wherein they'd given command that there should
be
Food and whatever else was necessary,
They went for pleasure all the livelong day.
And this was on the morning sixth of May,
And May had painted with his soft warm showers
This garden full of foliage and of flowers;
And work of man's hand had so curiously
Arrayed this lovely garden, truthfully,
That never was another of such price,
Unless it were the very Paradise.
The scent of flowers and the fair fresh sight
Would have made any heart dance for delight
That e'er was born, unless too great sickness
Or too great sorrow held it in distress;
So full it was of beauty and pleasance.
After their dinner all began to dance,
And sing, also, save Dorigen alone,
Who made alway her same complaint and moan.
For him she saw not through the dancing go,
Who was her husband and her love also.
Nevertheless, she must a time abide,
And with good hope held, let her sorrow slide.
Amid these mazes, with the other men,
There danced a squire before this Dorigen,
That was more blithe, and prettier of array,
In my opinion, than the month of May.
He sang and danced better than any man
That is, or was, since first the world began.
Therewith he was, description to contrive,
One of best conditioned men alive;
Young, strong, right virtuous, and rich, and wise,
And well beloved, and one to idealize.
And briefly, if I tell the truth withal,
Unknown to Dorigen—nay, least of all—
This pleasant squire, servant to Queen Venus,

Which mankinde is so fair part of thy werk
That thou it madest lyk to thyn owene merk.
Than semed it ye hadde a greet chiertee
Toward mankinde; but how than may it be
That ye swiche menes make it to destroyen,
Whiche menes do no good, but ever anoyen?
I woot wel clerkes wol seyn, as hem leste,
By arguments, that al is for the beste,
Though I ne can the causes nat y-knowe.
But thilke god, that made wind to blowe,
As kepe my lord! this my conclusioun;
To clerkes lete I al disputisoun.
But wolde god that alle thise rokkes blake
Were sonken in-to helle for his sake!
Thise rokkes sleen myn herte for the fere."
Thus wolde she seyn, with many a pitous tere.
Hir freendes sawe that it was no disport
To romen by the see, but disconfort;
And shopen for to pleyen somwher elles.
They leden hir by riveres and by welles,
And eek in othere places delitables;
They dauncen, and they pleyen at ches and
tables.[1]
So on a day, right in the morwe-tyde,
Un-to a gardin that was ther bisyde,
In which that they had maad hir
ordinaunce
Of vitaille and of other purveyaunce,
They goon and pleye hem al the longe day.
And this was on the sixte morwe of May,
Which May had peynted with his softe shoures
This gardin ful of leves and of floures;
And craft of mannes hand so curiously
Arrayed hadde this gardin, trewely,
That never was ther gardin of swich prys,
But-if it were the verray paradys.
Th'odour of floures and the fresshe sighte
Wolde han maad any herte for to lighte
That ever was born, but-if to gret siknesse,
Or to gret sorwe helde it in distresse;
So ful it was of beautee with plesaunce.
At-after diner gonne they to daunce,
And singe also, save Dorigen allone,
Which made alwey hir compleint and hir mone;
For she ne saugh him on the daunce go,
That was hir housbonde and hir love also.
But nathelees she moste a tyme abyde,
And with good hope lete hir sorwe slyde.
Up-on this daunce, amonges othere men,
Daunced a squyer biforen Dorigen,
That fressher was and jolyer of array,
As to my doom, than is the monthe of May.
He singeth, daunceth, passinge any man
That is, or was, sith that the world bigan.
Ther-with he was, if men sholde him discryve,
Oon of the beste faringe man on-lyve;
Yong, strong, right vertuous, and riche and wys,
And wel biloved, and holden in gret prys.
And shortly, if the sothe I tellen shal,
Unwiting of this Dorigen at al,
This lusty squyer, servant to Venus,

[1]Backgammon.

Which that y-cleped was Aurelius,
Had loved hir best of any creature
Two yeer and more, as was his aventure,
But never dorste he telle hir his grevaunce;
With-outen coppe he drank al his penaunce.
He was despeyred, no-thing dorste he seye,
Save in his songes somwhat wolde he wreye
His wo, as in a general compleyning;
He seyde he lovede, and was biloved nothing.
Of swich matere made he manye layes,
Songes, compleintes, roundels, virelayes,
How that he dorste nat his sorwe telle,
But languissheth, as a furie dooth in helle;
And dye he moste, he seyde, as dide Ekko
For Narcisus, that dorste nat telle hir wo.
In other manere than ye here me seye,
Ne dorste he nat to hir his wo biwreye;
Save that, paraventure, som-tyme at daunces,
Ther yonge folk kepen hir observaunces,
It may wel be he loked on hir face
In swich a wyse, as man that asketh grace;
But no-thing wiste she of his entente.
Nathelees, it happed, er they thennes wente,
By-cause that he was hir neighebour,
And was a man of worship and honour,
And hadde y-knowen him of tyme yore,
They fille in speche; and forth more and more
Un-to his purpos drough Aurelius,
And whan he saugh his tyme, he seyde thus:
"Madame," quod he, "by god that this world made,
So that I wiste it mighte your herte glade,
I wolde, that day that your Arveragus
Wente over the see, that I, Aurelius,
Had went ther never I sholde have come agayn;
For wel I woot my service is in vayn.
My guerdon is but bresting of myn herte;
Madame, reweth upon my peynes smerte;
For with a word ye may me sleen or save,
Heer at your feet god wolde that I were grave!
I ne have as now no leyser more to seye;
Have mercy, swete, or ye wol do me deye!"
She gan to loke up-on Aurelius:
"Is this your wil," quod she, "and sey ye thus?
Never erst," quod she, "ne wiste I what ye mente.
But now, Aurelie, I knowe your entente,
By thilke god that yaf me soule and lyf,
Ne shal I never been untrewe wyf
In word ne werk, as fer as I have wit:
I wol ben his to whom that I am knit;
Tak this for fynal answer as of me."
But after that in pley thus seyde she:
"Aurelie," quod she, "by heighe god above,
Yet wolde I graunte yow to been your love,
Sin I yow see so pitously complayne;
Loke what day that, endelong Britayne,
Ye remoeve alle the rokkes, stoon by stoon,
That they ne lette ship ne boot to goon—
I seye, whan ye han maad the coost so clene
Of rokkes, that ther nis no stoon y-sene,

The name of whom was this, Aurelius,
Had loved her best of anyone alive
Two years and more (since she did first arrive),
But never dared he tell her of his state;
Without a cup he drank his draught of fate.
He had despaired, for nothing dared he say,
Save that in songs he would somewhat betray
His woe, as of a general complaint;
He loved, but none loved him, though he went faint
Of such a subject made he many lays,
Songs and complaints, rondels and virelays,
How that he dared not his deep sorrow tell,
But languished, as a fury does in Hell;
And die he must, he said, as did Echo
For her Narcissus, daring not tell her woe.
In other manner than you hear me say
Dared he not unto her his woe betray;
Save that, perchance, there would be times at dances,
Where young folk honoured all that makes romances,
It may well be he looked upon her face
In such wise as a man who sued for grace;
But nothing knew she of his love's intent.
Nevertheless it chanced, ere thence they went,
Because it happened he was her neighbour,
And was a man of worship and honour,
And she had known him in the time of yore,
They fell to talking; and so, more and more,
Unto his purpose drew Aurelius,
And when he saw his time addressed her thus:
"Madam," said he, "by God Who this world made,
So that I knew it might your sad heart aid,
I would, that day when your Arviragus
Went overseas, that I, Aurelius,
Had gone whence never I should come again;
For well I know my service is in vain.
My guerdon is the breaking of my heart;
Madam, have pity on my pains that smart;
For with a word you may slay me or save,
Here at your feet would God I found my grave!
Time to say more, at present naught have I;
Have mercy, sweet, or you will make me die!"
So then she looked upon Aurelius:
"Is this your will?" asked she, "And say you thus?
Never before have I known what you meant.
But since, Aurelius, I know your intent,
By that same God Who gave me soul and life,
Never shall I become an untrue wife
In word or deed, so far as I have wit:
I will remain his own to whom I'm knit;
Take this for final answer as from me."
But after that she said thus sportively:
"Aurelius," said she, "by God above,
Yet would I well consent to be your love,
Since I hear you complain so piteously,
On that day when, from coasts of Brittany,
You've taken all the black rocks, stone by stone,
So that they hinder ship nor boat—I own,
I say, when you have made the coast so clean
Of rocks that there is no stone to be seen,

Then will I love you best of any man;
Take here my promise—all that ever I can."
"Is there no other grace in you?" asked he.
"No, by that Lord," said she, "Who has made me!
For well I know that it shall ne'er betide.
Let suchlike follies out of your heart slide.
What pleasure can a man have in his life
Who would go love another man's own wife,
That has her body when he wishes it?"
Deep sighs Aurelius did then emit;
Woe was Aurelius when this he heard,
And with a sorrowful heart he thus answered:
"Madam," said he, "this were impossible!
Then must I die a sudden death and fell."
And with that word he turned away anon.
Then came her other friends, and many a one,
And in the alleys wandered up and down,
And nothing knew of this decision shown,
But suddenly began to dance anew
Until the bright sun lost his golden hue;
For the horizon had cut off his light;
This is as much as saying, it was night.
And home they went in joy and with solace,
Except the wretch Aurelius, alas!
He to his house went with a woeful heart;
He saw he could not from his near death part.
It seemed to him he felt his heart grow cold;
Up toward Heaven his two hands did he hold,
And on his bare knees did he kneel him down
And in his raving said his orison.
For very woe out of his wits he fled.
He knew not what he spoke, but thus he said;
With mournful heart his plaint had he begun
Unto the gods, and first unto the sun.
He said: "Apollo, governor and god
Of every plant, herb, tree, and flower in sod,
That givest, according to thy declination,
To each of them its time of foliation,
All as thy habitation's low or high,
Lord Phoebus, cast thy merciful bright eye
On wretched Aurelius, who is lost and lorn.
Lo, Lord! My lady has my swift death sworn,
Without my guilt, save thy benignity
Upon my dying heart have some pity!
For well I know, Lord Phoebus, if you lest,
You can thus aid me, save my lady, best.
Now vouchsafe that I may for you devise
A plan to help me, telling in what wise.
"Your blessed sister, Lucina, serene,
That of the sea is goddess chief and queen
(Though Neptune is the deity in the sea,
Yet empress set above him there is she).
You know well, Lord, that just as her desire
Is to be quickened and lighted by your fire,
For which she follows you right busily,
Just so the sea desires, and naturally,
To follow her, she being high goddess
Both of the sea and rivers, great and less.
Wherefore, Lord Phoebus, this request I make—
Without this miracle, my heart will break—
That at the time of your next opposition,
Which will be in the Lion, make petition

Than wol I love yow best of any man;
Have heer my trouthe in al that ever I can."
"Is ther non other grace in yow?" quod he.
"No, by that lord," quod she, "that maked me!
For wel I woot that it shal never bityde.
Lat swiche folies out of your herte slyde.
What deyntee sholde a man han in his lyf
For to go love another mannes wyf,
That hath hir body whan so that him lyketh?"
Aurelius ful ofte sore syketh;
Wo was Aurelie, whan that he this herde,
And with a sorweful herte he thus answerde:
"Madame," quod he, "this were an inpossible!
Than moot I dye of sodein deth horrible."
And with that word he turned him anoon.
Tho come hir othere freendes many oon,
And in the aleyes romeden up and doun,
And no-thing wiste of this conclusioun,
But sodeinly bigonne revel newe
Til that the brighte sonne loste his hewe;
For th'orisonte hath reft the sonne his light;
This is as muche to seye as it was night.
And hoom they goon in joye and in solas,
Save only wrecche Aurelius, allas!
He to his hous is goon with sorweful herte;
He seeth he may nat fro his deeth asterte.
Him semed that he felte his herte colde;
Up to the hevene his handes he gan holde,
And on his knowes bare he sette him doun,
And in his raving seyde his orisoun.
For verray wo out of his wit he breyde.
He niste what he spak, but thus he seyde;
With pitous herte his pleynt hath he bigonne
Un-to the goddes, and first un-to the sonne:
He seyde, "Appollo, god and governour
Of every plaunte, herbe, tree and flour,
That yevest, after thy declinacioun,
To ech of hem his tyme and his sesoun,
As thyn herberwe chaungeth lowe or hye,
Lord Phebus, cast thy merciable yë
On wrecche Aurelie, which that am but lorn.
Lo, lord! my lady hath my deeth y-sworn
With-oute gilt, but thy benignitee
Upon my dedly herte have som pitee!
For wel I woot, lord Phebus, if yow lest,
Ye may me helpen, save my lady, best.
Now voucheth sauf that I may yow devyse
How that I may been holpe and in what wyse.
Your blisful suster, Lucina the shene,
That of the see is chief goddesse and quene,
Though Neptunus have deitee in the see,
Yet emperesse aboven him is she:
Ye knowen wel, lord, that right as hir desyr
Is to be quiked and lightned of your fyr,
For which she folweth yow ful bisily,
Right so the see desyreth naturelly
To folwen hir, as she that is goddesse
Bothe in the see and riveres more and lesse.
Wherfore, lord Phebus, this is my requeste—
Do this miracle, or do myn herte breste—
That now, next at this opposicioun,
Which in the signe shal be of the Leoun,

As preyeth hir so greet a flood to bringe,
That fyve fadme at the leeste it overspringe
The hyeste rokke in Armorik Briteyne;
And lat this flood endure yeres tweyne;
Than certes to my lady may I seye:
'Holdeth your heste, the rokkes been aweye.'
  Lord Phebus, dooth this miracle for me;
Preye hir she go no faster cours than ye;
I seye, preyeth your suster that she go
No faster cours than ye thise yeres two.
Than shal she been evene atte fulle alway,
And spring-flood laste bothe night and day.
And, but she vouche-sauf in swiche manere
To graunte me my sovereyn lady dere,
Prey hir to sinken every rok adoun
In-to hir owene derke regioun
Under the ground, ther Pluto dwelleth inne,
Or never-mo shal I my lady winne.
Thy temple in Delphos wol I barefoot seke;
Lord Phebus, see the teres on my cheke,
And of my peyne have som compassioun."
And with that word in swowne he fil adoun,
And longe tyme he lay forth in a traunce.
  His brother, which that knew of his penaunce,
Up caughte him and to bedde he hath him broght.
Dispeyred in this torment and this thoght
Lete I this woful creature lye;
Chese he, for me, whether he wol live or dye.
  Arveragus, with hele and greet honour,
As he that was of chivalrye the flour,
Is comen hoom, and othere worthy men.
O blisful artow now, thou Dorigen,
That hast thy lusty housbonde in thyne armes,
The fresshe knight, the worthy man of armes,
That loveth thee, as his owene hertes lyf.
No-thing list him to been imaginatyf
If any wight had spoke, whyl he was oute,
To hire of love; he hadde of it no doute.
He noght entendeth to no swich matere,
But daunceth, justeth, maketh hir good chere;
And thus in joye and blisse I lete hem dwelle,
And of the syke Aurelius wol I telle.
  In langour and in torment furious
Two yeer and more lay wrecche Aurelius,
Er any foot he mighte on erthe goon;
Ne confort in this tyme hadde he noon,
Save of his brother, which that was a clerk;
He knew of al this wo and al this werk.
For to non other creature certeyn
Of this matere he dorste no word seyn.
Under his brest he bar it more secree
Than ever dide Pamphilus for Galathee.
His brest was hool, with-oute for to sene,
But in his herte ay was the arwe kene.
And wel ye knowe that of a sursanure[1]
In surgerye is perilous the cure,
But men mighte touche the arwe, or come therby.
His brother weep and wayled prively,
Til atte laste him fil in remembraunce,
That whyl he was at Orliens in Fraunce,
As yonge clerkes, that been likerous

To her that she so great a flood will bring
That full five fathoms shall it over-spring
The highest rock in Armoric Brittany;
And let this flood endure two years for me;
Then truly to my lady may I say:
'Now keep your word, the rocks are gone away.'
  "Lord Phoebus, do this miracle for me;
Pray her she run no faster course, being free—
I say, Lord, pray your sister that she go
No faster course than you these next years two.
Then shall she be even at the full alway,
And spring-flood shall endure both night and day.
And save she vouchsafe, Lord, in such manner
To grant to me my sovereign lady dear,
Pray her to sink, then, every rock far down
Into that region dark and cold, her own,
Under the earth, the place Pluto dwells in,
Or nevermore shall I my lady win.
Thy temple in Delphi will I, barefoot, seek;
Lord Phoebus, see the tears upon my cheek,
And on my pain be some compassion shown."
And with that word in swoon he tumbled down,
And for a long time lay there in a trance.
  His brother, who knew all his suppliance,
Found him, and took him, and to bed him brought.
Despairing in the torment of his thought,
Let I this woeful fellow-creature lie,
To choose, for all of me, to live or die.
  Arviragus, with health, in honour's hour,
As he that was of chivalry the flower,
Came home again, with other gentlemen.
O happy are you now, my Dorigen,
Who have your pleasant husband in your arms,
The vigorous knight, the worthy man-at-arms,
That loves you as he loves his own heart's life.
Nothing he chose to question of his wife
If any man had said, while he was out,
Some words of love; of her he had no doubt.
He tended not that way, it would appear,
But danced and jousted, made for her good cheer;
And thus in joy and bliss I let them dwell
And of love-sick Aurelius will I tell.
  In weakness and in torment furious
Two years and more lay wretched Aurelius
Ere foot on earth he went—aye, even one;
For comfort in this long time had he none,
Save from his brother, who was a good clerk;
He knew of all this woe and all this work.
For to no other human, 'tis certain,
Dared he his cause of illness to explain.
In breast he kept more secret his idea
Than did Pamphilius for Galatea.
His breast was whole, with no wound to be seen,
But in his heart there was the arrow keen.
And well you know that of a sursanure[1]
In surgery is difficult the cure,
Unless they find the dart or take it out.
His brother wept, and long he sought about
Till at the last he called to remembrance
That while he was at Orléans in France—
For many young clerks are all ravenous

[1]A wound healed or healing outwardly only.

To read of arts that are most curious,
And into every nook and cranny turn
Particular strange sciences to learn—
He thus recalled that once upon a day,
At Orléans, while studying there, I say,
A book of natural magic there he saw
In a friend's room, a bachelor of law
(Though he was there to learn another craft),
Which book he'd privately on his desk left;
And which book said much of the operations
Touching the eight and twenty variations
That designate the moon, and such folly
As is, in our days, valued not a fly;
For Holy Church provides us with a creed
That suffers no illusion to mislead.
And when this book came to his remembrance,
At once, for joy, his heart began to dance,
And to himself he said in privacy:
"My brother shall be healed, and speedily;
For I am sure that there are sciences
Whereby men make divers appearances,
Such as these prestidigitators play.
For oft at feasts, have I well heard men say
That jugglers, in a hall both bright and large,
Have made come in there, water and a barge,
And in the hall the barge rowed up and down.
Sometimes there seemed to come a grim lion;
And sometimes flowers sprang as in a mead;
Or vines with grapes both red and white indeed;
Sometimes a castle built of lime and stone;
And when they wished it disappeared anon.
Thus seemed these things to be in each man's sight.
"Now, then, conclude I thus, that if I might
At Orléans some old school-fellow find,
Who has these mansions of the moon in mind,
Or other natural magic from above,
He could well make my brother have his love.
For with a mere appearance clerks may make
It seem in man's sight that all rocks that break
The seas of Brittany were banished, so
That right above them ships might come and go,
And in such wise endure a week or two;
Then were my brother cured of all his woe.
For she must keep the word she gave at feast.
Or he'll have right to shame her, at the least."
Why should I longer speak of this event?
He to the bedside of his brother went,
And urged him eagerly to get him gone
To Orléans; he started up anon
And forward on his way at once did fare
In hope to be relieved of all his care.
When they were come almost to that city,
Perhaps two furlongs short of it, or three,
A young clerk walking by himself they met,
Who, in good Latin, heartily did greet,
And after that he said a wondrous thing.
[illegible]now," said he, "the cause of your coming."
[illegible] farther foot the brothers went,
[illegible]ll the soul of their intent.
[illegible]asked after school-fellows
[illegible]ough former suns and

To reden artes that been curious,
Seken in every halke and every herne
Particuler sciences for to lerne,
He him remembred that, upon a day,
At Orliens in studie a book he say
Of magik naturel, which his felawe,
That was that tyme a bacheler of lawe,
Al were he ther to lerne another craft,
Had prively upon his desk y-laft;
Which book spak muchel of the operaciouns,
Touchinge the eighte and twenty mansiouns
That longen to the mone, and swich folye,
As in our dayes is nat worth a flye;
For holy chirches feith in our bileve
Ne suffreth noon illusion us to greve.
And whan this book was in his remembraunce,
Anon for joye his herte gan to daunce,
And to him-self he seyde prively:
"My brother shal be warisshed hastily;
For I am siker that ther be sciences,
By whiche men make diverse apparences
Swiche as thise subtile tregetoures pleye.
For ofte at festes have I wel herd seye,
That tregetours, with-inne an halle large,
Have maad come in a water and a barge,
And in the halle rowen up and doun.
Somtyme hath semed come a grim leoun;
And somtyme floures springe as in a mede;
Somtyme a vyne, and grapes whyte and rede;
Somtyme a castel, al of lym and stoon;
And whan hem lyked, voyded it anoon.
Thus semed it to every mannes sighte.
Now than conclude I thus, that if I mighte
At Orliens som old felawe y-finde,
That hadde this mones mansions in minde,
Or other magik naturel above,
He sholde wel make my brother han his love.
For with an apparence a clerk may make
To mannes sighte, that alle the rokkes blake
Of Britaigne weren y-voyded everichon,
And shippes by the brinke comen and gon,
And in swich forme endure a day or two;
Than were my brother warisshed of his wo.
Than moste she nedes holden hir biheste,
Or elles he shal shame hir atte leste."
What sholde I make a lenger tale of this?
Un-to his brotheres bed he comen is,
And swich confort he yaf him for to gon
To Orliens, that he up stirte anon,
And on his wey forthward thanne is he fare,
In hope for to ben lissed of his care.
Whan they were come almost to that citee,
But-if it were a two furlong or three,
A yong clerk rominge by him-self they mette,
Which that in Latin thriftily hem grette,
And after that he seyde a wonder thing:
"I knowe," quod he, "the cause of your coming";
And er they ferther any fote wente,
He tolde hem al that was in hir entente.
This Briton clerk him asked of felawes
The whiche that he had knowe in olde
dawes;

And he answerde him that they dede were,
For which he weep ful ofte many a tere.
Doun of his hors Aurelius lighte anon,
And forth with this magicien is he gon
Hoom to his hous, and made hem wel at ese.
Hem lakked no vitaille that mighte hem plese;
So wel arrayed hous as ther was oon
Aurelius in his lyf saugh never noon.
He shewed him, er he wente to sopeer,
Forestes, parkes ful of wilde deer;
Ther saugh he hertes with hir hornes hye,
The gretteste that ever were seyn with yë.
He saugh of hem an hondred slayn with houndes,
And somme with arwes blede of bittre woundes.
He saugh, whan voided were this wilde deer,
Thise fauconers upon a fair river,
That with hir haukes han the heron slayn.
Tho saugh he knightes justing in a playn;
And after this, he dide him swich plesaunce,
That he him shewed his lady on a daunce
On which him-self he daunced, as him thoughte.
And whan this maister, that this magik wroughte,
Saugh it was tyme, he clapte his handes two,
And farewel! al our revel was ago.
And yet remoeved they never out of the hous,
Whyl they saugh al this sighte merveillous,
But in his studie, ther-as his bookes be,
They seten stille, and no wight but they three.
To him this maister called his squyer,
And seyde him thus: "is redy our soper?
Almost an houre it is, I undertake,
Sith I yow bad our soper for to make,
Whan that thise worthy men wenten with me
In-to my studie, ther-as my bookes be."
"Sire," quod this squyer, "whan it lyketh yow,
It is al redy, though ye wol right now."
"Go we than soupe," quod he, "as for the beste;
This amorous folk som-tyme mote han reste."
At-after soper fille they in tretee,
What somme sholde this maistres guerdon be,
To remoeven alle the rokkes of Britayne,
And eek from Gerounde to the mouth of Sayne.
He made it straunge, and swoor, so god him save,
Lasse than a thousand pound he wolde nat have,
Ne gladly for that somme he wolde nat goon.
Aurelius, with blisful herte anoon,
Answerde thus, "fy on a thousand pound!
This wyde world, which that men seye is round,
I wolde it yeve, if I were lord of it.
This bargayn is ful drive, for we ben knit.
Ye shal be payed trewely, by my trouthe!
But loketh now, for no necligence or slouthe,
Ye tarie us heer no lenger than to-morwe."
"Nay," quod this clerk, "have heer my feith to borwe."
To bedde is goon Aurelius whan him leste,
And wel ny al that night he hadde his reste;
What for his labour and his hope of blisse,
His woful herte of penaunce hadde a lisse.
Upon the morwe, whan that it was day,
To Britaigne toke they the righte way,

And he replied to this that dead they were,
Whereat he wept, for sorrow, many a tear.
Down from his horse Aurelius leaped anon,
And onward with this wizard he was gone
Home to his house, where he was put at ease.
To him there lacked no victuals that might please;
So well appointed house as was that one
Aurelius in life before saw none.
He showed him, ere he went to supper here,
Forests and parks full of the dim wild deer;
There saw he harts of ten with their horns high,
The greatest ever seen by human eye.
He saw of them a hundred slain by hounds,
And some with arrows bled, with bitter wounds.
He saw, when vanished all were these wild deer,
Some falconers by river flowing clear,
Who with their hawks had many herons slain.
And then he saw knights jousting on a plain;
And after this he did him such pleasance
That he showed him his lady in a dance
Wherein he also joined, or so he thought.
And when this master who this magic wrought
Saw it was time, he clapped his two hands, lo!
Farewell to all! the revels out did go.
And yet they'd never moved out of the house
While they saw all these sights so marvelous,
But in his study, where his books would be,
They had sat still, and no one but they three.
Then unto him this master called his squire,
And asked him thus: "Is supper ready, sir?
Almost an hour it is, I'll undertake,
Since I bade you our evening meal to make,
When these two gentlemen came in with me
Into my study, wherein my books be."
"Sir," said this squire then, "when it pleases you
It is all ready, though you will right now."
"Then let us sup," said he, "for that is best;
These amorous folk must sometime have some rest."
After the supper they discussed, they three,
What sum should this said master's guerdon be
For moving all rocks Breton coasts contain
From the Gironde unto the mouth of Seine.
He played for time, and swore, so God him save,
Less than a thousand pounds he would not have,
Nor eagerly for that would take it on.
Aurelius, with blissful heart, anon
Answered him thus: "Fig for a thousand pound!
This great wide world, the which, men say, is round,
I'd give it all, if I were lord of it.
The bargain is concluded and we're knit.
You shall be truly paid, sir, by my troth!
But look you, for no negligence or sloth,
Delay no longer than tomorrow morn."
"Nay," said this clerk, "upon my faith I'm sworn."
To bed went this Aurelius and undressed,
And well-nigh all that night he had his rest;
What of his labour and his hope of bliss
The pain had left that woeful heart of his.
Upon the morrow, when it was full day,
To Brittany took they the nearest way,

Aurelius, with this wizard at his side,
And thus they came to where they would abide;
And that was, as the books say, I remember,
The cold and frosty season of December.
Phoebus was old and coloured like pale brass,
That in hot declination coloured was
And shone like burnished gold with streamers
bright;
But now in Capricorn did he alight,
Wherein he palely shone, I dare explain.
The bitter frosts, with all the sleet and rain,
Had killed the green of every garden-yard.
Janus sat by the fire, with double beard,
And drained from out his bugle horn the wine.
Before him stood the brawn of tuskèd swine,
And "Noël!" cried then every lusty man.
Aurelius, in all that he could plan,
Did to this master cheerful reverence,
And prayed of him he'd use all diligence
To bring him from his pains that so did smart,
Or else with sword that he would slit his heart.
This subtle clerk such ruth had for this man,
That night and day he sped about his plan,
To wait the proper time for his conclusion;
That is to say, the time to make illusion,
By such devices of his jugglery
(I understand not this astrology)
That she and everyone should think and say
That all the Breton rocks were gone away,
Or else that they were sunken underground.
So at the last the proper time he found
To do his tricks and all his wretchedness
Of such a superstitious wickedness.
For his Toletan Tables forth he brought,
All well corrected, and he lacked in naught,
The years collected nor the separate years,
Nor his known roots, nor any other gears,
As, say, his centres and his argument,
And his proportionals convenient
In estimating truly his equations.
The eighth sphere showed him in his calculations
How far removed was Alnath, passing by,
From head of that fixed Aries on high,
That in the ninth great sphere considered is;
Right cleverly he calculated this.
When he the moon's first mansion thus had found,
The rest proportionally he could expound;
And knew the moon's arising-time right well,
And in what face and term, and all could tell;
This gave him then the mansion of the moon—
He worked it out accordingly right soon,
And did the other necessary rites
To cause illusions and such evil sights
As heathen peoples practised in those days.
Therefore no longer suffered he delays,
But all the rocks by magic and his lore
Appeared to vanish for a week or more.
Aurelius, who yet was torn by this,
Whether he'd gain his love or fare amiss,
Awaited night and day this miracle;
And when he knew there was no obstacle,
That vanished were these black rocks, every one,

Aurelius, and this magicien bisyde,
And been descended ther they wolde abyde;
And this was, as the bokes me remembre,
The colde frosty seson of Decembre.
Phebus wex old, and hewed lyk latoun,
That in his hote declinacioun
Shoon as the burned gold with stremes
brighte;
But now in Capricorn adoun he lighte,
Wher-as he shoon ful pale, I dar wel seyn.
The bittre frostes, with the sleet and reyn,
Destroyed hath the grene in every yerd.
Janus sit by the fyr, with double berd,
And drinketh of his bugle-horn the wyn.
Biforn him stant braun of the tusked swyn,
And "Nowel" cryeth every lusty man.
Aurelius, in al that ever he can,
Doth to his maister chere and reverence,
And preyeth him to doon his diligence
To bringen him out of his peynes smerte,
Or with a swerd that he wolde slitte his herte.
This subtil clerk swich routhe had of this man,
That night and day he spedde him that he can,
To wayte a tyme of his conclusioun;
This is to seye, to make illusioun,
By swich an apparence or jogelrye,
I ne can no termes of astrologye,
That she and every wight sholde wene and seye,
That of Britaigne the rokkes were aweye,
Or elles they were sonken under grounde.
So atte laste he hath his tyme y-founde
To maken his japes and his wrecchednesse
Of swich a supersticious cursednesse.
His tables Toletanes forth he broght,
Ful wel corrected, ne ther lakked noght,
Neither his collect ne his expans yeres,
Ne his rotes ne his othere geres,
As been his centres and his arguments,
And his proporcionels convenients
For his equacions in every thing.
And, by his eighte spere in his wirking,
He knew ful wel how fer Alnath was shove
Fro the heed of thilke fixe Aries above
That in the ninthe speere considered is;
Ful subtilly he calculed al this.
Whan he had founde his firste mansioun,
He knew the remenant by proporcioun;
And knew the arysing of his mone weel,
And in whos face, and terme, and everydeel;
And knew ful weel the mones mansioun
Acordaunt to his operacioun,
And knew also his othere observaunces
For swiche illusiouns and swiche meschaunces
As hethen folk used in thilke dayes;
For which no lenger maked he delayes,
But thurgh his magik, for a wyke or tweye,
It semed that alle the rokkes were aweye.
Aurelius, which that yet despeired is
Wher he shal han his love or fare amis,
Awaiteth night and day on this miracle;
And whan he knew that ther was noon obstacle,
That voided were thise rokkes everichon,

Doun to his maistres feet he fil anon,
And seyde, "I woful wrecche, Aurelius,
Thanke yow, lord, and lady myn Venus,
That me han holpen fro my cares colde:"
And to the temple his wey forth hath he holde,
Wher-as he knew he sholde his lady see.
And whan he saugh his tyme, anon-right he,
With dredful herte and with ful humble chere,
Salewed hath his sovereyn lady dere:
"My righte lady," quod this woful man,
"Whom I most drede and love as I best can,
And lothest were of al this world displese,
Nere it that I for yow have swich disese,
That I moste dyen heer at your foot anon,
Noght wolde I telle how me is wo bigon;
But certes outher moste I dye or pleyne;
Ye slee me giltelees for verray peyne.
But of my deeth, thogh that ye have no routhe,
Avyseth yow, er that ye breke your trouthe.
Repenteth yow, for thilke god above,
Er ye me sleen by-cause that I yow love.
For, madame, wel ye woot what ye han hight;
Nat that I chalange any thing of right
Of yow my sovereyn lady, but your grace;
But in a gardin yond, at swich a place,
Ye woot right wel what ye bihighten me;
And in myn hand your trouthe plighten ye
To love me best, god woot, ye seyde so,
Al be that I unworthy be therto.
Madame, I speke it for the honour of yow,
More than to save myn hertes lyf right now;
I have do so as ye comanded me;
And if ye vouche-sauf, ye may go see.
Doth as yow list, have your biheste in minde,
For quik or deed, right ther ye shul me finde;
In yow lyth al, to do me live or deye;—
But wel I woot the rokkes been aweye!"
He taketh his leve, and she astonied stood,
In al hir face nas a drope of blood;
She wende never han come in swich a trappe:
"Allas!" quod she, "that ever this sholde happe!
For wende I never, by possibilitee,
That swich a monstre or merveille mighte be!
It is agayns the proces of nature:"
And hoom she gooth a sorweful creature.
For verray fere unnethe may she go,
She wepeth, wailleth, al a day or two
And swowneth, that it routhe was to see;
But why it was, to no wight tolde she;
For out of toune was goon Arveragus.
But to hir-self she spak, and seyde thus,
With face pale and with ful sorweful chere,
In hir compleynt, as ye shul after here:
"Allas," quod she, "on thee, Fortune, I pleyne,
That unwar wrapped hast me in thy cheyne;
For which, t'escape, woot I no socour
Save only deeth or elles dishonour;
Oon of thise two bihoveth me to chese.
But nathelees, yet have I lever lese
My lyf than of my body have a shame,
Or knowe my-selven fals, or lese my name,
And with my deth I may be quit, y-wis.

Down at the master's feet he fell anon
And said: "I, woeful wretch, Aurelius,
Thank you, my lord, and Lady mine Venus,
That have so saved me from my dreadful care."
And to the temple straightway did he fare,
Whereat he knew he should his lady see.
And when he saw his opportunity,
With fluttering heart and with an humble cheer
He greeted thus his sovereign lady dear.
"My own dear lady," said this woeful man,
"Whom I most fear and love best, as I can,
And whom, of all this world, I'd not displease,
Were it not that for you I've such unease
That I must die here at your feet anon,
I would not tell how I am woebegone;
But I must either die or else complain;
You slay me, for no crime, with utter pain.
But on my death, although you have no ruth,
Take heed now, ere you break your promised troth.
Repent you, for the sake of God above,
Ere me you slay, because it's you I love.
For well you know your promise apposite;
Not that I challenge aught, of my own right,
In you, my sovereign lady, save your grace;
But in a garden, in a certain place,
You know right well what you did promise me;
And in my hand you plighted troth," said he,
"To love me best, God knows you promised so,
Howe'er I may unworthy be thereto.
Madam, I say it for your honour's vow
More than to save my heart's dear life right now;
I have done all that you commanded me;
And if you will, you may well go and see.
Do as you please, but hold your word in mind,
For quick or dead, as you do, me you'll find;
In you lies all, to make me live or die,
But well I know the rocks are vanished, aye!"
He took his leave, and she astounded stood,
In all her face there was no drop of blood;
She never thought to have come in such a trap.
"Alas!" said she, "that ever this should hap!
For thought I never, by possibility,
That such prodigious marvel e'er might be!
It is against the way of all nature."
And home she went, a sorrowful creature.
For utter terror hardly could she go,
She wept, she wailed throughout a day or so,
And swooned so much 'twas pitiful to see;
But why this was to not a soul told she;
For out of town was gone Arviragus.
But to her own heart spoke she, and said thus,
With her face pale and with a heavy cheer,
All her complaint, as you'll hereafter hear:
"Of thee," she cried, "O Fortune, I complain,
That, unaware, I'm bound within thy chain;
From which to go, I know of no succour
Save only death, or else my dishonour;
One of these two I am compelled to choose.
Nevertheless, I would far rather lose
My life than of my body come to shame,
Or know myself untrue, or lose my name;
By death I know it well, I may be freed,

Has there not many a noble wife, indeed,
And many a maiden slain herself—alas!—
Rather than with her body do trespass?
"Yes, truly, lo, these stories bear witness;
When Thirty Tyrants, full of wickedness,
Had Phido slain in Athens, at a feast,
They gave command his daughters to arrest,
And had them brought before them, for despite,
All naked, to fufill their foul delight,
And in their father's blood they made them dance
Upon the pavement—God give them mischance!
For which these woeful maidens, full of dread,
Rather than they should lose their maidenhead,
Unseen they all leaped down into a well
And drowned themselves therein, as old books tell.
"They of Messina did require and seek
From Lacedaemon fifty maids to take,
On whom they would have done their lechery;
But there was none of all that company
Who was not slain, and who with good intent
Preferred not death rather than give consent
To be thus ravished of her maidenhead.
Why should I then hold dying in such dread?
"Lo, too, the tyrant Aristoclides,
Who loved a maiden called Stimphalides.
Whenas her father had been slain by night,
Unto Diana's temple she took flight
And grasped the image in her two hands so
That from this image would she not let go.
No one could tear her hands from that embrace
Till she was slaughtered in that self-same place.
Now since these maidens showed such scorn outright
Of being defiled to make man's foul delight,
Well ought a wife rather herself to slay
Than be defiled, I think, and so I say.
"What shall I say of Hasdrubal's fair wife,
Who in Carthage bereft herself of life?
For when she saw that Romans won the town,
She took her children all and leaped right down
Into the fire, choosing thus to die
Before a Roman did her villainy.
"Did not Lucretia slay herself—alas!—
At Rome, when she so violated was
By Tarquin? For she thought it was a shame
Merely to live when she had lost her name.
"The seven maidens of Miletus, too,
Did slay themselves, for very dread and woe,
Rather than men of Gaul should on them press.
More than a thousand stories, as I guess,
Could I repeat now of this matter here.
"With Abradates slain, his wife so dear
Herself slew, and she let her red blood glide
In Abradates' wounds so deep and wide,
And said: 'My body, at the least, I say,
No man shall now defile,' and passed away.
"Why should I of more instances be fain?
Since that so many have their bodies slain
Rather than that they should dishonoured be?
I will conclude it better is for me
To slay myself than be dishonoured thus.
I will be true unto Arviragus,
Or else I'll slay myself in some manner,

Hath ther nat many a noble wyf, er this,
And many a mayde y-slayn hir-self, allas!
Rather than with hir body doon trespas?
Yis, certes, lo, thise stories beren witnesse;
Whan thretty tyraunts, ful of cursednesse,
Had slayn Phidoun in Athenes, atte feste,
They comanded his doghtres for t'areste,
And bringen hem biforn hem in despyt
Al naked, to fulfille hir foul delyt,
And in hir fadres blood they made hem daunce
Upon the pavement, god yeve hem mischaunce!
For which thise woful maydens, ful of drede,
Rather than they wolde lese hir maydenhede,
They prively ben stirt in-to a welle,
And dreynte hem-selven, as the bokes telle.
They of Messene lete enquere and seke
Of Lacedomie fifty maydens eke,
On whiche they wolden doon hir lecherye;
But was ther noon of al that companye
That she nas slayn, and with a good entente
Chees rather for to dye than assente
To been oppressed of hir maydenhede.
Why sholde I thanne to dye been in drede?
Lo, eek, the tiraunt Aristoclides
That loved a mayden, heet Stimphalides,
Whan that hir fader slayn was on a night,
Un-to Dianes temple goth she right,
And hente the image in hir handes two,
Fro which image wolde she never go.
No wight ne mighte hir handes of it arace,
Til she was slayn right in the selve place.
Now sith that maydens hadden swich despyt
To been defouled with mannes foul delyt,
Wel oghte a wyf rather hir-selven slee
Than be defouled, as it thinketh me.
What shal I seyn of Hasdrubales wyf,
That at Cartage birafte hir-self hir lyf?
For whan she saugh that Romayns wan the toun,
She took hir children alle, and skipte adoun
In-to the fyr, and chees rather to dye
Than any Romayn dide hir vileinye.
Hath nat Lucresse y-slayn hir-self, allas!
At Rome, whanne she oppressed was
Of Tarquin, for hir thoughte it was a shame
To liven whan she hadde lost hir name?
The sevene maydens of Milesie also
Han slayn hem-self, for verray drede and wo,
Rather than folk of Gaule hem sholde oppresse.
Mo than a thousand stories, as I gesse,
Coude I now telle as touchinge this matere.
Whan Habradate was slayn, his wyf so dere
Hirselven slow, and leet hir blood to glyde
In Habradates woundes depe and wyde,
And seyde, "my body, at the leeste way,
Ther shal no wight defoulen, if I may."
What sholde I mo ensamples heer-of sayn,
Sith that so manye han hem-selven slayn
Wel rather than they wolde defouled be?
I wol conclude, that it is bet for me
To sleen my-self, than been defouled thus.
I wol be trewe un-to Arveragus,
Or rather sleen my-self in som manere,

As dide Demociones doghter dere,
By-cause that she wolde not defouled be.
O Cedasus! it is ful greet pitee,
To reden how thy doghtren deyde, allas!
That slowe hem-selven for swich maner cas.
As greet a pitee was it, or wel more,
The Theban mayden, that for Nichanore
Hir-selven slow, right for swich maner wo.
Another Theban mayden dide right so;
For oon of Macedoine hadde hir oppressed,
She with hir deeth hir maydenhede redressed.
What shal I seye of Nicerates wyf,
That for swich cas birafte hir-self hir lyf?
How trewe eek was to Alcebiades
His love, that rather for to dyen chees
Than for to suffre his body unburied be!
Lo which a wyf was Alcestė," quod she.
"What seith Omer of gode Penalopee?
Al Grece knoweth of hir chastitee.
Pardee, of Laodomya is writen thus,
That whan at Troye was slayn Protheselaus,
No lenger wolde she live after his day.
The same of noble Porcia telle I may;
With-oute Brutus coude she nat live,
To whom she hadde al hool hir herte yive.
The parfit wyfhod of Arthemesye
Honoured is thurgh al the Barbarye.
O Teuta, queen! thy wyfly chastitee
To alle wyves may a mirour be.
The same thing I seye of Bilia, [11,766*a*]
Of Rodogone, and eek Valeria." [*b*]
Thus pleyned Dorigene a day or tweye,
Purposinge ever that she wolde deye.
But nathelees, upon the thridde night,
Hom cam Arveragus, this worthy knight,
And asked hir, why that she weep so sore?
And she gan wepen ever lenger the more.
"Allas!" quod she, "that ever was I born!
Thus have I seyd," quod she, "thus have I sworn"—
And told him al as ye han herd bifore;
It nedeth nat reherce it yow na-more.
This housbond with glad chere, in freendly wyse,
Answerde and seyde as I shal yow devyse:
"Is ther oght elles, Dorigen, but this?"
"Nay, nay," quod she, "god help me so, as wis;
This is to muche, and it were goddes wille."
"Ye, wyf," quod he, "lat slepen that is stille:
It may be wel, paraventure, yet to-day.
Ye shul your trouthe holden, by my fay!
For god so wisly have mercy on me,
I hadde wel lever y-stiked for to be,
For verray love which that I to yow have,
But-if ye sholde your trouthe kepe and save.
Trouthe is the hyeste thing that man may kepe:"—
But with that word he brast anon to wepe,
And seyde, "I yow forbede, up peyne of deeth,
That never, whyl thee lasteth lyf ne breeth
To no wight tel thou of this aventure.
As I may best, I wol my wo endure,

As did Demotions's virgin daughter dear
Because she would not violated be.
"O Cedasus, it rouses great pity
To read of how your daughters died, alas!
That slew themselves in such another case.
"As great a pity was it, aye and more,
That a fair Theban maid, for Nicanor,
Did slay herself in such a kind of woe.
"Another Theban maiden did also;
For one of Macedonia her had pressed,
And she, by death, her maidenhead redressed.
"What shall I say of Nicerates' wife,
Who, for like cause, bereft herself of life?
"How true, too, was to Alcibiades
His love, who chose to drain death to the lees
And would not let his corpse unburied be!
Lo, what a wife was Alcestis," said she.
"What says Homer of good Penelope?
The whole of Hellas knew her chastity.
"*Pardieu*, of Laodamia they wrote thus,
That when at Troy was slain Protesilaus,
No longer would she live after his day.
"The same of noble Portia may I say;
Without her Brutus could she no wise live,
To whom in youth her whole heart she did give.
"The perfect wifehood of Artemisia
Was honoured throughout all old Caria.
"O Teuta, queen! Your wifely chastity,
To all wives may a very mirror be.
The same thing may I say of Bilia,
Of Rhodogune and of Valeria."
Thus Dorigen went on a day or so,
Purposing ever that to death she'd go.
But notwithstanding, upon the third night
Home came Arviragus, this worthy knight,
And asked her why it was she wept so sore.
And thereat she began to weep the more.
"Alas!" cried she, "that ever I was born!
Thus have I said," quoth she, "thus have I sworn"—
And told him all, as you have heard before;
It needs not to re-tell it to you more.
This husband, with glad cheer, in friendly wise,
Answered and said as I shall you apprise:
"Is there naught else, my Dorigen, than this?"
"Nay, nay," said she, "God help me, as it is
This is too much, though it were God's own will."
"Yea, wife," said he, "let sleep what's lying still;
It may be well with us, perchance, today.
But you your word shall hold to, by my fay!
As God may truly mercy have on me,
Wounded to death right now I'd rather be,
For sake of this great love of you I have,
Than you should not your true word keep and save.
Truth is the highest thing that man may keep."
But with that word began he then to weep,
And said; "I you forbid, on pain of death,
That ever, while to you last life and breath,
To anyone you tell this adventure.
As I best may, I will my woe endure,

Nor show a countenance of heaviness,
That folk no harm may think of you, or guess."
And then he called a squire and a maid:
"Go forth anon with Dorigen," he said,
"And bring her to a certain place anon."
They took their leave and on their way were gone,
But nothing knew of why she thither went
Nor would he to a soul tell his intent.
Perhaps a lot of you will certainly
Hold him a wicked man that wilfully
Put his wife's honour thus in jeopardy;
Hearken the tale, ere you upon her cry.
She may have better luck than you suppose;
And when you've heard all, let your judgment close.
This squire I've told you of, Aurelius,
Of Dorigen he being so amorous,
Chanced, as it seems, his lady fair to meet
In middle town, right in the busiest street,
As she was going forth, as you have heard,
Toward the garden where she'd pledged her word
And he was going gardenward also;
For he was always watching when she'd go
Out of her house to any kind of place.
But thus they met, by chance perhaps or grace;
And he saluted her with good intent,
And asked her, now, whither it was she went.
And she replied, as if she were half mad:
"Unto the garden, as my husband bade,
My promise there to keep, alas, alas!"
Aurelius then pondered on this case,
And in his heart he had compassion great
On her and her lamenting and her state,
And on Arviragus, the noble knight,
Who'd bidden her keep promise, as she might,
Being so loath his wife should break with truth;
And in his heart he gained, from this, great ruth,
Considering the best on every side,
That from possession rather he'd abide
Than do so great a churlish grievousness
Against free hearts and all high nobleness;
For which, and in few words, he told her thus:
"Madam, say to your lord Arviragus
That since I see his noble gentleness
To you, and since I see well your distress,
That he'd have rather shame (and that were ruth)
Than you to me should break your word of truth,
I would myself far rather suffer woe
Than break apart the love between you two.
So I release, madam, into your hand,
And do return, discharged, each surety and
Each bond that you have given and have sworn,
Even from the very time that you were born.
My word I pledge, I'll ne'er seek to retrieve
A single promise, and I take my leave
As of the truest and of the best wife
That ever yet I've known in all my life.
Let every wife of promises take care,
Remember Dorigen, and so beware!
Thus can a squire perform a gentle deed
As well as can a knight, of that take heed."

Ne make no contenance of hevinesse,
That folk of yow may demen harm or gesse."
And forth he cleped a squyer and a mayde:
"Goth forth anon with Dorigen," he sayde,
"And bringeth hir to swich a place anon."
They take hir leve, and on hir wey they gon;
But they ne wiste why she thider wente.
He nolde no wight tellen his entente.
Paraventure an heep of yow, y-wis, [11,802*a*]
Wol holden him a lewed man in this, [*b*]
That he wol putte his wyf in jupartye; [*c*]
Herkneth the tale, er ye up-on hir crye. [*d*]
She may have bettre fortune than yow semeth; [*e*]
And whan that ye han herd the tale demeth. [*f*]
This squyer, which that highte Aurelius
On Dorigen that was so amorous,
Of aventure happed hir to mete
Amidde the toun, right in the quikkest strete,
As she was boun to goon the wey forthright
Toward the gardin ther-as she had hight.
And he was to the gardinward also;
For wel he spyed, whan she wolde go
Out of hir hous to any maner place.
But thus they mette, of aventure or grace;
And he saleweth hir with glad entente,
And asked of hir whiderward she wente?
And she answerde, half as she were mad,
"Un-to the gardin, as myn housbond bad,
My trouthe for to holde, allas! allas!"
Aurelius gan wondren on this cas,
And in his herte had greet compassioun
Of hir and of hir lamentacioun,
And of Arveragus, the worthy knight,
That bad hir holden al that she had hight,
So looth him was his wyf sholde breke hir trouthe;
And in his herte he caughte of this greet routhe,
Consideringe the beste on every syde,
That fro his lust yet were him lever abyde
Than doon so heigh a cherlish wrecchednesse
Agayns franchyse and alle gentillesse;
For which in fewe wordes seyde he thus:
"Madame, seyth to your lord Arveragus,
That sith I see his grete gentillesse
To yow, and eek I see wel your distresse,
That him were lever han shame (and that were routhe)
Than ye to me sholde breke thus your throuthe,
I have wel lever ever to suffre wo
Than I departe the love bitwix yow two.
I yow relesse, madame, in-to your hond
Quit every surement and every bond,
That ye han maad to me as heer-biforn,
Sith thilke tyme which that ye were born.
My trouthe I plighte, I shal yow never repreve
Of no biheste, and here I take my leve,
As of the treweste and the beste wyf
That ever yet I knew in al my lyf.
But every wyf be-war of hir biheste,
On Dorigene remembreth atte leste.
Thus can a squyer doon a gentil dede,
As well as can a knight, with-outen drede."

She thonketh him up-on hir knees al bare,
And hoom un-to hir housbond is she fare,
And tolde him al as ye han herd me sayd;
And be ye siker, he was so weel apayd,
That it were inpossible me to wryte;
What sholde I lenger of this cas endyte?

Arveragus and Dorigene his wyf
In sovereyn blisse leden forth hir lyf.
Never eft ne was ther angre hem bitwene;
He cherisseth hir as though she were a quene;
And she was to him trewe for evermore.
Of thise two folk ye gete of me na-more.

Aurelius, that his cost hath al forlorn,
Curseth the tyme that ever he was born:
"Allas," quod he, "allas! that I bihighte
Of pured gold a thousand pound of wighte
Un-to this philosophre! how shal I do?
I see na-more but that I am fordo.
Myn heritage moot I nedes selle,
And been a begger; heer may I nat dwelle,
And shamen al my kinrede in this place,
But I of him may gete bettre grace.
But nathelees, I wol of him assaye,
At certeyn dayes, yeer by yeer, to paye,
And thanke him of his grete curteisye;
My trouthe wol I kepe, I wol nat lye."

With herte soor he gooth un-to his cofre,
And broghte gold un-to this philosophre,
The value of fyve hundred pound, I gesse,
And him bisecheth, of his gentillesse,
To graunte him dayes of the remenaunt,
And seyde, "maister, I dar wel make avaunt,
I failled never of my trouthe as yit;
For sikerly my dette shal be quit
Towardes yow, how-ever that I fare
To goon a-begged in my kirtle bare.
But wolde ye vouche-sauf, up-on seurtee,
Two yeer or three for to respyten me,
Than were I wel; for elles moot I selle
Myn heritage; ther is na-more to telle."

This philosophre sobrely answerde,
And seyde thus, whan he thise wordes herde:
"Have I nat holden covenant un-to thee?"
"Yes, certes, wel and trewely," quod he.
"Hastow nat had thy lady as thee lyketh?"
"No, no," quod he, and sorwefully he syketh.
"What was the cause? tel me if thou can."
Aurelius his tale anon bigan,
And tolde him al, as ye han herd bifore;
It nedeth nat to yow reherce it more.

He seide, "Arveragus, of gentillesse,
Had lever dye in sorwe and in distresse
Than that his wyf were of hir trouthe fals."
The sorwe of Dorigen he tolde him als,
How looth hir was to been a wikked wyf,
And that she lever had lost that day hir lyf,
And that hir trouthe she swoor, thurgh innocence:
"She never erst herde speke of apparence;
That made me han of hir so greet pitee.
And right as frely as he sente hir me,
As frely sente I hir to him ageyn.
This al and som, ther is na-more to seyn."

Upon her bare knees did she thank him there,
And home unto her husband did she fare,
And told him all, as you have heard it said;
And be assured, he was so pleased and glad
That 'twere impossible of it to write.
What should I further of this case indite?

Arviragus and Dorigen his wife
In sovereign happiness led forth their life.
Never did any anger come between;
He cherished her as if she were a queen;
And she to him was true for evermore.
Of these two folk you get from me no more.

Aurelius, whose wealth was now forlorn,
He cursed the time that ever he was born;
"Alas!" cried he, "Alas! that I did state
I'd pay fine gold a thousand pounds by weight
To this philosopher! What shall I do?
I see no better than I'm ruined too.
All of my heritage I needs must sell
And be a beggar; here I cannot dwell
And shame all of my kindred in this place,
Unless I gain of him some better grace.
And so I'll go to him and try, today,
On certain dates, from year to year, to pay,
And thank him for his princely courtesy;
For I will keep my word, and I'll not lie."

With sore heart he went then to his coffer,
And took gold unto this philosopher,
The value of five hundred pounds, I guess,
And so besought him, of his nobleness,
To grant him dates for payment of the rest,
And said: "Dear master, I may well protest
I've never failed to keep my word, as yet;
For certainly I'll pay my entire debt
To you, however after I may fare,
Even to begging, save for kirtle, bare.
But if you'd grant, on good security,
Two years or three of respite unto me,
Then all were well; otherwise must I sell
My heritage; there is no more to tell."

Then this philosopher soberly answered
And spoke in this wise, when these words he'd heard:
"Have I not fairly earned my promised fee?"
"Yes, truly, you have done so, sir," said he.
"Have you not had the lady at your will?"
"No, no," said he, and sighed, and then was still.
"What was the reason? Tell me if you can."

Aurelius his tale anon began,
And told him all, as you have heard before;
It needs not I repeat it to you more.

He said: "Arviragus, of nobleness,
Had rather die in sorrow and distress
Than that his wife were to her promise false."
He told of Dorigen's grief, too, and how else
She had been loath to live a wicked wife
And rather would that day have lost her life,
And that her troth she swore through ignorance:
"She'd ne'er before heard of such simulance;
Which made me have for her such great pity.
And just as freely as he sent her me,
As freely sent I her to him again.
This is the sum, there's no more to explain."

Then answered this philosopher: "Dear brother,
Each one of you has nobly dealt with other.
You are a squire, true, and he is a knight,
But God forbid, what of His blessed might,
A clerk should never do a gentle deed
As well as any of you. Of this take heed!
"Sir, I release to you your thousand pound,
As if, right now, you'd crept out of the ground
And never, before now, had known of me.
For, sir, I'll take of you not one penny
For all my art and all my long travail.
You have paid well for all my meat and ale;
It is enough, so farewell, have good day!"
And took his horse and went forth on his way.
Masters, this question would I ask you now:
Which was most generous, do you think, and how?
Pray tell me this before you farther wend.
I can no more, my tale is at an end.

This philosophre answerde, "leve brother,
Everich of yow dide gentilly til other.
Thou art a squyer, and he is a knight;
But god forbede, for his blisful might,
But-if a clerk coude doon a gentil dede
As wel as any of yow, it is no drede!
Sire, I relesse thee thy thousand pound,
As thou right now were cropen out of the ground,
Ne never er now ne haddest knowen me.
For sire, I wol nat take a peny of thee
For al my craft, ne noght for my travaille.
Thou hast y-payed wel for my vitaille;
It is y-nogh, and farewel, have good day:"
And took his hors, and forth he gooth his way.
Lordinges, this question wolde I aske now,
Which was the moste free, as thinketh yow?
Now telleth me, er that ye ferther wende.
I can na-more, my tale is at an ende.

HERE IS ENDED THE FRANKLIN'S TALE

THE PHYSICIAN'S TALE

HERE FOLLOWETH THE PHYSICIAN'S TALE[1]

There was, as tells us Titus Livius,
A knight whose name was called Virginius,
Fulfilled of honour and of worthiness,
Who many friends and much wealth did possess.
This knight had had a daughter by his wife,
Nor children more had he in all his life.
Fair was this maid, in excellent beauty
Above all others that a man may see;
For Nature had, with sovereign diligence,
Moulded her to so great an excellence
She seemed to say: "Behold now, I, Nature,
Thus can I form and paint a creature pure
When I desire. Who can it counterfeit?
Pygmalion? Nay, not though he forge and beat,
Or curve, or paint; and I dare say again,
Apelles, Zeuxis too, should work in vain,
Either to carve or paint, or forge or beat,
If they presumed my work to counterfeit.
For He Who is Creator Principal
Has made of me His Vicar General
To form and colour earthly creatures all,
Just as I like, for they're mine, great and small
Under the moon, the which may wax and wane;
And for my work I ask no payment vain;
My Lord and I are of one sole accord;
I made her in the worship of my Lord.
So do I other fair or foul creatures,
What colours though they have, or what figures."
It seems to me that Nature thus would say.
This maid was fourteen years of age, this may
In whom Dame Nature had so great delight.
For just as she can paint a lily white
Or redden rose, even with such a stroke
She did this creature by her art evoke
Ere she was born, painting her sweet limbs free
In such true colours as they'd come to be;

Ther was, as telleth Titus Livius,
A knight that called was Virginius,
Fulfild of honour and of worthinesse,
And strong of freendes and of greet richesse.
This knight a doghter hadde by his wyf,
No children hadde he mo in al his lyf.
Fair was this mayde in excellent beautee
Aboven every wight that man may see;
For nature hath with sovereyn diligence
Y-formed hir in so greet excellence,
As though she wolde seyn, "lo! I, Nature,
Thus can I forme and peynte a creature,
Whan that me list; who can me countrefete?
Pigmalion noght, though he ay forge and bete,
Or grave, or peynte; for I dar wel seyn,
Apelles, Zanzis, sholde werche in veyn,
Outher to grave or peynte or forge or bete,
If they presumed me to countrefete.
For he that is the former principal
Hath maked me his vicaire general,
To forme and peynten erthely creaturis
Right as me list, and ech thing in my cure is
Under the mone, that may wane and waxe,
And for my werk right no-thing wol I axe;
My lord and I ben ful of oon accord;
I made hir to the worship of my lord.
So do I alle myne othere creatures,
What colour that they han, or what figures."—
Thus semeth me that Nature wolde seye.
This mayde of age twelf yeer was and tweye,
In which that Nature hadde swich delyt.
For right as she can peynte a lilie whyt
And reed a rose, right with swich peynture
She peynted hath this noble creature
Er she were born, up-on hir limes free,
Wher-as by right swiche colours sholde be;

[1] The Prologue [11,929-34], held spurious by Skeat, is omitted.

And Phebus dyed hath hir tresses grete
Lyk to the stremes of his burned hete.
And if that excellent was hir beautee,
A thousand-fold more vertuous was she.
In hir ne lakked no condicioun,
That is to preyse, as by discrecioun.
As wel in goost as body chast was she;
For which she floured in virginitee
With alle humilitee and abstinence,
With alle attemperaunce and pacience,
With mesure eek of bering and array.
Discreet she was in answering alway;
Though she were wys as Pallas, dar I seyn,
Hir facound eek ful wommanly and pleyn,
No countrefeted termes hadde she
To seme wys; but after hir degree
She spak, and alle hir wordes more and lesse
Souninge in vertu and in gentillesse.
Shamfast she was in maydens shamfastnesse,
Constant in herte, and ever in bisinesse
To dryve hir out of ydel slogardye.
Bacus hadde of hir mouth right no maistrye;
For wyn and youthe doon Venus encrece,
As men in fyr wol casten oile or grece.
And of hir owene vertu, unconstreyned,
She hath ful ofte tyme syk hir feyned,
For that she wolde fleen the companye
Wher lykly was to treten of folye,
As is at festes, revels, and at daunces.
That been occasions of daliaunces
Swich thinges maken children for to be
To sone rype and bold, as men may see,
Which is ful perilous, and hath ben yore.
For al to sone may she lerne lore
Of boldnesse, whan she woxen is a wyf.
  And ye maistresses in your olde lyf,
That lordes doghtres han in governaunce,
Ne taketh of my wordes no displesaunce;
Thenketh that ye ben set in governinges
Of lordes doghtres, only for two thinges;
Outher for ye han kept your honestee,
Or elles ye han falle in freletee,
And knowen wel y-nough the olde daunce,
And han forsaken fully swich meschaunce
For evermo; therfore, for Cristes sake,
To teche hem vertu loke that ye ne slake.
A theef of venisoun, that hath forlaft
His likerousnesse, and al his olde craft,
Can kepe a forest best of any man.
Now kepeth hem wel, for if ye wol, ye can;
Loke wel that ye un-to no vice assente,
Lest ye be dampned for your wikke entente;
For who-so doth, a traitour is certeyn.
And taketh kepe of that that I shal seyn;
Of alle tresons sovereyn pestilence
Is whan a wight bitrayseth innocence.
  Ye fadres and ye modres eek also,
Though ye han children, be it oon or two,
Your is the charge of al hir surveyaunce,
Whyl that they been under your governaunce.
Beth war that by ensample of your livinge,
Or by your necligence in chastisinge,

And Phoebus dyed her long hair with such gold
As have his burning streamers manifold.
But if right excellent was her beauty,
A thousand-fold more virtuous was she.
In her there lacked not one condition known
That's praiseworthy when by discretion shown.
As well in soul as body chaste was she;
For which she flowered in virginity
With all humility and abstinence,
And with all temperance and with patience,
And with a modest bearing and array.
Discreet in her replies she was alway;
Though she was wise as Pallas, and not vain,
Her speech was always womanly and plain,
No highfalutin pretty words had she
To ape deep knowledge; after her degree
She spoke, and all her words, greater and less,
Tended to virtue and to gentleness.
Modest she was, with maiden bashfulness,
Constant of heart, and full of busyness
To keep her from all idle sluggardry.
Bacchus had of her mouth no mastery;
For wine and youth help Venus to increase,
As when on fire is scattered oil or grease.
And of her virtue, free and unconstrained,
She had ofttimes some little illness feigned
In order to avoid a company
Which likely was to do some great folly,
As people do at revels and at dances,
Which are occasions when young folk take chances.
Such things but make young men and maidens be
Too ripe and bold, as everyone may see,
Which is right dangerous, as 'twas of yore.
For all too soon a virgin learns the lore
Of wantonness when she becomes a wife.
  You governesses, who in older life
Have great lords' daughters in your governance,
Take from my words no foolish petulance;
Remember you've been set to governings
Of lords' daughters for but one of two things:
Either that you have kept your honesty,
Or else that you've succumbed to your frailty,
And having learned the measures of love's dance,
Have now forsaken such ways of mischance
For evermore; therefore, for Jesus' sake,
See that you teach them virtue, nor mistake.
A poacher of the deer, who has reformed,
Left wicked ways and been by goodness warmed,
Can guard a forest best of any man.
So guard them well, for if you will you can;
Look that to no vice do you give assent,
Lest you be damned for your so vile intent;
For who does thus is traitor, that's certain.
And take good care that I speak not in vain;
Of treacheries all, the sovereign pestilence
Is when adults betray young innocence.
  You fathers and you mothers fond, also,
If you have children, be it one or two,
Yours is the burden of their wise guidance
The while they are within your governance.
Beware that not from your own lax living,
Or by your negligence in chastening

They fall and perish; for I dare well say,
If that should chance you'll dearly have to pay.
Under a shepherd soft and negligent
Full many a sheep and lamb by wolf is rent.
Suffice one instance, as I give it here,
For I must in my story persevere.
  This maid, of whom I do this praise express,
Guarded herself, nor needed governess;
For in her daily life all maids might read,
As in a book, every good word or deed
That might become a maiden virtuous;
She was so prudent and so bounteous.
From all this grew the fame on every side
Of both her beauty and her goodness wide;
Throughout that land they praised her, every one
That virtue loved; and Envy stood alone,
That sorry is when others live in weal
And for their woe will ever gladness feel.
(Doctor Augustine's are these words, I own).
  This maid, upon a day, went into town
Unto a temple, with her mother dear,
As the wont is of young maids everywhere.
  Now there was then a justice in that town
Was governor of all the region known.
And so befell, this judge his two eyes cast
Upon this maid, noting her beauty fast,
As she went by the place wherein he stood.
Swiftly his heart was altered, and his mood,
He was so caught by beauty of the maid,
And to his own dark secret heart he said:
"She shall be mine in spite of any man!"
  Anon the Fiend into his bosom ran
And taught him swiftly how, by treachery,
The maiden to his purpose might win he.
For truly not to bribery or force
Would it avail, he thought, to have recourse,
Since she had many friends, and was so good,
So strong in virtue, that he never could
By any subtle means her favour win
And make her give her body unto sin.
Therefore, and with great scheming up and down,
He sent to find a fellow of the town,
Which man, he knew, was cunning and was bold.
And unto this man, when the judge had told
His secret, then he made himself right sure
That it should come to ears of no creature,
For if it did the fellow'd lose his head.
And when assent to this crime had been said,
Glad was the judge, and then he made great cheer
And gave the fellow precious gifts and dear.
  When plotted out was their conspiracy,
From point to point, how all his lechery
Should have its will, performing craftily,
As you shall hear it now told openly,
Home went the churl, whose name was Claudius.
This false judge, who was known as Appius
(Such was his name, for this is no fable,
But an historical event I tell,
At least the gist is true, beyond a doubt)—
This false judge goes now busily about
To hasten his delight in all he may.
And so befell soon after, on a day,

That they ne perisse; for I dar wel seye,
If that they doon, ye shul it dere abeye.
Under a shepherde softe and necligent
The wolf hath many a sheep and lamb to-rent.
Suffyseth oon ensample now as here,
For I mot turne agayn to my matere.
  This mayde, of which I wol this tale expresse,
So kepte hir-self, hir neded no maistresse;
For in hir living maydens mighten rede,
As in a book, every good word or dede,
That longeth to a mayden vertuous;
She was so prudent and so bountevous.
For which the fame out-sprong on every syde
Bothe of hir beautee and hir bountee wyde;
That thurgh that land they preysed hir echone,
That loved vertu, save envye allone,
That sory is of other mennes wele,
And glad is of his sorwe and his unhele;
(The doctour maketh this descripcioun).
  This mayde up-on a day wente in the toun
Toward a temple, with hir moder dere,
As is of yonge maydens the manere.
  Now was ther thanne a justice in that toun,
That governour was of that regioun.
And so bifel, this juge his eyen caste
Up-on this mayde, avysinge him ful faste,
As she cam forby ther this juge stood.
Anon his herte chaunged and his mood,
So was he caught with beautee of this mayde;
And to him-self ful prively he sayde,
"This mayde shal be myn, for any man."
  Anon the feend in-to his herte ran,
And taughte him sodeynly, that he by slighte
The mayden to his purpos winne mighte.
For certes, by no force, ne by no mede,
Him thoughte, he was nat able for to spede;
For she was strong of freendes, and eek she
Confermed was in swich soverayn bountee,
That wel he wiste he mighte hir never winne
As for to make hir with hir body sinne.
For which, by greet deliberacioun,
He sente after a cherl, was in the toun,
Which that he knew for subtil and for bold.
This juge un-to this cherl his tale hath told
In secree wyse, and made him to ensure,
He sholde telle it to no creature,
And if he dide, he sholde lese his heed.
Whan that assented was this cursed reed,
Glad was this juge and maked him greet chere,
And yaf him yiftes preciouse and dere.
  Whan shapen was al hir conspiracye
Fro point to point, how that his lecherye
Parfourned sholde been ful subtilly,
As ye shul here it after openly,
Hoom gooth the cherl, that highte Claudius.
This false juge that highte Apius,
So was his name (for this is no fable,
But knowen for historial thing notable,
The sentence of it sooth is, out of doute),
This false juge gooth now faste aboute
To hasten his delyt al that he may.
And so bifel sone after, on a day,

This false juge, as telleth us the storie,
As he was wont, sat in his consistorie,
And yaf his domes up-on sondry cas.
This false cherl cam forth a ful greet pas,
And seyde, "lord, if that it be your wille,
As dooth me right up-on this pitous bille,
In which I pleyne up-on Virginius.
And if that he wol seyn it is nat thus,
I wol it preve, and finde good witnesse,
That sooth is that my bille wol expresse."

The juge answerde, "of this, in his absence,
I may nat yeve diffinitif sentence.
Lat do him calle, and I wol gladly here;
Thou shalt have al right, and no wrong here."

Virginius cam, to wite the juges wille,
And right anon was rad this cursed bille;
The sentence of it was as ye shul here.

"To yow, my lord, sire Apius so dere,
Sheweth your povre servant Claudius,
How that a knight, called Virginius,
Agayns the lawe, agayn al equitee,
Holdeth, expres agayn the wil of me,
My servant, which that is my thral by right,
Which fro myn hous was stole up-on a night,
Whyl that she was ful yong; this wol I preve
By witnesse, lord, so that it nat yow greve.
She nis his doghter nat, what so he seye;
Wherfore to yow, my lord the juge, I preye,
Yeld me my thral, if that it be your wille."
Lo! this was al the sentence of his bille.

Virginius gan up-on the cherl biholde,
But hastily, er he his tale tolde,
And wolde have preved it, as sholde a knight,
And eek by witnessing of many a wight,
That it was fals that seyde his adversarie,
This cursed juge wolde no-thing tarie,
Ne here a word more of Virginius,
But yaf his jugement, and seyde thus:—

"I deme anon this cherl his servant have;
Thou shalt no lenger in thyn hous hir save.
Go bring hir forth, and put hir in our warde,
The cherl shal have his thral, this I awarde."

And whan this worthy knight Virginius,
Thurgh sentence of this justice Apius,
Moste by force his dere doghter yiven
Un-to the juge, in lecherye to liven,
He gooth him hoom, and sette him in his halle,
And leet anon his dere doghter calle,
And, with a face deed as asshen colde,
Upon hir humble face he gan biholde,
With fadres pitee stiking thurgh his herte,
Al wolde he from his purpos nat converte.

"Doghter," quod he, "Virginia, by thy name,
Ther been two weyes, outher deeth or shame,
That thou most suffre; allas! that I was bore!
For never thou deservedest wherfore
To dyen with a swerd or with a knyf.
O dere doghter, ender of my lyf,
Which I have fostred up with swich plesaunce,
That thou were never out of my remembraunce!
O doghter, which that art my laste wo,
And in my lyf my laste joye also,

This false judge, as recounts the ancient story,
As he was wont, sat in his auditory
And gave his judgment upon every case.
Forthwith the wicked churl advanced a pace,
And said: "Your honour, if it be your will,
Then give me justice prayed for in this bill
Of my complaint against Virginius
And if he claim the matter stands not thus,
I will so prove, by many a good witness,
That truth is what my bill does here express."

The judge replied: "On this, in his absence,
I may not give definitive sentence.
Let him be called and I will gladly hear;
You shall have all your right, and no wrong, here."

Virginius came to learn the judge's will,
And then was read to him this wicked bill,
The substance of it being as you shall hear.

"To you, Judge Appius, may it so appear
That comes and says your servant Claudius,
How that a knight, by name Virginius,
Against the law, against all equity,
Holds, expressly against the will of me,
My servant who is slave to me by right,
Who from my house was stolen, on a night,
While yet she was but young; this will I prove,
My lord, by witness competent thereof.
She's not his child, whatever he may say;
Wherefore to you, my lord the judge, I pray,
Yield me my slave, if that it be your will."
Lo, this was all the substance of his bill.

Virginius' eyes the churl's began to hold,
But hastily, before his tale he'd told,
Ready to prove it, as befits a knight,
And by the evidence of many a wight,
That false was this charge of his adversary.
The wicked judge, he would no moment tarry,
Nor hear a word more from Virginius,
But gave his judgment then and there, as thus:

"I do decree in favour of the churl:
No longer shall you hold this servant girl.
Go bring her here and leave her as my ward.
This man shall have his slave, as my award."

And when this noble knight Virginius,
By judgment of this Justice Appius,
Must now, perforce, his darling daughter give
Unto the judge, in lechery to live,
He did go home and sat down in his hall,
And gave command his daughter there to call:
And, with a face dead white and ashen cold,
Her modest mien his eyes did then behold,
With father's pity striking through his heart,
Though from his purpose he would not depart.

"Daughter," said he, "Virginia by your name,
There are two ways, for either death or shame
You now must suffer. Ah, that I was born!
For you have not deserved to be thus lorn,
To die by means of sword or any knife.
O my dear daughter, ender of my life,
Whom I have bred up with so deep pleasance
That you were never from my remembrance!
O daughter who are now my final woe,
Aye, and in life my final joy also,

O gem of chastity, in brave patience
Receive your death, for that is my sentence.
For love and not for hate you must be dead;
My pitying hand must strike your innocent head.
Alas! That ever Appius saw you! Nay,
Thus has he falsely judged of you today."—
And told her all the case, as you before
Have heard; there is no need to tell it more.
"O mercy, my dear father," said this maid,
And with that word both of her arms she laid
About his neck, as she was wont to do;
Then broke the bitter tears from her eyes two.
She said: "O my good father, must I die?
Is there no grace? Is there no remedy?"
"No, truly, darling daughter mine," said he.
"Then give me leisure, father mine," quoth she,
"But to lament my death a little space;
For even Jephtha gave his daughter grace
To weep a little ere he slew, alas!
And God knows that in naught did she trespass,
Save that she ran to be the first to see
And welcome him with greetings, merrily."
And with that word she fell into a swoon,
And after, when the faint was past and gone,
She rose up and unto her father said:
"Praise be to God that I shall die a maid.
Give me death before I come to shame;
Do with your child your will, and in God's name!"
And then she prayed him, as he was expert,
He'd strike her swiftly, lest the blow should hurt,
Whereon again a-swooning down she fell.
Her father, with a heavy heart and will,
Struck off her head, and bore it by the hair
Straight to the judge and did present it there
While yet he sat on bench in auditory.
And when the judge saw this, so says the story,
He bade them take him out and swiftly hang.
But then a thousand people rose and sprang
To save the knight, for ruth and for pity,
For known was now the false iniquity.
The people had suspected some such thing,
By the churl's manner in his challenging,
That it was done to please this Appius;
They knew right well that he was lecherous.
Wherefore they ran this Appius upon
And cast him into prison cell anon,
Wherein he slew himself; and Claudius,
Who had been creature of this Appius,
Was sentenced to be hanged upon a tree;
But then Virginius, of his great pity,
So pleaded for him that he was exiled,
For, after all, the judge had him beguiled.
The rest were hanged, the greater and the less,
Who had been parties to this wickedness.
Here may men see how sin has its desert!
Beware, for no man knows whom God will hurt,
Nor how profoundly, no, nor in what wise
The hidden worm of conscience terrifies
The wicked soul, though secret its deeds be
And no one knows thereof but God and he.

O gemme of chastitee, in pacience
Take thou thy deeth, for this is my sentence.
For love and nat for hate, thou most be deed;
My pitous hand mot smyten of thyn heed.
Allas! that ever Apius thee say!
Thus hath he falsly juged thee to-day"—
And tolde hir al the cas, as ye bifore
Han herd; nat nedeth for to telle it more.
"O mercy, dere fader," quod this mayde,
And with that word she both hir armes layde
About his nekke, as she was wont to do:
The teres broste out of hir eyen two,
And seyde, "gode fader, shal I dye?
Is ther no grace? is ther no remedye?"
"No, certes, dere doghter myn," quod he.
"Thanne yif me leyser, fader myn," quod she,
"My deeth for to compleyne a litel space;
For pardee, Jepte yaf his doghter grace
For to compleyne, er he hir slow, allas!
And god it woot, no-thing was hir trespas,
But for she ran hir fader first to see,
To welcome him with greet solempnitee."
And with that word she fil aswowne anon,
And after, whan hir swowning is agon,
She ryseth up, and to hir fader sayde,
"Blessed be god, that I shal dye a mayde.
Yif me my deeth, er that I have a shame;
Doth with your child your wil, a goddes name!"
And with that word she preyed him ful ofte,
That with his swerd he wolde smyte softe,
And with that word aswowne down she fil.
Hir fader, with ful sorweful herte and wil,
Hir heed of smoot, and by the top if hente,
And to the juge he gan it to presente,
As he sat yet in doom in consistorie.
And whan the juge it saugh, as seith the storie,
He bad to take him and anhange him faste.
But right anon a thousand peple in thraste,
To save the knight, for routhe and for pitee,
For knowen was the false iniquitee.
The peple anon hath suspect of this thing,
By manere of the cherles chalanging,
That it was by th'assent of Apius;
They wisten wel that he was lecherous.
For which un-to this Apius they gon,
And caste him in a prison right anon,
Wher-as he slow him-self; and Claudius,
That servant was un-to this Apius,
Was demed for to hange upon a tree;
But that Virginius, of his pitee,
So preyde for him that he was exyled;
And elles, certes, he had been bigyled.
The remenant were anhanged, more and lesse,
That were consentant of this cursednesse.—
Heer men may seen how sinne hath his meryte!
Beth war, for no man woot whom god wol smyte
In no degree, ne in which maner wyse
The worm of conscience may agryse
Of wikked lyf, though it so privee be,
That no man woot ther-of but god and he.

For be he lewed man, or elles lered,
He noot how sone that he shal been afered.
Therfore I rede yow this conseil take,
Forsaketh sinne, er sinne yow forsake.

For be he ignorant or learned, yet
He cannot know when fear will make him sweat
Therefore I counsel you, this counsel take:
Forsake your sin ere sin shall you forsake.

HERE ENDETH THE PHYSICIAN'S TALE

THE WORDS OF THE HOST

THE WORDS OF THE HOST TO THE PHYSICIAN AND THE PARDONER

Our Hoste gan to swere as he were wood,
"Harrow!" quod he, "by nayles and by blood!
This was a fals cherl and a fals justyse!
As shamful deeth as herte may devyse
Come to thise juges and hir advocats!
Algate this sely mayde is slayn, allas!
Allas! to dere boghte she beautee!
Wherfore I seye al day, as men may see,
That yiftes of fortune or of nature
Ben cause of deeth to many a creature.
Hir beautee was hir deeth, I dar wel sayn;
Allas! so pitously as she was slayn!
Of bothe yiftes that I speke of now
Men han ful ofte more harm than prow.
But trewely, myn owene mayster dere,
This is a pitous tale for to here.
But natheles, passe over, is no fors;
I prey to god, so save thy gentil cors,
And eek thyne urinals and thy jordanes,
Thyn Ypocras, and eek thy Galianes,
And every boist ful of thy letuarie;
God blesse hem, and our lady seinte Marie!
So mot I theen, thou art a propre man,
And lyk a prelat, by seint Ronyan!
Seyde I nat wel? I can nat speke in terme;
But wel I woot, thou doost my herte to erme,
That I almost have caught a cardiacle.
By corpus bones! but I have triacle,
Or elles a draught of moyste and corny ale,
Or but I here anon a mery tale,
Myn herte is lost for pitee of this mayde.
Thou bel amy, thou Pardoner," he seyde,
"Tel us som mirthe or japes right anon."
"It shall be doon," quod he, "by seint Ronyon!
But first," quod he, "heer at this alestake
I wol both drinke, and eten of a cake."
But right anon thise gentils gonne to crye,
"Nay! lat him telle us of no ribaudye;
Tel us som moral thing, that we may lere
Som wit, and thanne wol we gladly here."
"I graunte, y-wis," quod he, "but I mot thinke
Up-on som honest thing, whyl that I drinke."

Our host began to swear as madman would:
"Halloo!" he cried, "now by the Nails and Blood!
This was a false churl and a false justice!
As shameful death as thinking may devise
Come to such judge who such a helper has!
And so this luckless maid is slain, alas!
Alas, too dearly paid she for beauty!
Wherefore I always say, as men may see,
That Fortune's gifts, or those of Dame Nature,
Are cause of death to many a good creature.
Her beauty was her death, I say again;
Alas, so pitiably she there was slain!
From both the kinds of gift I speak of now
Men often take more harm than help, I vow.
But truly, my own master lief and dear,
This is a very pitiful tale to hear,
Yet let us pass it by as of no force.
I pray to God to save your gentle corse,
Your urinals and all your chamberpots,
Your hippocras and medicines and tots
And every boxful of electuary;
God bless them, and Our Lady, holy Mary!
So may I prosper, you're a proper man,
And like a prelate too, by Saint Ronan!
Said I not well? I can't speak in set terms;
But well I know my heart with grief so warms
That almost I have caught a cardiac pain.
Body and Bones! Save I some remedy gain,
Or else a draught of fresh-drawn, malty ale,
Or save I hear, anon, a merry tale,
My heart is lost for pity of this maid.
You, *bon ami*, you pardoner," he said,
"Tell us some pleasant tale or jest, anon."
"It shall be done," said he, "by Saint Ronan!
But first," he said, "just here, at this ale-stake,
I will both drink and eat a bite of cake."
But then these gentle folk began to cry:
"Nay, let him tell us naught of ribaldry;
Tell us some moral thing, that we may hear
Wisdom, and then we gladly will give ear."
"I grant it, aye," said he, "but I must think
Upon some seemly tale the while I drink."

THE PROLOGUE OF THE PARDONER'S TALE

HERE FOLLOWETH THE PROLOGUE OF THE PARDONER'S TALE

Radix malorum est Cupiditas: Ad Thimotheum, sexto

"Masters," quoth he, "in churches, when I preach,
I am at pains that all shall hear my speech,
And ring it out as roundly as a bell,
For I know all by heart the thing I tell.
My theme is always one, and ever was:
'*Radix malorum est cupiditas*.'

"First I announce the place whence I have come,
And then I show my pardons, all and some.
Our liege-lord's seal on my patent perfect,
I show that first, my safety to protect,
And then no man's so bold, no priest nor clerk,
As to disturb me in Christ's holy work;
And after that my tales I marshal all.
Indulgences of pope and cardinal,
Of patriarch and bishop, these I do
Show, and in Latin speak some words, a few,
To spice therewith a bit my sermoning
And stir men to devotion, marvelling.
Then show I forth my hollow crystal-stones,
Which are crammed full of rags, aye, and of bones;
Relics are these, as they think, every one.
Then I've in latten box a shoulder bone
Which came out of a holy Hebrew's sheep.
'Good men,' say I, 'my words in memory keep;
If this bone shall be washed in any well,
Then if a cow, calf, sheep, or ox should swell
That's eaten snake, or been by serpent stung,
Take water of that well and wash its tongue,
And 'twill be well anon; and furthermore,
Of pox and scab and every other sore
Shall every sheep be healed that of this well
Drinks but one draught; take heed of what I tell.
And if the man that owns the beasts, I trow,
Shall every week, and that before cock-crow,
And before breakfast, drink thereof a draught,
As that Jew taught of yore in his priestcraft,
His beasts and all his store shall multiply.
And, good sirs, it's a cure for jealousy;
For though a man be fallen in jealous rage,
Let one make of this water his pottage
And nevermore shall he his wife mistrust,
Though he may know the truth of all her lust,
Even though she'd taken two priests, aye, or three.

"'Here is a mitten, too, that you may see.
Who puts his hand therein, I say again,
He shall have increased harvest of his grain,
After he's sown, be it of wheat or oats,
Just so he offers pence or offers groats.

"'Good men and women, one thing I warn you,
If any man be here in church right now
That's done a sin so horrible that he
Dare not, for shame, of that sin shriven be,

"Lordings," quod he, "in chirches whan I preche,
I peyne me to han an hauteyn speche,
And ringe it out as round as gooth a belle,
For I can al by rote that I telle.
My theme is alwey oon, and ever was—
'*Radix malorum est Cupiditas*.'

First I pronounce whennes that I come,
And than my bulles shewe I, alle and somme.
Our lige lordes seel on my patente,
That shewe I first, my body to warente,
That no man be so bold, ne preest ne clerk,
Me to destourbe of Cristes holy werk;
And after that than telle I forth my tales,
Bulles of popes and of cardinales,
Of patriarkes, and bishoppes I shewe;
And in Latyn I speke a wordes fewe,
To saffron with my predicacioun,
And for to stire men to devocioun.
Than shewe I forth my long cristal stones,
Y-crammed ful of cloutes and of bones;
Reliks been they, as wenen they echoon.
Than have I in latoun a sholder-boon
Which that was of an holy Jewes shepe.
'Good men,' seye I, 'tak of my wordes kepe;
If that this boon be wasshe in any welle,
If cow, or calf, or sheep, or oxe swelle
That any worm hath ete, or worm y-stonge,
Tak water of that welle, and wash his tonge,
And it is hool anon; and forthermore,
Of pokkes and of scabbe, and every sore
Shal every sheep be hool, that of this welle
Drinketh a draughte; tak kepe eek what I telle.
If that the good-man, that the bestes oweth,
Wol every wike, er that the cok him croweth,
Fastinge, drinken of this welle a draughte,
As thilke holy Jewe our eldres taughte,
His bestes and his stoor shal multiplye.
And, sirs, also it heleth jalousye;
For, though a man be falle in jalous rage,
Let maken with this water his potage,
And never shal he more his wyf mistriste,
Though he the sooth of hir defaute wiste;
Al had she taken preestes two or three.

Heer is a miteyn eek, that ye may see.
He that his hond wol putte in this miteyn,
He shal have multiplying of his greyn,
Whan he hath sowen, be it whete or otes,
So that he offre pens, or elles grotes.

Good men and wommen, o thing warne I yow,
If any wight be in this chirche now,
That hath doon sinne horrible, that he
Dar nat, for shame, of it y-shriven be,

Or any womman, be she yong or old,
That hath y-maad hir housbond cokewold,
Swich folk shul have no power ne no grace
To offren to my reliks in this place.
And who-so findeth him out of swich blame,
He wol com up and offre in goddes name,
And I assoille him by the auctoritee
Which that by bulle y-graunted was to me.'
By this gaude have I wonne, yeer by yeer,
An hundred mark sith I was Pardoner.
I stonde lyk a clerk in my pulpet,
And whan the lewed peple is doun y-set,
I preche, so as ye han herd bifore,
And telle an hundred false japes more.
Than peyne I me to strecche forth the nekke,
And est and west upon the peple I bekke,
As doth a dowve sitting on a berne.
Myn hondes and my tonge goon so yerne,
That it is joye to see my bisinesse.
Of avaryce and of swich cursednesse
Is al my preching, for to make hem free
To yeve her pens, and namely un-to me.
For my entente is nat but for to winne,
And no-thing for correccioun of sinne.
I rekke never, whan that they ben beried,
Though that her soules goon a-blakeberied!
For certes, many a predicacioun
Comth ofte tyme of yvel entencioun;
Som for plesaunce of folk and flaterye,
To been avaunced by ipocrisye,
And som for veyne glorie, and som for hate.
For, whan I dar non other weyes debate,
Than wol I stinge him with my tonge smerte
In preching, so that he shal nat asterte
To been defamed falsly, if that he
Hath trespased to my brethren or
to me.
For, though I telle noght his propre name,
Men shal wel knowe that it is the same
By signes and by othere circumstances.
Thus quyte I folk that doon us displesances;
Thus spitte I out my venim under hewe
Of holynesse, to seme holy and trewe.
But shortly myn entente I wol devyse;
I preche of no-thing but for coveityse.
Therfor my theme is yet, and ever was—
'*Radix malorum est cupiditas.*'
Thus can I preche agayn that same vyce
Which that I use, and that is avaryce.
But, though my-self be gilty in that sinne,
Yet can I maken other folk to twinne
From avaryce, and sore to repente.
But that is nat my principal entente.
I preche no-thing but for coveityse;
Of this matere it oughte y-nogh suffyse.
Than telle I hem ensamples many oon
Of olde stories, longe tyme agoon:
For lewed peple loven tales olde;
Swich thinges can they wel reporte and holde.
What? trowe ye, the whyles I may
preche,
And winne gold and silver for I teche,

Or any woman, be she young or old,
That's made her husband into a cuckold,
Such folk shall have no power and no grace
To offer to my relics in this place.
But whoso finds himself without such blame,
He will come up and offer, in God's name,
And I'll absolve him by authority
That has, by bull, been granted unto me.'
"By this fraud have I won me, year by year,
A hundred marks, since I've been pardoner.
I stand up like a scholar in pulpit,
And when the ignorant people all do sit,
I preach, as you have heard me say before,
And tell a hundred false japes, less or more.
I am at pains, then, to stretch forth my neck,
And east and west upon the folk I beck,
As does a dove that's sitting on a barn.
With hands and swift tongue, then, do I so yarn
That it's a joy to see my busyness.
Of avarice and of all such wickedness
Is all my preaching, thus to make them free
With offered pence, the which pence come to me.
For my intent is only pence to win,
And not at all for punishment of sin.
When they are dead, for all I think thereon
Their souls may well black-berrying have gone!
For, certainly, there's many a sermon grows
Ofttimes from evil purpose, as one knows;
Some for folks' pleasure and for flattery,
To be advanced by all hypocrisy,
And some for vainglory, and some for hate.
For, when I dare not otherwise debate,
Then do I sharpen well my tongue and sting
The man in sermons, and upon him fling
My lying defamations, if but he
Has wronged my brethren or—much worse—
wronged me.
For though I mention not his proper name,
Men know whom I refer to, all the same,
By signs I make and other circumstances.
Thus I pay those who do us displeasances.
Thus spit I out my venom under hue
Of holiness, to seem both good and true.
"But briefly my intention I'll express;
I preach no sermon, save for covetousness.
For that my theme is yet, and ever was,
'*Radix malorum est cupiditas.*'
Thus can I preach against that self-same vice
Which I indulge, and that is avarice.
But though myself be guilty of that sin,
Yet can I cause these other folk to win
From avarice and really to repent.
But that is not my principal intent.
I preach no sermon, save for covetousness;
This should suffice of that, though, as I guess.
"Then do I cite examples, many a one,
Out of old stories and of time long gone,
For vulgar people all love stories old;
Such things they can re-tell well and can hold.
What? Think you that because I'm good at preach-
ing
And win me gold and silver by my teaching

I'll live of my free will in poverty?
No, no, that's never been my policy!
For I will preach and beg in sundry lands;
I will not work and labour with my hands,
Nor baskets weave and try to live thereby,
Because I will not beg in vain, say I.
I will none of the apostles counterfeit;
I will have money, wool, and cheese, and wheat,
Though it be given by the poorest page,
Or by the poorest widow in village,
And though her children perish of famine.
Nay! I will drink good liquor of the vine
And have a pretty wench in every town.
But hearken, masters, to conclusion shown:
Your wish is that I tell you all a tale.
Now that I've drunk a draught of musty ale,
By God, I hope that I can tell something
That shall, in reason, be to your liking.
For though I am myself a vicious man,
Yet I would tell a moral tale, and can,
The which I'm wont to preach more gold to win.
Now hold your peace! my tale I will begin."

That I wol live in povert wilfully?
Nay, nay, I thoghte it never trewely!
For I wol preche and begge in sondry londes;
I wol not do no labour with myn hondes,
Ne make baskettes, and live therby,
Because I wol nat beggen ydelly.
I wol non of the apostles counterfete;
I wol have money, wolle, chese, and whete,
Al were it yeven of the povrest page,
Or of the povrest widwe in a village,
Al sholde hir children sterve for famyne.
Nay! I wol drinke licour of the vyne,
And have a joly wenche in every toun.
But herkneth, lordings, in conclusioun;
Your lyking is that I shal telle a tale.
Now, have I dronke a draughte of corny ale,
By god, I hope I shal yow telle a thing
That shal, by resoun, been at your lyking.
For, though myself be a ful vicious man,
A moral tale yet I yow telle can,
Which I am wont to preche, for to winne.
Now holde your pees, my tale I wol beginne."

THE PARDONER'S TALE

HERE BEGINNETH THE PARDONER'S TALE

In Flanders, once, there was a company
Of young companions given to folly,
Riot and gambling, brothels and taverns;
And, to the music of harps, lutes, gitterns,
They danced and played at dice both day and night,
And ate also and drank beyond their might,
Whereby they made the devil's sacrifice
Within that devil's temple, wicked wise,
By superfluity both vile and vain.
So damnable their oaths and so profane
That it was terrible to hear them swear;
Our Blessed Saviour's Body did they tear;
They thought the Jews had rent Him not enough;
And each of them at others' sins would laugh.
Then entered dancing-girls of ill repute,
Graceful and slim, and girls who peddled fruit,
Harpers and bawds and women selling cake,
Who do their office for the Devil's sake,
To kindle and blow the fire of lechery,
Which is so closely joined with gluttony;
I call on holy writ, now, to witness
That lust is in all wine and drunkenness.
  Lo, how the drunken Lot unnaturally
Lay with his daughters two, unwittingly;
So drunk he was he knew not what he wrought.
  Herod, as in his story's clearly taught,
When full of wine and merry at a feast,
Sitting at table idly gave behest
To slay John Baptist, who was all guiltless.
  Seneca says a good word too, doubtless;
He says there is no difference he can find
Between a man that's quite out of his mind

In Flaundres whylom was a companye
Of yonge folk, that haunteden folye,
As ryot, hasard, stewes, and tavernes,
Wher-as, with harpes, lutes, and gitернes,
They daunce and pleye at dees bothe day and night,
And ete also and drinken over hir might,
Thurgh which they doon the devel sacrifyse
With-in that develes temple, in cursed wyse,
By superfluitee abhominable;
Hir othes been so grete and so dampnable,
That it is grisly for to here hem swere;
Our blissed lordes body they to-tere;
Hem thoughte Jewes rente him noght y-nough;
And ech of hem at otheres sinne lough.
And right anon than comen tombesteres
Fetys and smale, and yonge fruytesteres,
Singers with harpes, baudes, wafereres,
Whiche been the verray develes officeres
To kindle and blowe the fyr of lecherye,
That is annexed un-to glotonye;
The holy writ take I to my witnesse,
That luxurie is in wyn and dronkenesse.
  Lo, how that dronken Loth, unkindely,
Lay by his doghtres two, unwitingly;
So dronke he was, he niste what he wroghte.
  Herodes, (who-so wel the stories soghte),
Whan he of wyn was replet at his feste,
Right at his owene table he yaf his heste
To sleen the Baptist John ful giltelees.
  Senek seith eek a good word doutelees;
He seith, he can no difference finde
Bitwix a man that is out of his minde

And a man which that is dronkelewe,
But that woodnesse, y-fallen in a shrewe,
Persevereth lenger than doth dronkenesse.
O glotonye, ful of cursednesse,
O cause first of our confusioun,
O original of our dampnacioun,
Til Crist had boght us with his blood agayn!
Lo, how dere, shortly for to sayn,
Aboght was thilke cursed vileinye;
Corrupt was al this world for glotonye!
Adam our fader, and his wyf also,
Fro Paradys to labour and to wo
Were driven for that vyce, it is no drede;
For whyl that Adam fasted, as I rede,
He was in Paradys; and whan that he
Eet of the fruyt defended on the tree,
Anon he was out-cast to wo and peyne.
O glotonye, on thee wel oghte us pleyne!
O, wiste a man how many maladyes
Folwen of excesse and of glotonyes,
He wolde been the more mesurable
Of his diete, sittinge at his table.
Allas! the shorte throte, the tendre mouth,
Maketh that, Est and West, and North and South,
In erthe, in eir, in water men to-swinke
To gete a glotoun deyntee mete and drinke!
Of this matere, o Paul, wel canstow trete,
"Mete un-to wombe, and wombe eek un-to mete,
Shal god destroyen bothe," as Paulus seith.
Allas! a foul thing is it, by my feith,
To seye this word, and fouler is the dede,
Whan man so drinketh of the whyte and rede,
That of his throte he maketh his privee,
Thurgh thilke cursed superfluitee.
The apostel weping seith ful pitously,
"Ther walken many of whiche yow told have I,
I seye it now weping with pitous voys,
[That] they been enemys of Cristes croys,
Of whiche the ende is deeth, wombe is her god."
O wombe! O bely! O stinking cod,
Fulfild of donge and of corrupcioun!
At either ende of thee foul is the soun.
How greet labour and cost is thee to finde!
Thise cokes, how they stampe, and streyne, and
grinde,
And turnen substaunce in-to accident,
To fulfille al thy likerous talent!
Out of the harde bones knokke they
The mary, for they caste noght a-wey
That may go thurgh the golet softe and swote;
Of spicerye, of leef, and bark, and rote
Shal been his sauce y-maked by delyt,
To make him yet a newer appetyt.
But certes, he that haunteth swich delyces
Is deed, whyl that he liveth in tho vyces.
A lecherous thing is wyn, and dronkenesse
Is ful of stryving and of wrecchednesse.
O dronke man, disfigured is thy face,
Sour is thy breeth, foul artow to embrace,
And thurgh thy dronke nose semeth the soun
As though thou seydest ay "Sampsoun, Samp-
soun";

And one that's drunken, save perhaps in this
That when a wretch in madness fallen is,
The state lasts longer than does drunkenness.
O gluttony, full of all wickedness,
O first cause of confusion to us all,
Beginning of damnation and our fall,
Till Christ redeemed us with His blood again!
Behold how dearly, to be brief and plain,
Was purchased this accursed villainy;
Corrupt was all this world with gluttony!
Adam our father, and his wife also,
From Paradise to labour and to woe
Were driven for that vice, no doubt; indeed
The while that Adam fasted, as I read,
He was in Paradise; but then when he
Ate of the fruit forbidden of the tree,
Anon he was cast out to woe and pain.
O gluttony, of you we may complain!
Oh! knew a man how many maladies
Follow on excess and on gluttonies,
Surely he would be then more moderate
In diet, and at table more sedate.
Alas! The throat so short, the tender mouth,
Causing that east and west and north and south,
In earth, in air, in water men shall swink
To get a glutton dainty meat and drink!
Of this same matter Paul does wisely treat:
"Meat for the belly and belly for the meat:
And both shall God destroy," as Paul does say.
Alas! A foul thing is it, by my fay,
To speak this word, and fouler is the deed,
When man so guzzles of the white and red
That of his own throat makes he his privy,
Because of this cursed superfluity.
The apostle, weeping, says most piteously:
"For many walk, of whom I've told you, aye,
Weeping I tell you once again they're dross,
For they are foes of Christ and of the Cross,
Whose end is death, whose belly is their god."
O gut! O belly! O you stinking cod,
Filled full of dung, with all corruption found!
At either end of you foul is the sound.
With how great cost and labour do they find
Your food! These cooks, they pound and strain and
grind;
Substance to accident they turn with fire,
All to fulfill your gluttonous desire!
Out of the hard and riven bones knock they
The marrow, for they throw nothing away
That may go through the gullet soft and sweet;
With spicery, with leaf, bark, root, replete
Shall be the sauces made for your delight,
To furnish you a sharper appetite.
But truly, he that such delights entice
Is dead while yet he wallows in this vice.
A lecherous thing is wine, and drunkenness
Is full of striving and of wretchedness.
O drunken man, disfigured is your face,
Sour is your breath, foul are you to embrace,
And through your drunken nose there comes a sound
As if you snored out "Samson, Samson"
round;

And yet God knows that Samson drank no wine.
You fall down just as if you were stuck swine;
Your tongue is loose, your honest care obscure;
For drunkenness is very sepulture
Of any mind a man may chance to own.
In whom strong drink has domination shown
He can no counsel keep for any dread.
Now keep you from the white and from the red,
And specially from the white wine grown at Lepe
That is for sale in Fish Street or in Cheap.
This wine of Spain, it mixes craftily
With other wines that chance to be near by,
From which there rise such fumes, as well may be,
That when a man has drunk two draughts, or three,
And thinks himself to be at home in Cheap,
He finds that he's in Spain, and right at Lepe,—
Not at Rochelle nor yet at Bordeaux town,
And then will he snore out "Samson, Samson."
 But hearken, masters, one word more I pray:
The greatest deeds of all, I'm bold to say,
Of victories in the old testament,
Through the True God, Who is omnipotent,
Were gained by abstinence and after prayer:
Look in the Bible, you may learn this there.
 Lo, Attila, the mighty conqueror,
Died in his sleep, in shame and dishonour,
And bleeding at the nose for drunkenness;
A great captain should live in soberness.
Above all this, advise yourself right well
What was commanded unto Lemuel—
Not Samuel, but Lemuel, say I—
The Bible's words you cannot well deny:
Drinking by magistrates is called a vice.
No more of this, for it may well suffice.
 And now that I have told of gluttony,
I'll take up gambling, showing you thereby
The curse of chance, and all its evils treat;
From it proceeds false swearing and deceit,
Blaspheming, murder, and—what's more—the waste
Of time and money; add to which, debased
And shamed and lost to honour quite is he,
Who once a common gambler's known to be.
And ever the higher one is of estate,
The more he's held disgraced and desolate.
And if a prince plays similar hazardry
In all his government and policy,
He loses in the estimate of men
His good repute, and finds it not again.
 Chilon, who was a wise ambassador,
Was sent to Corinth, all in great honour,
From Lacedaemon, to make alliance.
And when he came, he noticed there, by chance,
All of the greatest people of the land
Playing at hazard there on every hand.
Wherefore, and all as soon as it might be,
He stole off home again to his country,
And said: "I will not thus debase my name;
Nor will I take upon me so great shame
You to ally with common hazarders.
Send, if you will, other ambassadors;
For, by my truth, I say I'd rather die

And yet, god wot, Sampsoun drank never no wyn.
Thou fallest, as it were a stiked swyn;
Thy tonge is lost, and al thyn honest cure;
For dronkenesse is verray sepulture
Of mannes wit and his discrecioun.
In whom that drinke hath dominacioun,
He can no conseil kepe, it is no drede.
Now kepe yow fro the whyte and fro the rede,
And namely fro the whyte wyn of Lepe,
That is to selle in Fish-strete or in Chepe.
This wyn of Spayne crepeth subtilly
In othere wynes, growing fast by,
Of which ther ryseth swich fumositee,
Than whan a man hath dronken draughtes three,
And weneth that he be at hoom in Chepe,
He is in Spayne, right at the toune of Lepe,
Nat at the Rochel, ne at Burdeux toun;
And thanne wol he seye, "Sampsoun, Sampsoun."
 But herkneth, lordings, o word, I yow preye,
That alle the sovereyn actes, dar I seye,
Of victories in th'olde testament,
Thurgh verray god, that is omnipotent,
Were doon in abstinence and in preyere;
Loketh the Bible, and ther ye may it lere.
 Loke, Attila, the grete conquerour,
Deyde in his sleep, with shame and dishonour,
Bledinge ay at his nose in dronkenesse;
A capitayn shoulde live in sobrenesse.
And over al this, avyseth yow right wel
What was comaunded un-to Lamuel—
Nat Samuel, but Lamuel, seye I—
Redeth the Bible, and finde it expresly
Of wyn-yeving to hem that han justyse.
Na-more of this, for it may wel suffyse.
 And now that I have spoke of glotonye,
Now wol I yow defenden hasardrye.
Hasard is verray moder of lesinges.
And of deceite, and cursed forsweringes,
Blaspheme of Crist, manslaughtre, and wast also
Of catel and of tyme; and forthermo,
It is repreve and contrarie of honour
For to ben holde a commune hasardour.
And ever the hyër he is of estaat,
The more is he holden desolaat.
If that a prince useth hasardrye,
In alle governaunce and policye
He is, as by commune opinioun,
Y-holde the lasse in reputacioun.
 Stilbon, that was a wys embassadour,
Was sent to Corinthe, in ful greet honour,
Fro Lacidomie, to make hir alliaunce.
And whan he cam, him happede, par chaunce,
That alle the grettest that were of that lond,
Pleyinge atte hasard he hem fond.
For which, as sone as it mighte be,
He stal him hoom agayn to his contree,
And seyde, "ther wol I nat lese my name;
N' I wol nat take on me so greet defame,
Yowe for to allye un-to none hasardours.
Sendeth othere wyse embassadours;
For, by my trouthe, me were lever dye,

Than I yow sholde to hasardours allye.
For ye that been so glorious in honours
Shul nat allyen yow with hasardours
As by my wil, ne as by my tretee."
This wyse philosophre thus seyde he.
  Loke eek that, to the king Demetrius
The king of Parthes, as the book seith us,
Sente him a paire of dees of gold in scorn,
For he hadde used hasard ther-biforn;
For which he heeld his glorie or his renoun
At no value or reputacioun.
Lordes may finden other maner pley
Honeste y-nough to dryve the day awey.
  Now wol I speke of othes false and grete
A word or two, as olde bokes trete.
Gret swering is a thing abhominable,
And false swering is yet more reprevable.
The heighe god forbad swering at al,
Witnesse on Mathew; but in special
Of swering seith the holy Jeremye,
"Thou shalt seye sooth thyn othes, and nat lye,
And swere in dome, and eek in rightwisnesse";
But ydel swering is a cursednesse.
Bihold and see, that in the firste table
Of heighe goddes hestes honurable,
How that the seconde heste of his is this—
"Tak nat my name in ydel or amis."
Lo, rather he forbedeth swich swering
Than homicyde or many a cursed thing;
I seye that, as by ordre, thus it stondeth;
This knowen, that his hestes understondeth,
How that the second heste of god is that.
And forther over, I wol thee telle al plat,
That vengeance shal nat parten from his hous,
That of his othes is to outrageous.
"By goddes precious herte, and by his nayles,
And by the blode of Crist, that it is in Hayles,
Seven is my chaunce, and thyn is cink and treye;
By goddes armes, if thou falsly pleye,
This dagger shal thurgh-out thyn herte go"—
This fruyt cometh of the bicched bones two,
Forswering, ire, falsnesse, homicyde.
Now, for the love of Crist that for us dyde,
Leveth your othes, bothe grete and smale;
But, sirs, now wol I telle forth my tale.
  Thise ryotoures three, of whiche I telle,
Longe erst er pryme rong of any belle,
Were set hem in a taverne for to drinke;
And as they satte, they herde a belle clinke
Biforn a cors, was caried to his grave;
That oon of hem gan callen to his knave,
"Go bet," quod he, "and axe redily,
What cors is this that passeth heer forby;
And look that thou reporte his name wel."
  "Sir," quod this boy, "it nedeth never-a-del.
It was me told, er ye cam heer, two houres;
He was, pardee, an old felawe of youres;
And sodeynly he was y-slayn to-night,
For-dronke, as he sat on his bench upright;
Ther cam a privee theef, men clepeth Deeth,
That in this contree al the peple sleeth,
And with his spere he smoot his herte a-two,

Than you with gamblers like to them ally.
For you that are so glorious in honours
Shall never ally yourselves with hazarders
By my consent, or treaty I have made."
This wise philosopher, 'twas thus he said.
  Let us look, then, at King Demetrius.
The king of Parthia, as the book tells us,
Sent him a pair of golden dice, in scorn,
Because the name of gambler he had borne;
Wherefore he marked his reputation down
As valueless despite his wide renown.
Great lords may find sufficient other play
Seemly enough to while the time away.
  Now will I speak of oaths both false and great
A word or two, whereof the old books treat.
Great swearing is a thing abominable,
And vain oaths yet more reprehensible.
The High God did forbid swearing at all,
As witness Matthew; but in especial
Of swearing says the holy Jeremiah,
"Thou shalt not swear in vain, to be a liar,
But swear in judgment and in righteousness";
But idle swearing is a wickedness.
Behold, in the first table of the Law,
That should be honoured as High God's, sans flaw,
This second one of His commandments plain:
"Thou shalt not take the Lord God's name in vain."
Nay, sooner He forbids us such swearing
Than homicide or many a wicked thing;
I say that, as to order, thus it stands;
'Tis known by him who His will understands
That the great second law of God is that.
Moreover, I will tell you full and flat,
That retribution will not quit his house
Who in his swearing is too outrageous.
"By God's own precious heart, and by His nails,
And by the blood of Christ that's now at Hales,
Seven is my chance, and yours is five and trey!"
"By God's good arms, if you do falsely play,
This dagger through your heart I'll stick for you!"
Such is the whelping of the bitched bones two:
Perjury, anger, cheating, homicide.
Now for the love of Christ, Who for us died,
Forgo this swearing oaths, both great and small;
But, sirs, now will I tell to you my tale.
  Now these three roisterers, whereof I tell,
Long before prime was rung by any bell,
Were sitting in a tavern for to drink;
And as they sat they heard a small bell clink
Before a corpse being carried to his grave;
Whereat one of them called unto his knave:
"Go run," said he, "and ask them civilly
What corpse it is that's just now passing by,
And see that you report the man's name well."
  "Sir," said the boy, "it needs not that they tell.
I learned it, ere you came here, full two hours;
He was, by gad, an old comrade of yours;
And he was slain, all suddenly, last night,
When drunk, as he sat on his bench upright;
An unseen thief, called Death, came stalking by,
Who hereabouts makes all the people die,
And with his spear he clove his heart in two

And went his way and made no more ado.
He's slain a thousand with this pestilence;
And, master, ere you come in his presence,
It seems to me to be right necessary
To be forewarned of such an adversary:
Be ready to meet him for evermore.
My mother taught me this, I say no more."
"By holy Mary," said the innkeeper,
"The boy speaks truth, for Death has slain, this year,
A mile or more hence, in a large village,
Both man and woman, child and hind and page.
I think his habitation must be there;
To be advised of him great wisdom 'twere,
Before he did a man some dishonour."
"Yea, by God's arms!" exclaimed this roisterer,
"Is it such peril, then, this Death to meet?
I'll seek him in the road and in the street,
As I now vow to God's own noble bones!
Hear, comrades, we're of one mind, as each owns;
Let each of us hold up his hand to other
And each of us become the other's brother,
And we three will go slay this traitor Death;
He shall be slain who's stopped so many a breath,
By God's great dignity, ere it be night."
Together did these three their pledges plight
To live and die, each of them for the other,
As if he were his very own blood brother.
And up they started, drunken, in this rage,
And forth they went, and towards that village
Whereof the innkeeper had told before.
And so, with many a grisly oath, they swore
And Jesus' blessed body once more rent—
"Death shall be dead if we find where he went."
When they had gone not fully half a mile,
Just as they would have trodden over a stile,
An old man, and a poor, with them did meet.
This ancient man full meekly them did greet,
And said thus: "Now, lords, God keep you and see!"
The one that was most insolent of these three
Replied to him: "What? Churl of evil grace,
Why are you all wrapped up, except your face?
Why do you live so long in so great age?"
This ancient man looked upon his visage
And thus replied: "Because I cannot find
A man, nay, though I walked from here to Ind,
Either in town or country who'll engage
To give his youth in barter for my age;
And therefore must I keep my old age still,
As long a time as it shall be God's will.
Not even Death, alas! my life will take;
Thus restless I my wretched way must make,
And on the ground, which is my mother's gate,
I knock with my staff early, aye, and late,
And cry: 'O my dear mother, let me in!
Lo, how I'm wasted, flesh and blood and skin!
Alas! When shall my bones come to their rest?
Mother, with you fain would I change my chest,
That in my chamber so long time has been,
Aye! For a haircloth rag to wrap me in!'
But yet to me she will not show that grace,
And thus all pale and withered is my face.

And wente his wey with-outen wordes mo.
He hath a thousand slayn this pestilence:
And, maister, er ye come in his presence,
Me thinketh that it were necessarie
For to be war of swich an adversarie:
Beth redy for to mete him evermore.
Thus taughte me my dame, I sey na-more."
"By seinte Marie," seyde this taverner,
"The child seith sooth, for he hath slayn this yeer,
Henne over a myle, with-in a greet village,
Both man and womman, child and hyne, and page.
I trowe his habitacioun be there;
To been avysed greet wisdom it were,
Er that he dide a man a dishonour."
"Ye, goddes armes," quod this ryotour.
"Is it swich peril with him for to mete?
I shal him seke by wey and eek by strete,
I make avow to goddes digne bones!
Herkneth, felawes, we three been al ones;
Lat ech of us holde up his hond til other,
And ech of us bicomen otheres brother,
And we wol sleen this false traytour Deeth;
He shal be slayn, which that so many sleeth,
By goddes dignitee, er it be night."
Togidres han thise three her trouthes plight,
To live and dyen ech of hem for other,
As though he were his owene y-boren brother.
And up they sterte al dronken, in this rage,
And forth they goon towardes that village,
Of which the taverner had spoke biforn,
And many a grisly ooth than han they sworn,
And Cristes blessed body they to-rente—
"Deeth shal be deed, if that they may him hente."
Whan they han goon nat fully half a myle,
Right as they wolde han troden over a style,
An old man and a povre with hem mette.
This olde man ful mekely hem grette,
And seyde thus, "now, lordes, god yow see!"
The proudest of thise ryotoures three
Answerde agayn, "what? carl, with sory grace,
Why artow al forwrapped save thy face?
Why livestow so longe in so greet age?"
This olde man gan loke in his visage,
And seyde thus, "for I ne can nat finde
A man, though that I walked in-to Inde,
Neither in citee nor in no village,
That wolde chaunge his youthe for myn age;
And therfore moot I han myn age stille,
As longe time as it is goddes wille.
Ne deeth, allas! ne wol nat han my lyf;
Thus walke I, lyk a restelees caityf,
And on the ground, which is my modres gate,
Iknokke with my staf, bothe erly and late,
And seye, 'leve moder, leet me in!
Lo, how I vanish, flesh, and blood, and skin!
Allas! whan shul my bones been at reste?
Moder, with yow wolde I chaunge my cheste,
That in my chambre longe tyme hath be,
Ye! for an heyre clout to wrappe me!'
But yet to me she wol nat do that grace,
For which ful pale and welked is my face.

But, sires, to yow it is no curteisye
To speken to an old man vileinye,
But he trespasse in worde, or elles in dede.
In holy writ ye may your-self wel rede,
'Agayns an old man, hoor upon his heed,
Ye sholde aryse'; wherfor I yeve yow reed,
Ne dooth un-to an old man noon harm now,
Na-more than ye wolde men dide to yow
In age, if that ye so longe abyde;
And god be with yow, wher ye go or ryde.
I moot go thider as I have to go."
"Nay, olde cherl, by god, thou shalt nat so,"
Seyde this other hasardour anon;
"Thou partest nat so lightly, by seint John!
Thou spak right now of thilke traitour Deeth,
That in this contree alle our frendes sleeth.
Have heer my trouthe, as thou art his aspye,
Tel wher he is, or thou shalt it abye,
By god, and by the holy sacrament!
For soothly thou art oon of his assent,
To sleen us yonge folk, thou false theef!"
"Now, sirs," quod he, "if that yow be so leef
To finde Deeth, turne up this croked wey,
For in that grove I lafte him, by my fey,
Under a tree, and ther he wol abyde;
Nat for your boost he wol him no-thing hyde.
See ye that ook? right ther ye shul him finde.
God save yow, that boghte agayn mankinde,
And yow amende!"—thus seyde this olde man.
And everich of thise ryotoures ran,
Til he cam to that tree, and ther they founde
Of florins fyne of golde y-coyned rounde
Wel ny an eighte busshels, as hem thoughte.
No lenger thanne after Deeth they soughte,
But ech of hem so glad was of that sighte,
For that the florins been so faire and brighte,
That doun they sette hem by this precious hord.
The worste of hem he spake the firste word.
"Brethren," quod he, "tak kepe what I seye;
My wit is greet, though that I bourde and pleye.
This tresor hath fortune un-to us yiven,
In mirthe and jolitee our lyf to liven,
And lightly as it comth, so wol we spende.
Ey! goddes precious dignitee! who wende
To-day, that we sholde han so fair a grace?
But mighte this gold be caried fro this place
Hoom to myn hous, or elles un-to youres—
For wel ye woot that al this gold is oures—
Than were we in heigh felicitee.
But trewely, by daye it may nat be;
Men wolde seyn that we were theves stronge,
And for our owene tresor doon us honge.
This tresor moste y-caried be by nighte
As wysly and as slyly as it mighte.
Wherfore I rede that cut among us alle
Be drawe, and lat see wher the cut wol falle;
And he that hath the cut with herte blythe
Shal renne to the toune, and that ful swythe,
And bringe us breed and wyn ful prively.
And two of us shul kepen subtilly
This tresor wel; and, if he wol nat tarie,
Whan it is night, we wol this tresor carie

"But, sirs, in you it is no courtesy
To speak to an old man despitefully,
Unless in word he trespass or in deed.
In holy writ you may, yourselves, well read
'Before an old man, hoar upon the head,
You should arise.' Which I advise you read,
Nor to an old man any injury do
More than you would that men should do to you
In age, if you so long time shall abide;
And God be with you, whether you walk or ride.
I must pass on now where I have to go."
"Nay, ancient churl, by God it sha'n't be so,"
Cried out this other hazarder, anon;
"You sha'n't depart so easily, by Saint John!
You spoke just now of that same traitor Death,
Who in this country stops our good friends' breath
Hear my true word, since you are his own spy,
Tell where he is or you shall rue it, aye
By God and by the holy Sacrament!
Indeed you must be, with this Death, intent
To slay all us young people, you false thief."
"Now, sirs," said he, "if you're so keen, in brief,
To find out Death, turn up this crooked way,
For in that grove I left him, by my fay,
Under a tree, and there he will abide;
Nor for your boasts will he a moment hide.
See you that oak? Right there you shall him find.
God save you, Who redeemed all humankind,
And mend your ways!"—thus said this ancient man.
And every one of these three roisterers ran
Till he came to that tree; and there they found,
Of florins of fine gold, new-minted, round,
Well-nigh eight bushels full, or so they thought.
No longer, then, after this Death they sought,
But each of them so glad was of that sight,
Because the florins were so fair and bright,
That down they all sat by this precious hoard.
The worst of them was first to speak a word.
"Brothers," said he, "take heed to what I say;
My wits are keen, although I mock and play.
This treasure here Fortune to us has given
That mirth and jollity our lives may liven,
And easily as it's come, so will we spend.
Eh! By God's precious dignity! Who'd pretend,
Today, that we should have so fair a grace?
But might this gold be carried from this place
Home to my house, or if you will, to yours—
For well we know that all this gold is ours—
Then were we all in high felicity.
But certainly by day this may not be;
For men would say that we were robbers strong,
And we'd, for our own treasure, hang ere long.
This treasure must be carried home by night
All prudently and slyly, out of sight.
So I propose that cuts among us all
Be drawn, and let's see where the cut will fall;
And he that gets the short cut, blithe of heart
Shall run to town at once, and to the mart,
And fetch us bread and wine here, privately.
And two of us shall guard, right cunningly,
This treasure well; and if he does not tarry,
When it is night we'll all the treasure carry

Where, by agreement, we may think it best."
  That one of them the cuts brought in his fist
And bade them draw to see where it might fall;
And it fell on the youngest of them all;
And so, forth toward the town he went anon.
And just as soon as he had turned and gone,
That one of them spoke thus unto the other:
  "You know well that you are my own sworn brother,
So to your profit I will speak anon.
You know well how our comrade is just gone;
And here is gold, and that in great plenty,
That's to be parted here among us three.
Nevertheless, if I can shape it so
That it be parted only by us two,
Shall I not do a turn that is friendly?"
  The other said: "Well, now, how can that be?
He knows well that the gold is with us two.
What shall we say to him? What shall we do?"
  "Shall it be secret?" asked the first rogue, then,
"And I will tell you in eight words, or ten,
What we must do, and how bring it about."
  "Agreed," replied the other, "Never doubt,
That, on my word, I nothing will betray."
  "Now," said the first, "we're two, and I dare say
The two of us are stronger than is one.
Watch when he sits, and soon as that is done
Arise and make as if with him to play;
And I will thrust him through the two sides, yea,
The while you romp with him as in a game,
And with your dagger see you do the same;
And then shall all this gold divided be,
My right dear friend, just between you and me;
Then may we both our every wish fulfill
And play at dice all at our own sweet will."
And thus agreed were these two rogues, that day,
To slay the third, as you have heard me say.
  This youngest rogue who'd gone into the town,
Often in fancy rolled he up and down
The beauty of those florins new and bright.
"O Lord," thought he, "if so be that I might
Have all this treasure to myself alone,
There is no man who lives beneath the throne
Of God that should be then so merry as I."
  And at the last the Fiend, our enemy,
Put in his thought that he should poison buy
With which he might kill both his fellows; aye,
The Devil found him in such wicked state,
He had full leave his grief to consummate;
For it was utterly the man's intent
To kill them both and never to repent.
And on he strode, no longer would he tarry,
Into the town, to an apothecary,
And prayed of him that he'd prepare and sell
Some poison for his rats, and some as well
For a polecat that in his yard had lain,
The which, he said, his capons there had slain,
And fain he was to rid him, if he might,
Of vermin that thus damaged him by night.
  The apothecary said: "And you shall have
A thing of which, so God my spirit save,

By oon assent, wher-as us thinketh best."
  That oon of hem the cut broughte in his fest,
And bad hem drawe, and loke wher it wol falle;
And it fil on the yongeste of hem alle;
And forth toward the toun he wente anon.
And al-so sone as that he was gon,
That oon of hem spak thus un-to that other,
  "Thou knowest wel thou art my sworne brother,
Thy profit wol I telle thee anon.
Thou woost wel that our felawe is agon;
And heer is gold, and that ful greet plentee,
That shal departed been among us three.
But natheles, if I can shape it so
That it departed were among us two
Hadde I nat doon a freendes torn to thee?"
  That other answerde, "I noot how that may be;
He woot how that the gold is with us tweye,
What shal we doon, what shal we to him seye?"
  "Shal it be conseil?" seyde the firste shrewe,
"And I shal tellen thee, in wordes fewe,
What we shal doon, and bringe it wel aboute."
  "I graunte," quod that other, "out of doute,
That, by my trouthe, I wol thee nat biwreye."
  "Now," quod the firste, "thou woost wel we be tweye,
And two of us shul strenger be than oon.
Look whan that he is set, and right anoon
Arys, as though thou woldest with him pleye;
And I shal ryve him thurgh the sydes tweye
Whyl that thou strogelest with him as in game,
And with thy dagger look thou do the same;
And than shal al this gold departed be,
My dere freend, bitwixen me and thee;
Than may be bothe our lustes al fulfille,
And pleye at dees right at our owene wille."
And thus acorded been thise shrewes tweye
To sleen the thridde, as ye han herd me seye.
  This yongest, which that wente un-to the toun,
Ful ofte in herte he rolleth up and doun
The beautee of thise florins newe and brighte.
"O lord!" quod he, "if so were that I mighte
Have al this tresor to my-self allone,
Ther is no man that liveth under the trone
Of god, that sholde live so mery as I!"
  And atte laste the feend, our enemy,
Putte in his thought that he shold poyson beye,
With which he mighte sleen his felawes tweye;
For-why the feend fond him in swich lyvinge,
That he had leve him to sorwe bringe,
For this was outrely his fulle entente
To sleen hem bothe, and never to repente.
And forth he gooth, no lenger wolde he tarie,
Into the toun, un-to a pothecarie,
And preyed him, that he him wolde selle
Som poyson, that he mighte his rattes quelle;
And eek ther was a polcat in his hawe,
That, as he seyde, his capouns hadde y-slawe,
And fayn he wolde wreke him, if he mighte,
On vermin, that destroyed him by nighte.
  The pothecarie answerde, "and thou shalt have
A thing that, al-so god my soule save,

In al this world ther nis no creature,
That ete or dronke hath of this confiture
Noght but the mountance of a corn of whete,
That he ne shal his lyf anon forlete;
Ye, sterve he shal, and that in lasse whyle
Than thou wolt goon a paas nat but a myle;
This poyson is so strong and violent."
This cursed man hath in his hond y-hent
This poyson in a box, and sith he ran
In-to the nexte strete, un-to a man,
And borwed [of] him large botels three;
And in the two his poyson poured he;
The thridde he kepte clene for his drinke.
For al the night he shoop him for to swinke
In caryinge of the gold out of that place.
And whan this ryotour, with sory grace,
Had filled with wyn his grete botels three,
To his felawes agayn repaireth he.
What nedeth it to sermone of it more?
For right as they had cast his deeth bifore,
Right so they han him slayn, and that anon.
And whan that this was doon, thus spak that oon,
"Now lat us sitte and drinke, and make us merie,
And afterward we wol his body berie."
And with that word it happed him, par cas,
To take the botel ther the poyson was,
And drank, and yaf his felawe drinke also,
For which anon they storven bothe two.
But, certes, I suppose that Avicen
Wroot never in no canon, ne in no fen,
Mo wonder signes of empoisoning
Than hadde thise wrecches two, er hir ending.
Thus ended been thise homicydes two,
And eek the false empoysoner also.
O cursed sinne, ful of cursednesse!
O traytours homicyde, o wikkednesse!
O glotonye, luxurie, and hasardrye!
Thou blasphemour of Crist with vileinye
And othes grete, of usage and of pryde!
Allas! mankinde, how may it bityde,
That to thy creatour which that thee wroghte,
And with his precious herte-blood thee boghte,
Thou art so fals and so unkinde, allas!
Now, goode men, god forgeve yow your trespas,
And ware yow fro the sinne of avaryce.
Myn holy pardoun may yow alle waryce,
So that ye offre nobles or sterlinges,
Or elles silver broches, spones, ringes.
Boweth your heed under this holy bulle!
Cometh up, ye wyves, offreth of your wolle!
Your name I entre heer in my rolle anon;
In-to the blisse of hevene shul ye gon;
I yow assoile, by myn heigh power,
Yow that wol offre, as clene and eek as cleer
As ye were born;
and, lo, sirs, thus I preche.
And Jesu Crist, that is our soules leche,
So graunte yow his pardon to receyve;
For that is best; I wol yow nat deceyve.
But sirs, o word forgat I in my tale,
I have relikes and pardon in my male,
As faire as any man in Engelond,

In all this world there is no live creature
That's eaten or has drunk of this mixture
As much as equals but a grain of wheat,
That shall not sudden death thereafter meet;
Yea, die he shall, and in a shorter while
Than you require to walk but one short mile;
This poison is so violent and strong."
This wicked man the poison took along
With him boxed up, and then he straightway ran
Into the street adjoining, to a man,
And of him borrowed generous bottles three;
And into two his poison then poured he;
The third one he kept clean for his own drink.
For all that night he was resolved to swink
In carrying the florins from that place.
And when this roisterer, with evil grace,
Had filled with wine his mighty bottles three,
Then to his comrades forth again went he.
What is the need to tell about it more?
For just as they had planned his death before,
Just so they murdered him, and that anon.
And when the thing was done, then spoke the one:
"Now let us sit and drink and so be merry,
And afterward we will his body bury."
And as he spoke, one bottle of the three
He took wherein the poison chanced to be
And drank and gave his comrade drink also,
For which, and that anon, lay dead these two.
I feel quite sure that Doctor Avicena
Within the sections of his *Canon* never
Set down more certain signs of poisoning
Than showed these wretches two at their ending.
Thus ended these two homicides in woe;
Died thus the treacherous poisoner also.
O cursed sin, full of abominableness!
O treacherous homicide! O wickedness!
O gluttony, lechery, and hazardry!
O blasphemer of Christ with villainy,
And with great oaths, habitual for pride!
Alas! Mankind, how may this thing betide
That to thy dear Creator, Who thee wrought,
And with His precious blood salvation bought,
Thou art so false and so unkind, alas!
Now, good men, God forgive you each trespass,
And keep you from the sin of avarice.
My holy pardon cures and will suffice,
So that it brings me gold, or silver brings
Or else, I care not—brooches, spoons or rings.
Bow down your heads before this holy bull!
Come up, you wives, and offer of your wool!
Your names I'll enter on my roll, anon,
And into Heaven's bliss you'll go, each one.
For I'll absolve you, by my special power,
You that make offering, as clean this hour
As you were born.
And lo, sirs, thus I preach.
And Jesus Christ, who is our souls' great leech,
So grant you each his pardon to receive;
For that is best; I will not you deceive.
But, sirs, one word forgot I in my tale;
I've relics in my pouch that cannot fail,
As good as England ever saw, I hope,

The which I got by kindness of the pope.
If gifts your change of heart and mind reveal,
You'll get my absolution while you kneel.
Come forth, and kneel down here before, anon,
And humbly you'll receive my full pardon;
Or else receive a pardon as you wend,
All new and fresh as every mile shall end,
So that you offer me each time, anew,
More gold and silver, all good coins and true.
It is an honour to each one that's here
That you may have a competent pardoner
To give you absolution as you ride,
For all adventures that may still betide.
Perchance from horse may fall down one or two,
Breaking his neck, and it might well be you.
See what insurance, then, it is for all
That I within your fellowship did fall,
Who may absolve you, both the great and less,
When soul from body passes, as I guess.
I think our host might just as well begin,
For he is most enveloped in all sin.
Come forth, sir host, and offer first anon,
And you shall kiss the relics, every one,
Aye, for a groat! Unbuckle now your purse.
  "Nay, nay," said he, "then may I have Christ's curse!
It sha'n't be," said he, "as I've hope for riches,
Why, you would have me kissing your old breeches,
And swear they were the relics of a saint,
Though with your excrement 'twere dabbed like paint.
By cross Saint Helen found in Holy Land,
I would I had your ballocks in my hand
Instead of relics in a reliquary;
Let's cut them off, and them I'll help you carry;
They shall be shrined within a hog's fat turd."
  This pardoner, he answered not a word;
So wrathy was he no word would he say.
  "Now," said our host, "I will no longer play
With you, nor any other angry man."
  But at this point the worthy knight began,
When that he saw how all the folk did laugh:
"No more of this, for it's gone far enough;
Sir pardoner, be glad and merry here;
And you, sir host, who are to me so dear,
I pray you that you kiss the pardoner.
And, pardoner, I pray you to draw near,
And as we did before, let's laugh and play."
And then they kissed and rode forth on their way.

Whiche were me yeven by the popes hond,
If any of yow wol, of devocioun,
Offren, and han myn absolucioun,
Cometh forth anon, and kneleth heer adoun,
And mekely receyveth my pardoun:
Or elles, taketh pardon as ye wende,
Al newe and fresh, at every tounes ende,
So that ye offren alwey newe and newe
Nobles and pens, which that be gode and trewe.
It is an honour to everich that is heer,
That ye mowe have a suffisant pardoneer
T'assoille yow, in contree as ye ryde,
For aventures which that may bityde.
Peraventure ther may falle oon or two
Doun of his hors, and breke his nekke atwo.
Look which a seuretee is it to yow alle
That I am in your felaweship y-falle,
That may assoille yow, bothe more and lasse,
Whan that the soule shal fro the body passe.
I rede that our hoste heer shal biginne,
For he is most envoluped in sinne.
Com forth, sir hoste, and offre first anon,
And thou shalt kisse the reliks everichon,
Ye, for a grote! unbokel anon thy purs.
  "Nay, nay," quod he, "than have I Cristes curs!
Lat be," quod he, "it shal nat be, so thee'ch!
Thou woldest make me kisse thyn old breech,
And swere it were a relik of a seint,
Thogh it were with thy fundement depeint!
But by the croys which that seint Eleyne fond,
I wolde I hadde thy coillons in myn hond
In stede of relikes or of seintuarie;
Lat cutte hem of, I wol thee helpe hem carie;
They shul be shryned in an hogges tord."
  This pardoner answerde nat a word;
So wrooth he was, no word ne wolde he seye.
  "Now," quod our host, "I wol no lenger pleye
With thee, ne with noon other angry man."
  But right anon the worthy Knight bigan,
Whan that he saugh that al the peple lough,
"Na-more of this, for it is right y-nough;
Sir Pardoner, be glad and mery of chere;
And ye, sir host, that been to me so dere,
I prey yow that ye kisse the Pardoner.
And Pardoner, I prey thee, drawe thee neer,
And, as we diden, lat us laughe and pleye."
Anon they kiste, and riden forth hir weye.

HERE IS ENDED THE PARDONER'S TALE

THE SHIPMAN'S PROLOGUE

HERE BEGINNETH THE SHIPMAN'S PROLOGUE

OUR host upon his stirrups stood, anon,
And said: "Good men, now hearken, every one;
This was a useful story, for the nonce!
Sir parish priest," quoth he, "for God His bones.
Tell us a tale, as you agreed before.

OUR hoste up-on his stiropes stood anon,
And seyde, "good men, herkneth everich on;
This was a thrifty tale for the nones!
Sir parish prest," quod he, "for goddes bones,
Tel us a tale, as was thy forward yore.

I see wel that ye lerned men in lore
Can moche good, by goddes dignitee!"
  The Persone him answerde, "*ben'cite!*
What eyleth the man, so sinfully to swere?"
  Our hoste answerde, "O Jankin, be ye there?
I smelle a loller in the wind," quod he.
"How! good men," quod our hoste, "herkneth me;
Abydeth, for goddes digne passioun,
For we shal han a predicacioun;
This loller heer wil prechen us som-what."
  "Nay, by my fader soule! that shal be nat,"
Seyde the Shipman; "heer he shal nat preche,
He shal no gospel glosen heer ne teche.
We leve alle in the grete god," quod he,
"He wolde sowen som difficultee,
Or springen cokkel in our clene corn;
And therfor, hoste, I warne thee biforn,
My joly body shal a tale telle,
And I shal clinken yow so mery a belle,
That I shal waken al this companye;
But it shal nat ben of philosophye,
Ne *physices*, ne termes queinte of lawe;
Ther is but litel Latin in my mawe."

I see well that you learned men of lore
Have learned much good, by God's great dignity!"
  The parson answered: "*Benedicite!*
What ails the man, so sinfully to swear?"
  Our host replied: "Ho, Jenkin, are you there?
I smell a Lollard in the wind," quoth he.
"Ho, good men!" said our host, "now hearken me;
Wait but a bit, for God's high passion do,
For we shall have a sermon ere we're through;
This Lollard here will preach to us somewhat."
  "Nay, by my father's soul, that shall he not!"
Replied the sailor; "Here he shall not preach,
Nor comment on the gospels here, nor teach.
We all believe in the great God," said he,
"But he would sow among us difficulty,
Or sprinkle cockles in our good clean corn;
And therefore, host, beforehand now, I warn
My jolly body shall a story tell
And I will clink for you so merry a bell
That it shall waken all this company;
But it shall not be of philosophy,
Nor yet of physics, nor quaint terms of law;
There is but little Latin in my maw."

HERE ENDETH THE SHIPMAN HIS PROLOGUE

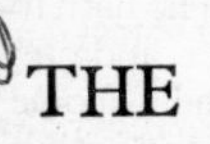

THE SHIPMAN'S TALE

HERE BEGINNETH THE SHIPMAN'S TALE

A MARCHANT whylom dwelled at Seint Denys,
That riche was, for which men helde him wys;
A wyf he hadde of excellent beautee,
And compaignable and revelous was she,
Which is a thing that causeth more dispence
Than worth is al the chere and reverence
That men hem doon at festes and at daunces;
Swiche salutaciouns and contenaunces
Passen as dooth a shadwe up-on the wal.
But wo is him that payen moot for al;
The sely housbond, algate he mot paye;
He moot us clothe, and he moot us arraye,
Al for his owene worship richely,
In which array we daunce jolily.
And if that he noght may, par-aventure,
Or elles, list no swich dispence endure,
But thinketh it is wasted and y-lost,
Than moot another payen for our cost,
Or lene us gold, and that is perilous.
  This noble Marchant heeld a worthy hous,
For which he hadde alday so greet repair
For his largesse, and for his wyf was fair,
That wonder is; but herkneth to my tale.
Amonges alle his gestes, grete and smale,
Ther was a monk, a fair man and a bold,
I trowe of thritty winter he was old,
That ever in oon was drawing to that place.
This yonge monk, that was so fair of face,
Aqueinted was so with the gode man,
Sith that hir firste knoweliche bigan,

A MERCHANT, dwelling, once, at Saint-Denis,
Was rich, for which men held him wise, and he
Had got a wife of excellent beauty,
And very sociable and gay was she,
Which is a thing that causes more expense
Than all the good cheer and the deference
That men observe at festivals and dances;
Such salutations and masked countenances
Pass by as does a shadow on the wall;
But woe to him that must pay for it all.
The foolish husband, always he must pay;
He must buy clothes and other fine array,
And all for his own worship, wealthily,
In which, indeed, women dance jollily.
And if he cannot thus, peradventure,
Or cares not such expenses to endure,
But thinks his money wasted or quite lost,
Why then another man must pay the cost,
Or else lend gold, and that is dangerous.
  This noble merchant had a worthy house,
To which, each day, so many did repair,
Since he was generous and his wife was fair,
'Twas to be wondered at; but hear my tale.
Among his many guests of great and small
There was a monk, a handsome man and bold,
I think that he was thirty winters old,
Who was for ever coming to that place.
This youthful monk, who was so fair of face,
Was so far intimate with the worthy man,
And had been since their friendship first began,

That in the house familiar was he
As it is possible for friend to be.
And in as much as this same goodly man
And too, this monk of whom I first began,
Were both born in the village they'd lived in,
The monk claimed him for cousin, or such kin;
And he again, he never said him nay,
But was as glad thereof as bird of day;
For to his heart it was a great pleasance.
Thus they were knit by endless alliance,
And each of them did other one assure
Of brotherhood the while their lives endure.
Free was Dan John with money and expense
When in that house; and full of diligence
To please all there, whatever be his age.
He ne'er forgot to tip the humblest page
In all that house; according to degree
He gave the master, then the company,
Whene'er he came, some kind of honest thing;
For which they were as glad of his coming
As bird is glad when the new sun up-rises.
No more of all this now, for it suffices.
It so befell, this merchant, on a day,
Prepared to make all ready his array,
Since to the town of Bruges he was to fare
To purchase there a quantity of ware;
To which end he'd to Paris sent someone
With messages, and he had prayed Dan John
That he should come to Saint-Denis to pay
Him and his wife a visit for a day,
Said 'twas a thing he certainly must do.
This noble monk, whereof I'm telling you,
Had from his abbot, when he wished, license,
Because he was a man of great prudence,
An officer, indeed, who out did ride
To see to barns and granges, far and wide;
And now to Saint-Denis he came anon.
Who was so welcome as my lord Dan John,
Our cousin dear, so full of courtesy?
With him he brought a jug of rare malmsey,
And still another full of fine vernage,[1]
And wild fowls, too, as was his long usage.
And so I let them eat and drink and play,
This monk and merchant, for a night and day.
Upon the third day this good trader rises,
And on his needs discreetly he advises;
And up into his counting-house goes he
To reckon up his books, as well may be,
For the past year, to learn how matters stood
And what he'd spent, and whether it were good,
And whether he were wealthier than before.
His books and bags, all that he had in store,
He put before him on his counting-board;
He was right rich in goods and rich in hoard,
For the which cause he bolted fast his door;
He'd have no one disturb him while before
Him stood his books and monies at that time;
And thus he sat till it was well past prime.
Dan John had risen with the dawn, also,
And in the garden wandered to and fro,
Having said all his prayers full reverently.

That in his hous a famulier was he
As it possible is any freend to be.
And for as muchel as this gode man
And eek this monk, of which that I bigan,
Were bothe two y-born in o village,
The monk him claimeth as for cosinage;
And he again, he seith nat ones nay,
But was as glad ther-of as fowel of day;
For to his herte it was a greet plesaunce.
Thus been they knit with eterne alliaunce,
And ech of hem gan other for t'assure
Of bretherhede, whyl that hir lyf may dure.
Free was daun John, and namely of dispence,
As in that hous; and ful of diligence
To doon plesaunce, and also greet costage.
He noght forgat to yeve the leeste page
In al that hous; but, after hir degree,
He yaf the lord, and sitthe al his meynee,
When that he cam, som maner honest thing;
For which they were as glad of his coming
As fowel is fayn, whan that the sonne up-ryseth.
Na more of this as now, for it suffyseth.
But so bifel, this marchant on a day
Shoop him to make redy his array
Toward the toun of Brugges for to fare,
To byën ther a porcioun of ware;
For which he hath to Paris sent anon
A messager, and preyed hath daun John
That he sholde come to Seint Denys to pleye
With him and with his wyf a day or tweye,
Er he to Brugges wente, in alle wyse.
This noble monk, of which I yow devyse,
Hath of his abbot, as him list, licence,
By-cause he was a man of heigh prudence,
And eek an officer, our for to ryde,
To seen hir graunges and hir bernes wyde;
And un-to Seint Denys he comth anon.
Who was so welcome as my lord daun John,
Our dere cosin, ful of curteisye?
With him broghte he a jubbe of Malvesye,
And eek another, ful of fyn Vernage,[1]
And volatyl, as ay was his usage.
And thus I lete hem ete and drinke and pleye,
This marchant and this monk, a day or tweye.
The thridde day, this marchant up aryseth,
And on his nedes sadly him avyseth,
And up in-to his contour-hous goth he
To rekene with him-self, as wel may be,
Of thilke yeer, how that it with him stood,
And how that he despended hadde his good;
And if that he encressed were or noon.
His bokes and his bagges many oon
He leith biforn him on his counting-bord;
Ful riche was his tresor and his hord,
For which ful faste his countour-dore he shette;
And eek he nolde that no man sholde him lette
Of his accountes, for the mene tyme;
And thus he sit til it was passed pryme.
Daun John was risen in the morwe also,
And in the gardin walketh to and fro,
And hath his thinges seyd ful curteisly.

[1]An old wine of Italy.

This gode wyf cam walking prively
In-to the gardin, ther he walketh softe,
And him saleweth, as she hath don ofte.
A mayde child cam in hir companye,
Which as hir list she may governe and gye,
For yet under the yerde was the mayde.
"O dere cosin myn, daun John," she sayde,
"What eyleth yow so rathe for to ryse?"
"Nece," quod he, "it oghte y-nough suffyse
Fyve houres for to slepe up-on a night,
But it were for an old appalled wight,
As been thise wedded men, that lye and dare
As in a forme sit a wery hare,
Were al for-straught with houndes grete and
smale.
But dere nece, why be ye so pale?
I trowe certes that our gode man
Hath yow laboured sith the night bigan,
That yow were nede to resten hastily?"
And with that word he lough ful merily,
And of his owene thought he wex al reed.
This faire wyf gan for to shake hir heed,
And seyde thus, "ye, god wot al," quod she;
"Nay, cosin myn, it stant nat so with me.
For, by that god that yaf me soule and lyf,
In al the reme of France is ther no wyf
That lasse lust hath to that sory pley.
For I may singe 'allas' and 'weylawey,
That I was born,' but to no wight," quod she,
"Dar I nat telle how that it stant with me.
Wherfore I thinke out of this land to wende,
Or elles of my-self to make an ende,
So ful am I of drede and eek of care."
This monk bigan up-on this wyf to stare,
And seyde, "allas, my nece, god forbede
That ye, for any sorwe or any drede,
Fordo your-self; but telleth me your grief;
Paraventure I may, in your meschief,
Conseille or helpe, and therfore telleth me
Al your anoy, for it shal been secree;
For on my porthors here I make an ooth,
That never in my lyf, for lief ne looth,
Ne shal I of no conseil yow biwreye."
"The same agayn to yow," quod she, "I seye;
By god and by this porthors, I yow swere,
Though men me wolde al in-to peces tere,
Ne shal I never, for to goon to helle,
Biwreye a word of thing that ye me telle,
Nat for no cosinage ne alliance,
But verraily, for love and affiance."
Thus been they sworn, and heer-upon they kiste,
And ech of hem tolde other what hem liste.
"Cosin," quod she, "if that I hadde a space,
As I have noon, and namely in this place,
Than wolde I telle a legende of my lyf,
What I have suffred sith I was a wyf
With myn housbonde, al be he your cosyn."
"Nay," quod this monk, "by god and seint
Martyn,
He is na more cosin un-to me
Than is this leef that hangeth on the tree!
I clepe him so, by Seint Denys of Fraunce,

Then came this goodwife, walking secretly
Into the garden, walking slow and soft.
And kissed him in salute, as she'd done oft.
A little girl came walking at her side,
Was in her charge to govern and to guide,
For yet beneath the rod was this small maid.
"O my dear cousin, O Dan John," she said,
"What ails you that so early you arise?"
"Dear niece," said he, "surely it should suffice
To sleep for five full hours of any night,
Unless 'twere for some old and languid wight,
As are these married men, who doze and dare
About as in the form the weary hare,
Worn all distraught by hounds both great and
small.
But, my dear niece, just why are you so pale?
I must suppose of course that our good man
Has you belaboured since the night began,
And you were forced to sleep but scantily."
And with that word he laughed right merrily,
And, what of his own thoughts, he blushed all red.
This pretty wife began to shake her head,
And answered thus: "Aye, God knows all!" said she:
"Nay, cousin mine, it stands not so with me.
For by that God Who gave me soul and life,
In all the realm of France there is no wife
Who has less lust for that some sorry play.
For I may sing 'Alas!' and 'Welaway
That I was born!' but to no man," said she,
"Dare I to tell how this thing stands with me.
Wherefore I'm thinking from this land to wend,
Or else of my own life to make an end,
I am so fearful and so full of care."
This monk began, then, at the wife to stare,
And said: "Alas, my niece, may God forbid
That you, for any care or fear morbid,
Destroy yourself! But tell me of your grief;
Perhaps I may, whatever the mischief,
Counsel or help, and therefore do tell me
All the annoyance, for 'twill secret be;
For on my breviary I make oath
That never in my life, though lief or loath,
Shall I your secret whisper or betray."
"The same to you again," said she, "I say;
By God and by this breviary, I swear,
Though men this body of mine a-pieces tear,
No I will never, though I go to Hell,
Betray a single word that you may tell,
And this, not for our kinship and alliance,
But verily for love and true reliance."
Thus are they sworn, and thereupon they kissed,
And each told other such things as they list.
"Cousin," said she, "if I had time and space,
As I have not, and specially in this place,
Then would I tell a legend of my life,
What I have suffered since I've been a wife,
From my husband, though he is your cousin."
"Nay," quoth the monk, "by God and Saint
Martin,
He is no more a cousin unto me
Than is this leaf a-hanging on the tree!
I call him so, by Saint-Denis of France,

To have but better reason to advance
With you, whom I have loved especially
Above all other women, and truly;
I swear this to you on the faith I own.
Tell me your grief before your man comes down,
Come, hasten now, and go your way anon."
"My dearest love," said she, "O my Dan John,
Right glad I were this counsel for to hide,
But it must out, I can't it more abide.
To me my husband is the poorest man
That ever was, since first the world began.
But since I am a wife, becomes not me
To tell a living soul our privity,
Either abed or in some other place;
God guard that I should tell it, of His grace!
For wife must never talk of her husband,
Save to his honour, as I understand.
But now to you thus much I can and shall:
So help me God, he is not worth, at all,
In any wise, the value of a fly.
But yet this grieves me most—he's niggardly;
And well you know that women naturally
Desire six things, and even so do I.
For women all would have their husbands be
Hardy, and wise, and rich, and therewith free,
Obedient to the wife, and fresh in bed.
But by that very Lord Who for us bled,
Though in his honour, myself to array
On Sunday next, I must yet go and pay
A hundred francs, or else be but forlorn.
Yet would I rather never have been born
Than have a scandal or disgrace, say I.
And if my husband such a thing should spy,
I were but lost, and therefore do I pray,
Lend me this sum, or else I perish, yea!
Dan John, I say, lend me these hundred francs;
By gad, I will not fail to give you thanks,
If only you will do the thing I pray.
For on a certain day I will repay,
And give to you what pleasure and service
I can give, aye, just as you may devise.
And if I don't, God take on me vengeance
As foul as once on Ganelon of France!"
This gentle monk replied as you shall hear:
"Now truthfully, my own sweet lady dear,
I have," said he, "on you so great a ruth
That I do swear and promise you, in truth,
That when your husband goes to Flanders there,
I will deliver you from all this care;
For I will bring to you a hundred francs."
And with that word he caught her by the flanks
And hugged her to him hard and kissed her oft.
"Go now your way," he said, "all still and soft,
And let us dine as soon as ever we may,
For by my dial it's the prime of day.
Go now, and be as true as I shall be."
"Now all else God forbid, sir," then said she.
And in she went as jolly as a pie,
And bade the cooks that they to kitchen hie,
So that her men might dine, and that anon.

To have the more cause of aqueintaunce
Of yow, which I have loved specially
Aboven alle wommen sikerly;
This swere I yow on my professioun.
Telleth your grief, lest that he come adoun,
And hasteth yow, and gooth your wey anon."
"My dere love," quod she, "o my daun John,
Ful lief were me this conseil for to hyde,
But out it moot, I may namore abyde.
Myn housbond is to me the worste man
That ever was, sith that the world bigan.
But sith I am a wyf, it sit nat me
To tellen no wight of our privetee,
Neither a-bedde, ne in non other place;
God shilde I sholde it tellen, for his grace!
A wyf ne shal nat seyn of hir housbonde
But al honour, as I can understonde;
Save un-to yow thus muche I tellen shal;
As help me god, he is noght worth at al
In no degree the value of a flye.
But yet me greveth most his nigardye;
And wel ye woot that wommen naturelly
Desyren thinges sixe, as wel as I.
They wolde that hir housbondes sholde be
Hardy, and wyse, and riche, and ther-to free,
And buxom to his wyf, and fresh a-bedde.
But, by that ilke lord that for us bledde,
For his honour, my-self for to arraye,
A Sonday next, I moste nedes paye
An hundred frankes, or elles am I lorn.
Yet were me lever that I were unborn
Than me were doon a sclaundre or vileinye;
And if myn housbond eek it mighte espye,
I nere but lost, and therfore I yow preye
Lene me this somme, or elles moot I deye.
Daun John, I seye, lene me this hundred frankes;
Pardee, I wol nat faille yow my thankes,
If that yow list to doon that I yow praye.
For at a certein day I wol yow paye,
And doon to yow what plesance and servyce
That I may doon, right as yow list devyse.
And but I do, god take on me vengeance
As foul as ever had Geniloun of France!"
This gentil monk answerde in this manere;
"Now, trewely, myn owene lady dere,
I have," quod he, "on yow so greet a routhe,
That I yow swere and plighte yow my trouthe,
That whan your housbond is to Flaundres fare,
I wol delivere yow out of this care;
For I wol bringe yow an hundred frankes."
And with that word he caughte hir by the flankes,
And hir embraceth harde, and kiste hir ofte.
"Goth now your wey," quod he, "al stille and softe,
And lat us dyne as sone as that ye may;
For by my chilindre it is pryme of day.
Goth now, and beeth as trewe as I shal be."
"Now, elles god forbede, sire," quod she,
And forth she gooth, as jolif as a pye,
And bad the cokes that they sholde hem hye,
So that men mighte dyne, and that anon.

Up to hir housbonde is this wyf y-gon,
And knokketh at his countour boldely.
"*Qui la?*" quod he.
"Peter![1] it am I,"
Quod she, "what, sire, how longe wol ye faste?
How longe tyme wol ye rekene and caste
Your sommes, and your bokes, and your thinges?
The devel have part of alle swiche rekeninges!
Ye have y-nough, pardee, of goddes sonde;
Com doun to-day, and lat your bagges stonde.
Ne be ye nat ashamed that daun John
Shal fasting al this day elenge goon?
What! lat us here a messe, and go we dyne."
"Wyf," quod this man, "litel canstow devyne
The curious bisinesse that we have.
For of us chapmen, al-so god me save,
And by that lord that cleped is Seint Yve,
Scarsly amonges twelve ten shul thryve,
Continuelly, lastinge un-to our age.
We may wel make chere and good visage,
And dryve forth the world as it may be,
And kepen our estaat in privetee,
Til we be deed, or elles that we pleye
A pilgrimage, or goon out of the weye.
And therfor have I greet necessitee
Up-on this queinte world t'avyse me;
For evermore we mote stonde in drede
Of hap and fortune in our chapmanhede.
To Flaundres wol I go to-morwe at day,
And come agayn, as sone as ever I may.
For which, my dere wyf, I thee biseke,
As be to every wight buxom and meke,
And for to kepe our good be curious,
And honestly governe wel our hous.
Thou hast y-nough, in every maner wyse,
That to a thrifty houshold may suffyse.
Thee lakketh noon array ne no vitaille,
Of silver in thy purs shaltow nat faille."
And with that word his countour-dore he shette,
And doun he gooth, no lenger wolde he lette,
But hastily a messe was ther seyd,
And spedily the tables were y-leyd,
And to the diner faste they hem spedde;
And richely this monk the chapman fedde.
At-after diner daun John sobrely
This chapman took a-part, and prively
He seyde him thus, "cosyn, it standeth so,
That wel I see to Brugges wol ye go.
God and seint Austin spede yow and gyde!
I prey yow, cosin, wysly that ye ryde;
Governeth yow also of your diete
Atemprely, and namely in this hete.
Bitwix us two nedeth no strange fare;
Fare-wel, cosyn; god shilde yow fro care.
If any thing ther be by day or night,
If it lye in my power and my might,
That ye me wol comande in any wyse,
It shal be doon, right as ye wol devyse.
O thing, er that ye goon, if it may be,
I wolde prey yow; for to lene me
An hundred frankes, for a wyke or tweye,

Up to her husband is this wife then gone,
And knocked upon his counting-room boldy.
"*Qui est là?*" asked he.
"Peter![1] It is I,"
Said she; "What, sir, and how long will you fast?
How long time will you reckon up and cast
Your sums and books and other tiresome things?
The devil take away such reckonings!
You have enough, by gad, of God's mercy;
Come down today, and let your gold-bags be.
Why, are you not ashamed that our Dan John
Has fasted miserably all morning gone?
What! Let us hear a Mass and then go dine."
"Wife," said this man, "little can you divine
The curious businesses that merchants have.
As for us traders, as may God me save,
And by that lord that all we call Saint Yve,
Among twelve merchants scarcely two shall thrive
Continually, and lasting into age.
We must keep open house and blithe visage,
While goes the world as it may chance to be,
And hold all our affairs in secrecy
Till we are dead; or else we must go play
At pilgrimage, or else go clean away.
And therefore have I great necessity
That on this curious world advised I be;
For evermore we merchants stand in dread
Of chance and mishap as our ways we tread.
"To Flanders go I at the break of day,
And I'll come back as soon as ever I may.
For which, my dearest wife, your aid I seek
To be, to all, both courteous and meek,
And to maintain our wealth be studious,
And govern honourably and well our house.
You have enough in every sort of wise
That, to a thrifty household, should suffice.
You've clothes and food, I've seen to each detail,
And silver in your purse shall never fail."
And with that word his counting-door he shut
And down he went, no longer tarrying, but
Right hastily a Mass for them was said,
And speedily the tables there were spread,
And to the dinner swiftly all they sped;
And richly then the monk this merchant fed.
After the dinner Dan John soberly
This merchant took aside, and privately
He said to him, "Cousin, it stands just so,
For I see well that you to Bruges will go.
God and good Saint Augustine speed and guide!
I pray you, cousin, that you'll wisely ride;
Guard your health well, and govern your diet
Temperately, especially in this heat.
Neither of us requires outlandish fare;
Farewell, dear cousin; God shield you from care.
If anything there be, by day or night,
If it lie in my power and my might,
That you would have me do, in any wise,
It shall be done, just as you may devise.
"One thing, before you go, if it may be,
I pray you do, and that is, to lend me
A hundred francs, for but a week or two,

[1]That is, Saint Peter.

For certain cattle I must buy, to do
The stocking of a little place of ours.
So help me God, I would that it were yours!
I will not fail you, come next settling day,
Not for a thousand francs, a mile away.
But let this thing be secret, pray, for I,
Even tonight, must go these beasts to buy;
And farewell now, my own good cousin dear.
And many thanks for entertainment here."
This noble merchant, civilly, anon,
Answered and said: "O cousin mine, Dan John,
Now surely this is but a small request;
My gold is yours and aye at your behest.
And not gold only, no but all my ware;
Take what you like, God shield that you should spare.
"There's but one thing, which you know well enow
Of traders, for their money is their plow.
We may on credit trade, while we've a name,
But to be goldless is to lose the game.
Pay it again when you are at your ease;
In all I can, full fain am I to please."
These hundred francs he went and got anon,
And privately he gave them to Dan John.
No one in all the world knew of this loan,
Saving this merchant and Dan John alone.
They drink and talk, and walk awhile, and play,
Until Dan John sets out for his abbey.
The morrow came and forth this merchant rides
Toward Flanders; and his apprentice guides
Until he came to Bruges all happily.
Now went this merchant fast and busily
About his trade, and bought, and borrowed gold;
He neither played at dice nor danced, I'm told,
But like a merchant, briefly here to tell,
He led his life, and there I let him dwell.
On the first Sunday after he was gone,
To Saint-Denis is come again Dan John,
With face and tonsure shining from a shave.
In all the house was not so small a knave,
Nor any other, but was right glad, then,
Because my lord Dan John was come again.
And coming briefly to the point, anon
This lovely wife agreed with her Dan John
That for these hundred francs he should, all night,
Have her within his arms and bolt upright;
And this agreement was performed in bed.
In mirth all night a busy life they led
Till it was dawn, when Dan John went his way,
Bidding the household "Farewell!" and "Good-day!"
For none of them, nor any in the town,
Had of Dan John the least suspicion shown.
So forth he rode, home to his own abbey,
Or where he wished; no more of him I say.
This merchant, when all ended was the fair,
To Saint-Denis made ready to repair;
And with his wife he feasted and made cheer,
And told her that, since goods were very dear,
He needs must get more cash at his command,

For certein beestes that I moste beye,
To store with a place that is oures.
God help me so, I wolde it were youres!
I shal nat faille surely of my day,
Nat for a thousand frankes, a myle-way.
But lat this thing be secree, I yow preye,
For yet to-night thise beestes moot I beye;
And fare-now wel, myn owene cosin dere,
Graunt mercy of your cost and of your chere."
This noble marchant gentilly anon
Answerde, and seyde, "o cosin myn, daun John,
Now sikerly this is a smal requeste;
My gold is youres, whan that it yow leste.
And nat only my gold, but my chaffare;
Take what yow list, god shilde that ye spare.
But o thing is, ye knowe it wel y-nogh,
Of chapmen, that hir moneye is hir plogh.
We may creaunce whyl we have a name,
But goldlees for to be, it is no game.
Paye it agayn whan it lyth in your ese;
After my might ful fayn wolde I yow plese."
Thise hundred frankes he fette forth anon,
And prively he took hem to daun John.
No wight in al this world wiste of this lone,
Savinge this marchant and daun John allone.
They drinke, and speke, and rome a whyle and pleye,
Til that daun John rydeth to his abbeye.
The morwe cam, and forth this marchant rydeth
To Flaundres-ward; his prentis wel him gydeth,
Til he cam in-to Brugges merily.
Now gooth this marchant faste and bisily
Aboute his nede, and byeth and creaunceth.
He neither pleyeth at the dees ne daunceth;
But as a marchant, shortly for to telle,
He let his lyf, and there I lete him dwelle.
The Sonday next this Marchant was agon,
To Seint Denys y-comen is daun John,
With crowne and berd all fresh and newe y-shave.
In al the hous ther nas so litel a knave,
Ne wo wight elles, that he nas ful fayn,
For that my lord daun John was come agayn.
And shortly to the point right for to gon,
This faire wyf accorded with daun John,
That for thise hundred frankes he sholde al night
Have hir in his armes bolt-upright;
And this acord parfourned was in dede.
In mirthe al night a bisy lyf they lede
Til it was day, that daun John wente his way,
And bad the meynee "fare-wel, have good day!"
For noon of hem, ne no wight in the toun,
Hath of daun John right no suspecioun.
And forth he rydeth hoom to his abbeye,
Or where him list; namore of him I seye.
This marchant, whan that ended was the faire,
To Seint Denys he gan for to repaire,
And with his wyf he maketh feste and chere,
And telleth hir that chaffare is so dere,
That nedes moste he make a chevisaunce.

For he was bounde in a reconissaunce
To paye twenty thousand sheeld anon.
For which this marchant is to Paris gon,
To borwe of certein frendes that he hadde
A certein frankes; and somme with him he ladde.
And whan that he was come in-to the toun,
For greet chertee and greet affeccioun,
Un-to daun John he gooth him first, to pleye;
Nat for to axe or borwe of him moneye,
But for to wite and seen of his welfare,
And for to tellen him of his chaffare,
As freendes doon whan they ben met y-fere.
Daun John him maketh feste and mery chere;
And he him tolde agayn ful specially,
How he hadde wel y-boght and graciously,
Thanked be god, al hool his marchandyse.
Save that he moste, in alle maner wyse,
Maken a chevisaunce, as for his beste,
And thanne he sholde been in joye and reste.
Daun John answerde, "certes, I am fayn
That ye in hele ar comen hoom agayn.
And if that I were riche, as have I blisse,
Of twenty thousand sheeld shold ye nat misse,
For ye so kindely this other day
Lente me gold; and as I can and may,
I thanke yow, by god and by seint Jame!
But nathelees I took un-to our dame,
Your wyf at hoom, the same gold ageyn
Upon your bench; she woot it wel, certeyn,
By certein tokenes that I can hir telle.
Now, by your leve, I may no lenger dwelle,
Our abbot wol out of this toun anon;
And in his companye moot I gon.
Grete wel our dame, myn owene nece swete,
And fare-wel, dere cosin, til we mete."
This Marchant, which that was ful war and wys,
Creaunced hath, and payd eek in Parys,
To certeyn Lumbardes, redy in hir hond,
The somme of gold, and gat of hem his bond;
And hoom he gooth, mery as a papejay.
For wel he knew he stood in swich array,
That nedes moste he winne in that viage
A thousand frankes above al his costage.
His wyf ful redy mette him atte gate,
As she was wont of old usage algate,
And al that night in mirthe they bisette;
For he was riche and cleerly out of dette.
Whan it was day, this marchant gan embrace
His wyf al newe, and kiste hir on hir face,
And up he gooth and maketh it ful tough.
"Namore," quod she, "by god, ye have
y-nough!"
And wantounly agayn with him she pleyde;
Til, atte laste, that this Marchant seyde,
"By god," quod he, "I am a litel wrooth
With yow, my wyf, al-thogh it be me looth.
And woot ye why? by god, as that I gesse,
That ye han maad a maner straungenesse
Bitwixen me and my cosyn daun John.
Ye sholde han warned me, er I had gon,
That he yow hadde an hundred frankes payed
By redy tokene; and heeld him yvel apayed,

For he was bound by his own note of hand
To pay some twenty thousand crowns anon.
For which this merchant is to Paris gone
To borrow there, from certain friends he had,
Some certain francs unto his own to add.
And when he'd come at length into the town,
Out of great friendship never yet outgrown,
Unto Dan John he went first, there to play,
Not to talk business, nor ask money, nay,
But to inquire and see to his welfare,
And, too, to tell about his Flemish ware,
As friends are wont when come from far or near.
Dan John made him a feast and merry cheer;
And he told him again, and specially,
How he had purchased well and luckily—
Thanks be to God!—all of his merchandise.
Save that he must, nor fail in any wise,
Obtain a loan, at least it would be best,
And then he'd have some time for joy and rest.
Dan John replied: "No gladness do I feign
That sound in health you are come home again.
And if I were but rich, as I have bliss,
These twenty thousand crowns you should not miss,
Since you so kindly, but the other day,
Lent me some gold; and as I can and may,
I thank you, by the Lord and by Saint James!
Nevertheless, to no hand but our dame's,
Your wife at home, I gave the gold again
Upon your counter; she'll remember when
By certain tokens that I gave to her.
Now, by your leave, I must get up and stir,
Our abbot will be leaving town anon;
And in his company I must be gone.
Greet well our dame, your wife and my niece sweet,
And farewell, cousin dear, until we meet."
This merchant, being a man full wary-wise,
Has got his loan and paid there in Paris,
To certain Lombards, ready in their hand,
The sum of gold, and got his note back, and
Now home he goes as merry as a jay.
For well he knew he stood in such array
That now he needs must make, with nothing lost,
A thousand francs above his total cost.
His wife, all ready, met him at the gate,
As she was wont, though he came soon or late,
And all that night with pleasure did they pet,
For he was rich and cleanly out of debt.
When it was day, this merchant did embrace
His wife anew, and kissed her on her face,
And up he goes and makes it rather tough.
"No more," cried she, "by God, you've had
enough!"
And wantonly again with him she played,
Till, at the last, this merchant sighed and said:
"By God," said he, "I am a little wroth
With you, my wife, though to be so I'm loath.
And know you why? By God, and as I guess,
You've been the causing of some small strangeness
Between me and my cousin, dear Dan John.
You should have warned me, really, ere I'd gone,
That he to you a hundred francs had paid
In cash; he was put out, I am afraid,

Because I spoke to him of loans, by chance,
At least I judged so by his countenance.
Nevertheless, by God our Heavenly King,
I never thought to ask him such a thing.
I pray you, wife, never again do so;
But always tell me, ere away I go,
If any debtor has, in my absence,
Repaid to you, lest through your negligence
I might demand a sum already paid."
  This wife was not astounded nor afraid,
But boldly she spoke up and that anon:
"Marry, I challenge that false monk, Dan John!
I kept, of all his coins, not one to tell.
He brought me certain gold— that know I well!
What! Ill success upon his friar's snout!
For God knows that I thought, with never a doubt.
That he had given it me because of you,
To advance thus my honour, and yours too,
In cousinhood, and for the merry cheer
That he has found so many a time right here.
But since I see our peace is thus disjoint,
I'll answer you but briefly, to the point.
You have far slacker debtors than am I!
For I will pay you well and readily
From day to day; and if it be I fail,
I am your wife, tally it on my tail,
And I will pay as soon as ever I may.
For by my truth I have, on new array,
And not on rubbish, spent it, every sou.
And since so well I've spent it, all for you,
All for your honour, for God's sake, I say,
Do not be angry, but let's laugh and play.
My jolly body's yours in pledge," she said,
"By God, I will not pay you, save in bed!
Forgive me, then, my own sweet husband dear;
Let us be happy now—turn over here!"
  This merchant saw there was no remedy,
And, thought he, chiding were but great folly,
Since that the thing might not amended be.
  "Now wife," he said, "I do forgive, you see;
But on your life, don't run so far at large;
Conserve our wealth hereafter, so I charge."
  Thus ends my tale, and may the good God send
Tales fair enough until our lives shall end! Amen.

For that I to him spak of chevisaunce,
Me semed so, as by his contenaunce.
But nathelees, by god our hevene king,
I thoghte nat to axe of him no-thing.
I prey thee, wyf, ne do namore so;
Tel me alwey, er that I fro thee go,
If any dettour hath in myn absence
Y-payëd thee; lest, thurgh thy necligence,
I mighte him axe a thing that he hath payed."
  This wyf was nat afered nor affrayed,
But boldely she seyde, and that anon:
"Marie, I defye the false monk, daun John!
I kepe nat of hise tokenes never a deel;
He took me certein gold, that woot I weel!
What! yvel thedom on his monkes snoute!
For, god it woot, I wende, withouten doute,
That he had yeve it me bycause of yow,
To doon ther-with myn honour and my prow,
For cosinage, and eek for bele chere
That he hath had ful ofte tymes here.
But sith I see I stonde in this disjoint,
I wol answere yow shortly, to the point.
Ye han mo slakker dettours than am I!
For I wol paye yow wel and redily
Fro day to day; and, if so be I faille,
I am your wyf; score it up-on my taille,
And I shal paye, as sone as ever I may.
For, by my trouthe, I have on myn array,
And nat on wast, bistowed every deel.
And for I have bistowed it so weel
For your honour, for goddes sake, I seye,
As be nat wrooth, but lat us laughe and pleye.
Ye shal my joly body have to wedde;
By god, I wol nat paye yow but a-bedde.
Forgive it me, myn owene spouse dere;
Turne hiderward and maketh bettre chere."
  This marchant saugh ther was no remedye,
And, for to chyde, it nere but greet folye,
Sith that the thing may nat amended be.
  "Now, wyf," he seyde, "and I foryeve it thee;
But, by thy lyf, ne be namore so large;
Keep bet our good, this yeve I thee in charge."
  Thus endeth now my tale, and god us sende
Taling y-nough, un-to our lyves ende, Amen.

HERE ENDETH THE SHIPMAN'S TALE

THE PRIORESS'S PROLOGUE

BEHOLD THE MERRY WORDS OF THE HOST TO THE SHIPMAN AND TO THE LADY PRIORESS

"Well said, by *corpus dominus*," said our host,
"Now long time may you sail along the coast,
Sir gentle master, gentle mariner!
God give this monk a thousand years bitter!
Aha, comrades, beware of such a jape!
The monk put into that man's hood an ape,
And in the wife's too, by Saint Augustine!
Invite no more monks to your house or inn.
  "But let that pass, and let us look about

"Wel seyd, by *corpus dominus*," quod our hoste,
"Now longe moot thou sayle by the coste,
Sir gentil maister, gentil marineer!
God yeve this monk a thousand last quad yeer!
A ha! felawes! beth ware of swiche a jape!
The monk putte in the mannes hood an ape,
And in his wyves eek, by seint Austin!
Draweth no monkes more un-to your in.
  But now passe over, and lat us seke aboute,

Who shal now telle first, of al this route,
Another tale;"
and with that word he sayde,
As curteisly as it had been a mayde,
"My lady Prioresse, by your leve,
So that I wiste I sholde yow nat greve,
I wolde demen that ye tellen sholde
A tale next, if so were that ye wolde.
Now wol ye vouche-sauf, my lady dere?"
"Gladly," quod she, and seyde as ye shal here.

To see who shall be next, of all this rout,
To tell a tale."
And after that he said,
As courteously as it had been a maid:
"My lady prioress, and by your leave,
So that I knew I should in no way grieve,
I would opine that tell a tale you should,
The one that follows next if you but would.
Now will you please vouchsafe it, lady dear?"
"Gladly," said she, and spoke as you shall hear.

HERE IT ENDETH

THE PRIORESS'S TALE

THE PROLOGUE OF THE PRIORESS'S TALE

Domine, dominus noster

O Lord our lord, thy name how merveillous
Is in this large worlde y-sprad—quod she:—
For noght only thy laude precious
Parfourned is by men of dignitee,
But by the mouth of children thy bountee
Parfourned is, for on the brest soukinge
Som tyme shewen they thyn heryinge.

Wherfor in laude, as I best can or may,
Of thee, and of the whyte lily flour
Which that thee bar, and is a mayde alway,
To telle a storie I wol do my labour;
Not that I may encresen hir honour;
For she hir-self is honour, and the rote
Of bountee, next hir sone, and soules bote.—

O moder mayde! o mayde moder free!
O bush unbrent, brenninge in Moyses sighte,
That ravisedest doun fro the deitee,
Thurgh thyn humblesse, the goost that in th'alighte,
Of whos vertu, whan he thyn herte lighte,
Conceived was the fadres sapience,
Help me to telle it in thy reverence!

Lady! thy bountee, thy magnificence,
Thy vertu, and thy grete humilitee
Ther may no tonge expresse in no science;
For som-tyme, lady, er men praye to thee,
Thou goost biforn of thy benignitee,
And getest us the light, thurgh thy preyere,
To gyden us un-to thy sone so dere.

My conning is so wayk, o blisful quene,
For to declare thy grete worthinesse,
That I ne may the weighte nat sustene,
But as a child of twelf monthe old, or lesse,
That can unnethes any word expresse,
Right so fare I, and therfor I yow preye,
Gydeth my song that I shal of yow seye.

"O Lord, Our Lord, Thy name how marvelous
Is spread through all this mighty world," said she;
"For not alone Thy praise so glorious
Is given by men of worth and dignity,
But from the mouths of children Thy bounty
Is hymned, yea, even sucklings at the breast
Do sometimes Thy laudation manifest.

"Wherefore in praise, as best I can or may,
Of Thee and of that pure white Lily-flower
Who bore Thee, and is yet a maid alway,
I tell a tale as best is in my power,
Not that I may increase Her heavenly dower,
For She Herself is honour and the one
From Whom spring wealth and goodness, next Her Son.

"O Mother-Maid! O Maiden-Mother free!
O bush unburnt, burning in Moses' sight,
Who ravished so the Soul of Deity,
With Thy meekness, the Spirit of the Light,
That His virtue, which was Thy soul's delight,
Conceived in Thee the Father's wise Essence,
Help me to speak now with all reverence!

"Lady, Thy goodness and Thy generous grace,
Thy virtue and Thy great humility—
No tongue may say, no pen may fully trace;
For sometimes, Lady, ere men pray to Thee,
Thou goest before, of Thy benignity,
And givest us the true light, by Thy prayer,
To guide us all unto Thy Son so dear.

"I cannot bear the burden, blessed Queen,
Of fitly praising all Thy worthiness,
My wisdom and my knowledge are too mean;
But as a child of twelve months old, or less,
That scarcely any word can well express,
So fare I now, and therefore do I pray,
Guide Thou that song of Thee which I shall say!"

HERE IT ENDETH

HERE BEGINNETH THE PRIORESS'S TALE

In Asia, in a city rich and great
There was a Jewry set amidst the town,
Established by a rich lord of the state
For usury and gain of ill renown,
Hateful to Christ and those who are His own;
And through that street a man might ride or wend,
For it was free and open at each end.

Ther was in Asie, in a greet citee,
Amonges Cristen folk, a Jewerye,
Sustened by a lord of that contree
For foule usure and lucre of vilanye,
Hateful to Crist and to his companye;
And thurgh the strete men mighte ryde or wende,
For it was free, and open at either ende.

A little school for Christian folk there stood,
Down at the farther end, in which there were
A many children born of Christian blood,
Who learned in that same school, year after year,
Such teachings as with men were current there,
Which is to say, to sing well and to read,
As children do of whatsoever creed.

A litel scole of Cristen folk ther stood
Doun at the ferther ende, in which ther were
Children an heep, y-comen of Cristen blood,
That lerned in that scole yeer by yere
Swich maner doctrine as men used there,
This is to seyn, to singen and to rede,
As smale children doon in hir childhede.

Among these children was a widow's son,
A little choir boy, seven years of age,
Who went to school as days passed one by one,
And who, whenever saw he the image
Of Jesus' Mother, it was his usage,
As he'd been taught, to kneel down there and say
Ave Maria, ere he went his way.

Among thise children was a widwes sone,
A litel clergeon, seven yeer of age,
That day by day to scole was his wone,
And eek also, wher-as he saugh th'image
Of Cristes moder, hadde he in usage,
As him was taught, to knele adoun and seye
His *Ave Marie*, as he goth by the weye.

Thus had this widow her small son well taught
Our Blessed Lady, Jesus' Mother dear,
To worship always, and he ne'er forgot,
For simple child learns easily and clear;
But ever, when I muse on matters here,
Saint Nicholas stands aye in my presence,
For he, when young, did do Christ reverence.

Thus hath this widwe hir litel sone y-taught
Our blisful lady, Cristes moder dere,
To worshipe ay, and he forgat it naught,
For sely child wol alday sone lere;
But ay, whan I remembre on this matere,
Seint Nicholas stant ever in my presence,
For he so yong to Crist did reverence.

This little child, his little lesson learning
Sat at his primer in the school, and there,
While boys were taught the antiphons, kept turning
And heard the *Alma redemptoris* fair,
And drew as near as ever he did dare,
Marking the words, remembering every note,
Until the first verse he could sing by rote.

This litel child, his litel book lerninge,
As he sat in the scole at his prymer,
As children lerned hir antiphoner;
He *Alma redemptoris* herde singe,
And, as he dorste, he drough him ner and ner,
And herkned ay the wordes and the note,
Til he the firste vers coude al by rote.

He knew not what this Latin meant to say,
Being so young and of such tender age,
But once a young school-comrade did he pray
To expound to him the song in his language,
Or tell him why the song was in usage;
Asking the boy the meaning of the song,
On his bare knees he begged him well and long.

Noght wiste he what this Latin was to seye,
For he so yong and tendre was of age;
But on a day his felaw gan he preye
T'expounden him this song in his langage,
Or telle him why this song was in usage;
This preyde he him to construe and declare
Ful ofte tyme upon his knowes bare.

His fellow was an older lad than he,
And answered thus: "This song, as I've heard say,
Was made to praise Our Blessed Lady free,
Her to salute and ever Her to pray
To be our help when comes our dying day.
I can expound to you only so far;
I've learned the song; I know but small grammar."

His felaw, which that elder was than he,
Answerde him thus: "this song, I have herd seye,
Was maked of our blisful lady free,
Hir to salue, and eek hir for to preye
To been our help and socour whan we deye.
I can no more expounde in this matere;
I lerne song, I can but smal grammere."

"And is this song made in all reverence
Of Jesus' Mother?" asked this innocent;
"Now truly I will work with diligence
To learn it all ere Christmas sacrament,

"And is this song maked in reverence
Of Cristes moder?" seyde this innocent;
"Now certes, I wol do my diligence
To conne it al, er Cristemasse is went;

Though that I for my prymer shal be shent,
And shal be beten thryës in an houre,
I wol it conne, our lady for to honoure."

His felaw taughte him homward prively,
Fro day to day, til he coude it by rote,
And than he song it wel and boldely
Fro word to word, acording with the note;
Twyës a day it passed thurgh his throte,
To scoleward and homward whan he wente;
On Cristes moder set was his entente.

As I have seyd, thurgh-out the Jewerye
This litel child, as he cam to and fro,
Ful merily than wolde he singe, and crye
O Alma redemptoris ever-mo.
The swetnes hath his herte perced so
Of Cristes moder, that, to hir to preye,
He can nat stinte of singing by the weye.

Our firste fo, the serpent Sathanas,
That hath in Jewes herte his waspes nest,
Up swal, and seide, "O Hebraik peple, allas!
Is this to yow a thing that is honest,
That swich a boy shal walken as him lest
In your despyt, and singe of swich sentence,
Which is agayn your lawes reverence?"

Fro thennes forth the Jewes han conspyred
This innocent out of this world to chace;
An homicyde ther-to han they hyred,
That in an aley hadde a privee place;
And as the child gan for-by for to pace,
This cursed Jew him hente and heeld him faste,
And kitte his throte, and in a pit him caste.

I seye that in a wardrobe they him threwe
Wher-as these Jewes purgen hir entraille.
O cursed folk of Herodes al newe,
What may your yvel entente yow availle?
Mordre wol out, certein, it wol nat faille,
And namely ther th'onour of god shal sprede,
The blood out cryeth on your cursed dede.

"O martir, souded to virginitee,
Now maystou singen, folwing ever in oon
The whyte lamb celestial," quod she,
"Of which the grete evangelist, seint John,
In Pathmos wroot, which seith that they that goon
Biforn this lamb, and singe a son al newe,
That never, fleshly, wommen they ne knewe."

This povre widwe a awaiteth al that night
After hir litel child, but he cam noght;
For which, as sone as it was dayes light,
With face pale of drede and bisy thoght,
She hath at scole and elles-wher him soght,
Til finally she gan so fer espye
That he last seyn was in the Jewerye.

With modres pitee in hir brest enclosed,
She gooth, as she were half out of hir minde,

Though for my primer I take punishment
And though I'm beaten thrice within the hour,
Yet will I learn it by Our Lady's power!"

His fellow taught him on their homeward way
Until he learned the antiphon by rote.
Then clear and bold he sang it day by day,
Each word according with its proper note;
And twice each day it welled from out his throat,
As schoolward went he and as homeward went;
On Jesus' Mother was his fixed intent.

As I have said, as through the Jewry went
This little school-boy, out the song would ring,
And joyously the notes he upward sent;
O Alma redemptoris would he sing;
To his heart's core it did the sweetness bring
Of Christ's dear Mother, and, to Her to pray,
He could not keep from singing on his way.

Our primal foe, the serpent Sathanas,
Who has in Jewish heart his hornets' nest,
Swelled arrogantly: "O Jewish folk, alas!
Is it to you a good thing, and the best,
That such a boy walks here, without protest,
In your despite and doing such offense
Against the teachings that you reverence?"

From that time forth the Jewish folk conspired
Out of the world this innocent to chase;
A murderer they found, and thereto hired,
Who in an alley had a hiding-place;
And as the child went by at sober pace,
This cursed Jew did seize and hold him fast,
And cut his throat, and in a pit him cast.

I say, that in a cesspool him they threw,
Wherein these Jews did empty their entrails.
O cursed folk of Herod, born anew,
How can you think your ill intent avails?
Murder will out, 'tis sure, nor ever fails,
And chiefly when God's honour vengeance needs,
The blood cries out upon your cursed deeds.

"O martyr firm in thy virginity,
Now mayest thou sing, and ever follow on
The pure white Lamb Celestial" —quoth she—
"Whereof the great evangelist, Saint John,
In Patmos wrote, saying that they are gone
Before the Lamb, singing a song that's new,
And virgins all, who never woman knew."

This widow poor awaited all that night
Her child's return to her, but he came not;
For which, so soon as it was full daylight,
With pale face full of dread, and busy thought,
At school she sought and everywhere she sought,
Until, at last, from all her questioning she
Learned that he last was seen in the Jewry.

With mother's pity in her breast enclosed
She ran, as she were half out of her mind,

To every place where it might be supposed,
In likelihood, that she her son should find;
And ever on Christ's Mother meek and kind
She called until, at last, Our Lady wrought
That amongst the cursed Jews the widow sought.

She asked and she implored, all piteously,
Of every Jew who dwelt in that foul place,
To tell her where her little child could be.
They answered "Nay." But Jesus, of His grace,
Put in her mind, within a little space,
That after him in that same spot she cried
Where he'd been cast in pit, or near beside.

O Thou great God, Who innocents hast called
To give Thee praise, now shown is Thy great might!
This gem of chastity, this emerald,
Of martyrdom the ruby clear and bright,
Began, though slain and hidden there from sight,
The *Alma redemptoris* loud to sing,
So clear that all the neighbourhood did ring.

The Christian folk that through the ghetto went
Came running for the wonder of this thing,
And hastily they for the provost sent;
He also came without long tarrying,
And gave Christ thanks, Who is of Heaven King,
And, too, His Mother, honour of mankind;
And after that the Jews there did he bind.

This child, with piteous lamentation, then
Was taken up, singing his song alway;
And, honoured by a great concourse of men,
Carried within an abbey near, that day.
Swooning, his mother by the black bier lay,
Nor easily could people who were there
This second Rachel carry from the bier.

With torture and with shameful death, each one,
The provost did these cursed Hebrews serve
Who of the murder knew, and that anon;
From justice to the villains he'd not swerve.
Evil shall have what evil does deserve.
And therefore, with wild horses, did he draw,
And after hang, their bodies, all by law.

Upon the bier lay this poor innocent
Before the altar, while the mass did last,
And after that the abbot and monks went
About the coffin for to close it fast;
But when the holy water they did cast,
Then spoke the child, at touch of holy water,
And sang, "*O Alma redemptoris mater!*"

This abbot, who was a right holy man,
As all monks are, or as they ought to be,
The dead young boy to conjure then began,
Saying: "O dear child, I do beg of thee,
By virtue of the Holy Trinity,
Tell me how it can be that thou dost sing
After thy throat is cut, to all seeming?"

To every place wher she hath supposed
By lyklihede hir litel child to finde;
And ever on Cristes moder meke and kinde
She cryde, and atte laste thus she wroghte,
Among the cursed Jewes she him soghte.

She frayneth and she preyeth pitously
To every Jew that dwelte in thilke place,
To telle hir, if hir child wente oght for-by.
They seyde, "nay"; but Jesu, of his grace,
Yaf in hir thought, inwith a litel space,
That in that place after hir sone she cryde,
Wher he was casten in a pit bisyde.

O grete god, that parfournest thy laude
By mouth of innocents, lo heer thy might!
This gemme of chastitee, this emeraude,
And eek of martirdom the ruby bright,
Ther he with throte y-corven lay upright,
He "*Alma redemptoris*" gan to singe
So loude, that al the place gan to ringe.

The Cristen folk, that thurgh the strete wente,
In coomen, for to wondre up-on this thing,
And hastily they for the provost sente;
He cam anon with-outen tarying,
And herieth Crist that is of heven king,
And eek his moder, honour of mankinde,
And after that, the Jewes leet he binde.

This child with pitous lamentacioun
Up-taken was, singing his song alway;
And with honour of greet processioun
They carien him un-to the nexte abbay.
His moder swowning by the bere lay;
Unnethe might the peple that was there
This newe Rachel bringe fro his bere.

With torment and with shamful deth echon
This provost dooth thise Jewes for to sterve
That of this mordre wiste, and that anon;
He nolde no swich cursednesse observe.
Yvel shal have, that yvel wol deserve.
Therfor with wilde hors he dide hem drawe,
And after that he heng hem by the lawe.

Up-on his bere ay lyth this innocent
Biforn the chief auter, whyl masse laste,
And after that, the abbot with his covent
Han sped hem for to burien him ful faste;
And whan they holy water on him caste,
Yet spak this child, whan spreynd was holy water,
And song—"*O Alma redemptoris mater*!"

This abbot, which that was an holy man
As monkes been, or elles oghten be,
This yonge child to conjure he bigan,
And seyde, "o dere child, I halse thee,
In vertu of the holy Trinitee,
Tel me what is thy cause for to singe,
Sith that thy throte is cut, to my seminge?"

"My throte is cut un-to my nekke-boon,"
Seyde this child, "and, as by wey of kinde,
I sholde have deyed, ye, longe tyme agoon,
But Jesu Crist, as ye in bokes finde,
Wil that his glorie laste and be in minde;
And, for the worship of his moder dere,
Yet may I singe '*O Alma*' loude and clere.

This welle of mercy, Cristes moder swete,
I lovede alwey, as after my conninge;
And whan that I my lyf sholde forlete,
To me she cam, and bad me for to singe
This antem verraily in my deyinge,
As ye han herd, and, whan that I had songe,
Me thoughte, she leyde a greyn up-on my tonge.

Wherfor I singe, and singe I moot certeyn
In honour of that blisful mayden free,
Til fro my tonge of-taken is the greyn;
And afterward thus seyde she to me,
'My litel child, now wol I fecche thee
Whan that the greyn is fro thy tonge y-take;
Be nat agast, I wol thee nat forsake.' "

This holy monk, this abbot, him mene I,
Him tonge out-caughte, and took a-wey the greyn,
And he yaf up the goost ful softely.
And whan this abbot had this wonder seyn,
His salte teres trikled doun as reyn,
And gruf he fil al plat up-on the grounde.
And stille he lay as he had been y-bounde.

The covent eek lay on the pavement
Weping, and herien Cristes moder dere,
And after that they ryse, and forth ben went,
And toke awey this martir fro his bere,
And in a tombe of marbul-stones clere
Enclosen they his litel body swete;
Ther he is now, god leve us for to mete.

O yonge Hugh of Lincoln,[1] slayn also
With cursed Jewes, as it is notable,
For it nis but a litel whyle ago;
Preye eek for us, we sinful folk unstable,
That, of his mercy, god so merciable
On us his grete mercy multiplye,
For reverence of his moder Marye. Amen.

"My throat is cut unto the spinal bone,"
Replied the child. "By nature of my kind
I should have died, aye, many hours agone,
But Jesus Christ, as you in books shall find,
Wills that His glory last in human mind;
Thus for the honour of His Mother dear,
Still may I sing '*O Alma*' loud and clear.

"This well of mercy, Jesus' Mother sweet,
I always loved, after my poor knowing;
And when came time that I my death must meet,
She came to me and bade me only sing
This anthem in the pain of my dying,
As you have heard, and after I had sung,
She laid a precious pearl upon my tongue.

"Wherefore I sing, and sing I must, 'tis plain,
In honour of that blessed Maiden free,
Till from my tongue is taken away the grain;
And afterward she said thus unto me:
'My little child, soon will I come for thee,
When from thy tongue the little bead they take;
Be not afraid, thee I will not forsake.' "

The holy monk, this abbot, so say I,
The tongue caught out and took away the grain,
And he gave up the ghost, then, easily,
And when the abbot saw this wonder plain,
The salt tears trickled down his cheeks like rain,
And humbly he fell prone upon the ground,
Lying there still as if he had been bound.

And all the monks lay there on the pavement,
Weeping and praising Jesus' Mother dear,
And after that they rose and forth they went,
Taking away this martyr from his bier,
And in a tomb of marble, carved and clear,
Did they enclose his little body sweet;
Where he is now—God grant us him to meet!

O you young Hugh of Lincoln,[1] slain also
By cursed Jews, as is well known to all,
Since it was but a little while ago,
Pray you for us, sinful and weak, who call,
That, of His mercy, God will still let fall
Something of grace, and mercy multiply,
For reverence of His Mother dear on high. Amen.

[1]Referring to a murder that had attracted much attention in England during the reign of Henry III.

HERE IS ENDED THE PRIORESS'S TALE

PROLOGUE TO SIR THOPAS

BEHOLD THE MERRY WORDS OF THE HOST TO CHAUCER

WHAN seyd was al this miracle, every man
As sobre was, that wonder was to see,
Til that our hoste japen tho bigan,
And than at erst he loked up-on me,
And seyde thus, "what man artow?" quod he;

WHEN told was all this miracle, every man
So sober fell 'twas wonderful to see,
Until our host in jesting wise began,
And for the first time did he glance at me,
Saying, "What man are you?"—'twas thus quoth he—

"You look as if you tried to find a hare, For always on the ground I see you stare.	"Thou lokest as thou woldest finde an hare, For ever up-on the ground I see thee stare.
"Come near me then, and look up merrily. Now make way, sirs, and let this man have place; He in the waist is shaped as well as I; This were a puppet in an arm's embrace For any woman, small and fair of face. Why, he seems absent, by his countenance, And gossips with no one for dalliance.	Approche neer, and loke up merily. Now war yow, sirs, and lat this man have place; He in the waast is shape as well as I; This were a popet in an arm t'enbrace For any womman, smal and fair of face. He semeth elvish by his contenaunce, For un-to no wight dooth he daliaunce.
"Since other folk have spoken, it's your turn; Tell us a mirthful tale, and that anon." "Mine host," said I, "don't be, I beg, too stern, For of good tales, indeed, sir, have I none, Save a long rhyme I learned in years agone." "Well, that is good," said he; "now shall we hear It seems to me, a thing to bring us cheer."	Sey now somwhat, sin other folk han sayd; Tel us a tale of mirthe, and that anoon";— "Hoste," quod I, "ne beth nat yvel apayd, For other tale certes can I noon, But of a ryme I lerned longe agoon." "Ye, that is good," quod he; "now shul we here Som deyntee thing, me thinketh by his chere."

HERE IT ENDETH

SIR THOPAS

HERE BEGINNETH CHAUCER'S TALE OF THOPAS

The First Fit

Listen, lords, with good intent, I truly will a tale present Of mirth and of solace; All of a knight was fair and gent[1] In battle and in tournament. His name was Sir Thopas.	Listeth, lordes, in good entent, And I wol telle verrayment Of mirthe and of solas; Al of a knyght was fair and gent[1] In bataille and in tourneyment, His name was sir Thopas.
Born he was in a far country, In Flanders, all beyond the sea, And Poperinghe the place; His father was a man full free, And lord he was of that countree, As chanced to be God's grace.	Y-born he was in fer contree, In Flaundres, al biyonde the see, At Popering, in the place; His fader was a man ful free, And lord he was of that contree, As it was goddes grace.
Sir Thopas was a doughty swain, White was his brow as paindemaine,[2] His lips red as a rose; His cheeks were like poppies in grain, And I tell you, and will maintain, He had a comely nose.	Sir Thopas wex a doghty swayn, Whyt was his face as payndemayn,[2] His lippes rede as rose; His rode is lyk scarlet in grayn, And I yow telle in good certayn, He hadde a semely nose.
His hair and beard were like saffron And to his girdle reached adown, His shoes were of cordwain;[3] From Bruges were come his long hose brown, His rich robe was of ciclatoun[4]— And cost full many a jane.[5]	His heer, his berd was lyk saffroun, That to his girdel raughte adoun; His shoon of Cordewane.[3] Of Brugges were his hosen broun, His robe was of ciclatoun,[4] That coste many a jane.[5]
Well could he hunt the dim wild deer And ride a-hawking by river, With grey goshawk on hand; Therewith he was a good archer,	He coude hunte at wilde deer, And ryde an hauking for riveer, With grey goshauk on honde; Ther-to he was a good archeer,

[1]Of gentle birth. [2]White bread of the finest quality. [3]Cordovan leather.
[4]A costly kind of thin cloth.
[5]A Genoese coin, current in England in the 14th century.

Of wrestling was ther noon his peer,
Ther any ram[1] shal stonde.

Ful many a mayde, bright in bour,
They moorne for him, paramour,
Whan hem were bet to slepe;
But he was chast and no lechour,
And sweet as is the bremble-flour
That bereth the rede hepe.[2]

And so bifel up-on a day,
For sothe, as I yow telle may,
Sir Thopas wolde out ryde;
He worth upon his stede gray,
And in his honde a launcegay,
A long swerd by his syde.

He priketh thurgh a fair forest,
Ther-inne is many a wilde best,
Ye, bothe bukke and hare;
And, as he priketh north and est,
I telle it yow, him hadde almest
Bitid a sory care.

Ther springen herbes grete and smale,
The lycorys and cetewale,
And many a clowe-gilofre;
And notemuge to putte in ale,
Whether it be moyste or stale,
Or for to leye in cofre.

The briddes singe, it is no nay,
The sparhauk and the papejay,
That joye it was to here;
The thrustelcok made eek his lay,
The wodedowve upon the spray
She sang ful loude and clere.

Sir Thopas fil in love-longinge
Al whan he herde the thrustel singe,
And priked as he were wood:
His faire stede in his prikinge
So swatte that men mighte him wringe,
His sydes were al blood.

Sir Thopas eek so wery was
For prikinge on the softe gras,
So fiers was his corage,
That doun he leyde him in that plas
To make his stede som solas,
And yaf him good forage.

"O seinte Marie, *ben'cite!*
What eyleth this love at me
To binde me so sore?
Me dremed al this night, pardee,
An elf-queen shal my lemman be,
And slepe under my gore.[3]

"An elf-queen wol I love, y-wis,[4]
For in this world no womman is

At wrestling was there none his peer
Where any ram[1] did stand.

Full many a maiden, bright in bower,
Did long for him for paramour
When they were best asleep;
But chaste he was, no lecher sure,
And sweet as is the bramble-flower
That bears a rich red hepe.[2]

And so befell, upon a day,
In truth, as I can tell or may,
Sir Thopas out would ride;
He mounted on his stallion grey,
And held in hand a lance, I say,
With longsword by his side.

He spurred throughout a fair forest
Wherein was many a dim wild beast,
Aye, both the buck and hare;
And as he spurred on, north and east,
I tell you now he had, in breast,
A melancholy care.

There herbs were springing, great and small,
The licorice blue and white setwall,
And many a gillyflower,
And nutmeg for to put in ale,
All whether it be fresh or stale,
Or lay in chest in bower.

The birds they sang, upon that day,
The sparrow-hawk and popinjay,
Till it was joy to hear;
The missel thrush he made his lay,
The tender stockdove on the spray,
She sang full loud and clear.

Sir Thopas fell to love-longing
All when he heard the throstle sing,
And spurred as madman would:
His stallion fair, for this spurring,
Did sweat till men his coat might wring,
His two flanks were all blood.

Sir Thopas grown so weary was
With spurring on the yielding grass,
So fierce had been his speed,
That down he laid him in that place
To give the stallion some solace
And let him find his feed.

"O holy Mary, *ben'cite!*
What ails my heart that love in me
Should bind me now so sore?
For dreamed I all last night, pardie,
An elf-queen shall my darling be,
And sleep beneath my gore.[3]

"An elf-queen will I love, ywis,[4]
For in this world no woman is

[1]The usual prize in wrestling. [2]Hip. [3]The gore of his garment. [4]Truly, certainly.

Worthy to be my make
In town;
All other women I forsake,
And to an elf-queen I'll betake
Myself, by dale and down!"

Into his saddle he climbed anon
And spurred then over stile and stone,
An elf-queen for to see,
Till he so far had ridden on
He found a secret place and won
The land of Faëry
So wild;
For in that country was there none
That unto him dared come, not one,
Not either wife or child.

Until there came a great giant,
Whose name it was Sir Oliphant,[1]
A dangerous man indeed;
He said: "O Childe, by Termagant,
Save thou dost spur from out my haunt,
Anon I'll slay thy steed
With mace.
For here the queen of Faëry,
With harp and pipe and harmony,
Is dwelling in this place."

The Childe said: "As I hope to thrive,
We'll fight the morn, as I'm alive,
When I have my armour;
For well I hope, and *par ma fay*,
That thou shalt by this lance well pay,
And suffer strokes full sore;
Thy maw
Shall I pierce through, and if I may,
Ere it be fully prime of day,
Thou'lt die of wounds most raw."

Sir Thopas drew aback full fast;
This giant at him stones did cast
Out of a fell staff-sling;
But soon escaped was Childe Thopas,
And all it was by God's own grace,
And by his brave bearing.

And listen yet, lords, to my tale,
Merrier than the nightingale,
Whispered to all and some,
How Sir Thopas, with pride grown pale,
Hard spurring over hill and dale,
Came back to his own home.

His merry men commanded he
To make for him both game and glee,
For needs now must he fight
With a great giant of heads three,
For love in the society
Of one who shone full bright.

"Do come," he said, "my minstrels all,

Worthy to be my make
In toune;
Alle othere wommen I forsake,
And to an elf-queen I me take
By dale and eek by doune!"

In-to his sadel he clamb anoon,
And priketh over style and stoon
An elf-queen for t'espye,
Til he so longe had riden and goon
That he fond, in a privee woon,
The contree of Fairye [13,731]
So wilde; [13,734]
For in that contree was ther noon
That to him dorste ryde or goon,
Neither wyf ne childe.

Til that ther cam a greet geaunt,
His name was sir Olifaunt,[1]
A perilous man of dede;
He seyde, "child, by Termagaunt,
But-if thou prike out of myn haunt,
Anon I slee thy stede
With mace.
Heer is the queen of Fayërye,
With harpe and pype and simphonye
Dwelling in this place."

The child seyde, "al-so mote I thee,
Tomorwe wol I mete thee
Whan I have myn armoure;
And yet I hope, *par ma fay*,
That thou shalt with this launcegay
Abyen it ful soure;
Thy mawe
Shal I percen, if I may,
Er it be fully pryme of day,
For heer thou shalt be slawe."

Sir Thopas drow abak ful faste;
This geaunt at him stones caste
Out of a fel staf-slinge;
But faire escapeth child Thopas,
And al it was thurgh goddes gras,
And thurgh his fair beringe.

Yet listeth, lordes, to my tale
Merier than the nightingale,
For now I wol yow roune
How sir Thopas with sydes smale,
Priking over hil and dale,
Is come agayn to toune.

His merie men comanded he
To make him bothe game and glee,
For nedes moste he fighte
With a geaunt with hevedes three,
For paramour and jolitee
Of oon that shoon ful brighte.

"Do come," he seyde, "my minstrales,

[1]An old form of elephant.

And gestours, for to tellen tales
Anon in myn arminge;
Of romances that been royales,
Of popes and of cardinales,
And eek of love-lykinge."

They fette him first the swete wyn,
And mede eek in a maselyn,[1]
And royal spicerye
Of gingebreed that was ful fyn,
And lycorys, and eek comyn,
With sugre that is so trye.

He dide next his whyte lere
Of clooth of lake fyn and clere
A breech and eek a sherte;
And next his sherte an aketoun,[2]
And over that an habergeoun[3]
For percinge of his herte;

And over that a fyn hauberk,[4]
Was al y-wroght of Jewes werk,
Ful strong it was of plate;
And over that his cote-armour
As whyt as is a lily-flour,
In which he wol debate.

His sheeld was al of gold so reed,
And ther-in was a bores heed,
A charbocle bisyde;
And there he swoor, on ale and breed,
How that "the geaunt shal be deed,
Bityde what bityde!"

His jambeux[5] were of quirboilly,[6]
His swerdes shethe of yvory,
His helm of laton[7] bright;
His sadel was of rewel-boon,[8]
His brydel as the sonne shoon,
Or as the mone light.

His spere was of fyn ciprees,
That bodeth werre, and no-thing pees,
The heed ful sharpe y-grounde;
His stede was al dappel-gray,
It gooth an ambel in the way
Ful softely and rounde
In londe.
Lo, lordes myne, heer is a fit![9]
If ye wol any more of it,
To telle it wol I fonde.

And jesters, tell me tales in hall
Anon in mine arming;
Of old romances right royal,
Of pope and king and cardinal,
And e'en of love-liking."

They brought him, first, the sweet, sweet wine,
And mead within a maselyn,[1]
And royal spicery
Of gingerbread that was full fine,
Cumin and licorice, I opine,
And sugar so dainty.

He drew on, next his white skin clear,
Of finest linen, clean and sheer,
His breeches and a shirt;
And next the shirt a stuffed acton,[2]
And over that a habergeon[3]
'Gainst piercing of his heart.

And over that a fine hauberk[4]
That was wrought all of Jewish work
And reinforced with plate;
And over that his coat-of-arms,
As white as lily-flower that charms,
Wherein he will debate.

His shield was all of gold so red,
And thereon was a wild boar's head
A carbuncle beside;
And now he swore, by ale and bread,
That soon "this giant shall be dead,
Betide what may betide!"

His jambeaux[5] were of cuir-bouilli,[6]
His sword sheath was of ivory,
His helm of latten[7] bright;
His saddle was of rewel bone,[8]
And as the sun his bridle shone,
Or as the full moonlight.

His spear was of fine cypress wood,
That boded war, not brotherhood,
The head full sharply ground;
His steed was all a dapple grey
Whose gait was ambling, on the way,
Full easily and round
In land.
Behold, my lords, here is a fit![9]
If you'll have any more of it,
You have but to command.

The Second Fit

Now hold your mouth, *par charitee*,
Bothe knight and lady free,
And herkneth to my spelle;
Of bataille and of chivalry,
And of ladyes love-drury[10]
Anon I wol yow telle.

Now hold your peace, *par charitee*,
Both knight and lady fair and free,
And hearken to my spell;
Of battle and of chivalry
And all of ladies' love-drury[10]
Anon I will you tell.

[1]A maple bowl. [2]A quilted jacket. [3]A short coat of mail.
[4]A long coat of mail. [5]Leg armour. [6]Hardened leather. [7]A brass-like alloy.
[8]Probably whale or walrus ivory. [9]A part of a ballad. [10]Love, passion.

Romances men recount of price,
Of King Horn and of Hypotis,
  Of Bevis and Sir Guy,
Of Sir Libeaux and Plain-d' Amour;
But Sir Thopas is flower sure
  Of regal chivalry.

His good horse all he then bestrode,
And forth upon his way he rode
  Like spark out of a brand;
Upon his crest he bore a tower,
Wherein was thrust a lily-flower;
  God grant he may withstand!

He was a knight adventurous,
Wherefore he'd sleep within no house,
  But lay down in his hood;
His pillow was his helmet bright,
And by him browsed his steed all night
  On forage fine and good.

Himself drank water of the well,
As did the knight Sir Percival,
  So worthy in his weeds,
Till on a day . . .

Men speke of romances of prys,
Of Horn child and of Ypotys,
  Of Bevis and sir Gy,
Of sir Libeux and Pleyn-damour;
But sir Thopas, he bereth the flour
  Of royal chivalry.

His gode stede al he bistrood,
And forth upon his wey he glood
  As sparkle out of the bronde;
Up-on his crest he bar a tour,
And ther-in stiked a lily-flour,
  God shilde his cors fro shonde!

And for he was a knight auntrous,
He nolde slepen in non hous,
  But liggen in his hode;
His brighte helm was his wonger,
And by him baiteth his dextrer
  Of herbes fyne and gode.

Him-self drank water of the wel,
As did the knight sir Percivel,
  So worthy under wede,
Til on a day——

HERE THE HOST STINTETH CHAUCER OF HIS TALE OF THOPAS

PROLOGUE TO MELIBEUS

"No more of this, for God's high dignity!"
Exclaimed our host, "For you, sir, do make me
So weary with your vulgar foolishness
That, as may God so truly my soul bless,
My two ears ache from all your worthless speech;
Now may such rhymes the devil have, and each!
This sort of thing is doggerel," said he.
  "Why so?" I asked, "Why will you hinder me
In telling tales more than another man,
Since I have told the best rhyme that I can?"
  "By God!" cried he, "now plainly, in a word,
Your dirty rhyming is not worth a turd;
You do naught else but waste and fritter time.
Sir, in one word, you shall no longer rhyme.
Let's see if you can use the country verse,
Or tell a tale in prose—you might do worse—
Wherein there's mirth or doctrine good and plain."
  "Gladly," said I, " by God's sweet tears and pain,
I will relate a little thing in prose
That ought to please you, or so I suppose,
For surely, else, you're contumelious.
It is a moral tale, right virtuous,
Though it is told, sometimes, in different wise
By different folk, as I shall you apprise.
As thus: You know that each evangelist
Who tells the passion of Lord Jesus Christ
Says not in all things as his fellows do,
But nonetheless, each gospel is all true,
And all of them accord in their essence,
Howbeit there's in telling difference.

"No more of this, for goddes dignitee,"
Quod oure hoste, "for thou makest me
So wery of thy verray lewednesse
That, also wisly god my soule blesse,
Myn eres aken of thy drasty speche;
Now swiche a rym the devel I biteche!
This may wel be rym dogerel," quod he.
  "Why so?" quod I, "why wiltow lette me
More of my tale than another man,
Sin that it is the beste rym I can?"
  "By god," quod he, "for pleynly, at a word,
Thy drasty ryming is nat worth a tord!
Thou doost nought elles but despendest tyme,
Sir, at o word, thou shalt no lenger ryme.
Lat see wher thou canst tellen aught in geste,
Or telle in prose somwhat at the leste
In which ther be some mirthe or som doctryne."
  "Gladly," quod I, "by goddes swete pyne,
I wol yow telle a litel thing in prose,
That oghte lyken yow, as I suppose,
Or elles, certes, ye been to daungerous.
It is a moral tale vertuous,
Al be it told som-tyme in sondry wyse
Of sondry folk, as I shal yow devyse.
As thus; ye woot that every evangelist,
That telleth us the peyne of Jesu Crist,
Ne saith nat al thing as his felaw dooth,
But natheles, hir sentence is al sooth,
And alle acorden as in hir sentence,
Al be ther in hir telling difference.

For somme of hem seyn more, and somme lesse,
Whan they his pitous passioun expresse;
I mene of Mark [and] Mathew, Luk and John;
But doutelees hir sentence is al oon.
Therfor, lordinges alle, I yow biseche,
If that ye thinke I varie as in my speche,
As thus, thogh that I telle som-what more
Of proverbes, than ye han herd bifore,
Comprehended in this litel tretis here,
To enforce with the th'effect of my matere,
And thogh I nat the same wordes seye
As ye han herd, yet to yow alle I preye,
Blameth me nat; for, as in my sentence,
Ye shul not fynden moche difference
Fro the sentence of this tretis lyte
After the which this mery tale I wryte.
And therfor herkneth what that I shal seye,
And lat me tellen al my tale, I preye."

For some of them say more and some say less
When they His piteous passion would express;
I mean now Mark and Matthew, Luke and John;
Yet, without doubt, their meaning is all one.
And therefore, masters all, I do beseech,
If you should think I vary in my speech,
As thus: That I do quote you somewhat more
Of proverbs than you've ever heard before,
Included in this little treatise here,
To point the morals out, as they appear,
And though I do not quite the same words say
That you have heard before, yet now, I pray,
You'll blame me not; for in the basic sense
You will not find a deal of difference
From the true meaning of that tale polite
After the which this happy tale I write.
And therefore hearken now to what I say,
And let me tell you all my tale, I pray."

HERE IT ENDETH

THE TALE OF MELIBEUS

HERE BEGINNETH CHAUCER'S TALE OF MELIBEUS

1. A YONG man called Melibeus, mighty and riche, bigat up-on his wyf that called was Prudence, a doghter which that called was Sophie.

2. Upon a day bifel, that he for his desport is went in-to the feeldes him to pleye. His wyf and eek his doghter hath he left inwith his hous, of which the dores weren fast y-shette. Three of his olde foos han it espyed, and setten laddres to the walles of his hous, and by the windowes been entred, and betten his wyf, and wounded his doghter with fyve mortal woundes in fyve sondry places; this is to seyn, in hir feet, in hir handes, in hir eres, in hir nose, and in hir mouth; and leften hir for deed, and wenten awey.

3. Whan Melibeus retourned was in-to his hous, and saugh al this meschief, he, lyk a mad man, rendinge his clothes, gan to wepe and crye.

4. Prudence his wyf, as ferforth as she dorste, bisoghte him of his weping for to stinte; but nat forthy he gan to crye and wepen ever lenger the more.

5. This noble wyf Prudence remembered hir upon the sentence of Ovide, in his book that cleped is The Remedie of Love, wher-as he seith; "he is a fool that destourbeth the moder to wepen in the deeth of hir child, til she have wept hir fille, as for a certein tyme; and thanne shal man doon his diligence with amiable wordes hir to reconforte, and preyen hir of hir weping for to stinte." For which resoun this noble wyf Prudence suffred hir housbond for to wepe and crye as for a certein space; and whan she saugh hir tyme, she seyde him in this wyse. "Allas, my lord," quod she, "why make ye your-self for to be lyk a fool? For sothe, it aperteneth nat to a wys man, to maken swiche a sorwe. Your doghter, with the grace of god, shal warisshe and escape. And al were it so that she right now

A YOUNG man named Melibeus, mighty and rich, begot on Prudence, his wife, a daughter who was called Sophie.

It happened one day that, for his amusement he went into the fields to play. His wife and daughter remained at home, the doors of his house being all fast shut and locked. But three of his old enemies, having spied out the state of things, set ladders to the wall of the house and entered therein by a window; and they beat the wife and wounded the daughter with five dangerous wounds in five different places; that is to say, in her feet, in her hands, in her ears, in her nose, and in her mouth; and they left her for dead and went away.

When Melibeus returned to his house and saw all this mischief, he, like a madman, rending his clothes, began to weep and cry.

Prudence his wife, so far as she dared, besought him to cease his weeping; nevertheless he wept and cried but the more.

This noble wife Prudence remembered then the opinion of Ovid, in his book *The Remedy for Love*, wherein he says: "He is but a fool who interferes with the mother weeping for the death of her child, until she shall have wept her fill, and for a certain time; and only then may a man be diligent, with kind words, to comfort her, and pray her to forgo her tears." For which reason this noble wife Prudence suffered her husband to weep and cry for a time; and when she saw her opportunity, she spoke to him. "Alas, my lord!" said she, "Why do you allow yourself to act like a fool? For truly it becomes not a wise man to show such sorrow. Your daughter, by the grace of God, shall be healed and will recover. And were she dead even now, you ought not, for this, to destroy yourself. Seneca says: 'The wise man will not take too sorrowfully to heart the death of his children, but will suffer it with patience, just as he awaits the death of his own body.' "

Melibeus answered, saying: "What man should cease his weeping who has so great a cause to weep? Jesus Christ Our Lord Himself wept for the death of His friend Lazarus."

Prudence replied: "Indeed, well do I know that moderate weeping is not forbidden to anyone who sorrows, among sorrowing folk; but, rather, it is permitted him to weep. The Apostle Paul writes unto the Romans: 'Rejoice with them that do rejoice, and weep with them that weep.' But though a tempered weeping may be granted, excessive weeping certainly is forbidden. Moderation in grief should be considered, according to the teaching of Seneca. 'When your friend is dead,' says he, 'let not your eyes be too wet with tears, nor yet too dry; and though your tears rise to the eyes, let them not fall.' So, when you have given over your friend, be diligent in procuring another; and this is wiser than to weep for the friend who is lost; for therein is no profit. And therefore, if you govern yourself with wisdom, put away sorrow out of your heart. Remember how Jesus son of Sirach says: 'A joyous and glad heart makes a man flourish in his age; but truly a sorrowful heart drieth the bones.' He says also that sorrow hath killed many a man. Solomon says that as moths in the sheep's fleece annoy the clothes, and as small worms the tree, so sorrow annoys the heart. Wherefore we ought to be patient, not less for the death of our children than for the loss of worldly goods.

"Remember the patient Job, when he had lost his children and his substance, and had in his body received and endured many a grievous tribulation, yet said he thus: 'The Lord gave, and the Lord hath taken away; blessed be the name of the Lord.' "

To these things Melibeus answered, saying to Prudence his wife: "All your words are true, and likewise profitable, but verily my heart is troubled so grievously with this sorrow that I know not what to do."

"Call, then," said Prudence, "all of your true friends and those of your kindred who are wise; tell them your trouble and hearken to what they say in council; and then govern yourself according to their advice. Says Solomon: 'Do nothing without advice, and thou shalt never repent.' "

Then, upon the advice of his wife Prudence, Melibeus called together a great gathering of people, old and young; and some among them were surgeons and physicians; and some were of his old enemies who seemed to have become reconciled to him; and there came some of his neighbours who respected him more out of fear than of love, as often happens;

were deed, ye ne oghte nat as for hir deeth yourself to destroye. Senek seith: 'the wise man shal nat take to greet disconfort for the deeth of his children, but certes he sholde suffren it in pacience, as wel as he abydeth the deeth of his owene propre persone.' "

6. This Melibeus answerde anon and seyde, "What man," quod he, "sholde of his weping stinte, that hath so greet a cause for to wepe? Jesu Crist, our lord, him-self wepte for the deeth of Lazarus his freend." Prudence answerde, "Certes, well woot, attempree weping is no-thing defended to him that sorweful is, amonges folk in sorwe, but it is rather graunted him to wepe. The Apostle Paul un-to the Romayns wryteth, 'man shal rejoyse with hem that maken joye, and wepen with swich folk as wepen.' But thogh attempree weping be y-graunted, outrageous weping certes is defended. Mesure of weping sholde be considered, after the lore that techeth us Senek. 'Whan that thy freend is deed,' quod he, 'lat nat thyne eyen to moyste been of teres, ne to muche drye; althogh the teres come to thyne eyen, lat hem nat falle.' And whan thou hast for-goon thy freend, do diligence to gete another freend; and this is more wysdom than for to wepe for thy freend which that thou hast lorn; for ther-inne is no bote. And therfore, if ye governe yow by sapience, put awey sorwe out of your herte. Remembre yow that Jesus Syrak seith: 'a man that is joyous and glad in herte, it him conserveth florisshing in his age; but soothly sorweful herte maketh his bones drye.' He seith eek thus: 'that sorwe in herte sleeth ful many a man.' Salomon seith: 'that, right as motthes in the shepes flees anoyeth to the clothes, and the smale wormes to the tree, right so anoyeth sorwe to the herte.' Wherfore us oghte, as wel in the deeth of our children as in the losse of our goodes temporels, have pacience.

7. Remembre yow up-on the pacient Job, whan he hadde lost his children and his temporel substance, and in his body endured and receyved ful many a grevous tribulacioun; yet seyde he thus: 'our lord hath yeven it me, our lord hath biraft it me; right as our lord hath wold, right so it is doon; blessed be the name of our lord.' " To thise foreseide thinges answerde Melibeus un-to his wyf Prudence: "Alle thy wordes," quod he, "been sothe, and therto profitable; but trewely myn herte is troubled with this sorwe so grevously, that I noot what to done." "Lat calle," quod Prudence, "thy trewe freendes alle, and thy linage whiche that been wyse; telleth your cas, and herkneth what they seye in conseiling, and yow governe after hir sentence. Salomon seith: 'werk alle thy thinges by conseil, and thou shalt never repente.' "

8. Thanne, by the conseil of his wyf Prudence, this Melibeus leet callen a greet congregacioun of folk; as surgiens, phisiciens, olde folk and yonge, and somme of hise olde enemys reconsiled as by hir semblaunt to his love and in-to his grace; and ther-with-al ther comen somme of hise neighebores that diden him reverence more for drede than for

love, as it happeth ofte. Ther comen also ful many subtile flatereres, and wyse advocats lerned in the lawe.

there came also a great many subtle flatterers; and there were wise advocates learned in the law.

9. And whan this folk togidre assembled weren, this Melibeus in sorweful wyse shewed hem his cas; and by the manere of his speche it semed that in herte he bar a cruel ire, redy to doon vengeaunce up-on hise foos, and sodeynly desired that the werre sholde biginne; but nathelees yet axed he hir conseil upon this matere. A surgien, by licence and assent of swiche as weren wyse, up roos and un-to Melibeus seyde as ye may here.

And when all these folks were assembled together, Melibeus, with sorrowful words and mien, told them his trouble; and by the manner of his speech it appeared that in his heart he bore a savage anger, ready to take vengeance upon his foes, and was desirous that the war upon them should quickly come. Nevertheless, he asked their advice upon this matter. Then a surgeon, by leave and voice of all present who were wise, rose up and spoke to Melibeus as you shall hear.

10. "Sir," quod he, "as to us surgiens aperteneth, that we do to every wight the beste that we can, wher-as we been with-holde, and to our pacients that we do no damage; wherfore it happeth, many tyme and ofte, that whan twey men han everich wounded other, oon same surgien heleth hem bothe; wherefore un-to our art it is nat pertinent to norice werre, ne parties to supporte. But certes, as to the warisshinge of your doghter, al-be-it so that she perilously be wounded, we shullen do so ententif bisinesse fro day to night, that with the grace of god she shal be hool and sound as sone as is possible." Almost right in the same wyse the phisiciens answerden, save that they seyden a fewe wordes more: "That, right as maladyes been cured by hir contraries, right so shul men warisshe werre by vengeaunce." His neighebores, ful of envye, his feyned freendes that semeden reconsiled, and his flatereres, maden semblant of weping, and empeireden and agreggeden muchel of this matere, in preising greetly Melibee of might, of power, of richesse, and of freendes, despysinge the power of his adversaries, and seiden outrely that he anon sholde wreken him on his foos and biginne werre.

"Sir," said he, "as for us surgeons, it belongs to us that we do for everyone the best that we can, when we have been retained, and that we do no harm to our patients. Wherefore it happens, many times and oft, that when two men have wounded one another, the same surgeon heals them both. Therefore it does not become us to foment warfare nor to support factions. And certainly, as to the healing of your daughter, although she is dangerously wounded, we will be so attentive, by day and by night, that, with God's grace, she shall be made sound and whole again, and that as soon as may be possible."

Almost in the same words the physicians answered, save that they added: "Just as diseases are cured by their contraries, so shall men cure war by vengeance."

His neighbours full of envy, his false friends who feigned to be reconciled to him, and his flatterers, made a semblance of weeping; and they greatly aggravated the matter by praising Melibeus, speaking of his might, his power, his wealth, and his friends, and disparaging the strength of his enemies; and they said outright, that very swiftly he should begin the war and wreak vengeance upon his foes.

11. Up roos thanne an advocat that was wys, by leve and by conseil of othere that were wyse, and seyde: "Lordinges, the nede for which we been assembled in this place is a ful hevy thing and an heigh matere, by-cause of the wrong and of the wikkednesse that hath be doon, and eek by resoun of the grete damages that in tyme cominge been possible to fallen for this same cause; and eek by resoun of the grete richesse and power of the parties bothe; for the whiche resouns it were a ful greet peril to erren in this matere. Wherfore, Melibeus, this is our sentence: we conseille yow aboven alle thing, that right anon thou do thy diligence in kepinge of thy propre persone, in swich a wyse that thou ne wante noon espye ne wacche, thy body for to save. And after that we conseille, that in thyn hous thou sette suffisant garnisoun, so that they may as wel thy body as thyn hous defende. But certes, for to moeve werre, or sodeynly for to doon vengeaunce, we may nat demen in so litel tyme that it were profitable. Wherfore we axen leyser and espace to have deliberacioun in this cas to deme. For the commune proverbe seith thus: 'he that sone demeth, sone shal repente.' And eek men seyn that thilke juge is wys, that sone understondeth a matere and juggeth by leyser. For al-be-it so that alle tary-

Then arose an advocate, a wise man, by leave and advice of others who were wise, and said: "Masters, the matter for which we are assembled here is a heavy thing, and a high, what with the wrong and wickedness that have been done, and by reason of the great evil that may follow hereafter from this same cause; and, too, by reason of the great wealth and power of both parties. For all of these reasons it were dangerous indeed to err in this matter. Wherefore, Melibeus, this is our judgment: we counsel you above all things, that, without delay, you take steps to guard your own person in such wise that you shall lack neither spy nor watchman. And we counsel, that in your house you establish a sufficient garrison, so that the house may be as well defended as you yourself. But, to say truth, as to initiating warfare in order to obtain a sudden revenge, we can give no opinion, in so short a time, on whether such a move will be profitable. Therefore we ask for leisure and time wherein to deliberate upon the matter more fully. For the common proverb runs 'Resolve in haste, in haste repent.' And besides, men hold that he is a wise judge who quickly understands a case and leisurely pronounces thereupon. For though delay may be annoying, nevertheless it is not to be blamed when it is a question of rendering just judgments, or of securing vengeance, when the delay is both sufficient and reasonable. And that was shown, in example, by Our Lord Jesus Christ. For when the woman taken in adultery was brought into His presence, in order to learn what He would have them to do with her, though He well knew what He would thereafter answer, yet would He not answer quickly, but deliberated; and He stooped down and wrote twice upon the ground. For all these reasons, we ask time in which to deliberate, and thereafter we will counsel you, by the grace of God, as to the most profitable course."

Up started, then, all of the young folk, at once, and the greater part of them scorned the counsel of the old wise men; and they raised a clamour and said: that just as it is well to strike while the iron is hot, so should men wreak their vengeance while they are fresh in anger. And they all cried loudly, "War, war!"

Upon this, one of the old wise ones arose, and with his hand commanding silence and attention, he said: "Masters, there is many a man to cry 'War, War!' who yet knows but little of the meaning of it. War, in the beginning, has so high an entrance, and so wide, that every man may enter when he pleases, and may find war easily. But truly, what the end of war shall be is not so easy to know. For when a war is once begun, many an unborn child shall die in the womb because of the strife, or else shall be born into sorrow and die in wretchedness. Therefore, ere any war begins, men should take much counsel together and act only after much deliberation."

But when this old man thought to reinforce his words with reasons, then well-nigh all the younger folk arose and began to heckle him and to break up his argument, bidding him cut short his remarks. For indeed, he that preaches to those who have ears but hear not, makes of himself a nuisance. As Jesus son of Sirach says: "A tale out of season is as musick in mourning." Which is to say, it avails as much to speak to folk to whom the speech is annoying as to sing before one who weeps. And when this wise man understood that he lacked an audience, he sat down again, much confused. For Solomon says: "When there is none will hear thee, cease to speak." "I see well," said this wise man, "that the proverb says truth, which runs, 'Good counsel is wanting when it is most needed.' "

Again, Melibeus had in his council many men who said one thing in his private ear and spoke otherwise in general audience.

When Melibeus heard that the greater part of his councillors were agreed on war, straightway he showed himself in accord with them and confirmed their judgment. Then Dame Prudence, seeing that her husband shaped his course for war and revenge, humbly and after biding her time, said to him: "My lord, I beseech you as earnestly as I dare and can,

ing be anoyful, algates it is nat to repreve in yevinge of jugement, ne in vengeance-taking, whan it is suffisant and resonable. And that shewed our lord Jesu Crist by ensample; for whan that the womman that was taken in avoutrie was broght in his presence, to knowen what sholde be doon with hir persone, al-be-it so that he wiste wel him-self what that he wolde answere, yet ne wolde he nat answere sodeynly, but he wolde have deliberacioun, and in the ground he wroot twyes. And by thise causes we axen deliberacioun, and we shal thanne, by the grace of god, conseille thee thing that shal be profitable."

12. Up stirten thanne the yonge folk at-ones, and the moste partie of that companye han scorned the olde wyse men, and bigonnen to make noyse, and seyden: that, right so as whyl that iren is hoot, men sholden smyte, right so, men sholde wreken hir wronges whyle that they been fresshe and newe; and with loud voys they cryden, "werre! werre!"

Up roos tho oon of thise olde wyse, and with his hand made contenaunce that men sholde holden hem stille and yeven him audience. "Lordinges," quod he, "ther is ful many a man that cryeth 'werre! werre!' that woot ful litel what werre amounteth. Werre at his biginning hath so greet an entree and so large, that every wight may entre whan him lyketh, and lightly finde werre. But, certes, what ende that shal ther-of bifalle, it is nat light to knowe. For sothly, whan that werre is ones bigonne, ther is ful many a child unborn of his moder, that shal sterve yong by-cause of that ilke werre, or elles live in sorwe and dye in wrecchednesse. And ther-fore, er that any werre biginne, men moste have greet conseil and greet deliberacioun." And whan this olde man wende to enforcen his tale by resons, wel ny alle at-ones bigonne they to ryse for to breken his tale, and beden him ful ofte his wordes for to abregge. For soothly, he that precheth to hem that listen nat heren his wordes, his sermon hem anoyeth. For Jesus Syrak seith: that "musik in wepinge is anoyous thing"; this is to seyn: as muche availleth to speken bifore folk to whiche his speche anoyeth, as dooth to singe biforn him that wepeth. And whan this wyse man saugh that him wanted audience, al shamefast he sette him doun agayn. For Salomon seith: "ther-as thou ne mayst have noon audience, enforce thee nat to speke." "I see wel," quod this wyse man, "that the commune proverbe is sooth; that 'good conseil wanteth whan it is most nede.' "

13. Yet hadde this Melibeus in his conseil many folk, that prively in his ere conseilled him certeyn thing, and conseilled him the contrarie in general audience.

Whan Melibeus hadde herd that the gretteste partie of his conseil weren accorded that he sholde maken werre, anoon he consented to hir conseilling, and fully affermed hir sentence. Thanne dame Prudence, whan that she saugh how that hir housbonde shoop him for to wreken him on his foos, and to biginne werre, she in ful humble wyse, when she saugh hir tyme, seide him thise wordes: "My lord," quod she, "I yow biseche as hertely as I dar and can, ne haste yow nat to faste, and for alle guerdons as yeveth me audience. For Piers Alfonce seith: 'who-so that dooth to that other good or harm, haste thee nat to quyten it; for in this wyse thy freend wol abyde, and thyn enemy shal the lenger live in drede.' The proverbe seith: 'he hasteth wel that wysely can abyde'; and in wikked haste is no profit."

that you go not too hastily in this matter; and for your own good give me a hearing. For Petrus Alfonsus says: 'And if one man do to another any good or any evil, let there be no haste to repay it in kind; for then will the friend remain friendly, while the enemy shall but the longer fear.' The proverb has it: 'He hastens well who wisely can delay.' And in foolish haste there is no profit."

14. This Melibee answerde un-to his wyf Prudence: "I purpose nat," quod he, "to werke by thy conseil, for many causes and resouns. For certes every wight wolde holde me thanne a fool; this is to seyn, if I, for thy conseilling, wolde chaungen thinges that been ordeyned and affermed by so manye wyse. Secoundly I seye, that alle wommen been wikke and noon good of hem alle. For 'of a thousand men,' seith Salomon, 'I fond a good man: but certes, of alle wommen, good womman fond I never.' And also certes, if I governed me by thy conseil, it sholde seme that I hadde yeve to thee over me the maistrie; and god forbede that it so were. For Jesus Syrak seith; 'that if the wyf have maistrie, she is contrarious to hir housbonde.' And Salomon seith: 'never in thy lyf, to thy wyf, ne to thy child, ne to thy freend, ne yeve no power over thyself. For bettre it were that thy children aske of thy persone thinges that hem nedeth, than thou see thy-self in the handes of thy children.' And also, if I wolde werke by thy conseilling, certes my conseilling moste som tyme be secree, til it were tyme that it moste be knowe; and this ne may noght be. [For it is writen, that 'the janglerie of wommen can hyden thinges that they witen noght.' Furthermore, the philosophre seith, 'in wikked conseil wommen venquisshe men'; and for thise resouns I ne ow nat usen thy conseil."

This Melibeus answered Prudence his wife: "I purpose not to work by your counsel, for many causes and reasons. For truly every man would then take me for a fool; by which I mean: if I by your advising, should change things that have been ordained and confirmed by so many wise men. Secondly, I say that all women are evil and none good. 'Behold, this have I found (saith the Preacher), counting one by one, to find out the account; which yet my soul seeketh, but I found not: one man among a thousand have I found; but a woman among all those have I not found.' And certainly, if I were to be governed by your counsel, it would appear as if I had given over to you my sovereignty; and may God forbid that such a thing should ever be. For Jesus son of Sirach says: 'A woman, if she maintain her husband, is full of anger, impudence, and much reproach.' And Solomon says: 'Give not thy son and wife, thy brother and friend, power over thee while thou livest, and give not thy goods to another: lest it repent thee, and thou entreat for the same again. As long as thou livest and hast breath in thee, give not thyself over to any. For better it is that thy children should seek to thee, than that thou shouldest stand to their courtesy.' And also, if I were to work according to your counselling, certain it is that my counsels must be kept secret until the proper time to make them known; and this could not thus be. For it is written that 'The chattering of women can conceal nothing except that which they do not know.' Furthermore, the philosopher says: 'In evil counsel women surpass men.' And for all these reasons I will not follow your advice."

15. Whanne dame Prudence, ful debonairly and with greet pacience, hadde herd al that hir housbonde lyked for to seye, thanne axed she of him licence for to speke, and seyde in this wyse. "My lord," quod she, "as to your firste resoun, certes it may lightly been answered. For I seye, that it is no folie to chaunge conseil whan the thing is chaunged; or elles whan the thing semeth otherweyes than it was biforn. And more-over I seye, that though ye han sworn and bihight to perfourne your emprise, and nathelees ye weyve to perfourne thilke same emprise by juste cause, men sholde nat seyn therefore that ye were a lyer ne forsworn. For the book seith, that 'the wyse man maketh no lesing whan he turneth his corage to the bettre.' And al-be-it so that your emprise be establissed and ordeyned by greet multitude of folk, yet thar ye nat accomplice thilke same ordinaunce but yow lyke. For the trouthe of thinges and the profit been rather foun-

When Dame Prudence, very affably and with great patience, had heard all that her husband chose to say, then she asked of him leave to speak, and said: "My lord, as to your first reason, surely it may readily be answered. For I say that it is no folly to over-rule counsel when circumstances are changed, or when the cause appears otherwise than at the first. And, moreover, I say that though you have sworn and warranted to perform your enterprise, nevertheless, should you refuse for just cause to perform it, men will not therefore say that you are a liar and forsworn. For the book says that the wise man deals not falsely when he changes his first purpose for a better one. And although your undertaking be ordained and established by a great many men, yet you need not accomplish it, unless you like. For the truth of things, and the profit thereof, are found rather among a few folk who are wise and reasonable than among the multitude, where every man cries and gabbles as he likes. Truly such a crowd is not worthy of honour. As to the second reason, wherein you say that all women are evil, then certainly, saving your grace, you must despise all women by so saying; and he that despises all displeases all, as the book says. And Seneca says that 'Whoso has sapience will not any man dispraise; but he will gladly impart such knowledge as he can, and that without presumption and pride. And for such things as he knows not, he will not be ashamed to inquire of and learn from lesser folk.' And, sir, that there has been many a good woman may be easily proved. For certainly, sir, Our Lord Jesus Christ would never have condescended to be born of a woman if all women had been evil. And thereafter, for the great worth that is in women, Our Lord Jesus Christ, when He had risen from death unto life, appeared to a woman, rather than to His disciples. And although Solomon says that he never found good in any woman, it follows not, therefore, that all women are wicked. For, though he may never have found a good woman, surely many another man has found full many a woman to be both good and true. Or perchance Solomon's meaning was this: that so far as the highest virtue is concerned, he found no such woman; which is to say, that there is no one who has sovereign goodness and worth, save God alone, as He Himself has caused to be recorded in His gospels. For there is no creature so good that he is not somehow wanting in the perfection of God, Who is his Maker. Your third reason is this: You say that if you were to be governed by my counsel, it should appear as if you had given over to me the mastery and sovereignty of your person. Sir, saving your presence, it is not so. For, if it were true, then, in order that no man should ever be advised, save by those who had mastery over his person, men could not so often be advised. For truly, every man who asks counsel concerning any purpose yet retains his freedom to choose whether he will or will not proceed by that counselling. And as to your fourth reason, wherein you say that the chattering of women can hide things of the which they are not aware, as one might say that a woman cannot hide what she knows—sir, these words are only to be understood of women who are both evil and gossipy; of which women men say that three things will drive a man out of his own house: smoke, and the dripping of rain, and a wicked wife. And further, of such women, Solomon says: 'It were better to dwell in a corner of the housetop than with a brawling woman in a wide house.' And, sir, by your leave, that I am not; for you have often enough tested my ability to keep silence, and tried my patience, and even how I can hide and conceal matters that men ought to keep secret. And, in good truth, as to your fifth reason, wherein you say that in evil counsel women surpass men, God knows that this reason has no standing here. For understand now, you ask counsel to do wickedness; and if your will is to work wickedness, and your wife restrains such an ill purpose and overcomes you by reason and good counsel given, then, certainly, your wife ought rather to be praised than

den in fewe folk that been wyse and ful of resoun, than by greet multitude of folk, ther every man cryeth and clatereth what that him lyketh. Soothly swich multitude is nat honeste. As to the seconde resoun, where-as ye seyn that 'alle wommen been wikke,' save your grace, certes ye despysen alle wommen in this wyse; and 'he that alle despyseth alle displeseth,' as seith the book. And Senek seith that 'who-so wole have sapience, shal no man dispreise; but he shal gladly techen the science that he can, with-outen presumpcioun or pryde. And swiche thinges as he nought ne can, he shal nat been ashamed to lerne hem and enquere of lasse folk than him-self.' And sir, that ther hath been many a good womman, may lightly be preved. For certes, sir, our lord Jesu Crist wolde never have descended to be born of a womman, if alle wommen hadden ben wikke. And after that, for the grete bountee that is in wommen, our lord Jesu Crist, whan he was risen fro deeth to lyve, appeered rather to a womman than to his apostles. And though that Salomon seith, that 'he ne fond never womman good,' it folweth nat therfore that alle wommen ben wikke. For though that he ne fond no good womman, certes, ful many another man hath founden many a womman ful good and trewe. Or elles per-aventure the entente of Salomon was this; that, as in sovereyn bountee, he fond no womman; this is to seyn, that ther is no wight that hath sovereyn bountee save god allone; as he him-self recordeth in his Evaungelie. For ther nis no creature so good that him ne wanteth somwhat of the perfeccioun of god, that is his maker. Your thridde resoun is this: ye seyn that 'if ye governe yow by my conseil, it sholde seme that ye hadde yeve me the maistrie and the lordshipe over your persone.' Sir, save your grace, it is nat so. For if it were so, that no man sholde be conseilled but only of hem that hadden lordshipe and maistrie of his persone, men wolden nat be conseilled so ofte. For soothly, thilke man that asketh conseil of a purpos, yet hath he free chois, wheither he wole werke by that conseil or noon. And as to your fourthe resoun, ther ye seyn that 'the janglerie of wommen hath hid thinges that they woot noght,' as who seith, that 'a womman can nat hyde that she woot'; sir, thise wordes been understonde of wommen that been jangleresses and wikked; of whiche wommen, men seyn that 'three thinges dryven a man out of his hous; that is to seyn, smoke, dropping of reyn, and wikked wyves'; and of swiche wommen seith Salomon, that 'it were bettre dwelle in desert, than with a womman that is riotous.' And sir, by your leve, that am nat I; for ye han ful ofte assayed my grete silence and my gret pacience; and eek how wel that I can hyde and hele thinges that men oghte secreely to hyde. And soothly, as to your fifthe resoun, wher-as ye seyn, that 'in wikked conseil wommen venquisshe men'; god woot, thilke resoun stant here in no stede. For understond now, ye asken conseil to do wikkednesse; and if ye wole werken wikkednesse, and your wyf restreyneth thilke wikked purpos, and overcometh yow by resoun and by good conseil; certes, your wyf oghte rather to be preised than y-blamed. Thus sholde ye understonde the philosophre that seith, 'in wikked conseil wommen venquisshen hir housbondes.' And ther-as ye blamen alle wommen and hir resouns, I shal shewe yow by manye ensamples that many a womman hath ben ful good, and yet been; and hir conseils ful hoolsome and profitable. Eek som men han seyd, that 'the conseillinge of wommen is outher to dere, or elles to litel of prys.' But al-be-it so, that ful many a womman is badde, and hir conseil vile and noght worth, yet han men founde ful many a good womman, and ful discrete and wise in conseillinge. Lo, Jacob, by good conseil of his moder Rebekka, wan the benisoun of Ysaak his fader, and the lordshipe over alle his bretheren. Judith, by hir good conseil, delivered the citee of Bethulie, in which she dwelled, out of the handes of Olofernus, that hadde it biseged and wolde have al destroyed it. Abigail delivered Nabal hir housbonde fro David the King, that wolde have slayn him, and apaysed the ire of the king by hir wit and by hir good conseilling. Hester by hir good conseil enhaunced greetly the peple of god in the regne of Assuerus the king. And the same bountee in good conseilling of many a good womman may men telle. And moreover, whan our lord hadde creat Adam our forme-fader, he seyde in this wyse: 'it is nat good to been a man allone; make we to him an help semblable to himself.' Here may ye se that, if that wommen were nat goode, and hir conseils goode and profitable, our lord god of hevene wolde never han wroght hem, ne called hem help of man, but rather confusioun of man. And ther seyde ones a clerk in two vers: 'what is bettre than gold? Jaspre. What is bettre than jaspre? Wisdom. And what is bettre than wisdom? Womman. And what is bettre than a good womman? No-thing.' And sir, by manye of othre resons may ye seen, that manye wommen been goode, and hir conseils goode and profitable. And therfore sir, if ye wol triste to my conseil, I shal restore yow your doghter hool and sound. And eek I wol do to yow so muche, that ye shul have honour in this cause."

16. Whan Melibee hadde herd the wordes of his wyf Prudence, he seyde thus: "I see wel that the word of Salomon is sooth; he seith, that 'wordes that been spoken discreetly by ordinaunce, been honycombes; for they yeven swetnesse to the soule, and hoolsomnesse to the body.' And wyf, by-cause of thy swete wordes, and eek for I have assayed and preved thy grete sapience and thy grete trouthe, I wol governe me by thy conseil in alle thing."

17. "Now sir," quod dame Prudence, "and sin ye vouche-sauf to been governed by my conseil, I wol enforme yow how ye shul governe your-self in chesinge of your conseillours. Ye shul first, in alle your werkes, mekely biseken to the heighe god that he wol be your conseillour; and shapeth yow to swich entente, that he yeve yow conseil and confort, as taughte Thobie his sone: 'at alle tymes thou

blamed. Thus should you understand the saw of the philosopher who says that in evil counsel women surpass their husbands. And whereas you blame all women and their reasonings, I will show you, by many examples, that many women have been good and are yet, and have given counsel both wholesome and profitable. True, some men have said that the advice of women is either too dear or too cheap in price. But, be it that many a woman is bad, and her counsel vile and worthless, yet men have found many a good woman, full wise and full discreet in giving counsel. Behold how Jacob, by following the good advice of his mother Rebecca, won the blessing of Isaac, his father, and came to authority over all his brethren. Judith, by her good counsel, delivered the city of Bethulia, wherein she dwelt, out of the hands of Holofernes, who besieged it and who would have completely destroyed it. Abigail delivered her husband Nabal from David the king, who would have slain him, and appeased the anger of the king by her wit and good advising. Esther, by her good counsel, greatly exalted the people of God in the reign of King Ahasuerus. And men may tell much of the same excellence of good advice in many a good woman. Moreover, when Our Lord had created Adam, our forefather, he said thus: 'It is not good that the man should be alone: I will make him a help meet for him.' Here you may see that, if women were not good, and their counsels good and profitable, Our Lord God of Heaven would never have wrought them, nor called them the help of man, but, rather, the confusion of man. And once a writer said, in two verses: 'What is better than gold? Jasper. What is better than jasper? Wisdom. What is better than wisdom? Woman. And what is better than woman? Nothing.' And, sir, by many other examples you may see that women are good and their counselling both good and profitable. And thereupon, sir, if you will trust to my advice, I will restore to you your daughter whole and sound. And moreover, I will do for you so much that you shall come out of this affair with honour."

When Melibeus had listened to the words of his wife Prudence, he said: "I see well that the word of Solomon is true. He says, 'Pleasant words are as a honeycomb, sweet to the soul and health to the bones.' And, wife, because of your sweet words, and because, moreover, I have tried and proved your great wisdom and your great truthfulness, I will be governed in all things by your counsels."

"Now, sir," said Dame Prudence, "since you give yourself to be governed by my advice, I will tell you how to choose your councillors. You shall first, in all your works, meekly pray to the high God that He will be your adviser, and you shall mould your understanding in such wise that He may give you counsel and comfort, as Tobit taught his son, that is to say: 'Bless the Lord thy God always, and desire of Him that thy ways may be directed and that all thy paths and counsels may prosper.' And look to it that all your counsels are in Him for evermore. Saint James, also, says: 'If any of you lack wisdom, let him ask of God.' And after that, then shall you take counsel within yourself, and examine well your thoughts, concerning all things that seem to be the best for your own profit. And then shall you drive from your heart three things that are opposed to the following of good counsel, and they are anger, and covetousness, and hastiness.

"First, he that takes counsel within himself, certainly he must be free from anger, and this for many reasons. The first one is this: He that has great ire and wrath within himself thinks always that he is capable of doing things that he cannot do. Secondly, he that is angry and full of wrath cannot think or judge well, and he that cannot judge well cannot well advise. The third reason is this: That 'He that is angry,' as says Seneca, 'can speak only to berate and blame.' And thus with his vicious words he drives others into a like state.

"And too, sir, you must drive covetousness out of your heart. For the Apostle says that 'The love of money is the root of all evil.' And, trust me, a covetous man cannot judge correctly, nor can he think well, save only to the furtherance of his covetousness; and that, in truth, can never really be accomplished, because the richer he becomes, the greater desire has he for yet a larger abundance.

"And, sir, you must drive hastiness out of your inmost heart. For certain it is that you cannot hold to be best the sudden thought that comes into your heart, but you must weigh it and advise upon it. For, as you have heard before, the common proverb has it that he who resolves in haste soon repents. Sir, you are not always in like mood and of a like disposition; for surely that which at one time seems good to you, at another appears to be quite the contrary.

"When you have taken counsel within yourself, and have, after due deliberation, deemed such, or such, a thing to be for the best, then, I advise you, keep it secret. Reveal not your intentions to any person, save to such as you may certainly know will be of help to render your position more tenable through such revelation. For Jesus son of Sirach says: 'Whether it be to a friend or a foe, talk not of other men's lives; and if thou canst without offense, reveal them not. For he heard and observed thee, and when time cometh he will hate thee.' And another writer says: 'Hardly shalt thou find one person who can keep secrets.' The Book says: 'While thou dost keep thy counsel in thine own heart, thou keepest it imprisoned; and when thou revealest it to anyone, he holdeth thee imprisoned.' And therefore it is better that you hide your thoughts within your own heart, than pray to him to whom you have told them that he will be close and keep silence. For Seneca says: 'If thou canst not keep thine own counsel, how darest thou beg of another that he will do so?' But, nevertheless, if you deem certainly that the revealing of your secret to anyone will better your condition,

shalt blesse god, and praye him to dresse thy weyes'; and looke that alle thy conseils been in him for evermore. Seint Jame eek seith: 'if any of yow have nede of sapience, axe it of god.' And afterward thanne shul ye taken conseil in your-self, and examine wel your thoghtes, of swich thing as yow thinketh that is best for your profit. And thanne shul ye dryve fro your herte three thinges that been contrariouse to good conseil, that is to seyn, ire, coveitise, and hastifnesse.

18. First, he that axeth conseil of him-self, certes he moste been with-outen ire, for manye causes. The firste is this: he that hath greet ire and wratthe in him-self, he weneth alwey that he may do thing that he may nat do. And secoundely, he that is irous and wroth, he ne may nat wel deme; and he that may nat wel deme, may nat wel conseille. The thridde is this; that 'he that is irous and wrooth,' as seith Senek, 'ne may nat speke but he blame thinges'; and with his viciouse wordes he stireth other folk to angre and to ire. And eek sir, ye moste dryve coveitise out of your herte. For the apostle seith, that 'coveitise is rote of alle harmes.' And trust wel that a coveitous man ne can noght deme ne thinke, but only to fulfille the ende of his coveitise; and certes, that ne may never been accompliced; for ever the more habundaunce that he hath of richesse, the more he desyreth. And sir, ye moste also dryve out of your herte hastifnesse; for certes, ye ne may nat deme for the beste a sodeyn thought that falleth in youre herte, but ye moste avyse yow on it ful ofte. For as ye herde biforn, the commune proverbe is this, that 'he that sone demeth, sone repenteth.'

19. Sir, ye ne be nat alwey in lyke disposicioun; for certes, som thing that somtyme semeth to yow that it is good for to do, another tyme it semeth to yow the contrarie.

20. Whan ye han taken conseil in your-self, and han demed by good deliberacion swich thing as you semeth best, thanne rede I yow, that ye kepe it secree. Biwrey nat your conseil to no persone, but-if so be that ye wenen sikerly that, thurgh your biwreying, your condicioun shal be to yow the more profitable. For Jesus Syrak seith: 'neither to thy foo ne to thy freend discovere nat thy secree ne thy folie; for they wol yeve yow audience and loking and supportacioun in thy presence, and scorne thee in thyn absence.' Another clerk seith, that 'scarsly shaltou finden any persone that may kepe conseil secreely.' The book seith: 'whyl that thou kepest thy conseil in thyn herte, thou kepest it in thy prisoun: and whan thou biwreyest thy conseil to any wight, he holdeth thee in his snare.' And therefore yow is bettre to hyde your conseil in your herte, than praye him, to whom ye han biwreyed your conseil, that he wole kepen it cloos and stille. For Seneca seith: 'if so be that thou ne mayst nat thyn owene conseil hyde, how darstou prayen any other wight thy conseil secreely to kepe?' But nathelees, if thou wene sikerly that the biwreying of thy con-

seil to a persone wol make thy condicioun to stonden in the bettre plyt, thanne shaltou tellen him thy conseil in this wyse. First, thou shalt make no semblant whether thee were lever pees or werre, or this or that, ne shewe him nat thy wille and thyn entente; for trust wel, that comunly thise conseillours been flatereres, namely the conseillours of grete lordes; for they enforcen hem alwey rather to speken plesante wordes, enclyninge to the lordes lust, than wordes that been trewe or profitable. And therfore men seyn, that 'the riche man hath seld good conseil but-if he have it of himself.' And after that, thou shalt considere thy freendes and thyne enemys. And as touchinge thy freendes, thou shalt considere whiche of hem been most feithful and most wyse, and eldest and most approved in conseilling. And of hem shalt thou aske thy conseil, as the caas requireth.

then tell it to him in this wise. First, you shall give no indication whether you prefer peace or war, or this or that, and show him not your determination and intent; for, trust me, councillors are commonly flatterers, especially the councillors of great lords. For they are at pains always to speak pleasantly, inclining toward the lord's desire, rather than to use words that are, in themselves, true and profitable. And therefore men say that the rich man rarely receives good counsel, save as he has it from himself. And after that, you shall consider your friends and your enemies. Touching your friends, you must consider which of them are most old and faithful, and wisest, and most approved in counselling. And of them shall you ask advice, as the event requires.

21. I seye that first ye shul clepe to your conseil your freendes that been trewe. For Salomon seith: that 'right as the herte of a man delyteth in savour that is sote, right so the conseil of trewe freendes yeveth swetenesse to the soule.' He seith also: 'ther may no-thing be lykned to the trewe freend.' For certes, gold ne silver beth nat so muche worth as the gode wil of a trewe freend. And eek he seith, that 'a trewe freend is a strong deffense; who-so that it findeth, certes he findeth a greet tresour.' Thanne shul ye eek considere, if that your trewe freendes been discrete and wyse. For the book seith: 'axe alwey thy conseil of hem that been wyse.' And by this same resoun shul ye clepen to your conseil, of your freendes that been of age, swiche as han seyn and been expert in manye thinges, and been approved in conseillinges. For the book seith, that 'in olde men is the sapience and in longe tyme the prudence.' And Tullius seith: that 'grete thinges ne been nat ay accompliced by strengthe, ne by delivernesse of body, but by good conseil, by auctoritee of persones, and by science; the whiche three thinges ne been nat feble by age, but certes they enforcen and encreesen day by day.' And thanne shul ye kepe this for a general reule. First shul ye clepen to your conseil a fewe of your freendes that been especiale; for Salomon seith: 'manye freendes have thou; but among a thousand chese thee oon to be thy conseillour.' For al-be-it so that thou first ne telle thy conseil but to a fewe, thou mayst afterward telle it to mo folk, if it be nede. But loke alwey that thy conseillours have thilke three condiciouns that I have seyd bifore; that is to seyn, that they be trewe, wyse, and of old experience. And werke nat alwey in every nede by oon conseillour allone; for somtyme bihoveth it to been conseilled by manye. For Salomon seith: 'salvacioun of thinges is wheras ther been manye conseillours'.

"I say that first you must call into council such of your friends as are true. For Solomon says: 'Ointment and perfume rejoice the heart; so doth the sweetness of a man's friend by hearty counsel.' He says also: 'Nothing doth countervail a faithful friend, and his excellency is invaluable.' For certain it is that neither gold nor silver are worth so much as the goodwill of a true friend. Again he says: 'A faithful friend is a strong defence: and he that hath found such an one hath found a treasure.'

"Then, too, shall you consider whether your real, friends are discreet and wise. For the Book says: 'Stand in the multitude of the elders, and cleave unto him that is wise.' And for this reason you should call to your council, of your friends that have arrived at a proper age, those who have seen and experienced many things, and who have been approved in parliaments. For the Book says: 'With the ancient is wisdom; and in length of days understanding.' And Tullius says: 'Great things are not accomplished by strength and activity of body, but by counsel, authority, and knowledge; and these things do not become enfeebled with age, but rather grow stronger and increase day after day.'

"And then you shall keep this for a general rule. First, you shall call to your council but a few of your most special friends. For Solomon says: 'Have thou many friends, but of a thousand choose but one to be thy councillor.' And although you should, at the first, tell your secrets to but a few, afterward you may tell them to others, if there be need. But look to it always that your councillors have the three attributes that I have mentioned, namely: that they are true, wise, and experienced. And act not always, and in every need, by the advice of one councillor alone; for sometimes it is well to have the advice of many. Says Solomon: 'Without counsel purposes are disappointed: but in the multitude of councillors they are established.'

22. Now sith that I have told yow of which folk ye sholde been counseilled, now wol I teche yow which conseil ye oghte to eschewe. First ye shul eschewe the conseilling of foles; for Salomon seith:

"Now that I have told you of the sort of folk by whom you should be counselled, I will teach you which sort of counsel you ought to eschew. First, you shall avoid the counselling of fools. For Solomon says: 'Consult not with a fool, for he cannot keep counsel.' It is said in a book that the characteristic of a fool is this: he readily believes evil of everyone, and as readily believes all good of himself. You shall also eschew the counselling of all flatterers, such as force themselves rather to praise your person than to tell you the truth about things.

"Wherefore Tullius says, that of all the pestilences of friendship, the greatest is flattery. And so it is more needful that you eschew and fear flatterers than any other kind of men. The Book says that one should rather flee from and fear the sweet words of flatterers than the earnest words of the friend who tells one the truth. Solomon says that the words of a flatterer are a snare wherewith to catch innocents. He says also, that he who speaks sweet words to his friend, sets before his feet a net to catch him. And therefore says Tullius Cicero: 'Incline not thine ears to flatterers, nor take counsel of flattering words.' And Cato says: 'Be well advised, and avoid sweet and pleasant words.' And you must also eschew the counsels of such of your former enemies as have become reconciled to you. The Book says that no one can safely trust to the goodwill of a former enemy. And Æsop says: 'Trust not to those with whom you have been sometime at war or in enmity, neither tell them of your intentions.' And Seneca tells us the reason for this. 'It may not be.' says he, 'that, where fire has long existed there shall remain no vapour of heat.' And thereto says Solomon: 'The kisses of an enemy are deceitful.' For, certainly, though your enemy may be reconciled, and appear before you in all humility, and bow his head to you, you should never trust him. Surely he feigns this humility more for his advantage than for any love of you; for he thinks to gain some victory over you by such feigning, the which he could not gain by strife of open war. And Petrus Alfonsus says: 'Have no fellowship with ancient foes; for if you do good to them, they will pervert it into evil.' And, too, you must eschew the advice of those who are your own servants and bear themselves toward you with all reverence; for perchance they speak more out of fear than for love. And therefore says a philosopher thus: 'There is no one perfectly true to him of whom he is afraid.' And Tullius says: 'There is no power of any emperor, fitted to endure, save it be founded more in the love of the people than in the fears.' You must also avoid the counselling of drunkards; for they can retain nothing. Solomon says that there is no secrecy where drunkenness reigns. You should also suspect the counsels of such as advise you privately to one thing and to a contrary thing in public. For Cassiodorus says that it is but an artifice to hinder when a man does one thing openly and its contrary in private. You should also hold suspect the counselling of the wicked. For the Book says that the advice of the wicked is always full of fraud. And David says that he is a happy man who has not followed the counselling of villains. You should also avoid and shun

'taak no conseil of a fool, for he ne can noght conseille but after his owene lust and his affeccioun.' The book seith: that 'the propretee of a fool is this; he troweth lightly harm of every wight, and lightly troweth alle bountee in himself.' Thou shalt eek eschewe the conseilling of alle flatereres, swiche as enforcen hem rather to preise your persone by flaterye than for to telle yow the sothfastnesse of thinges.

23. Wherfore Tullius seith: 'amonges alle the pestilences that been in freendshipe, the gretteste is flaterye.' And therfore is it more nede that thou eschewe and drede flatereres than any other peple. The book seith: 'thou shalt rather drede and flee fro the swete wordes of flateringe preiseres, than fro the egre wordes of thy freend that seith thee thy sothes.' Salomon seith, that 'the wordes of a flaterere is a snare to cacche with innocents.' He seith also, that 'he that speketh to his freend wordes of swetnesse and of plesaunce, setteth a net biforn his feet to cacche him.' And therfore seith Tullius: 'enclyne nat thynes eres to flatereres, ne taketh no conseil of wordes of flaterye.' And Caton seith: 'avyse thee wel, and eschewe the wordes of swetnesse and of plesaunce.' And eek thou shalt eschewe the conseilling of thyne olde enemys that been reconsiled. The book seith: that 'no wight retourneth saufly in-to the grace of his olde enemy.' And Isope seith: 'ne trust nat to hem to whiche thou hast had som-tyme werre or enmitee, ne telle hem nat thy conseil.' And Seneca telleth the cause why. 'It may nat be,' seith he, 'that, where greet fyr hath longe tyme endured, that ther ne dwelleth som vapour of warmnesse.' And therfore seith Salomon: 'in thyn olde foo trust never.' For sikerly, though thyn enemy be reconsiled and maketh thee chere of humilitee, and louteth to thee with his heed, ne trust him never. For certes, he maketh thilke feyned humilitee more for his profit than for any love of thy persone; by-cause that he demeth to have victorie over thy persone by swich feyned contenance, the which victorie he mighte nat have by stryf or werre. And Peter Alfonce seith: 'make no felawshipe with thyne olde enemys; for if thou do hem bountee, they wol perverten it into wikkednesse.' And eek thou most eschewe the conseilling of hem that been thy servants, and beren thee greet reverence; for peraventure they seyn it more for drede than for love. And therfore seith a philosophre in this wyse: 'ther is no wight parfitly trewe to him that he to sore dredeth.' And Tullius seith: 'ther nis no might so greet of any emperour, that longe may endure, but-if he have more love of the peple than drede.' Thou shalt also eschewe the conseiling of folk that been dronkelewe; for they ne can no conseil hyde. For Salomon seith: 'ther is no privetee ther-as regneth dronkenesse.' Ye shul also han in suspect the conseilling of swich folk as conseille yow a thing prively, and conseille yow the contrarie openly. For Cassidorie seith: that 'it is a maner sleighte to hindre, whan he sheweth to doon a thing openly

and werketh prively the contrarie.' Thou shalt also have in suspect the conseilling of wikked folk. For the book seith: 'the conseilling of wikked folk is alwey ful of fraude': And David seith: 'blisful is that man that hath nat folwed the conseilling of shrewes.' Thou shalt also eschewe the conseilling of yong folk; for hir conseil is nat rype.

24. Now sir, sith I have shewed yow of which folk ye shul take your conseil, and of which folk ye shul folwe the conseil, now wol I teche yow how ye shal examine your conseil, after the doctrine of Tullius. In the examininge thanne of your conseillour, ye shul considere manye thinges. Alderfirst thou shalt considere, that in thilke thing that thou purposest, and upon what thing thou wolt have conseil, that verray trouthe be seyd and conserved; this is to seyn, telle trewely thy tale. For he that seith fals may nat wel be conseilled, in that cas of which he lyeth. And after this, thou shalt considere the thinges that acorden to that thou purposest for to do by thy conseillours, if resoun accorde therto; and eek, if thy might may atteine ther-to; and if the more part and the bettre part of thy conseillours acorde ther-to, or no. Thanne shaltou considere what thing shal folwe of that conseilling; as hate, pees, werre, grace, profit, or damage; and manye othere thinges. And in alle thise thinges thou shalt chese the beste, and weyve alle other thinges. Thanne shaltow considere of what rote is engendred the matere of thy conseil, and what fruit it may conceyve and engendre. Thou shalt eek considere alle thise causes, fro whennes they been sprongen. And whan ye han examined your conseil as I have seyd, and which partie is the bettre and more profitable, and hast approved it by manye wyse folk and olde; thanne shaltou considere, if thou mayst parfourne it and maken of it a good ende. For certes, resoun wol nat that any man sholde biginne a thing, but-if he mighte parfourne it as him oghte. Ne no wight sholde take up-on hym so hevy a charge that he mighte nat bere it. For the proverbe seith: 'he that to muche embraceth, distreyneth litel.' And Catoun seith: 'assay to do swich thing as thou hast power to doon, lest that the charge oppresse thee so sore, that thee bihoveth to weyve thing that thou hast bigonne.' And if so be that thou be in doute, whether thou mayst parfourne a thing or noon, chese rather to suffre than biginne. And Piers Alphonce seith: 'if thou hast might to doon a thing of which thou most repente thee, it is bettre "nay" than "ye";' this is to seyn, that thee is bettre holde thy tonge stille, than for to speke. Thanne may ye understonde by strenger resons, that if thou hast power to parfourne a werk of which thou shalt repente, thanne is it bettre that thou suffre than biginne. Wel seyn they, that defenden every wight to assaye any thing of which he is in doute, whether he may parfourne it or no. And after, whan ye han examined your conseil as I have seyd biforn, and knowen wel that ye may parfourne youre emprise, conferme it thanne sadly til it be at an ende.

the advice of the young; for their judgments are not mature.

"And now, sir, that I have shown you as to the folk from whom you may take counsel, and what counsel you may accept and follow, now will I teach you how that counsel should be examined, according to the doctrines of Tullius. In bringing a councillor to the test, you must consider many things. First, you should consider that, in this very thing that you purpose, and upon which you are in need of advice, only the truth may be told; that is to say, state your case truthfully. For he that lies or prevaricates may not well be counselled, at least in so far as he has deceived. And after this, you must consider the things that agree with your purpose in council; whether reason agrees therewith; and whether you have power to attain your purpose; and whether the major and the better part of your council agree with it. Then shall you consider the probable result of acting upon all your advices: as hate, peace, war, honour, gain, loss, and many other things. And in all these things you must choose the best and avoid all else. Then must you take into consideration the root whereof is grown the matter of your counselling, and what fruit it may engender. Then, too, you shall consider all of the causes and examine into the causes of causes. And when you have examined your counselling as I have outlined to you, and have determined which part of it is the better and more profitable, and have found it to be approved by many wise and elderly men: then shall you consider whether you have power to carry it to a good end. For surely reason will not permit a man to begin a thing, save he carry it through as he should. Nor should anyone take upon himself a burden so heavy that he cannot bear it. For says the proverb: He that too much embraces, confines but little. And Cato says: 'Attempt only what thou hast power to do, lest the great task so oppress thee that it shall behoove thee to forgo that which thou hast begun.' And if it be that you are in doubt whether you can perform a thing, choose rather to suffer than to begin. For Petrus Alfonsus says: 'If you have power to do any thing which you must later regret, it is better to say nay than yea.' That is to say, it is better to keep silence than to speak. Then may you apprehend, and for stronger reasons, that if you have the ability to carry out any work whereof it is likely that later you must repent, then it is better to suffer it to remain undone than to begin it. Well do they speak who forbid a man to attempt a thing of which he has doubt of his ability to perform it. And afterward, when you have thoroughly examined your counsels, as I have set forth, and are convinced that you can carry through your enterprise to its goal, conform to it, then, gravely and carefully to the end.

"Now it is time that I instruct you when and for what you may change your intention without reproach. For truly a man may change purpose and plan when the cause for them is removed, or when a new condition arises. For the law says that new conditions demand new counsels. And Seneca says: 'If thy plan be come to the ears of thine enemy, change thy plan.' You may also change your plan if it develops that, through error or for other reason, harm will ensue from following it. Also, if your counselling is dishonest, or comes of a false premise, change your plan. For the laws provide that all dishonest mandates are invalid. And plans may be altered if they are impossible of fulfilment, or may not well be performed.

"And take this for a general rule: That every counsel that is so rigorously established that it cannot be altered, for any condition that may arise, I say that that counsel is vicious."

This Melibeus, when he had heard all the doctrines of his wife, Dame Prudence, answered her thus: "Dame, so far you have well and agreeably taught me, in a general way, how I should govern myself in the choosing and in the rejecting of councillors. But now I would fain have you descend to the particular, and tell me how you like them and how they appear to you—I mean, the councillors who have been already chosen in the present need."

"My lord," said she, "I beg of you, in all humility, that you will not wilfully object to my reasons,nor allow anger to enter your heart, even though I should say things that must displease you. For God knows that, as for my intention, I speak to your best interest, your honour, and your advantage. And, truly, I hope that your benignity will take it all in patience. Trust me, your counselling in this case should not be called counselling, properly speaking, but only a motion to do folly; and you have erred in many ways.

"First and foremost, you have erred in the method and manner of assembling your councillors. For you should have called, at first, but a few, and thereafter, had there arisen a need, you might have called in more. But, indeed, you have suddenly called into council a great multitude of persons, all very burdensome and all very tiresome to hear. Also, you have erred thus: whereas you should have called into council only your true friends, elderly and wise, you have gathered here many strange men, and young men, false flatterers, reconciled enemies, and men who do you reverence without love. Again, you have erred in that you have brought with you into council anger, covetousness, and hastiness, the which three things are antagonistic to every honest and profitable parliament; nor have you voided nor destroyed them, either in yourself or in your councillors, as you ought to have done. You have erred, again, in that you have revealed your wishes to your councillors, and your desire to make war and obtain vengeance; they have learned from your speeches the thing toward

25. Now is it resoun and tyme that I shewe yow, whanne, and wherfore, that ye may chaunge your conseil with-outen your repreve. Soothly, a man may chaungen his purpos and his conseil if the cause cesseth, or whan a newe caas bitydeth. For the lawe seith: that 'upon thinges that newely bityden bihoveth newe conseil.' And Senek seith: 'if thy conseil is comen to the eres of thyn enemy, chaunge thy conseil.' Thou mayst also chaunge thy conseil if so be that thou finde that, by errour or by other cause, harm or damage may bityde. Also, if thy conseil be dishonest, or elles cometh of dishoneste cause, chaunge thy conseil. For the lawes seyn: that 'alle bihestes that been dishonest been of no value.' And eek, if it so be that it be inpossible, or may nat goodly be parfourned or kept.

26. And take this for a general reule, that every conseil that is affermed so strongly that it may nat be chaunged, for no condicioun that may bityde, I seye that thilke conseil is wikked."

27. This Melibeus, whanne he hadde herd the doctrine of his wyf dame Prudence, answerde in this wyse. "Dame," quod he, "as yet in-to this tyme ye han wel and covenably taught me as in general, how I shal governe me in the chesinge and in the withholdinge of my conseillours. But now wolde I fayn that ye wolde condescende in especial, and telle me how lyketh yow, or what semeth yow, by our conseillours that we han chosen in our present nede."

28. "My lord," quod she, "I biseke yow in al humblesse, that ye wol nat wilfully replye agayn my resouns, ne distempre your herte thogh I speke thing that yow displese. For god wot that, as in myn entente, I speke it for your beste, for your honour and for your profite eke. And soothly, I hope that your benignitee wol taken it in pacience. Trusteth me wel," quod she, "that your conseil as in this caas ne sholde nat, as to speke properly, be called a conseilling, but a mocioun or a moevyng of folye; in which conseil ye han erred in many a sondry wyse.

29. First and forward, ye han erred in th'assemblinge of your conseillours. For ye sholde first have cleped a fewe folk to your conseil, and after ye mighte han shewed it to mo folk, if it hadde been nede. But certes, ye han sodeynly cleped to your conseil a greet multitude of peple, ful chargeant and ful anoyous for to here. Also ye han erred, for there-as ye sholden only have cleped to your conseil your trewe freendes olde and wyse, ye han y-cleped straunge folk, and yong folk, false flatereres, and enemys reconsiled, and folk that doon yow reverence withouten love. And eek also ye have erred, for ye han broght with yow to your conseil ire, covetise, and hastifnesse; the whiche three thinges been contrariouse to every conseil honeste and profitable; the whiche three thinges ye han nat anientissed or destroyed hem, neither in your-self ne in your conseillours, as yow oghte. Ye han erred also, for ye han shewed to your conseillours your talent, and your affeccioun to make werre anon and for to do vengeance; they han espyed by your

wordes to what thing ye been enclyned. And therfore han they rather conseilled yow to your talent than to your profit. Ye han erred also, for it semeth that yow suffyseth to han been conseilled by thise conseillours only, and with litel avys; wher-as, in so greet and so heigh a nede, it hadde been necessarie mo conseillours, and more deliberacioun to parfourne your emprise. Ye han erred also, for ye han nat examined your conseil in the forseyde manere, ne in due manere as the caas requireth. Ye han erred also, for ye han maked no divisioun bitwixe your conseillours; this is to seyn, bitwixen your trewe freendes and your feyned conseillours; ne ye han nat knowe the wil of your trewe freendes olde and wyse; but ye han cast alle hir wordes in an hochepot, and enclyned your herte to the more part and to the gretter nombre; and ther been ye condescended. And sith ye wot wel that men shal alwey finde a gretter nombre of foles than of wyse men, and therfore the conseils that been at congregaciouns and multitudes of folk, ther-as men take more reward to the nombre than to the sapience of persones, ye see wel that in swiche conseillinges foles han the maistrie." Melibeus answerde agayn, and seyde: "I graunte wel that I have erred; but ther-as thou hast told me heer-biforn, that he nis nat to blame that chaungeth hise conseillours in certein caas, and for certeine juste causes, I am al redy to chaunge my conseillours, right as thou wolt devyse. The proverbe seith: that 'for to do sinne is mannish, but certes for to persevere longe in sinne is werk of the devel.' "

30. To this sentence answerde anon dame Prudence, and seyde: "Examineth," quod she, "your conseil, and lat us see the whiche of hem han spoken most resonably, and taught yow best conseil. And for-as-muche as that the examinacioun is necessarie, lat us biginne at the surgiens and at the phisiciens, that first speken in this matere. I sey yow, that the surgiens and phisiciens han seyd yow in your conseil discreetly, as hem oughte; and in hir speche seyden ful wysly, that to the office of hem aperteneth to doon to every wight honour and profit, and no wight for to anoye; and, after hir craft, to doon greet diligence un-to the cure of hem whiche that they han in hir governaunce. And sir, right as they han answered wysly and discreetly, right so rede I that they been heighly and sovereynly guerdoned for hir noble speche; and eek for they sholde do the more ententif bisinesse in the curacioun of your doghter dere. For al-be-it so that they been your freendes, therfore shal ye nat suffren that they serve yow for noght; but ye oghte the rather guerdone hem and shewe hem your largesse. And as touchinge the proposicioun which that the phisiciens entreteden in this caas, this is to seyn, that, in maladyes, that oon contrarie is warisshed by another contrarie, I wolde fayn knowe how ye understonde thilke text, and what is your sentence." "Certes," quod Melibeus, "I understonde it in this wyse: that, right as they han

which you incline. Therefore, they have advised you agreeably to your wishes, rather than to your profit You have erred, also, in that it appears to have sufficed you to be counselled by these councillors only, and with little advising; whereas, in so great and high a matter, it was really encumbent upon you to have procured more councillors and to have deliberated longer upon the means of performing your enterprise. Again you have erred, for you have not examined and tested your council in the manner aforesaid, nor in any manner required by the cause. You have erred, again, in that you have made no division between your councillors; that is to say, between your true friends and your feigned; nor have you learned the desire of your true friends, the elderly and wise of them; but you have cast the words of every man into a hotchpot, and you have then inclined your heart toward the majority, and upon that side have you stooped to folly. And since you well know that men must always exhibit, in any gathering, a greater number of fools than of wise heads, therefore in those councils composed of large numbers, where rather is considered the will of the majority than the wisdom of individuals, you may see easily enough that in such cases the fools must have the mastery."

Melibeus answered her again, saying: "I grant that I have erred; but since you have already told me that he is not to blame who changes councillors under certain conditions and for just causes, I stand ready to change mine, just as you shall prompt. The proverb runs: To err is human, but to persist in sin is the work of the devil."

To this replied Dame Prudence: "Examine your council, and let us see which of them have spoken most reasonably and given the best advice. And since such an examination is necessary, let us begin with the surgeons and physicians who spoke the first in this cause. I say that the surgeons and physicians have spoken discreetly, as they should; and they wisely spoke when they said that to their profession belongs the duty of dealing honourably with every man, and to his profit, and to harm no one; and, according to their skill, to set diligently about the healing of those under their care. And sir, since they have answered wisely and discreetly, I advise that they be richly and nobly rewarded for their noble speech, and, too, that they may be the more attentive to the healing of your dear daughter. For, though they are your friends, you must not suffer it that they serve you for nothing; you ought, indeed, but the more to reward them and to give them largess. And, touching the proposition that the physicians introduced into this case, namely, that, in diseases, the thing is cured by its contrary, I would fain learn how you understand that saying and what is your opinion of it."

"Indeed." said Melibeus, "I understand it thus: That just as they have done me an injury, so should I do them another. For just as they have revenged themselves upon me, and have thereby done me a wrong, so shall I now take my revenge and do them a wrong. And then shall I have cured one contrary by another."

"Lo, lo," exclaimed Dame Prudence, "how easily is every man inclined toward his own desire and to the securing of his own pleasure! Surely the words of the physicians should not have been interpreted in this sense. For, indeed, wickedness is not the contrary of wickedness, nor is vengeance of vengeance, nor wrong of wrong; but they are their likenesses. And therefore one vengeance is not to be cured by another vengeance, nor one wrong by another wrong; but, rather, each of them fructifies and engenders upon the other. But the words of the physicians should be understood in this wise: good and evil are opposites, and peace and war, revenge and forgiveness, discord and concord, and many others. But, certainly, wickedness shall be cured by goodness, discord by concord, war by peace, and so on of other things. And with this Saint Paul the Apostle accords in many places. Says he: 'See that none render evil for evil unto any man; but ever follow that which is good, both among yourselves, and to all men.' And in many other places he admonishes to peace and harmony.

"But now will I speak of the counselling that was given by the lawyers and suchlike wise men, who were all of one accord, as you heard: to the effect that, above all else, you should be diligent in guarding your person and in garrisoning and provisioning your house. And they held, also, that in these matters you ought to act advisedly and after much deliberation. Sir, as to the first point, which touches upon the safety of your person, you must understand that he who is at war should meekly and devoutly pray, above all things, that Jesus Christ, of His great mercy, will keep him under His protection and be his sovereign and very present help in time of need. For assuredly, in this world there is no man who can be safeguarded by advice, save and except he be within the keeping of Our Lord Jesus Christ. With this opinion agrees the prophet David, who says: 'Except the Lord keep the city, the watchman wakes but in vain.' Now then, sir, you shall commit the guarding of your person to your true friends, approved and well known; for of them only should you ask such help. For Cato says: 'If thou hast need of aid, ask it of thy friends; for there is no physician so valuable as thy true friend.' And hereafter you must keep always from all strange folk, and from liars, and hold them always suspect. For Petrus Alfonsus says: 'Never take company of a strange man, on the way, unless it is that you have known him longer than the present moment. And if it be that he fall in with you by accident, and without your assent, inquire then, as subtly as you may, into his conversation and into his life, and do you dissemble for yourself; say that you are going where you do not intend to go; and if he carry a spear, walk upon the right side of him, and if he bear a sword, walk

doon me a contrarie, right so sholde I doon hem another. For right as they han venged hem on me and doon me wrong, right so shal I venge me upon hem and doon hem wrong; and thanne have I cured oon contrarie by another."

31. "Lo, lo!" quod dame Prudence, "how lightly is every man enclyned to his owene desyr and to his owene plesaunce! Certes," quod she, "the wordes of the phisiciens ne sholde nat han been understonden in this wyse. For certes, wikkednesse is nat contrarie to wikkednesse, ne vengeaunce to vengeaunce, ne wrong to wrong; but they been semblable. And therfore, o vengeaunce is nat warisshed by another vengeaunce, ne o wrong by another wrong; but everich of hem encreesceth and aggreggeth other. But certes, the wordes of the phisiciens sholde been understonden in this wyse: for good and wikkednesse been two contraries, and pees and werre, vengeaunce and suffraunce, discord and accord, and manye othere thinges. But certes, wikkednesse shal be warisshed by goodnesse, discord by accord, werre by pees, and so forth of othere thinges. And heer-to accordeth Seint Paul the apostle in manye places. He seith: 'ne yeldeth nat harm for harm, ne wikked speche for wikked speche; but do wel to him that dooth thee harm, and blesse him that seith to thee harm.' And in manye othere places he amonesteth pees and accord. But now wol I speke to yow of the conseil which that was yeven to yow by the men of lawe and the wyse folk, that seyden alle by oon accord as ye han herd bifore; that, over alle thynges, ye sholde doon your diligence to kepen your persone and to warnestore your hous. And seyden also, that in this caas ye oghten for to werken ful avysely and with greet deliberacioun. And sir, as to the firste point, that toucheth to the keping of your persone; ye shul understonde that he that hath werre shal evermore mekely and devoutly preyen biforn alle thinges, that Jesus Crist of his grete mercy wol han him in his proteccioun, and been his sovereyn helping at his nede. For certes, in this world ther is no wight that may be conseilled ne kept suffisantly withouten the keping of our lord Jesu Crist. To this sentence accordeth the prophete David, that seith: 'if god ne kepe the citee, in ydel waketh he that it kepeth.' Now sir, thanne shul ye committe the keping of your persone to your trewe freendes that been approved and y-knowe; and of hem shul ye axen help your persone for to kepe. For Catoun seith: 'if thou hast nede of help, axe it of thy freendes; for ther nis noon so good a phisicien as thy trewe freend.' And after this, thanne shul ye kepe yow fro alle straunge folk, and fro lyeres, and have alwey in suspect hir companye. For Piers Alfonce seith: 'ne take no companye by the weye of a straunge man, but-if so be that thou have known him of a lenger tyme. And if so be that he falle in-to thy companye paraventure withouten thyn assent, enquere thanne, as subtilly as thou mayst, of his conversacioun and of his lyf bifore, and feyne thy wey; seye that thou

goost thider as thou wolt nat go; and if he bereth a spere, hold thee on the right syde, and if he bere a swerd, hold thee on the lift syde.' And after this, thanne shul ye kepe yow wysely from alle swich manere peple as I have seyd bifore, and hem and hir conseil eschewe. And after this, thanne shul ye kepe yow in swich manere, that for any presumpcioun of your strengthe, that ye ne dispyse nat ne acounte nat the might of your adversarie so litel, that ye lete the keping of your persone for your presumpcioun; for every wys man dredeth his enemy. And Salomon seith: 'weleful is he that of alle hath drede; for certes, he that thurgh the hardinesse of his herte and thurgh the hardinesse of him-self hath to greet presumpcioun, him shal yvel bityde.' Thanne shul ye evermore countrewayte embusshements and alle espiaille. For Senek seith: that 'the wyse man that dredeth harmes escheweth harmes; ne he ne falleth in-to perils, that perils escheweth.' And al-be-it so that it seme that thou art in siker place, yet shaltow alwey do thy diligence in kepinge of thy persone; this is to seyn, ne be nat necligent to kepe thy persone, nat only fro thy gretteste enemys but fro thy leeste enemy. Senek seith: 'a man that is wel avysed, he dredeth his leste enemy.' Ovide seith: that 'the litel wesele wot slee the grete bole and the wilde hert.' And the book seith: 'a litel thorn may prikke a greet king ful sore; and an hound wol holde the wilde boor.' But nathelees, I sey nat thou shalt be so coward that thou doute ther wher-as is no drede. The book seith: that 'somme folk han greet lust to deceyve, but yet they dreden hem to be deceyved.' Yet shaltou drede to been empoisoned, and kepe yow from the companye of scorneres. For the book seith: 'with scorneres make no companye, but flee hir wordes as venim.'

32. Now as to the seconde point, wher-as your wyse conseillours conseilled yow to warnestore your hous with gret diligence, I wolde fayn knowe, how that ye understonde thilke wordes, and what is your sentence."

33. Melibeus answerde and seyde, "Certes I understonde it in this wise; that I shal warnestore myn hous with toures, swiche as han castelles and othere manere edifices, and armure and artelleries, by whiche thinges I may my persone and myn hous so kepen and defenden, that myne enemys shul been in drede myn hous for to approche."

34. To this sentence answerde anon Prudence; "warnestoring," quod she, "of heighe toures and of grete edifices apperteneth som-tyme to pryde; and eek men make heighe toures and grete edifices with grete costages and with greet travaille; and whan that they been accompliced, yet be they nat worth a stree, but-if they be defended by trewe freendes that been olde and wyse. And understond wel, that the gretteste and strongeste garnison that a riche man may have, as wel to kepen his persone as hise goodes, is that he be biloved amonges his subgets and with hise neighebores. For thus seith Tullius: that 'ther is a maner garnison that no man

on his left.' And hereafter shall you wisely hold yourself verily aloof from the sorts of people I have described, and eschew both them and their counsel. And you shall not presume so much upon your strength that you are led to despise and hold as naught the might of your adversary, thus endangering your person by this presumption; for every wise man fears his enemy. And Solomon says that it is well for him that suspects all others; for verily he that, because of the courage of his heart and the strength of his body, presumes too much upon them—him shall evil befall. Then, you should guard always against all ambushments and all espionage. For Seneca says: 'The wise man that fears danger avoids danger; he does not fall into peril who peril shuns.' And though it may seem that you are secure in a place, yet shall you be always upon your guard; that is to say, be not negligent either before your greatest enemy or your least. Seneca says: 'A man that is well advised dreads his weakest foe.' Ovid says that the little weasel may kill the great bull and the wild hart. And the Book says that a little thorn may sorely prick a great king; and that a hound will hold the wild boar. But, nevertheless, I do not say that you are to be so cowardly as to be afraid where there is no just cause for fear. It is said in a book that some folk have a great wish to deceive, who yet fear deception. But you shall fear poisoning, and withhold yourself from the company of scoffers. For the Book says that with the scoffer one should have no fellowship, and should avoid his words as venom.

"Now, as to the second point, wherein your wise councillors have advised you to provision and garrison your house, I would know how you understand their words, and what is your opinion of them."

Melibeus answered and said: "Verily, I understand them in this wise: that I am to equip my house with towers, such as castles have, and other such buildings, and with armour and with artilleries; by means of which I may keep my house and may so defend and keep my person that my enemies will not dare to approach me."

To this judgment Prudence then replied: "The garrisoning, provisioning, and equipping of high towers is sometimes but the pandering to pride. And it sometimes happens that even when men build high towers and great fortresses, at much cost and with untold labour, when they are completed they are not worth a straw, unless they be defended by true friends, who are both old and wise. And understand well that the greatest and strongest garrison a powerful man may have, as well to defend his person as his property, is the love of his vassals and his neighbours. For Tullius says that there is a kind of garrison which no man can vanquish or disperse, and that is the love of a lord's own citizens and people.

"Now, sir, as to the third point, whereof your older and wiser councillors averred that you ought not suddenly and hastily to proceed in this matter, but that you should provide for and array yourself with great diligence and after much careful thought, indeed I think that they spoke wisely and truthfully. For Tullius says: 'In every act, or ever thou begin it, array thyself with great diligence.' Then, say I, in seeking vengeance, in war, in battle, and in making arrangements, before you begin you must thoroughly prepare yourself and do it with much forethought. For Tullius says that a swift victory is the result of long preparation. And Cassiodorus says that the garrison is the stronger for being well prepared.

"But let us now speak of the counsel that was given by your neighbours, those who do you reverence without love; by your old reconciled enemies; by your flatterers who counselled you privately to certain things and openly to quite others; and by the younger men, also, who advised a speedy taking of vengeance and an immediate opening of hostilities. And certainly, sir, as I have said before, you were greatly in error in calling such folk into your council; such councillors are sufficiently discredited by the reasons hitherto adduced. But, nonetheless, let us descend to the particular. You should first proceed after the teaching of Tullius. Certainly the truth of this matter, or of this counselling, needs no long inquiry. For we know well who they are that have done to you this injury and this villainy, and how many offenders there are, and in what manner they have wrought against you this wrong and harm. And after this, then shall you examine the second condition which this same Tullius added. For Tullius puts forth a condition which he calls 'complying,' by which he means: who they are, and how many of them, that complied with your wishes to do hasty vengeance on your enemies, as you expressed it in council. And let us consider, also, who they are and how many, that complied with the wishes of your adversaries. As to the first group, it is well known who they are that complied with your hasty wilfulness; for truly all those who counselled you to make a sudden war are not your friends. Let us now consider who they are that you hold so steadfastly to be friends of your person. For though you are a mighty man, and a rich, true it is that you do but stand alone. For you have no child, save a daughter; nor have you any brothers, or cousins, or other near kinsmen for the dread of whom your enemies might forgo treating with you or attempting to destroy your person. You know also that your wealth, when apportioned out, will be distributed to a few men not closely related to you; and when each of them shall have received his share, then he will have but little incentive to avenge your death. But your enemies are three, and they have many children, brothers, cousins, and other near kinsmen; and though it were that you had slain two or three of them, yet there

may venquisse ne disconfite, and that is, a lord to be biloved of hise citezeins and of his peple.'

35. Now sir, as to the thridde point; wher-as your olde and wise conseillours seyden, that yow ne oghte nat sodeynly ne hastily proceden in this nede, but that yow oghte purveyen and apparaillen yow in this caas with greet diligence and greet deliberacioun; trewely, I trowe that they seyden right wysly and right sooth. For Tullius seith, 'in every nede, er thou biginne it, apparaille thee with greet diligence.' Thanne seye I, that in vengeance-taking, in werre, in bataille, and in warnestoring, er thow biginne, I rede that thou apparaille thee therto, and do it with greet deliberacioun. For Tullius seith: that 'long apparailling biforn the bataille maketh short victorie.' And Cassidorus seith: 'the garnison is stronger whan it is longe tyme avysed.'

36. But now lat us speken of the conseil that was accorded by your neighebores, swiche as doon yow reverence withouten love, your olde enemys reconsiled, your flatereres that conseilled yow certeyne thinges prively, and openly conseilleden yow the contrarie; the yonge folk also, that conseilleden yow to venge yow and make werre anon. And certes, sir, as I have seyd biforn, ye han greetly erred to han cleped swich maner folk to your conseil; which conseillours been y-nogh repreved by the resouns afore-seyd. But nathelees, lat us now descende to the special. Ye shuln first procede after the doctrine of Tullius. Certes, the trouthe of this matere or of this conseil nedeth nat diligently enquere; for it is wel wist whiche they been that han doon to yow this trespas and vileinye, and how manye trespassours, and in what manere they han to yow doon al this wrong and al this vileinye. And after this, thanne shul ye examine the seconde condicioun, which that the same Tullius addeth in this matere. For Tullius put a thing, which that he clepeth 'consentinge,' this is to seyn; who been they and how manye, and whiche been they, that consenteden to thy conseil, in thy wilfulnesse to doon hastif vengeance. And lat us considere also who been they, and how manye been they, and whiche been they, that consenteden to your adversaries. And certes, as to the firste poynt, it is wel knowen whiche folk been they that consenteden to your hastif wilfulnesse; for trewely, alle tho that conseilleden yow to maken sodeyn werre ne been nat your freendes. Lat us now considere whiche been they, that ye holde so greetly your freendes as to your persone. For al-be-it so that ye be mighty and riche, certes ye ne been nat but allone. For certes, ye ne han no child but a doghter; ne ye ne han bretheren ne cosins germayns, ne noon other neigh kinrede, wherfore that your enemys, for drede, sholde stinte to plede with yow or to destroye your persone. Ye knowen also, that your richesses moten been dispended in diverse parties; and whan that every wight hath his part, they ne wollen taken but litel reward to venge thy deeth. But thyne enemys been three, and they han manie children, bretheren, cosins, and other ny kinrede;

and, though so were that thou haddest slayn of hem two or three, yet dwellen ther y-nowe to wreken hir deeth and to slee thy persone. And though so be that your kinrede be more siker and stedefast than the kin of your adversarie, yet nathelees your kinrede nis but a fer kinrede; they been but litel sib to yow, and the kin of your enemys been ny sib to hem. And certes, as in that, hir condicioun is bet than youres. Thanne lat us considere also if the conseilling of hem that conseilleden yow to taken sodeyn vengeaunce, whether it accorde to resoun? And certes, ye knowe wel 'nay.' For as by right and resoun, ther may no man taken vengeance on no wight, but the juge that hath the jurisdiccioun of it, whan it is graunted him to take thilke vengeance, hastily or attemprely, as the lawe requireth. And yet more-over, of thilke word that Tullius clepeth 'consentinge,' thou shalt considere if thy might and thy power may consenten and suffyse to thy wilfulnesse and to thy conseillours. And certes, thou mayst wel seyn that 'nay.' For sikerly, as for to speke proprely, we may do no-thing but only swich thing as we may doon rightfully. And certes, rightfully ne mowe ye take no vengeance as of your propre auctoritee. Thanne mowe ye seen, that your power ne consenteth nat ne accordeth nat with your wilfulnesse. Lat us now examine the thridde point that Tullius clepeth 'consequent.' Thou shalt understonde that the vengeance that thou purposest for to take is the consequent. And ther-of folweth another vengeaunce, peril, and werre; and othere damages with-oute nombre, of whiche we be nat war as at this tyme. And as touchinge the fourthe point, that Tullius clepeth 'engendringe,' thou shalt considere, that this wrong which that is doon to thee is engendred of the hate of thyne enemys; and of the vengeance-takinge upon that wolde engendre another vengeance, and muchel sorwe and wastinge of richesses, as I seyde.

should remain enough to avenge those deaths by killing you. And though it were that your own kindred are true and more steadfast than those of your enemies, yet, nevertheless, your own kinsmen are but distantly related to you, whereas the kinsmen of your adversaries are closely sib to them. And, certainly, as for that, their condition is better than yours. Then let us consider, also, whether the advice of those who urged you to a sudden vengeance accords with reason. Certainly you know here that the answer is nay. For you know well that there is no man who may take vengeance upon anyone, save the judge who has proper jurisdiction, and when it has been granted to him to take such vengeance, hastily or slowly, as the law requires. And, moreover, as to that same word which Tullius calls 'complying,' you should consider whether your might and power may consent to comply with your wilfulness and that of your councillors. And, surely, to that also you must answer no. For indeed, properly speaking, we should do nothing save such things as we may do rightfully. And, in truth, rightfully you may take no vengeance as of your own authority. Thus you may see that your power does not rightfully consent to comply with your wilfulness. Let us now examine the third point, which Tullius calls the 'consequence.' You must understand that the vengeance which you purpose is the consequence. And from that follows another vengeance, another peril, and another war, and further injuries and damages without number whereof we are not at this time aware. And, touching the fourth point, which Tullius calls 'engendering,' you should consider that this wrong done to you was engendered of the hate of your enemies; and of the vengeance taken on that evil would be begotten another vengeance, and therewithal much sorrow and wastage of wealth, as I have pointed out.

37. Now sir, as to the point that Tullius clepeth 'causes,' which that is the laste point, thou shalt understonde that the wrong that thou hast receyved hath certeine causes, whiche that clerkes clepen *Oriens* and *Efficiens*, and *Causa longinqua* and *Causa propinqua*; this is to seyn, the fer cause and the ny cause. The fer cause is almighty god, that is cause of alle thinges. The neer cause is thy three enemys. The cause accidental was hate. The cause material been the fyve woundes of thy doghter. The cause formal is the manere of hir werkinge, that broghten laddres and cloumben in at thy windowes. The cause final was for to slee thy doghter; it letted nat in as muche as in hem was. But for to speken of the fer cause, as to what ende they shul come, or what shal finally bityde of hem in this caas, ne can I nat deme but by conjectinge and by supposinge. For we shul suppose that they shul come to a wikked ende, by-cause that the Book of Decrees seith: 'selden or with greet peyne been causes y-broght to good ende whanne they been baddely bigonne.'

"Now, sir, as to the point which Tullius calls 'causes,' which is the last point to consider, you must understand that the wrong that has been done you had certain causes, the which scholars call *Oriens* and *Efficens*, and *Causa longinqua* and *Causa propinqua*, which is to say, the ultimate cause and the proximate cause. The ultimate cause is Almighty God, Who is the Cause of all things. The proximate cause is your three enemies. The accidental cause is hate. The material cause is the five wounds of your daughter. The formal cause is the method of their working who brought ladders and climbed in at your windows. The final cause was the wish to slay your daughter; it hindered them not, in so far as they did their best. But, to speak now of the ultimate cause, as to what end they shall reach, or what shall finally betide your enemies in this case, I cannot judge, save in conjecture and supposition. Yet we may suppose that they shall come to an evil end, for the *Book of Decrees* says: 'Seldom, and only with great pain, are causes brought to a good end, when they have been badly begun.'

"Now, sir, if men ask me why God has suffered men to do this villainy, certainly I can answer nothing in any reliable language. For the Apostle says that the wisdom and the judgments of Our Lord God Almighty are very deep, whereof no man may comprehend anything, nor search into them. Nevertheless, by certain presumptions and conjecturings, I hold and believe that God, Who is justice and righteousness, has permitted this villainy upon a just and reasonable cause.

"Your name is Melibee, which is to say, a man who drinks honey.[1] You have drunk so much of the sweet honey of mundane riches and delights and honours that you are intoxicated therewith, and have forgotten Jesus Christ, your Creator: you have not honoured Him as you should have done, nor have you showed Him a proper reverence. Nor have you well observed those words of Ovid, who says: 'Under the honey of the good things of the flesh is hidden the venom that slays the soul.' And Solomon says that if you have found honey, eat of it only a sufficiency; for if you eat of it overmuch, you shall vomit, and so be again hungry and in want. And perchance Christ holds you in scorn, and has turned away His face from you, and shut up the ears of His mercy; and also He has suffered it that you have been punished in that manner in which you have sinned. You have sinned against Our Lord Christ; for, certainly, those three enemies of mankind, the world, the flesh, and the devil, you have wilfully suffered to enter into your heart through the windows of your body, and you have not sufficiently defended yourself against their assaults and temptations, so that they have wounded your soul in five different places; that is to say, the deadly sins that have entered into your heart through your five senses. In the same manner Our Lord Christ has willed and permitted it that your three enemies have entered your house through the windows thereof, and have wounded your daughter in the manner whereof you know."

"Certainly," said Melibeus, "I see well that you so strengthen your arguments that I shall not revenge myself upon my enemies, showing me thus the perils and the evils that may result from this taking of vengeance. But if everyone were to consider, in every revenge, the dangers and ills that might ensue therefrom, no man would ever take vengeance, and that would be harmful; for by vengeance-taking the wicked are set apart from the good men. And they that have the will to do wickedly restrain their evil purpose when they see the punishment and chastisement of other wrongdoers."

To this replied Dame Prudence: "Surely," said she, "I grant that much good and much evil come of vengeance; but vengeance-taking does not belong to everyone, but only to judges and such as have a proper jurisdiction and authority over wrongdoers. And I say, further, that just as an individual sins in wreaking vengeance upon another man, so sins the judge if he does not fully exact payment from those who have deserved to be punished. For Seneca says:

38. Now sir, if men wolde axe me, why that god suffred men to do yow this vileinye, certes, I can nat well answere as for no sothfastnesse. For th'apostle seith, that 'the sciences and the juggementz of our lord god almighty been ful depe; ther may no man comprehende ne serchen hem suffisantly.' Nathelees, by certeyne presumpcions and conjectinges, I holde and bileve that god, which that is ful of justice and of rightwisnesse, hath suffred this bityde by juste cause resonable.

39. Thy name is Melibee, this is to seyn, 'a man that drinketh hony.'[1] Thou hast y-dronke so muchel hony of swete temporel richesses and delices and honours of this world, that thou art dronken; and hast forgeten Jesu Crist thy creatour; thou ne hast nat doon to him swich honour and reverence as thee oughte. Ne thou ne hast nat wel y-taken kepe to the wordes of Ovide, that seith: 'under the hony of the godes of the body is hid the venim that sleeth the soule.' And Salomon seith, 'if thou hast founden hony, ete of it that suffyseth; for if thou ete of it out of mesure, thou shalt spewe,' and be nedy and povre. And peraventure Crist hath thee in despit, and hath turned awey fro thee his face and hise eres of misericorde; and also he hath suffred that thou hast been punisshed in the manere that thow hast y-trespassed. Thou hast doon sinne agayn our lord Crist; for certes, the three enemys of mankinde, that is to seyn, the flessh, the feend, and the world, thou hast suffred hem entre in-to thyn herte wilfully by the windowes of thy body, and hast nat defended thy-self suffisantly agayns hir assautes and hir temptaciouns, so that they han wounded thy soule in fyve places; this is to seyn, the deedly sinnes that been entred in-to thyn herte by thy fyve wittes. And in the same manere our lord Crist hath wold and suffred, that thy three enemys been entred in-to thyn hous by the windowes, and han y-wounded thy doghter in the fore-seyde manere."

40. "Certes," quod Melibee, "I see wel that ye enforce yow muchel by wordes to overcome me in swich manere, that I shal nat venge me of myne enemys; shewinge me the perils and the yveles that mighten falle of this vengeance. But who-so wolde considere in alle vengeances the perils and yveles that mighte sewe of vengeance-takinge, a man wolde never take vengeance, and that were harm; for by the vengeance-takinge been the wikked men dissevered fro the gode men. And they that han wil to do wikkednesse restreyne hir wikked purpos, whan they seen the punissinge and chastysinge of the trespassours." [And to this answerde dame Prudence: "Certes," seyde she, "I graunte wel that of vengeaunce cometh muchel yvel and muchel good; but vengeaunce-taking aperteneth nat unto everichoon, but only unto juges and unto hem that han jurisdiccioun upon the trespassours.] And yet seye I more, that right as a singuler persone sinneth in takinge vengeance of another man, right so sinneth the juge if he do no vengeance of hem that

[1] Meliboeus, a shepherd in Virgil's First Eclogue.

it han deserved. For Senek seith thus: 'that maister,' he seith, 'is good that proveth shrewes.' And as Cassidore seith: 'A man dredeth to do outrages, whan he woot and knoweth that it displeseth to the juges and sovereyns.' And another seith: 'the juge that dredeth to do right, maketh men shrewes.' And Seint Paule the apostle seith in his epistle, whan he wryteth un-to the Romayns: that 'the juges beren nat the spere with-outen cause'; but they beren it to punisse the shrewes and misdoeres, and for to defende the gode men. If ye wol thanne take vengeance of your enemys, ye shul retourne or have your recours to the juge that hath the jurisdiccion up-on hem; and he shal punisse hem as the lawe axeth and requyreth."

41. "A!" quod Melibee, "this vengeance lyketh me no-thing. I bithenke me now and take hede, how fortune hath norissed me fro my childhede, and hath holpen me to passe many a strong pas. Now wol I assayen hir, trowinge, with goddes help, that she shal helpe me my shame for to venge."

42. "Certes," quod Prudence, "if ye wol werke by my conseil, ye shul nat assaye fortune by no wey; ne ye shul nat lene or bowe unto hir, after the word of Senek: for 'thinges that been folily doon, and that been in hope of fortune, shullen never come to good ende.' And as the same Senek seith: 'the more cleer and the more shyning that fortune is, the more brotil and the sonner broken she is.' Trusteth nat in hir, for she nis nat stidefast ne stable; for whan thow trowest to be most seur or siker of hir help, she wol faille thee and deceyve thee. And wheras ye seyn that fortune hath norissed yow fro your childhede, I seye, that in so muchel shul ye the lasse truste in hir and in hir wit. For Senek seith: 'what man that is norissed by fortune, she maketh him a greet fool.' Now thanne, sin ye desyre and axe vengeance, and the vengeance that is doon after the lawe and bifore the juge ne lyketh yow nat, and the vengeance that is doon in hope of fortune is perilous and uncertein, thanne have ye noon other remedie but for to have your recours unto the sovereyn juge that vengeth alle vileinyes and wronges; and he shal venge yow after that himself witnesseth, wher-as he seith: 'leveth the vengeance to me, and I shal do it.' "

43. Melibee answerde, "if I ne venge me nat of the vileinye that men han doon to me, I sompne or warne hem that han doon to me that vileinye and alle othere, to do me another vileinye. For it is writen: 'if thou take no vengeance of an old vileinye, thou sompnest thyne adversaries to do thee a newe vileinye.' And also, for my suffrance, men wolden do to me so muchel vileinye, that I mighte neither bere it ne sustene; and so sholde I been put and holden over lowe. For men seyn: 'in muchel suffringe shul manye thinges falle un-to thee whiche thou shalt nat mowe suffre.' "

44. "Certes," quod Prudence, "I graunte yow that over muchel suffraunce nis nat good; but yet ne folweth it nat ther-of, that every persone to

'That is a good master who convicts criminals.' And as Cassiodorus says: 'A man shrinks from crime when he understands and knows that it angers the judges and the sovereigns.' And yet another says: 'The judge who fears to deal justly makes criminals of men.' And Saint Paul the Apostle says in his Epistle to the Romans that not without reason are the fasces borne before the magistrates. For they are borne to punish criminals and miscreants, and for the security of good and just men. If, then, you would have revenge upon your enemies, you should turn to and have recourse unto the judge having a proper jurisdiction over them; and he will punish them as the law demands and requires."

"Ah!" exclaimed Melibeus. "This idea of vengeance is no longer to my liking. I remember, now, how Fortune has nourished me from my childhood, helping me over many a difficult place. I give heed to this; and now will I make trial of her again, believing that, with God's help, she will aid me to avenge my shame."

"Indeed," said Prudence, "if you will act according to my advice, you shall not make trial of Fortune in any way; you shall not bow down before her. For, to quote Seneca: 'Things done foolishly and in the hope of Fortune, shall never come to any good end.' And as the same Seneca says: 'The clearer and the more shining Fortune appears, the more brittle she is and the more easily broken.' Trust not in her, for she is neither steadfast nor stable; for when you believe yourself to be most secure and most certain of her help, she will deceive and fail you. And whereas you say that Fortune has nourished you from your childhood, I say that by so much the less should you trust now to her and to her ingenuity. For Seneca says: 'As for the man who is nursed by Fortune, she will make of him a great fool.' Now then, since you desire and demand vengeance, and since the sort of vengeance that is to be had according to law and before a judge is not to your taste, and since the vengeance that is attempted in reliance upon Fortune is dangerous and uncertain, then remains to you no other remedy than to have recourse unto the sovereign Judge Who punishes all villainies and avenges all wrongs. And He will avenge you, as He Himself promises, for 'Vengeance is mine', saith the Lord."

Melibee answered: "If I do not revenge myself for the injury that men have done to me, I invite and advertise to those who have injured me, and to all others, that they are free to do me another wrong. For it is written: 'If thou take no revenge for an old injury, thou invitest thine enemies to do thee a new evil.' And also, what of my sufferance, men would do to me so much of villainy that I could neither endure it nor sustain it; and I should be held in contempt. For men say: 'In patient sufferance shall many things happen to one, the which one may not grin and bear.' "

"Certainly," said Prudence, "I grant you that too much of sufferance is not a good thing; but yet it follows not therefrom that every person to whom men do a rascality may take vengeance for it; for that is the duty of and belongs only to the proper judges. Wherefore the two authorities that you have quoted are only to be understood as speaking to and of the judges; for when they suffer overmuch that wrong and crime remain unpunished, they not only invite new injury and wrong, but they command that they be done. Also a wise man says: 'The judge who does not chasten the sinner, bids him to sin again.' And it is conceivable that the judges and sovereigns of any realm might show so much leniency to criminals and evil-doers that, from such sufferance, in process of time, they might so wax in power as to turn out the judges and the monarchs from their places, and thus, at last, deprive them of the mastery.

whom men doon vileinye take of it vengeance; for that aperteneth and longeth al only to the juges, for they shul venge the vileinyes and iniuries. And ther-fore tho two auctoritees that ye han seyd above, been only understonden in the juges; for whan they suffren over muchel the wronges and the vileinyes to be doon withouten punisshinge, they sompne nat a man al only for to do newe wronges, but they comanden it. Also a wys man seith: that 'the juge that correcteth nat the sinnere comandeth and biddeth him do sinne.' And the juges and sovereyns mighten in hir land so muchel suffre of the shrewes and misdoeres, that they sholden by swich suffrance, by proces of tyme, wexen of swich power and might, that they sholden putte out the juges and the sovereyns from hir places, and atte laste maken hem lesen hir lordshipes.

"But now let us assume that you have a proper leave to avenge yourself. I say that you have not now the power to avenge yourself. For if you will compare your own with the power and might of your adversaries, you shall find, in many ways, as I have previously pointed out, that their condition is better than yours. And therefore say I that it is well, as for this time, to suffer your injuries in patience.

45. But lat us now putte, that ye have leve to venge yow. I seye ye been nat of might and power as now to venge yow. For if ye wole maken comparisoun un-to the might of your adversaries, ye shul finde in manye thinges, that I have shewed yow er this, that hir condicioun is bettre than youres. And therfore seye I, that it is good as now that ye suffre and be pacient.

"Furthermore, you know well the common saw: It is madness in a man to strive with one who is stronger than himself; and to strive with a man of even strength is dangerous; but to strive with a weaker man is foolish. And for this reason a man should avoid all strife, in so far as he may. For Solomon says that it is to a man's honour if he withhold himself from noise and strife. And if it so happen that a man of greater power or strength does you an injury, make it your business to study how to stop the pain of it, rather than how to avenge it. For Seneca says: 'He puts himself into great peril who strives with a greater than himself.' And Cato says: 'If a man of higher degree or estate, or one more mighty than thou do thee an annoyance or grievance, tolerate him; for he that once has grieved thee, at another time he may relieve and help.' Yet I am assuming that you have both the power and the license to avenge yourself. I say, nevertheless, that there are very many things which ought to constrain you to withhold your punishment, and make you rather incline toward sufferance and to have patience under whatever may have been done to you. First and foremost, if you will, consider the faults in your own person, for which defects God has permitted that you have this tribulation, as I said before. For the poet says that we ought patiently to endure the tribulations that come to us when we think upon and well consider that we have deserved them. And Saint Gregory says: 'When a man considers well the multitude of his faults and sins, the trials and tribulations that he suffers will seem but the lighter to be borne; and just in so much as he holds his sins to be the more heavy and grievous, in so much will seem his pains the lighter and the easier to be borne.' Also, you ought to incline and bow down your heart to observe and learn the patience of Our Lord Jesus

46. Forther-more, ye knowen wel that, after the comune sawe, 'it is a woodnesse a man to stryve with a strenger or a more mighty man than he is him-self; and for to stryve with a man of evene strengthe, that is to seyn, with as strong a man as he, it is peril; and for to stryve with a weyker man, it is folie.' And therfore sholde a man flee stryvinge as muchel as he mighte. For Salomon seith: 'it is a greet worship to a man to kepen him fro noyse and stryf.' And if it so bifalle or happe that a man of gretter might and strengthe than thou art do thee grevaunce, studie and bisie thee rather to stille the same grevaunce, than for to venge thee. For Senek seith: that 'he putteth him in greet peril that stryveth with a gretter man than he is him-self.' And Catoun seith: 'if a man of hyer estaat or degree, or more mighty than thou, do thee anoy or grevaunce, suffre him: for he that ones hath greved thee may another tyme releve thee and helpe.' Yet sette I caas, ye have bothe might and licence for to venge yow. I seye, that ther be ful manye thinges that shul restreyne yow of vengeance-takinge, and make yow for to enclyne to suffre, and for to han pacience in the thinges that han been doon to yow. First and foreward, if ye wole considere the defautes that been in your owene persone, for whiche defautes god hath suffred yow have this tribulacioun, as I have seyd yow heer-biforn. For the poete seith, that 'we oghte paciently taken the tribulacions that comen to us, whan we thinken and consideren that we han deserved to have hem.' And Seint Gregorie seith: that 'whan a man considereth wel the nombre of hise defautes and of his sinnes, the peynes and the tribulaciouns that he suffreth semen the lesse un-to hym; and in-as-muche as him thinketh hise sinnes more hevy and grevous, in-so-muche semeth his peyne the lighter and the

esier un-to him.' Also ye owen to enclyne and bowe your herte to take the pacience of our lord Jesu Crist, as seith seint Peter in hise epistles: 'Jesu Crist,' he seith, 'hath suffred for us, and yeven ensample to every man to folwe and sewe him; for he dide never sinne, ne never cam ther a vileinous word out of his mouth: whan men cursed him, he cursed hem noght; and whan men betten him, he manaced hem noght.' Also the grete pacience, which the seintes that been in paradys han had in tribulaciouns that they han y-suffred, with-outen hir desert or gilt, oghte muchel stiren yow to pacience. Forthermore, ye sholde enforce yow to have pacience, consideringe that the tribulaciouns of this world but litel whyle endure, and sone passed been and goon. And the joye that a man seketh to have by pacience in tribulaciouns is perdurable, after that the apostle seith in his epistle: 'the joye of god,' he seith, 'is perdurable,' that is to seyn, everlastinge. Also troweth and bileveth stedefastly, that he nis nat wel y-norissed ne wel y-taught, that can nat have pacience or wol nat receyve pacience. For Salomon seith: that 'the doctrine and the wit of a man is knowen by pacience.' And in another place he seith: that 'he that is pacient governeth him by greet prudence.' And the same Salomon seith: 'the angry and wrathful man maketh noyses, and the pacient man atempreth hem and stilleth.' He seith also: 'it is more worth to be pacient than for to be right strong; and he that may have the lordshipe of his owene herte is more to preyse, than he that by his force or strengthe taketh grete citees.' And therfore seith seint Jame in his epistle: that 'pacience is a greet vertu of perfeccioun.' "

Christ, as Saint Peter says in his Epistle. 'Jesus Christ,' he says, 'hath suffered for us, and hath given example to every man to follow Him and to pray unto Him; for He did never sin, nor ever came there a vicious word out of His mouth; when men cursed Him, he cursed them not, and when men belaboured Him with blows, He would not menace them.' Also, the great patience which the saints in Paradise showed in bearing the tribulations of this world, and all without their deserving or their guilt—this ought greatly to prompt you to patience. Furthermore, you should enforce patience upon yourself when you consider that the tribulations of this world can but a little while endure, being soon over and ended. But the happiness that a man looks to receive by bearing tribulations patiently is perdurable, as the apostle says in his Epistle. 'The joy of God,' he says, 'is perdurable.' Which is to say, it is everlasting. Also, hold and believe steadfastly that he is neither well bred nor well taught who cannot have patience, or will not receive training in patience. For Solomon says that the belief and the knowledge of a man are known by his patience. And in another place he says that he who is patient will govern himself prudently. And this same Solomon says that the angry and wrathful man is noisy, while the patient man moderates and quiets noise. He says, also, that it is better to be patient than to be very strong; and he that governeth his own heart is more praiseworthy than he that taketh a city. And thereto says Saint James in his Epistle: 'Let patience have her perfect work.' "

47. "Certes," quod Melibee, "I graunte yow, dame Prudence, that pacience is a greet vertu of perfeccioun; but every man may nat have the perfeccioun that ye seken; ne I nam nat of the nombre of right parfite men, for myn herte may never been in pees un-to the tyme it be venged. And albe-it so that it was greet peril to myne enemys, to do me a vileinye in takinge vengeance up-on me, yet token they noon hede of the peril, but fulfilleden hir wikked wil and hir corage. And therfore, me thinketh men oghten nat repreve me, though I putte me in a litel peril for to venge me, and though I do a greet excesse, that is to seyn, that I venge oon outrage by another."

"Surely," said Melibeus, "I will grant you, Dame Prudence, that patience is a great virtue of perfection; but every man may not attain to the perfection that you seek; nor am I of the number of perfect men, for my heart will never find peace until I have revenged myself. And though it was dangerous to my enemies to do me an injury in taking vengeance upon me, yet took they no heed of their own peril, but fulfilled their evil purpose. And therefore it seems to me that men ought not to find fault with me if I incur a little peril in taking vengeance, even though I go to great excess, that is to say, that I avenge one outrage with another."

48. "A!" quod dame Prudence, "ye seyn your wil and as yow lyketh; but in no caas of the world a man sholde nat doon outrage ne excesse for to vengen him. For Cassidore seith: that 'as yvel doth he that vengeth him by outrage, as he that doth the outrage.' And therfore ye shul venge yow after the ordre of right, that is to seyn by the lawe, and noght by excesse ne by outrage. And also, if ye wol venge yow of the outrage of your adversaries in other maner than right comandeth, ye sinnen; and therfore seith Senek: that 'a man shal never vengen shrewednesse by shrewednesse.' And if ye seye, that right axeth a man to defenden violence by violence, and fighting by fighting, certes ye seye sooth,

"Ah," said Dame Prudence, "you speak out of your purpose as you desire it to happen; but never in this world should any man commit an outrage or go to excess to obtain his vengeance. For Cassiodorus says: 'As much evil does he who avenges himself by outrage as did he who first committed outrage.' And therefore you must avenge yourself in an orderly manner, and rightfully, that is to say, according to law, and not by excess nor by outrage. For if you avenge yourself in any other way, you sin. And thereupon Seneca says: 'A man must not avenge villainy with villainy.' If you say that right demands that a man defend himself violently against violence, and fightingly against fighting, certainly you speak but the truth, when the fighting is done immediately, without interval of tarrying or delay, and simply for defence and not for vengeance. And it behooves a man that he conduct his defence with such moderation that men will have no cause to accuse him of excess and outrage; for otherwise the thing were unreasonable. By God, you know well that you are not now defending yourself, but are going to revenge yourself; and so it follows that you have no wish to do your deed with moderation. That is why I hold that patience would be good for you. For Solomon says: 'He that is not patient shall endure great evil.' "

"Certainly," said Melibeus, "I grant you that when a man is impatient and wroth because of that which touches him not, and in no way concerns him, if he be harmed thereby it is not to be wondered at. For the law provides that he is culpable who interferes or meddles with what does not concern him. And Solomon says that he who interferes in the strife of other men is like one who seizes a hound by the ears. For just as he who takes a strange dog by the ears is likely to be bitten, just so is it reasonable to suppose that he may be injured who, by his impatience, meddles in the strife of other men, when it does not concern him. But you know well that this deed, that is to say, my grief and unrest, touches me closely. Therefore, if I am angry and impatient, it is no marvel. And, saving your presence, I cannot see wherein it can greatly harm me if I wreak my revenge; for I am richer and stronger than are my enemies. And well do you know that with money and great possessions are governed all the matters of this world. Solomon says that all things obey great wealth."

When Prudence had heard her husband boast thus of his possessions and money, despising the power of his enemies, she answered and said: "Surely, dear sir, I grant that you are mighty and rich, and that wealth is a good thing for those who have acquired it honestly and know well how to use it. For just as the body of man cannot live without the soul, neither can it exist without worldly goods. And by means of riches a man may acquire powerful friends. Thereupon says Pamphilius: 'If a cowherd's daughter be rich, she may make choice of a thousand men, which she will take for her husband; for, of a thousand, not one will forsake or refuse her.' And this Pamphilius also says: 'If thou be very happy, that is to say, if thou be very rich, thou shalt find a great many comrades and friends. And if thy fortune change, so that thou become poor, then farewell fellowship and friendship; for thou shalt be left alone, without any company, save it be the company of the poor.' And still further says Pamphilius: 'Those who are thralls and born of bondmen's blood shall be made worthy and noble by wealth.' And just as from riches come many good things, so from poverty come many ills and evils. For deep poverty forces a man into evil deeds. Therefore Cassiodorus calls poverty the 'mother

whan the defense is doon anon with-outen intervalle or with-outen tarying or delay, for to defenden him and nat for to vengen him. And it bihoveth that a man putte swich attemperance in his defence, that men have no cause ne matere to repreven him that defendeth him of excesse and outrage; for elles were it agayn resoun. Pardee, ye knowen wel, that ye maken no defence as now for to defende yow, but for to venge yow; and so seweth it that ye han no wil to do your dede attemprely. And therfore, me thinketh that pacience is good. For Salomon seith: that 'he that is nat pacient shal have greet harm.' "

49. "Certes," quod Melibee, "I graunte yow, that whan a man is inpacient and wroth, of that that toucheth him noght and that aperteneth nat un-to him, though it harme him, it is no wonder. For the lawe seith: that 'he is coupable that entremetteth or medleth with swich thyng as aperteneth nat un-to him.' And Salomon seith: that 'he that entremetteth him of the noyse or stryf of another man, is lyk to him that taketh an hound by the eres.' For right as he that taketh a straunge hound by the eres is outherwhyle biten with the hound, right in the same wyse is it resoun that he have harm, that by his inpacience medleth him of the noyse of another man, wher-as it aperteneth nat un-to him. But ye knowen wel that this dede, that is to seyn, my grief and my disese, toucheth me right ny. And therfore, though I be wroth and inpacient, it is no merveille. And savinge your grace, I can nat seen that it mighte greetly harme me though I toke vengeaunce; for I am richer and more mighty than myne enemys been. And wel knowen ye, that by moneye and by havinge grete possessions been all the thinges of this world governed. And Salomon seith: that 'alle thinges obeyen to moneye.' "

50. Whan Prudence hadde herd hir housbonde avanten him of his richesse and of his moneye, dispreisinge the power of hise adversaries, she spak, and seyde in this wyse: "certes, dere sir, I graunte yow that ye been rich and mighty, and that the richesses been goode to hem that han wel y-geten hem and wel conne usen hem. For right as the body of a man may nat liven withoute the soule, namore may it live withouten temporel goodes. And by richesses may a man gete him grete freendes. And therfore seith Pamphilles: 'if a netherdes doghter,' seith he, 'be riche, she may chesen of a thousand men which she wol take to hir housbonde; for, of a thousand men, oon wol nat forsaken hir ne refusen hir.' And this Pamphilles seith also: 'if thou be right happy, that is to seyn, if thou be right riche, thou shalt find a greet nombre of felawes and freendes. And if thy fortune change that thou wexe povre, farewel freendshipe and felaweshipe; for thou shalt be allone with-outen any companye, but-if it be the companye of povre folk.' And yet seith this Pamphilles moreover: that 'they that been thralle and bonde of linage shullen been maad worthy and noble by the richesses.' And right so as by richesses ther comen manye goodes, right so by poverte come

ther manye harmes and yveles. For greet poverte constreyneth a man to do manye yveles. And therfore clepeth Cassidore poverte 'the moder of ruine,' that is to seyn, the moder of overthrowinge or fallinge doun. And therfore seith Piers Alfonce: 'oon of the gretteste adversitees of this world is whan a free man, by kinde or by burthe, is constreyned by poverte to eten the almesse of his enemy.' And the same seith Innocent in oon of hise bokes; he seith: that 'sorweful and mishappy is the condicioun of a povre begger; for if he axe nat his mete, he dyeth for hunger; and if he axe, he dyeth for shame; and algates necessitee constreyneth him to axe.' And therfore seith Salomon: that 'bet it is to dye than for to have swich poverte.' And as the same Salomon seith: 'bettre it is to dye of bitter deeth than for to liven in swich wyse.' By thise resons that I have seid un-to yow, and by manye othere resons that I coude seye, I graunte yow that richesses been goode to hem that geten hem wel, and to hem that wel usen tho richesses. And therfore wol I shewe yow how ye shul have yow, and how ye shul bere yow in gaderinge of richesses, and in what manere ye shul usen hem.

of ruin,' which is to say, the mother of overthrowing or of falling down. And thereupon says Petrus Alfonsus: 'One of the greatest adversities of this world is when a man free by kindred and birth is constrained by poverty to eat of the alms of his enemy.' And the same thing is said by Innocent in one of his books, for he says: 'Sorrowful and unhappy is the condition of the poor beggar; for if he beg not his food, he dies of hunger; and if he beg it, he dies of shame; and yet necessity constrains him to beg.' And thereupon Solomon says that it is better to die than to live in poverty. And this same Solomon says that it is better to die the bitter death than to live in such wise. For these reasons that I have given, and for many others that I could adduce, I grant you that riches are good for those who have well acquired them, and for those who use them well. And therefore will I show you how you should bear yourself in acquiring wealth, and how you should use it.

51. First, ye shul geten hem withouten greet desyr, by good leyser sokingly, and nat over hastily. For a man that is to desyringe to gete richesses abaundoneth him first to thefte and to alle other yveles. And therfore seith Salomon: 'he that hasteth him to bisily to wexe riche shal be noon innocent.' He seith also: that 'the richesse that hastily cometh to a man, sone and lightly gooth and passeth fro a man; but that richesse that cometh litel and litel wexeth alwey and multiplyeth.' And sir, ye shul geten richesses by your wit and by your travaille un-to your profit; and that with-outen wrong or harm-doinge to any other persone. For the lawe seith: that 'ther maketh no man himselven riche, if he do harm to another wight'; this is to seyn, that nature defendeth and forbedeth by right, that no man make himself riche un-to the harm of another persone. And Tullius seith: that 'no sorwe ne no drede of deeth, ne no-thing that may falle un-to a man is so muchel agayns nature, as a man to encressen his owene profit to the harm of another man. And though the grete men and the mighty men geten richesses more lightly than thou, yet shaltou nat been ydel ne slow to do thy profit; for thou shalt in alle wyse flee ydelnesse.' For Salomon seith: that 'ydelnesse techeth a man to do manye yveles.' And the same Salomon seith: that 'he that travailleth and bisieth him to tilien his land, shal eten breed; but he that is ydel and casteth him to no bisinesse ne occupacioun, shal falle in-to poverte, and dye for hunger.' And he that is ydel and slow can never finde covenable tyme for to doon his profit. For ther is a versifiour seith: that 'the ydel man excuseth hym in winter, by cause of the grete cold; and in somer, by enchesoun of the hete.' For thise causes seith Caton: 'waketh and enclyneth nat yow over muchel for to slepe; for over muchel reste norisseth and causeth manye

"First, you should get it without any great desire, and leisurely, and gradually, and not over eagerly. For the man who is too desirous of gathering riches abandons himself first to theft and to all other evils. And thereupon says Solomon: 'A merchant shall hardly keep himself from doing wrong, and a huckster shall not be freed from sin.' He says also: 'The wealth that cometh hastily unto a man goeth soon and passeth lightly away from him; but the wealth that cometh by a little and a little waxeth alway and multiplieth.' And sir, you shall acquire riches by your wisdom and by your labour to your own profit; and that without wronging or doing harm to any other person. For the law provides that no man shall legally become rich who injures another in the process; that is to say, that Nature forbids, and rightfully, that a man acquire wealth at another's expense. And Tullius says: 'No sorrow, no fear of death, nay nothing that may befall a man, is so much against Nature as for a man to increase and take his profit at the expense of another. And though the great man and the mighty man acquire riches more easily than thou, yet be not idle nor slow in gaining thine own profit; for thou must, in all things, avoid idleness.' For Solomon says that idleness teaches a man to do many evil things. And the same Solomon says that he that labours and busies himself to till his land shall eat bread; but he that is given over to idleness and has no business or occupation shall fall into poverty and die of hunger. And he that is idle and slow can never find a convenient time wherein to transact his business. For there is a versifier who says: 'The lazy man excuses himself in winter because of the great cold, and in summer because of the great heat.' For these reasons Cato says: 'Wake, and be not overly inclined toward sleep; for a superfluity of rest causes and nourishes many vices.' And thereupon says Saint Jerome: 'Do some good deeds, that the Devil, our

Enemy, find you not unoccupied. For the Devil takes not easily into his service those whom he finds occupied in good deeds.'

"Thus, then, in getting riches, you must avoid idleness. And afterward you shall use the wealth, which you have acquired by your knowledge and by your labour, in such manner that men will not hold you to be too stingy, or too sparing, or too foolishly generous, that is to say, too great a spendthrift. For just as men blame an avaricious man for his meanness and penuriousness, in the same wise is he to be blamed that spends too freely. Thereupon says Cato: 'Use the wealth which thou hast acquired in such manner that men shall have no reason to call thee either wretch or niggard; for it is shameful for a man to have a poor heart and a rich purse.' He says also: 'Use the wealth which thou hast measureably.' That is to say, spend it within measure; for those who foolishly spend and waste what riches they have, when they have no longer any property of their own, scheme then to take that of another man. I say, then, that you shall flee avarice; using your riches in such manner that men shall not say that you have buried them, but that you hold them in your power and at your wielding. For a wise man reproves an avaricious man thus, in two verses: 'Wherefore and why does a man bury his wealth, of his great avarice, when he knows well that he must needs die; for death is the end of every man in this present life? And for what cause or occasion does he join or knit himself so closely to his goods that all his wit may not dissever or part him therefrom; when he knows, or ought to know, that when he is dead he shall have borne with him nothing at all from this world? Thereupon says Saint Augustine: 'The avaricious man is like unto Hell; for the more it swallows the more desire has it to swallow and devour.' And just as you would hate to be called an avaricious man, or a stingy, just so should you govern yourself that men will not call you a spendthrift. Therefore says Tullius: 'The riches of thy house should not be hid, nor should they be kept so closely that they may not be opened by pity and good will.' That is to say, in order to give a part to those in need. 'But yet thy wealth should not be so openly exposed as to become the goods of every man,' Afterward, in getting your wealth and in using it, you should have always three things in mind, that is to say, Our Lord God, conscience, and your own good name. First, you should have God in your heart, and for the sake of no riches at all should you do anything which may in any manner displease God, Who is your Creator and Maker. For, after the word of Solomon: Better it is to have little and therewith the love of God, than great riches and treasure and the loss of God's love thereby. And the prophet says that it is better to be held for a good man and to have but little of the wealth and treasure of this world, than to be held for a villain and have great riches. And yet say I still, that you should always do your business in the gathering of

vices.' And therfore seith seint Jerome: 'doth somme gode dedes, that the devel which is our enemy ne finde yow nat unoccupied.' For the devel ne taketh nat lightly un-to his werkinge swiche as he findeth occupied in gode werkes.'

52. Thanne thus, in getinge richesses, ye mosten flee ydelnesse. And afterward, ye shul use the richesses, whiche ye have geten by your wit and by your travaille, in swich a manere, than men holde nat yow to scars, ne to sparinge, ne to fool-large, that is to seyn, over-large a spender. For right as men blamen an avaricious man by-cause of his scarsetee and chincherye, in the same wyse is he to blame that spendeth over largely. And therfore seith Caton: 'use,' he seith, 'thy richesses that thou hast geten in swich a manere, that men have no matere ne cause to calle thee neither wrecche ne chinche; for it is a greet shame to a man to have a povere herte and a riche purs.' He seith also: 'the goodes that thou hast y-geten, use hem by mesure,' that is to seyn, spende hem mesurably; for they that folily wasten and despenden the goodes that they han, whan they han namore propre of hir owene, they shapen hem to take the goodes of another man. I seye thanne, that ye shul fleen avarice; usinge your richesses in swich manere, that men seye that your richesses been y-buried, but that ye have hem in your might and in your weeldinge. For a wys man repreveth the avaricious man, and seith thus, in two vers: 'wherto and why burieth a man hise goodes by his grete avarice, and knoweth wel that nedes moste he dye; for deeth is the ende of every man as in this present lyf.' And for what cause or enchesoun joyneth he him or knitteth he him so faste un-to hise goodes, that alle his wittes mowen nat disseveren him or departen him from hise goodes; and knoweth wel, or oghte knowe, that whan he is deed, he shal nothing bere with him out of this world? And therfore seith seint Augustin: that 'the avaricious man is likned un-to helle; that the more it swelweth, the more desyr it hath to swelwe and devoure.' And as wel as ye wolde eschewe to be called an avaricious man or chinche, as wel sholde ye kepe yow and governe yow in swich a wyse that men calle yow nat fool-large. Therfore seith Tullius: 'the goodes,' he seith, 'of thyn hous ne sholde nat been hid, ne kept so cloos but that they mighte been opened by pitee and debonairetee'; that is to seyn, to yeven part ot hem that han greet nede; 'ne thy goodes shullen nat been so opene, to been every mannes goodes.' Afterward, in getinge of your richesses and in usinge hem, ye shul alwey have three thinges in your herte; that is to seyn, our lord god, conscience, and good name. First, ye shul have god in your herte; and for no richesse ye shullen do nothing, which may in any manere displese god, that is your creatour and maker. For after the word of Salomon: 'it is bettre to have a litel good with the love of god, than to have muchel good and tresour, and lese the love of his lord god.' And the prophete seith: that 'bettre it is to been a good man and have

litel good and tresour, than to been holden a shrewe and have grete richesses.' And yet seye I ferthermore, that ye sholde alwey doon your bisinesse to gete yow richesses, so that ye gete hem with good conscience. And th'apostle seith: that 'ther nis thing in this world, of which we sholden have so greet joye as whan our conscience bereth us good witnesse.' And the wyse man seith: 'the substance of a man is ful good, whan sinne is nat in mannes conscience.' Afterward, in getinge of your richesses, and in usinge of hem, yow moste have greet bisinesse and greet diligence, that your goode name be alwey kept and conserved. For Salomon seith: that 'bettre it is and more it availleth a man to have a good name, than for to have grete richesses.' And therfore he seith in another place: 'do greet diligence,' seith Salomon, 'in keping of thy freend and of thy gode name; for it shal lenger abide with thee than any tresour, be it never so precious.' And certes he sholde nat be called a gentil man, that after god and good conscience, alle thinges left, ne dooth his diligence and bisinesse to kepen his good name. And Cassidore seith: that 'it is signe of a gentil herte, whan a man loveth and desyreth to han a good name.' And therfore seith seint Augustin: that 'ther been two thinges that arn necessarie and nedefulle, and that is good conscience and good loos; that is to seyn, good conscience to thyn owene persone inward, and good loos for thy neighebore outward.' And he that trusteth him so muchel in his gode conscience, that he displeseth and setteth at noght his gode name or loos, and rekketh noght though he kepe nat his gode name, nis but a cruel cherl.

wealth so that you gather it with a good conscience. And the apostle says that there is not anything in all this world whereof a man should have so great a joy as when his conscience bears a good witness unto himself. And the wise man says that the substance a man has is righteous when sin lies not upon the conscience of that man. Afterward, in gathering your riches and in the using them, you must busy yourself and be diligent to observe that your good name be kept and conserved. For Solomon says: 'A good name is rather to be chosen than great riches.' And thereupon he says elsewhere: 'Do thy diligence in keeping of thy friend and of thine own good name; for these shall abide longer than any treasure, be it never so precious.' And surely he should not be called a good man who, after God and his own conscience, in all things else is not diligent in the business of maintaining his good name. Cassiodorus says: 'It is a sign of a good heart in a man when he loves and desires to have and to keep an honoured name.' And thereupon says Saint Augustine: 'Two things there be which are necessary and needful, and they are: good conscience and a good name; that is to say, a good conscience for the sake of thy soul, and a good name for the sake of thy neighbour.' And he who will trust so much in his own good conscience that he recks not of displeasing and setting at naught the value of his neighbour's opinion of his good name, and cares nothing if he keep not his good name toward his neighbour—he is but a boor.

53. Sire, now have I shewed yow how ye shul do in getinge richesses, and how ye shullen usen hem; and I see wel, that for the trust that ye han in youre richesses, ye wole moeve werre and bataille. I conseille yow, that ye biginne no werre in trust of your richesses; for they ne suffysen noght werres to mayntene. And therfore seith a philosophre: 'that man that desyreth and wole algates han werre, shal never have suffisaunce; for the richer that he is, the gretter despenses moste he make, if he wole have worship and victorie.' And Salomon seith: that 'the gretter richesses that a man hath, the mo despendours he hath.' And dere sire, al-be-it so that for your richesses ye mowe have muchel folk, yet bihoveth it nat, ne it is nat good, to biginne werre, where-as ye mowe in other manere have pees, unto your worship and profit. For the victories of batailles that been in this world, lyen nat in greet nombre or multitude of the peple ne in the vertu of man; but it lyth in the wil and in the hand of our lord god almighty. And therfore Judas Machabeus, which was goddes knight, whan he sholde fighte agayn his adversarie that hadde a greet nombre, and a gretter multitude of folk and strenger than was this peple of Machabee, yet he reconforted his litel companye, and seyde right in this wyse: 'als lightly,' quod he, 'may our lord god almighty yeve victorie to a fewe folk as to many folk; for the vic-

"My lord, now have I showed you how you should act in acquiring riches, and how you should employ them; and well I understand that, because of the faith you rest in your wealth you will move toward war and battle. I counsel you that you begin no war upon faith in the continuance of your wealth; for your wealth is not sufficient to maintain war. Wherefore says a philosopher: 'He who intrigues for and will always have war, shall never have sufficient funds; for the richer he is, the more must his expenses be, always providing he wants respect and victory.' And Solomon says that the greater a man's riches the more leeches hang upon him. And, dear sir, though because of your wealth you may have many followers, yet it behooves you not, nor is it a good thing, to initiate a war when you may have a peace, and that to your own honour and profit. For victory in battle in this world lies not in a great multitude of people, neither lies it in the virtue of man; but it lies alone within the will and in the hands of Our Lord God Almighty. And therefore Judas Maccabeus, God's own knight, when called upon to fight against an adversary greatly superior in numbers and stronger than his own people, comforted his little army, saying: 'As easily may Our Lord God Almighty give victory unto a few as unto a multitude; for the fortune of war lieth not in numbers, but cometh solely from Our Lord God of

Heaven.' And, dear sir, for as much as there is no man certain whether he be worthy that God give him the victory, any more than he can be certain whether he is worthy of the love of God, therefore Solomon says that every man should greatly fear to begin a war. Also, in battle, many perils befall, and many chances of evil, and therein is a great man as easily slain as a poor; and thereupon is it written in the *Second Book of the Kings* that the issue of battle is all at chance and is not to be known beforehand; for as easily hurt with a spear is one man as any other. And since there lies great peril in war, therefore should a man flee and eschew warfare, in so far as he may with honour. For Solomon says: 'He that liveth by the sword shall perish by the sword.' "

After Dame Prudence had spoken in this manner, Melibeus answered and said: "I see well, Dame Prudence, that by your fair words and by the reasons you have adduced before me, you are not in favour of war; but I have not yet heard you advise as to what course I ought to pursue in this extremity."

"Certainly," quoth she, "I counsel you that you accord with your adversaries, and that you have peace with them. For Saint James says in his Epistle that by concord and peace little fortunes grow great, and by discord and warfare are great fortunes brought low. And well you know that one of the greatest things there is in all this world is unity and peace. Wherefore says Our Lord Jesus Christ in this wise to His disciples: 'Blessed are the peacemakers, for they shall be called the children of God.' "

"Ah," said Melibee, "now do I see well that you love neither my honour nor my reputation. You know well that my adversaries have begun this quarrel and contention by their outrage; and you see well that they neither require nor ask peace from me, nor even do they ask to be reconciled. Will you, then, that I go and show myself meek and make myself humble before them, and cry mercy of them? Forsooth that were not to my honour. For just as men say that too much familiarity breeds contempt, so fares it with overmuch humility or meekness."

Then began Dame Prudence to make a show of wrath, and she said: "Certainly, sir, saving your grace, I love your honour and your profit as I do my own, and so have I ever; nor have you or any other hitherto said anything to the contrary. And yet, if I had said that you should have bought a peace and a reconciliation, I had not been much mistaken nor said very far amiss. For the wise man says that dissension begins with another, but reconciliation with oneself. And the prophet says: 'Flee evil and do good; seek peace and follow it.' Yet say I not that you shall rather sue to your enemies than they to you; for well I know that you are so hard-hearted that you will do nothing for me. And Solomon says that he that is too hard of heart shall in the end have evil fortune."

torie of bataile cometh nat by the grete nombre of peple, but it cometh from our lord god of hevene.' And dere sir, for as muchel as there is no man certein, if he be worthy that god yeve him victorie, [namore than he is certein whether he be worthy of the love of god] or naught, after that Salomon seith, therfore every man sholde greetly drede werres to biginne. And by-cause that in batailles fallen manye perils, and happeth outher-while, that as sone is the grete man sleyn as the litel man; and, as it is written in the seconde book of Kinges, 'the dedes of batailles been aventurouse and nothing certeyne; for as lightly is oon hurt with a spere as another.' And for ther is gret peril in werre, therfore sholde a man flee and eschewe werre, in as muchel as a man may goodly. For Salomon seith: 'he that loveth peril shal falle in peril.' "

54. After that Dame Prudence hadde spoken in this manere, Melibee answerde and seyde, "I see wel, dame Prudence, that by your faire wordes and by your resons that ye han shewed me, that the werre lyketh yow no-thing; but I have nat yet herd your conseil, how I shal do in this nede."

55. "Certes," quod she, "I conseille yow that ye accorde with youre adversaries, and that ye have pees with hem. For seint Jame seith in hise epistles: that 'by concord and pees the smale richesses wexen grete, and by debaat and discord the grete richesses fallen doun.' And ye knowen wel that oon of the gretteste and most sovereyn thing, that is in this world, is unitee and pees. And therfore seyde oure lord Jesu Crist to hise apostles in this wyse: 'wel happy and blessed been they that loven and purchacen pees; for they been called children of god.' " "A !"quod Melibee, "now see I wel that ye loven nat myn honour ne my worshipe. Ye knowen wel that myne adversaries han bigonnen this debaat and brige by hir outrage; and ye see wel that they ne requeren ne preyen me nat of pees, ne they asken nat to be reconsiled. Wol ye thanne that I go and meke me and obeye me to hem, and crye hem mercy? For sothe, that were nat my worship. For right as men seyn, that 'over-greet homlinesse engendreth dispreysinge,' so fareth it by to greet humylitee or mekenesse."

56. Thanne bigan dame Prudence to maken semblant of wratthe, and seyde, "certes, sir, sauf your grace, I love your honour and your profit as I do myn owene, and ever have doon; ne ye ne noon other syen never the contrarie. And yit, if I hadde seyd that ye sholde han purchaced the pees and the reconsiliacioun, I ne hadde nat muchel mistaken me, ne seyd amis. For the wyse man seith: 'the dissensioun biginneth by another man, and the reconsiling biginneth by thy-self.' And the prophete seith: 'flee shrewednesse and do goodnesse; seke pees and folwe it, as muchel as in thee is.' Yet seye I nat that ye shul rather pursue to your adversaries for pees than they shuln to yow; for I knowe wel that ye been so hard-herted, that ye wol do nothing for me. And Salomon seith: 'he that hath over-hard an herte, atte laste he shal mishappe and mistyde.' "

57. Whanne Melibee hadde herd dame Prudence maken semblant of wratthe, he seyde in this wyse, "dame, I prey yow that ye be nat displesed of thinges that I seye; for ye knowe wel that I am angry and wrooth, and that is no wonder; and they that been wrothe witen nat wel what they doon, ne what they seyn. Therfore the prophete seith: that 'troubled eyen han no cleer sighte.' But seyeth and conseileth me as yow lyketh; for I am redy to do right as ye wol desyre; and if ye repreve me of my folye, I am the more holden to love yow and to preyse yow. For Salomon seith: that 'he that repreveth him that doth folye, he shal finde gretter grace than he that deceyveth him by swete wordes.' "

58. Thanne seide dame Prudence, "I make no semblant of wratthe ne anger but for your grete profit. For Salomon seith: 'he is more worth, that repreveth or chydeth a fool for his folye, shewinge him semblant of wratthe, than he that supporteth him and preyseth him in his misdoinge, and laugheth at his folye.' And this same Salomon seith afterward: that 'by the sorweful visage of a man,' that is to seyn, by the sory and hevy countenaunce of a man, 'the fool correcteth and amendeth him-self.' "

59. Thanne seyde Melibee, "I shal nat conne answere to so manye faire resouns as ye putten to me and shewen. Seyeth shortly your wil and your conseil, and I am al ready to fulfille and parforne it."

60. Thanne dame Prudence discovered al hir wil to him, and seyde, "I conseille yow," quod she, aboven alle thinges, that ye make pees bitwene god and yow; and beth reconsiled un-to him and to his grace. For as I have seyde yow heerbiforn, god hath suffred yow to have this tribulacioun and disese for your sinnes. And if ye do as I sey yow, god wol sende your adversaries un-to yow, and maken hem fallen at your feet, redy to do your wil and your comandements. For Salomon seith: 'whan the condicioun of man is plesaunt and likinge to god, he chaungeth the hertes of the mannes adversaries, and constreyneth hem to biseken him of pees and of grace.' And I prey yow, lat me speke with your adversaries in privee place; for they shul nat knowe that it be of your wil or your assent. And thanne, whan I knowe hir wil and hir entente, I may conseille yow the more seurly."

61. "Dame," quod Melibee, "dooth your wil and your lykinge, for I putte me hoolly in your disposicioun and ordinaunce."

62. Thanne Dame Prudence, whan she saugh the gode wil of her housbonde, delibered and took avys in hir-self, thinkinge how she mighte bringe this nede un-to a good conclusioun and to a good ende. And whan she saugh hir tyme, she sente for thise adversaries to come un-to hir in-to a privee place, and shewed wysly un-to hem the grete goodes that comen of pees, and the grete harmes and perils that been in werre; and seyde to hem in a goodly manere, how that hem oughte have greet repentaunce of the injurie and wrong that they hadden doon to Melibee hir lord, and to hir, and to hir doghter.

When Melibee had heard Dame Prudence show anger thus, he said: "Dame, I pray you that you be not displeased at things I say, for you know well that I am in my angry mood, and that it is no wonder; and that those who are angry cannot judge well of what they say or do. Wherefore the prophet says: 'The troubled eyes have no clear sight.' But speak to and counsel me as you like; for I am ready to do as you wish; and if you reprove me for my folly I am but bound the more to love you and praise you. For Solomon says that he that reproves him who has done a folly shall have more grace than he that deceives him with sweet words."

Then said Dame Prudence: "I make no show of wrath or anger save for your great profit. For Solomon says that more worth is he who reproves and chides a fool for his folly than is he that supports him and praises him and laughs at his foolishness. And this same Solomon says that by the sorrowful visage of a man (that is to say, by the sorry and heavy countenance of a man) the fool corrects and amends himself."

Then said Melibee: "I shall not know how to answer so many fair and good reasons as you show and lay before me. Speak out briefly your counsel and your wish, for I am ready to fulfill and to perform it."

Then Dame Prudence showed him all her wish and desire, saying: "I counsel you, above all things, that you make peace with God and become reconciled to Him and to His grace. For, as I have heretofore said, God has suffered you to have this tribulation and unrest because of your sins. And if you do as I tell you to do, God will send your adversaries unto you and make them fall at your feet, ready to do your will and to obey your commands. For Solomon says that when the condition of a man is pleasant and to God's liking, He changes the hearts of that man's enemies and constrains them to seek peace of him, and grace. And I pray you, let me have private speech with your adversaries; for they shall not know that it is done with your consent. And then, when I have learned their whole intent and will, I may the more surely counsel you."

"Dame," quoth Melibee, "do your whole will and whatsoever pleases you. For I put myself entirely at your disposal and command."

Then Dame Prudence, when she saw the goodwill of her husband, deliberated and took advice of herself how she might bring this whole matter to a good end. And when she saw her time, she sent for these adversaries to come to her privately; and truly showed them the great good to be gained from peace and the great harms and dangers that are in war; and told them in a gracious manner that they ought to be repentant for the injury and wrong they had done to Melibee, her lord, and to herself, and to her daughter.

And when they heard the gracious words of Dame Prudence they were so taken by surprise and so ravished with delight of her, that it was wonderful to tell. "Ah, lady," they said, "you have showed us the 'blessings of sweetness' in the words of David the prophet; for the reconciliation we are in no way worthy of, though we ought but in the greater contrition and humility to ask it—this, of your goodness, you have offered to us. Now see we well that the wisdom and knowledge of Solomon are true indeed, for he says that sweet words multiply and increase friends and cause villains to become courteous and humble.

"Certainly," said they, "we will put our actions and all our matter and cause wholly in your good keeping; and we stand ready to obey the word and command of Lord Melibee. Therefore, dear and benign lady, we pray and beseech you, as humbly as we can, that it shall please you, in your great goodness, to fulfill your goodly words in deeds; for we consider and acknowledge that we have offended and grieved Lord Melibee beyond measure; so far indeed that it lies not within our power to make him any amends. Therefore we obligate and bind ourselves and our friends to do whatsoever he commands. But perchance he has for us such a heaviness of wrath, what of our offense, that he will impose upon us so great a pain of punishment that we shall not be able to bear it. And therefore, noble lady, we beseech you of your womanly pity to take such advisement in this need that we, and our friends, shall not be disinherited and destroyed because of our folly."

"Certainly," said Prudence, "it is a hard thing, and a dangerous, for a man to put himself utterly into the arbitrament and judgment and into the might and power of his enemies. For Solomon says: 'Give not thy son and wife, thy brother and friend, power over thee while thou livest, and give not thy goods to another: lest it repent thee, and thou entreat for the same again. As long as thou livest and hast breath in thee, give not thyself over to any.' Now, since he counsels that a man give not even to a brother or a friend the power over his body, by a stronger reason he forbids a man to give himself over to his enemy. Nevertheless, I counsel you that you mistrust not my lord. For I know well and truly that he is kindly and meek, large-hearted, courteous, and nothing desirous nor covetous of goods and riches. For there is nothing in all the world that he desires, save only respect and honour. Furthermore, I know well and am right sure that he will do nothing in this case without my counsel. And I shall so work therein that, by the grace of Our Lord God, you shall be reconciled unto us."

Then said they with one voice: "Worshipful lady, we put ourselves and our property all fully at your command and disposal; and we are ready to come, upon whatever day is agreeable to your goodness, to make and give our obligation and bond, and that as

63. And whan they herden the goodliche wordes of dame Prudence, they weren so surprised and ravisshed, and hadden so greet joye of hir, that wonder was to telle. "A! lady!" quod they, "ye han shewed un-to us 'the blessinge of swetnesse,' after the sawe of David the prophete; for the reconsilinge which we been nat worthy to have in no manere, but we oghte requeren it with greet contricioun and humilitee, ye of your grete goodnesse have presented unto us. Now see we wel that the science and the conninge of Salomon is ful trewe; for he seith: that 'swete wordes multiplyen and encresen freendes, and maken shrewes to be debonaire and meke.'

64. Certes," quod they, "we putten our dede and al our matere and cause al hoolly in your goode wil; and been redy to obeye to the speche and comandement of my lord Melibee. And therfore, dere and benigne lady, we preyen yow and biseke yow as mekely as we conne and mowen, that it lyke unto your grete goodnesse to fulfillen in dede your goodliche wordes; for we consideren and knowlichen that we han offended and greved my lord Melibee out of mesure; so ferforth, that we be nat of power to maken hise amendes. And therfore we oblige and binden us and our freendes to doon al his wil and hise comandements. But peraventure he hath swich hevinesse and swich wratthe to usward, by-cause of our offence, that he wole enjoyne us swich a peyne as we mowe nat bere ne sustene. And therfore, noble lady, we biseke to your wommanly pitee, to taken swich avysement in this nede, that we, ne our freendes, be nat desherited ne destroyed thurgh our folye."

65. "Certes," quod Prudence, "it is an hard thing and right perilous, that a man putte al outrely in the arbitracioun and juggement, and in the might and power of hise enemys. For Salomon seith: 'leveth me, and yeveth credence to that I shal seyn; I seye,' quod he, 'ye peple, folk, and governours of holy chirche, to thy sone, to thy wyf, to thy freend, ne to thy brother ne yeve thou never might ne maistrie of thy body, whyl thou livest.' Now sithen he defendeth, that man shal nat yeven to his brother ne to his freend the might of his body, by a strenger resoun he defendeth and forbedeth a man to yeven him-self to his enemy. And nathelees I conseille you, that ye mistruste nat my lord. For I woot wel and knowe verraily, that he is debonaire and meke, large, curteys, and nothing desyrous ne coveitous of good ne richesse. For ther nis no-thing in this world that he desyreth, save only worship and honour. Forther-more I knowe wel, and am right seur, that he shal no-thing doon in this nede with-outen my conseil. And I shal so werken in this cause, that, by grace of our lord god, ye shul been reconsiled un-to us."

66. Thanne seyden they with o vois, "worshipful lady, we putten us and our goodes al fully in your wil and disposicioun; and been redy to comen, what day that it lyke un-to your noblesse to limite us or assigne us, for to maken our obligacioun and

bond as strong as it lyketh un-to your goodnesse; that we mowe fulfille the wille of yow and of my lord Melibee."

strong as your goodness may desire: all that we may fulfill your will and that of Lord Melibee."

67. Whan dame Prudence hadde herd the answeres of thise men, she bad hem goon agayn prively; and she retourned to hir lord Melibee, and tolde him how she fond hise adversaries ful repentant, knowlechinge ful lowely hir sinnes and trespas, and how they were redy to suffren al peyne, requiringe and preyinge him of mercy and pitee.

When Dame Prudence had heard the answers of these men, she sent them away again, secretly. And she returned to Lord Melibee and reported to him how she had found these adversaries ready to suffer pain and punishment, praying him, however, for mercy and pity.

68. Thanne seyde Melibee, "he is wel worthy to have pardoun and foryifnesse of his sinne, that excuseth nat his sinne, but knowlecheth it and repenteth him, axinge indulgence. For Senek seith: 'ther is the remissioun and foryifnesse, wheras confessioun is'; for confession is neighebore to innocence. And he seith in another place: 'he that hath shame for his sinne and knowlecheth it, is worthy remissioun.' And therfore I assente and conferme me to have pees; but it is good that we do it nat with-outen the assent and wil of our freendes."

"Then," said Melibee, "he is well worthy of pardon and to have his sins forgiven who excuses not his crime but acknowledges it and repents, asking indulgence. For Seneca says: 'There is the remission and the forgiveness where confession is.' For confession is neighbour to innocence. And he says in another place: 'He that is ashamed for his sin and acknowledges it, is worthy of remission.' Therefore I assent to peace; but it is best that we do this with the advice and consent of our friends."

69. Thanne was Prudence right glad and joyeful, and seyde, "Certes, sir," quod she, "ye han wel and goodly answered. For right as by the conseil, assent, and help of your freendes, ye han been stired to venge yow and maken werre, right so withouten hir conseil shul ye nat accorden yow, ne have pees with your adversaries. For the lawe seith: 'ther nis no-thing so good by wey of kinde, as a thing to been unbounde by him that it was y-bounde.'"

Then was Dame Prudence right glad and joyful, and she said: "Certainly, sir, you have well answered. For just as by the counsel, assent, and help of your friends you have been stirred to avenge yourself and go to war, just so you should not, without their consent, accord and make peace with your adversaries. For the law says: There is nothing so good in kind as that a thing shall be unbound by him by whom it was bound."

70. And thanne dame Prudence, with-outen delay or taryinge, sente anon hir messages for hir kin, and for hir olde freendes whiche that were trewe and wyse, and tolde hem by ordre, in the presence of Melibee, al this matere as it is aboven expressed and declared; and preyden hem that they wolde yeven hir avys and conseil, what best were to doon in this nede. And whan Melibees freendes hadde taken hir avys and deliberacioun of the forseide matere, and hadden examined it by greet bisinesse and greet diligence, they yave ful conseil for to have pees and reste; and that Melibee sholde receyve with good herte hise adversaries to foryifnesse and mercy.

And then Dame Prudence, without delay or tarrying, sent messengers for their kindred and for their old friends who were true and wise, and told them in detail and in order, in the presence of Melibee, all of this matter, as it has been here expressed and declared; and she prayed them that they would advise and counsel what best were to be done in this need. And when Melibee's friends had taken their advices in this said matter, and had examined into it with diligence, they gave their counsel for peace and rest; and that Melibee should receive, with good heart, the prayers of his adversaries for forgiveness and mercy.

71. And whan dame Prudence hadde herd the assent of hir lord Melibee, and the conseil of hise freendes, accorde with hir wille and hir entencioun, she was wonderly glad in hir herte, and seyde: "ther is an old proverbe," quod she, "seith: that 'the goodnesse that thou mayst do this day, do it; and abyde nat ne delaye it nat til to-morwe.' And therfore I conseille that ye sende your messages, swiche as been discrete and wyse, un-to your adversaries; tellinge hem, on your bihalve, that if they wole trete of pees and of accord, that they shape hem, with-outen delay or tarying, to comen un-to us." Which thing parfourned was in dede. And whanne thise trespassours and repentinge folk of hir folies, that is to seyn, the adversaries of Melibee, hadden herd what thise messagers seyden un-to hem, they weren right glad and joyeful, and answereden ful mekely and benignely, yeldinge graces and thank-

And when Dame Prudence had heard the assent of her lord, Melibee, and the counsel of these friends, how they accorded with her will and intention, she was wonderfully glad of heart; and she said: "There is an old proverb which advises that the goodness you may do this day, do it; and delay it not until the morrow. Therefore I counsel you that you send wise and discreet messengers to your adversaries, bidding them that, if they are still minded to treat with you of peace and concord, they come hither to us without delay or tarrying."

Which thing was done. And when these trespassers and repentant folk, that is to say, the adversaries of Melibeus, had heard the messengers' words, they were right glad and joyful, and they replied full meekly and favourably, yielding grace and giving thanks to their Lord Melibee and to all his party; and they made ready, without delay, to accompany the messengers in obedience to the command of Lord Melibee.

Soon, then, they took their way toward Melibee's court, and they took with them some of their true friends to stand as sureties for them, and as hostages. And when they were come into the presence of Melibee, he spoke to them as follows: "It stands thus, and true it is, that you, without just cause, and without right or reason, have done great injury and wrong to me, to my wife Prudence, and to my daughter also. For you have entered my house with violence, and you did such outrage here that all men know well enough that you have fully deserved death; therefore do I ask of you whether you will leave the punishment, the chastisement, and the vengeance of this thing to me and to my wife Prudence? Or will you not?"

Then the wisest of these three answered for all of them, saying: "Sir, we know well that we are unworthy to come into the court of so great and so worthy a lord as you are. For we have so greatly erred, and have offended guiltily in such wise against your lordship, that verily we have been deserving of death. But yet, for the great goodness and kindness that all the world witnesses in your person, we submit ourselves to the excellence and benignity of your gracious lordship, and stand ready to obey all your commands, beseeching you, that of your mercy and pity you will consider our great repentance and humble submission, and will grant us forgiveness for our outrageous trespass and offence. For well we know that your liberal grace and mercy reach out farther into goodness than reach our outrageous guilts and trespasses into wickedness; and this despite the fact that we have wickedly and damnably offended against your high lordship."

Then Melibee took them benignly up from the ground, and received their obligations and bonds, by their oaths, and their pledges and sureties and hostages, and assigned a day for their reappearance before his court to receive and accept his sentence and judgment, the which he should impose; and after this, each man returned to his own home.

And when Dame Prudence saw her opportunity, she asked her lord, Melibee, what vengeance he purposed taking on these adversaries.

To which Melibee replied: "Surely I think and fully purpose to confiscate all that they have and to strip them out of their inheritances, and then to send them into perpetual banishment."

"Certainly," said Dame Prudence, "that were a cruel sentence and much against reason. For you are rich enough, and have no need of other men's property. And you could easily in this way acquire a name for covetousness, which is a vicious thing and ought to be avoided by every good man. For, after the word of the apostle, covetousness is the root of all evil.

inges to hir hord Melibee and to al his companye; and shopen hem, with-outen delay, to go with the messagers, and obeye to the comandement of hir lord Melibee.

72. And right anon they token hir wey to the court of Melibee, and token with hem somme of hir trewe freendes, to maken feith for hem and for to been hir borwes. And whan they were comen to the presence of Melibee, he seyde hem thise wordes: "it standeth thus," quod Melibee, "and sooth it is, that ye, causeless, and with-outen skile and resoun, han doon grete injuries and wronges to me and to my wyf Prudence, and to my doghter also. For ye han entred in-to myn hous by violence, and have doon swich outrage, that alle men knowen wel that ye have deserved the deeth; and therfore wol I knowe and wite of yow, whether ye wol putte the punissement and the chastysinge and the vengeance of this outrage in the wil of me and of my wyf Prudence; or ye wol nat?"

73. Thanne the wyseste of hem three answerde for hem alle, and seyde: "sire," quod he, "we knowen wel, that we been unworthy to comen un-to the court of so greet a lord and so worthy as ye been. For we han so greetly mistaken us, and han offended and agilt in swich a wyse agayn your heigh lordshipe, that trewely we han deserved the deeth. But yet, for the grete goodnesse and debonairetee that all the world witnesseth of your persone, we submitten us to the excellence and benignitee of your gracious lordshipe, and been redy to obeie to alle your comandements; bisekinge yow, that of your merciable pitee ye wol considere our grete repentaunce and lowe submissioun, and graunten us foryevenesse of our outrageous trespas and offence. For wel we knowe, that your liberal grace and mercy strecchen hem ferther in-to goodnesse, than doon our outrageouse giltes and trespas in-to wikkednesse; al-be-it that cursedly and dampnably we han agilt agayn your heigh lordshipe."

74. Thanne Melibee took hem up fro the ground ful benignely, and receyved hir obligaciouns and hir bondes by hir othes up-on hir plegges and borwes, and assigned hem a certeyn day to retourne un-to his court, for to accepte and receyve the sentence and jugement that Melibee wolde comande to be doon on hem by the causes afore-seyd; whiche thinges ordeyned, every man retourned to his hous.

75. And whan that dame Prudence saugh hir tyme, she freyned and axed hir lord Melibee, what vengeance he thoughte to taken of hise adversaries?

76. To which Melibee answerde and seyde, "certes," quod he, "I thinke and purpose me fully to desherite hem of al that ever they han, and for to putte hem in exil for ever."

77. "Certes," quod dame Prudence, "this were a cruel sentence, and muchel agayn resoun. For ye been riche y-nough, and han no nede of other mennes good; and ye mighte lightly in this wyse gete yow a coveitous name, which is a vicious thing, and oghte been eschewed of every good man. For after the sawe of the word of the apostle: 'conveitise is

rote of alle harmes.' And therfore, it were bettre for yow to lese so muchel good of your owene, than for to taken of hir good in this manere. For bettre it is to lesen good with worshipe, than it is to winne good with vileinye and shame. And every man oghte to doon his diligence and his bisinesse to geten him a good name. And yet shal he nat only bisie him in kepinge of his good name, but he shal also enforcen him alwey to do som-thing by which ne may renovelle his good name; for it is writen, that 'the olde good loos or good name of a man is sone goon and passed, whan it is nat newed ne renovelled.' And as touchinge that ye seyn, ye wole exile your adversaries, that thinketh me muchel agayn resoun and out of mesure, considered the power that they han yeve yow up-on hem-self. And it is writen, that 'he is worthy to lesen his privilege that misuseth the might and the power that is yeven him.' And I sette cas ye mighte enjoyne hem that peyne by right and by lawe, which I trowe ye mowe nat do, I seye, ye mighte nat putten it to execucioun per-aventure, and thanne were it lykly to retourne to the werre as it was biforn. And therfore, if ye wole that men do yow obeisance, ye moste demen more curteisly; this is to seyn, ye moste yeven more esy sentences and jugements. For it is writen, that 'he that most curteisly comandeth, to him men most obeyen.' And therfore, I prey yow that in this necessitee and in this nede, ye caste yow to overcome your herte. For Senek seith: that 'he that overcometh his herte, overcometh twyes.' And Tullius seith: 'ther is no-thing so comendable in a greet lord as whan he is debonaire and meke, and appeseth him lightly.' And I prey yow that ye wol forbere now to do vengeance, in swich a manere, that your goode name may be kept and conserved; and that men mowe have cause and matere to preyse yow of pitee and of mercy; and that ye have no cause to repente yow of thing that ye doon. For Senek seith: 'he overcometh in an yvel manere, that repenteth him of his victorie.' Wherfore I pray yow, lat mercy been in your minde and in your herte, to th'effect and entente that god almighty have mercy on yow in his laste jugement. For seint Jame seith in his epistle: 'jugement withouten mercy shal be doon to him, that hath no mercy of another wight.' "

78. Whanne Melibee hadde herd the grete skiles and resouns of dame Prudence, and hir wise informaciouns and techinges, his herte gan enclyne to the wil of his wyf, consideringe hir trewe entente; and conformed him anon, and assented fully to werken after hir conseil; and thonked god, of whom procedeth al vertu and alle goodnesse, that him sente a wyf of so greet discrecioun. And whan the day cam that hise adversaries sholde apperen in his presence, he spak unto hem ful goodly, and seyde in this wyse: "al-be-it so that of your pryde and presumpcioun and folie, and of your necligence and unconninge, ye have misborn yow and trespassed un-to me; yet, for as much as I see and biholde your grete humilitee, and that ye been sory and repentant of your giltes, it constreyneth me to

Therefore were it better for you to lose an equal property of your own than to take theirs from them in this manner. For better it is to lose goods with honour than to win them by villainy and shame. And every man ought to be diligent about getting and keeping a good name. And he should not only busy himself with the keeping of a good name, but he should impose upon himself the constant task of renewing it. For it is written that 'The good fame or good name of a man is soon passed and forgotten, unless it be renewed.' And touching what you say, that you will exile your adversaries, that seems to me much against reason and out of all measure, considering how they have placed themselves within your power. And it is written that 'He deserves to lose his privilege who abuses and misuses the might and the power that are given to him.' And I submit that, even if you might impose upon them that pain by right and by law, which I think that you could not, I say that you might not be able to put it into execution, by some chance, and then were you as likely to fall again into war as you were before. Therefore, if you would have men render you obedience, you must judge more courteously, that is to say, you must give more easy sentences. For it is written that 'He who most courteously commands, men most readily obey.' Therefore I pray you that in this need you contrive to conquer your own heart. For Seneca says: 'He that overcomes his own heart, conquers twice.' And Tullius says: 'There is nothing so commendable in a great lord as when he is kindly and meek and easily satisfied.' And I pray you that you will forgo your vengeance in this manner, in order that your good name may be kept and preserved; and that men may have cause and reason to praise you for pity and for mercy, and that you yourself shall not have cause to repent for what you have done. For Seneca says: 'He conquers but evilly who repents of his victory.' Wherefore, I pray you, let there be mercy in your mind and in your heart, to the end that God Almighty may have mercy upon you at His last judgment. For Saint James says in his Epistle: 'For he shall have judgment without mercy who hath showed no mercy.' "

When Melibee had heard the great arguments and reasons of Dame Prudence, and her wise information and teaching, his heart began to incline toward the desire of his wife, considering her true intent; and he conformed his will to hers and assented fully to her counselling. And he thanked God, from Whom proceeds all virtue and goodness, that He had sent him a wife of so very great discretion.

And when the day arrived for his adversaries to appear before him, he spoke to them kindly, in this wise: "Howbeit that of your pride and presumption and folly, and in your negligence and ignorance, you have borne yourselves badly and have trespassed against me, yet for as much as I see and behold your great humility and that you are sorry and repentant for your crimes, it constrains me to show you grace and mercy. Therefore do I receive you into my grace and forgive you utterly all the offences, injuries, and wrongs that you have done against me and mine; to this effect and to this end: that God of His endless mercy will, at our dying day, forgive us our sins that we have sinned against Him in this wretched world. For doubtless, if we be sorry and repentant for the sins and crimes which we have committed in the sight of Our Lord, He is so free and so merciful that He will forgive us our guilt and bring us into His everlasting bliss. Amen."

doon yow grace and mercy. Therfore I receyve yow to my grace, and foryeve yow outrely alle the offences, injuries, and wronges, that ye have doon agayn me and myne; to this effect and to this ende, that god of his endelees mercy wole at the tyme of our dyinge foryeven us our giltes that we han trespassed to him in this wrecched world. For doutelees, if we be sory and repentant of the sinnes and giltes whiche we han trespassed in the sighte of our lord god, he is so free and so merciable, that he wole foryeven us our giltes, and bringen us to his blisse that never hath ende. Amen."

HERE IS ENDED CHAUCER'S TALE OF MELIBEUS AND OF DAME PRUDENCE

THE MONK'S PROLOGUE

THE MERRY WORDS OF THE HOST TO THE MONK

When ended was my tale of Melibee
And of Prudence and her benignity,
Our host remarked: "As I am faithful man,
And by the precious *corpus Madrian*,
I'd rather than a barrel of good ale
That my wife Goodlief could have heard this
tale!
For she has no such patience, I'll avow,
As had this Melibeus' Prudence, now.
By God's own bones! When I do beat my knaves
She fetches forth the stoutest gnarly staves
And cries out: 'Slay the damned dogs, every one!
And break their bones, backbone and every bone!'
And if but any neighbour, aye, of mine
Will not, in church, bow to her and incline,
Or happens to usurp her cherished place,
Why, she comes home and ramps right in my
face,
Crying, 'False coward, go avenge your wife!
By *corpus* bones! Come, let me have your knife,
And you shall take my distaff and go spin!'
From day to day like this will she begin:
'Alas!' she cries, 'that ever fate should shape
My marriage with a milksop coward ape
That may be overborne by every wight!
You dare not stand up for your own wife's right!'
This is my life, unless I choose to fight;
And through the door anon I must take flight,
Or else I'm lost, unless, indeed, that I
Be like a young wild lion, foolhardy.
I know well she will make me kill, one day,
Some neighbour man and have to run away.
For I am dangerous with a knife in hand,
Albeit that I dare not her withstand;
For she's big of arm, and wickedly inclined,
As anyone who crosses her will find.
But let us leave that doleful subject here.
"My lord the monk," said he, "be of good
cheer;
For you shall tell a tale, and verily.

When ended was my tale of Melibee,
And of Prudence and hir benignitee,
Our hoste seyde, "as I am faithful man,
And by the precious *corpus Madrian*,
I hadde lever than a barel ale
That goode lief my wyf hadde herd this
tale!
For she nis no-thing of swich pacience
As was this Melibeus wyf Prudence.
By goddes bones! whan I bete my knaves,
She bringth me forth the grete clobbed staves,
And cryeth, 'slee the dogges everichoon,
And brek hem, bothe bak and every boon.'
And if that any neighebor of myne
Wol nat in chirche to my wyf enclyne,
Or be so hardy to hir to trespace,
Whan she comth hoom, she rampeth in my
face,
And cryeth, 'false coward, wreek thy wyf!
By *corpus* bones! I wol have thy knyf,
And thou shalt have my distaf and go spinne!'
Fro day to night right thus she wol beginne;—
'Allas!' she seith, 'that ever I was shape
To wedde a milksop or a coward ape,
That wol be overlad with every wight!
Thou darst nat stonden by thy wyves right!'
This is my lyf, but-if that I wol fighte;
And out at dore anon I moot me dighte,
Or elles I am but lost, but-if that I
Be lyk a wilde leoun fool-hardy.
I woot wel she wol do me slee som day
Som neighebor, and thanne go my wey.
For I am perilous with knyf in honde,
Al be it that I dar nat hir withstonde,
For she is big in armes, by my feith,
That shal he finde, that hir misdooth or seith.
But lat us passe awey fro this matere.
My lord the Monk," quod he, "be mery of
chere;
For ye shul telle a tale trewely.

Lo! Rouchestre stant heer faste by!
Ryd forth, myn owene lord, brek nat our game,
But, by my trouthe, I knowe nat your name,
Wher shal I calle yow my lord dan John,
Or dan Thomas, or elles dan Albon?
Of what hous be ye, by your fader kin?
I vow to god, thou hast a ful fair skin,
It is a gentil pasture ther thou goost;
Thou art nat lyk a penaunt or a goost.
Upon my feith, thou art som officer,
Some worthy sexteyn, or som celerer,
For by my fader soule, as to my doom,
Thou art a maister whan thou art at hoom;
No povre cloisterer, ne no novys,
But a governour, wyly and wys.
And therwithal of brawnes and of bones
A wel-faring persone for the nones.
I pray to god, yeve him confusioun
That first thee broghte un-to religioun;
Thou woldest han been a trede-foul aright.
Haddestow as greet a leve, as thou hast might
To parfourne al thy lust in engendrure,
Thou haddest bigeten many a creature.
Alas! why werestow so wyd a cope?
God yeve me sorwe! but, and I were a pope,
Not only thou, but every mighty man,
Thogh he were shorn ful hye upon his pan,
Sholde have a wyf; for al the world is lorn!
Religioun hath take up al the corn
Of treding, and we borel men ben shrimpes!
Of feble trees ther comen wrecched impes.
This maketh that our heires been so sclendre
And feble, that they may nat wel engendre.
This maketh that our wyves wol assaye
Religious folk, for ye may bettre paye
Of Venus payements than mowe we;
God woot, no lussheburghes payen ye!
But be nat wrooth, my lord, for that I pleye;
Ful ofte in game a sooth I have herd seye."
  This worthy monk took al in pacience,
And seyde, "I wol doon al my diligence,
As fer as souneth in-to honestee,
To telle yow a tale, or two or three.
And if yow list to herkne hiderward,
I wol yow seyn the lyf of seint Edward;
Or elles first Tragedies wol I telle
Of whiche I have an hundred in my celle.
Tragedie is to seyn a certeyn storie,
As olde bokes maken us
  memorie,
Of him that stood in greet prosperitee
And is y-fallen out of heigh degree
Into miserie, and endeth wrecchedly.
And they ben versifyed comunly
Of six feet, which men clepe *exametron*.
In prose eek been endyted many oon,
And eek in metre, in many a sondry wyse.
Lo! this declaring oughte y-nough suffise.
  Now herkneth, if yow lyketh for to here;
But first I yow biseke in this matere,
Though I by ordre telle nat thise thinges,
Be it of popes, emperours, or kinges,

Lo, Rochester is standing there hard by!
Ride up, my own liege lord, break not our game,
But, by my truth, I do not know your name,
Whether I ought to call you lord Don John,
Or Don Thomas, or else Don Albion?
Of what house are you, by your father's kin?
I vow to God you have a right fair skin;
It is a noble pasture where you're most;
You are not like a penitent or ghost.
Upon my faith, you are some officer,
Some worthy sexton, or a cellarer,
For by my father's soul, I guess, in sum,
You are a master when you are at home.
No cloisterer or novice can you be:
A wily governor you seem to me,
And therewithal a man of brawn and bone.
A person of some consequence you've grown.
I pray that God confound the silly fool
That put you first in a religious school;
You would have been a hen-hopper, all right!
Had you as good a chance as you have might
To work your lust in good engendering;
Why, you'd beget full many a mighty thing.
Alas! Why do you wear so wide a cope?
God give me sorrow but, if I were pope,
Not only you, but every mighty man,
Though he were shorn full high upon the pan,
Should have a wife. For all the world's forlorn!
Religion, why it's gathered all the corn
Of treading, and we laymen are but shrimps!
From feeble trees there come but wretched imps.
That's why our heirs are all so very slender
And feeble that they may not well engender.
That's why our goodwives always will essay
Religious folk, for you may better pay
With Venus' payments than we others do;
God knows, in no light weight of coin pay you!
But be not wroth, my lord, because I play;
Full oft in jest have I heard truth, I say."
  This worthy monk took all with sober sense,
And said: "I will do all my diligence,
So far as it accords with decency,
To tell to you a tale, or two, or three.
And if you care to hear, come hitherward,
And I'll repeat the life of Saint Edward;
Or rather, first some tragedies I'll tell,
Whereof I have a hundred in my cell.
Tragedy is to say a certain story
From ancient books which have preserved
  the glory
Of one that stood in great prosperity
And is now fallen out of high degree
In misery, where he ends wretchedly.
Such tales are versified most commonly
In six feet, which men call hexameter.
In prose are many written; some prefer
A quantitative metre, sundry wise.
Lo, this short prologue will enough suffice.
  "Now hearken, if you'd like my speech to hear;
But first I do beseech, let it be clear
That I, in order, tell not all these things,
Be it of popes, of emperors, or kings,

Each in his place, as men in writings find,
But I put some before and some behind,
As they to memory may come by chance;
Hold me excused, pray, of my ignorance."

After hir ages, as men writen finde,
But telle hem som bifore and som bihinde,
As it now comth un-to my remembraunce;
Have me excused of myn ignoraunce."

HERE IT ENDETH

THE MONK'S TALE

HERE BEGINNETH THE MONK'S TALE OF THE FALLS OF FAMOUS MEN

I WILL bewail in manner of tragedy
The ills of those that stood in high degree
And fell so far there was no remedy
To bring them out of their adversity;
For certain 'tis, when Fortune wills to flee,
There may no man the course of her withhold;
Let no man trust in blind prosperity;
Be warned by these examples true and old.

I WOL biwayle in maner of Tragedie
The harm of hem that stode in heigh degree,
And fillen so that ther nas no remedie
To bringe hem out of hir adversitee;
For certein, whan that fortune list to flee,
Ther may no man the cours of hir withholde;
Lat no man truste on blind prosperitee;
Be war by thise ensamples trewe and olde.

LUCIFER

With Lucifer, though he was angel fair
And not a man, with him will I begin;
For though Fortune may not an angel dare,
From high degree yet fell he for his sin
Down into Hell, and he lies yet therein.
O Lucifer, brightest of angels all,
Now art thou Satan, and thou may'st not win
From misery wherein thou far did'st fall!

At Lucifer, though he an angel were,
And nat a man, at him I wol biginne;
For, thogh fortune may non angel dere,
From heigh degree yet fel he for his sinne
Doun in-to helle, wher he yet is inne.
O Lucifer! brightest of angels alle,
Now artow Sathanas, that maist nat twinne
Out of miserie, in which that thou art falle.

ADAM

Lo, Adam, in the garden Damascene,
By God Almighty's finger wrought was he,
And not begotten of man's sperm unclean;
He ruled all Paradise, except one tree.
Had never earthly man so high degree
As Adam, till he, for misgovernance,
Was driven from his high prosperity
To labour, and to Hell, and to mischance.

Lo Adam, in the feld of Damassene,
With goddes owene finger wroght was he,
And nat bigeten of mannes sperme unclene,
And welte al Paradys, saving o tree.
Had never worldly man so heigh degree
As Adam, til he for misgovernaunce
Was drive out of his hye prosperitee
To labour, and to helle, and to meschaunce.

SAMPSON

Lo, Samson, whose birth was annunciated
By angel, long ere his nativity,
And was to God Almighty consecrated,
And had nobility while he could see.
Was never such another as was he
For body's strength, and therewith hardiness;
But to his wives he told his privity,
Whereby he slew himself for
wretchedness.

Lo Sampson, which that was annunciat
By th'angel, longe er his nativitee,
And was to god almighty consecrat,
And stood in noblesse, whyl he mighte see.
Was never swich another as was he,
To speke of strengthe, and therwith hardinesse;
But to his wyves tolde he his secree,
Through which he slow him-self, for wrecched-
nesse.

Samson, this noble mighty champion,
Without a weapon in his hands, I say,
He slew and rent in two a young lion,
While to his wedding walking in the way.
His false wife could so please him, she did
pray
Till she his secret held, when she, untrue,
Unto his foes that secret did betray
And him forsook for other loves and new.

Sampson, this noble almighty champioun,
Withouten wepen save his hondes tweye,
He slow and al to-rente the leoun,
Toward his wedding walking by the weye.
His false wyf coude him so plese and
preye
Til she his conseil knew, and she untrewe
Un-to his foos his conseil gan biwreye,
And him forsook, and took another newe.

Three hundred foxes took Sampson for ire,
And alle hir tayles he togider bond,
And sette the foxes tayles alle on fire,
For he on every tayl had knit a brond;
And they brende alle the cornes in that lond,
And alle hir oliveres and vynes eek.
A thousand men he slow eek with his hond,
And had no wepen but an asses cheek.

Whan they were slayn, so thursted him that he
Was wel ny lorn, for which he gan to preye
That god wolde on his peyne han som pitee,
And sende him drinke, or elles moste he deye;
And of this asses cheke, that was dreye,
Out of a wang-tooth sprang anon a welle,
Of which he drank y-nogh, shortly to seye,
Thus heelp him god, as *Judicum* can telle.

By verray force, at Gazan, on a night,
Maugree Philistiens of that citee,
The gates of the toun he hath up-plight,
And on his bak y-caried hem hath he
Hye on an hille, that men mighte hem see.
O noble almighty Sampson, leef and dere,
Had thou nat told to wommen thy secree,
In al this worlde ne hadde been thy pere!

This Sampson never sicer drank ne wyn,
Ne on his heed cam rasour noon ne shere,
By precept of the messager divyn,
For alle his strengthes in his heres were;
And fully twenty winter, yeer by yere,
He hadde of Israel the governaunce.
But sone shal he wepen many a tere,
For wommen shal him bringen to meschaunce!

Un-to his lemman Dalida he tolde
That in his heres al his strengthe lay,
And falsly to his fo-men she him solde.
And sleping in hir barme up-on a day
She made to clippe or shere his heer awey,
And made his fo-men al his craft espyen;
And whan that they him fonde in this array,
They bounde him faste, and putten out his yën.

But er his heer were clipped or y-shave,
Ther was no bond with which men might him
binde;
But now is he in prisoun in a cave,
Wher-as they made him at the querne grinde.
O noble Sampson, strongest of mankinde,
O whylom juge in glorie and in richesse,
Now maystow wepen with thyn yën
blinde,
Sith thou fro wele art falle in wrecchednesse.

Th'ende of this caytif was as I shal seye;
His fo-men made a feste upon a day,
And made him as hir fool bifore hem pleye,
And this was in a temple of greet array.
But atte last he made a foul affray;
For he two pilers shook, and made hem falle,

Three hundred foxes Samson took, for ire,
And bound their brushes well together, and
Then set those foxes' tails alight with fire,
For he to every one had fixed a brand;
And they burned all the corn of all that land
And all the olive trees and vines, each one.
A thousand men he slew with his own hand,
With no weapon save an ass's jaw-bone.

When they were slain, he thirsted so that he
Was well nigh lost, for which he prayed, say I,
That God would on his pain have some pity
And send him drink, or must he surely die;
And from that ass's jaw-bone, then but dry,
Out of a tooth there sprang anon a well,
Whereof he drank his fill and laid it by.
Thus helped him God, as *Judges*, fifteen, tell.

By very force at Gaza, on a night,
Maugre Philistines of that said city,
The great gates of the town he took with might,
And on his shoulders carried them, did he,
High on a hill where every man might see.
O noble mighty Samson, lief and dear,
Had'st thou not woman told thy privity,
In all this world had never been thy peer.

This Samson never liquor drank, nor wine,
Nor on his head came razor, nor a shear,
Obeying thus the angel's word divine,
For all his forces in his long locks were;
And fully twenty winters, year by year,
He held of Israel the governance.
But all too soon should he weep many a tear,
For women should betray him to mischance!

Delilah being his darling, her he told
That in his unshorn locks all his strength lay,
And him to foemen then she falsely sold.
For, sleeping in her bosom, on a day,
She clipped and sheared all his long hair away,
Then showed his state unto his enemies,
And when they found him lying in this array
They bound him fast and put out both his eyes.

Before his hair was sheared and shaven close,
There were no bonds wherewith men might him
bind;
But now he lies in prison cell, morose,
And labours, when at mill they make him grind.
O noble Samson, strongest of mankind,
O judge, but late, in glory measureless,
Now may'st thou shed hot tears from thine eyes
blind,
For thou from wealth art fallen to wretchedness.

This captive's end was as I now shall say;
His foes they made a feast upon a day,
And made him as their fool before them play,
All in a temple great, of rich array.
But at the last he made a stern affray;
For he two pillars took and caused them fall,

And down came roof and all, and there it lay,
Killing himself and enemies, each and all.

That is to say, those princes, every one,
And full three thousand others who were slain
By falling of that temple built of stone.
To Samson now I'll not revert again.
Be warned by this example old and plain.
Men should not tell their business to their wives
In such things as of secrecy they're fain,
And if it touch their limbs or touch their lives.

And doun fil temple and al, and ther it lay,
And slow him-self, and eek his fo-men alle.

This is to seyn, the princes everichoon,
And eek three thousand bodies wer ther slayn
With falling of the grete temple of stoon.
Of Sampson now wol I na-more seyn.
Beth war by this ensample old and playn
That no men telle hir conseil til hir wyves
Of swich thing as they wolde han secree fayn,
If that it touche hir limmes or hir lyves.

HERCULES

Of Hercules, the sovereign conquering power,
Sing his deeds' praise and sing his high renown;
For in his time of strength he was the flower.
He slew, and made a lion's skin his own;
Of centaurs laid he all the boastings down;
He killed the cruel Harpies, those birds fell;
Brought golden apples from the dragon thrown;
And he stole Cerberus, the hound of Hell.

He slew the cruel tyrant Busiris
And made his horses eat him, flesh and bone;
To a fiery, venomous worm he wrote finis;
Achelous had two horns, but he broke one;
Cacus he slew within his cave of stone;
He slew the giant Anthaeus the strong;
He killed the Erymanthian boar anon;
And bore the heavens upon his shoulders long.

Was never man, since this old world began,
That slew so many monsters as did he.
Throughout all earth's wide realms his honour ran,
What of his strength and his high chivalry,
And every kingdom went he out to see.
He was so strong no man could hinder him;
At both ends of the world, as says Trophy,
In lieu of limits he set pillars grim.

A darling had this noble champion,
Deianira, sweet as is the May;
And as these ancient writers say, each one,
She sent to him a new shirt, fresh and gay.
Alas that shirt, alas and welaway!
Envenomed was so cunningly withal
That, ere he'd worn the thing but half a day,
It made the flesh from off his bones to fall.

Yet are there writers who do her excuse
Because of Nessus, who the shirt had made;
Howe'er it be, I will not her accuse;
But all his naked back this poison flayed
Until the flesh turned black, and torn, and frayed.
And when he saw no other remedy,
Upon a pyre of hot brands he was laid,
For of no poison would he deign to die.

Thus died this mighty worthy, Hercules.
Lo, who may trust to Fortune any throw?
And he who seeks on earth for fame and ease
Ere he's aware, he's often brought down low.

Of Hercules the sovereyn conquerour
Singen his workes laude and heigh renoun;
For in his tyme of strengthe he was the flour.
He slow, and rafte the skin of the leoun;
He of Centauros leyde the boost adoun;
He Arpies slow, the cruel briddes felle;
He golden apples rafte of the dragoun;
He drow out Cerberus, the hound of helle:

He slow the cruel tyrant Busirus,
And made his hors to frete him, flesh and boon;
He slow the firy serpent venimous;
Of Achelois two hornes, he brak oon;
And he slow Cacus in a cave of stoon;
He slow the geaunt Antheus the stronge;
He slow the grisly boor, and that anoon,
And bar the heven on his nekke longe.

Was never wight, sith that the world bigan,
That slow so many monstres as dide he.
Thurgh-out this wyde world his name ran,
What for his strengthe, and for his heigh bountee,
And every reaume wente he for to see.
He was so strong that no man mighte him lette;
At bothe the worldes endes, seith Trophee,
In stede of boundes, he a piler sette.

A lemman hadde this noble champioun,
That highte Dianira, fresh as May;
And, as thise clerkes maken mencioun,
She hath him sent a sherte fresh and gay.
Allas! this sherte, allas and weylaway!
Envenimed was so subtilly with-alle,
That, er that he had wered it half a day,
It made his flesh al from his bones falle.

But nathelees somme clerkes hir excusen
By oon that highte Nessus, that it maked;
Be as be may, I wol hir noght accusen;
But on his bak this sherte he wered al naked,
Til that his flesh was for the venim blaked.
And whan he sey noon other remedye,
In hote coles he hath him-selven raked,
For with no venim deyned him to dye.

Thus starf this worthy mighty Hercules,
Lo, who may truste on fortune any throwe?
For him that folweth al this world of prees,
Er he be war, is ofte y-leyd ful lowe.

Ful wys is he that can him-selven knowe.
Beth war, for whan that fortune list to glose,
Than wayteth she hir man to overthrowe
By swich a wey as he wolde leest suppose.

Right wise is he that can his own heart know.
Beware, when Fortune may her smile disclose,
She lies in wait her man to overthrow,
And in such wise as he would least suppose.

NEBUCHADNEZZAR

The mighty trone, the precious tresor,
The glorious ceptre and royal magestee
That hadde the king Nabugodonosor,
With tonge unnethe may discryved be.
He twyës wan Jerusalem the citee;
The vessel of the temple he with him ladde.
At Babiloyne was his sovereyn see,
In which his glorie and his delyt he hadde.

The precious treasure and the mighty throne,
The glorious sceptre and royal majesty
That Nebuchadnezzar counted as his own
With tongue or pen not easily told may be.
Twice of Jerusalem the victor he;
The Temple's vessels took he and was glad.
And Babylon was the ancient sovereign see
Wherein his glory and delight he had.

The fairest children of the blood royal
Of Israel he leet do gelde anoon,
And maked ech of hem to been his thral.
Amonges othere Daniel was oon,
That was the wysest child of everichoon;
For he the dremes of the king expouned,
Wher-as in Chaldey clerk ne was ther noon
That wiste to what fyn his dremes
souned.

The fairest children of the blood royal
Of Israel, he gelded them anon,
And made each one of them to be his thrall.
Among the number Daniel thus was one,
Of all the youth the nation's wisest son;
For he the dreams of the great king expounded
When in Chaldea wise clerk was there none
Who knew to what end those dreams were pro-
pounded.

This proude king leet make a statue of golde,
Sixty cubytes long, and seven in brede,
To which image bothe yonge and olde
Comaunded he to loute, and have in drede;
Or in a fourneys ful of flambes rede
He shal be brent, that wolde noght obeye.
But never wolde assente to that dede
Daniel, ne his yonge felawes tweye.

This proud king made a statue of pure gold
Full sixty cubits long by seven wide,
Unto which image both the young and old
Commanded he to bow down, nor deride,
Else in a furnace full of flames go bide
And burn to ashes, who would not obey.
But no assent to that, whate'er betide,
Would Daniel and his pair of comrades say.

This king of kinges proud was and elaat,
He wende that god, that sit in magestee,
Ne mighte him nat bireve of his estaat:
But sodeynly he loste his dignitee,
And lyk a beste him semed for to be,
And eet hay as an oxe, and lay ther-oute;
In reyn with wilde bestes walked he,
Til certein tyme was y-come aboute.

This king of kings right proud was and elate,
And thought that God, Who sits in majesty,
Could not bereave him of his high estate:
Yet suddenly he lost all dignity,
And like a brute beast then he seemed to be,
And ate hay like an ox, and lay without;
In rain and storm with all wild beasts walked he,
Until a certain time was come about.

And lyk an egles fetheres wexe his heres,
His nayles lyk a briddes clawes were;
Til god relessed him a certein yeres,
And yaf him wit; and than with many a tere
He thanked god, and ever his lyf in fere
Was he to doon amis, or more trespace,
And, til that tyme he leyd was on his bere,
He knew that god was ful of might and grace.

And like an eagle's feathers were his hairs,
His nails like any bird's claws hookèd were;
Till God released him after certain years
And gave him sense; and then, with many a tear,
He gave God thanks; thereafter all in fear
He lived of doing ever again trespass,
And till the time they laid him on his bier,
He knew that God was full of might and grace.

BELSHAZZAR

His sone, which that highte Balthasar,
That heeld the regne after his fader day,
He by his fader coude nought be war,
For proud he was of herte and of array;
And eek an ydolastre was he ay.
His hye estaat assured him in pryde.
But fortune caste him doun, and ther he
lay,
And sodeynly his regne gan divyde.

His son, called Belshazzar, or Balthasar,
Who held the realm after his father's day,
He for his father's fate would not beware,
For proud he was of heart and of array;
He was a worshipper of idols aye.
His high estate assured him in his pride.
But Fortune cast him down and there he
lay,
And suddenly his kingdom did divide.

A feast he made unto a thousand lords,
Upon a time, and bade them merry be.
Then to his officers he said these words:
"Go fetch me forth the vessels all," said he,
"Of which my father, in prosperity,
The temple in Jerusalem bereft,
And unto our high gods give thanks that we
Retain the honour that our elders left."

His wife, his lords, and all his concubines,
They drank then, while that mighty feast did last,
Out of those noble vessels sundry wines.
But on a wall this king his eyes did cast
And saw an armless hand that wrote full fast,
For fear whereof he shook with trouble sore.
This hand that held Belshazzar so aghast
Wrote *Mene*, *mene*, *teḳel*, and no more.

In all that land magician was there none
Who could explain what thing this writing meant;
But when they sent for Daniel it was done,
Who said: "O king, God to your father lent
Glory and honour, treasure, government,
And he was proud, nor feared God, being mad,
Wherefore Lord God great misery on him sent,
And him bereft of all the realm he had.

"He was cast out of human company;
With asses was his habitation known;
He ate hay like a beast, through wet and dry,
Until he learned, by grace and reason shown,
That Heaven's God has dominion, up and down,
Over all realms and everything therein;
And then did God to him compassion own
And gave him back his kingdom and his kin.

"Now you, who are his son, are proud also,
Though you knew all these things, aye verily;
You are a rebel and you are God's foe.
You drank from out His vessels boastfully;
Your wife and all your wenches sinfully
Drank from those sacred vessels sundry wines,
And praised false gods, and hailed them, wickedly;
Whereof toward you the wrath of God inclines.

"That hand was sent from God which on the wall
Wrote *Mene*, *mene*, *teḳel*. Oh, trust me,
Your reign is done, you have no worth at all,
Divided is your realm, and it shall be
To Medes and Persians given now," said he.
And that night went the king to fill death's maw,
And so Darius took his high degree,
Though he thereto had naught of right in law.

Masters, therefrom a moral may you take,
That in dominion is no certainness;
For when Fortune will any man forsake,
She takes his realm and all he may possess,
And all his friends, too, both the great and less;
For when a man has friends that Fortune gave,
Mishap but turns them enemies, as I guess:
This word is true for king as well as slave.

A feste he made un-to his lordes alle
Up-on a tyme, and bad hem blythe be,
And than his officeres gan he calle—
"Goth, bringeth forth the vessels," [tho] quod he,
"Which that my fader, in his prosperitee,
Out of the temple of Jerusalem birafte,
And to our hye goddes thanke we
Of honour, that our eldres with us lafte."

His wyf, his lordes, and his concubynes
Ay dronken, whyl hir appetytes laste,
Out of thise noble vessels sundry wynes;
And on a wal this king his yën caste,
And sey an hond armlees, that wroot ful faste,
For fere of which he quook and syked sore.
This hond, that Balthasar to sore agaste,
Wroot *Mane*, *techel*, *phares*, and na-more.

In al that lond magicien was noon
That coude expoune what this lettre mente;
But Daniel expouned it anoon,
And seyde, "king, god to thy fader lente
Glorie and honour, regne, tresour, rente
And he was proud, and no-thing god ne dradde,
And therfor god gret wreche up-on him sente,
And him birafte the regne that he hadde.

He was out cast of mannes companye,
With asses was his habitacioun,
And eet hey as a beste in weet and drye,
Til that he knew, by grace and by resoun,
That god of heven hath dominacioun
Over every regne and every creature;
And thanne had god of him compassioun,
And him restored his regne and his figure.

Eek thou, that art his sone, art proud also,
And knowest alle thise thinges verraily,
And art rebel to god, and art his fo.
Thou drank eek of his vessels boldely;
Thy wyf eek and thy wenches sinfully
Dronke of the same vessels sondry wynes,
And heriest falst goddes cursedly;
Therfor to thee y-shapen ful gret pyne is.

This hand was sent from god, that on the walle
Wroot *mane*, *techel*, *phares*, truste me;
Thy regne is doon, thou weyest noght at alle;
Divyded is thy regne, and it shal be
To Medes and to Perses yeven," quod he.
And thilke same night this king was slawe,
And Darius occupyeth his degree,
Thogh he therto had neither right no lawe.

Lordinges, ensample heer-by may ye take
How that in lordshipe is no sikernesse;
For whan fortune wol a man forsake,
She bereth awey his regne and his richesse,
And eek his freendes, bothe more and lesse;
For what man that hath freendes thurgh fortune,
Mishap wol make hem enemys, I gesse:
This proverbe is ful sooth and ful commune.

ZENOBIA

Cenobia, of Palimerie quene,
As writen Persiens of hir noblesse,
So worthy was in armes and so kene,
That no wight passed hir in hardinesse,
Ne in linage, ne in other gentillesse.
Of kinges blode of Perse is she descended;
I seye nat that she hadde most fairnesse,
But of hir shape she mighte nat been amended.

From hir childhede I finde that she fledde
Office of wommen, and to wode she wente;
And many a wilde hertes blood she shedde
With arwes brode that she to hem sente.
She was so swift that she anon hem hente,
And whan that she was elder, she wolde kille
Leouns, lepardes, and beres al to-rente,
And in hir armes welde hem at hir wille.

She dorste wilde beestes dennes seke,
And rennen in the montaignes al the night,
And slepen under a bush, and she coude eke
Wrastlen by verray force and verray might
With any yong man, were he never so wight;
Ther mighte no-thing in hir armes stonde.
She kepte hir maydenhod from every wight,
To no man deigned hir for to be bonde.

But atte laste hir frendes han hir maried
To Odenake, a prince of that contree,
Al were it so that she hem longe taried;
And ye shul understonde how that he
Hadde swiche fantasyes as hadde she.
But nathelees, whan they were knit infere,
They lived in joye and in felicitee;
For ech of hem hadde other leef and dere.

Save o thing, that she never wolde assente
By no wey, that he sholde by hir lye
But ones, for it was hir pleyn entente
To have a child, the world to multiplye;
And al-so sone as that she mighte espye
That she was nat with childe with that dede,
Than wolde she suffre him doon his fantasye
Eft-sone, and nat but ones, out of drede.

And if she were with childe at thilke cast,
Na-more sholde he pleyen thilke game
Til fully fourty dayes weren past;
Than wolde she ones suffre him do the same.
Al were this Odenake wilde or tame,
He gat na-more of hir, for thus she seyde,
"It was to wyves lecherye and shame
In other cas, if that men with hem pleyde."

Two sones by this Odenake hadde she,
The whiche she kepte in vertu and lettrure;
But now un-to our tale turne we.
I seye, so worshipful a creature,
And wys therwith, and large with mesure,
So penible in the werre, and curteis eke,

Zenobia, of all Palmyra queen
(As write old Persians of her nobleness),
So mighty was in warfare, and so keen,
That no man her surpassed in hardiness,
Nor yet in lineage, nor in gentleness.
Of blood of Persia's kings she was descended;
I say not she had greatest beauteousness,
But of her figure naught could be amended.

From childhood on I find that she had fled
Duties of women, and to wildwood went;
And many a wild hart's blood therein she shed
With arrows broad that she within them sent.
So swift she was, she ran them down all spent;
And when she was grown older she would kill
Lions and leopards, and bears too she rent,
And in her arms she broke them at her will.

She even dared the wild beasts' dens to seek,
And ran upon the mountains all the night,
Sleeping beneath a bush; and, nothing weak,
Wrestled by very force and very might
With any man, however brave in fight;
For there was nothing in her arms could stand.
She kept her maidenhead from every wight,
And unto no man would she yield her hand.

But at the last her friends did make her marry
Odenathus, a prince of that country,
Albeit she long waited and did tarry;
And you must understand that also he
Held to the same queer fancies as had she.
Nevertheless, when wedded, 'twould appear
They lived in joy and all felicity,
For each of them held other lief and dear.

But to one thing she never would consent,
For any prayers, that he should near her lie
Save one night only, when 'twas her intent
To have a child, since men should multiply;
Yet when she learned she'd got no pregnancy
From that night's work together on her bed,
Then would she suffer him again to try,
But only once indeed, and then with dread.

And when she was with child, all at the last,
Then no more might he play at that same game
Till fully forty days were gone and past;
Then would she once more suffer him the same.
And were Odenathus grown wild or tame,
He got no more of her; for thus she'd say:
"In wives it is but lechery and shame
When, oftener, men with their bodies play."

Two sons by this Odenathus had she,
The which she bred in virtue and learning;
But now again unto our tale turn we.
I say, so worshipful a young being,
Wise, and right generous in everything,
Careful in war and courteous as well,

And hardy in the field, and full daring,
Was not in all the world where men do dwell.

Her rich array may not be rightly told,
Either of vessels or of fine clothing;
She was clad all in jewels and in gold;
And she did never cease, despite hunting,
To gain of divers tongues a full knowing,
Whenever she had time; she did intend
To learn from books, which were to her liking,
How she in virtue might her whole life spend.

And briefly of this story now to treat,
So doughty was her husband, as was she,
That they two conquered many kingdoms great
Throughout the East, with many a fair city
That did pertain unto the majesty
Of Rome; and with strong hands they held them
  fast;
Nor might a foe escape by trying to flee
The while Odenathus' good days did last.

Her battles all (as whoso wills may read)
Against Sapor the king and others too,
And all her story as it fell, indeed,
Why she was victor and had right thereto,
And, after, all her misfortune and woe,
How they besieged her and at last did take,
Let him unto my master Petrarch go,
Who wrote the whole of this, I undertake.

Now when Odenathus was dead, then she
The kingdom held within her own strong hand;
Against her foes she fought so bitterly
There was no king or prince in all that land
But was right glad, if mercy make her bland,
That she turned not against him her array;
With her they made alliance, bond and band,
To keep the peace and let her ride and play.

The emperor of Rome, one Claudius
(His predecessor, Galien too, that man),
Had never courage to oppose her thus;
Nor was Egyptian nor Armenian,
Nor Syrian, nor yet Arabian
That dared against her in the field to fight,
For fear that at her hands they might be slain,
Or by her army put to sudden flight.

In kingly habit went her sons also,
As being heirs to their sire's kingdoms all,
Athenodorus and Thymalao
Their names were (or the Greeks did so them call).
But Fortune's honey is aye mixed with gall;
This mighty queen could no great while endure.
And Fortune from her high throne made her fall
To wretchedness and into ways obscure.

Aurelian, when Roman governance
Came to his two strong hands, made no delay,
But swore that on this queen he'd wreak vengeance,
And so with mighty legions took his way

Ne more labour mighte in werre endure,
Was noon, thogh al this world men sholde seke.

Hir riche array ne mighte nat be told
As wel in vessel as in hir clothing;
She was al clad in perree and in gold,
And eek she lafte noght, for noon hunting,
To have of sondry tonges ful knowing,
Whan that she leyser hadde, and for to entende
To lernen bokes was al hir lyking,
How she in vertu mighte hir lyf dispende.

And, shortly of this storie for to trete,
So doughty was hir housbonde and eek she,
That they conquered many regnes grete
In th'orient, with many a fair citee,
Apertenaunt un-to the magestee
Of Rome, and with strong hond helde hem ful
  faste;
Ne never mighte hir fo-men doon hem flee,
Ay whyl that Odenakes dayes laste.

Hir batailes, who-so list hem for to rede,
Agayn Sapor the king and othere mo,
And how that al this proces fil in dede,
Why she conquered and what title had therto,
And after of hir meschief and hir wo,
How that she was biseged and y-take,
Let him un-to my maister Petrark go,
That writ y-nough of this, I undertake.

When Odenake was deed, she mightily
The regnes heeld, and with hir propre honde
Agayn hir foos she faught so cruelly,
That ther nas king ne prince in al that londe
That he nas glad, if that he grace fonde,
That she ne wolde up-on his lond werreye;
With hir they made alliaunce by bonde
To been in pees, and lete hir ryde and pleye.

The emperour of Rome, Claudius,
Ne him bifore, the Romayn Galien,
Ne dorste never been so corageous,
Ne noon Ermyn, ne noon Egipcien,
Ne Surrien, ne noon Arabien,
Within the feld that dorste with hir fighte
Lest that she wolde hem with hir hondes slen
Or with hir meynee putten hem to flighte.

In kinges habit wente hir sones two,
As heires of hir fadres regnes alle,
And Hermanno, and Thymalaö
Her names were, as Persiens hem calle.
But ay fortune hath in hir hony galle;
This mighty quene may no whyl endure.
Fortune out of hir regne made hir falle
To wrecchednesse and to misaventure.

Aurelian, whan that the governaunce
Of Rome cam in-to his hondes tweye,
He shoop up-on this queen to do vengeaunce,
And with his legiouns he took his weye

Toward Cenobie, and, shortly for to seye,
He made hir flee, and atte laste hir hente,
And fettred hir, and eek hir children tweye,
And wan the lond, and hoom to Rome he wente.

Against Zenobia; let me briefly say
He made her flee; and at the last he sent
And fettered her and her two sons one day,
And won the land, and home to Rome he went.

Amonges othere thinges that he wan,
Hir char, that was with gold wrought and perree,
This grete Romayn, this Aurelian,
Hath with him lad, for that men sholde it see.
Biforen his triumphe walketh she
With gilte cheynes on hir nekke hanging;
Corouned was she, as after hir degree,
And ful of perree charged hir clothing.

Among the other booty Asian
Her chariot was, of gold and jewellery,
And this great Roman, this Aurelian,
He carried it away for men to see.
Before his car in triumph then walked she
With golden chains upon her neck hanging;
Crowned was she, too, to show her high degree,
And full of priceless gems was her clothing.

Allas, fortune! she that whylom was
Dredful to kinges and to emperoures,
Now gaureth al the peple on hir, allas!
And she that helmed was in starke stoures,
And wan by force tounes stronge and toures,
Shal on hir heed now were a vitremyte;
And she that bar the ceptre ful of floures
Shal bere a distaf, hir cost for to quyte.

Alas, Fortune! She that but lately was
The scourge of kings and emperors and powers,
Now may the rabble gape at her, alas!
And she that, armed, rode where grim battle lowers
And took by force great cities and strong towers,
Must wear a cap now while her two eyes weep;
And she that bore the sceptre of carved flowers
May bear a distaff and thus earn her keep.

NERO

Al-though that Nero were as vicious
As any feend that lyth ful lowe adoun,
Yet he, as telleth us Swetonius.
This wyde world hadde in subjeccioun,
Both Est and West, South and Septemtrioun;
Of rubies, saphires, and of perles whyte
Were alle his clothes brouded up and doun;
For he in gemmes greetly gan delyte.

Though viciousness had Nero in overplus,
As ever fiend that's low in torment thrown,
Yet he, as tells us old Suetonius,
This whole wide world held subject; aye, did own,
East, west, south, north, wherever Rome was known.
Of rubies, sapphires, and of great pearls white
Were all his garments broidered up and down,
For he in jewels greatly did delight.

More delicat, more pompous of array,
More proud was never emperour than he;
That ilke cloth, that he had wered o day,
After that tyme he nolde it never see.
Nettes of gold-thred hadde he gret plentee
To fisshe in Tybre, whan him liste pleye.
His lustes were al lawe in his decree,
For fortune as his freend him wolde obeye.

More delicate, more pompous of array,
More proud was never emperor than he;
That toga which he wore on any day,
After that time he nevermore would see.
Nets of gold thread he had in great plenty
To fish in Tiber when he pleased to play.
His lusts were all the laws in his decree,
For Fortune was his friend and would obey.

He Rome brende for his delicacye;
The senatours he slow up-on a day,
To here how men wolde wepe and crye;
And slow his brother, and by his sister lay.
His moder made he in pitous array;
For he hir wombe slitte, to biholde
Wher he conceyved was; so weilawey!
That he so litel of his moder tolde!

He burned Rome for his delicate profligacy;
Some senators he slew upon a day
Only to learn how men might weep and cry;
He killed his brother and with his sister lay.
His mother put he into piteous way,
For he her belly ripped up just to see
Where he had been conceived; alack-a-day,
That but so little for her life cared he!

No tere out of his yën for that sighte
Ne cam, but seyde, "a fair womman was she."
Gret wonder is, how that he coude or mighte
Be domesman of hir dede beautee.
The wyn to bringen him comaunded he,
And drank anon; non other wo he made.
Whan might is joyned un-to crueltee,
Allas! to depe wol the venim wade!

No tear out of his two eyes for that sight
Came, but he said: "A woman fair was she."
Great wonder is it how he could or might
Pass judgment thus upon her dead beauty.
Wine to be brought him then commanded he
And drank anon; no other sign he made.
When might is wedded unto cruelty,
Alas, too deep its venom will pervade!

In youthe a maister hadde this emperour,

A master had, in youth, this emperor,

To teach him letters and all courtesy,
For of morality he was the flow'r
In his own time, unless the old books lie;
And while this master held his mastery,
So well he taught him wiles and subtle ways
That ere could tempt him vice or tyranny
Was, it is said, the length of many days.

This Seneca, of whom I do apprise,
By reason Nero held him in such dread,
Since he for vices spared not to chastise,
Discreetly, though, by word and not by deed—
"Sir," would he say, "an emperor must need
Be virtuous and hate all tyranny"—
For which, in bath, did Nero make him bleed
From both his arms until he had to die.

This Nero had, though, out of arrogance,
Been wont, in youth, against the rod to rise,
Which afterward he thought a great grievance;
Wherefore he made him perish in this wise.
Nevertheless, this Seneca the wise
Chose in a bath to die, as you did hear,
Rather than suffer in some other guise;
And thus did Nero slay his master dear.

Now it befell that Fortune cared no longer
To Nero's high pride to be accomplice;
For though he might be strong, yet she was
stronger;
She thought thus: "By God, I am none too nice,
Setting a man who is but filled with vice
In high degree, emperor over all.
By God, up from his seat I will him trice;
When he least thinks of it, then shall he fall."

The people rose against him, on a night,
For all his faults; and when he it espied,
Out of the doors he went and took to flight
Alone; and where he thought he was allied
He knocked; but always, and the more he cried
The faster did they bar the doors, aye all;
Then learned he well he'd been his own worst guide,
And went his way, nor longer dared to call.

The people cried and rumbled up and down,
And, having ears, he heard the thing they said:
"Where's this false tyrant Nero ,where's he flown?"
For fear almost out of his wits he strayed,
And to his gods, then, piously he prayed
For succour, but no help might him betide.
For fear of this he wished himself unmade,
And ran into a garden, there to hide.

And in this garden were two fellows, yea,
Who sat before a great fire and a red,
And to those fellows he began to pray
That they would slay him and strike off his head,
But of his body, after he was dead,
They should do nothing to its further shame.
Himself he slew, no better counsel sped,
Whereat Dame Fortune laughed and made a game.

To teche him letterure and curteisye,
For of moralitee he was the flour,
As in his tyme, but-if bokes lye;
And whyl this maister hadde of him maistrye,
He maked him so conning and so souple
That longe tyme it was er tirannye
Or any vyce dorste on him uncouple.

This Seneca, of which that I devyse,
By-cause Nero hadde of him swich drede,
For he fro vyces wolde him ay chastyse
Discreetly as by worde and nat by dede;—
"Sir," wolde he seyn, "an emperour moot nede
Be vertuous, and hate tirannye"—
For which he in a bath made him to blede
On bothe his armes, til he moste dye.

This Nero hadde eek of acustumaunce
In youthe ageyn his maister for to ryse,
Which afterward him thoughte a greet grevaunce;
Therfor he made him deyen in this wyse.
But natheles this Seneca the wyse
Chees in a bath to deye in this manere
Rather than han another tormentyse;
And thus hath Nero slayn his maister dere.

Now fil it so that fortune list no lenger
The hye pryde of Nero to cheryce;
For though that he were strong, yet was she
strenger;
She thoughte thus, "by god, I am to nyce
To sette a man that is fulfild of vyce
In heigh degree, and emperour him calle.
By god, out of his sete I wol him tryce;
When he leest weneth, sonest shal he falle."

The peple roos up-on him on a night
For his defaute, and whan he it espyed,
Out of his dores anon he hath him dight
Alone, and, ther he wende han ben allyed,
He knokked faste, and ay, the more he cryed,
The faster shette they the dores alle;
Tho wiste he wel he hadde him-self misgyed,
And wente his wey, no lenger dorste he calle.

The peple cryde and rombled up and doun,
That with his eres herde he how they seyde,
"Wher is this false tyraunt, this Neroun?"
For fere almost out of his wit he breyde,
And to his goddes pitously he preyde
For socour, but it mighte nat bityde.
For drede of this, him thoughte that he deyde,
And ran in-to a gardin, him to hyde.

And in this gardin fond he cherles tweye
That seten by a fyr ful greet and reed,
And to thise cherles two he gan to preye
To sleen him, and to girden of his heed,
That to his body, whan that he were deed,
Were no despyt y-doon, for his defame.
Him-self he slow, he coude no better reed,
Of which fortune lough, and hadde a game.

OF HOLOFERNES

Was never capitayn under a king
That regnes mo putte in subjeccioun,
Ne strenger was in feeld of alle thing,
As in his tyme, ne gretter of renoun,
Ne more pompous in heigh presumpcioun
Than Oloferne, which fortune ay kiste
So likerously, and ladde him up and doun
Til that his heed was of, er that he wiste.

Was never captain, no, of any king's
That had more kingdoms in subjection thrown,
Nor stronger was, in field, above all things,
Nor in his time a greater of renown,
Nor had more pomp with high presumption shown,
Than Holofernes, whom Dame Fortune kissed
Right lecherously, and led him up and down
Until his head was off before 'twas missed.

Nat only that this world hadde him in awe
For lesinge of richesse or libertee,
But he made every man reneye his lawe.
"Nabugodonosor was god," seyde he,
"Noon other god sholde adoured be."
Ageyns his heste no wight dar trespace
Save in Bethulia, a strong citee,
Wher Eliachim a prest was of that place.

Not only did this world hold him in awe
For taking all its wealth and liberty,
But he made every man renounce old law.
"Nebuchadnezzar is your god," said he,
"And now no other god shall worshipped be."
Against his order no man dared to stand,
Save in Bethulia, a strong city,
Where Eliachim priest was of the land.

But tak kepe of the deeth of Olofern;
Amidde his host he dronke lay a night,
With-inne his tente, large as is a bern,
And yit, for al his pompe and al his might,
Judith, a womman, as he lay upright,
Sleping, his heed of smoot, and from his tente
Ful privelу she stal from every wight,
And with his heed unto hir toun she wente.

But from the death of Holofernes learn.
Amidst his host he lay drunk, on a night,
Within his tent, as large as ever barn,
And yet, for all his pomp and all his might,
Judith, a woman, as he lay upright,
Sleeping, smote off his head and from his tent
Stole secretly away every wight,
And with the head to her own town she went.

OF THE FAMOUS KING ANTIOCHUS

What nedeth it of King Anthiochus
To telle his hye royal magestee,
His hye pryde, his werkes venimous?
For swich another was ther noon as he.
Rede which that he was in Machabee,
And rede the proude wordes that he seyde,
And why he fil fro heigh prosperitee,
And in an hil how wrechedly he deyde.

What needs it, as for King Antiochus,
To tell his high and royal majesty,
His great pride and his deeds so venomous?
There never was another such as he.
Go read what's said of him in Maccabee,
And all the haughty sayings that he said,
And how he fell from high prosperity,
And on a hill how wretchedly lay dead.

Fortune him hadde enhaunced so in pryde
That verraily he wende he mighte attayne
Unto the sterres, upon every syde,
And in balance weyen ech montayne,
And alle the flodes of the see restrayne.
And goddes peple hadde he most in hate,
Hem wolde he sleen in torment and in payne,
Wening that god ne mighte his pryde abate.

Fortune had so enhanced the man's great pride
That verily he thought he might attain
Unto the utter stars on every side,
And in a balance weigh the high mountain,
And all the flood-tides of the sea restrain.
And God's own people held he most in hate.
Them would he slay with torment and with pain,
Thinking that God his pride would not abate.

And for that Nichanor and Thimothee
Of Jewes weren venquisshed mightily,
Unto the Jewes swich an hate hadde he
That he bad greithe his char ful hastily,
And swoor, and seyde, ful despitously,
Unto Jerusalem he wolde eft-sone,
To wreken his ire on it ful cruelly;
But of his purpos he was let ful sone.

And because Nicanor and Timothy
Were vanquished by the Jews so mightily,
Unto all Jews so great a hate had he
That he bade bring his chariot hastily,
And swore an oath and said, impiteously,
That to Jerusalem he'd go ere noon
To wreak his ire on it full cruelly;
But from his purpose he was turned, and soon.

God for his manace him so sore smoot
With invisible wounde, ay incurable,
That in his guttes carf it so and boot
That his peynes weren importable.

God, for this menace, smote him then full sore
With wound invisible, incurable,
For in his guts he was so carved, aye more,
The pain of it was insupportable.

And certainly the thing was reasonable,
For many a man's guts he had caused to pain;
But from his purpose, cursed, damnable,
In spite of all he would not him restrain.

He gave command to marshal his great host,
And suddenly, or ere he was aware,
God daunted all his pride and all his boast.
For he so heavily fell from his car
That from his very bones the flesh did tear,
So that he might not either walk or ride,
But in a litter men were forced to bear
Him with them, bruised upon the back and side.

The wrath of God smote him so cruelly
That through his body loathsome maggots crept;
And therewithal he stank so horribly
That none of those that round his person kept,
Whether he lay awake or whether slept,
Could, for the very stench of him, endure.
In this foul state he wailed and howled and wept;
That God was Lord of all he then was sure.

To all his host and to himself also
Full loathsome was his carrion, one great blain;
There were no men could bear him to and fro.
And in this stink and in this horrid pain
He died full wretchedly on a mountain.
Thus had this robber and this homicide,
Who made so many men weep and complain,
Such guerdon as belongs to too great pride.

And certeinly, the wreche was resonable,
For many a mannes guttes dide he peyne;
But from his purpos cursed and dampnable
For al his smert he wolde him nat restreyne;

But bad anon apparaillen his host,
And sodeynly, er he of it was war,
God daunted al his pryde and al his bost.
For he so sore fil out of his char,
That it his limes and his skin to-tar,
So that he neither mighte go ne ryde,
But in a chayer men aboute him bar,
Al for-brused, bothe bak and syde.

The wreche of god him smoot so cruelly
That thurgh his body wikked wormes crepte;
And ther-with-al he stank so horribly,
That noon of al his meynee that him kepte,
Whether so he wook or elles slepte,
Ne mighte noght for stink of him endure.
In this meschief he wayled and eek wepte,
And knew god lord of every creature.

To al his host and to him-self also
Ful wlatsom was the stink of his careyne;
No man ne mighte him bere to ne fro.
And in this stink and this horrible peyne
He starf ful wrecchedly in a monteyne.
Thus hath this robbour and this homicyde,
That many a man made to wepe and pleyne,
Swich guerdon as bilongeth unto pryde.

OF ALEXANDER

Alexander's tale is so well known a tune
That everyone who is not simple grown
Has heard somewhat, or all, of his fortune
This whole wide world, to state conclusion known,
He won by strength, or else for his renown
Right gladly men to sue for peace did send.
The pride of man and beast he tumbled down
Where'er he went, and that was the world's end.

Comparison might never yet be staked
Upon a single similar conquering power;
For all this world in dread of him has quaked.
He was of knighthood and of freedom flower;
Fortune made him her heir to honour's bower;
Save wine and women, nothing might assuage
His high intent in arms; all men must cower,
So filled he was of leonine courage.

What praise were it to him, though 'gain were told
Darius' tale or of others brought low—
Of kings and dukes and earls and princes bold,
The which he conquered and brought down to woe?
I say, as far as man may ride or go
The world was his, to tell it in a trice.
For though I wrote or told you always, so,
Of his knighthood, the time would not suffice.

Twelve years he reigned, as tells us Maccabee;

The storie of Alisaundre is so comune,
That every wight that hath discrecioun
Hath herd somwhat or al of his fortune.
This wyde world, as in conclusioun,
He wan by strengthe, or for his hye renoun
They weren glad for pees un-to him sende.
The pryde of man and beste he leyde adoun,
Wher-so he cam, un-to the worldes ende.

Comparisoun might never yit be maked
Bitwixe him and another conquerour;
For al this world for drede of him hath quaked,
He was of knighthode and of fredom flour;
Fortune him made the heir of hir honour;
Save wyn and wommen, no-thing mighte aswage
His hye entente in armes and labour;
So was he ful of leonyn corage.

What preys were it to him, though I yow tolde
Of Darius, and an hundred thousand mo,
Of kinges, princes, erles, dukes bolde,
Whiche he conquered, and broghte hem in-to wo?
I seye, as fer as man may ryde or go,
The world was his, what sholde I more devyse?
For though I write or tolde you evermo
Of his knighthode, it mighte nat suffyse.

Twelf yeer he regned, as seith Machabee;

Philippes sone of Macedoyne he was,
That first was king in Grece the contree.
O worthy gentil Alisaundre, allas!
That ever sholde fallen swich a cas!
Empoisoned of thyn owene folk thou were;
Thy *sys* fortune hath turned into *as*,
And yit for thee ne weep she never a tere!

Who shal me yeven teres to compleyne
The deeth of gentillesse and of fraunchyse,
That al the world welded in his demeyne,
And yit him thoughte it mighte nat suffyse?
So ful was his corage of heigh empryse.
Allas! who shal me helpe to endyte
False fortune, and poison to despyse,
The whiche two of al this wo I wyte?

And Philip's son of Macedon he was,
Who first was king of Greece, the whole country.
O noble Alexander, O alas!
That ever you should come to such a pass!
For poisoned by your very own you were;
Your six did Fortune turn into an ace,
And yet for you she never wept a tear!

Who shall give me the tears now to complain
For death of gentle blood and high franchise?
He all the world did wield as one domain,
And yet he thought it could not long suffice,
So full his heart was of high enterprise.
Alas! And who shall help me to indict
False Fortune, and all poison to despise?
For these I blame for all the woe I write.

OF JULIUS CAESAR

By wisdom, manhede, and by greet labour
Fro humble bed to royal magestee,
Up roos he, Julius the conquerour,
That wan al th'occident by lond and see,
By strengthe of hond, or elles by tretee,
And un-to Rome made hem tributarie;
And sitthe of Rome the emperour was he,
Til that fortune wex his adversarie.

O mighty Cesar, that in Thessalye
Ageyn Pompeius, fader thyn in lawe,
That of th'orient hadde al the chivalrye
As fer as that the day biginneth dawe,
Thou thurgh thy knighthode hast hem take and
slawe,
Save fewe folk that with Pompeius fledde,
Thurgh which thou puttest al th'orient in awe.
Thanke fortune, that so wel thee spedde!

But now a litel whyl I wol biwaille
This Pompeius, this noble governour
Of Rome, which that fleigh at this bataille;
I seye, oon of his men, a fals traitour,
His heed of smoot, to winnen him favour
Of Julius, and him the heed he broghte.
Allas, Pompey, of th'orient conquerour,
That fortune unto swich a fyn thee broghte!

To Rome ageyn repaireth Julius
With his triumphe, laureat ful hye,
But on a tyme Brutus Cassius,
That ever hadde of his hye estaat envye,
Ful prively hath maad conspiracye
Ageins this Julius, in subtil wyse,
And cast the place, in whiche he sholde dye
With boydekins, as I shal yow devyse.

This Julius to the Capitolie wente
Upon a day, as he was wont to goon,
And in the Capitolie anon him hente
This false Brutus, and his othere foon,
And stikede him with boydekins anoon
With many a wounde, and thus they lete him
lye;

By wisdom, manhood, and by great labour,
From humble bed to royal majesty
Up rose he, Julius the conqueror,
Who won the Occident by land and sea,
By force of arms, or else by clear treaty,
And unto Rome made all this tributary;
And then of Rome the emperor was he,
Till Fortune came to be his adversary.

O mighty Caesar, who in Thessaly
Against great Pompey, father of yours in law,
That of the East had all the chivalry
From farthest places that the sun e'er saw,
You, by your knighthood broke them for death's
maw,
Save those few men who thence with Pompey fled,
Whereby you put the Orient in awe.
Thank Fortune now that you so well have sped.

But now a little while I well bewail
This Pompey, this so noble governor
Of Rome, who fled when battle's chance did fail;
I say, one of his men, a false traitor,
Smote off his head to win himself favour
With Julius, and there the head he brought.
Alas, Pompey! Of Orient conqueror,
That Fortune such an end for thee hath wrought!

To Rome again repaired great Julius,
To have his triumph, laureate full high;
But on a time Brutus and Cassius,
Who ever had of great estate envy,
Full secretly did lay conspiracy
Against this Julius, in subtle wise,
And fixed the place at which he soon should die
By dagger thrusts, as I shall you apprise.

This Julius, to the Capitol he went
Upon a day, as he'd been wont to go,
And there they seized on him, as well they meant,
This treacherous Brutus and each other foe,
And struck him with their daggers, high and low,
And gave him many a wound and let him
die;

But never groaned he, save at one stroke, no
(Or two perchance), unless his legend lie.

But never gronte he at no strook but oon,
Or elles at two, but-if his storie lye.

So manly was this Julius in his heart,
And so well loved he stately decency,
That, though his deadly wounds did burn and smart,
His mantle yet about his hips cast he,
That no man there should see his privity.
And as he lay there, dying, in a trance,
And knew that he was dying, verily,
Of decency yet had he remembrance.

So manly was this Julius at herte
And so wel lovede estaatly honestee,
That, though his deedly woundes sore smerte,
His mantel over his hippes casteth he,
For no man sholde seen his privitee.
And, as he lay on deying in a traunce,
And wiste verraily that deed was he,
Of honestee yit hadde he remembraunce.

Lucan to tell this story I commend,
Suetonius too, Valerius also,
Who of the tale have written to the end
And told how, of these mighty conquerors two,
Fortune was first the friend and then the foe.
No man may trust in Fortune's favour long,
But as one fearing ambush must he go.
Witness the end of all these conquerors strong.

Lucan, to thee this storie I recomende,
And to Sweton, and to Valerie also,
That of this storie wryten word and ende,
How that to thise grete conqueroures two
Fortune was first freend, and sithen fo.
No man ne truste up-on hir favour longe,
But have hir in awayt for ever-mo.
Witnesse on alle thise conqueroures stronge.

CROESUS

The wealthy Croesus, Lydia's sometime king,
Of which Croesus King Cyrus had such dread,
Yet was he taken, in his pride swelling,
And to be burned upon a pyre was led.
But such a rain down from the clouds was shed
As quenched the fire and let him there escape;
But to be warned, no grace was in him spread
Till Fortune on the gallows made him gape.

This riche Cresus, whylom king of Lyde,
Of whiche Cresus Cyrus sore him dradde,
Yit was he caught amiddes al his pryde,
And to be brent men to the fyr him ladde.
But swich a reyn doun fro the welkne shadde
That slow the fyr, and made him to escape;
But to be war no grace yet he hadde,
Til fortune on the galwes made him gape.

When he'd escaped, not changed was his intent
To march at once into new wars again.
He thought right well 'twas Fortune that had sent
Such chance that he'd escape because of rain,
And that by foes he never should be slain;
And then a vision in the night he met,
At which he waxed so proud and grew so fain
That upon vengeance all his heart was set.

Whan he escaped was, he can nat stente
For to biginne a newe werre agayn.
He wende wel, for that fortune him sente
Swich hap, that he escaped thurgh the rayn,
That of his foos he mighte nat be slayn;
And eek a sweven up-on a night he mette,
Of which he was so proud and eek so fayn,
That in vengeaunce he al his herte sette.

Upon a tree he was, or so he thought,
Where Jupiter did wash him, back and side,
And Phoebus, then a fair white towel brought
To dry him with and thereby swell his pride;
And to his daughter, who stood there beside,
And well, he knew, in knowledge did abound,
He bade interpret what it signified,
And she his dream in this wise did expound.

Up-on a tree he was, as that him thoughte,
Ther Juppiter him wesh, bothe bak and syde,
And Phebus eek a fair towaille him broughte
To drye him with, and ther-for wex his pryde;
And to his doghter, that stood him bisyde,
Which that he knew in heigh science habounde,
He bad hir telle him what it signifyde,
And she his dreem bigan right thus expounde.

"The tree," she said, "the gallows is to mean,
And Jupiter betokens snow and rain,
While Phoebus with his towel white and clean,
That is the sunbeams beating down amain;
You shall be hanged, O father, 'tis certain;
The rain shall wash you and the sun shall dry."
And thus she gave him warning flat and plain,
His daughter, who was Phania, say I.

"The tree," quod she, "the galwes is to mene,
And Juppiter bitokneth snow and reyn,
And Phebus, with his towaille so clene,
Tho ben the sonne stremes for to seyn,
Thou shalt anhanged be, fader, certeyn;
Reyn shal thee wasshe, and sonne shal thee drye";
Thus warned she him ful plat and ful pleyn,
His doughter, which that called was Phanye.

So hanged was Croesus, that proud Lydian king,
His royal throne could nothing then avail.
Tragedy is no other kind of thing;

Anhanged was Cresus, the proude king,
His royal trone mighte him nat availle.—
Tragedie is noon other maner thing,

Ne can in singing crye ne biwaille,
But for that fortune alwey wol assaille
With unwar strook the regnes that ben proude;
For when men trusteth hir, than wol she faille,
And covere hir brighte face with a cloude.

Nor can the singer cry aught, or bewail,
But that Dame Fortune always will assail
With unwarned stroke rose great ones who are proud;
For when men trust her most, then will she fail
And cover her bright face as with a cloud.

OF KING PEDRO OF SPAIN

O noble, o worthy Petro, glorie of Spayne,
Whom fortune heeld so hy in magestee,
Wel oughten men thy pitous deeth complayne!
Out of thy lond thy brother made thee flee;
And after, at a sege, by subtiltee,
Thou were bitrayed, and lad un-to his tente,
Wher-as he with his owene hond slow thee,
Succeding in thy regne and in thy rente.

O noble Pedro, glory once of Spain,
Whom Fortune held so high in majesty,
Well ought men read thy piteous death with pain!
Out of thy land thy brother made thee flee;
And later, at a siege, by scheme crafty,
Thou wert betrayed, and led into his tent,
Where he then, and with his own hand, slew thee,
Succeeding to thy realm and government.

The feeld of snow, with th'egle of blak ther-inne,[1]
Caught with the lymrod, coloured as the glede,
He brew this cursednes and al this sinne.
The "wikked nest"[2] was werker of this nede;
Noght Charles Oliver, that ay took hede
Of trouthe and honour, but of Armorike
Genilon Oliver, corrupt for mede,
Broghte this worthy king in swich a brike.

The field of snow, with eagle black therein,[1]
Caught by the lime-rod, coloured as the gleed,
He brewed this wickedness and all this sin.
The "Wicked Nest"[2] was worker of this deed;
Not that Charles Oliver who aye took heed
Of truth and honour, but the Armorican
Ganelon Oliver, corrupt for mead,
Brought low this worthy king by such a plan.

OF KING PETER OF CYPRUS

O worthy Petro, king of Cypre, also,
That Alisaundre wan by heigh maistrye,
Ful many a hethen wroghtestow ful wo,
Of which thyn owene liges hadde envye,
And, for no thing but for thy chivalrye,
They in thy bedde han slayn thee by the morwe.
Thus can fortune hir wheel governe and gye,
And out of joye bringe men to sorwe.

O noble Peter, Cyprus' lord and king,
Which Alexander won by mastery,
To many a heathen ruin did'st thou bring;
For this thy lords had so much jealousy,
That, for no crime save thy high chivalry,
All in thy bed they slew thee on a morrow.
And thus does Fortune's wheel turn treacherously
And out of happiness bring men to sorrow.

OF BERNABO OF LOMBARDY

Of Melan grete Barnabo Viscounte,
God of delyt, and scourge of Lumbardye,
Why sholde I nat thyn infortune acounte,
Sith in estaat thou clombe were so hye?
Thy brother sone, that was thy double allye,
For he thy nevew was, and sone-in-lawe,
With-inne his prisoun made thee to dye;
But why, ne how, noot I that thou were slawe.

Of Milan, great Bernabo Visconti,
God of delight and scourge of Lombardy,
Why should I tell not of thy misery,
Since in all power thou did'st climb so high?
Thy brother's son, and doubly thine ally,
For he thy nephew was and son-in-law,
Within his prison shut thee up to die,
But I know not how death to thee did draw.

OF UGOLINO, COUNT OF PISA

Of the erl Hugelyn of Pyse the langour
Ther may no tonge telle for pitee;
But litel out of Pyse stant a tour,
In whiche tour in prisoun put was he,
And with him been his litel children three.
The eldeste scarsly fyf yeer was of age.
Allas, fortune! it was greet crueltee
Swiche briddes for to putte in swiche a cage!

Of Ugolino, Count of Pisa's woe
No tongue can tell the half for hot pity.
Near Pisa stands a tower, and it was so
That to be there imprisoned doomed was he,
While with him were his little children three,
The eldest child was scarce five years of age.
Alas, Fortune! It was great cruelty
To lock such birds up into such a cage!

Dampned was he to deye in that prisoun,
For Roger, which that bisshop was of Pyse,
Hadde on him maad a fals suggestioun,
Thurgh which the peple gan upon him ryse,

Condemned was he to die in that prison,
Since Ruggieri, Pisa's bishop, twice
Had lied, intrigued, and egged old passions on,
Whereby the people did against him rise,

[1]The arms of Bertrand du Guesclin.
[2]Chaucer puts this for OF. *mau ni,* meaning thereby Sir Oliver Mauny.

And thrust him into prison in such wise
As you have heard; and meat and drink he had
So little that it could not long suffice,
And was, moreover, very poor and bad.

And on a day befell it, at the hour
When commonly to him his food was brought,
The gaoler shut the great doors of the tower.
He heard it well enough, but he said naught,
And to his heart anon there came the thought
That they by hunger would leave him to die.
"Alas," said he, "that ever I was wrought!"
And thereupon the tears fell from his eye.

His youngest son, who three years was of age,
Unto him said: "Father, why do you weep?
When will the gaoler bring us our pottage?
Is there no crumb of bread that you did keep?
I am so hungry that I cannot sleep.
Now would God that I might sleep on for aye!
Then should not hunger through my belly creep;
For nothing more than bread I'd rather pray."

Thus, day by day, this little child did cry,
Till on his father's breast at length he lay
And said: "Farewell, my father, I must die."
And kissed the man and died that very day.
And when the father saw it dead, I say,
For grief his arms gnawed he until blood came,
And said: "Alas, Fortune and welaway,
It is thy treacherous wheel that I must blame!"

His children thought that it for hunger was
He gnawed his arms, and not that 'twas for woe,
And cried: "O father, do not thus, alas!
But rather eat our young flesh, even so;
This flesh you gave us; take it back and go
And eat enough!" 'Twas thus those children cried,
And after that, within a day or two,
They laid themselves upon his knees and died.

Himself, despairing, all by hunger starved,
Thus ended this great count of Pisa's cries;
All his vast riches Fortune from him carved.
Of his fate tragic let thus much suffice.
Whoso would hear it told in longer wise,
Let him read the great bard of Italy
Whom men call Dante; seen through Dante's eyes
No point is slurred, nor in one word fails he.

And putten him to prisoun in swich wyse
As ye han herd, and mete and drink he hadde
So smal, that wel unnethe it may suffyse,
And therwith-al it was ful povre and badde.

And on a day bifil that, in that hour,
Whan that his mete wont was to be broght,
The gayler shette the dores of the tour.
He herde it wel,—but he spak right noght,
And in his herte anon ther fil a thoght,
That they for hunger wolde doon him dyen.
"Allas!" quod he, "allas! that I was wroght!"
Therwith the teres fillen from his yën.

His yonge sone, that three yeer was of age,
Un-to him seyde, "fader, why do ye wepe?
Whan wol the gayler bringen our potage,
Is ther no morsel breed that ye do kepe?
I am so hungry that I may nat slepe.
Now wolde god that I mighte slepen ever!
Than sholde nat hunger in my wombe crepe;
Ther is no thing, save breed, that me were lever."

Thus day by day this child bigan to crye,
Til in his fadres barme adoun it lay,
And seyde, "far-wel, fader, I moot dye,"
And kiste his fader, and deyde the same day.
And whan the woful fader deed it sey,
For wo his armes two he gan to byte,
And seyde, "allas, fortune! and weylaway!
Thy false wheel my wo al may I wyte!"

His children wende that it for hunger was
That he his armes gnow, and nat for wo,
And seyde, "fader, do nat so, allas!
But rather eet the flesh upon us two;
Our flesh thou yaf us, tak our flesh us fro
And eet y-nough": right thus they to him seyde,
And after that, with-in a day or two,
They leyde hem in his lappe adoun, and deyde.

Him-self, despeired, eek for hunger starf;
Thus ended in this mighty Erl of Pyse;
From heigh estaat fortune awey him carf.
Of this Tragedie it oghte y-nough suffyse.
Who-so wol here it in a lenger wyse,
Redeth the grete poete of Itaille,
That highte Dant, for he can al devyse
Fro point to point, nat o word wol he faille.

HERE ENDETH THE TRAGEDY

HERE STINTETH THE KNIGHT THE MONK OF HIS TALE

THE PROLOGUE OF THE NUN'S PRIEST'S TALE

THE PROLOGUE OF THE NUN'S PRIEST'S TALE

"Ho!" quod the knight, "good sir, namore of this,
That ye han seyd is right y-nough, y-wis,
And mochel more; for litel hevinesse
Is right y-nough to mochel folk, I gesse.
I seye for me, it is a greet disese
Wher-as men han ben in greet welthe and ese,
To heren of hir sodeyn fal, allas!
And the contrarie is joie and greet solas,
As whan a man hath been in povre estaat,
And clymbeth up, and wexeth fortunat,
And ther abydeth in prosperitee,
Swich thing is gladsom, as it thinketh me,
And of swich thing were goodly for to telle."
"Ye," quod our hoste, "by seint
Poules belle,
Ye seye right sooth; this monk, he clappeth loude,
He spak how 'fortune covered with a cloude'
I noot never what, and als of a 'Tragedie'
Right now ye herde, and parde! no remedie
It is for to biwaille, ne compleyne
That that is doon, and als it is a peyne,
As ye han seyd, to here of hevinesse.
Sir monk, na-more of this, so god yow blesse!
Your tale anoyeth al this companye;
Swich talking is nat worth a boterflye;
For ther-in is ther no desport ne game.
Wherfor, sir Monk, or dan Piers by your name,
I preye yow hertely, telle us somwhat elles,
For sikerly, nere clinking of your belles,
That on your brydel hange on every syde,
By heven king, that for us alle dyde,
I sholde er this han fallen doun for slepe,
Although the slough had never been so depe;
Than had your tale al be told in vayn.
For certeinly, as that thise clerkes seyn,
'Wher-as a man may have noon audience,
Noght helpeth it to tellen his sentence.'
And wel I woot the substance is in me,
If any thing shal wel reported be.
Sir, sey somwhat of hunting, I yow preye."
"Nay," quod this monk, "I have no lust to pleye;
Now let another telle, as I have told."
Than spak our host, with rude speche and bold,
And seyde un-to the Nonnes Preest anon,
"Com neer, thou preest, com hider, thou sir John,
Tel us swich thing as may our hertes glade,
Be blythe, though thou ryde up-on a jade.
What though thyn hors be bothe foule and
lene,
If he wol serve thee, rekke nat a bene;
Look that thyn herte be mery evermo."
"Yis, sir," quod he, "yis, host, so mote I go,
But I be mery, y-wis, I wol be blamed":—

Hold!" cried the knight. "Good sir, no more of this,
What you have said is right enough, and is
Very much more; a little heaviness
Is plenty for the most of us, I guess.
For me, I say it's saddening, if you please,
As to men who've enjoyed great wealth and ease,
To hear about their sudden fall, alas!
But the contrary's joy and great solace,
As when a man has been in poor estate
And he climbs up and waxes fortunate,
And there abides in all prosperity.
Such things are gladsome, as it seems to me,
And of such things it would be good to tell."
"Yea," quoth our host, "and by Saint Paul's
great bell,
You say the truth; this monk, his clapper's loud.
He spoke how 'Fortune covered with a cloud'
I know not what, and of a 'tragedy,'
As now you heard, and gad! no remedy
It is to wail and wonder and complain
That certain things have happened, and it's pain,
As you have said, to hear of wretchedness.
Sir monk, no more of this, so God you bless!
Your tale annoys the entire company;
Such talking is not worth a butterfly;
For in it is no sport nor any game.
Wherefore, sir monk, Don Peter by your name,
I pray you heartily tell us something else,
For truly, but for clinking of the bells
That from your bridle hang on either side,
By Heaven's king, Who for us all has died,
I should, ere this, have fallen down for sleep,
Although the mud had never been so deep;
Then had your story all been told in vain.
For certainly, as all these clerks complain,
'Whenas a man has none for audience,
It's little help to speak his evidence.'
And well I know the substance is in me
To judge of things that well reported be.
Sir, tell a tale of hunting now, I pray."
"Nay," said this monk, "I have no wish to play;
Now let another tell, as I have told."
Then spoke our host out, in rude speech and bold,
And said he unto the nun's priest anon:
"Come near, you priest, come hither, you Sir John,
Tell us a thing to make our hearts all glad;
Be blithe, although you ride upon a jade.
What though your horse may be both foul and
lean?
If he but serves you, why, don't care a bean;
Just see your heart is always merry. So."
"Yes, sir," said he, "yes, host, so may I go,
For, save I'm merry, I know I'll be blamed."

And right away his story has he framed,
And thus he said unto us, every one,
This dainty priest, this goodly man, Sir John.

And right anon his tale he hath attamed,
And thus he seyde un-to us everichon,
This swete preest, this goodly man, sir John.

HERE IT ENDETH

THE NUN'S PRIEST'S TALE

HERE BEGINNETH THE NUN'S PRIEST'S TALE OF THE COCK AND HEN, CHANTECLEER AND PERTELOTE

A WIDOW poor, somewhat advanced in age,
Lived, on a time, within a small cottage
Beside a grove and standing down a dale.
This widow, now, of whom I tell my tale,
Since that same day when she'd been last a wife
Had led, with patience, her strait simple life,
For she'd small goods and little income-rent;
By husbanding of such as God had sent
She kept herself and her young daughters twain.
Three large sows had she, and no more, 'tis plain,
Three cows and a lone sheep that she called Moll.
Right sooty was her bedroom and her hall,
Wherein she'd eaten many a slender meal.
Of sharp sauce, why she needed no great deal,
For dainty morsel never passed her throat;
Her diet well accorded with her coat.
Repletion never made this woman sick;
A temperate diet was her whole physic,
And exercise, and her heart's sustenance.
The gout, it hindered her nowise to dance,
Nor apoplexy spun within her head;
And no wine drank she, either white or red;
Her board was mostly garnished, white and black,
With milk and brown bread, whereof she'd no lack,
Broiled bacon and sometimes an egg or two,
For a small dairy business did she do.
A yard she had, enclosed all roundabout
With pales, and there was a dry ditch without,
And in the yard a cock called Chanticleer.
In all the land, for crowing, he'd no peer.
His voice was merrier than the organ gay
On Mass days, which in church begins to play;
More regular was his crowing in his lodge
Than is a clock or abbey horologe.
By instinct he'd marked each ascension down
Of equinoctial value in that town;
For when fifteen degrees had been ascended,
Then crew he so it might not be amended.
His comb was redder than a fine coral,
And battlemented like a castle wall.
His bill was black and just like jet it shone;
Like azure were his legs and toes, each one;
His spurs were whiter than the lily flower;
And plumage of the burnished gold his dower.
This noble cock had in his governance
Seven hens to give him pride and all pleasance,
Which were his sisters and his paramours
And wondrously like him as to colours,
Whereof the fairest hued upon her throat
Was called the winsome Mistress Pertelote.

A POVRE widwe, somdel stape in age,
Was whylom dwelling in a narwe cotage,
Bisyde a grove, stonding in a dale.
This widwe, of which I telle you my tale,
Sin thilke day that she was last a wyf,
In pacience ladde a ful simple lyf,
For litel was hir catel and hir rente;
By housbondrye, of such as God hir sente,
She fond hir-self, and eek hir doghtren two.
Three large sowes hadde she, and namo,
Three kyn, and eek a sheep that highte Malle,
Ful sooty was hir bour, and eek hir halle,
In which she eet ful many a sclendre meel.
Of poynaunt sauce hir neded never a deel.
No deyntee morsel passed thurgh hir throte;
Hir dyete was accordant to hir cote.
Repleccioun ne made hir never syk;
Attempree dyete was al hir phisyk,
And exercyse, and hertes suffisaunce.
The goute lette hir no-thing for to daunce,
N'apoplexye shente nat hir heed;
No wyn ne drank she, neither whyt ne reed;
Hir bord was served most with whyt and blak,
Milk and broun breed, in which she fond no lak,
Seynd bacoun, and somtyme an ey or tweye,
For she was as it were a maner deye.
A yerd she hadde, enclosed al aboute
With stikkes, and a drye dich with-oute,
In which she hadde a cok, hight Chauntecleer,
In al the land of crowing nas his peer.
His vois was merier than the mery orgon
On messe-dayes that in the chirche gon;
Wel sikerer was his crowing in his logge,
Than is a clokke, or an abbey orlogge.
By nature knew he ech ascencioun
Of equinoxial in thilke toun;
For whan degrees fiftene were ascended,
Thanne crew he, that it mighte nat ben amended.
His comb was redder than the fyn coral,
And batailed, as it were a castel-wal.
His bile was blak, and as the jeet it shoon;
Lyk asur were his legges, and his toon;
His nayles whytter than the lilie flour,
And lyk the burned gold was his colour.
This gentil cok hadde in his governaunce
Sevene hennes, for to doon al his plesaunce,
Whiche were his sustres and his paramours,
And wonder lyk to him, as of colours.
Of whiche the faireste hewed on hir throte
Was cleped faire damoysele Pertelote.

Curteys she was, discreet, and debonaire,
And compaignable, and bar hir-self so faire,
Sin thilke day that she was seven night old,
That trewely she hath the herte in hold
Of Chauntecleer loken in every lith;
He loved hir so, that wel was him therwith.
But such a joye was it to here hem singe,
Whan that the brighte sonne gan to springe,
In swete accord, "my lief is faren in londe."
For thilke tyme, as I have understonde,
Bestes and briddes coude speke and singe.
And so bifel, that in a daweninge,
As Chauntecleer among his wyves alle
Sat on his perche, that was in the halle,
And next him sat this faire Pertelote,
This Chauntecleer gan gronen in his throte,
As man that in his dreem is drecched sore.
And whan that Pertelote thus herde him rore,
She was agast, and seyde, "O herte dere,
What eyleth yow, to grone in this manere?
Ye been a verray sleper, fy for shame!"
And he answerde and seyde thus, "madame,
I pray yow, that ye take it nat a-grief:
By god, me mette I was in swich meschief
Right now, that yet myn herte is sore afright.
Now god," quod he, "my swevene recche aright,
And keep my body out of foul prisoun!
Me mette, how that I romed up and doun
Withinne our yerde, wher-as I saugh a beste,
Was lyk an hound, and wolde han maad areste
Upon my body, and wolde han had me deed.
His colour was bitwixe yelwe and reed;
And tipped was his tail, and bothe his eres,
With blak, unlyk the remenant of his heres;
His snowte smal, with glowinge eyen tweye.
Yet of his look for fere almost I deye;
This caused me my groning, doutelees."
"Avoy!" quod she, "fy on yow, hertelees!
Allas!" quod she, "for, by that god above,
Now han ye lost myn herte and al my love;
I can nat love a coward, by my feith.
For certes, what so any womman seith,
We alle desyren, if it mighte be,
To han housbondes hardy, wyse, and free,
And secree, and no nigard, ne no fool,
Ne him that is agast of every tool,
Ne noon avauntour, by that god above!
How dorste ye seyn for shame unto your love,
That any thing mighte make yow aferd?
Have ye no mannes herte, and han a berd?
Allas! and conne ye been agast of swevenis?
No-thing, god wot, but vanitee, in sweven is.
Swevenes engendren of replecciouns,
And ofte of fume, and of complecciouns,
Whan humours been to habundant in a wight.
Certes this dreem, which ye han met to-night,
Cometh of the grete superfluitee
Of youre rede *colera*, pardee,
Which causeth folk to dreden in here dremes
Of arwes, and of fyr with rede lemes,
Of grete bestes, that they wol hem byte,
Of contek, and of whelpes grete and lyte;

Courteous she was, discreet and debonnaire,
Companionable, and she had been so fair
Since that same day when she was seven nights old,
That truly she had taken the heart to hold
Of Chanticleer, locked in her every limb;
He loved her so that all was well with him.
But such a joy it was to hear them sing,
Whenever the bright sun began to spring,
In sweet accord, "My love walks through the land."
For at that time, and as I understand,
The beasts and all the birds could speak and sing.
So it befell that, in a bright dawning,
As Chanticleer 'midst wives and sisters all
Sat on his perch, the which was in the hall,
And next him sat the winsome Pertelote,
This Chanticleer he groaned within his throat
Like man that in his dreams is troubled sore.
And when fair Pertelote thus heard him roar,
She was aghast and said: "O sweetheart dear,
What ails you that you groan so? Do you hear?
You are a sleepy herald. Fie, for shame!"
And he replied to her thus: "Ah, *madame*,
I pray you that you take it not in grief:
By God, I dreamed I'd come to such mischief,
Just now, my heart yet jumps with sore affright.
Now God," cried he, "my vision read aright
And keep my body out of foul prison!
I dreamed, that while I wandered up and down
Within our yard, I saw there a strange beast
Was like a dog, and he'd have made a feast
Upon my body, and have had me dead.
His colour yellow was and somewhat red;
And tipped his tail was, as were both his ears,
With black, unlike the rest, as it appears;
His snout was small and gleaming was each eye.
Remembering how he looked, almost I die;
And all this caused my groaning, I confess."
"Aha," said she, "fie on you, spiritless!
Alas!" cried she, "for by that God above,
Now have you lost my heart and all my love;
I cannot love a coward, by my faith.
For truly, whatsoever woman saith,
We all desire, if only it may be,
To have a husband hardy, wise, and free,
And trustworthy, no niggard, and no fool,
Nor one that is afraid of every tool,
Nor yet a braggart, by that God above!
How dare you say, for shame, unto your love
That there is anything that you have feared?
Have you not man's heart, and yet have a beard?
Alas! And are you frightened by a vision?
Dreams are, God knows, a matter for derision.
Visions are generated by repletions
And vapours and the body's bad secretions
Of humours overabundant in a wight.
Surely this dream, which you have had tonight,
Comes only of the superfluity
Of your bilious irascibility,
Which causes folk to shiver in their dreams
For arrows and for flames with long red gleams,
For great beasts in the fear that they will bite,
For quarrels and for wolf whelps great and slight;

Just as the humour of melancholy
Causes full many a man, in sleep, to cry,
For fear of black bears or of bulls all black,
Or lest black devils put them in a sack.
Of other humours could I tell also,
That bring, to many a sleeping man, great woe;
But I'll pass on as lightly as I can.
"Lo, Cato, and he was a full wise man,
Said he not, we should trouble not for dreams?
Now, sir," said she, "when we fly from the beams,
For God's love go and take some laxative;
On peril of my soul, and as I live,
I counsel you the best, I will not lie,
That both for choler and for melancholy
You purge yourself; and since you shouldn't tarry,
And on this farm there's no apothecary,
I will myself go find some herbs for you
That will be good for health and pecker too;
And in our own yard all these herbs I'll find,
The which have properties of proper kind
To purge you underneath and up above.
Forget this not, now, for God's very love!
You are so very choleric of complexion.
Beware the mounting sun and all dejection,
Nor get yourself with sudden humours hot;
For if you do, I dare well lay a groat
That you shall have the tertian fever's pain,
Or some ague that may well be your bane.
A day or two you shall have digestives
Of worms before you take your laxatives
Of laurel, centuary, and fumitory,
Or else of hellebore purificatory,
Or caper spurge, or else of dogwood berry,
Or herb ivy, all in our yard so merry;
Peck them just as they grow and gulp them in.
Be merry, husband, for your father's kin!
Dread no more dreams. And I can say no more."
"Madam," said he, "gramercy for your lore.
Nevertheless, not running Cato down,
Who had for wisdom such a high renown,
And though he says to hold no dreams in dread,
By God, men have, in many old books, read
Of many a man more an authority
That ever Cato was, pray pardon me,
Who say just the reverse of his sentence,
And have found out by long experience
That dreams, indeed, are good significations,
As much of joys as of all tribulations
That folk endure here in this life present.
There is no need to make an argument;
The very proof of this is shown indeed.
"One of the greatest authors that men read
Says thus: That on a time two comrades went
On pilgrimage, and all in good intent;
And it so chanced they came into a town
Where there was such a crowding, up and down,
Of people, and so little harbourage,
That they found not so much as one cottage
Wherein the two of them might sheltered be.
Wherefore they must, as of necessity,

Right as the humour of malencolye
Causeth ful many a man, in sleep, to crye,
For fere of blake beres, or boles blake,
Or elles, blake develes wole hem take.
Of othere humours coude I telle also,
That werken many a man in sleep ful wo;
But I wol passe as lightly as I can.
Lo Catoun, which that was so wys a man,
Seyde he nat thus, ne do no fors of dremes?
Now, sire," quod she, "whan we flee fro the bemes,
For Goddes love, as tak som laxatyf;
Up peril of my soule, and of my lyf,
I counseille yow the beste, I wol nat lye,
That bothe of colere and of malencolye
Ye purge yow; and for ye shul nat tarie,
Though in this toun is noon apotecarie,
I shal my-self to herbes techen yow,
That shul ben for your hele, and for your prow;
And in our yerd tho herbes shal I finde,
The whiche han of hir propretee, by kinde,
To purgen yow binethe, and eek above.
Forget not this, for goddes owene love!
Ye been ful colerik of compleccioun.
Ware the sonne in his ascencioun
Ne fynde yow nat repleet of humours hote;
And if it do, I dar wel leye a grote,
That ye shul have a fevere terciane,
Or an agu, that may be youre bane.
A day or two ye shul have digestyves
Of wormes, er ye take your laxatyves,
Of lauriol, centaure, and fumetere,
Or elles of ellebor, that groweth there.
Of catapuce, or of gaytres beryis,
Of erbe yve, growing in our yerd, that mery is;
Pekke hem up right as they growe, and ete hem in.
Be mery, housbond, for your fader kin!
Dredeth no dreem; I can say yow namore."
"Madame," quod he, "*graunt mercy* of your lore.
But nathelees, as touching daun Catoun,
That hath of wisdom such a greet renoun,
Though that he bad no dremes for to drede,
By god, men may in olde bokes rede
Of many a man, more of auctoritee
Than ever Catoun was, so mote I thee,
That al the revers seyn of his sentence,
And han wel founden by experience,
That dremes ben significaciouns,
As wel of joye as tribulaciouns
That folk enduren in this lyf present.
Ther nedeth make of this noon argument;
The verray preve sheweth it in dede.
"Oon of the gretteste auctours that men rede
Seith thus, that whylom two felawes wente
On pilgrimage, in a ful good entente;
And happed so, thay come into a toun,
Wher-as ther was swich congregacioun
Of peple, and eek so streit of herbergage
That they ne founde as muche as o cotage
In which they bothe might y-logged be.
Wherfor thay mosten, of necessitee,

As for that night, departen compaignye;
And ech of hem goth to his hostelrye,
And took his logging as it wolde falle.
That oon of hem was logged in a stalle,
Fer in a yerd, with oxen of the plough;
That other man was logged wel y-nough,
As was his aventure, or his fortune,
That us governeth alle as in commune.
"And so bifel, that, longe er it were day,
This man mette in his bed, ther-as he lay,
How that his felawe gan up-on him calle,
And seyde, 'allas! for in an oxes stalle
This night I shal be mordred ther I lye.
Now help me, dere brother, er I dye;
In alle haste com to me,' he sayde.
This man out of his sleep for fere abrayde;
But whan that he was wakned of his sleep,
He turned him, and took of this no keep;
Him thoughte his dreem nas but a vanitee.
Thus twyës in his sleping dremed he.
And atte thridde tyme yet his felawe
Cam, as him thoughte, and seide, 'I am now slawe;
Bihold my blody woundes, depe and wyde!
Arys up erly in the morwe-tyde,
And at the west gate of the toun,' quod he,
'A carte ful of dong ther shaltow see,
In which my body is hid ful prively;
Do thilke carte aresten boldely.
My gold caused my mordre, sooth to sayn';
And tolde him every poynt how he was slayn,
With a ful pitous face, pale of hewe.
And truste wel, his dreem he fond ful trewe;
For on the morwe, as sone as it was day,
To his felawes in he took the way;
And whan that he cam to this oxes stalle,
After his felawe he bigan to calle.
The hostiler answered him anon,
And seyde, 'sire, your felawe is agon,
As sone as day he wente out of the toun.'
This man gan fallen in suspecioun,
Remembring on his dremes that he mette,
And forth he goth, no lenger wolde he lette,
Unto the west gate of the toun, and fond
A dong-carte, as it were to donge lond,
That was arrayed in the same wyse
As ye han herd the dede man devyse;
And with an hardy herte he gan to crye
Vengeaunce and justice of this felonye:—
'My felawe mordred is this same night,
And in this carte he lyth gapinge upright.
I crye out on the ministres,' quod he,
'That sholden kepe and reulen this citee;
Harrow! allas! her lyth my felawe slayn!'
What sholde I more un-to this tale sayn?
The peple out-sterte, and caste the cart to grounde,
And in the middel of the dong they founde
The dede man, that mordred was al newe.
O blisful god, that art so just and trewe!
Lo, how that thou biwreyest mordre alway!
Mordre wol out, that see we day by day.

For that one night at least, part company;
And each went to a different hostelry
And took such lodgment as to him did fall.
Now one of them was lodged within a stall,
Far in a yard, with oxen of the plow;
That other man found shelter fair enow,
As was his luck, or was his good fortune,
Whatever 'tis that governs us, each one.
"So it befell that, long ere it was day,
This last man dreamed in bed, as there he lay,
That his poor fellow did unto him call,
Saying: 'Alas! For in an ox's stall
This night shall I be murdered where I lie.
Now help me, brother dear, before I die.
Come in all haste to me.' 'Twas thus he said.
This man woke out of sleep, then, all afraid;
But when he'd wakened fully from his sleep,
He turned upon his pillow, yawning deep,
Thinking his dream was but a fantasy.
And then again, while sleeping, thus dreamed he.
And then a third time came a voice that said
(Or so he thought): 'Now, comrade, I am dead;
Behold my bloody wounds, so wide and deep!
Early arise tomorrow from your sleep,
And at the west gate of the town,' said he,
A wagon full of dung there shall you see,
Wherein is hid my body craftily;
Do you arrest this wagon right boldly.
They killed me for what money they could gain.
And told in every point how he'd been slain,
With a most pitiful face and pale of hue.
And trust me well, this dream did all come true;
For on the morrow, soon as it was day,
Unto his comrade's inn he took the way;
And when he'd come into that ox's stall,
Upon his fellow he began to call.
"The keeper of the place replied anon,
And said he: 'Sir, your friend is up and gone;
As soon as day broke he went out of town.'
This man, then, felt suspicion in him grown,
Remembering the dream that he had had,
And forth he went, no longer tarrying, sad,
Unto the west gate of the town, and found
A dung-cart on its way to dumping-ground,
And it was just the same in every wise
As you have heard the dead man advertise;
And with a hardy heart he then did cry
Vengeance and justice on this felony:
'My comrade has been murdered in the night,
And in this very cart lies, face upright.
I cry to all the officers,' said he
'That ought to keep the peace in this city.
Alas, alas, here lies my comrade slain!'
"Why should I longer with this tale detain?
The people rose and turned the cart to ground,
And in the center of the dung they found
The dead man, lately murdered in his sleep.
"O Blessed God, Who art so true and deep!
Lo, how Thou dost turn murder out alway!
Murder will out, we see it every day.

Murder's so hateful and abominable
To God, Who is so just and reasonable,
That He'll not suffer that it hidden be;
Though it may skulk a year, or two, or three,
Murder will out, and I conclude thereon.
Immediately the rulers of that town,
They took the carter and so sore they racked
Him and the host, until their bones were cracked,
That they confessed their wickedness anon,
And hanged they both were by the neck, and soon.
"Here may men see that dreams are things to
dread.
And certainly, in that same book I read,
Right in the very chapter after this
(I spoof not, as I may have joy and bliss),
Of two men who would voyage oversea,
For some cause, and unto a far country,
If but the winds had not been all contrary,
Causing them both within a town to tarry,
Which town was builded near the haven-side.
But then, one day, along toward eventide,
The wind did change and blow as suited
best.
Jolly and glad they went unto their rest.
And were prepared right early for to sail;
But unto one was told a marvelous tale.
For one of them, a-sleeping as he lay,
Did dream a wondrous dream ere it was day,
He thought a strange man stood by his bedside
And did command him, he should there abide,
And said to him: 'If you tomorrow wend,
You shall be drowned; my tale is at an end.'
He woke and told his fellow what he'd met
And prayed him quit the voyage and forget;
For just one day he prayed him there to bide.
His comrade, who was lying there beside,
Began to laugh and scorned him long and fast.
'No dream,' said he, 'may make my heart aghast,
So that I'll quit my business for such things.
I do not care a straw for your dreamings,
For visions are but fantasies and japes.
Men dream, why, every day, of owls and apes,
And many a wild phantasm therewithal;
Men dream of what has never been, nor shall.
But since I see that you will here abide,
And thus forgo this fair wind and this tide,
God knows I'm sorry; nevertheless, good day!'
"And thus he took his leave and went his way.
But long before the half his course he'd sailed,
I know not why, nor what it was that failed,
But casually the vessel's bottom rent,
And ship and men under the water went,
In sight of other ships were there beside.
The which had sailed with that same wind and tide.
"And therefore, pretty Pertelote, my dear,
By such old-time examples may you hear
And learn that no man should be too reckless
Of dreams, for I can tell you, fair mistress,
That many a dream is something well to dread.
"Why in the 'Life' of Saint Kenelm I read
(Who was Kenelphus' son, the noble king
Of Mercia), how Kenelm dreamed a thing;

Mordre is so wlatsom and abhominable
To god, that is so just and resonable,
That he ne wol nat suffre it heled be;
Though it abyde a yeer, or two, or three,
Mordre wol out, this my conclusioun.
And right anoon, ministres of that toun
Han hent the carter, and so sore him pyned,
And eek the hostiler so sore engyned,
That thay biknewe hir wikkednesse anoon,
And were an-hanged by the nekke-boon.
Here may men seen that dremes been to
drede.
And certes, in the same book I rede,
Right in the nexte chapitre after this,
(I gabbe nat, so have I joye or blis,)
Two men that wolde han passed over see,
For certeyn cause, in-to a fer contree,
If that the wind ne hadde been contrarie,
That made hem in a citee for to tarie,
That stood ful mery upon an havensyde.
But on a day, agayn the even-tyde,
The wind gan chaunge, and blew right as hem
leste.
Jolif and glad they wente un-to hir reste,
And casten hem ful erly for to saille;
But to that oo man fil a greet mervaille.
That oon of hem, in sleping as he lay,
Him mette a wonder dreem, agayn the day;
Him thoughte a man stood by his beddes syde,
And him comaunded, that he sholde abyde,
And seyde him thus, 'if thou to-morwe wende,
Thou shalt be dreynt; my tale is at an ende.'
He wook, and tolde his felawe what he mette,
And preyde him his viage for to lette;
As for that day, he preyde him to abyde.
His felawe, that lay by his beddes syde,
Gan for to laughe, and scorned him ful faste.
'No dreem,' quod he, 'may so myn herte agaste,
That I wol lette for to do my thinges.
I sette not a straw by thy dreminges,
For swevenes been but vanitees and japes.
Men dreme al-day of owles or of apes,
And eke of many a mase therwithal;
Men dreme of thing that never was ne shal.
But sith I see that thou wolt heer abyde,
And thus for-sleuthen wilfully thy tyde,
God wot it reweth me; and have good day.'
And thus he took his leve, and wente his way.
But er that he hadde halfe his cours y-seyled,
Noot I nat why, ne what mischaunce it eyled,
But casuelly the shippes botme rente,
And ship and man under the water wente
In sighte of othere shippes it byside,
That with hem seyled at the same tyde.
And therfor, faire Pertelote so dere,
By swiche ensamples olde maistow lere,
That no man sholde been to recchelees
Of dremes, for I sey thee, doutelees,
That many a dreem ful sore is for to drede.
Lo, in the lyf of seint Kenelm, I rede,
That was Kenulphus sone, the noble king
Of Mercenrike, how Kenelm mette a thing;

A lyte er he was mordred, on a day,
His mordre in his avisioun he say.
His norice him expouned every del
His sweven, and bad him for to kepe him wel
For traisoun; but he nas but seven yeer old,
And therfore litel tale hath he told
Of any dreem, so holy was his herte.
By god, I hadde lever than my sherte
That ye had rad his legende, as have I.
Dame Pertelote, I sey yow trewely,
Macrobeus, that writ th'avisioun
In Affrike of the worthy Cipioun,
Affermeth dremes, and seith that they been
Warning of thinges that men after seen.
  And forther-more, I pray yow loketh wel
In th'olde testament, of Daniel,
If he held dremes any vanitee.
Reed eek of Joseph, and ther shul ye see
Wher dremes ben somtyme (I sey nat alle)
Warning of thinges that shul after falle.
Loke of Egipt the king, daun Pharao,
His bakere and his boteler also,
Wher they ne felte noon effect in dremes.
Who-so wol seken actes of sondry remes,
May rede of dremes many a wonder thing.
  Lo Cresus, which that was of Lyde king,
Mette he nat that he sat upon a tree,
Which signified he sholde anhanged be?
Lo heer Andromacha, Ectores wyf,
That day that Ector sholde lese his lyf,
She dremed on the same night biforn,
How that the lyf of Ector sholde be lorn,
If thilke day he wente in-to bataille;
She warned him, but it mighte nat availle;
He wente for to fighte nathelees,
But he was slayn anoon of Achilles.
But thilke tale is al to long to telle,
And eek it is ny day, I may nat dwelle.
Shortly I seye, as for conclusioun,
That I shal han of this avisioun
Adversitee; and I seye forther-more,
That I ne telle of laxatyves no store,
For they ben venimous, I woot it wel;
I hem defye, I love hem never a del.
  Now let us speke of mirthe, and stinte al this;
Madame Pertelote, so have I blis,
Of o thing god hath sent me large grace;
For whan I see the beautee of your face,
Ye ben so scarlet-reed about your yën,
It maketh al my drede for to dyen;
For, also siker as *In principio,*
Mulier est hominis confusio;
Madame, the sentence of this Latin is—
Womman is mannes joye and al his blis.
For whan I fele a-night your softe syde,
Al-be-it that I may nat on you ryde,
For that our perche is maad so narwe, alas!
I am so ful of joye and of solas
That I defye bothe sweven and dreem."
  And with that word he fley doun fro the beem,
For it was day, and eek his hennes alle;
And with a chuk he gan hem for to calle,

A while ere he was murdered, so they say,
His own death in a vision saw, one day.
His nurse interpreted, as records tell,
That vision, bidding him to guard him well
From treason; but he was but seven years old,
And therefore 'twas but little he'd been told
Of any dream, so holy was his heart.
By God! I'd rather than retain my shirt
That you had read this legend, as have I.
Dame Pertelote, I tell you verily,
Macrobius, who wrote of Scipio
The African a vision long ago,
He holds by dreams, saying that they have been
Warnings of things that men have later seen.
  "And furthermore, I pray you to look well
In the Old Testament at Daniel,
Whether he held dreams for mere vanity.
Read, too, of Joseph, and you there shall see
Where dreams have sometimes been (I say not all)
Warnings of things that after did befall.
Consider Egypt's king, Dan Pharaoh,
His baker and his butler, these also,
Whether they knew of no effect from dreams.
Whoso will read of sundry realms the themes
May learn of dreams full many a wondrous thing.
  Lo, Croesus, who was once of Lydia king,
Dreamed he not that he sat upon a tree,
Which signified that hanged high he should be?
Lo, how Andromache, great Hector's wife,
On that same day when Hector lost his life,
She dreamed upon the very night before
That Hector's life should be lost evermore,
If on that day he battled, without fail.
She warned him, but no warning could avail;
He went to fight, despite all auspices,
And so was shortly slain by Achilles.
But that same tale is all too long to tell,
And, too, it's nearly day, I must not dwell
Upon this; I but say, concluding here,
That from this vision I have cause to fear
Adversity; and I say, furthermore,
That I do set by laxatives no store,
For they are poisonous, I know it well.
Them I defy and love not, truth to tell.
  "But let us speak of mirth and stop all this;
My lady Pertelote, on hope of bliss,
In one respect God's given me much grace;
For when I see the beauty of your face,
You are so rosy-red beneath each eye,
It makes my dreadful terror wholly die.
For there is truth in *In principio*
Mulier est hominis confusio
(Madam, the meaning of this Latin is,
Woman is man's delight and all his bliss).
For when I feel at night your tender side,
Although I cannot then upon you ride,
Because our perch so narrow is, alas!
I am so full of joy and all solace
That I defy, then, vision, aye and dream."
  And with that word he flew down from the beam,
For it was day, and down went his hens all;
And with a cluck he them began to call,

For he had found some corn within the yard.
Regal he was, and fears he did discard.
He feathered Pertelote full many a time
And twenty times he trod her ere 'twas prime.
He looked as if he were a grim lion
As on his toes he strutted up and down;
He deigned not set his foot upon the ground.
He clucked when any grain of corn he found,
And all his wives came running at his call.
Thus regal, as a prince is in his hall,
I'll now leave busy Chanticleer to feed,
And with events that followed I'll proceed.

When that same month wherein the world began,
Which is called March, wherein God first made man
Was ended, and were passed of days also,
Since March began, full thirty days and two,
It fell that Chanticleer, in all his pride,
His seven wives a-walking by his side,
Cast up his two eyes toward the great bright sun
(Which through the sign of Taurus now had run
Twenty degrees and one, and somewhat more),
And knew by instinct and no other lore
That it was prime, and joyfully he crew,
"The sun, my love," he said, "has climbed anew
Forty degrees and one, and somewhat more.
My lady Pertelote, whom I adore,
Mark now these happy birds, hear how they sing,
And see all these fresh flowers, how they spring;
Full is my heart of revelry and grace."

But suddenly he fell in grievous case;
For ever the latter end of joy is woe.
God knows that worldly joys do swiftly go;
And if a rhetorician could but write,
He in some chronicle might well indite
And mark it down as sovereign in degree.
Now every wise man, let him hark to me:
This tale is just as true, I undertake,
As is the book of *Launcelot of the Lake*,
Which women always hold in such esteem.
But now I must take up my proper theme.

A brant-fox, full of sly iniquity,
That in the grove had lived two years, or three,
Now by a fine premeditated plot
That same night, breaking through the hedge, had got
Into the yard where Chanticleer the fair
Was wont, and all his wives too, to repair;
And in a bed of greenery still he lay
Till it was past the quarter of the day,
Waiting his chance on Chanticleer to fall,
As gladly do these killers one and all
Who lie in ambush for to murder men.
O murderer false, there lurking in your den!
O new Iscariot, O new Ganelon!
O false dissimulator, Greek Sinon
That brought down Troy all utterly to sorrow!
O Chanticleer, accursed be that morrow
When you into that yard flew from the beams!
You were well warned, and fully, by your dreams
That this day should hold peril damnably.
But that which God foreknows, it needs must be,
So says the best opinion of the clerks.

For he had founde a corn, lay in the yerd.
Royal he was, he was namore aferd;
He fethered Pertelote twenty tyme,
And trad as ofte, er that it was pryme.
He loketh as it were a grim leoun;
And on his toos he rometh up and doun,
Him deyned not to sette his foot to grounde.
He chukketh, whan he hath a corn y-founde,
And to him rennen thanne his wyves alle.
Thus royal, as a prince is in his halle,
Leve I this Chauntecleer in his pasture;
And after wol I telle his aventure.

Whan that the month in which the world bigan,
That highte March, whan god first maked man,
Was complet, and [y]-passed were also,
Sin March bigan, thritty dayes and two,
Bifel that Chauntecleer, in al his pryde,
His seven wyves walking by his syde,
Caste up his eyen to the brighte sonne,
That in the signe of Taurus hadde y-ronne
Twenty degrees and oon, and somwhat more;
And knew by kynde, and by noon other lore,
That it was pryme, and crew with blisful stevene.
"The sonne," he sayde, "is clomben up on hevene
Fourty degrees and oon, and more, y-wis.
Madame Pertelote, my worldes blis,
Herkneth thise blisful briddes how they singe,
And see the fresshe floures how they springe;
Ful is myn herte of revel and solas."

But sodeinly him fil a sorweful cas;
For ever the latter ende of joye is wo.
God woot that worldly joye is sone ago;
And if a rethor coude faire endyte,
He in a cronique saufly mighte it wryte,
As for a sovereyn notabilitee.
Now every wys man, lat him herkne me;
This storie is al-so trewe, I undertake,
As is the book of Launcelot de Lake,
That wommen holde in ful gret reverence.
Now wol I torne agayn to my sentence.

A col-fox, ful of sly iniquitee,
That in the grove hadde woned yeres three,
By heigh imaginacioun forn-cast,
The same night thurgh-out the hegges brast
Into the yerd, ther Chauntecleer the faire
Was wont, and eek his wyves, to repaire;
And in a bed of wortes stille he lay,
Til it was passed undern of the day,
Wayting his tyme on Chauntecleer to falle,
As gladly doon thise homicydes alle,
That in awayt liggen to mordre men.
O false mordrer, lurking in thy den!
O newe Scariot, newe Genilon!
False dissimilour, O Greek Sinon,
That broghtest Troye al outrely to sorwe!
O Chauntecleer, acursed be that morwe,
That thou into that yerd flough fro the bemes!
Thou were ful wel y-warned by thy dremes,
That thilke day was perilous to thee.
But what that god forwoot mot nedes be,
After the opinioun of certeyn clerkis.

Witnesse on him, that any perfit clerk is,
That in scole is gret altercacioun
In this matere, and greet disputisoun,
And hath ben of an hundred thousand men.
But I ne can not bulte it to the bren,
As can the holy doctour Augustyn,
Or Boëce, or the bishop Bradwardyn,
Whether that goddes worthy forwiting
Streyneth me nedely for to doon a thing,
(Nedely clepe I simple necessitee);
Or elles, if free choys be graunted me
To do that same thing, or do it noght,
Though god forwoot it, er that it was wroght;
Or if his witing streyneth nevere a del
But by necessitee condicionel.
I wol not han to do of swich matere;
My tale is of a cok, as ye may here,
That took his counseil of his wyf, with sorwe,
To walken in the yerd upon that morwe
That he had met the dreem, that I yow tolde.
Wommennes counseils been ful ofte colde;
Wommannes counseil broghte us first to wo,
And made Adam fro paradys to go,
Ther-as he was ful mery, and wel at ese.—
But for I noot, to whom it mighte displese,
If I counseil of wommen wolde blame,
Passe over, for I seyde it in my game.
Rede auctours, wher they trete of swich matere,
And what they seyn of wommen ye may here.
Thise been the cokkes wordes, and nat myne;
I can noon harm of no womman divyne.—
Faire in the sond, to bathe hir merily,
Lyth Pertelote, and alle hir sustres by,
Agayn the sonne; and Chauntecleer so free
Song merier than the mermayde in the see;
For Phisiologus seith sikerly,
How that they singen wel and merily.
And so bifel that, as he caste his yë,
Among the wortes, on a boterflye,
He was war of this fox that lay ful lowe.
No-thing ne liste him thanne for to crowe,
But cryde anon, "cok, cok," and up he sterte,
As man that was affrayed in his herte.
For naturelly a beest desyreth flee
Fro his contrarie, if he may it see,
Though he never erst had seyn it with his yë.
This Chauntecleer, whan he gan him espye,
He wolde han fled, but that the fox anon
Seyde, "Gentil sire, allas! wher wol ye gon?
Be ye affrayed of me that am your freend?
Now certes, I were worse than a feend,
If I to yow wolde harm or vileinye.
I am nat come your counseil for t'espye;
But trewely, the cause of my cominge
Was only for to herkne how that ye singe.
For trewely ye have as mery a stevene
As eny aungel hath, that is in hevene;
Therwith ye han in musik more felinge
Than hadde Boëce, or any that can singe.
My lord your fader (god his soule blesse!)
And eek your moder, of hir gentilesse,

Witness some cleric perfect for his works.
That in the schools there's a great altercation
In this regard, and much high disputation
That has involved a hundred thousand men.
But I can't sift it to the bran with pen,
As can the holy Doctor Augustine,
Or Boethius, or Bishop Bradwardine,
Whether the fact of God's great foreknowing
Makes it right needful that I do a thing
(By needful, I mean, of necessity);
Or else, if a free choice he granted me,
To do that same thing, or to do it not,
Though God foreknew before the thing was wrought;
Or if His knowing constrains never at all,
Save by necessity conditional.
I have no part in matters so austere;
My tale is of a cock, as you shall hear,
That took the counsel of his wife, with sorrow,
To walk within the yard upon that morrow
After he'd had the dream whereof I told.
Now women's counsels oft are ill to hold;
A woman's counsel brought us first to woe,
And Adam caused from Paradise to go,
Wherein he was right merry and at ease.
But since I know not whom it may displease
If woman's counsel I hold up to blame,
Pass over, I but said in it my game.
Read authors where such matters do appear,
And what they say of women, you may hear.
These are the cock's words, they are none of mine;
No harm in women can I e'er divine.
All in the sand, a-bathing merrily,
Lay Pertelote, with all her sisters by,
There in the sun; and Chanticleer so free
Sang merrier than a mermaid in the sea
(For Physiologus says certainly
That they *do* sing, both well and merrily).
And so befell that, as he cast his eye
Among the herbs and on a butterfly,
He saw this fox that lay there, crouching low.
Nothing of urge was in him, then, to crow;
But he cried "Cock-cock-cock" and did so start
As man who has a sudden fear at heart.
For naturally a beast desires to flee
From any enemy that he may see,
Though never yet he's clapped on such his eye.
When Chanticleer the fox did then espy,
He would have fled but that the fox anon
Said: "Gentle sir, alas! Why be thus gone?
Are you afraid of me, who am your friend?
Now, surely, I were worse than any fiend
If I should do you harm or villainy.
I came not here upon your deeds to spy;
But, certainly, the cause of my coming
Was only just to listen to you sing.
For truly, you have quite as fine a voice
As angels have that Heaven's choirs rejoice;
Boethius to music could not bring
Such feeling, nor do others who can sing.
My lord your father (God his soul pray bless!)
And too your mother, of her gentleness,

Have been in my abode, to my great ease;
And truly, sir, right fain am I to please.
But since men speak of singing, I will say
(As I still have my eyesight day by day),
Save you, I never heard a man so sing
As did your father in the grey dawning;
Truly 'twas from the heart, his every song.
And that his voice might ever be more strong,
He took such pains that, with his either eye,
He had to blink, so loudly would he cry,
A-standing on his tiptoes therewithal,
Stretching his neck till it grew long and small.
And such discretion, too, by him was shown,
There was no man in any region known
That him in song or wisdom could surpass.
I have well read, in *Dan Burnell the Ass*,
Among his verses, how there was a cock,
Because a priest's son gave to him a knock
Upon the leg, while young and not yet wise,
He caused the boy to lose his benefice.
But, truly, there is no comparison
With the great wisdom and the discretion
Your father had, or with his subtlety.
Now sing, dear sir, for holy charity,
See if you can your father counterfeit."
This Chanticleer his wings began to beat,
As one that could no treason there espy,
So was he ravished by this flattery.
Alas, you lords! Full many a flatterer
Is in your courts, and many a cozener,
That please your honours much more, by my fay,
Than he that truth and justice dares to say.
Go read the Ecclesiast on flattery;
Beware, my lords, of all their treachery!
This Chanticleer stood high upon his toes,
Stretching his neck, and both his eyes did close,
And so did crow right loudly, for the nonce;
And Russel Fox, he started up at once,
And by the gorget grabbed our Chanticleer,
Flung him on back, and toward the wood did steer,
For there was no man who as yet pursued.
O destiny, you cannot be eschewed!
Alas, that Chanticleer flew from the beams!
Alas, his wife recked nothing of his dreams!
And on a Friday fell all this mischance.
O Venus, who art goddess of pleasance,
Since he did serve thee well, this Chanticleer,
And to the utmost of his power here,
More for delight than cocks to multiply,
Why would'st thou suffer him that day to die?
O Gaufred,[1] my dear master sovereign,
Who, when King Richard Lionheart was slain
By arrow, sang his death with sorrow sore,
Why have I not your faculty and lore
To chide Friday, as you did worthily?
(For truly, on a Friday slain was he).
Then would I prove how well I could complain
For Chanticleer's great fear and all his pain.
Certainly no such cry and lamentation
Were made by ladies at Troy's desolation,

Han in myn hous y-been, to my gret ese;
And certes, sire ful fayn wolde I yow plese.
But for men speke of singing, I wol saye,
So mote I brouke wel myn eyen tweye,
Save yow, I herde never man so singe,
As dide your fader in the morweninge;
Certes, it was of herte, al that he song.
And for to make his voys the more strong,
He wolde so peyne him, that with bothe his yën
He moste winke, so loude he wolde cryen,
And stonden on his tiptoon ther-with-al,
And strecche forth his nekke long and smal.
And eek he was of swich discrecioun,
That ther nas no man in no regioun
That him in song or wisdom mighte passe.
I have wel rad in daun Burnel the Asse,
Among his vers, how that ther was a cok,
For that a preestes sone yaf him a knok
Upon his leg, whyl he was yong and nyce,
He made him for to lese his benefyce.
But certeyn, ther nis no comparisoun
Bitwix the wisdom and discrecioun
Of youre fader, and of his subtiltee.
Now singeth, sire, for seinte Charitee,
Let see, conne ye your fader countrefete?"
This Chauntecleer his winges gan to bete,
As man that coude his tresoun nat espye,
So was he ravisshed with his flaterye.
Allas! ye lordes, many a fals flatour
Is in your courtes, and many a losengeour,
That plesen yow wel more, by my feith,
Than he that soothfastnesse unto yow seith.
Redeth Ecclesiaste of flaterye;
Beth war, ye lordes, of hir trecherye.
This Chauntecleer stood hye up-on his toos,
Strecching his nekke, and heeld his eyen cloos,
And gan to crowe loude for the nones;
And daun Russel the fox sterte up at ones,
And by the gargat hente Chauntecleer,
And on his bak toward the wode him beer,
For yet ne was ther no man that him sewed.
O destinee, that mayst nat been eschewed!
Allas, that Chauntecleer fleigh fro the bemes!
Allas, his wyf ne roghte nat of dremes!
And on a Friday fil al this meschaunce.
O Venus, that art goddesse of plesaunce,
Sin that thy servant was this Chauntecleer,
And in thy service dide al his poweer,
More for delyt, than world to multiplye,
Why woldestow suffre him on thy day to dye?
O Gaufred,[1] dere mayster soverayn,
That, whan thy worthy king Richard was slayn
With shot, compleynedest his deth so sore,
Why ne hadde I now thy sentence and thy lore,
The Friday for to chyde, as diden ye?
(For on a Friday soothly slayn was he.)
Than wolde I shewe yow how that I coude pleyne
For Chauntecleres drede, and for his peyne.
Certes, swich cry ne lamentacioun
Was never of ladies maad, whan Ilioun

[1]Gaufred de Vinsauf.

Was wonne, and Pirrus with his streite swerd,
Whan he hadde hent king Priam by the berd,
And slayn him (as saith us *Eneydos*),
As maden alle the hennes in the clos,
Whan they had seyn of Chauntecleer the sighte.
But sovereynly dame Pertelote shrighte,
Ful louder than dide Hasdrubales wyf,
Whan that hir housbond hadde lost his lyf,
And that the Romayns hadde brend Cartage;
She was so ful of torment and of rage,
That wilfully into the fyr she sterte,
And brende hir-selven with a stedfast herte.
O woful hennes, right so cryden ye,
As, whan that Nero brende the citee
Of Rome, cryden senatoures wyves,
For that hir housbondes losten alle hir lyves;
Withouten gilt this Nero hath hem slayn.
Now wol I torne to my tale agayn:—
  This sely widwe, and eek hir doghtres two,
Herden thise hennes crye and maken wo,
And out at dores sterten they anoon,
And syen the fox toward the grove goon,
And bar upon his bak the cok away;
And cryden, "Out! harrow! and weylaway!
Ha, ha, the fox!" and after him they ran,
And eek with staves many another man;
Ran Colle our dogge, and Talbot, and Gerland,
And Malkin, with a distaf in hir hand;
Ran cow and calf, and eek the verray hogges
So were they fered for berking of the dogges
And shouting of the men and wimmen eke,
They ronne so, hem thoughte hir herte berke.
They yelleden as feendes doon in helle;
The dokes cryden as men wolde hem quelle;
The gees for fere flowen over the trees;
Out of the hyve cam the swarm of bees;
So hidous was the noyse, a! *benedicite!*
Certes, he Jakke Straw,[1] and his meynee,
Ne made never shoutes half so shrille,
Whan that they wolden any Fleming kille,
As thilke day was maad upon the fox.
Of bras thay broghten bemes, and of box,
Of horn, of boon, in whiche they blewe and pouped,
And therwithal thay shryked and they houped;
It semed as that heven sholde falle.
Now, gode men, I pray yow herkneth alle!
  Lo, how fortune turneth sodeinly
The hope and pryde eek of hir enemy!
This cok, that lay upon the foxes bak,
In al his drede, un-to the fox he spak,
And seyde, "sire, if that I were as ye,
Yet sholde I seyn (as wis god helpe me),
Turneth agayn, ye proude cherles alle!
A verray pestilence up-on yow falle!
Now am I come un-to this wodes syde,
Maugree your heed, the cok shal heer abyde;
I wol him ete in feith and that anon."—
  The fox answerde, "in feith, it shal be don,"—

When Pyrrhus with his terrible bared sword
Had taken old King Priam by the beard
And slain him (as the Aeneid tells to us),
As made then all those hens in one chorus
When they had caught a sight of Chanticleer.
But fair Dame Pertelote assailed the ear
Far louder than did Hasdrubal's good wife
When that her husband bold had lost his life,
And Roman legionaries burned Carthage;
For she so full of torment was, and rage,
She voluntarily to the fire did start
And burned herself there with a steadfast heart.
And you, O woeful hens, just so you cried
As when base Nero burned the city wide
Of Rome, and wept the senators' stern wives
Because their husbands all had lost their lives,
For though not guilty, Nero had them slain.
Now will I turn back to my tale again.
  This simple widow and her daughters two
Heard these hens cry and make so great ado,
And out of doors they started on the run
And saw the fox into the grove just gone,
Bearing upon his back the cock away.
And then they cried, "Alas, and weladay!
Oh, oh, the fox!" and after him they ran,
And after them, with staves, went many a man;
Ran Coll, our dog, ran Talbot and Garland,
And Malkin with a distaff in her hand;
Ran cow and calf and even the very hogs,
So were they scared by barking of the dogs
And shouting men and women all did make,
They all ran so they thought their hearts would break.
They yelled as very fiends do down in Hell;
The ducks they cried as at the butcher fell;
The frightened geese flew up above the trees;
Out of the hive there came the swarm of bees;
So terrible was the noise, ah *ben' cite!*
Certainly old Jack Straw[1] and his army
Never raised shouting half so loud and shrill
When they were chasing Flemings for to kill,
As on that day was raised upon the fox.
They brought forth trumpets made of brass, of box,
Of horn, of bone, wherein they blew and pooped,
And therewithal they screamed and shrieked and whooped;
It seemed as if the heaven itself should fall!
And now, good men, I pray you hearken all.
  Behold how Fortune turns all suddenly
The hope and pride of even her enemy!
This cock, which lay across the fox's back,
In all his fear unto the fox did clack
And say: "Sir, were I you, as I should be,
Then would I say (as God may now help me!),
'Turn back again, presumptuous peasants all!
A very pestilence upon you fall!
Now that I've gained here to this dark wood's side,
In spite of you this cock shall here abide.
I'll eat him, by my faith, and that anon!'"
  The fox replied: "In faith, it shall be done!"

[1]One of the leaders in Wat Tyler's rebellion, 1381.

And as he spoke that word, all suddenly
This cock broke from his mouth, full cleverly,
And high upon a tree he flew anon.
And when the fox saw well that he was gone,
"Alas," quoth he, "O Chanticleer, alas!
I have against you done a base trespass
In that I frightened you, my dear old pard,
When you I seized and brought from out that yard;
But, sir, I did it with no foul intent;
Come down, and I will tell you what I meant.
I'll tell the truth to you, God help me so!"
"Nay then," said he, "beshrew us both, you know,
But first, beshrew myself, both blood and bones,
If you beguile me, having done so once,
You shall no more, with any flattery,
Cause me to sing and close up either eye.
For he who shuts his eyes when he should see,
And wilfully, God let him ne'er be free!"
"Nay," said the fox, "but God give him mischance
Who is so indiscreet in governance
He chatters when he ought to hold his peace."
Lo, such it is when watch and ward do cease,
And one grows negligent with flattery.
But you that hold this tale a foolery,
As but about a fox, a cock, a hen,
Yet do not miss the moral, my good men.
For Saint Paul says that all that's written well
Is written down some useful truth to tell.
Then take the wheat and let the chaff lie still.
And now, good God, and if it be Thy will,
As says Lord Christ, so make us all good men
And bring us into His high bliss. Amen.

And as he spak that word, al sodeinly
This cok brak from his mouth deliverly,
And heighe up-on a tree he fleigh anon.
And whan the fox saugh that he was y-gon,
"Allas!" quod he, "O Chauntecleer, allas!
I have to yow," quod he, "y-doon trespas,
In-as-muche as I maked yow aferd,
Whan I yow hente, and broghte out of the yerd;
But, sire, I dide it in no wikke entente;
Com doun, and I shal telle yow what I mente.
I shal seye sooth to yow, god help me so."
"Nay than," quod he, "I shrewe us bothe two,
And first I shrewe my-self, bothe blood and bones,
If thou bigyle me ofter than ones.
Thou shalt na-more, thurgh thy flaterye,
Do me to singe and winke with myn yë.
For he that winketh, whan he sholde see,
Al wilfully, god lat him never thee!"
"Nay," quod the fox, "but god yeve him meschaunce,
That is so undiscreet of governaunce,
That jangleth whan he sholde holde his pees."
Lo, swich it is for to be recchelees,
And necligent, and truste on flaterye.
But ye that holden this tale a folye,
As of a fox, or of a cok and hen,
Taketh the moralitee, good men.
For seint Paul seith, that al that writen is,
To our doctryne it is y-write, y-wis.
Taketh the fruyt, and lat the chaf be stille.
Now, gode god, if that it be thy wille,
As seith my lord, so make us alle good men;
And bringe us to his heighe blisse. Amen.

HERE IS ENDED THE NUN'S PRIEST'S TALE

EPILOGUE TO THE NUN'S PRIEST'S TALE

Sir nun's priest," said our host, and that anon,
"Now blessed be your breech and every stone!
This was a merry tale of Chanticleer.
But, truth, if you were secular, I swear
You would have been a hen-hopper, all right!
For if you had the heart, as you have might,
You'd need some hens, I think it will be seen,
And many more than seven times seventeen.
For see what muscles has this noble priest,
So great a neck and such a splendid chest!
He's got a hawk's fierce fire within his eye;
And certainly he has no need to dye
His cheeks with any stain from Portugal.
Sir, for your tale, may blessings on you fall!"
And after that he, with right merry cheer,
Spoke to another one, as you shall hear.

"Sir Nonnes Preest," our hoste seyde anoon,
"Y-blessed by thy breche, and every stoon!
This was a mery tale of Chauntecleer.
But, by my trouthe, if thou were seculer,
Thou woldest been a trede-foul a-right.
For, if thou have corage as thou hast might,
Thee were nede of hennes, as I wene,
Ya, mo than seven tymes seventene.
See, whiche braunes hath this gentil Preest,
So greet a nekke, and swich a large breest!
He loketh as a sperhauk with his yën;
Him nedeth nat his colour for to dyen
With brasil, ne with greyn of Portingale.
Now sire, faire falle yow for youre tale!"
And after that he, with ful mery chere,
Seide to another, as ye shullen here.

THE SECOND NUN'S PROLOGUE

THE PROLOGUE OF THE SECOND NUN'S TALE

THE ministre and the norice un-to vyces,
Which that men clepe in English ydelnesse,
That porter of the gate is of delyces,
T'eschue, and by hir contrarie hir oppresse,
That is to seyn, by leveful bisinesse,
Wel oghten we to doon al our entente,
Lest that the feend thurgh ydelnesse us hente.

For he, that with his thousand cordes slye
Continuelly us waiteth to biclappe,
Whan he may man in ydelnesse espye,
He can so lightly cacche him in his trappe,
Til that a man be hent right by the lappe,
He nis nat war the feend hath him in honde;
Wel oughte us werche, and ydelnes withstonde.

And though men dradden never for to dye,
Yet seen men wel by reson doutelees,
That ydelnesse is roten slogardye,
Of which ther never comth no good encrees;
And seen, that slouthe hir holdeth in a lees
Only to slepe, and for to ete and drinke,
And to devouren al that othere swinke.

And for to putte us fro swich ydelnesse,
That cause is of so greet confusioun,
I have heer doon my feithful bisinesse,
After the legende, in translacioun
Right of thy glorious lyf and passioun,
Thou with thy gerland wroght of rose and lilie;
Thee mene I, mayde and martir, seint Cecilie!

THAT servant and that nurse unto the vices
Which men do call in English Idleness,
Portress at Pleasure's gate, by all advices
We should avoid, and by her foe express,
That is to say, by lawful busyness,
We ought to live with resolute intent,
Lest by the Fiend through sloth we should be rent.

For he, that with his thousand cords and sly
Continually awaits us all to trap,
When he a man in idleness may spy
He easily the hidden snare will snap,
And till the man has met the foul mishap,
He's not aware the Fiend has him in hand;
We ought to work and idleness withstand.

And though men never dreaded they must die,
Yet men see well, by reason, idleness
Is nothing more than rotten sluggardry,
Whereof comes never good one may possess;
And see sloth hold her in a leash, no less,
Only to sleep and eat and always drink
And to absorb all gain of others' swink.

And so, to save us from such idleness
Through which great trouble and distress have grown,
I have here done my faithful busyness,
Translating the old legend, to make known
All of that glorious life which was thine own,
Thou ever with the rose and lily crowned,
Cecilia, for virtues high renowned.

Invocation to Mary

AND thou that flour of virgines art alle,
Of whom that Bernard list so wel to wryte,
To thee at my biginning first I calle;
Thou comfort of us wrecches, do me endyte
Thy maydens deeth, than wan thurgh hir meryte
The eternal lyf, and of the feend victorie,
As man may after reden in hir storie.

Thou mayde and mooder, doghter of thy sone,
Thou welle of mercy, sinful soules cure,
In whom that god, for bountee, chees to wone,
Thou humble, and heigh over every creature,
Thou nobledest so ferforth our nature,
That no desdeyn the maker hadde of kinde,
His sone in blode and flesh to clothe and winde.

Withinne the cloistre blisful of thy sydes
Took mannes shap the eternal love and pees,
That of the tryne compas lord and gyde is,
Whom erthe and see and heven, out of relees,
Ay herien; and thou, virgin wemmelees,

And Thou that art the flower of virgins all
Of whom Saint Bernard loved so well to write,
To Thee at my beginning do I call;
Thou comfort of us wretches, help me indite
Thy maiden's death, who won through her merit
The eternal life, and from the Fiend such glory
As men may read hereafter in her story.

Thou Maid and Mother, Daughter of Thy Son,
Thou well of ruth, of sinful souls the cure,
In Whom, for goodness, God was embryon,
Thou humble One, high over each creature,
Thou did'st ennoble so far our nature
That no disdain God had of humankind
His Son in blood and flesh to clothe and wind.

Within the blessed cloister of Thy sides
Took human shape eternal love and peace
Who all the threefold world as sovereign guides,
Whom earth and sea and heaven, without cease,
Do praise; and Thou, O stainless Maid, increase

Bore of Thy body—and wert kept a maid—
The mighty God Who every creature made.

Assembled is in Thee magnificence,
With mercy, goodness, and with such pity
That Thou, Who art the sun of excellence,
Not only keepest those that pay to Thee,
But oftentimes, of Thy benignity,
Freely, or ever men Thy help beseech,
Thou goest before and art their spirits' leech.

Now help, Thou meek and blessed, Thou fair Maid,
Me, banished wretch, in wilderness of gall;
Think how the Canaanitish woman said
That even dogs may eat of the crumbs all
Which from the master's laden table fall;
And though I, now, unworthy son of Eve,
Am sinful, yet accept me, who believe.

And since all faith is dead divorced from works,
That I may do the right, O give me space
To free me from that darkness of deep murks!
O Thou, Who art so fair and full of grace,
Be Thou my advocate in that high place
Where without ever end is sung "Hosanna,"
Thou, Mother of Christ and daughter of Saint Anna!

And of Thy light my soul illuminate,
That troubled is by the contagion sown
Here in my body, also by the weight
Of earthly lust and false loves I have known;
O haven of refuge, O salvation shown
To those that are in sorrow and distress,
Now help, for to my work I'll me address.

Yet pray I all who read what I do write,
Forgive me that I do no diligence
By subtle change to make the story right;
For I have taken both the words and sense
From him who wrote the tale in reverence
Of this one saint; I follow her legend
And pray you that you will my work amend.

Bar of thy body, and dweltest mayden pure,
The creatour of every creature.

Assembled is in thee magnificence
With mercy, goodnesse, and with swich pitee
That thou, that art the sonne of excellence,
Nat only helpest hem that preyen thee,
But ofte tyme, of thy benignitee,
Ful frely, er that men thyn help biseche,
Thou goost biforn, and art hir lyves leche.

Now help, thou meke and blisful fayre mayde,
Me, flemed wrecche, in this desert of galle;
Think on the womman Cananee, that sayde
That whelpes eten somme of the crommes alle
That from hir lordes table been y-falle;
And though that I, unworthy sone of Eve,
Be sinful, yet accepte my bileve.

And, for that feith is deed with-outen werkes,
So for to werken yif me wit and space,
That I be quit fro thennes that most derk is!
O thou, that art so fayr and ful of grace,
Be myn advocat in that heighe place
Ther-as withouten ende is songe "Osanne,"
Thou Cristes mooder, doghter dere of Anne!

And of thy light my soule in prison lighte,
That troubled is by the contagioun
Of my body, and also by the wighte
Of erthly luste and fals affeccioun;
O haven of refut, o salvacioun
Of hem that been in sorwe and in distresse,
Now help, for to my werk I wol me dresse.

Yet preye I yow that reden that I wryte,
Foryeve me, that I do no diligence
This ilke storie subtilly to endyte;
For both have I the wordes and sentence
Of him that at the seintes reverence
The storie wroot, and folwe hir legende,
And prey yow, that ye wol my werk amende.

The interpretation of the name Cecilia, which Friar Jacobus Januensis put in the Legenda Aurea

First would I you the name of Saint Cecilia
Expound, as men may in her story see.
It is to say, in English, "Heaven's lily," a
Symbol of pure and virgin chastity;
Or, since she had the white of modesty,
And green of good conscience, and of good fame
The savour sweet, so "lily" was her name.

Or else Cecilia means "path for the blind,"
For she example was, by good teaching;
Or else Cecilia, as I written find,
Is made, after a manner of joining,
Of "Heaven" and "Lia"; and, in figuring,
The "Heaven" is put for "thought of holiness"
And "Lia" for enduring busyness.

Cecilia may mean, too, in this wise,

FIRST wolde I yow the name of seint Cecilie
Expoune, as men may in hir storie see,
It is to seye in English "hevenes lilie,"
For pure chastnesse of virginitee;
Or, for she whytnesse hadde of honestee,
And grene of conscience, and of good fame
The sote savour, "lilie" was hir name.

Or Cecile is to seye "the wey to blinde,"
For she ensample was by good techinge;
Or elles Cecile, as I writen finde,
Is joyned, by a maner conjoininge
Of "hevene" and "Lia"; and heer, in figuringe,
The "heven" is set for thoght of holinesse,
And "Lia" for hir lasting bisinesse.

Cecile may eek be seyd in this manere,

"Wanting of blindnesse," for hir grete light
Of sapience, and for hir thewes clere;
Or elles, lo! this maydens name bright
Of "hevene" and "leos" comth, for which by
right
Men mighte hir wel "the heven of peple" calle,
Ensample of gode and wyse werkes alle.

"Lacking in blindness," for her shining light
Of sapience, and for good qualities;
Or else, behold! this maiden's name so bright
From "Heaven" and "*leos*" comes, for which, by
right,
Men well might her the "Heaven of people" call,
Example of good and wise works unto all.

For "leos" "peple" in English is to seye,
And right as men may in the hevene see
The sonne and mone and sterres every weye,
Right so men gostly, in this mayden free,
Seyen of feith the magnanimitee,
And eek the cleernesse hool of sapience,
And sondry werkes, brighte of excellence.

Leos is folk in English, so to say,
And just as men may in the heavens see
The sun and moon and stars strewn every way,
Just so men ghostly, in this maiden free,
See of her faith the magnanimity,
And the whole glory of her sapience,
And many actions, bright of excellence.

And right so as thise philosophres wryte
That heven is swift and round and eek brenninge,
Right so was fayre Cecilie the whyte
Ful swift and bisy ever in good werkinge,
And round and hool in good perseveringe,
And brenning ever in charitee ful brighte;
Now have I yow declared what she highte.

And just as these philosophers do write
That heaven is round and moving and burning,
Just so was fair Cecilia the white
Eager and busy ever in good working,
Large and whole-hearted, steadfast in each thing,
And shining ever in charity full bright;
Now have I told you of her name aright.

HERE IT ENDETH

THE SECOND NUN'S TALE

HERE BEGINNETH THE SECOND NUN'S TALE, OF THE LIFE OF SAINT CECILIA

This mayden bright Cecilie, as hir lyf seith,
Was comen of Romayns, and of noble kinde,
And from hir cradel up fostred in the feith
Of Crist, and bar his gospel in hir minde;
She never cessed, as I writen finde,
Of hir preyere, and god to love and drede,
Biseking him to kepe hir maydenhede.

This maiden bright, Cecilia, her life saith,
Was Roman born and of a noble kind,
And from the cradle tutored in the faith
Of Christ, and bore His gospel in her mind;
She never ceased, as written do I find,
To pray to God, and love Him, and to dread,
Beseeching Him to keep her maidenhead.

And when this mayden sholde unto a man
Y-wedded be, that was ful yong of age,
Which that y-cleped was Valerian,
And day was comen of hir mariage,
She, ful devout and humble in hir corage,
Under hir robe of gold, that sat ful fayre,
Had next hir flesh y-clad hir in an heyre.

And when this maiden must unto a man
Be wedded, who was a young man in age,
And who had to his name Valerian,
And when the day was come for her marriage,
She, meek of heart, devout, and ever sage,
Under her robe of gold, well-made and fair,
Had next her body placed a shirt of hair.

And whyl the organs maden melodye,
To god alone in herte thus sang she;
"O lord, my soule and eek my body gye
Unwemmed, lest that I confounded be":
And, for his love that deyde upon a tree,
Every seconde or thridde day she faste,
Ay biddinge in hir orisons ful faste.

And while the organ made its melody,
To God alone within her heart sang she:
"O Lord, my soul and body guide to Thee
Unsoiled, lest I in spirit ruined be."
And for His love Who died upon a tree,
Each second or third day she used to fast,
And ever prayed she till the day was past.

The night cam, and to bedde moste she gon
With hir housbonde, as ofte is the manere,
And prively to him she seyde anon,
"O swete and wel biloved spouse dere,
Ther is a conseil, and ye wolde it here,
Which that right fain I wolde unto yow seye,
So that ye swere ye shul me nat biwreye."

The night came, and to bed she must be gone
With her young husband, but she had no fear,
And privately to him she said anon:
"O sweet and well-beloved spouse so dear,
There is a secret if you will to hear,
Which I am fain enough to you to say,
So that you swear that me you'll not betray."

Valerian to her his oath did swear
That evermore, whatever thing might be,
He never would betray what she said there;
And so beginning straightway thus said she:
"I have an angel lover that loves me,
And with a great love, whether I wake or sleep,
He will my body ever guard and keep.

"And if he feels (and this is truth," she said)
"That you will touch or love me vulgarly,
At once he'll slay and leave you with the dead,
And in your days of youth thus shall you die;
And if you love me cleanly, so say I,
He'll love you as now me, for your cleanness,
And show you all his joy and his brightness."

Valerian, checked thus as God would mould,
Replied: "If I'm to trust you, let me see
That angel with my eyes and him behold;
And if that it a very angel be,
Then will I do as you have asked of me;
And if you love another man, forsooth
Right with this sword then will I slay you both."

Cecilia replied right in this wise:
"If you so wish, that angel shall you see,
So you believe in Christ and you baptize.
Go forth to Via Appia,"[1] said she,
"That from this town is distant but miles three,
And to the poor folk who in that place dwell
Say to them what I'll now proceed to tell.

"Tell them that I, Cecilia, have sent
You to the good man Urban, who is old,
For secret need, and with a good intent.
And when this holy Urban you behold,
Tell him the thing that I to you have told;
And when he shall have purged you of your sin.
That angel shall you see ere thence you win."

Valerian to that place got him gone,
And just as he'd been told about the thing,
He found this ancient saint, Urban, anon,
Among the holy catacombs lurking.
And he anon, with never tarrying,
Told him his errand; and when it was told,
Urban for joy his two hands did uphold.

Some teardrops from his two eyes he let fall—
"Almighty Lord, O Jesus Christ," said he,
"Sower of counsel chaste, herd of us all,
The fruit of that same seed of chastity
Which Thou sowed'st in Cecilia, take to Thee!
Lo, like a busy bee, and without guile,
Thy thrall Cecilia serves Thee all the while!

"For that same spouse that lately wedded she,
Who was like lion fierce, she sends him here,
As meek as ever was a lamb, to Thee!"
And with that word anon there did appear
An old, old man, clothed all in white clothes clear,

Valerian gan faste unto hir swere,
That for no cas, ne thing that mighte be,
He sholde never-mo biwreyen here;
And thanne at erst to him thus seyde she,
"I have an angel which that loveth me,
That with greet love, wher-so I wake or slepe,
Is redy ay my body for to kepe.

And if that he may felen, out of drede,
That ye me touche or love in vileinye,
He right anon wol slee yow with the dede,
And in your yowthe thus ye shulden dye;
And if that ye in clene love me gye,
He wol yow loven as me, for your clennesse,
And shewen yow his joye and his brightnesse."

Valerian, corrected as god wolde,
Answerde agayn, "if I shal trusten thee,
Lat me that angel see, and him biholde;
And if that it a verray angel be,
Than wol I doon as thou hast preyed me;
And if thou love another man, for sothe
Right with this swerd than wol I slee yow bothe."

Cecile answerde anon right in this wyse,
"If that yow list, the angel shul ye see,
So that ye trowe on Crist and yow baptyse.
Goth forth to Via Apia,"[1] quod she,
"That fro this toun ne stant but myles three,
And, to the povre folkes that ther dwelle,
Sey hem right thus, as that I shal yow telle.

Telle hem that I, Cecile, yow to hem sente,
To shewen yow the gode Urban the olde,
For secree nedes and for good entente.
And whan that ye seint Urban han biholde,
Telle him the wordes whiche I to yow tolde;
And whan that he hath purged yow fro sinne,
Thanne shul ye see that angel, er ye twinne."

Valerian is to the place y-gon,
And right as him was taught by his lerninge,
He fond this holy olde Urban anon
Among the seintes buriels lotinge.
And he anon, with-outen taryinge,
Dide his message; and whan that he it tolde,
Urban for joye his hondes gan up holde.

The teres from his yën leet he falle—
"Almighty lord, O Jesu Crist," quod he,
"Sower of chast conseil, herde of us alle,
The fruit of thilke seed of chastitee
That thou hast sowe in Cecile, tak to thee!
Lo, lyk a bisy bee, with-outen gyle,
Thee serveth ay thyn owene thral Cecile!

For thilke spouse, that she took but now
Ful lyk a fiers leoun, she sendeth here,
As meke as ever was any lamb, to yow!"
And with that worde, anon ther gan appere
An old man, clad in whyte clothes clere,

[1]A district near Rome (not the famous highway) where the earliest catacombs were located.

That hadde a book with lettre of golde in honde, And gan biforn Valerian to stonde.	Who had a golden-lettered book in hand, And who before Valerian did stand.
Valerian as deed fil doun for drede Whan he him saugh, and he up hente him tho, And on his book right thus he gan to rede— "Oo Lord, oo feith, oo god with-outen mo, Oo Cristendom, and fader of alle also, Aboven alle and over al everywhere"— Thise wordes al with gold y-writen were.	Valerian for fear fell down as dead When him he saw, who raised him from the floor, And from his book (whereof I told) he read— "One Lord, one faith, one God with never more, One Christian Church, One Father of all to adore, Above all, over all, and everywhere"— These words in very gold were written there.
Whan this was rad, than seyde this olde man, "Levestow this thing or no? sey ye or nay." "I leve al this thing," quod Valerian, "For sother thing than this, I dar wel say, Under the hevene no wight thinke may." Tho vanisshed th'olde man, he niste where, And pope Urban him cristened right there.	When this was read, then said the ancient man: "Do you believe or not? Say 'Yea' or 'Nay' " "I do believe this," said Valerian, "For truer thing than this, I dare well say, Under the heavens none can think, nor may." Then vanished the old man, he knew not where, And Pope Urban baptized him even there.
Valerian goth hoom, and fint Cecilie With-inne his chambre with an angel stonde; This angel hadde of roses and of lilie Corones two, the which he bar in honde; And first to Cecile, as I understonde, He yaf that oon, and after gan he take That other to Valerian, hir make.	Valerian, going home, Cecilia found In chamber, wherein did an angel stand; This angel had two coronals, woven round Of roses and of lilies, in his hand; And to Cecilia, as I understand, He gave the one, and gave the other straight Unto this said Valerian, her mate.
"With body clene and with unwemmed thoght Kepeth ay wel thise corones," quod he; "Fro Paradys to yow have I hem broght, Ne never-mo ne shal they roten be, Ne lese her sote savour, trusteth me; Ne never wight shal seen hem with his yë, But he be chaast and hate vileinyë.	"With body clean and with unsullied thought Keep well these crowns for ever," then said he; "To you from Paradise have I them brought, Nor ever shall they fade or withered be, Nor lose their perfume sweet, so you trust me; And never man shall see them with his eye, Save he be chaste and hate depravity.
And thou, Valerian, for thou so sone Assentedest to good conseil also, Sey what thee list, and thou shalt han thy bone." "I have a brother," quod Valerian tho, "That in this world I love no man so. I pray yow that my brother may han grace To know the trouthe, as I do in this place."	"And you, Valerian, since you so soon Consented to accept the Faith also, Say what you will and you shall have your boon." "I have a brother," said Valerian, "Oh, And in the wide world I love no man so. I pray you that my brother may have grace To know the truth, as I do in this place."
The angel seyde, "god lyketh thy requeste, And bothe, with the palm of martirdom, Ye shullen come unto his blisful feste." And with that word Tiburce his brother com. And whan that he the savour undernom Which that the roses and the lilies caste, With-inne his herte he gan to wondre faste,	The angel answered: "God likes your request, And both of you, with palm of martyrdom, Shall come at last unto His blessed rest." Whereon his brother Tibertius was come. And when he smelled the sweet perfume that from The roses and the lilies filled the air, In heart he wondered much how came it there,
And seyde, "I wondre, this tyme of the yeer, Whennes that sote savour cometh so Of rose and lilies that I smelle heer. For though I hadde hem in myn hondes two, The savour mighte in me no depper go. The sote smel that in myn herte I finde Hath chaunged me al in another kinde."	And said: "I wonder much, this time of year, Whence comes the sweetness that arises so, Of rose and lily, to my senses here? For though I held them in my two hands—no The savour could in me no deeper go. The gentle scent that in my heart I find Has changed me to a man of other kind."
Valerian seyde, "two corones han we, Snow-whyte and rose-reed, that shynen clere,	Valerian replied: "Two crowns have we, Snow white and rose red, and they're bright and fair,

The which your two eyes have no power to see;
And as you smell them, brother, through my prayer,
So shall you see them also, brother dear,
If you but will, without delay forsooth,
Rightly believe and know the very truth."

Tibertius answered: "Say you this to me
In truth? Or do I dream I hear all this?"
"In dreams," replied Valerian, then, "have we
Lived to this time, O brother mine, ywis.
In truth now for the first time our life is."
"How know you?" asked Tibertius: "In what wise?"
Valerian said: "You will I now apprise.

"God's angel unto me the truth has taught,
Which you shall see, if only you'll put by
All idols and be clean, else you'll learn naught."
(And of these crowns miraculous, say I,
Saint Ambrose of the two does testify
In his Preface; this noble doctor dear
Commends the story, making it all clear:

The palm of martyrdom, thus to receive,
This Saint Cecilia, filled with God's gift,
The world and even her chamber did she leave;
Witness Tibertius' and Valerian's shrift,
To whom the good God sent by angel swift
Two crowns of flowers fair and sweet smelling,
And bade the angel take them as fitting.

The maiden brought these men to bliss above;
The world has learned what it is worth, 'tis plain,
Devotion to fair chastity to love.)
Then did Cecilia show him and explain
That every idol is a thing all vain;
For they are dumb, and they are deaf also,
And charged him that his idols he forgo.

"Whoso believes not this, a beast he is,"
Said then Tibertius, "if I shall not lie."
And then she kissed his breast, when she heard this,
And was full glad that truth he could espy.
"This day I take you for my own ally,"
So said this blessed, lovely maiden dear;
And after that said on as you shall hear:

"Lo, even as the love of Christ," said she,
"Made me your brother's wife, just in that wise
I take you now my close ally to be,
Since you'll forgo your idols and despise.
Go with your brother, let them you baptize
And make you clean; so that you may behold
The angel's face whereof your brother told."

Tibertius answered, saying: "Brother dear,
First tell me where to go and to what man."
"To whom?" said he, "Come forth, and with good cheer,
For I will lead you unto Pope Urban."
"To Urban? Brother mine, Valerian,"

Whiche that thyn yën han no might to see;
And as thou smellest hem thurgh my preyere,
So shaltow seen hem, leve brother dere,
If it so be thou wolt, withouten slouthe,
Bileve aright and knowen verray trouthe."

Tiburce answerde, "seistow this to me
In soothnesse, or in dreem I herkne this?"
"In dremes," quod Valerian, "han we be
Unto this tyme, brother myn, y-wis.
But now at erst in trouthe our dwelling is."
"How woostow this," quod Tiburce, "in what wyse?"
Quod Valerian, "that shal I thee devyse.

The angel of god hath me the trouthe y-taught
Which thou shalt seen, if that thou wolt reneye
The ydoles and be clene, and elles naught."—
And of the miracle of thise corones tweye
Seint Ambrose in his preface list to seye;
Solempnely this noble doctour dere
Commendeth it, and seith in this manere:

The palm of martirdom for to receyve,
Seinte Cecile, fulfild of goddes yifte,
The world and eek hir chambre gan she weyve;
Witnes Tyburces and Valerians shrifte,
To whiche god of his bountee wolde shifte
Corones two of floures wel smellinge,
And made his angel hem the corones bringe:

The mayde hath broght thise men to blisse above;
The world hath wist what it is worth, certeyn,
Devocioun of chastitee to love.—
Tho shewede him Cecile al open and pleyn
That alle ydoles nis but a thing in veyn;
For they been dombe, and therto they been deve,
And charged him his ydoles for to leve.

"Who so that troweth nat this, a beste he is,"
Quod tho Tiburce, "if that I shal nat lye."
And she gan kisse his brest, that herde this,
And was ful glad he coude trouthe espye.
"This day I take thee for myn allye,"
Seyde this blisful fayre mayde dere;
And after that she seyde as ye may here:

"Lo, right so as the love of Crist," quod she,
"Made me thy brotheres wyf, right in that wyse
Anon for myn allye heer take I thee,
Sin that thou wolt thyn ydoles despyse.
Go with thy brother now, and thee baptyse,
And make thee clene; so that thou mowe biholde
The angels face of which thy brother tolde."

Tiburce answerde and seyde, "brother dere,
First tel me whider I shal, and to what man?"
"To whom?" quod he, "com forth with right good chere,
I wol thee lede unto the pope Urban."
"Til Urban? brother myn Valerian,"

Quod tho Tiburce, "woltow me thider lede?
Me thinketh that it were a wonder dede.

Ne menestow nat Urban," quod he tho,
"That is so ofte dampned to be deed,
And woneth in halkes alwey to and fro,
And dar nat ones putte forth his heed?
Men sholde him brennen in a fyr so reed
If he were founde, or that men mighte him spye;
And we also, to bere him companye—

And whyl we seken thilke divinitee
That is y-hid in hevene prively,
Algate y-brend in this world shul we be!"
To whom Cecile answerde boldely,
"Men mighten dreden wel and skilfully
This lyf to lese, myn owene dere brother,
If this were livinge only and non other.

But ther is better lyf in other place,
That never shal be lost, ne drede thee noght,
Which goddes sone us tolde thurgh his grace;
That fadres sone hath alle thinges wroght;
And al that wroght is with a skilful thoght,
The goost, that fro the fader gan procede,
Hath sowled hem, withouten any drede.

By word and by miracle goddes sone,
Whan he was in this world, declared here
That ther was other lyf ther men may wone."
To whom answerde Tiburce, "O suster dere,
Ne seydestow right now in this manere,
Ther nis but o god, lord in soothfastnesse;
And now of three how maystow bere witnesse?"

"That shal I telle," quod she, "er I go.
Right as a man hath sapiences three,
Memorie, engyn, and intellect also,
So, in o being of divinitee,
Three persones may ther right wel be."
Tho gan she him ful bisily to preche
Of Cristes come and of his peynes teche,

And many pointes of his passioun;
How goddes sone in this world was withholde,
To doon mankinde pleyn remissioun,
That was y-bounde in sinne and cares colde:
Al this thing she unto Tiburce tolde.
And after this Tiburce, in good entente,
With Valerian to pope Urban he wente,

That thanked god; and with glad herte and light
He cristned him, and made him in that place
Parfit in his lerninge, goddes knight.
And after this Tiburce gat swich grace,
That every day he saugh, in tyme and space,
The angel of god; and every maner bone
That he god axed, it was sped ful sone.

It were ful hard by ordre for to seyn
How many wondres Jesus for hem wroghte;
But atte laste, to tellen short and pleyn,

Tibertius said, "and thither will you lead?
I think this were a wondrous thing indeed.

"Surely you mean not Urban!" he cried out,
"Who's been so often ordered to be dead,
And lives in corners, dodging ever about,
And dares not once by day to show his head?
Why, men would burn him in a fire right red
If he were found, or any him could spy;
And us, if we should bear him company.

"And while we seek for that Divinity
Who is in Heaven where we may not see,
Burned in this world to ashes shall we be!"
To whom Cecilia answered, and boldly:
"Men might well dread, and very reasonably,
This life on earth to lose, my own dear brother,
If this alone were living, and no other.

"But there's a better life in other place,
That never shall be lost, nay, fear you naught,
Whereof God's Son has told us, through His grace;
That Father's Son all things that He has wrought,
And all that is has made with reasoned thought,
The Spirit which from Father did proceed
Has given a soul to each, fear not indeed.

"By word and miracle God's only Son,
When He was in this world, declared us here
There was another life that could be won."
To whom replied Tibertius: "Sister dear,
Did you not say, just now, in manner clear,
There's but one God, the Lord in truth, no less;
And now to three, how can you bear witness?"

"That will I tell," said she, "before I go.
Just as a man has kinds of wisdom three,
Memory, genius, intellect also,
So in one Being of Divinity
Three Persons, truly may there right well be."
Then she to him full earnestly did preach
Of Jesus' coming, and of His pain did teach,

And many points His agony had shown:
How God's Son in this world a time did hold
To man a full remission to make known,
Who had been bound in sin and care of old:
All these things to Tibertius first she told.
And then Tibertius, with a good intent,
He with Valerian to Pope Urban went,

Who thanked God; and with a glad heart and light
He christened him, and made him in that place
Perfect in knowledge, and God's very knight.
And after this Tibertius got such grace
That every day he saw, in time and space,
God's angel; aye, and every kind of boon
He asked of God, the same was granted soon.

'Twere hard in proper order to explain
How many wonders Jesus for them wrought;
But at the last, to tell it short and plain,

They by the sergeants of Rome town were sought,
And to Almachius the prefect brought,
Who questioned them and learned their whole
intent,
And unto Jupiter's image had them sent,

Saying: "Who will not go and sacrifice,
Strike off his head, that is my sentence here."
These martyrs, then, of whom I do apprise,
One Maximus, who was an officer
Of the prefect's, and his corniculer,
Took them; and when the saints forth he had led,
Himself he wept, for pity that he had.

When Maximus had learned their creed and lore,
Of executioners obtained he leave,
And to his house he led them, without more;
And by their preaching, ere it came to eve,
They from the executioners did reave,
And Maximus and from his folk, each one,
The false faith, to believe in God alone.

Cecilia came, when it was fully night,
With priests, who christened them together there;
And afterward, when day came with its light,
Cecilia them bade, with steadfast cheer:
"Now Christ's own knights together, lief and dear,
The works of darkness cast you all away,
And arm you in the armour of the day.

"You have indeed fought the good fight—all hail!
Your course is done, your faith you have preserved,
Go to the crown of life that shall not fail;
The Righteous Judge, Whom you have so well
served,
Will give it to you, since you've it deserved."
And when, as I have told this thing was said,
To make the sacrifice they forth were led.

But when before the image they were brought,
Briefly to tell the end as it is known,
They'd not incense, and sacrificed they naught,
But on their knees they reverently knelt down,
With humble heart and firm devotion shown,
And so they lost their heads there in that place.
Their spirits went unto the King of Grace.

This Maximus, who saw this thing betide,
With pitying tears he told folk then, forthright,
That he their souls had seen to Heaven glide
With angels full of glory and of light,
And by his words converted many a wight;
For which Almachius had him beaten so,
With whips of lead, he did his life forgo.

Cecilia him buried with the others,
Valerian and Tibertius, quietly.
Thus in the tomb he rested with the brothers;
And after this Almachius speedily
Ordered his servants fetch him openly
Cecilia, that she might in his presence
Make sacrifice to Jove and burn incense.

The sergeants of the toun of Rome hem soghte,
And hem biforn Almache the prefect broghte,
Which hem apposed, and knew al hir
entente,
And to the image of Jupiter hem sente,

And seyde, "who so wol nat sacrifyse,
Swap of his heed, this is my sentence here."
Anon thise martirs that I yow devyse,
Oon Maximus, that was an officere
Of the prefectes and his corniculere,
Hem hente; and whan he forth the seintes ladde,
Him-self he weep, for pitee that he hadde.

Whan Maximus had herd the seintes lore,
He gat him of the tormentoures leve,
And ladde hem to his hous withoute more;
And with hir preching, er that it were eve,
They gonnen fro the tormentours to reve,
And fro Maxime, and fro his folk echone
The false feith, to trowe in god allone.

Cecilie cam, whan it was woxen night,
With preestes that hem cristned alle y-fere;
And afterward, whan day was woxen light,
Cecile hem seyde with a ful sobre chere,
"Now, Cristes owene knightes leve and dere,
Caste alle awey the werkes of derknesse,
And armeth yow in armure of brightnesse.

Ye han for sothe y-doon a greet bataille,
Your cours is doon, your feith han ye conserved,
Goth to the corone of lyf that may nat faille;
The rightful juge, which that ye han
served,
Shall yeve it yow, as ye han it deserved."
And whan this thing was seyd as I devyse,
Men ladde hem forth to doon the sacrifyse.

But whan they weren to the place broght,
To tellen shortly the conclusioun,
They nolde encense ne sacrifice right noght,
But on hir knees they setten hem adoun
With humble herte and sad devocioun,
And losten bothe hir hedes in the place.
Hir soules wenten to the king of grace.

This Maximus, that saugh this thing bityde,
With pitous teres tolde it anon-right,
That he hir soules saugh to heven glyde
With angels ful of cleernesse and of light,
And with his word converted many a wight;
For which Almachius dide him so to-bete
With whippe of leed, til he his lyf gan lete.

Cecile him took and buried him anoon
By Tiburce and Valerian softely,
Withinne hir burying-place, under the stoon.
And after this Almachius hastily
Bad his ministres fecchen openly
Cecile, so that she mighte in his presence
Doon sacrifyce, and Jupiter encense.

But they, converted at hir wyse lore,
Wepten ful sore, and yaven ful credence
Unto hir word, and cryden more and more,
"Crist, goddes sone withouten difference,
Is verray god, this is al our sentence,
That hath so good a servant him to serve;
This with o voys we trowen, thogh we sterve!"

Almachius, that herde of this doinge,
Bad fecchen Cecile, that he might hir see,
And alderfirst, lo! this was his axinge,
"What maner womman artow?" tho quod he.
"I am a gentil womman born," quod she.
"I axe thee," quod he, "thogh it thee greve,
Of thy religioun and of thy bileve."

"Ye han bigonne your question folily,"
Quod she, "that wolden two answeres conclude
In oo demande; ye axed lewedly."
Almache answerde unto that similitude,
"Of whennes comth thyn answering so rude?"
"Of whennes?" quod she, whan that she was freyned,
"Of conscience and of good feith unfeyned."

Almachius seyde, "ne takestow non hede
Of my power?" and she answerde him this—
"Your might," quod she, "ful litel is to drede;
For every mortal mannes power nis
But lyk a bladdre, ful of wind, y-wis.
For with a nedles poynt, whan it is blowe,
May al the boost of it be leyd ful lowe."

"Ful wrongfully bigonne thou," quod he,
"And yet in wrong is thy perseveraunce;
Wostow nat how our mighty princes free
Han thus comanded and maad ordinaunce,
That every Cristen wight shal han penaunce
But-if that he his Cristendom withseye,
And goon al quit, if he wol it reneye?"

"Your princes erren, as your nobley dooth,"
Quod tho Cecile, "and with a wood sentence
Ye make us gilty, and it is nat sooth;
For ye, that knowen wel our innocence,
For as muche as we doon a reverence
To Crist, and for we bere a Cristen name,
Ye putte on us a cryme, and eek a blame.

But we that knowen thilke name so
For vertuous, we may it nat withseye."
Almache answerde, "chees oon of thise two,
Do sacrifyce, or Cristendom reneye,
That thou mowe now escapen by that weye."
At which the holy blisful fayre mayde
Gan for to laughe, and to the juge seyde,

"O juge, confus in thy nycetee,
Woltow that I reneye innocence,
To make me a wikked wight?" quod she;
"Lo! he dissimuleth here in audience,

But since they were converted by her lore,
They wept, and to a full belief they came
In what she said, and cried out more and more,
"O Christ, God's Son, Whose substance is the same,
Thou'rt very God, and blessed be Thy name,
Who hast so good a servant Thee to serve;
This with one voice we say, nor will we swerve."

Almachius, who heard of this same thing,
Commanded that they bring her him to see,
And when she came, this was his questioning:
"What manner of woman are you?" then asked he.
"I am a noblewoman born," said she.
"I ask," said he, "though to your harm and grief,
Of your religion and of your belief."

"You have begun your questions foolishly,"
Said she, "who would two answers so include
In one demand; you asked me ignorantly."
Almachius answered that exactitude:
"Whence comes your answering so rough and rude?"
"Whence?" asked she, when that she was thus constrained,
"From conscience and from simple faith unfeigned."

Almachius said: "And do you take no heed
Of power I wield?" And she replied like this:
"Your might," said she, "is scarce a thing to dread;
For power of every mortal man but is
Like to a bladder full of wind, ywis.
For with a needle's point, when it is blown,
Prick it, and all the pride of it comes down."

"Erroneously have you begun," said he,
"And deep in error do you still remain;
Know you not how our mighty princes free
Have ordered us such error to restrain,
That every Christian man shall suffer pain,
Unless his Christianity he deny?
He shall be free if he'll do that, say I."

"Your princes err, and your nobility,"
Cecilia said, "and with a mad sentence
Condemn our guilt all guiltless though we be;
And you, who know full well our innocence,
Merely because we do our reverence
To Christ and bear ourselves the Christian name,
You thus impute to us a crime and blame.

"But we, who know far better than can you
Its virtue, will not once the name gainsay."
Almachius said: "Choose one of these things two:
Deny that faith, or sacrifice today,
That you may now escape from death that way."
Whereat the holy, blessed, lovely maid
Began to laugh, and to the judge she said:

"O judge, convicted by your own folly,
Will you that I deny my innocence
And make myself a criminal?" asked she.
"Lo, he dissimulates in audience,

He glares and rages in his violence!"
To whom Almachius: "O unhappy wretch,
Do you not know how far my might may stretch?

"Did not our mighty princes to me give,
Aye, both the power and authority
To give to people death or make them live?
Why do you speak so proudly then to me?"
"I speak to you but steadfastly," said she,
"Not proudly, for I say, upon my side,
We've deadly hatred for the vice of pride.

"And if to hear a truth you do not fear,
Then will I show, all openly, by right,
That you have said a full great falsehood here.
You say, your princes have you given the might
Both to condemn and give life to a wight;
But you can merely him of life bereave,
You have no other power or other leave!

"You may but say, your princes did declare
You were death's officer; if more you claim,
You lie, for of more power you are bare."
"This bold speech drop!" Almachius did exclaim,
"And do your sacrifice in our gods' name,
I care not what you wrongfully impute;
Like a philospher I'll bear it, mute;

"But those same wrongs which I cannot endure
Are those you speak against our gods," said he.
Cecilia replied: "O vain creature,
You've nothing said, since speaking first to me,
That I've not learned thereby your great folly,
And that you were and are, in every wise,
An ignorant officer and vain justice.

"There is no proving, by your outward eye,
That you're not blind; what can be seen by all,
That it is stone—that men see well, say I—
Yet that same stone a god you think and call.
I charge you, let your hand upon it fall,
And test it well, and 'twill be stone, you'll find,
Since you can see it not with your eyes blind.

"It is a shame that all the people shall
So scorn you, judge, and laugh at your folly;
For commonly men know it above all
That mighty God is in His heaven high,
And idols such as these, they testify,
May bring no profit to themselves or you—
They have no power, nothing can they do."

These words and many other such said she,
And he grew wroth and bade she should be led
Home to her house. "And in her house," said he,
"Boil her in bath heated by great flames red."
And as he bade, so was it done, 'tis said;
For in a bath they locked her and began
(All night and day) a great fire to fan.

The long night through, and a long day also,
For all the fire and all the bath's great heat,

He stareth and woodeth in his advertence!"
To whom Almachius, "unsely wrecche,
Ne woostow nat how far my might may strecche?

Han noght our mighty princes to me yeven,
Ye, bothe power and auctoritee
To maken folk to dyen or to liven?
Why spekestow so proudly than to me?"
"I speke noght but stedfastly," quod she,
"Nat proudly, for I seye, as for my syde,
We haten deedly thilke vyce of pryde.

And if thou drede nat a sooth to here,
Than wol I shewe al openly, by right,
That thou hast maad a ful gret lesing here.
Thou seyst, thy princes han thee yeven might
Bothe for to sleen and for to quiken a wight;
Thou, that ne mayst but only lyf bireve,
Thou hast non other power ne no leve!

But thou mayst seyn, thy princes han thee maked
Ministre of deeth; for if thou speke of mo,
Thou lyest, for thy power is ful naked."
"Do wey thy boldnes," seyde Almachius tho,
"And sacrifyce to our goddes, er thou go;
I recche nat what wrong that thou me profre,
For I can suffre it as a philosophre;

But thilke wronges may I nat endure
That thou spekest of our goddes here," quod he.
Cecile answerede, "O nyce creature,
Thou seydest no word sin thou spak to me
That I ne knew therwith thy nycetee;
And that thou were, in every maner wyse,
A lewed officer and a veyn justyse.

Ther lakketh no-thing to thyn utter yën
That thou nart blind, for thing that we seen alle
That it is stoon, that men may wel espyen,
That ilke stoon a god thou wolt it calle.
I rede thee, lat thyn hand upon it falle,
And taste it wel, and stoon thou shalt it finde,
Sin that thou seest nat with thyn yën blinde.

It is a shame that the peple shal
So scorne thee, and laughe at thy folye;
For comunly men woot it wel overal,
That mighty god is in his hevenes hye,
And thise images, wel thou mayst espye,
To thee ne to hem-self mowe nought profyte,
For in effect they been nat worth a myte."

Thise wordes and swiche othere seyde she,
And he weex wroth, and bad men sholde hir lede
Hom til hir hous, "and in hir hous," quod he,
"Brenne hir right in a bath of flambes rede."
And as he bad, right so was doon in dede;
For in a bath they gonne hir faste shetten,
And night and day greet fyr they under betten.

The longe night and eek a day also,
For al the fyr and eek the bathes hete,

She sat al cold, and felede no wo,
It made hir nat a drope for to swete.
But in that bath hir lyf she moste lete;
For he, Almachius, with ful wikke entente
To sleen hir in the bath his sonde sente.

Three strokes in the nekke he smoot hir tho,
The tormentour, but for no maner chaunce
He mighte noght smyte al hir nekke a-two;
And for ther was that tyme an ordinaunce,
That no man sholde doon man swich penaunce
The ferthe strook to smyten, softe or sore,
This tormentour ne dorste do na-more.

But half-deed, with hir nekke y-corven there,
He lefte hir lye, and on his wey is went.
The Cristen folk, which that aboute hir were,
With shetes han the blood ful faire y-hent.
Three dayes lived she in this torment,
And never cessed hem the feith to teche;
That she hadde fostred, hem she gan to preche;

And hem she yaf hir moebles and hir thing,
And to the pope Urban bitook hem tho.
And seyde, "I axed this at hevene king,
To han respyt three dayes and na-mo,
To recomende to yow, er that I go,
Thise soules, lo! and that I mighte do werche
Here of myn hous perpetuelly a cherche."

Seint Urban, with his deknes, prively
The body fette, and buried it by nighte
Among his othere seintes honestly.
Hir hous the chirche of seint Cecilie highte;
Seint Urban halwed it, as he wel mighte;
In which, into this day, in noble wyse,
Men doon to Crist and to his seint servyse.

She sat there cool and calm and felt no woe,
Nor did it make her any drop to sweat.
But in that bath her life should she lose yet;
For he, Almachius, with bad intent,
To slay her in the bath his headsman sent.

The executioner three times her smote
Upon the neck, and could not strike again,
Although he failed to cut in two her throat,
For at that time the ordinance was plain
That no man might another give the pain
Of striking four blows, whether soft or sore;
This executioner dared do no more.

But half dead, with her neck cut three times there,
He let her lie, and on his way he went.
The Christian folk that all about her were,
With sheets caught up the precious blood she spent;
And three days lived she in this same torment,
But never ceased at all the faith to teach,
That she had fostered; dying did she preach;

To them she gave her goods and everything,
And of Pope Urban put them in the care,
And said: "This much I asked of Heaven's King,
A respite of three days, that you might share
With me these souls; and too I would prepare
Before I go my house a church to make.
That it be kept forever for my sake."

Saint Urban, with his deacons, privately,
The body took and buried it by night
Among his other saints, right honourably.
Her house is Church of Saint Cecilia hight;
Saint Urban hallowed it, as well he might;
Wherein in noble wise unto this day
To Christ and to His saint men service pay.

HERE IS ENDED THE SECOND NUN'S TALE

THE CANON'S YEOMAN'S PROLOGUE

THE PROLOGUE OF THE CANON'S YEOMAN'S TALE

WHAN ended was the lyf of seint Cecyle,
Er we had riden fully fyve myle,
At Boghton under Blee us gan atake
A man, that clothed was in clothes blake,
And undernethe he hadde a whyt surplys.
His hakeney, that was al pomely grys,
So swatte, that it wonder was to see;
It semed he had priked myles three.
The hors eek that his yeman rood upon
So swatte, that unnethe mighte it gon.
Aboute the peytrel stood the foom ful hye,
He was of fome al flekked as a pye.
A male tweyfold on his croper lay,
It semed that he caried lyte array.
Al light for somer rood this worthy man,
And in myn herte wondren I bigan
What that he was, til that I understood

WHEN Saint Cecilia's Life was done, and whiles
We had not farther gone a good five miles,
At Boughton-under-Blean us did o'ertake
A man, who was clothed all in clothes of black,
And underneath he had a surplice white.
His hackney was of dappled-grey, so bright
With sweat that it was marvelous to see;
It seemed that he had spurred him for miles three,
The horse too that his yeoman rode upon
So sweat that scarcely could it go; and on
The breast strap of the harness foam stood high,
Whereof he was as flecked as is a pie.
A double wallet on his crupper lay,
And as it seemed, he went in light array.
Lightly, for summer, rode this worthy man,
And in my heart to wonder I began
What he could be, until I understood

The way he had his cloak sewed to his hood;
From which, when long I had communed with me,
I judged at length some canon he must be.
His hat hung on his back down by a lace,
For he had ridden more than trot or pace;
He had spurred hard, indeed, as madman would.
A burdock leaf he had beneath his hood
To curb the sweat and keep his head from heat.
But what a joy it was to see him sweat!
His forehead dripped as a distillatory
Were full of plantain and of pellitory.
And this man when he came began to cry:
"God save," said he, "this jolly company!
Fast I have spurred," said he then, "for your sake,
Because I wanted you to overtake,
To ride on in this merry company."
His yeoman too was full of courtesy,
And said: "Good sirs, all in the morningtide
Out of your hostelry I saw you ride,
And warned my lord and master, full and plain,
And he to ride with you is truly fain
For his amusement; he loves dalliance."
"Friend, for your warning, God give you good chance,"
Said then our host, "for truly it would seem
Your lord is wise, and so I may well deem;
He is right jocund also, I dare lay.
Can he a merry tale tell, on the way,
Wherewith to gladden this our company?"
"Who, sir? My lord? Yea, yea, without a lie,
He knows of mirth and of all jollity
Not but enough; and also, sir, trust me,
If you but knew him as well as do I,
You'd wonder much how well and craftily
He can behave, and that in different wise.
He's taken on him many an enterprise
That were right hard for anyone that's here
(Unless he learned it) to effect, I fear.
As plainly as he rides, here among you,
It would be to your profit if you knew
Him well; you'd not give up his acquaintance
For much of wealth, I dare lay in balance
All that I have of goods in my possession.
He is a man of wondrous high discretion,
I warn you well, he's a surpassing man."
"Well," said our host, "then pray tell, if you can,
Is he a clerk, or not? Tell what he is."
"Nay, he is greater than a clerk, ywis,"
This yeoman said, "and briefly, if you'll wait,
Host, of his craft a little I'll relate.
"I say, my lord has so much subtlety
(But all his art you cannot learn from me,
And yet I help by working at his side),
That all this pleasant land through which we ride,
From here right into Canterbury town,
Why, he could turn it all clean upside-down
And pave it all with silver and with gold."
And when this yeoman had this story told
Unto our host, our host said: "*Ben'cite!*
This thing is wondrous marvelous to me,
Since your lord is a man of such science,
For which men should hold him in reverence,

How that his cloke was sowed to his hood;
For which, when I had longe avysed me,
I demed him som chanon for to be.
His hat heng at his bak doun by a laas,
For he had riden more than trot or paas;
He had ay priked lyk as he were wood.
A clote-leef he hadde under his hood
For swoot, and for to kepe his heed from hete.
But it was joye for to seen him swete!
His forheed dropped as a stillatorie,
Were ful of plantain and of paritorie.
And whan that he was come, he gan to crye,
"God save," quod he, "this joly companye!
Faste have I priked," quod he, "for your sake,
By-cause that I wolde yow atake,
To ryden in this mery companye."
His yeman eek was ful of curteisye,
And seyde, "sires, now in the morwe-tyde
Out of your hostelrye I saugh you ryde,
And warned heer my lord and my soverayn,
Which that to ryden with yow is ful fayn,
For his desport; he loveth daliaunce."
"Freend, for thy warning god yeve thee good chaunce,"
Than seyde our host, "for certes, it wolde seme
Thy lord were wys, and so I may wel deme;
He is ful jocund also, dar I leye.
Can he oght telle a mery tale or tweye,
With which he glade may this companye?"
"Who, sire? my lord? ye, ye, withouten lye,
He can of murthe, and eek of jolitee
Nat but ynough; also sir, trusteth me,
And ye him knewe as wel as do I,
Ye wolde wondre how wel and craftily
He coude werke, and that in sondry wyse.
He hath take on him many a greet empryse,
Which were ful hard for any that is here
To bringe aboute, but they of him it lere.
As homely as he rit amonges yow,
If ye him knewe, it wolde be for your prow;
Ye wolde nat forgoon his aqueyntaunce
For mochel good, I dar leye in balaunce
Al that I have in my possessioun.
He is a man of heigh discrecioun,
I warne you wel, he is a passing man."
"Wel," quod our host, "I pray thee, tel me than,
Is he a clerk, or noon? tel what he is."
"Nay, he is gretter than a clerk, y-wis,"
Seyde this yeman, "and in wordes fewe,
Host, of his craft som-what I wol yow shewe.
I seye, my lord can swich subtilitee—
(But al his craft ye may nat wite at me;
And som-what helpe I yet to his werking)—
That al this ground on which we been ryding,
Til that we come to Caunterbury toun,
He coude al clene turne it up-so-doun,
And pave it al of silver and of gold."
And whan this yeman hadde thus y-told
Unto our host, he seyde, "'*ben'cite!*
This thing is wonder merveillous to me,
Sin that thy lord is of so heigh prudence,
By-cause of which men sholde him reverence,

That of his worship rekketh he so lyte;
His oversloppe nis nat worth a myte,
As in effect, to him, so mote I go!
It is al baudy and to-tore also.
Why is thy lord so sluttish, I thee preye,
And is of power better cloth to beye,
If that his dede accorde with thy speche?
Telle me that, and that I thee biseche."
"Why?" quod this yeman, "wherto axe ye me?
God help me so, for he shal never thee!
(But I wol nat avowe that I seye,
And therfor kepe it secree, I yow preye).
He is to wys, in feith, as I bileve;
That that is overdoon, it wol nat preve
Aright, as clerkes seyn, it is a vyce.
Wherfor in that I holde him lewed and nyce.
For whan a man hath over-greet a wit,
Ful oft him happeth to misusen it;
So dooth my lord, and that me greveth sore.
God it amende, I can sey yow na-more."
"Ther-of no fors, good yeman," quod our host;
"Sin of the conning of thy lord thou wost,
Tel how he dooth, I pray thee hertely,
Sin that he is so crafty and so sly.
Wher dwellen ye, if it to telle be?"
"In the suburbes of a toun," quod he,
"Lurkinge in hernes and in lanes blinde,
Wher-as thise robbours and thise theves by kinde
Holden hir privee fereful residence,
As they that dar nat shewen hir presence;
So faren we, if I shal seye the sothe."
"Now," quod our host, "yit lat me talke to the;
Why artow so discoloured of thy face?"
"Peter!" quod he, "god yeve it harde grace,
I am so used in the fyr to blowe,
That it hath chaunged my colour, I trowe.
I am nat wont in no mirour to prye,
But swinke sore and lerne multiplye.[1]
We blondren ever and pouren in the fyr,
And for al that we fayle of our desyr,
For ever we lakken our conclusioun.
To mochel folk we doon illusioun,
And borwe gold, be it a pound or two,
Or ten, or twelve, or many sommes mo,
And make hem wenen, at the leeste weye,
That of a pound we coude make tweye!
Yet is it fals, but ay we han good hope
It for to doon, and after it we grope.
But that science is so fer us biforn,
We mowen nat, al-though we hadde it sworn,
It overtake, it slit awey so faste;
It wol us maken beggers atte laste."
Whyl this yeman was thus in his talking,
This chanoun drough him neer, and herde al thing
Which this yeman spak, for suspecioun
Of mennes speche ever hadde this chanoun.
For Catoun seith, that he that gilty is
Demeth al thing be spoke of him, y-wis.
That was the cause he gan so ny him drawe

That of his dignity his care's so slight;
His over-garment is not worth a mite
For such a man as he, so may I go!
It is all dirty and it's torn also.
Why is your lord so slovenly, pray I,
And yet has power better clothes to buy,
If but his deeds accord well with your speech?
Tell me that, sir, and that I do beseech."
"Why?" asked this yeoman, "Why ask this of me?
God help me, wealthy he will never be!
(But I will not stand back of what I say,
And therefore keep it secret, I you pray).
He is too wise, in faith, as I believe;
That which is overdone, as I conceive,
Won't turn out right, clerks say, and that's a vice.
In that, I hold him ignorantly nice.
For when a man has overmuch of wit,
It often happens he misuses it;
So does my lord, and this thing grieves me sore.
May God amend it, I can say no more."
"No matter then, good yeoman," said our host;
"Since of the learning of your lord you boast,
Tell how he works, I pray you heartily,
Since he's so clever and withal so sly.
Where do you dwell, if you may tell it me?"
"Within the suburbs of a town, "said he,
"Lurking in corners and in alleys blind,
Wherein these thieves and robbers, every kind,
Have all their privy fearful residence,
As those who dare not show men their presence;
So do we live, if I'm to tell the truth."
"Now, "said our host, "let me go on, forsooth.
Why are you so discoloured in the face?"
"Peter!" cried he, "God give it evil grace!
I am so wont upon the fire to blow
That it has changed my colour, as I trow.
I'm not wont in a mirror, sir, to pry,
But I work hard to learn to multiply.[1]
We stir and mix and stare into the fire,
But for all that we fail of our desire,
And never do we come to our conclusion.
To many folk we bring about illusion,
And borrow gold, perhaps a pound or two,
Or ten, or twelve, or any sum will do,
And make them think, aye, at the least, it's plain,
That from a pound of gold we can make twain!
It is all false, but yet we have great hope
That we can do it, and after it we grope.
But that science is so far us before,
We never can, in spite of all we swore,
Come up with it, it slides away so fast;
And it will make us beggars at the last."
The while this yeoman chattered on like this,
The canon nearer drew and did not miss
A thing he said; suspicion always woke
In him, indeed, when anybody spoke.
For Cato says suspicion's ever fed
In any guilty man when aught is said.
That was the reason why he drew so near

[1]To increase gold or silver in amount by alchemy.

To his yeoman, his gossiping to hear.
And thus he said unto his yeoman then:
"Now hold your peace and do not speak again,
For if you do you'll pay it ruefully;
You slander me, here in this company,
And you uncover that which you should hide."
"Yea?" said our host, "Tell on, whate'er betide;
For all his threatening do not care a mite!"
"In faith," said he, "my caring is but slight."
And when this canon saw how it would be,
That his yeoman would tell his privity,
He fled away for very grief and shame.
"Ah, "said the yeoman, "hence shall come a game.
All that I know anon now will I tell.
Since he is gone, the Fiend take him to Hell!
With him hereafter I'll have naught to do
For penny or for pound, I promise you!
He that first brought me into that ill game,
Before he die, sorrow have he and shame!
For it's no game to me, sirs, by my fay;
That I feel well, whatever man may say.
And yet, for all my smart and all my grief,
For all the sorrow, labour, and mischief,
I never could leave off, in any wise.
Now would to God that my wit might suffice
To tell of all pertaining to that art!
Nevertheless, I will relate a part;
Since now my lord is gone, I will not spare;
The things I know about I will declare."

To his yeman, to herknen al his sawe.
And thus he seyde un-to his yeman tho,
"Hold thou thy pees, and spek no wordes mo,
For if thou do, thou shalt it dere abye;
Thou sclaundrest me heer in this companye,
And eek discoverest that thou sholdest hyde."
"Ye," quod our host, "telle on, what so bityde;
Of al his threting rekke nat a myte!"
"In feith," quod he, "namore I do but lyte."
And whan this chanon saugh it wolde nat be,
But his yeman wolde telle his privetee,
He fledde awey for verray sorwe and shame.
"A!" quod the yeman, "heer shal aryse game,
Al that I can anon now wol I telle.
Sin he is goon, the foule feend him quelle!
For never her-after wol I with him mete
For peny ne for pound, I yow bihete!
He that me broghte first unto that game,
Er that he dye, sorwe have he and shame!
For it is ernest to me, by my feith;
That fele I wel, what so any man seith.
And yet, for al my smerte and al my grief,
For al my sorwe, labour, and meschief,
I coude never leve it in no wyse.
Now wolde god my wit mighte suffyse
To tellen al that longeth to that art!
But natheles yow wol I tellen part;
Sin that my lord is gon, I wol nat spare;
Swich thing as that I knowe, I wol declare."—

HERE ENDETH THE PROLOGUE OF THE CANON'S YEOMAN'S TALE

THE CANON'S YEOMAN'S TALE

HERE BEGINNETH THE CANON'S YEOMAN HIS TALE

First Part

SEVEN years I've served this canon, but no more
I know about his science than before.
All that I had I have quite lost thereby;
And, God knows, so have many more than I.
Where I was wont to be right fresh and gay
Of clothing and of other good array,
Now may I wear my old hose on my head;
And where my colour was both fresh and red,
Now it is wan and of a leaden hue;
Whoso this science follows, he shall rue.
And from my toil yet bleary is my eye,
Behold the gain it is to multiply!
That slippery science has made me so bare
That I've no goods, wherever I may fare;
And I am still indebted so thereby
For gold that I have borrowed, truthfully,
That while I live I shall repay it never.
Let every man be warned by me for ever!
And any man who casts his lot thereon,
If he continue, I hold his thrift gone.
So help me God, thereby he shall not win,
But empty purse and have his wits grow thin.
And when he, through his madness and folly,
Has lost his own, by willing jeopardy,

WITH this chanoun I dwelt have seven yeer,
And of his science am I never the neer.
Al that I hadde, I have y-lost ther-by;
And god wot, so hath many mo than I.
Ther I was wont to be right fresh and gay
Of clothing and of other good array,
Now may I were an hose upon myn heed;
And wher my colour was bothe fresh and reed,
Now is it wan and of a leden hewe;
Who-so it useth, sore shal he rewe.
And of my swink yet blered is myn yë,
Lo! which avantage is to multiplye!
That slyding science hath me maad so bare,
That I have no good, wher that ever I fare;
And yet I am endetted so ther-by
Of gold that I have borwed, trewely,
That whyl I live, I shal it quyte never.
Lat every man be war by me for ever!
What maner man that casteth him ther-to,
If he continue, I holde his thrift y-do.
So helpe me god, ther-by shal he nat winne,
But empte his purs, and make his wittes thinne.
And whan he, thurgh his madnes and folye,
Hath lost his owene good thurgh jupartye,

Thanne he excyteth other folk ther-to,
To lese hir good as he him-self hath do.
For unto shrewes joye it is and ese
To have hir felawes in peyne and disese;
Thus was I ones lerned of a clerk.
Of that no charge, I wol speke of our werk.
When we been ther as we shul exercyse
Our elvish craft, we semen wonder wyse,
Our termes been so clergial and so queynte.
I blowe the fyr til that myn herte feynte.

What sholde I tellen ech proporcioun
Of thinges whiche that we werche upon,
As on fyve or sixe ounces, may wel be,
Of silver or som other quantitee,
And bisie me to telle yow the names
Of orpiment, brent bones, yren squames,
That into poudre grounden been ful smal?
And in an erthen potte how put is al,
And salt y-put in, and also papeer,
Biforn thise poudres that I speke of heer,
And wel y-covered with a lampe of glas,
And mochel other thing which that ther was?
And of the pot and glasses enluting,
That of the eyre mighte passe out no-thing?
And of the esy fyr and smart also,
Which that was maad, and of the care and wo
That we hadde in our matires sublyming,
And in amalgaming and calcening
Of quik-silver, y-clept Mercurie crude?
For alle our sleightes we can nat conclude.
Our orpiment and sublymed Mercurie,
Our grounden litarge eek on the porphurie,
Of ech of thise of ounces a certeyn
Nought helpeth us, our labour is in veyn.
Ne eek our spirites ascencioun,
Ne our materes that lyen al fixe adoun,
Mowe in our werking no-thing us avayle.
For lost is al our labour and travayle,
And al the cost, a twenty devel weye,
Is lost also, which we upon it leye.
Ther is also ful many another thing
That is unto our craft apertening;
Though I by ordre hem nat reherce can,
By-cause that I am a lewed man,
Yet wol I telle hem as they come to minde,
Though I ne can nat sette hem in hir kinde;
As bole armoniak, verdegrees, boras,
And sondry vessels maad of erthe and glas,
Our urinales and our descensories,
Violes, croslets, and sublymatories,
Cucurbites, and alembykes eek,
And othere swiche, dere y-nough a leek.
Nat nedeth it for to reherce hem alle,
Watres rubifying and boles galle,
Arsenik, sal armoniak, and brimstoon;
And herbes coude I telle eek many oon,
As egremoine, valerian, and lunarie,
And othere swiche, if that me liste tarie.
Our lampes brenning bothe night and day,
To bringe about our craft, if that we may.
Our fourneys eek of calcinacioun,

Then will he incite others, many a one,
To lose their wealth as he himself has done.
For unto scoundrels it's a pleasant thing
Their fellows in distress and pain to bring,
Thus was I taught once by a learned clerk.
Of that no matter, I'll speak of our work.
When we are where we choose to exercise
Our elvish craft, why, we seem wondrous wise,
Our terms are all so learned and so quaint.
I blow the fire till my heart's like to faint.

Why tell you what proportions of things went
In working out each new experiment,
As five ounces, or six, it may well be,
Of silver, or some other quantity?
Or tell you all the names, my memory fails,
Of orpiment, burnt bones, and iron scales
That into powder we ground fine and small?
Or in an earthen pot how we put all,
And salt put in, and also pepper dear,
Before these powders that I speak of here,
And covered all these with a plate of glass,
And of the various other gear there was?
And of the sealing of the pot and glass,
So that the air might no way from it pass?
And of the slow fire and the forced also,
Which we made there, and of the care and woe
That we took in our matter's sublimating,
And in calcining and amalgamating
Quicksilver, which is known as mercury crude?
For all our skill, we never could conclude.
Our orpiment and sublimed mercury,
Our litharge that we ground on porphyry,
Of each some certain ounces—it is plain
Naught helped us, all our labour was in vain.
Neither the gases that by nature rose
Nor solid matter either—none of those
Might, in our working, anything avail.
For lost was all our labour and travail,
And all the cost, the devil's own to pay,
Was lost also, for we made no headway.
There is also full many another thing
That to our craft pertains in labouring.
Though name them properly I never can,
Because, indeed, I am an ignorant man,
Yet will I tell them as they come to mind,
Though I'll not try to class each one by kind;
Armenian bole, borax, the green of brass,
And sundry vessels made of earth and glass,
Our urinals and all our descensories,
Vials and crucibles, sublimatories,
Cucurbites, and alembics, and such freaks,
All dear enough if valued at two leeks.
There is no need to specify them all,
The reddening waters and the dark bull's gall,
Arsenic, sal ammoniac, and brimstone;
And, too, of herbs could I name many a one,
Valerian, agrimony, and lunary,
And others such, if I but wished to tarry.
Our lamps that burned by day and burned by night
To bring about our end, if but we might,
Our furnace, too, white-hot for calcination,

And waters all prepared for albication,
Unslaked lime, chalk, and white of egg, I say,
Powders diverse, and ashes, dung, piss, clay,
Little waxed bags, saltpetre, vitriol;
And many a different fire of wood and coal;
Alkali, salt, potassium carbonate,
And our burnt matters, and coagulate,
Clay mixed with horses' or men's hair, and oil
Of tartar, alum, glass, yeast, wort, argoil,
Realgar, and our matters absorbent,
And with them, too, our matters resorbent,
And how we practised silver citrination
And our cementing and our fermentation,
Our moulds and testers, aye, and many more.
I will tell you, as I was taught before,
The bodies seven and the spirits four,
In order, as my master named of yore.
The first of spirits, then, quicksilver is,
The second arsenic, the third, ywis,
Is sal ammoniac, the fourth brimstone.
The seven bodies I'll describe anon:
Sol, gold is, Luna's silver, as we see,
Mars iron, and quicksilver's Mercury,
Saturn is lead, and Jupiter is tin,
And Venus copper, by my father's kin!
This wicked craft, whoso will exercise,
He shall gain never wealth that may suffice;
For all the coin he spends therein goes out
And is but lost, of which I have no doubt.
Whoso, then, will exhibit such folly,
Let him come forth and learn to multiply;
And every man that has aught in coffer,
Let him appear and be philosopher.
Perhaps that craft is easy to acquire?
Nay, nay, God knows! And be he monk or friar
Canon, or priest, or any other wight,
Though he sit at his books both day and night
In learning of this elvish, fruitless lore,
All is in vain, and by gad it's much more!
To teach an ignorant man this subtlety—
Fie! Speak not of it, for it cannot be;
And though he has booklore, or though he's none,
In final count he shall find it all one.
For both of them, and this by my salvation,
Come to one end seeking multiplication;
They fare the same when they've done everything;
That is to say, they both fail, sorrowing.
Yet I forgot to tell you in detail
Of the corrosive waters and limaille,
And some of bodies the mollification,
And on the other hand of induration,
Oils, and ablutions, metals fusible—
More than a bible it would need to tell,
The largest ever; therefore I think best
That of these names I say no more, but rest.
For I believe that I've told you enough
To raise a devil, be he never so rough.
Ah no! Let be; the old philosopher's stone
Is called elixir, which we seek, each one;
For had we that, then were we safe enow.
But unto God in Heaven do I vow,
For all our art, when we've done all things thus,

And of watres albificacioun,
Unslekked lym, chalk, and gleyre of an ey,
Poudres diverse, asshes, dong, pisse, and cley,
Cered pokets, sal peter, vitriole;
And divers fyres maad of wode and cole;
Sal tartre, alkaly, and sal preparat,
And combust materes and coagulat,
Cley maad with hors or mannes heer, and oile
Of tartre, alum, glas, berm, wort, and argoile,
Resalgar, and our materes enbibing;
And eek of our materes encorporing,
And of our silver citrinacioun,
Our cementing and fermentacioun,
Our ingottes, testes, and many mo.
I wol yow telle, as was me taught also,
The foure spirites and the bodies sevene,
By ordre, as ofte I herde my lord hem nevene.
The firste spirit quik-silver called is,
The second orpiment, the thridde, y-wis,
Sal armoniak, and the ferthe brimstoon.
The bodies sevene eek, lo! hem heer anoon:
Sol gold is, and Luna silver we threpe,
Mars yren, Mercurie quik-silver we clepe,
Saturnus leed, and Jupiter is tin,
And Venus coper, by my fader kin!
This cursed craft who-so wol exercyse,
He shal no good han that him may suffyse;
For al the good he spendeth ther-aboute,
He lese shal, ther-of have I no doute.
Who-so that listeth outen his folye,
Lat him come forth, and lerne multiplye;
And every man that oght hath in his cofre,
Lat him appere, and wexe a philosofre.
Ascaunce that craft is so light to lere?
Nay, nay, god woot, al be he monk or frere,
Preest or chanoun, or any other wight,
Though he sitte at his book bothe day and night,
In lernyng of this elvish nyce lore,
Al is in veyn, and parde, mochel more!
To lerne a lewed man this subtiltee,
Fy! spek nat ther-of, for it wol nat be;
Al conne he letterure, or conne he noon,
As in effect, he shal finde it al oon.
For bothe two, by my savacioun,
Concluden, in multiplicacioun,
Y-lyke wel, whan they han al y-do;
This is to seyn, they faylen bothe two.
Yet forgat I to maken rehersaille
Of watres corosif and of limaille,
And of bodyes mollificacioun,
And also of hir induracioun,
Oiles, ablucions, and metal fusible,
To tellen al wolde passen any bible
That o-wher is; wherfor, as for the beste,
Of alle thise names now wol I me reste,
For, as I trowe, I have yow told y-nowe
To reyse a feend, al loke he never so rowe.
A! nay! lat be; the philosophres stoon,
Elixir clept, we sechen faste echoon;
For hadde we him, than were we siker y-now.
But, unto god of heven I make avow,
For al our craft, whan we han al y-do,

And al our sleighte, he wol nat come us to.
He hath y-maad us spenden mochel good,
For sorwe of which almost we wexen wood,
But that good hope crepeth in our herte,
Supposinge ever, though we sore smerte,
To be releved by him afterward;
Swich supposing and hope is sharp and hard;
I warne yow wel, it is to seken ever;
That futur temps hath maad men to dissever,
In trust ther-of, from al that ever they hadde.
Yet of that art they can nat wexen sadde,
For unto hem it is a bitter swete;
So semeth it; for nadde they but a shete
Which that they mighte wrappe hem inne a-night,
And a bak to walken inne by day-light,
They wolde hem selle and spenden on this craft;
They can nat stinte til no-thing be laft.
And evermore, wher that ever they goon,
Men may hem knowe by smel of brimstoon;
For al the world, they stinken as a goot;
Her savour is so rammish and so hoot,
That, though a man from hem a myle be,
The savour wol infecte him, trusteth me;
Lo, thus by smelling and threedbare array,
If that men liste, this folk they knowe may.
And if a man wol aske hem prively,
Why they been clothed so unthriftily,
They right anon wol rownen in his ere,
And seyn, that if that they espyed were,
Men wolde hem slee, by-cause of hir science;
Lo, thus this folk bitrayen innocence!
Passe over this; I go my tale un-to.
Er than the pot be on the fyr y-do,
Of metals with a certein quantitee,
My lord hem tempreth, and no man but he—
Now he is goon, I dar seyn boldely—
For, as men seyn, he can don craftily;
Algate I woot wel he hath swich a name,
And yet ful ofte he renneth in a blame;
And wite ye how? ful ofte it happeth so,
The pot to-breketh, and farewel! al is go!
Thise metals been of so greet violence,
Our walles mowe nat make hem resistence,
But if they weren wroght of lym and stoon;
They percen so, and thurgh the wal they goon,
And somme of hem sinken in-to the ground—
Thus han we lost by tymes many a pound—
And somme are scatered al the floor aboute,
Somme lepe in-to the roof; with-outen doute,
Though that the feend noght in our sighte him shewe,
I trowe he with us be, that ilke shrewe!
In helle wher that he is lord and sire,
Nis ther more wo, ne more rancour ne ire.
Whan that our pot is broke, as I have sayd,
Every man chit, and halt him yvel apayd.
Som seyde, it was long on the fyr-making,
Som seyde, nay! it was on the blowing;
(Than was I fered, for that was myn office);
"Straw!" quod the thridde, "ye been lewed and nyce,

And all our tricks, it will not come to us.
The thing has caused us to spend all we had,
For grief of which almost we should go mad,
Save that good hope comes creeping in the heart,
Supposing ever, though we sorely smart,
The elixir will relieve us afterward;
The tension of such hope is sharp and hard;
I warn you well, it means go seeking ever;
That future time has made men to dissever,
Trusting that hope, from all that ever they had.
Yet of that art they cannot well grow sad,
For unto them it is a bitter-sweet;
So it appears; for had they but a sheet
With which to wrap themselves about by night,
And a coarse cloak to walk in by daylight,
They'd sell them both and spend it on this craft;
They can withhold naught till there's nothing left
And evermore, wherever they'll be gone,
Men know them by their smell of foul brimstone;
For all the world they stink as does a goat;
Their savour is so rammish and so hot
That, though a man a mile away may be,
The odour will infect him, trust to me!
Thus by their smell and their threadbare array,
If men but wish, these folk they'll know, I say.
And if a man but ask them privately
Why they do go clothed so unthriftily,
They right away will whisper in his ear
And say that if they should be noticed here,
Why, men would slay them, what of their science;
Lo, thus these folk impose on innocence!
Pass over this; unto my tale I'll run.
Before the pot upon the fire be done,
Of metals in a certain quantity
My lord it tempers, and no man save he—
Now he is gone I dare say this boldly—
For, as men say, he can work artfully;
Always I well know he has such a name,
And yet full often has he been to blame;
And know you how? Full oft it happens so,
The pot broke, and farewell! All vanished, O!
These metals have such violence and force
That crucibles cannot resist their course
Unless they are built up of lime and stone;
They penetrate, and through the wall they're gone,
And some of them sink right into the ground—
Thus have we lost, at times, full many a pound—
And some are scattered all the floor about,
Some leap up to the roof. Beyond a doubt,
Although the Fiend's to us not visible,
I think he's with us, aye, that same scoundrel!
In Hell, wherein he is the lord and sire,
There's not more woe, nor rancour, nor more ire.
For when our pot is broken, as I've said,
Each man will scold and think that he's been bled.
One said that it was due to fire-making,
One said it was the blowing of the thing
(There I was scared, for that was what I did);
"O straw! You silly fool!" the third one chid,

"It was not tempered as it ought to be."
"Nay," said the fourth, "shut up and list to me;
It was because our fire was not of beech,
That's why, by all the wealth I hope to reach!"
I cannot tell where one should put the blame;
There was a dreadful quarrel, just the same.
"What!" cried my lord, "there's no more to be done,
Whatever 'twas, I'll know the reason soon;
I am quite certain that the pot was crazed.
Be as it may, do not stand there amazed;
As always, sweep the floor up quickly, lad,
Pluck up your hearts and be both blithe and glad."
The rubbish in a heap then swept up was,
And on the floor was spread a large canvas,
And all this rubbish in a sieve was thrown,
And sifted, picked, and whirled, both up and down.
"By gad," said one, "something of our metal
There is yet here, although we have not all.
Although this thing has gone awry for now,
Another time it may be well enow.
We must put all our wealth at adventure;
A merchant's luck, gad! will not aye endure,
Believe me, in his high prosperity;
Sometimes his freight will sink beneath the sea,
And sometimes comes it safely unto land."
"Peace," said my lord, "next time I'll understand
How to proceed and with a better aim;
And, save I do, sirs, let me be to blame;
There was defect in something, well I know 't."
Another said the fire was far too hot.
But were it hot or cold, I dare say this,
That we concluded evermore amiss.
We fail of that which we desire to have,
And in our madness evermore we rave.
And when we're all together, then each one
Seems as he were a very Solomon.
But everything that glisters like fine gold
Is not gold, as I've often heard it told;
And every apple that is fair to eye
Is yet not sound, whatever hucksters cry;
And even so, that's how it fares with us:
For he that seems the wisest, by Jesus,
Is greatest fool, when proof is asked, in brief;
And he that seems the truest is a thief;
That shall you know ere I from you do wend,
When of my tale I've made at length an end.

It was nat tempred as it oghte be."
"Nay!" quod the ferthe, "stint, and herkne me;
By-cause our fyr ne was nat maad of beech,
That is the cause, and other noon, so theech!"
I can nat telle wher-on it was long,
But wel I wot greet stryf is us among.
"What!" quod my lord, "ther is na-more to done,
Of thise perils I wol be war eft-sone;
I am right siker that the pot was crased.
Be as be may, be ye no-thing amased;
As usage is, lat swepe the floor as swythe,
Plukke up your hertes, and beth gladde and blythe."
The mullok on an hepe y-sweped was,
And on the floor y-cast a canevas,
And al this mullok in a sive y-throwe,
And sifted, and y-piked many a throwe.
"Pardee," quod oon, "somwhat of our metal
Yet is ther heer, though that we han nat al.
Al-though this thing mishapped have as now,
Another tyme it may be wel y-now,
Us moste putte our good in aventure;
A marchant, parde! may nat ay endure
Trusteth me wel, in his prosperitee;
Somtyme his good is drenched in the see,
And somtym comth it sauf un-to the londe."
"Pees!" quod my lord, "the next tyme I wol fonde
To bringe our craft al in another plyte;
And but I do, sirs, lat me han the wyte;
Ther was defaute in som-what, wel I woot."
Another seyde, the fyr was over hoot:—
But, be it hoot or cold, I dar seye this,
That we concluden evermore amis.
We fayle of that which that we wolden have,
And in our madnesse evermore we rave.
And whan we been togidres everichoon,
Every man semeth a Salomon.
But al thing which that shyneth as the gold
Nis nat gold, as that I have herd it told;
Ne every appel that is fair at yë
Ne is nat good, what-so men clappe or crye.
Right so, lo! fareth it amonges us;
He that semeth the wysest, by Jesus!
Is most fool, whan it cometh to the preef;
And he that semeth trewest is a theef;
That shul ye knowe, er that I fro yow wende,
By that I of my tale have maad an ende.

HERE ENDETH THE FIRST PART

HERE FOLLOWETH THE SECOND PART

There is a canon of religion known
Among us, who'd contaminate a town,
Though 'twere as great as Nineveh the free,
Rome, Alexandria, Troy, and others three.
His tricks and all his infinite treacherousness
No man could write down fully, as I guess,
Though he should live unto his thousandth year.
In all this world for falsehood he's no peer;
For in his terms he will so twist and wind
And speak in words so slippery of kind,

Ther is a chanoun of religioun
Amonges us, wolde infecte al a toun,
Though it as greet were as was Ninivee,
Rome, Alisaundre, Troye, and othere three.
His sleightes and his infinit falsnesse
Ther coude no man wryten, as I gesse,
Thogh that he mighte liven a thousand yeer.
In al this world of falshede nis his peer;
For in his termes so he wolde him winde,
And speke his wordes in so sly a kinde,

Whan he commune shal with any wight,
That he wol make him doten anon right,
But it a feend be, as him-selven is.
Ful many a man hath he bigyled er this,
And wol, if that he live may a whyle;
And yet men ryde and goon ful many a myle
Him for to seke and have his aqueyntaunce,
Noght knowinge of his false governaunce.
And if yow list to yeve me audience,
I wol it tellen heer in your presence.
But worshipful chanouns religious,
Ne demeth nat that I sclaundre your hous,
Al-though my tale of a chanoun be.
Of every ordre som shrewe is, parde,
And god forbede that al a companye
Sholde rewe a singuler mannes folye.
To sclaundre yow is no-thing myn entente,
But to correcten that is mis I mente.
This tale was nat only told for yow,
But eek for othere mo; ye woot wel how
That, among Cristes apostelles twelve,
Ther nas no traytour but Judas him-selve.
Than why sholde al the remenant have blame
That giltlees were? by yow I seye the same.
Save only this, if ye wol herkne me,
If any Judas in your covent be,
Remeveth him bitymes, I yow rede,
If shame or los may causen any drede.
And beth no-thing displesed, I yow preye,
But in this cas herkneth what I shal seye.

In London was a preest, an annueleer,[1]
That therin dwelled hadde many a yeer,
Which was so plesaunt and so servisable
Unto the wyf, wher-as he was at table,
That she wolde suffre him no-thing for to paye
For bord ne clothing, wente he never so gaye;
And spending-silver hadde he right y-now.
Therof no fors; I wol procede as now,
And telle forth my tale of the chanoun,
That broghte this preest to confusioun.
This false chanoun cam up-on a day
Unto this preestes chambre, wher he lay,
Biseching him to lene him a certeyn
Of gold, and he wolde quyte it him ageyn.
"Lene me a mark," quod he, "but dayes three,
And at my day I wol it quyten thee.
And if so be that thou me finde fals,
Another day do hange me by the hals!"
This preest him took a mark, and that as swythe,
And this chanoun him thanked ofte sythe,
And took his leve, and wente forth his weye,
And at the thridde day broghte his moneye,
And to the preest he took his gold agayn,
Wherof this preest was wonder glad and fayn.
"Certes," quod he, "no-thing anoyeth me
To lene a man a noble, or two or three,
Or what thing were in my possessioun,
Whan he so trewe is of condicioun,
That in no wyse he breke wol his day;
To swich a man I can never seye nay."

When he communicates with any wight,
That he soon makes a fool of him outright,
Unless it be a devil, as he is.
Full many a man has he beguiled ere this,
And will, if he may live a further while;
And yet men walk and ride full many a mile
To seek him out and have his acquaintance,
Naught knowing of his treacherous simulance.
And if you care to listen to me here,
I'll make the proof of what I say quite clear.
But most religious canons, just and true,
Don't think I'm slandering your house, or you,
Although my tale may of a canon be.
Some rogue's in every order, pardon me,
And God forbid that for one rascal's sake
Against a group we condemnation make.
To slander you is nowise my intent,
But to correct what is amiss I'm bent.
This tale I tell here not alone for you,
But even for others, too; you know well how
Among Christ's twelve disciples there was not
One to play traitor, save Iscariot.
Then why should all the rest be put to blame
Who guiltless were? Of you I say the same.
Save only this, if you will list to me,
If any Judas in your convent be,
Remove the man betimes, I counsel you,
Lest shame or loss or trouble should ensue.
And be displeased in nothing, I you pray,
But hear what on this matter I may say.

In London was a priest, an annualeer[1]
Who had therein dwelt many a quiet year,
A man so pleasant and so serviceable
To the goodwife who shared with him her table,
That she would never suffer him to pay
For board or clothing, went he ever so gay;
Of spending-silver, too, he had enow.
No matter; I'll proceed as I said, now,
And tell about the canon all my tale,
Who gave this priest good cause to weep and wail.
This canon false, he came, upon a day
Into the chaplain's chamber, where he lay,
Beseeching him to lend him a certain
Amount in gold, the which he'd pay again.
"Lend me a mark," said he, "for three days, say,
And when that time's done, I will it repay.
And if you find me false, I shall not reck
If, on a day, you hang me by the neck!"
This priest brought him a mark, and quickly, too,
Whereat this canon thanked him, said adieu,
And took his leave and went forth on his way,
And brought the money back on the third day,
And to the priest he gave his gold again,
Whereof this priest was wondrous glad, 'tis plain.
"Truly," he said, "it no wise bothers me
To lend a man a noble, or two, or three,
Or any modest thing that is my own,
To him who has the disposition shown
That in no wise will he forgo to pay;
To such a man I never can say nay."

[1]A priest employed in singing anniversary Masses.

"What!" cried this canon, "Should I be untrue?
Nay, that for me would be a thing quite new.
Truth is a thing that I will ever keep
Unto that day, at last, when I shall creep
Into my grave, or elsewise God forbid!
Trust this as surely as you trust your creed.
I thank God, and in good time be it said,
That there was never yet man ill repaid
For gold or silver that to me he lent,
Nor ever falsehood in my heart I've meant.
And, sir," said he, "out of my privity,
Since you have been so very good to me,
And showed to me so great a nobleness,
Somewhat to quit you for your kindliness,
I'll show to you, and if you'd learn it here,
I'll teach you plainly all the methods dear
I use in working at philosophy.
Give it good heed, for you'll see with your eye
I'll do a masterpiece before I go."
"Yes?" asked the priest, "Yes, sir, and will you so?
Mary! Thereof I pray you heartily."
"Right at your service, sir, and truthfully,"
Replied the canon, "else, may God forbid!"
Service this thief could offer, and he did!
Full true it is that service in this guise
Stinks, as take witness of these old men wise;
And soon enough I will this verify
By this canon, the root of treachery,
Who always had delight, nor could refrain—
Such devilish thoughts within his heart did reign—
When he brought Christian folk to tribulation.
God keep us from his false dissimulation!
Naught understood this priest with whom he dealt,
And of his coming harm he nothing felt.
O hapless priest! O hapless innocent!
Blinded by avarice malevolent!
O luckless one, full blind is your conceit,
Nothing are you aware of the deceit
Which this sly fox arranges here to be!
His wily stratagems you cannot flee.
Wherefore, at once to make the ending known,
By which your troubles will be clearly shown,
Unhappy man, I'll hasten on to tell
The folly into which you blindly fell,
And, too, the treachery of that other wretch,
As far as what I know of him may stretch.
This canon was my lord, you think I mean?
Sir host, in faith, and by the Heaven's Queen,
It was another canon, and not he,
Who has a hundred-fold more subtlety!
He has betrayed the people many a time;
Of his deceit it wearies me to rhyme.
Whatever of his falsehood I have said,
For shame of him I feel my cheeks grow red;
At any rate, my cheeks begin to glow,
For redness have I none, right well I know,
In all my visage; for the fumes diverse
Of metals, whereof you've heard me rehearse,
Have all consumed and wasted my redness.

"What!" quod this chanoun, "sholde I be untrewe?
Nay, that were thing y-fallen al of-newe
Trouthe is a thing that I wol ever kepe
Un-to that day in which that I shal crepe
In-to my grave, and elles god forbede;
Bileveth this as siker as is your crede.
God thanke I, and in good tyme be it sayd,
That ther was never man yet yvel apayd
For gold ne silver that he to me lente,
Ne never falshede in myn herte I mente.
And sir," quod he, "now of my privetee,
Sin ye so goodlich han been un-to me,
And kythed to me so greet gentillesse,
Somwhat to quyte with your kindenesse,
I wol yow shewe, and, if yow list to lere,
I wol yow teche pleynly the manere,
How I can werken in philosophye.
Taketh good heed, ye shul wel seen at yë,
That I wol doon a maistrie er I go."
"Ye," quod the preest, "ye, sir, and wol ye so?
Marie! ther-of I pray yow hertely!"
"At your comandement, sir, trewely,"
Quod the chanoun, "and elles god forbede!"
Lo, how this theef coude his servyse bede!
Ful sooth it is, that swich profred servyse
Stinketh, as witnessen thise olde wyse;
And that ful sone I wol it verifye
In this chanoun, rote of al trecherye,
That ever-more delyt hath and gladnesse—
Swich feendly thoughtes in his herte impresse—
How Cristes peple he may be meschief bringe;
God kepe us from his fals dissimulinge!
Noght wiste this preest with whom that he delte,
Ne of his harm cominge he no-thing felte.
O sely preest! O sely innocent!
With coveityse anon thou shalt be blent!
O gracelees, ful blind is thy conceit,
No-thing ne artow war of the deceit
Which that this fox y-shapen hath to thee!
His wyly wrenches thou ne mayst nat flee.
Wherfor, to go to the conclusioun
That refereth to thy confusioun,
Unhappy man! anon I wol me hye
To tellen thyn unwit and thy folye,
And eek the falsnesse of that other wrecche,
As ferforth as that my conning may strecche.
This chanoun was my lord, ye wolden wene?
Sir host, in feith, and by the hevenes quene,
It was another chanoun, and nat he,
That can an hundred fold more subtiltee!
He hath bitrayed folkes many tyme;
Of his falshede it dulleth me to ryme.
Ever whan that I speke of his falshede,
For shame of him my chekes wexen rede;
Algates, they biginnen for to glowe,
For reednesse have I noon, right wel I knowe,
In my visage; for fumes dyverse
Of metals, which ye han herd me reherce,
Consumed and wasted han my reednesse.

Now tak heed of this chanouns cursednesse!
"Sir," quod he to the preest, "lat your man gon
For quik-silver, that we it hadde anon;
And lat him bringen ounces two or three;
And whan he comth, as faste shul ye see
A wonder thing, which ye saugh never er this."
"Sir," quod the preest, "it shal be doon, y-wis."
He bad his servant fecchen him this thing,
And he al redy was at his bidding,
And wente him forth, and cam anon agayn
With this quik-silver, soothly for to sayn,
And took thise ounces three to the chanoun;
And he hem leyde fayre and wel adoun,
And bad the servant coles for to bringe,
That he anon mighte go to his werkinge.
The coles right anon weren y-fet,
And this chanoun took out a crosselet
Of his bosom, and shewed it the preest.
"This instrument," quod he, "which that thou seest,
Tak in thyn hand, and put thy-self therinne
Of this quik-silver an ounce, and heer biginne,
In the name of Crist, to wexe a philosofre.
Ther been ful fewe, whiche that I wolde profre
To shewen hem thus muche of my science.
For ye shul seen heer, by experience,
That this quik-silver wol I mortifye
Right in your sighte anon, withouten lye,
And make it as good silver and as fyn
As ther is any in your purs or myn,
Or elleswher, and make it malliable;
And elles, holdeth me fals and unable
Amonges folk for ever to appere!
I have a poudre heer, that coste me dere,
Shal make al good, for it is cause of al
My conning, which that I yow shewen shal.
Voydeth your man, and lat him be theroute,
And shet the dore, whyls we been aboute
Our privetee, that no man us espye
Whyls that we werke in this philosophye."
Al as he bad, fulfilled was in dede,
This ilke servant anon-right out yede,
And his maister shette the dore anon,
And to hir labour speedily they gon.
This preest, at this cursed chanouns bidding,
Up-on the fyr anon sette this thing,
And blew the fyr, and bisied him ful faste;
And this chanoun in-to the croslet caste
A poudre, noot I wher-of that it was
Y-maad, other of chalk, other of glas,
Or som-what elles, was nat worth a flye
To blynde with the preest; and bad him hye
The coles for to couchen al above
The croslet; "for, in tokening I thee love,"
Quod this chanoun, "thyn owene hondes two
Shul werche al thing which that shal heer be do."
"Graunt mercy," quod the preest, and was ful glad,
And couched coles as the chanoun bad.
And whyle he bisy was, this feendly wrecche,
This fals chanoun, the foule feend him fecche!
Out of his bosom took a bechen cole,

Now take heed of this canon's wickedness.
"Sir," this to the priest, "let your man be gone
For quicksilver, that we have some anon;
And let him bring us ounces two or three;
And when he comes, just so soon shall you see
A wondrous thing you've never seen ere this."
"Sir," said the priest, "it shall be done, ywis."
He bade his servant go to fetch them all,
And since the lad was ready at his call,
He got him forth and came anon again
With this quicksilver, truly to explain,
And gave these ounces three to the canon;
And he took them and laid them fairly down,
And bade the servant coals to go and bring,
That he might get to work with everything.
The coals at once were brought, and all was well;
And then this canon took a crucible
Out of his bosom, showing it to the priest.
"This instrument," said he, "you see—at least
Take in your hand, and put yourself therein
An ounce of quicksilver, and here begin,
And in God's name, to be philosopher!
There are but few to whom I would proffer
To make my science clear and evident.
For you shall learn here, by experiment,
That this quicksilver will I mortify
Right in your sight anon, without a lie,
And make it as good silver and as fine
As any that's in your purse or in mine,
Or elsewhere, aye, and make it malleable;
Otherwise hold me false, unfit as well
Among good folk for ever to appear.
I have a powder here that cost me dear,
Shall do all this, for it's the root of all
My craft; you'll see what shall therewith befall.
Dismiss your man and let him stay without,
And shut the door fast while we are about
Our secret work, that no man may espy
The way we work in this philosophy."
All was then done as canon had decreed;
This servant took himself straight out, indeed,
Whereat his master barred the door anon,
And to their labour quickly they were gone.
The priest, at this damned canon's ordering,
Upon the fire anon did set this thing,
And blew the fire and busied him full fast;
Within the crucible the canon cast
A powder (I know not whereof it was
Compounded, whether of chalk, or maybe glass,
Or something else—it was not worth a fly)
To blind the priest with; and he bade him high
The coals to pile the crucible above.
"In token of how much I bear you love,"
This canon said, "your own two hands, and none
Other, shall do this thing that shall be done."
"Thank you," the priest replied, and was right glad,
And heaped the coals up as the canon bade.
And while he laboured thus, this fiendish wretch,
This canon false—may him the foul Fiend fetch!—
Out of his bosom took a beechen coal,

Wherein right cunningly he'd bored a hole
In which, before, he'd put of silver limail
An ounce, and which he'd stopped up, without fail,
With blackened wax, to keep the filings in.
And understand you well that this false gin
Was not made there, but it was made before;
And there were other things I'll tell you more
About hereafter, which with him he'd brought;
Ere he came there, to cheat he'd taken thought,
And ere they parted he did even so;
Till he had skinned him he could not forgo.
It wearies me when of him I do speak,
For on his falsehood I myself would wreak,
If I knew how; but he is here and there:
He is so restless he abides nowhere.
  But take heed now, sirs, for God's very love!
He took this coal whereof I spoke above,
And in his hand he bore it privily.
And while the priest did pile up busily
The burning coals, as I told you ere this,
This canon said: "My friend, you do amiss;
This is not piled up as it ought to be;
But soon I shall amend all that," said he.
"Now let me thereof have a hand the whiles,
For I've great pity on you, by Saint Giles!
You are right hot, I see well how you sweat,
Take here a cloth and wipe away the wet."
And while the simple priest did wipe his face,
This canon took his coal, and with grave grace,
Laid it above and well to middleward
Upon the crucible, and blew it hard
Until the flames did blaze up hot again.
  "Now give us drink, sir," said the canon then,
"For soon all shall be well, I undertake;
Let us sit down, and let us merry make."
And when this treacherous canon's beechen coal
Was burnt, then all the filings from the hole
Into the crucible fell down anon;
As so, in reason, it must needs have done,
Since so well centred over it it was;
But thereof nothing knew the priest, alas!
He deemed that all the coals alike were good,
For of the trick he nothing understood.
And when this alchemist was ready, he
Said to the priest: "Rise up and stand by me;
And since I know that metal mould you've none,
Go sally forth and bring here a chalk-stone;
For I will make one of the very shape
That ingot moulds have, if I can them ape.
And, too, bring in with you a bowl or pan
Full of clear water, and you'll see, dear man,
How well our business here shall thrive, in brief.
And yet, that you may have no unbelief,
Or think that somehow I'm not doing right,
I'll never be a moment out of sight,
But go with you and come with you again."
  The chamber door, then, briefly to explain,
They opened and they shut, and went their way.
And as they went they took the key, I say,
And came again, without a long delay,

In which ful subtilly was maad an hole,
And ther-in put was of silver lymaille
An ounce, and stopped was, with-outen fayle,
The hole with wex, to kepe the lymail in.
And understondeth, that this false gin
Was nat maad ther, but it was maad bifore;
And othere thinges I shal telle more
Herafterward, which that he with him broghte
Er he cam ther, him to bigyle he thoghte,
And so he dide, er that they wente a-twinne;
Til he had terved him, coude he not blinne.
It dulleth me whan that I of him speke,
On his falshede fayn wolde I me wreke,
If I wiste how; but he is heer and ther:
He is so variaunt, he abit no-wher.
  But taketh heed now, sirs, for goddes love!
He took his cole of which I spak above,
And in his hond he baar it prively.
And whyls the preest couchede busily
The coles, as I tolde yow er this,
This chanoun seyde, "freend, ye doon amis;
This is nat couched as it oghte be;
But sone I shal amenden it," quod he.
"Now lat me medle therwith but a whyle,
For of yow have I pitee, by seint Gyle!
Ye been right hoot, I see wel how ye swete,
Have heer a cloth, and wype awey the wete."
And whyles that the preest wyped his face,
This chanoun took his cole with harde grace,
And leyde it above, up-on the middeward
Of the croslet, and blew wel afterward,
Til that the coles gonne faste brenne.
  "Now yeve us drinke," quod the chanoun thenne,
"As swythe al shal be wel, I undertake;
Sitte we doun, and lat us mery make."
And whan that this chanounes bechen cole
Was brent, al the lymaille, out of the hole,
Into the croslet fil anon adoun;
And so it moste nedes, by resoun,
Sin it so even aboven couched was;
But ther-of wiste the preest no-thing, alas!
He demed alle the coles y-liche good,
For of the sleighte he no-thing understood.
And whan this alkamistre saugh his tyme,
"Rys up," quod he, "sir preest, and stondeth by me;
And for I woot wel ingot have ye noon,
Goth, walketh forth, and bring us a chalkstoon;
For I wol make oon of the same shap
That is an ingot, if I may han hap.
And bringeth eek with yow a bolle or a panne,
Ful of water, and ye shul see wel thanne
How that our bisinesse shal thryve and preve.
And yet, for ye shul han no misbileve
Ne wrong conceit of me in your absence,
I ne wol nat been out of your presence,
But go with yow, and come with yow ageyn."
The chambre-dore, shortly for to seyn,
They opened and shette, and wente hir weye.
And forth with hem they carieden the keye,
And come agayn with-outen any delay.

What sholde I tarien al the longe day?
He took the chalk, and shoop it in the wyse
Of an ingot, as I shal yow devyse.
I seye, he took out of his owene sleve
A teyne[1] of silver (yvele mote he cheve!)
Which that ne was nat but an ounce of weighte;
And taketh heed now of his cursed sleighte!
He shoop his ingot, in lengthe and eek in brede,
Of this teyne, with-outen any drede,
So slyly, that the preest it nat espyde;
And in his sleve agayn he gan it hyde;
And fro the fyr he took up his matere,
And in th'ingot putte it with mery chere,
And in the water-vessel he it caste
Whan that him luste, and bad the preest as faste,
"Look what ther is, put in thyn hand and grope,
Thow finde shalt ther silver, as I hope;
What, devel of helle! sholde it elles be?
Shaving of silver silver is, pardee!"
He putte his hond in, and took up a teyne
Of silver fyn, and glad in every veyne
Was this preest, whan he saugh that it was so.
"Goddes blessing, and his modres also,
And alle halwes have ye, sir chanoun,"
Seyde this preest, "and I hir malisoun,
But, and ye vouche-sauf to techen me
This noble craft and this subtilitee,
I wol be youre, in al that ever I may!"
Quod the chanoun, "yet wol I make assay
The second tyme, that ye may taken hede
And been expert of this, and in your nede
Another day assaye in myn absence
This disciplyne and this crafty science.
Lat take another ounce," quod he tho,
"Of quik-silver, with-outen wordes mo,
And do ther-with as ye han doon er this
With that other, which that now silver is."
This preest him bisieth in al that he can
To doon as this chanoun, this cursed man,
Comanded him, and faste he blew the fyr,
For to come to th'effect of his desyr.
And this chanoun, right in the mene whyle,
Al redy was, the preest eft to bigyle,
And, for a countenance, in his hande he bar
An holwe stikke (tak keep and be war!)
In the ende of which an ounce, and na-more,
Of silver lymail put was, as bifore
Was in his cole, and stopped with wex weel
For to kepe in his lymail every deel.
And whyl this preest was in his bisinesse,
This chanoun with his stikke gan him dresse
To him anon, and his pouder caste in
As he did er; (the devel out of his skin
Him terve, I pray to god, for his falshede;
For he was ever fals in thoght and dede);
And with this stikke, above the croslet,
That was ordeyned with that false get,
He stired the coles, til relente gan
The wex agayn the fyr, as every man,
But it a fool be, woot wel it mot nede,
And al that in the stikke was out yede,

Why should I tarry here the livelong day?
He took the chalk and shaped it in such wise
As moulds are made, as further I'll apprise.
I say, he took, then, out of his own sleeve
A tain[1] of silver (Hell the man receive!)
Which was an ounce, no more or less, in weight;
Now here's the trick, the way of which I'll state!
He shaped his mould in length and breadth to be
Like to the tain of silver, as you see,
So slyly that the priest this never spied;
And in his sleeve did then the model hide;
And from the fire he took his crucible
And poured it in the mould, for all went well,
And in the bowl of water then did cast
The mould and all, and bade the priest, at last:
"Seek what there is, put in your hand and grope,
And you shall find there silver, as I hope;
What—devils out of Hell!—should it else be?
Filing of silver silver is!" cried he.
He put his hand in and a tain took out
Of silver fine, and glad, you cannot doubt,
Was this priest when he saw that it was so.
"God's blessing, and His Mother's dear also,
And all the saints', too, may you have, my friend,"
The priest replied, "and may they curse my end
Unless you will vouchsafe to teach to me
This noble craft and all this subtlety;
I will be yours in all that ever I may!"
Said then the canon: "Yet will I essay
A second time, that you may take good heed
And be expert in this, and at your need
When I am absent on another day,
You may this science and its arts essay.
Quicksilver take," said he, "one ounce, no more,
As you'll remember that we did before,
And as you treated that, so do with this
And like the first 'twill change, which silver is."
The priest then followed carefully the plan,
As he'd been bidden by this cursed man,
The canon; long and hard he blew the fire
To bring about the thing he did desire.
And this said canon waited all the while,
All ready there the poor priest to beguile,
And, for assurance in his hand did bear
A hollow stick (take heed, sirs, and beware!),
In end of which an ounce was, and no more,
Of silver filings put, all as before
Within the coal, and stopped with wax, a bit,
To keep the filings in the hole of it.
And while the priest was busy, as I say,
This canon, drawing close, got in his way,
And unobserved he threw the powder in
Just as before (the Devil from his skin
Strip him, I pray to God, for lies he wrought;
For he was ever false in deed and thought);
And with his stick, above the crucible,
Arranged for knavish trickery so well,
He stirred the coals until to melt began
The thin wax in the fire, as every man,
Except a fool, knows well it must, sans doubt,
And all that was within the stick slipped out,

[1]A thin slice.

And quickly in the crucible it fell.
Good sirs, what better do you wish than well?
When now the priest was thus beguiled again,
Supposing naught but truth, I should explain,
He was so glad that I cannot express,
In any way, his mirth and his gladness;
And to the canon he did proffer soon
Body and goods. "Yea," was the canon's tune,
"Though I am poor, I'm artful as you'll find;
I warn you plainly, there's yet more behind.
Is there some copper in your place?" asked he.
"Yea," said the priest, "I think there may well be."
"If not, go buy us some, and quickly too,
Good sir, make haste and fetch us it, pray do."
He went his way, and with the copper came,
And in his hands this canon took the same,
And of the copper weighed out but an ounce.
My tongue is far too simple to pronounce,
As servant to my wit, the doubleness
Within this canon, root of wickedness.
Friendly he seemed to those that knew him not
But he was fiendly both in heart and thought.
It wearies me to tell of his falseness,
Nevertheless yet will I it express
To end that all men may be warned thereby,
And for no other reason, truthfully.
Within the crucible he puts the ounce
Of copper which upon the fire he mounts,
And casts in powder, making the priest blow,
And at his labouring to stoop down low,
All as before, and all was but a jape;
Just as he pleased, he made the priest his ape.
And afterward into the mould he cast
The copper; into the water pan at last
Plunging the whole, and thrust therein his hand.
And in his sleeve (as you did understand
Before) he had a certain silver tain.
He slyly took it out, this damned villain,
While still the priest saw nothing of the plan,
And left it in the bottom of the pan;
And in the water groped he to and fro
And very stealthily took up also
The copper tain, of which the priest knew naught,
And hiding it, he by the breast him caught,
And spoke to him, thus carrying on his game:
"Stoop lower down, by God, you are to blame!
Come, help me now, as I did you whilere,
Put in your hand and search and learn what's there."
This priest took up the silver tain anon,
And then the canon said: "Let us be gone
With these three plates, the which we have so wrought,
To some goldsmith, to learn if they're worth aught.
For by my faith, I wouldn't, for my hood,
Have them, save they are silver fine and good,
And that immediately proved shall be."
Unto the goldsmith, then, with these tains three,
They went, and put the metal in assay

And in the croslet hastily it fel.
Now gode sirs, what wol ye bet than wel?
Whan that this preest thus was bigyled ageyn,
Supposing noght but trouthe, soth to seyn,
He was so glad, that I can nat expresse
In no manere his mirthe and his gladnesse;
And to the chanoun he profred eftsone
Body and good; "ye," quod the chanoun sone,
"Though povre I be, crafty thou shalt me finde;
I warne thee, yet is ther more bihinde.
Is ther any coper her-inne?" seyde he.
"Ye," quod the preest, "sir, I trowe wel ther be."
"Elles go bye us som, and that as swythe,
Now, gode sir, go forth thy wey and hy the."
He wente his wey, and with the coper cam,
And this chanoun it in his handes nam,
And of that coper weyed out but an ounce.
Al to simple is my tonge to pronounce,
As ministre of my wit, the doublenesse
Of this chanoun, rote of al cursednesse.
He semed freendly to hem that knewe him noght,
But he was feendly bothe in herte and thoght.
It werieth me to telle of his falsnesse,
And nathelees yet wol I it expresse,
To th'entente that men may be war therby,
And for noon other cause, trewely.
He putte his ounce of coper in the croslet,
And on the fyr as swythe he hath it set,
And caste in poudre, and made the preest to blowe,
And in his werking for to stoupe lowe,
As he dide er, and al nas but a jape;
Right as him liste, the preest he made his ape;
And afterward in th'ingot he it caste,
And in the panne putte it at the laste
Of water, and in he putte his owene hond.
And in his sleve (as ye biforn-hond
Herde me telle) he hadde a silver teyne.
He slyly took it out, this cursed heyne—
Unwiting this preest of his false craft—
And in the pannes botme he hath it laft;
And in the water rombled to and fro,
And wonder prively took up also
The coper teyne, noght knowing this preest,
And hidde it, and him hente by the breest,
And to him spak, and thus seyde in his game,
"Stoupeth adoun, by god, ye be to blame,
Helpeth me now, as I dide yow whyl-er,
Putte in your hand, and loketh what is ther."
This preest took up this silver teyne anon,
And thanne seyde the chanoun, "lat us gon
With thise three teynes, which that we han wroght,
To som goldsmith, and wite if they been oght.
For, by my feith, I nolde, for myn hood,
But-if that they were silver, fyn and good,
And that as swythe preved shal it be."
Un-to the goldsmith with thise teynes three
They wente, and putte thise teynes in assay

To fyr and hamer; mighte no man sey nay,
But that they weren as hem oghte be.
  This sotted preest, who was gladder than he?
Was never brid gladder agayn the day,
Ne nightingale, in the sesoun of May,
Nas never noon that luste bet to singe;
Ne lady lustier in carolinge
Or for to speke of love and wommanhede,
Ne knight in armes to doon an hardy dede
To stonde in grace of his lady dere,
Than had this preest this sory craft to lere;
And to the chanoun thus he spak and seyde,
"For love of god, that for us alle deyde,
And as I may deserve it un-to yow,
What shal this receit coste? telleth now!"
  "By our lady," quod this chanoun, "it is dere,
I warne yow wel; for, save I and a frere,
In Engelond ther can no man it make."
  "No fors," quod he, "now, sir, for goddes sake,
What shal I paye? telleth me, I preye."
  "Y-wis," quod he, "it is ful dere, I seye;
Sir, at o word, if that thee list it have,
Ye shul paye fourty pound, so god me save!
And, nere the freendship that ye dide er this
To me, ye sholde paye more, y-wis."
  This preest the somme of fourty pound anon
Of nobles fette, and took hem everichon
To this chanoun, for this ilke receit;
Al his werking nas but fraude and deceit.
  "Sir preest," he seyde, "I kepe han no loos
Of my craft, for I wolde it kept were cloos;
And as ye love me, kepeth it secree;
For, and men knewe al my subtilitee,
By god, they wolden han so greet envye
To me, by-cause of my philosophye,
I sholde be deed, ther were non other weye."
  "God it forbede!" quod the preest, "what sey ye?"
Yet hadde I lever spenden al the good
Which that I have (and elles wexe I wood!)
Than that ye sholden falle in swich mescheef."
  "For your good wil, sir, have ye right good preef,"
Quod the chanoun, "and far-wel, grant mercy!"
  He wente his wey and never the preest him sy
After that day; and whan that this preest sholde
Maken assay, at swich tyme as he wolde,
Of this receit, far-wel! it wolde nat be!
Lo, thus byjaped and bigyled was he!
Thus maketh he his introduccioun
To bringe folk to hir destruccioun.—
  Considereth, sirs, how that, in ech estaat,
Bitwixe men and gold ther is debaat
So ferforth, that unnethes is ther noon.
This multiplying blent so many oon,
That in good feith I trowe that it be
The cause grettest of swich scarsetee.
Philosophres speken so mistily
In this craft, that men can nat come therby,
For any wit that men han now a-dayes.
They mowe wel chiteren, as doon thise jayes,
And in her termes sette hir lust and peyne,

By fire and hammer; no man could say nay,
But they were silver, as they ought to be.
  This foolish priest, who was more glad than he?
Never was gladder bird for dawn of day,
Nor nightingale in season of the May,
Nor was there ever one more fain to sing;
Nor lady happier in carolling
Or speaking much of love and woman's meed;
Nor knight in arms to do a hardy deed
To stand in graces of his lady dear—
Than was the priest this sorry craft to hear;
And to the canon thus he spoke and said:
"For love of God, Who for us all was dead,
And as I may requite it unto you,
What shall this recipe cost? Come, tell me now?"
  "By 'r Lady," said this canon, "it is dear,
I warn you well; for now in England here
One friar and I are all who can it make."
  "No matter," said he, "now, sir, for God's sake,
What shall I pay? Oh, tell me this, I pray!"
  "Truly," said he, "it is right dear, I say;
Sir, in one word, if this thing you will have,
You shall pay forty pounds, so God me save!
And were it not for friendship shown ere this
To me, you should pay more than that, ywis."
  This priest the sum of forty pounds anon
In nobles fetched, and gave them, every one,
To this said canon for this said receipt;
His business was all fraud and all deceit.
  "Sir priest," he said, "I do not care to lose
My secret craft, and I would 'twere kept close;
So, as you love me, keep it privily;
For if men knew all of my subtlety,
By God above, they'd have so great envy
Of me, because of my philosophy,
I should be slain, there'd be no other way."
  "Nay, God forbid!" replied the priest. "What say?
Far rather would I spend all coin, by gad,
That I possess (and else may I grow mad!)
Than that you fall in any such distress."
  "For your good will, I wish you all success,"
Replied the canon, "farewell, many thanks."
  He went, and ne'er the priest this mountebank's
Face saw thereafter; and when this priest would
Make his own test, at such time as he could,
Of this receipt, farewell! it would not be!
Lo, thus bejaped and thus beguiled was he!
And thus he had his introduction in
The way men fall to ruin and to sin.
  Consider, sirs, how that, in each estate,
Between men and their gold there is debate
To such degree that gold is nearly done.
This multiplying blinds so many a one
That in good faith I think that it may be
The greatest cause of this said scarcity.
Philosophers they speak so mistily
About this craft, plain men can't come thereby
With any wit that men have nowadays.
They may well chatter, as do all these jays,
And in vague cant set their desire and pain,

But to their purpose shall they ne'er attain.
A man may easily learn, if he have aught,
To multiply, and bring his wealth to naught.
  Lo, such a gain is in this pleasant game
A man's mirth it will turn to grief and shame,
And it will empty great and heavy purses,
And causes alchemists to get the curses
Of all of those who thereunto have lent.
O fie! For shame! Those who the fire resent,
Alas! can they not flee the fire's fierce heat?
If you have tried it, leave it, I repeat,
Lest you lose all; better than never is late.
Never to thrive at all were a long date.
And though you prowl, you never gold shall find,
You are as bold as Bayard[1] is, the blind,
That blunders forth and thinks of danger, none;
He is as bold to run against a stone
As to go ambling down the broad highway.
And so fare you who multiply, I say.
If your two fleshly eyes can't see aright,
Look to it that your mind lack not for sight.
For, though you look about and though you stare,
You shall not win a mite in traffic there,
But you shall waste all you may scrape and turn.
Avoid that fire, lest much too fast it burn;
Meddle no more with that base art, I mean,
For if you do, you'll lose your savings clean.
  And now I'll tell you briefly, if I may,
What the philosophers about this say.
  Arnold of Villanovana I will cite.
In his *Rosarium* he brings to light
These facts, and says—in this I do not lie:
"No man can mercury ever mortify,
Unless its brother's aid to it he bring,
And also he who first did say this thing
Was father of philosophers, Hermes;
He said the dragon, doubtless, takes his ease
And never dies, unless there's also slain
His brother, which, to make the matter plain,
Means, by the dragon, mercury, none other,
And brimstone's understood to mean the brother,
That out of *Sol* and *Luna* we can draw.
And therefore," said he, "give heed to my saw,
Let no man busy him ever with this art
Unless philosophers to him impart
Their meaning clearly, for unless he can
Their language grasp, he's but an ignorant man.
This science and this learning, too," said he,
"Must ever the most secret secrets be."
  Also there was a student of Plato
Who on a time said to his master so,
As his book *Senior* will bear witness;
And this was his demand, in truthfulness:
"Tell me the name, sir, of the Secret Stone."
  And Plato answered in this wise anon:
"Take, now, the stone that Titanos men name."
  "What's that?" asked he. "Magnesia is the
    same,"
Plato replied. "Yea, sir, and is it thus?
This is *ignotum per ignotius*.
What is magnesia, good sir, I do pray?"

But to hir purpos shul they never atteyne.
A man may lightly lerne, if he have aught,
To multiplye, and bringe his good to naught!
  Lo! swich a lucre is in this lusty game,
A mannes mirthe it wol torne un-to grame,
And empten also grete and hevy purses,
And maken folk for to purchasen curses
Of hem, that han hir good therto y-lent.
O! fy! for shame! they that han been brent,
Allas! can they nat flee the fyres hete?
Ye that it use, I rede ye it lete,
Lest ye lese al; for bet than never is late.
Never to thryve were to long a date.
Though ye prolle ay, ye shul it never finde;
Ye been as bolde as is Bayard[1] the blinde,
That blundreth forth, and peril casteth noon;
He is as bold to renne agayn a stoon
As for to goon besydes in the weye.
So faren ye that multiplye, I seye.
If that your yën can nat seen aright,
Loke that your minde lakke nought his sight.
For, though ye loke never so brode, and stare,
Ye shul nat winne a myte on that chaffare,
But wasten al that ye may rape and renne.
Withdrawe the fyr, lest it to faste brenne;
Medleth na-more with that art, I mene,
For, if ye doon, your thrift is goon ful clene.
  And right as swythe I wol yow tellen here,
What philosophres seyn in this matere.
  Lo, thus seith Arnold of the Newe Toun,
As his Rosarie maketh mencioun;
He seith right thus, with-outen any lye,
"Ther may no man Mercurie mortifye,
But it be with his brother knowleching.
How that he, which that first seyde this thing,
Of philosophres fader was, Hermes;
He seith, how that the dragoun, doutelees,
Ne deyeth nat, but-if that he be slayn
With his brother; and that is for to sayn,
By the dragoun, Mercurie and noon other
He understood; and brimstoon by his brother,
That out of *sol* and *luna* were y-drawe.
And therfor," seyde he, "tak heed to my sawe,
Let no man bisy him this art for to seche,
But-if that he th'entencioun and speche
Of philosophres understonde can;
And if he do, he is a lewed man.
For this science and this conning," quod he,
"Is of the secree of secrees, parde."
  Also ther was a disciple of Plato,
That on a tyme seyde his maister to,
As his book Senior wol bere witnesse,
And this was his demande in soothfastnesse:
"Tel me the name of the privy stoon?"
  And Plato answerde unto him anoon,
"Tak the stoon that Titanos men name."
  "Which is that?" quod he. "Magnesia is the
    same,"
Seyde Plato. "Ye, sir, and is it thus?
This is *ignotum per ignotius*.
What is Magnesia, good sir, I yow preye?"

[1]Common name for a horse.

"It is a water that is maad, I seye,
Of elementes foure," quod Plato.
"Tel me the rote, good sir," quod he tho,
"Of that water, if that it be your wille?"
"Nay, nay," quod Plato, "certein, that I nille.
The philosophres sworn were everichoon,
That they sholden discovere it un-to noon,
Ne in no book it wryte in no manere;
For un-to Crist it is so leef and dere
That he wol nat that it discovered be,
But wher it lyketh to his deitee
Man for t'enspyre, and eek for to defende
Whom that him lyketh; lo, this is the ende."
Thanne conclude I thus; sith god of hevene
Ne wol nat that the philosophres nevene
How that a man shal come un-to this stoon,
I rede, as for the beste, lete it goon.
For who-so maketh god his adversarie,
As for to werken any thing in contrarie
Of his wil, certes, never shal he thryve,
Thogh that he multiplye terme of his lyve.
And ther a poynt; for ended is my tale;
God sende every trewe man bote of his bale!—
Amen.

"It is a water that is made, I say,
Out of four elements," replied Plato.
"Tell me the root, good sir," said he, "if so,
What then, is water, tell me if you will."
"Nay, nay," said Plato, "and now peace, be still."
Philosophers are sworn, aye, every one,
That they will thus discover it to none,
Nor in a book will write it for men here;
For unto Christ it is so lief and dear
That He wills that it not discovered be,
Save where it's pleasing to His deity
Man to inspire, and also, to defend
Whom that He will; and lo, this is the end.
And thus do I conclude: Since God in Heaven
Wills that philosophers shall not say even
How any man may come upon that stone,
I say, as for the best, let it alone.
For whoso makes of God his adversary,
To work out anything that is contrary
To what He wills, he'll surely never thrive,
Though he should multiply while he's alive.
And there's the end; for finished is my tale.
May God's salvation to no good man fail!
Amen.

HERE IS ENDED THE CANON'S YEOMAN'S TALE

THE MANCIPLE'S PROLOGUE

HERE FOLLOWETH THE PROLOGUE OF THE MANCIPLE'S TALE

Wite ye nat wher ther stant a litel toun
Which that y-cleped is Bob-up-and-doun,
Under the Blee, in Caunterbury weye?
Ther gan our hoste for to jape and pleye,
And seyde, "sirs, what! Dun is in the myre![1]
Is ther no man, for preyere ne for hyre,
That wol awake our felawe heer bihinde?
A theef mighte him ful lightly robbe and binde.
See how he nappeth! see, for cokkes bones,
As he wol falle from his hors at ones.
Is that a cook of Londoun, with meschaunce?
Do him come forth, he knoweth his penaunce,
For he shal telle a tale, by my fey!
Al-though it be nat worth a botel hey.
Awake, thou cook," quod he, "god yeve thee sorwe,
What eyleth thee to slepe by the morwe?
Hastow had fleen al night, or artow dronke,
Or hastow with som quene al night y-swonke,
So that thou mayst nat holden up thyn heed?"
This cook, that was ful pale and nothing reed,
Seyde to our host, "so god my soule blesse,
As ther is falle on me swich hevinesse,
Noot I nat why, that me were lever slepe
Than the beste galoun wyn in Chepe."
"Wel," quod the maunciple, "if it may doon ese
To thee, sir cook, and to no wight displese
Which that heer rydeth in this companye,

Do you not know where stands a little town
That's called by all about Bob-up-and-down,
Under the Blean, down Canterbury way?
There did our host begin to jape and play,
And he said: "Sirs, what! Dun is in the mire![1]
Is there no man, then, who, for prayer or hire,
Will wake our comrade who's so far behind?
A thief might easily rob him and bind.
See how he's nodding! See, now, by Cock's bones,
As if he'd fall down from his horse at once.
Is that a cook of London, with mischance?
Make him come forward, he knows his penance,
For he shall tell a tale here, by my fay,
Although it be not worth a bunch of hay.
Awake, you cook," cried he, "God give you sorrow!
What ails you that you sleep thus? It's good morrow!
Have you had fleas all night, or are you drunk?
Or did you toil all night in some quean's bunk?
So that you cannot now hold up your head?"
The cook, who was all pale and nothing red,
Said to our host: "So may God my soul bless,
As there is on me such a drowsiness,
I know not why, that I would rather sleep
Than drink a gallon of best wine in Cheap."
"Well," said the manciple, "if 'twill give ease
To you, sir cook, and in no way displease
The folk that ride here in this company,

[1]The name of an old rustic game.

And if our host will, of his courtesy,
I will, for now, excuse you from your tale.
For in good faith, your visage is full pale,
Your eyes are bleary also, as I think
And I know well your breath right sour does stink,
All of which shows that you are far from well;
No flattering lies about you will I tell.
See how he yawns. Just look, the drunken wight,
As if he'd swallow all of us outright.
Now close your mouth, man, by your father's kin;
Ah, may Hell's devil set his foot therein!
Your cursed breath will soon infect us all;
Fie, stinking swine, fie! Evil you befall!
Ah, take you heed, sirs, of this lusty man.
Now, sweet sir, would you like to ride at fan?[1]
It seems to me you're in the proper shape!
You've drunk the wine that makes a man an ape,
And that is when a man plays with a straw."
The cook grew wroth, for this had touched the raw,
And at the manciple he nodded fast
For lack of speech, and him his horse did cast,
And there he lay till up the rest him took,
Which was a feat of riding for a cook!
Alas! That he had kept not to his ladle!
For ere he was again within his saddle,
There was a mighty shoving to and fro
To lift him up, and hugeous care and woe,
So all unwieldy was this sorry ghost.
And to the manciple then spoke our host:
"Since drink has got such utter domination
Over this fellow here, by my salvation,
I think that badly he would tell his tale.
For whether wine or old or musty ale
Is what he's drunk, he speaks all through his nose;
He snorts hard and with cold he's lachrymose.
Also he has more than enough to do
To keep him and his nag out of the slough;
And if he fall down off his horse again,
We'll all have quite enough of labour then
In lifting up his heavy drunken corse.
Tell on your tale, he matters not, of course.
"Yet, manciple, in faith, you are not wise
Thus openly to chide him for his vice.
Some day he'll get revenge, you may be sure,
And call you like a falcon to the lure;
I mean he'll speak of certain little things,
As, say, to point out in your reckonings
Things not quite honest, were they put to proof."
"Nay," said the manciple, "that were ill behoof!
So might he easily catch me in his snare.
Yet would I rather pay him for the mare
Which he rides on than have him with me strive;
I will not rouse his rage, so may I thrive!
That which I said, I said as jesting word;
And know you what? I have here, in a gourd,
A draught of wine, yea, of a good ripe grape,
And now anon you shall behold a jape.

And that our host wol, of his curteisye,
I wol as now excuse thee of thy tale;
For, in good feith, thy visage is ful pale,
Thyn yën daswen eek, as that me thinketh,
And wel I woot, thy breeth ful soure stinketh,
That sheweth wel thou art not wel disposed;
Of me, certein, thou shalt nat been y-glosed.
Se how he ganeth, lo, this dronken wight,
As though he wolde us swolwe anon-right.
Hold cloos thy mouth, man, by thy fader kin!
The devel of helle sette his foot ther-in!
Thy cursed breeth infecte wol us alle;
Fy, stinking swyn, fy! foule moot thee falle!
A! taketh heed, sirs, of this lusty man.
Now, swete sir, wol ye justen atte fan?[1]
Ther-to me thinketh ye been wel y-shape!
I trowe that ye dronken han wyn ape,
And that is whan men pleyen with a straw"
And with this speche the cook wex wrooth and wraw,
And on the maunciple he gan nodde faste
For lakke of speche, and doun the hors him caste,
Wher as he lay, til that men up him took;
This was a fayr chivachee of a cook!
Allas! he nadde holde him by his ladel!
And, er that he agayn were in his sadel,
Ther was greet showving bothe to and fro,
To lifte him up, and muchel care and wo,
So unweldy was this sory palled gost.
And to the maunciple thanne spak our host,
"By-cause drink hath dominacioun
Upon this man, by my savacioun
I trowe he lewedly wolde telle his tale.
For, were it wyn, or old or moysty ale,
That he hath dronke, he speketh in his nose,
And fneseth faste, and eek he hath the pose.
He hath also to do more than y-nough
To kepe him and his capel out of slough;
And, if he falle from his capel eft-sone,
Than shul we alle have y-nough to done,
In lifting up his hevy dronken cors.
Telle on thy tale, of him make I no fors.
But yet, maunciple, in feith thou art to nyce,
Thus openly repreve him of his vyce.
Another day he wol, peraventure,
Reclayme thee, and bringe thee to lure;
I mene, he speke wol of smale thinges,
As for to pinchen at thy rekeninges,
That wer not honeste, if it cam to preef."
"No," quod the maunciple, "that were a greet mescheef!
So mighte he lightly bringe me in the snare.
Yet hadde I lever payen for the mare
Which he rit on, than he sholde with me stryve;
I wol nat wratthe him, al-so mote I thryve!
That that I spak, I seyde it in my bourde;
And wite ye what? I have heer, in a gourde,
A draught of wyn, ye, of a rype grape,
And right anon ye shul seen a good jape.

[1]A vane or quintain. To ride at fan (or at quintain) was to tilt at a board at one end of a pivoted crossbar, at the other end of which was suspended a sandbag. The object was to strike the board with the lance and to escape being hit by the sandbag.

This cook shal drinke ther-of, if I may;
Up peyne of deeth, he wol nat seye me nay!"
  And certeinly, to tellen as it was,
Of this vessel the cook drank faste, allas!
What neded him? he drank y-nough biforn.
And whan he hadde pouped in this horn
To the maunciple he took the gourde agayn;
And of that drinke the cook was wonder fayn,
And thanked him in swich wyse as he coude.
  Than gan our host to laughen wonder loude,
And seyde, "I see wel, it is necessarie,
Wher that we goon, good drink we with us carie;
For that wol turne rancour and disese
T'acord and love, and many a wrong apese.
  O thou Bachus, y-blessed be thy name,
That so canst turnen ernest in-to game!
Worship and thank be to thy deitee!
Of that matere ye gete na-more of me.
Tel on thy tale, maunciple, I thee preye."
  "Wel, sir," quod he, "now herkneth what I seye."

This cook shall drink thereof, sir, if I may;
On pain of death he will not say me nay!"
  And certainly, to tell it as it was,
Out of this gourd the cook drank deep, alas!
What need had he? He'd drunk enough that morn
And when he had blown into this said horn,
He gave the manciple the gourd again;
And of that drink the cook was wondrous fain,
And thanked him then in such wise as he could.
  Then did our host break into laughter loud,
And said: "I see well it is necessary,
Wher'er we go, good drink with us we carry;
For that will turn rancour and all unease
To accord and love, and many a wrong appease.
  "O Bacchus, thou, all blessed be thy name
Who canst so turn stern earnest into game!
Honour and thanks be to thy deity!
Concerning which you'll get no more from me.
Tell on your tale, good manciple, I pray."
  "Well, sir," said he, "now hear what I will say."

THUS ENDETH THE PROLOGUE OF THE MANCIPLE

THE MANCIPLE'S TALE

HERE BEGINNETH THE MANCIPLE'S TALE OF THE CROW

Whan Phebus dwelled here in this erthe adoun,
As olde bokes maken mencioun,
He was the moste lusty bachiler[1]
In al this world, and eek the beste archer;
He slow Phitoun, the serpent, as he lay
Slepinge agayn the sonne upon a day;
And many another noble worthy dede
He with his bowe wroghte, as men may rede.
  Pleyen he coude on every minstralcye,
And singen, that it was a melodye,
To heren of his clere vois the soun.
Certes the king of Thebes, Amphioun,
That with his singing walled that citee,
Coude never singen half so wel as he.
Therto he was the semelieste man
That is or was, sith that the world bigan.
What nedeth it his fetures to discryve?
For in this world was noon so fair on lyve.
He was ther-with fulfild of gentillesse,
Of honour, and of parfit worthinesse.
  This Phebus, that was flour of bachelrye,
As wel in fredom as in chivalrye,
For his desport, in signe eek of victorie
Of Phitoun, so as telleth us the storie,
Was wont to beren in his hand a bowe.
  Now had this Phebus in his hous a crowe,
Which in a cage he fostred many a day,
And taughte it speken, as men teche a jay.
Whyt was this crowe, as is a snow-whyt swan,
And countrefete the speche of every man
He coude, whan he sholde telle a tale.
Ther-with in al this world no nightingale

When Phoebus once on earth was dwelling, here,
As in the ancient books it is made clear,
He was the lustiest of bachelors[1]
In all this world, and even the best archer;
He slew Python, the serpent, as he lay
Sleeping within the sunlight, on a day;
And many another noble, worthy deed
He with his bow wrought, as all men may read.
  He played all instruments of minstrelsy,
And sang so that it made great harmony
To hear his clear voice in the joyous sun.
Truly the king of Thebes, that Amphion
Who, by his singing, walled that great city,
Could never sing one half so well as he.
Therewith he was the handsomest young man
That is or was since first the world began.
What needs it that his features I revive?
For in the world was none so fair alive.
Compact of honour and of nobleness,
Perfect he was in every worthiness.
  This Phoebus, of all youthful knights the flower,
Whom generous chivalry did richly dower,
For his amusement (sign of victory
Over that Python, says the old story),
Was wont to bear in hand a golden bow.
  Now Phoebus had within his house a crow,
Which in a cage he'd fostered many a day,
And taught to speak, as men may teach a jay.
White was this crow as is a snow white swan,
And counterfeit the speech of any man
He could, when he desired to tell a tale.
Therewith, in all this world, no nightingale

[1] A young knight.

Could, by a hundred-thousandth part, they tell,
Carol and sing so merrily and well.
Now had this Phoebus in his house a wife,
Whom he loved better than he loved his life,
And night and day he used much diligence
To please her and to do her reverence,
Save only, if it's truth that I shall say,
Jealous he was and so did guard her aye;
For he was very loath befooled to be.
And so is everyone in such degree;
But all in vain, for it avails one naught.
A good wife, who is clean in deed and thought,
Should not be kept a prisoner, that's plain;
And certainly the labour is in vain
That guards a slut, for, sirs, it just won't be.
This hold I for an utter idiocy,
That men should lose their labour guarding wives;
So say these wise old writers in their lives.
But now to purpose, as I first began:
This worthy Phoebus did all that a man
Could do to please, thinking that by such pleasures,
And by his manhood and his other measures
To make her love him and keep faithful, too.
But God knows well that nothing man may do
Will ever keep restrained a thing that nature
Has made innate in any human creature.
Take any bird and put it in a cage
And do your best affection to engage
And rear it tenderly with meat and drink
Of all the dainties that you can bethink,
And always keep it cleanly as you may;
Although its cage of gold be never so gay,
Yet would this bird, by twenty thousand-fold,
Rather, within a forest dark and cold,
Go to eat worms and all such wretchedness.
For ever this bird will do his business
To find some way to get outside the wires.
Above all things his freedom he desires.
Or take a cat, and feed him well with milk
And tender flesh, and make his bed of silk,
And let him see a mouse go by the wall;
Anon he leaves the milk and flesh and all
And every dainty that is in that house,
Such appetite has he to eat a mouse.
Desire has here its mighty power shown
And inborn appetite reclaims its own.
A she-wolf also has a vulgar mind;
The wretchedest he-wolf that she may find,
Or least of reputation, she'll not hate
Whenever she's desirous of a mate.
All these examples speak I of these men
Who are untrue, and not of sweet women.
For men have aye a lickerish appetite
On lower things to do their base delight
Than on their wives, though they be ne'er so fair
And ne'er so true and ne'er so debonair.
Flesh is so fickle, lusting beyond measure,
That we in no one thing can long have pleasure
Or virtuous keep more than a little while.
This Phoebus, who was thinking of no guile,
He was deceived, for all his quality;
For under him a substitute had she,

Ne coude, by an hondred thousand deel,
Singen so wonder merily and weel.
Now had this Phebus in his hous a wyf,
Which that he lovede more than his lyf,
And night and day dide ever his diligence
Hir for to plese, and doon hir reverence,
Save only, if the sothe that I shal sayn,
Jalous he was, and wolde have kept hir fayn;
For him were looth by-japed for to be.
And so in every wight in swich degree;
But al in ydel, for it availleth noght.
A good wyf, that is clene of werk and thoght,
Sholde nat been kept in noon await, certayn;
And trewely, the labour is in vayn
To kepe a shrewe, for it wol nat be.
This holde I for a verray nycetee,
To spille labour, for to kepe wyves;
Thus writen olde clerkes in hir lyves.
But now to purpos, as I first bigan:
This worthy Phebus dooth all that he can
To plesen hir, weninge by swich plesaunce,
And for his manhede and his governaunce,
That no man sholde han put him from hir grace.
But god it woot, ther may no man embrace
As to destreyne a thing, which that nature
Hath naturelly set in a creature.
Tak any brid, and put it in a cage,
And do al thyn entente and thy corage
To fostre it tendrely with mete and drinke,
Of alle deyntees that thou canst bithinke,
And keep it al-so clenly as thou may;
Al-though his cage of gold be never so gay,
Yet hath this brid, by twenty thousand fold,
Lever in a forest, that is rude and cold,
Gon ete wormes and swich wrecchednesse.
For ever this brid wol doon his bisinesse
To escape out of his cage, if he may;
His libertee this brid desireth ay.
Lat take a cat, and fostre him wel with milk,
And tendre flesh, and make his couche of silk,
And lat him seen a mous go by the wal;
Anon he weyveth milk, and flesh, and al,
And every deyntee that is in that hous,
Swich appetyt hath he to ete a mous.
Lo, here hath lust his dominacioun,
And appetyt flemeth discrecioun.
A she-wolf hath also a vileins kinde;
The lewedeste wolf that she may finde,
Or leest of reputacion wol she take,
In tyme whan hir lust to han a make.
Alle thise ensamples speke I by thise men
That been untrewe, and no-thing by wommen.
For men han ever a likerous appetyt
On lower thing to parfourne hir delyt
Than on hir wyves, be they never so faire,
Ne never so trewe, ne so debonaire.
Flesh is so newefangel, with meschaunce,
That we ne conne in no-thing han plesaunce
That souneth in-to vertu any whyle.
This Phebus, which that thoghte upon no gyle,
Deceyved was, for al his jolitee;
For under him another hadde she,

A man of litel reputacioun,
Noght worth to Phebus in comparisoun.
The more harm is; it happeth ofte so,
Of which ther cometh muchel harm and wo.
And so bifel, whan Phebus was absent,
His wyf anon hath for hir lemman[1] sent;
Hir lemman? certes, this is a knavish speche!
Foryeveth it me, and that I yow biseche.
The wyse Plato seith, as ye may rede,
The word mot nede accorde with the dede.
If men shal telle proprely a thing,
The word mot cosin be to the werking.
I am a boistous man, right thus seye I,
Ther nis no difference, trewely,
Bitwixe a wyf that is of heigh degree,
If of hir body dishonest she be,
And a povre wenche, other than this—
If it so be, they werke bothe amis—
But that the gentile, in estaat above,
She shal be cleped his lady, as in love;
And for that other is a povre womman,
She shal be cleped his wenche, or his lemman.
And, god it woot, myn owene dere brother,
Men leyn that oon as lowe as lyth that other.
Right so, bitwixe a titlelees tiraunt
And an outlawe, or a theef erraunt,
The same I seye, ther is no difference.
To Alisaundre told was this sentence;
That, for the tyrant is of gretter might,
By force of meynee for to sleen doun-right,
And brennen hous and hoom, and make al plain,
Lo! therfor is he cleped a capitain;
And, for the outlawe hath but smal meynee,
And may nat doon so greet an harm as he,
Ne bringe a contree to so greet mescheef,
Men clepen him an outlawe or a theef.
But, for I am a man noght textuel,
I wol noght telle of textes never a del;
I wol go to my tale, as I bigan.
Whan Phebus wyf had sent for hir lemman,
Anon they wroghten al hir lust volage.
The whyte crowe, that heng ay in the cage,
Biheld hir werk, and seyde never a word.
And whan that hoom was come Phebus, the lord,
This crowe sang "cokkow! cokkow! cokkow!"
"What, brid?" quod Phebus, "what song singestow?
Ne were thow wont so merily to singe
That to myn herte it was a rejoisinge
To here thy vois? allas! what song is this?"
"By god," quod he, "I singe nat amis;
Phebus," quod he, "for al thy worthinesse,
For al thy beautee and thy gentilesse,
For al thy song and al thy minstralcye,
For al thy waiting, blered is thyn yë
With oon of litel reputacioun,
Noght worth to thee, as in comparisoun,
The mountance of a gnat; so mote I thryve!
For on thy bed thy wyf I saugh him swyve."
What wol ye more? the crowe anon him tolde,
By sadde tokenes and by wordes bolde,

A man of little reputation, one
Worth naught to Phoebus, by comparison.
The more harm that; it often happens so,
Whereof there come so much of harm and woe.
And so befell, when Phoebus was absent,
His wife has quickly for her leman[1] sent.
Her leman? Truly, 'tis a knavish speech!
Forgive it me, I do indeed beseech.
The wise old Plato says, as you may read,
The word must needs accord well with the deed.
And if a man tell properly a thing,
The word must suited be to the acting.
But I'm a vulgar man, and thus say I,
There is no smallest difference, truly,
Between a wife who is of high degree,
If of her body she dishonest be,
And a poor unknown wench, other than this—
If it be true that both do what's amiss—
The gentlewoman, in her state above,
She shall be called his lady, in their love;
And since the other's but a poor woman,
She shall be called his wench or his leman.
And God knows very well, my own dear brother,
Men lay the one as low as lies the other.
Between a tyrant or usurping chief
And any outlawed man or errant thief,
It's just the same, there is no difference.
One told to Alexander this sentence:
That, since the tyrant is of greater might,
By force of numbers, to slay men outright
And burn down house and home even as a plane,
Lo! for that he's a captain, that's certain;
And since the outlaw has small company
And may not do so great a harm as he,
Nor bring a nation into such great grief,
Why, he's called but an outlaw or a thief.
But since I'm not a man the texts to spell,
Nothing at all from texts now will I tell;
I'll go on with my tale as I began.
When Phoebus' wife had sent for her leman,
At once they wrought all of their libertinage.
And the white crow, aye hanging in the cage,
Saw what they did, and never said a word.
And when again came Phoebus home, the lord,
This crow sang loud "Cuckoo! Cuckoo! Cuckoo!"
"What, bird?" asked Phoebus, "What song now sing you?
Were you not wont so merrily to sing
That in my heart it was a joyful thing
To hear your voice? Alas! What song is this?"
"By God," said he, "I do not sing amiss;
Phoebus," said he, "for all your worthiness,
For all your beauty and your nobleness,
For all your song and all your minstrelsy,
For all your watching, bleared is your bright eye
By one of small repute, as well is known,
Not worth, when I compare it with your own,
The value of a gnat, as I may thrive.
For on your bed your wife I saw him swive."
What will you more? The crow thereafter told,
In sober fashion, giving witness bold,

[1] Formerly applied to either sex.

How that his wife had done her lechery
To his great shame and with great villainy;
Repeating that he'd seen it with his eyes.
Then Phoebus turned away in sad surprise;
He thought his wretched heart would break for woe;
His bow he bent and set there an arrow,
And in his angry mood his wife did slay.
This the result; there is no more to say;
For grief of which he ceased his minstrelsy,
Broke harp and lute, gittern and psaltery;
And, too, he broke his arrows and his bow.
And after that he spoke thus to the crow.
"Traitor," cried he, "with tongue of scorpion,
You have brought me to ruin, treacherous one!
Alas, that I was born! Why died I not?
O my dear wife, jewel of joy, God wot,
Who were to me so trusty and so true,
Now you lie dead, with face all pale of hue,
And you were guiltless, I dare swear to this!
O hasty hand, to do so foul amiss!
O stupid brain, O anger all reckless,
That unadvisedly struck the guiltless!
O ill distrust that jealousy had sown!
Where were your thought and your discretion flown?
O every man, beware of hastiness,
Do not believe without a strong witness;
Strike not too soon, before you reason why,
And be advised full well and soberly
Ere you do any execution thus
In your wild anger when it is jealous.
Alas! A thousand folk has hasty ire
Ruined, and left them bleeding in the mire.
Alas! I'll slay myself forthwith for grief!"
And to the crow he said, "O you false thief!
I will anon requite you that false tale!
You sang but lately like a nightingale;
Now, you false thief, your songs are over and done,
And you'll all those white feathers lose, each one,
Nor ever in your life more shall you speak.
Thus men on traitors shall their justice wreak;
You and your offspring ever shall be black,
Nor evermore sweet noises shall you make,
But you shall cry in tempest and in rain
In token that through you my wife was slain."
And on the crow he leaped, and that anon,
And plucked out his white feathers, every one,
And made him black, and stilled for evermore
His song and speech, and flung him out the door
Unto the devil, where I leave this jack;
And for this reason, now all crows are black.
Masters, by this example, I do pray
You will beware and heed what I shall say:
Never tell any man, through all your life,
How that another man has humped his wife;
He'll hate you mortally, and that's certain.
Dan Solomon, as these wise clerks explain,
Teaches a man to keep his tongue from all;
But, as I said, I am not textual.
Nevertheless, thus taught me my good dame:
"My son, think of the crow, in high God's name;

How that his wyf had doon hir lecherye,
Him to gret shame and to gret vileinye;
And tolde him ofte, he saugh it with his yën.
This Phebus gan aweyward for to wryen,
Him thoughte his sorweful herte brast a-two;
His bowe he bente, and sette ther-inne a flo,
And in his ire his wyf thanne hath he slayn.
This is th'effect, ther is na-more to sayn;
For sorwe of which he brak his minstralcye,
Bothe harpe, and lute, and giterne, and sautrye;
And eek he brak his arwes and his bowe.
And after that, thus spak he to the crowe:
"Traitour," quod he, "with tonge of scorpioun,
Thou hast me broght to my confusioun!
Allas! that I was wroght! why nere I deed?
O dere wyf, O gemme of lustiheed,
That were to me so sad and eek so trew,
Now lystow deed, with face pale of hewe,
Ful giltelees, that dorste I swere, y-wis!
O rakel hand, to doon so foule amis!
O trouble wit, O ire recchelees,
That unavysed smytest giltelees!
O wantrust, ful of fals suspecioun,
Where was thy wit and thy discrecioun?
O every man, be-war of rakelnesse,
Ne trowe no-thing with-outen strong witnesse;
Smyt nat to sone, er that ye witen why,
And beeth avysed wel and sobrely
Er ye doon any execucioun,
Up-on your ire, for suspecioun.
Allas! a thousand fok hath rakel ire
Fully fordoon, and broght hem in the mire.
Allas! for sorwe I wol my-selven slee!"
And to the crowe, "O false theef!" seyde he,
"I wol thee quyte anon thy false tale!
Thou songe whylom lyk a nightingale;
Now shaltow, false theef, thy song forgon,
And eek thy whyte fetheres everichon,
Ne never in al thy lyf ne shaltou speke.
Thus shal men on a traitour been awreke;
Thou and thyn of-spring ever shul be blake,
Ne never swete noise shul ye make,
But ever crye agayn tempest and rayn,
In tokeninge that thurgh thee my wyf is slayn."
And to the crowe he stirte, and that anon,
And pulled his whyte fetheres everichon,
And made him blak, and refte him al his song,
And eek his speche, and out at dore him slong
Un-to the devel, which I him bitake
And for this caas ben alle crowes blake.—
Lordings, by this ensample I yow preye,
Beth war, and taketh kepe what I seye:
Ne telleth never no man in your lyf
How that another man hath dight his wyf;
He wol yow haten mortally, certeyn.
Daun Salomon, as wyse clerkes seyn,
Techeth a man to kepe his tonge wel;
But as I seyde, I am noght textuel.
But nathelees, thus taughte me my dame:
"My sone, thenk on the crowe, a goddes name;

My sone, keep wel thy tonge and keep thy freend.
A wikked tonge is worse than a feend.
My sone, from a feend men may hem blesse;
My sone, god of his endelees goodnesse
Walled a tonge with teeth and lippes eke,
For man sholde him avyse what he speke.
My sone, ful ofte, for to muche speche,
Hath many a man ben spilt, as clerkes teche;
But for a litel speche avysely
Is no men shent, to speke generally.
My sone, thy tonge sholdestow restreyne
At alle tyme, but whan thou doost thy peyne
To speke of god, in honour and preyere.
The firste vertu, sone, if thou wolt lere,
Is to restreyne and kepe wel thy tonge.—
Thus lerne children whan that they ben yonge.—
My sone, of muchel speking yvel-avysed,
Ther lasse speking hadde y-nough suffysed,
Comth muchel harm, thus was me told and taught.
In muchel speche sinne wanteth naught.
Wostow wher-of a rakel tonge serveth?
Right as a swerd forcutteth and forkerveth
An arm a-two, my dere sone, right so
A tonge cutteth frendship al a-two.
A jangler is to god abhominable;
Reed Salomon, so wys and honurable;
Reed David in his psalmes, reed Senekke.
My sone, spek nat, but with thyn heed thou bekke.
Dissimule as thou were deef, if that thou here
A jangler speke of perilous matere.
The Fleming seith, and lerne it, if thee leste,
That litel jangling causeth muchel reste.
My sone, if thou no wikked word hast seyd,
Thee thar nath drede for to be biwreyd;
But he that hath misseyd, I dar wel sayn,
He may by no wey clepe his word agayn.
Thing that is seyd, is seyd; and forth it gooth,
Though him repente, or be him leef or looth.
He is his thral to whom that he hath sayd
A tale, of which he is now yvel apayd.
My sone, be war, and be non auctour newe
Of tydinges, whether they ben false or trewe.
Wher-so thou come, amonges hye or lowe,
Kepe wel thy tonge, and thenk up-on the crowe."

My, son keep your tongue still, and keep your friend.
A wicked tongue is worse than any fiend.
My son, from devils men themselves may bless;
My son, high God, of His endless goodness,
Walled up the tongue with teeth and lips and cheeks
That man should speak advisedly when he speaks.
My son, full oftentimes, for too much speech,
Has many a man been killed, as clerics teach;
But, speaking little and advisedly,
Is no man harmed, to put it generally.
My son, your foolish tongue you should restrain
At all times, save those when your soul is fain
To speak of God, in honour and in prayer.
The first of virtues, son, if you'll but hear,
Is to restrain and to guard well your tongue—
Thus teach the children while they yet are young—
My son, of too much speaking, ill advised,
Where less had been enough and had sufficed,
Much harm may come; thus was I told and taught.
In fluent speaking evil wants for naught.
Know you of where a rash tongue has well served?
Just as a sword has cut deep and has carved
A many an arm in two, dear son, just so
A tongue can cut a friendship, well I know.
A gossip is to God abominable.
Read Solomon, so wise and honourable,
Or David's Psalms, what Seneca has said.
My son, speak not, but merely bow your head.
Dissemble like one deaf, if you but hear
A chatterer speak what's dangerous in your ear.
The Fleming says, and learn it, for it's best,
That little prattle gives us all much rest.
My son, if you no wicked word have said,
To be betrayed you need not ever dread;
But he that has missaid, I dare explain,
He may not aye recall his words again.
That which is said, is said, and goes, in truth,
Though he repent, and be he lief or loath.
A man's the slave of him to whom he's told
A tale to which he can no longer hold.
My son, beware and be not author new
Of tidings, whether they be false or true.
Where'er you come, among the high or low,
Guard well your tongue, and think upon the crow."

HERE IS ENDED THE MANCIPLE'S TALE OF THE CROW

THE PARSON'S PROLOGUE

HERE FOLLOWETH THE PROLOGUE OF THE PARSON'S TALE

By that the maunciple hadde his tale al ended,
The sonne fro the south lyne was descended
So lowe, that he nas nat, to my sighte,
Degreës nyne and twenty as in highte.
Foure of the clokke it was tho, as I gesse:
For eleven foot, or litel more or lesse,
My shadwe was at thilke tyme, as there,
Of swich feet as my lengthe parted were

What time the manciple his tale had ended,
The sun down from the south line had descended
So low that he was not, unto my sight,
Degrees full nine and twenty yet in height.
Four of the clock it was then, as I guess:
Four feet eleven, little more or less,
My shadow was extended then and there,
A length as if the shadow parted were

In six-foot equal parts, as I have shown.
Therewith the moon's high exaltation known,
I mean the sign of Libra, did ascend
As we were entering a village-end;
Whereat our host, since wont to guide was he,
As in this case, our jolly company,
Said in this wise: "Now, masters, every one,
We lack no tales except a single one.
My judgment is fulfilled and my decree,
I think that we have heard from each degree.
Almost fulfilled is all my ordinance;
I pray to God to give him right good chance
Who tells to us this story pleasantly.
Sir priest," he asked, "can you a vicar be?
Are you a parson? Tell truth, by your fay!
Be what you will, break not our jolly play;
For every man, save you, has told his tale,
Unbuckle, show us what is in your mail;
For truly, I think, judging by your cheer,
You should knit up a mighty matter here.
Tell us a fable now, by Cock's dear bones!"

This parson then replied to him at once:
"You'll get no foolish fable told by me;
For Paul, when writing unto Timothy,
Reproves all those that veer from truthfulness
And tell false fables and such wretchedness.
Why should I sow chaff out of my own fist
When I may sow good wheat, if I but list?
But if, I say, you something wish to hear
In which the moral virtues will appear,
And if you now will give me audience,
I will right gladly, in Christ's reverence,
Give you such lawful pleasure as I can.
But trust me, since I am a Southern man,
I can't romance with 'rum, ram, ruff'[1], by letter,
And, God knows, rhyme I hold but little better;
But if you wish the truth made plain and straight,
A pleasant tale in prose I will relate
To weave our feast together at the end.
May Jesus, of His grace, the wit me send
To show you, as we journey this last stage,
The way of that most perfect pilgrimage
To heavenly Jerusalem on high.
And if you will vouchsafe, anon shall I
Begin my tale, concerning which, I pray,
Choose what you will, I can no better say.
Yet this my meditation is, I own,
Perhaps not free from errors to be shown
By clerks, since I am not a learned man;
I do but grasp the meaning as I can.
Therefore, I do protest, I shall prepare
To take what comes, and all correction bear."

When he had spoken thus, we all agreed,
For, as it seemed to us, 'twas right indeed
To end with something virtuous in its sense,
And so to give him time and audience.
We bade our host that he to him convey
The wish of all that he begin straightway.

Our host, he had the very words for all.
"Sir priest," said he, "may good to you befall!
Say what you wish, and we will gladly hear."

In six feet equal of proporcioun.
Ther-with the mones exaltacioun,
I mene Libra, alwey gan ascende,
As we were entringe at a thropes ende;
For which our host, as he was wont to gye,
As in this caas, our joly companye,
Seyde in this wyse, "lordings everichoon,
Now lakketh us no tales mo than oon.
Fulfild is my sentence and my decree;
I trowe that we han herd of ech degree.
Almost fulfild is al myn ordinaunce;
I prey to god, so yeve him right good chaunce,
That telleth this tale to us lustily.
Sir preest," quod he, "artow a vicary?
Or art a person? sey sooth, by thy fey!
Be what thou be, ne breke thou nat our pley;
For every man, save thou, hath told his tale,
Unbokel, and shewe us what is in thy male;
For trewely, me thinketh, by thy chere,
Thou sholdest knitte up wel a greet matere.
Tel us a tale anon, for cokkes bones!"

This Persone him answerde, al at ones,
"Thou getest fable noon y-told for me;
For Paul, that wryteth unto Timothee,
Repreveth hem that weyven soothfastnesse,
And tellen fables and swich wrecchednesse.
Why sholde I sowen draf out of my fest,
Whan I may sowen whete, if that me lest?
For which I seye, if that yow list to here
Moralitee and vertuous matere,
And thanne that ye wol yeve me audience,
I wol ful fayn, at Cristes reverence,
Do yow plesaunce leefful, as I can.
But trusteth wel, I am a Southren man,
I can nat geste—rum, ram, ruf[1]—by lettre,
Ne, god wot, rym holde I but litel bettre;
And therfor, if yow list, I wol nat glose.
I wol yow telle a mery tale in prose
To knitte up al this feeste, and make an ende.
And Jesu, for his grace, wit me sende
To shewe yow the wey, in this viage,
Of thilke parfit glorious pilgrimage
That highte Jerusalem celestial.
And, if ye vouche-sauf, anon I shal
Biginne upon my tale, for whiche I preye
Telle your avys, I can no bettre seye.
But nathelees, this meditacioun
I putte it ay under correccioun
Of clerkes, for I am nat textuel;
I take but the sentens, trusteth wel.
Therfor I make protestacioun
That I wol stonde to correccioun."

Up-on this word we han assented sone,
For, as us semed, it was for to done,
To enden in som vertuous sentence,
And for to yeve him space and audience;
And bede our host he sholde to him seye,
That alle we to telle his tale him preye.

Our host hadde the wordes for us alle:—
"Sir preest," quod he, "now fayre yow bifalle!
Sey what yow list, and we wol gladly here"—

[1]Nonsense words, to imitate and mock at alliteration.

And with that word he seyde in this manere—
"Telleth," quod he, "your meditacioun,
But hasteth yow, the sonne wol adoun;
Beth fructuous, and that in litel space,
And to do wel god sende yow his grace!"

And after that he added, for his ear:
"Tell us," he said, "your meditation grown,
But pray make haste, the sun will soon be down;
Be fruitful, tell us in a little space,
And to do well God send to you His grace!"

HERE ENDETH THE PROEM

THE PARSON'S TALE

HERE BEGINNETH THE PARSON'S TALE

Jer. 6°. *State super vias et videte et interrogate de viis antiquis, que sit via bona; et ambulate in ea, et inuenietis refrigerium animabus vestris, &c.*

1. Our swete lord god of hevene, that no man wol perisse, but wole that we comen alle to the knoweleche of him, and to the blisful lyf that is perdurable, amonesteth us by the prophete Jeremie, that seith in this wyse: "stondeth upon the weyes, and seeth and axeth of olde pathes (that is to seyn, of olde sentences) which is the goode wey; and walketh in that wey, and ye shul finde refresshinge for your soules," &c. Manye been the weyes espirituels that leden folk to oure Lord Jesu Crist, and to the regne of glorie. Of whiche weyes, ther is a ful noble wey and a ful covenable, which may nat faile to man ne to womman, that thurgh sinne hath misgoon fro the righte wey of Jerusalem celestial; and this wey is cleped Penitence, of which man sholde gladly herknen and enquere with al his herte; to witen what is Penitence, and whennes it is cleped Penitence, and in how manye maneres been the accions of werkinges of Penitence, and how manye spyces ther been of Penitence, and whiche thinges apertenen and bihoven to Penitence, and whiche thinges destourben Penitence.

Our sweet Lord God of Heaven, Who will destroy no man, but would have all come unto the knowledge of Him and to the blessed life that is everlasting, admonishes us by the Prophet Jeremiah, who says thus: "Stand ye in the ways, and see, and ask for the old paths (that is to say, the old wisdom) where is the good way, and walk therein, and ye shall find rest for your souls," etc. Many are the spiritual ways that lead folk unto Our Lord Jesus Christ and to the Kingdom of Glory. Of which ways there is a right noble way and a proper one, which will not fail either man or woman who through sin has gone astray from the right way to the Heavenly Jerusalem; and this way is called penitence, as to which man should gladly hear and inquire with all his heart, in order that he may learn what penitence is, and why it is called penitence, and in how many ways penitence functions, and how many kinds of penitence there are, and what things appertain and are necessary to penitence, and what things hinder it.

2. Seint Ambrose seith, that "Penitence is the pleyninge of man for the gilt that he hath doon, and na-more to do any thing for which him oghte to pleyne." And som doctour seith: "Penitence is the waymentinge of man, that sorweth for his sinne and pyneth himself for he hath misdoon." Penitence, with certeyne circumstances, is verray repentance of a man that halt him-self in sorwe and other peyne for hise giltes. And for he shal be verray penitent, he shal first biwailen the sinnes that he hath doon, and stidefastly purposen in his herte to have shrift of mouthe, and to doon satisfaccioun, and never to doon thing for which him oghte more to biwayle or to compleyne, and to continue in goode werkes: or elles his repentance may nat availle. For as seith seint Isidre: "he is a japer and a gabber, and no verray repentant, that eftsoone dooth thing, for which him oghte repente." Wepinge, and nat for to stinte to doon sinne, may nat avaylle. But nathelees, men shal hope that every tyme that man falleth, be it never so ofte, that he may arise thurgh Penitence, if he have grace: but certeinly it is greet doute. For as seith Seint Gregorie: "unnethe aryseth he out of sinne, that is charged with the charge of yvel usage." And there-

Saint Ambrose says that "penitence is the mourning of man for the sin that he has done, and the resolve to do no more anything for which he ought to mourn." And another doctor says: "Penitence is the lamenting of man, who sorrows for his sin and punishes himself because he has done amiss." Penitence, under certain circumstances, is the true repentance of a man that goes in sorrow and other pain for his misdeeds. And that he shall be truly penitent, he shall first regret the sins that he has done, and steadfastly purpose in his heart to make oral confession, and to do penance, and nevermore to do anything for which he ought to feel regret or to mourn, and to continue on good works; or else his repentance will avail him nothing. For, as says Saint Isidore: "He is a mocker and a liar and no true penitent who does again a thing for which he ought to repent." Weeping, when not accompanied by a refusal to sin, shall not avail. But, nevertheless, men should hope that every time a man falls, be it never so often, he may arise through penitence, if he have grace; but certainly there is great doubt of this. For, as Saint Gregory says: "With difficulty shall he arise out of sin who is burdened with the burden of evil habit." And therefore repentant folk, who keep from sin and abandon sin ere sin abandon them, Holy Church holds them to be sure of their salvation. And he that sins and verily repents in his last moments, Holy Church yet hopes for his salvation, what of the great mercy of Our Lord Jesus Christ, because of his repentance; but take you the certain way.

And now, since I have declared unto you what penitence is, now shall you understand that there are three deeds required by penitence. The first deed is that a man be baptized after he has sinned. Saint Augustine says: "Save he be repentant for his former sinful life, he shall not begin to lead the new clean life." For truly, if he be baptized without repentance for his old offence, he receives the sign of baptism but not the grace nor the remission of his sins, until he have true repentance. Another defect is this, that men do deadly sin after they have received baptism. The third defect is that men fall into venial sins after their baptism, and from day to day. Thereof Saint Augustine says that "penitence of good and humble folk is the penitence of every day."

The kinds of penitence are three. One of them is public, another is general, and the third is private. That form of penitence which is public is of two kinds: as to be expelled from Holy Church in Lent, for the slaughter of children and such-like things. Another is, when a man has sinned openly, of which sin the shame is openly spoken of in the community; and then Holy Church, by judgment rendered, constrains him to do open penance. Common or general penitence is when priests enjoin men collectively in certain cases, as, peradventure, to go naked on pilgrimages, or barefoot. Private penitence is that which men do continually for their sins, whereof we confess privately and receive a private penance.

Now shall you understand what is necessary to a true and perfect penitence. And this stands upon three things: contrition of heart, confession by word of mouth, and restitution. As to which Saint John Chrysostom says: "Penitence constrains a man to accept cheerfully every pain that is put upon him, with contrition of heart and oral confession, with restitution; and in doing all of acts of humility." And this is a fruitful penitence for three things wherein we anger Our Lord Jesus Christ; that is to say, by delight in thinking, by recklessness in speaking, and by wicked sinful works. And over against these wicked offences is penitence, which may be likened unto a tree.

The root of this tree is contrition, which hides itself away in the heart of him who is truly repentant, just as the root of another tree hides within the earth. From the root contrition springs a trunk that bears branches and leaves of confession and the fruit of penance, as to which Christ says in His gospel: "Bring forth therefore fruits meet for repentance." For by this fruit may men know this tree, and not by the root that is hidden in the heart of man, nor

fore repentant folk, that stinte for to sinne, and forlete sinne er that sinne forlete hem, holy chirche holdeth hem siker of hir savacioun. And he that sinneth, and verraily repenteth him in his laste ende, holy chirche yet hopeth his savacioun, by the grete mercy of oure lord Jesu Crist, for his repentaunce; but tak the siker wey.

3. And now, sith I have declared yow what thing is Penitence, now shul ye understonde that ther been three accions of Penitence. The firste accion of Penitence is, that a man be baptized after that he hath sinned. Seint Augustin seith: "but he be penitent for his olde sinful lyf, he may nat biginne the newe clene lif." For certes, if he be baptized withouten penitence of his olde gilt, he receiveth the mark of baptisme, but nat the grace ne the remission of his sinnes, til he have repentance verray. Another defaute is this, that men doon deedly sinne after that they han received baptisme. The thridde defaute is, that men fallen in venial sinnes after hir baptisme, fro day to day. Ther-of seith Seint Augustin, that "penitence of goode and humble folk is the penitence of every day."

4. The spyces of Penitence been three. That oon of hem is solempne, another is commune, and the thridde is privee. Thilke penance that is solempne, is in two maneres; as to be put out of holy chirche in lente, for slaughtre of children, and swich maner thing. Another is, whan a man hath sinned openly, of which sinne the fame is openly spoken in the contree; and thanne holy chirche by jugement destreineth him for to do open penaunce. Commune penaunce is that preestes enjoinen men comunly in certeyn caas; as for to goon, peraventure, naked in pilgrimages, or bare-foot. Privee penaunce is thilke that men doon alday for privee sinnes, of whiche we shryve us prively and receyve privee penaunce.

5. Now shaltow understande what is bihovely and necessarie to verray parfit Penitence. And this stant on three thinges; Contricioun of herte, Confessioun of Mouth, and Satisfaccioun. For which seith Seint John Crisostom: "Penitence destreyneth a man to accepte benignely every peyne that him is enjoyned, with contricion of herte, and shrift of mouth, with satisfaccion; and in werkinge of alle maner humilitee." And this is fruitful Penitence agayn three thinges in whiche we wratthe oure lord Jesu Crist: this is to seyn, by delyt in thinkinge, by recchelesnesse in spekinge, and by wikked sinful werkinge. And agayns thise wikkede giltes is Penitence, that may be lykned un-to a tree.

6. The rote of this tree is Contricion, that hydeth him in the herte of him that is verray repentant, right as the rote of a tree hydeth him in the erthe. Of the rote of Contricion springeth a stalke, that bereth braunches and leves of Confession, and fruit of Satisfaccion. For which Crist seith in his gospel: "dooth digne fruit of Penitence"; for by this fruit may men knowe this tree, and nat by the rote that is hid in the herte of man, ne by the

braunches ne by the leves of Confession. And therefore oure Lord Jesu Crist seith thus: "by the fruit of hem ye shul knowen hem." Of this rote eek springeth a seed of grace, the which seed is moder of sikernesse, and this seed is egre and hoot. The grace of this seed springeth of god, thurgh remembrance of the day of dome and on the peynes of helle. Of this matere seith Salomon, that "in the drede of god man forleteth his sinne." The hete of this seed is the love of god, and the desiring of the joye perdurable. This hete draweth the herte of a man to god, and dooth him haten his sinne. For soothly, ther is no-thing that savoureth so wel to a child as the milk of his norice, ne no-thing is to him more abhominable than thilke milk whan it is medled with other mete. Right so the sinful man that loveth his sinne, him semeth that it is to him most swete of any-thing; but fro that tyme that he loveth sadly our lord Jesu Crist, and desireth the lif perdurable, ther nis to him no-thing more abhominable. For soothly, the lawe of god is the love of god; for which David the prophete seith: "I have loved thy lawe and hated wikkednesse and hate"; he that loveth god kepeth his lawe and his word. This tree saugh the prophete Daniel in spirit, up-on the avision of the king Nabugodonosor, whan he conseiled him to do penitence. Penaunce is the tree of lyf to hem that it receiven, and he that holdeth him in verray penitence is blessed; after the sentence of Salomon.

7. In this Penitence or Contricion man shal understonde foure thinges, that is to seyn, what is Contricion: and whiche been the causes that moeven a man to Contricion: and how he sholde be contrit: and what Contricion availleth to the soule. Thanne is it thus: that Contricion is the verray sorwe that a man receiveth in his herte for his sinnes, with sad purpos to shryve him, and to do penaunce, and nevermore to do sinne. And this sorwe shal been in this manere, as seith seint Bernard: "it shal been hevy and grevous, and ful sharpe and poinant in herte." First, for man hath agilt his lord and his creatour; and more sharpe and poinant, for he hath agilt his fader celestial; and yet more sharpe and poinant, for he hath wrathed and agilt him that boghte him; which with his precious blood hath delivered us fro the bondes of sinne, and fro the crueltee of the devel and fro the peynes of helle.

8. The causes that oghte moeve a man to Contricion been six. First, a man shal remembre him of hise sinnes; but loke he that thilke remembrance ne be to him no delyt by no wey, but greet shame and sorwe for his gilt. For Job seith: "sinful men doon werkes worthy of Confession." And therfore seith Ezechie: "I wol remembre me alle the yeres of my lyf, in bitternesse of myn herte." And god seith in the Apocalips: "remembreth yow fro whennes that ye been falle"; for biforn that tyme that ye sinned, ye were the children of god, and limes of the regne of god; but for your sinne ye been woxen thral and foul, and membres of the

by the branches, nor by the leaves of confession. And therefore Our Lord Jesus Christ says thus: "By their fruits ye shall know them." From this root, too, springs a seed of grace, the which seed is the mother of security, and this seed is eager and hot. The grace of this seed springs from God, through remembrance of the day of doom and the pains of Hell. Of this matter says Solomon: "Fear the Lord, and depart from evil." The heat of this seed is the love of God and the desiring of the joy everlasting. This heat draws the heart of man unto God and causes him to hate his sin. For truly there is nothing that tastes so well to a child as the milk of its nurse, nor is there anything more abhorrent to it than this same milk when it is mingled with other food. Just so, to the sinful man who loves his sin, it seems that it is sweeter than anything else; but from the time that he begins to love devoutly Our Lord Jesus Christ, and desires the life everlasting, there is to him nothing more abominable. For truly the law of God is the love of God; whereof David the prophet says: "Ye that love the Lord, hate evil." He that loves God keeps His law and His word. The Prophet Daniel saw this tree in spirit following upon the vision of King Nebuchadnezzar, when he counselled him to do penance. Penance is the tree of life to those who receive it, and he that holds himself in true penitence is blessed, according to the opinion of Solomon.

In this penitence or contrition man shall understand four things, that is to say, what contrition is, and what the causes are that move a man to contrition, and how he should be contrite, and what contrition avails the soul. Then it is thus: that contrition is the real sorrow that a man receives within his heart for his sins, with firm purpose to confess them and to do penance and nevermore to do sin. And this sorrow shall be in this manner, as says Saint Bernard: "It shall be heavy and grievous and sharp and poignant in the heart." First, because man has offended his Lord and his Creator; and more sharp and poignant because he has offended his Heavenly Father; and yet more sharp and poignant because he has angered and offended Him Who redeemed him, Who with His precious blood has delivered us from the bonds of sin and from the cruelty of the Devil and from the pains of Hell.

The causes that ought to move a man to contrition are six. First, a man should remember his sins, yet see to it that this same remembrance be not to him in any wise a delight, but only great shame and sorrow for his guilt. For Job says: that sinful men do things that ought to be confessed. And therefore Hezekiah says: "I will remember all the years of my life, in bitterness of heart." And God says in the Apocalypse: "Remember from whence thou art fallen." For before that time when first you sinned, you were the children of God and members of the Kingdom of God; but because of your sin you are become slavish and vile, and the children of the Fiend, hated of the angels, the slander of Holy Church, and food of the false serpent. You are perpetual fuel for the fire of Hell. And yet more vile and abominable, for you offend often and often, like the dog that returns to his vomit. And you are even yet more vile, for your long continuation in sin and your sinful habits, for which you are as filthy in your sin as a beast in its dung. Such thoughts cause a man to take shame to himself for his sinning, and not delight, as God says by the Prophet Ezekiel: "Thou shalt remember thy ways and be ashamed." Truly, sins are the ways that lead folk unto Hell.

The second reason why a man ought to have contempt for sin is this: that, as Saint Peter says, "He that sinneth is the slave of sin." And sin puts a man into deep thraldom. And thereupon the Prophet Ezekiel says: "I went sorrowfully, in abhorrence of myself." And truly, well ought a man to abhor sin and to release himself from that thraldom and degradation. And see what Seneca says about this matter. He says thus: "Though I knew that neither God nor man should ever be cognizant of it, yet would I disdain to commit a sin." And the same Seneca also says: "I am born to greater things than to be thrall to my body, or than to make of my body a thrall." Nor a viler thrall may man or woman make of his or her body than by giving that body over to sin. And were it the lowest churl, or the lowest woman, that lives, and the least worth, yet is he or she then more vile and more in servitude. Ever from the higher degree than man falls, the more is he enthralled, and by so much the more to God and to the world is he vile and abominable. O good God! Well ought a man to have disdain of sin; since, because of sin, whereas he was once free, now is he in bondage. And thereupon Saint Augustine says: "If thou have disdain for thy servant, if he offend or sin, have thou then disdain that thou shouldest do any sin." Have regard of your worth, that you be not foul unto yourself. Alas! Well ought they then to disdain to be servants and thralls to sin, and to be sorely ashamed of themselves, when God of His endless goodness has set them in high place, or given them understanding, bodily strength, health, beauty, prosperity, and redeemed them with His heart's blood, who now so unnaturally, in face of His nobleness, requite Him so vilely as to slaughter their own souls. O good God! You women, who are of so great beauty, remember the proverb of Solomon, who says: "A fair woman who is the fool of her body is like a gold ring in the snout of a sow." For just as a sow roots deep into every ordure, so does she root her beauty into the stinking filth of sin.

The third cause that ought to move a man to contrition is fear of the day of doom and of the horrible pains of Hell. For as Saint Jerome says: "Every time that I remember the day of doom I quake; for when I eat or drink or do whatever thing, ever it seems to me that the trump sounds in my ear, bidding the

feend, hate of aungels, sclaundre of holy chirche, and fode of the false serpent; perpetuel matere of the fyr of helle. And yet more foul and abhominable, for ye trespassen so ofte tyme, as doth the hound that retourneth to eten his spewing. And yet be ye fouler for your longe continuing in sinne and your sinful usage, for which ye be roten in your sinne, as a beest in his dong. Swiche manere of thoghtes maken a man to have shame of his sinne, and no delyt, as god seith by the prophete Ezechiel: "ye shal remembre yow of youre weyes, and they shuln displese yow." Sothly, sinnes been the weyes that leden folk to helle.

9. The seconde cause that oghte make a man to have desdeyn of sinne is this: that, as seith seint Peter, "who-so that doth sinne is thral of sinne"; and sinne put a man in greet thraldom. And therfore seith the prophete Ezechiel: "I wente sorweful in desdayn of my-self." And certes, wel oghte a man have desdayn of sinne, and withdrawe him from that thraldom and vileinye. And lo, what seith Seneca in this matere. He seith thus: "though I wiste that neither god ne man ne sholde nevere knowe it, yet wolde I have desdayn for to do sinne." And the same Seneca also seith: "I am born to gretter thinges than to be thral to my body, or than for to maken of my body a thral." Ne a fouler thral may no man ne womman maken of his body, than for to yeven his body to sinne. Al were it the fouleste cherl, or the fouleste womman that liveth, and leest of value, yet is he thanne more foule and more in servitute. Evere fro the hyer degree that man falleth, the more is he thral, and more to god and to the world vile and abhominable. O gode god, wel oghte man have desdayn of sinne; sith that, thurgh sinne, ther he was free, now is he maked bonde. And therfore seyth Seint Augustin: "if thou hast desdayn of thy servant, if he agilte or sinne, have thou thanne desdayn that thou thyself sholdest do sinne." Take reward of thy value, that thou ne be to foul to thy-self. Allas! wel oghten they thanne have desdayn to been servauntz and thralles to sinne, and sore been ashamed of hem-self, that god of his endelees goodnesse hath set hem in heigh estaat, or yeven hem wit, strengthe of body, hele, beautee, prosperitee, and boghte hem fro the deeth with his herte blood, that they so unkindely, agayns his gentilesse, quyten him so vileinsly, to slaughtre of hir owene soules. O gode god, ye wommen that been of so greet beautee, remembreth yow of the proverbe of Salomon, that seith: "he lykneth a fair womman, that is a fool of hir body, lyk to a ring of gold that were in the groyn of a sowe." For right as a sowe wroteth in everich ordure, so wroteth she hir beautee in the stinkinge ordure of sinne.

10. The thridde cause that oghte moeve a man to Contricion, is drede of the day of dome, and of the horrible peynes of helle. For as seint Jerome seith: "at every tyme that me remembreth of the day of dome, I quake; for whan I ete or drinke, or what-so that I do, evere semeth me that the trompe

sowneth in myn ere: riseth up, ye that been dede, and cometh to the jugement." O gode god, muchel oghte a man to drede swich a jugement, "ther-as we shullen been alle," as seint Poul seith, "biforn the sete of oure lord Jesu Crist"; wher-as he shal make a general congregacion, wher-as no man may been absent. For certes, there availleth noon essoyne ne excusacion. And nat only that oure defautes shullen be juged, but eek that alle oure werkes shullen openly be knowe. And as seith Seint Bernard: "ther ne shal no pledinge availle, ne no sleighte; we shullen yeven rekeninge of everich ydel word." Ther shul we han a juge that may nat been deceived ne corrupt. And why? For, certes, alle our thoghtes been discovered as to him; ne for preyere ne for mede he shal nat been corrupt. And therfore seith Salomon: "the wratthe of god ne wol nat spare no wight, for preyere ne for yifte"; and therfore, at the day of doom, ther nis noon hope to escape. Wherfore, as seith Seint Anselm: "ful greet angwissh shul the sinful folk have at that tyme; ther shal the sterne and wrothe juge sitte above, and under him the horrible put of helle open to destroyen him that moot biknowen hise sinnes, whiche sinnes openly been shewed biforn god and biforn every creature. And on the left syde, mo develes than herte may bithinke, for to harie and drawe the sinful soules to the pyne of helle. And with-inne the hertes of folk shal be the bytinge conscience, and with-oute-forth shal be the world al brenninge. Whider shal thanne the wrecched sinful man flee to hyden him? Certes, he may nat hyden him; he moste come forth and shewen him." For certes, as seith seint Jerome: "the erthe shal casten him out of him, and the see also; and the eyr also, that shal be ful of thonder-clappes and lightninges." Now sothly, who-so wel remembreth him of thise thinges, I gesse that his sinne shal nat turne him in-to delyt, but to greet sorwe, for drede of the peyne of helle. And therfore seith Job to god: "suffre, lord, that I may a whyle biwaille and wepe, er I go with-oute returning to the derke lond, covered with the derknesse of deeth; to the lond of misese and of derknesse, where-as is the shadwe of deeth; where-as ther is noon ordre or ordinance, but grisly drede that evere shal laste." Lo, here may ye seen that Job preyde respyt a whyle, to biwepe and waille his trespas; for soothly oon day of respyt is bettre than al the tresor of the world. And for-as-muche as a man may acquiten him-self biforn god by penitence in this world, and nat by tresor, therfore sholde he preye to god to yeve him respyt a whyle, to biwepe and biwaillen his trespas. For certes, al the sorwe that a man mighte make fro the beginning of the world, nis but a litel thing at regard of the sorwe of helle. The cause why that Job clepeth helle "the lond of derknesse"; understondeth that he clepeth it "londe" or erthe, for it is stable, and nevere shal faille; "derk," for he that is in helle hath defaute of light material. For certes, the derke light, that shal come out of the fyr that evere shal brenne, shal turne him al to peyne that is in helle;

dead arise and come to judgment." O good God! Greatly ought a man to fear such a judgment, "Where we shall be all," as Saint Paul says, "before the throne of Our Lord Jesus Christ." And there we shall compose a general congregation, whence no man shall absent himself. For truly there shall avail neither essoin nor excuse. And not only shall our faults be judged, but all our deeds shall openly be made known. As Saint Bernard says: "There shall no pleading avail, and no trickery; we shall give reckoning for every idle word." There shall we have a Judge that cannot be corrupted or deceived. And why? Because, in truth, all our thoughts are known unto Him; nor for prayer nor for bribing shall He be corrupted. And therefore says Solomon: "The wrath of God will spare no one, either for prayer or gifts." Therefore, at the day of doom, there shall be no hope of escape. Wherefore, as says Saint Anselm: "Great anguish shall all sinful folk have at that time; there shall the stern and angry Judge sit above, and under Him the horrible pit of Hell, open to destroy him who must acknowledge his sins, which sins shall be openly showed before God and before all creatures. And on the left side more devils than any heart can think, to harry and to draw the sinful souls to the punishment of Hell. And within the hearts of folk shall be the tearing of conscience and without shall be the world all burning. Whither then shall the wretched sinful man flee to hide himself? Certainly he shall not hide; he must come forth and show himself." For truly, as says Saint Jerome: "The earth shall cast him forth and the sea also; aye, and the air, which shall be filled with thunders and with lightnings." Now, indeed, whoso well thinks of these things, I suppose that his sin shall not be a delight within him, but a great sorrow, for fear of the pain of Hell. And therefore said Job to God: "Let me take comfort a little, before I go whence I shall not return, even to the land of darkness and the shadow of death; a land of darkness as darkness itself: and of the shadow of death, without any order, and where the light is as darkness." Lo, here may it be seen that Job prayed for respite to weep and to bewail his trespass; for indeed one day of respite is better than all the treasure of the world. And for as much as man may acquit himself before God by penitence in this world, and not by treasure, therefore should he pray to God to grant him respite for a while to weep and to bewail his sins. For truly, all the sorrow that a man might feel from the beginning of the world is but a little thing in comparison with the sorrows of Hell. As to the reason why Job called Hell the "land of darkness," it is to be understood that he called it "land" or "earth" because it is stable and never shall fail; "dark" because he that is in Hell lacks the materials for light. For truly the dark light that shall come out of the fire that burns for ever shall turn him all to pain who is in Hell; for it shall show unto him the horrible devils that torment him. "Covered with the darkness of death:" that is to say, that he who is in Hell shall lack the sight of God; for truly, to see God is life everlasting. "The darkness of death" is the sin which the wretched man has done, which hinders his seeing the face of God; just as does a cloud that comes between us and the sun. "Land of ill ease:" because there are three kinds of pains against three things that folk of the world have in this present life, that is to say, honours, delights, and riches. Over against honours they have in Hell shame and confusion. For well you know that men call "honour" the reverence that man gives to man; but in Hell is no honour or reverence. For indeed no more reverence shall be done there to a king than to a knave. As to which God says, by the Prophet Jeremiah: "They that scorn me shall be scorned." "Honour" is also called great lordship; but there no man shall serve another save to his harm and torment. "Honour," again, subsists in great dignity and rank; but in Hell all they shall be trodden upon by devils. And God says: "The horrible devils shall go and come upon the heads of the damned." And this is because the higher they were in this life, the lower shall they lie and be defiled in Hell. Against the riches of this world shall they have the misery of poverty; and this poverty shall be of four kinds: lack of treasure, whereof David says: "They that trust in their wealth, boast themselves in the multitude of their riches, they shall sleep in the darkness of death, and nothing shall they find in their hands of all their treasure." And, moreover, the misery of Hell shall consist of lack of food and drink. For God says thus, through Moses: "They shall be wasted with hunger, and the birds of Hell shall devour them with bitter death, and the gall of the dragon shall be their drink, and the venom of the dragon their morsels." And, furthermore, their misery shall be for lack of clothing, for they shall be naked of body save for the fire wherein they burn, and for other filth; and naked shall they be of soul, devoid of all virtues, which are the clothing of the soul. Where shall be then the gay robes and the soft sheets and the soft shirts? Behold what God says by the prophet Isaiah: "Under them shall be strewed moths and their covering shall be of the worms of Hell." And still further, their misery shall lie in lack of friends; for he is not poor who has good friends; but there there is no friend; for neither God nor any other shall be friend to them, and each of them shall hate all others with a deadly hatred. "The sons and the daughters shall rebel against father and mother, and kindred against kindred, and each of them shall curse and despise the others," both day and night, as says God through the Prophet Micah. And the loving people that once loved each other so passionately, each of them would eat the other if he might. For how should they love in the torments of Hell who hated each other in the prosperity of this life? For trust it well, their carnal love was deadly hate; as says the Prophet David: "Whoso loveth wickedness hateth his own soul." And whoso hates his own soul, truly he may love no other, in any wise. And therefore, in Hell is no solace nor any friendship, but ever the more fleshly relationships there are in Hell, the more cursings and

for it sheweth him to the horrible develes that him tormenten. "Covered with the derknesse of deeth": that is to seyn, that he that is in helle shal have defaute of the sighte of god; for certes, the sighte of god is the lyf perdurable. "The derknesse of deeth" been the sinnes that the wrecched man hath doon, whiche that destourben him to see the face of god; right as doth a derk cloude bitwixe us and the sonne. "Lond of misese": by-cause that ther been three maneres of defautes, agayn three thinges that folk of this world han in this present lyf, that is to seyn, honours, delyces, and richesses. Agayns honour, have they in helle shame and confusion. For wel ye woot that men clepen "honour" the reverence that man doth to man; but in helle is noon honour ne reverence. For certes, na-more reverence shal be doon there to a king than to a knave. For which god seith by the prophete Jeremye: "thilke folk that me despysen shul been in despyt." "Honour" is eek cleped greet lordshipe; ther shal no man serven other but of harm and torment. "Honour" is eek cleped greet dignitee and heighnesse; but in helle shul they been al fortroden of develes. And god seith: "the horrible develes shulle goon and comen up-on the hevedes of the dampned folk." And this is for-as-muche as, the hyer that they were in this present lyf, the more shulle they been abated and defouled in helle. Agayns the richesses of this world, shul they han misese of poverte; and this poverte shal been in foure thinges: in defaute of tresor, of which that David seith; "the riche folk, that embraceden and oneden al hir herte to tresor of this world, shul slepe in the slepinge of deeth; and no-thing ne shul they finden in hir handes of al hir tresor." And more-over, the miseise of helle shal been in defaute of mete and drinke. For god seith thus by Moyses; "they shul been wasted with hunger, and the briddes of helle shul devouren hem with bitter deeth, and the galle of the dragon shal been hir drinke, and the venim of the dragon hir morsels." And forther-over, hir miseise shal been in defaute of clothing: for they shulle be naked in body as of clothing, save the fyr in which they brenne and othere filthes; and naked shul they been of soule, of alle manere vertues, which that is the clothing of the soule. Where been thanne the gaye robes and the softe shetes and the smale shertes? Lo, what seith god of hem by the prophete Isaye: "that under hem shul been strawed motthes, and hir covertures shulle been of wormes of helle." And forther-over, hir miseise shal been in defaute of freendes; for he nis nat povre that hath goode freendes, but there is no freend; for neither god ne no creature shal been freend to hem, and everich of hem shal haten other with deedly hate. "The sones and the doghtren shullen rebellen agayns fader and mooder, and kinrede agayns kinrede, and chyden and despysen everich of hem other," bothe day and night, as god seith by the prophete Michias. And the lovinge children, that whylom loveden so fleshly everich other, wolden everich of hem eten other if they mighte. For how sholden they love hem togidre in the peyne of helle, whan they hated ech of hem other in the prosperitee of this lyf? For truste wel, hir fleshly love was deedly hate; as seith the prophete David: "who-so that loveth wikkednesse he hateth his soule." And who-so hateth his owene soule, certes, he may love noon other wight in no manere. And therfore, in helle is no solas ne no frendshipe, but evere the more fleshly kinredes that been in helle, the more cursinges, the more chydinges, and the more deedly hate ther is among hem. And forther-over, they shul have defaute of alle manere delyces; for certes, dèlyces been after the appetytes of the fyve wittes, as sighte, heringe, smellinge, savoringe, and touchinge. But in helle hir sighte shal be ful of derknesse and of smoke, and therfore ful of teres; and hir heringe, ful of waymentinge and of grintinge of teeth, as seith Jesu Crist; hir nosethirles shullen be ful of stinkinge stink. And as seith Isaye the prophete: "hir savoring shal be ful of bitter galle." And touchinge of al hir body, y-covered with "fyr that nevere shal quenche, and with wormes that nevere shul dyen," as god seith by the mouth of Isaye. And for-as-muche as they shul nat wene that they may dyen for peyne, and by hir deeth flee fro peyne, that may they understonden by the word of Job, that seith: "ther-as is the shadwe of deeth." Certes, a shadwe hath the lyknesse of the thing of which it is shadwe, but shadwe is nat the same thing of which it is shadwe. Right so fareth the payne of helle; it is lyk deeth for the horrible anguissh, and why? For it peyneth hem evere, as though they sholde dye anon; but certes they shal nat dye. For as seith Seint Gregorie: "to wrecche caytives shal be deeth with-oute deeth, and ende with-outen ende, and defaute with-oute failinge. For hir deeth shal alwey liven, and hir ende shal everemo biginne, and hir defaute shal nat faille." And therfore seith Seint John the Evangelist: "they shullen folwe deeth, and they shul nat finde him; and they shul desyren to dye, and deeth shal flee fro hem." And eek Job seith: that "in helle is noon ordre of rule." And al-be-it so that god hath creat alle thinges in right ordre, and no-thing with-outen ordre, but alle thinges been ordeyned and nombred; yet nathelees they that been dampned been no-thing in ordre, ne holden noon ordre. For the erthe ne shal bere hem no fruit. For, as the prophete David seith: "god shal destroye the fruit of the erthe as fro hem"; ne water ne shal yeve hem no moisture; ne the eyr no refresshing, ne fyr no light. For as seith seint Basilie: "the brenninge of the fyr of this world shal god yeven in helle to hem that been dampned; but the light and the cleernesse shal be yeven in hevene to hise children"; right as the gode man yeveth flesh to hise children, and bones to his houndes. And for they shullen have noon hope to escape, seith seint Job atte laste: that "ther shal horrour and grisly drede dwellen with-outen ende." Horrour is alwey drede of harm that is to come, and this drede shal evere dwelle in the hertes of hem that been dampned. And therfore han they lorn

the more deadly hates there are among them. And, again, they shall lack every kind of pleasure; for truly, pleasures are according to the appetites of the five senses, sight, hearing, smell, taste, and touch. But in Hell their sight shall be full of darkness and of smoke, and therefore full of tears; and their hearing full of wailing and the gnashing of teeth, as says Jesus Christ; their nostrils shall be full of a stinking smell. And, as the Prophet Isaiah says, "their savouring shall be of bitter gall." And as for touch, all the body shall be covered with "fire that never shall be quenched and with worms that never shall die," as God says by the mouth of Isaiah. And for as much as they shall not think that they may die of pain, and by death thus flee from pain, then may they understand the words of Job, who said, "There is the shadow of death." Certainly a shadow has the likeness of that whereof it is the shadow, but the shadow is not the substance. Just so it is with the pain of Hell; it is like unto death because of the horrible anguish. And why? Because it pains for ever, and as if they should die at every moment; but indeed they shall not die. For as Saint Gregory says: "To these wretched captives shall be given death without death, and end without end, and want without ceasing." And thereupon says Saint John the Evangelist: "They shall seek for death and they shall not find it; and they shall desire to die and death shall flee from them." And Job, also, says: "Death, without any order." And though it be that God has created all things in right order, and nothing at all without order, but all things are ordered and numbered; yet, nevertheless, they that are damned have no order, nor hold to any order. For the earth shall bear them no fruit. For, as the Prophet David says: "God shall destroy the fruits of the earth from them." No water shall give them moisture, nor the air refreshment, nor the fire a light. For, as Saint Basil says: "The burning of the fire of this world shall God send into Hell unto the damned souls there, but the light and the radiance thereof shall be given in Heaven unto His children"—just as the good man gives flesh to his children and bones to his dogs. And since they shall have no hope of escape, Saint Job says at the last that horror and grisly fear shall dwell there without end. Horror is always the fear of evil that is to come, and this fear shall dwell for ever in the hearts of the damned. And therefore have they lost all their hope, and for seven causes. First, because God their Judge shall be without mercy to them; they may not please Him, nor may they please any of His saints; they can give nothing for their ransom; they shall have no voice wherewith to speak to Him; they cannot flee from pain; and they have no goodness within themselves which they might show to deliver them out of pain. And therefore says Solomon: "The wicked man dieth; and when he is dead he shall have no hope of escaping from pain." Whosoever, then, will well understand these pains, and bethink him well that he has deserved these very pains for his sins, certainly he shall have more longing to sigh and weep than ever to sing and play. For, as Solomon says: "Whoso shall have the wisdom to know the pains that have been established and ordained for the punishment of pain, he will feel sorrow." "This same knowledge," says Saint Augustine, "maketh a man to bewail within his heart."

The fourth point that ought to cause a man to feel contrition is the unhappy memory of the good that he has left here on earth; also the good that he has lost. Truly, the good deeds that he has left are either those that he wrought before he fell into mortal sin, or the good deeds he did while he lived in sin. Indeed the good deeds he did before he fell into sin have been all deadened and stultified and rendered null and void by the repeated sinning. The other good deeds, which he wrought while he lay in mortal sin, they are utterly dead as to the effect they might have had on his life everlasting in Heaven. And then the same good deeds that have been rendered null by repeated sinning, which good works he wrought while he stood in a state of grace, shall never quicken again without an utter penitence. And thereof God says, by the mouth of Ezekiel: "If the righteous man shall turn again from his righteousness, and do wickedness, shall he live?" Nay, for all the good works that he has wrought shall never be held in memory, for he shall die in his sin. And thereupon, as to that same chapter, Saint Gregory says thus: "That we shall understand this principally: that when we do mortal sin it is for naught that we tell of or draw from memory the good works that we have wrought before." For, certainly, in the doing of mortal sin there is no trusting to the help of good that we have wrought before; that is to say, as it affects the everlasting life in Heaven. But notwithstanding this, the good deeds quicken again and return again, and help and are of avail in attaining the everlasting life in Heaven, when we have contrition. But indeed the good deeds that men do while they are in deadly sin, because they are done in deadly sin, shall never quicken again. For truly, that thing which never had life may never quicken; nevertheless, albeit these deeds avail nothing as to the perdurable life, yet they help to lighten the pains of Hell, or else to acquire temporal riches, or else, because of them, God will enlighten and illumine the heart of the sinful man to be repentant; and also they avail in accustoming a man to the doing of good deeds, to the end that the Fiend has less

al hir hope, for sevene causes. First, for god that is hir juge shal be with-outen mercy to hem; ne they may nat plese him, ne noon of hise halwes; ne they ne may yeve no-thing for hir raunson; ne they have no vois to speke to him; ne they may nat flee fro peyne; ne they have no goodnesse in hem, that they mowe shewe to delivere hem fro peyne. And therfore seith Salomon: "the wikked man dyeth; and whan he is deed, he shal have noon hope to escape fro peyne." Who-so thanne wolde wel understande these peynes, and bithinke him weel that he hath deserved thilke peynes for his sinnes, certes, he sholde have more talent to syken and to wepe than for to singen and to pleye. For as that seith Salomon: "who-so that hadde the science to knowe the peynes that been establissed and ordeyned for sinne, he wolde make sorwe." "Thilke science," as seith seint Augustin, "maketh a man to waymenten in his herte."

11. The fourthe point, that oghte maken a man to have contricion, is the sorweful remembrance of the good that he hath left to doon here in erthe; and eek the good that he hath lorn. Soothly, the gode werkes that he hath left, outher they been the gode werkes that he wroghte er he fel in-to deedly sinne, or elles the gode werkes that he wroghte while he lay in sinne. Soothly, the gode werkes, that he dide biforn that he fil in sinne, been al mortified and astoned and dulled by the ofte sinning. The othere gode werkes, that he wroghte whyl he lay in deedly sinne, they been outrely dede as to the lyf perdurable in hevene. Thanne thilke gode werkes that been mortified by ofte sinning, whiche gode werkes he dide whyl he was in charitee, ne mowe nevere quiken agayn with-outen verray penitence. And therof seith god, by the mouth of Ezechiel: that, "if the rightful man returne agayn from his rightwisnesse and werke wikkednesse, shal he live?" Nay; for alle the gode werkes that he hath wroght ne shul nevere been in remembrance; for he shal dyen in his sinne. And up-on thilke chapitre seith seint Gregorie thus: "that we shull understonde this principally; that whan we doon deedly sinne, it is for noght thanne to rehercen or drawen in-to memorie the gode werkes that we han wroght biforn." For certes, in the werkinge of the deedly sinne, ther is no trust to no good werk that we han doon biforn; that is to seyn, as for to have therby the lyf perdurable in hevene. But nathelees, the gode werkes quiken agayn, and comen agayn, and helpen, and availlen to have the lyf perdurable in hevene, whan we han contricion. But soothly, the gode werkes that men doon whyl they been in deedly sinne, for-as-muche as they were doon in deedly sinne, they may nevere quiken agayn. For certes, thing that nevere hadde lyf may nevere quikene; and nathelees, al-be-it that they ne availle noght to han the lyf perdurable, yet availlen they to abregge of the peyne of helle, or elles to geten temporal richesse, or elles that god wole the rather enlumine and lightne the herte of the sinful man to have repentance; and eek they availlen for to usen

a man to doon gode werkes, that the feend have the lasse power of his soule. And thus the curteis lord Jesu Crist wole that no good werk be lost; for in somwhat it shal availle. But for-as-muche as the gode werkes that men doon whyl they been in good lyf, been al mortified by sinne folwinge; and eek, sith that alle the gode werkes that men doon whyl they been in deedly synne, been outrely dede as for to have the lyf perdurable; wel may that man, that no good werke ne dooth, singe thilke newe Frenshe song: "*Jay tout perdu mon temps et mon labour.*" For certes, sinne bireveth a man bothe goodnesse of nature and eek the goodnesse of grace. For soothly, the grace of the holy goost fareth lyk fyr, that may nat been ydel; for fyr faileth anoon as it forleteth his wirkinge, and right so grace fayleth anoon as it forleteth his werkinge. Than leseth the sinful man the goodnesse of glorie, that only is bihight to gode men that labouren and werken. Wel may he be sory thanne, that oweth al his lif to god as longe as he hath lived, and eek as longe as he shal live, that no goodnesse ne hath to paye with his dette to god, to whom he oweth al his lyf. For trust wel, "he shal yeven acountes," as seith seint Bernard, "of alle the godes that han be yeven him in this present lyf, and how he hath hem despended; in so muche that ther shal nat perisse an heer of his heed, ne a moment of an houre ne shal nat perisse of his tyme, that he ne shal yeve of it a rekening."

12. The fifthe thing that oghte moeve a man to contricion, is remembrance of the passion that oure lord Jesu Crist suffred for oure sinnes. For, as seith seint Bernard: "whyl that I live, I shal have remembrance of the travailles that oure lord Crist suffred in preching; his werinesse in travailling, hise temptacions whan he fasted, hise longe wakinges whan he preyde, hise teres whan that he weep for pitee of good peple; the wo and the shame and the filthe that men seyden to him; of the foule spitting that men spitte in his face, of the buffettes that men yaven him, of the foule mowes, and of the repreves that men to him seyden; of the nayles with whiche he was nailed to the croys, and of al the remenant of his passion that he suffred for my sinnes, and no-thing for his gilt." And ye shul understonde, that in mannes sinne is every manere of ordre or ordinance turned up-so-doun. For it is sooth, that god, and reson, and sensualitee, and the body of man been so ordeyned, that everich of thise foure thinges sholde have lordshipe over that other; as thus: god sholde have lordshipe over reson, and reson over sensualitee, and sensualitee over the body of man. But sothly, whan men sinneth, al this ordre or ordinance is turned up-so-doun. And therfore thanne, for-as-muche as the reson of man ne wol nat be subget ne obeisant to god, that is his lord by right, therfore leseth it the lordshipe that it sholde have over sensualitee, and eek over the body of man. And why? For sensualitee rebelleth thanne agayns reson; and by that wey leseth reson the lordshipe over sensualitee and over the body.

power over his soul. And thus the compassionate Lord Jesus Christ wills that no good work be utterly lost; for in somewhat it shall avail. But for as much as the good deeds that men do while they are in a state of grace are all stultified by sin ensuing; and, also, since all the good works that men do while they are in mortal sin are utterly dead, in so far as the life everlasting is concerned, well may that man who does no good work sing that new French song, *J'ai tout perdu mon temps et mon labeur*. For certainly, sin bereaves a man of both goodness of nature and the goodness of grace. For indeed the grace of the Holy Ghost is like fire, which cannot be idle; for fire fails anon as it forgoes its working, and even so does grace fail immediately it forsakes its work. Then loses the sinful man the goodness of glory, which is promised only to good men who suffer and toil. Well then may he sorrow, who owes all his life to God, as long as he has lived and as long as he shall live, and who yet has no goodness wherewith to repay his debt to God. For trust well, "he shall give account," as Saint Bernard says, "of all the good things that have been given him in this present life, and of how he has used them; in so much that there shall not perish a hair of his head, nor shall a moment of an hour perish of all his time, that he shall not be called upon to give a reckoning for."

The fifth thing that ought to move a man to contrition is remembrance of the passion that Our Lord Jesus Christ suffered for our sins. For, as Saint Bernard says: "While I live I will keep in remembrance the travail that Our Lord Christ suffered in preaching; His weariness in travail; His temptations when He fasted; His long watchings when He prayed; His tears when He wept for pity of good people; the grievous and the shameful and the filthy things that men said of Him; the foul sputum that men spat into His face; the foul buffets that men gave Him; the foul grimaces and the chidings that men said; the nails wherewith He was nailed to the cross; and all the rest of His passion, which he suffered for my sins and not for his own guilt." And you shall understand that in man's sin is every order or ordinance turned upside-down. For it is true that God and reason and sensuality and the body of man have been so ordained and established that, of these four things, the next higher shall have lordship over the lower; as thus: God shall have lordship over reason, and reason over sensuality, and sensuality over the body of man. But indeed, when man sins, all of this order or ordinance is turned upside-down. Therefore, then, for as much as the reason of man will not be subject to nor obedient to God, Who is man's Lord by right, therefore it loses the lordship that it should hold over sensuality and also over the body of man? And why? Because sensuality rebels then against reason; and in that way reason loses the lordship over sensuality and over the body. For just as reason is rebel to God, just so is sensuality rebel to reason, and the body also. And truly, this confusion and this rebellion Our Lord Jesus Christ suffered upon His precious body, and paid full dearly thus, and hear you now in what wise. For as much, then, as reason is rebel to God, therefore is man worthy to have sorrow and to die. This Our Lord Jesus Christ suffered for mankind after He had been betrayed by His disciple, and secured and bound "so that the blood burst out at every nail of His hands," as says Saint Augustine. Moreover, for as much as reason of man will not subdue sensuality when it may, therefore man is worthy of shame; and this suffered Our Lord Jesus Christ for man when they spat in His face. Furthermore, for as much, then, as the wretched body of man is rebel both to reason and to sensuality, therefore is it worthy of death. And this Our Lord Jesus Christ suffered for man upon the cross, where there was no part of His body free from great pain and bitter passion. And all this Jesus Christ suffered, Who never did any wrong. And therefore it may be reasonably said of Jesus thus: "Too much am I tortured for things the punishment of which I do not deserve, and too much disgraced for shame that belongs to man." And therefore may the sinful man well say, as says Saint Bernard: "Accursed be the bitterness of my sin, for which there must be suffered so much bitterness." For truly, according to the diverse discordances of our wickedness, was the passion of Jesus Christ ordained in divers ways, as thus. Certainly sinful man's soul is betrayed unto the Devil by covetousness of temporal prosperity, and scorned by deceit when he chooses carnal delights; and it is tormented by impatience under adversity, and spat upon by servitude and subjection to sin; and at the last it is slain for ever. For this confusion by sinful man was Jesus Christ first betrayed and afterwards bound, Who came to loose us from sin and pain. Then was He scorned, Who should have been only honoured in all things. Then was His face, which all mankind ought to have desired to look upon, since into that face angels desire to look, villainously spat upon. Then was He scourged, Who had done nothing wrong; and finally, then was He crucified and slain. So was accomplished the word of Isaiah: "He was wounded for our misdeeds and defiled for our felonies." Now, since Jesus Christ took upon Himself the punishment for all our wickedness, much ought sinful man to weep and to bewail that for his sins the Son of God in Heaven should endure all this pain.

The sixth thing that ought to move a man to contrition is the hope of three things; that is to say, forgiveness of sin, and the gift of grace to do well, and the glory of Heaven, wherewith God shall reward man for his good deeds. And for as much as Jesus Christ gives us these gifts of His largess and of His sovereign bounty, therefore is He called *Iesus Nazarenus rex Judeorum*. Jesus means "saviour" or "salvation," in whom men shall hope to have for-

For right as reson is rebel to god, right so is bothe sensualitee rebel to reson and the body also. And certes, this disordinance and this rebellion oure lord Jesu Crist aboghte up-on his precious body ful dere, and herkneth in which wyse. For-as-muche thanne as reson is rebel to god, therfore is man worthy to have sorwe and to be deed. This suffred oure lord Jesu Crist for man, after that he hadde be bitraysed of his disciple, and distreyned and bounde, "so that his blood brast out at every nail of hise handes," as seith seint Augustin. And forther-over, for-as-muchel as reson of man ne wol nat daunte sensualitee whan it may, therfore is man worthy to have shame; and this suffred oure lord Jesu Crist for man, whan they spetten in his visage. And forther-over, for-as-muchel thanne as the caitif body of man is rebel bothe to reson and to sensualitee, therfore is it worthy the deeth. And this suffred oure lord Jesu Crist for man upon the croys, where-as ther was no part of his body free, with-outen greet peyne and bitter passion. And al this suffred Jesu Crist, that nevere forfeted. And therfore resonably may be seyd of Jesu in this manere: "to muchel am I peyned for the thinges that I nevere deserved, and to muche defouled for shendshipe that man is worthy to have." And therfore may the sinful man wel seye, as seith seint Bernard: "acursed by the bitternesse of my sinne, for which ther moste be suffred so muchel bitternesse." For certes, after the diverse discordances of oure wikkednesses, was the passion of Jesu Crist ordeyned in diverse thinges, as thus. Certes, sinful mannes soule is bitraysed of the devel by coveitise of temporel prosperitee, and scorned by deceite whan he cheseth fleshly delyces; and yet is it tormented by inpacience of adversitee, and bispet by servage and subjeccion of sinne; and atte laste it is slayn fynally. For this disordinaunce of sinful man was Jesu Crist first bitraysed, and after that was he bounde, that cam for to unbynden us of sinne and peyne. Thanne was he biscorned, that only sholde han been honoured in alle thinges and of alle thinges. Thanne was his visage, that oghte be desired to be seyn of al man-kinde, in which visage aungels desyren to looke, vileynsly bispet. Thanne was he scourged that no-thing hadde agilt; and fynally, thanne was he crucified and slayn. Thanne was acompliced the word of Isaye: "he was wounded for oure misdedes, and defouled for oure felonies." Now sith that Jesu Crist took up-on him-self the peyne of alle oure wikkednesses, muchel oghte sinful man wepen and biwayle, that for hise sinnes goddes sone of hevene sholde al this peyne endure.

13. The sixte thing that oghte moeve a man to contricion, is the hope of three thynges; that is to seyn, foryifnesse of sinne, and the yifte of grace wel for to do, and the glorie of hevene, with which god shal guerdone a man for hise gode dedes. And foras-muche as Jesu Crist yeveth us thise yiftes of his largesse and of his sovereyn bountee, therfore is he cleped *Jesus Nazarenus rex Judeorum*. Jesus is to seyn "saveour" or "salvacion," on whom men shul

hope to have foryifnesse of sinnes, which that is proprely salvacion of sinnes. And therfore seyde the aungel to Joseph: "thou shalt clepen his name Jesus, that shal saven his peple of hir sinnes." And heer-of seith seint Peter: "ther is noon other name under hevene that is yeve to any man, by which a man may be saved, but only Jesus." *Nazarenus* is as muche for to seye as "florisshinge," in which a man shal hope, that he that yeveth him remission of sinnes shal yeve him eek grace wel for to do. For in the flour is hope of fruit in tyme cominge; and in foryifnesse of sinnes hope of grace wel for to do. "I was atte dore of thyn herte." seith Jesus, "and cleped for to entre; he that openeth to me shal have foryifnesse of sinne. I wol entre in-to him by my grace, and soupe with him," by the goode werkes that he shal doon; whiche werkes been the foode of god; "and he shal soupe with me," by the grete joye that I shal yeven him. Thus shal man hope, for hise werkes of penaunce, that god shall yeven him his regne; as he bihoteth him in the gospel.

14. Now shal a man understonde, in which manere shal been his contricion. I seye, that it shal been universal and total; this is to seyn, a man shal be verray repentant for alle hise sinnes that he hath doon in delyt of his thoght; for delyt is ful perilous. For ther been two manere of consentinges; that oon of hem is cleped consentinge of affeccion, whan a man is moeved to do sinne, and delyteth him longe for to thinke on that sinne; and his reson aperceyveth it wel, that it is sinne agayns the lawe of god, and yet his reson refreyneth nat his foul delyt or talent, though he see wel apertly that it is agayns the reverence of god; al-though his reson ne consente noght to doon that sinne in dede, yet seyn somme doctours that swich delyt that dwelleth longe, it is ful perilous, al be it nevere so lite. And also a man sholde sorwe, namely, for al that evere he hath desired agayn the lawe of god with perfit consentinge of his reson; for ther-of is no doute, that it is deedly sinne in consentinge. For certes, ther is no deedly sinne, that it nas first in mannes thought, and after that in his delyt; and so forth in-to consentinge and in-to dede. Wherefore I seye, that many men ne repenten hem nevere of swiche thoghtes and delytes, ne nevere shryven hem of it, but only of the dede of grete sinnes outward. Wherfore I seye, that swiche wikked delytes and wikked thoghtes been subtile bigyleres of hem that shullen be dampned. Moreover, man oghte to sorwe for hise wikkede wordes as wel as for hise wikkede dedes; for certes, the repentance of a singuler sinne, and nat repente of alle hise othere sinnes, or elles repenten him of alle hise othere sinnes, and nat of a singuler sinne, may nat availle. For certes, god almighty is al good; and ther-fore he foryeveth al, or elles right noght. And heer-of seith seint Augustin: "I woot certeinly that god is enemy to everich sinnere"; and how thanne? He that observeth o sinne, shal he have foryifnesse of the remenaunt of hise othere sinnes? Nay. And forther-over, contricion sholde be wonder sorwe-

giveness of sins, which is, properly, salvation from sins. And therefore said the angel to Joseph: "Thou shalt call His name Jesus, Who shall save His people from their sins." And thereof says Saint Peter: "There is no other name under Heaven given to any man, whereby a man may be saved, save only Jesus." *Nazarenus* is as much as to say "flourishing," wherein a man may hope that He Who gives him remission of sins shall give him also the grace to do well. For in the flower is hope of fruit in time to come; and in forgiveness of sins is hope of grace to do well. "Behold, I stand at the door and knock," says Jesus: "if any man hear my voice, and open the door, I will come in to him, and will sup with him, and he with Me." That is to say, by the good works that he shall do, which good works are the food of God; "and he shall sup with Me"—by the great joy that I shall give him. Thus may man hope, for his deeds of penitence, that God shall allow him to enter His Kingdom, as is promised unto him in the gospel.

Now shall a man understand in what manner shall be his contrition. I say, that it shall be universal and total; that is to say, a man shall be truly repentant for all the sins that he has done in delight of his thought; for delight is very dangerous. For there are two ways of acquiescence; one called acquiescence of the affections, when a man is moved to do sin, and delights in long thinking thereon; and his reason well perceives that it is sin against the law of God, and yet his reason restrains not his foul delight or appetite, though he see well that it is opposed to the reverence that is due to God; although his reason consent not to do that sin in very deed, yet some doctors say that dwelling long on such delight is full dangerous, be it ever so little. And also a man should sorrow for all that he has ever desired against the law of God with perfect acquiescence of his reason; for there is no doubt of it, there is mortal sin in acquiescence. For truly, there is no mortal sin that was not first in man's thought, and after that in his delight, and so on unto acquiescence and unto deed. Wherefore I say, that many men never repent for such thoughts and delights, and never confess them, but only the actual performance of great sins. Wherefore I say that such wicked delights and wicked thoughts are subtle beguilers of those that shall be damned. Moreover, a man ought to sorrow for his wicked words as well as for his wicked deeds; for truly, the repentance for a single sin, unaccompanied by repentance for all other sins, or else repentance for all other sins and not for a single sin, shall not avail. For certainly God Almighty is all good; and therefore He forgives all or nothing. And thereupon says Saint Augustine: "I know certainly that God is the enemy of every sinner." And how then? He that continues to do one sin, shall be have forgiveness for the rest of his sins? No. Furthermore, contrition should be wondrous sorrowful and full of suffering; and for that God gives fully His mercy; and therefore, when my soul was suffering within me, I had remembrance of God, that my prayer might come unto Him. Moreover, contrition must be continual, and a man must keep and hold a steadfast purpose to shrive himself and to amend his way of life. For truly, while contrition lasts, man may continue to have hope of forgiveness; and of this comes hatred of sin, which destroys sin within himself and also in other folk, according to his ability. For which David says: "Ye that love God hate wickedness." For trust this well, to love God is to love what He loves and to hate what He hates.

ful and anguissous, and therfore yeveth him god pleynly his mercy; and therfore, whan my soule was anguissous with-inne me, I hadde remembrance of god that my preyere mighte come to him. Forther-over, contricion moste be continuel, and that man have stedefast purpos to shryven him, and for to amenden him of his lyf. For soothly, whyl contricion lasteth, man may evere have hope of foryifnesse; and of this comth hate of sinne, that destroyeth sinne bothe in himself, and eek in other folk, at his power. For which seith David: "ye that loven god hateth wikkednesse." For trusteth wel, to love god is for to love that he loveth, and hate that he hateth.

The last thing that man shall understand about contrition is this: What does contrition avail him? I say, that at times contrition delivers a man from sin; as to which David says: "I said I will confess my transgressions unto the Lord; and Thou forgavest the iniquity of my sin." And just as contrition nothing avails without firm purpose of shrift, if man have opportunity, just so shrift itself is of little worth without contrition. Moreover, contrition destroys the prison of Hell and makes weak and feeble all the strength of all the devils, and restores the gifts of the Holy Ghost and of all good virtues; and it cleanses the soul of sin, and delivers the soul from the pain of Hell and from the company of the Devil, and from the servitude of sin, and restores it unto all spiritual good and to the company and communion of Holy Church. And furthermore, it makes of him who was formerly the son of anger to be the son of grace; and all these things are proved by holy writ. And therefore he that would set his understanding to these things, he were full wise; for truly, he should not then, in all his life, have desire to sin, but should give his body and all his heart to the service of Jesus Christ, and do Him homage. For truly, Our sweet Lord Jesus Christ has spared us so graciously in our follies that, if He had not pity on man's soul, a sorry song indeed might all of us sing.

15. The laste thing that man shal understonde in contricion is this; wherof avayleth contricion. I seye, that som tyme contricion delivereth a man fro sinne; of which that David seith: "I seye," quod David, that is to seyn, "I purposed fermely to shryve me; and thow, Lord, relesedest my sinne." And right so as contricion availleth noght, withouten sad purpos of shrifte, if man have oportunitee, right so litel worth is shrifte or satisfaccion with-outen contricion. And more-over, contricion destroyeth the prison of helle, and maketh wayk and feble alle the strengthes of the develes, and restoreth the yiftes of the holy goost and of alle gode vertues; and it clenseth the soule of sinne, and delivereth the soule fro the peyne of helle, and fro the companye of the devel, and fro the servage of sinne, and restoreth it to alle godes espirituels, and to the companye and communion of holy chirche. And forther-over, it maketh him that whylom was sone of ire to be sone of grace; and alle thise thinges been preved by holy writ. And therfore, he that wolde sette his entente to thise thinges, he were ful wys; for soothly, he ne sholde nat thanne in al his lyf have corage to sinne, but yeven his body and al his herte to the service of Jesu Crist, and ther-of doon him hommage. For soothly, oure swete lord Jesu Crist hath spared us so debonairly in our folies, that if he ne hadde pitee of mannes soule, a sory song we mighten alle singe.

HERE ENDETH THE FIRST PART OF PENITENCE

HERE FOLLOWETH THE SECOND PART

The second part of penitence is confession, which is the sign of contrition. Now shall you understand what confession is, and whether it ought to be used or not, and which things are necessary to true confession.

First, you shall understand that confession is the true discovery of sins to the priest; I say "true," for a man must confess all the circumstances and conditions of his sin, in so far as he can. All must be told, and nothing excused or hidden, or covered up, and he must not vaunt his good deeds. And furthermore, it is necessary to understand whence his sins come, and how they increase, and what they are.

Of the birth of sins, Saint Paul says thus: that "as

16. The seconde partie of Penitence is Confession, that is signe of contricion. Now shul ye understonde what is Confession, and whether it oghte nedes be doon or noon, and whiche thinges been covenable to verray Confession.

17. First shaltow understonde that Confession is verray shewinge of sinnes to the preest; this is to seyn "verray," for he moste confessen him of alle the condiciouns that bilongen to his sinne, as ferforth as he can. Al moot be seyd, and no thing excused ne hid ne forwrapped, and noght avaunte him of his gode werkes. And forther over, it is necessarie to understonde whennes that sinnes springen, and how they encresen, and whiche they been.

18. Of the springinge of sinnes seith seint Paul

in this wise: that "right as by a man sinne entred first in-to this world, and thurgh that sinne deeth, right so thilke deeth entred in-to alle men that sinneden." And this man was Adam, by whom sinne entred in-to this world whan he brak the comaundement of god. And therfore, he that first was so mighty that he sholde not have dyed, bicam swich oon that he moste nedes dye, whether he wolde or noon; and all his progenie in this world that in thilke man sinneden. Loke that in th'estaat of innocence, when Adam and Eve naked weren in paradys, and no-thing ne hadden shame of hir nakednesse, how that the serpent, that was most wyly of alle othere bestes that god hadde maked, seyde to the womman: "why comaunded god to yow, ye sholde nat eten of every tree in paradys?" The womman answerde: "of the fruit," quod she, "of the trees in paradys we feden us; but soothly, of the fruit of the tree that is in the middel of paradys, god forbad us for to ete, ne nat touchen it, lest per-aventure we should dyen." The serpent seyde to the womman: "nay, nay, ye shul nat dyen of deeth; for sothe, god woot, that what day that ye eten ther-of, youre eyen shul opene, and ye shul been as goddes, knowinge good and harm." The womman thanne saugh that the tree was good to feding, and fair to the eyen, and delytable to the sighte; she tok of the fruit of the tree, and eet it, and yaf to hir housbonde, and he eet; and anoon the eyen of hem bothe openeden. And whan that they knewe that they were naked, they sowed of fige-leves a manere of breches to hiden hir membres. There may ye seen that deedly sinne hath first suggestion of the feend, as sheweth here by the naddre; and afterward, the delyt of the flesh, as sheweth here by Eve; and after that, the consentinge of resoun, as sheweth here by Adam. For trust wel, thogh so were that the feend tempted Eve, that is to seyn the flesh, and the flesh hadde delyt in the beautee of the fruit defended, yet certes, til that resoun, that is to seyn, Adam, consented to the etinge of the fruit, yet stood he in th'estaat of innocence. Of thilke Adam toke we thilke sinne original; for of him fleshly descended be we alle, and engendred of vile and corrupt matere. And whan the soule is put in our body, right anon is contract original sinne; and that, that was erst but only peyne of concupiscence, is afterward bothe peyne and sinne. And therfore be we alle born sones of wratthe and of dampnacion perdurable, if it nere baptesme that we receyven, which binimeth us the culpe; but for sothe, the peyne dwelleth with us, as to temptacion, which peyne highte concupiscence. Whan it is wrongfully disposed or ordeyned in man, it maketh him coveite, by coveitise of flesh, fleshly sinne, by sighte of hise eyen as to erthely thinges, and coveitise of hynesse by pryde of herte.

19. Now as for to speken of the firste coveitise, that is, concupiscence after the lawe of oure membres, that weren lawefulliche y-maked and by rightful jugement of god; I seye, for-as-muche as

by one man sin entered into the world, and death by sin; . . . so death passed upon all men, for that all have sinned." And this man was Adam, by whom sin entered into the world when he broke the commandment of God. And therefore, he that at first was so mighty that he should never have died became such a one as must needs die, whether he would or no; and all his progeny in this world, since they, in that man, sinned. Behold, in the state of innocence, when Adam and Eve were naked in Paradise, and had no shame for their nakedness, how that the serpent, which was the wiliest of all the beasts that God had made, said to the woman: "Yea, hath God said, ye shall not eat of every tree of the garden?" And the woman said unto the serpent: "We may eat of the fruit of the trees of the garden: but of the fruit of the tree which is in the midst of the garden, God hath said, 'Ye shall not eat of it, neither shall ye touch it, lest ye die.' " And the serpent said unto the woman: "Ye shall not surely die: for God doth know, that in the day ye eat thereof, then your eyes shall be opened; and ye shall be as gods, knowing good and evil." And when the woman saw that the tree was good for food, and that it was pleasant to the eyes, and delectable in the sight, she took of the fruit thereof and did eat; and gave also unto her husband, and he did eat. And the eyes of them both were opened. And when they knew that they were naked, they sewed fig-leaves together into a kind of breeches to hide their members. There may you see that mortal sin had first suggestion from the Fiend, who is here figured by the serpent; and afterward the delight of the flesh, as shown here by Eve; and after that the acquiescence of reason, as is shown by Adam. For trust this well, though it were that the Fiend tempted Eve, that is to say, the flesh, and the flesh delighted in the beauty of the forbidden fruit, certainly until reason, that is, Adam, consented to the eating of the fruit, yet stood he in the state of innocence. From that same Adam caught we all that original sin; for we are all descended from him in the flesh, engendered of vile and corrupt matter. And when the soul is put into a body, immediately is contracted original sin; and that which was at first merely the penalty of concupiscence becomes afterwards both penalty and sin. And therefore are we all born the sons of wrath and of everlasting damnation, were it not for the baptism we receive, which washes away the culpability; but, forsooth, the penalty remains within us, as temptation, and that penalty is called concupiscence. When it is wrongly disposed or established in man, it makes him desire, by the lust of the flesh, fleshly sin; desire, by the sight of his eyes, earthly things; and desire high place, what of the pride of his heart.

Now, to speak of the first desire, that is, concupiscence, according to the law for our sexual parts, which were lawfully made and by rightful word of God; I say, for as much as man is not obedient to

God, Who is his Lord, therefore is the flesh disobedient to Him, through concupiscence, which is also called the nourishing of and the reason for sin. Therefore all the while that a man has within himself the penalty of concupiscence, it is impossible but that he will be sometimes tempted and moved in his flesh to do sin. And this shall not fail so long as he lives; it may well grow feeble and remote by virtue of baptism and by the grace of God through penitence; but it shall never be fully quenched so that he shall never be moved within himself, unless he be cooled by sickness or by maleficence of sorcery or by opiates. For behold what Saint Paul says: "The flesh lusteth against the spirit, and the spirit against the flesh: and these are contrary, the one to the other; so that ye cannot do the things that ye would." The same Saint Paul, after his great penance on water and on land (on water by night and by day, in great peril and in great pain; on land in famine, in thirst, in cold, and naked, and once stoned almost unto death), yet said he: "O wretched man that I am! Who shall deliver me from the body of this death?" And Saint Jerome, when he had long lived in the desert, where he had no company but that of wild beasts, where he had no food but herbs, with only water to drink, and no bed but the naked earth, for which his flesh was black as an Ethiopian's with heat and well-nigh destroyed with cold, yet said he that the heat of lechery boiled through all his body. Wherefore I know well and surely that they are deceived who say that they are never tempted in the flesh. Witness Saint James the apostle, who says that everyone is tempted in his own concupiscence. That is to say, each of us has cause and occasion to be tempted by sin that is nourished in the body. And thereupon says Saint John the Evangelist: "If we say that we have no sin, we deceive ourselves, and the truth is not in us."

Now shall you understand in what manner sin waxes or increases in man. The first thing to be considered is this same nurturing of sin, whereof I spoke before, this same fleshly concupiscence. And after that comes the subjection to the Devil, that is to say, the Devil's bellows, wherewith he blows into man the fire of concupiscence. And after that a man bethinks himself whether he will do, or not, the thing to which he is tempted. And then, if a man withstand and put aside the first enticement of his flesh and the Fiend, then it is no sin; and if it be that he do not, he feels anon a flame of delight. And then it is well to be wary, and to guard himself, else he will fall anon into acquiescence to sin; and then he will do it, if he have time and place. And of this matter Moses says that the Devil says thus: "I will pursue, I will overtake, I will divide the spoil; my lust shall be satisfied upon them; I will draw my sword, my hand shall destroy them." For certainly, just as a sword may part a thing in two pieces, just so acquiescence separates God from man. "And then will I slay him in his sinful deed." Thus says the

man is nat obeisaunt to god, that is his lord, therfore is the flesh to him disobeisaunt thurgh concupiscence, which yet is cleped norissinge of sinne and occasion of sinne. Therfore, al the whyle that a man hath in him the peyne of concupiscence, it is impossible but he be tempted somtyme, and moeved in his flesh to sinne. And this thing may nat faille as longe as he liveth; it may wel wexe feble and faille, by vertu of baptesme and by the grace of god thurgh penitence; but fully ne shal it nevere quenche, that he ne shal som tyme be moeved in him-self, but-if he were al refreyded by siknesse, or by malefice of sorcerie or colde drinkes. For lo, what seith seint Paul: "the flesh coveiteth agayn the spirit, and the spirit agayn the flesh; they been so contrarie and so stryven that a man may nat alwey doon as he wolde." The same seint Paul, after his grete penaunce in water and in lond (in water by night and by day, in greet peril and in greet peyne, in lond, in famine, in thurst, in cold and clothlees, and ones stoned almost to the deeth) yet seyde he: "allas! I, caytif man, who shal delivere me fro the prisoun of my caytif body?" And seint Jerome, whan he longe tyme hadde woned in desert, where-as he hadde no companye but of wilde bestes, where-as he ne hadde no mete but herbes and water to his drinke, ne no bed but the naked erthe, for which his flesh was blak as an Ethiopen for hete and ny destroyed for cold, yet seyde he: that "the brenninge of lecherie boiled in al his body." Wherfore I woot wel sikerly, that they been deceyved that seyn, that they ne be nat tempted in hir body. Witnesse on Seint Jame the Apostel, that seith: that "every wight is tempted in his owen concupiscence"; that is to seyn, that everich of us hath matere and occasion to be tempted of the norissinge of sinne that is in his body. And therfore seith Seint John the Evaungelist: "if that we seyn that we beth with-oute sinne, we deceyve us-selve, and trouthe is nat in us."

20. Now shal ye understonde in what manere that sinne wexeth or encreseth in man. The firste thing is thilke norissinge of sinne, of which I spak biforn, thilke fleshly concupiscence. And after that comth the subjeccion of the devel, this is to seyn, the develes bely, with which he bloweth in man the fyr of fleshly concupiscence. And after that, a man bithinketh him whether he wol doon, or no, thilke thing to which he is tempted. And thanne, if that a man withstonde and weyve the firste entysinge of his flesh and of the feend, thanne is it no sinne; and if it so be that he do nat so, thanne feleth he anon a flambe of delyt. And thanne is it good to be war, and kepen him wel, or elles he wol falle anon in-to consentinge of sinne; and thanne wol he do it, if he may have tyme and place. And of this matere seith Moyses by the devel in this manere: "the feend seith, I wole chace and pursue the man by wikked suggestion, and I wole hente him by moevynge or stiringe of sinne. I wol departe my pryse or my praye by deliberacion, and my lust shal been accompliced in delyt; I wol

drawe my swerd in consentinge": for certes, right as a swerd departeth a thing in two peces, right so consentinge departeth god fro man: "and thanne wol I sleen him with myn hand in dede of sinne"; thus seith the feend. For certes, thanne is a man al deed in soule. And thus is sinne accompliced by temptacion, by delyt, and by consentinge; and thanne is the sin cleped actuel.

Fiend. For truly, then is a man dead in soul. And thus is sin accomplished by temptation and by acquiescence; and then is the sin called actual.

21. For sothe, sinne is in two maneres; outher it is venial, or deedly sinne. Soothly, whan man loveth any creature more than Jesu Crist oure creatour, thanne is it deedly sinne. And venial synne is it, if man love Jesu Crist lasse than him oghte. For sothe, the dede of this venial sinne is ful perilous; for it amenuseth the love that men sholde han to god more and more. And therfore, if a man charge him-self with manye swiche venial sinnes, certes, but-if so be that he som tyme descharge him of hem by shrifte, they mowe ful lightly amenuse in him al the love that he hath to Jesu Crist; and in this wise skippeth venial in-to deedly sinne. For certes, the more that a man chargeth his soule with venial sinnes, the more is he enclyned to fallen in-to deedly sinne. And therfore, lat us nat be necligent to deschargen us of venial sinnes. For the proverbe seith: that manye smale maken a greet. And herkne this ensample. A greet wawe of the see comth som-tyme with so greet a violence that it drencheth the ship. And the same harm doth som-tyme the smale dropes of water, that entren thurgh a litel crevace in-to the thurrok, and in-to the botme of the ship, if men be so necligent that they ne descharge hem nat by tyme. And therfore, althogh ther be a difference bitwixe thise two causes of drenchinge, algates the ship is dreynt. Right so fareth it somtyme of deedly sinne, and of anoyouse veniale sinnes, whan they multiplye in a man so greetly, that thilke worldly thinges that he loveth, thurgh whiche he sinneth venially, is as greet in his herte as the love of god, or more. And therfore, the love of every thing, that is nat biset in god ne doon principally for goddes sake, al-though that a man love it lasse than god, yet is it venial sinne; and deedly sinne, whan the love of any thing weyeth in the herte of man as muchel as the love of god, or more. "Deedly sinne," as seith seint Augustin, "is, whan a man turneth his herte fro god, which that is verray sovereyn bountee, that may nat chaunge, and yeveth his herte to thing that may chaunge and flitte"; and certes, that is every thing, save god of hevene. For sooth is, that if a man yeve his love, the which that he oweth al to god with al his herte, un-to a creature, certes, as muche of his love as he yeveth to thilke creature, so muche he bireveth fro god; and therfore doth he sinne. For he, that is dettour to god, ne yeldeth nat to god al his dette, that is to seyn, al the love of his herte.

Forsooth, sin is of two kinds; it is either venial or mortal sin. Verily, when man loves any creature more than he loves Jesus Christ our Creator, then is it mortal sin. And venial sin it is if a man love Jesus Christ less than he ought. Forsooth the effect of this venial sin is very dangerous; for it diminishes more and more the love that man should have for God. And therefore, if a man charge himself with many such venial sins, then certainly, unless he discharge them occasionally by shriving, they may easily lessen in him all the love that he has for Jesus Christ; and in this wise venial sin passes over into mortal sin. Therefore let us not be negligent in ridding ourselves of venial sins. For the proverb has it: "Mony a mickle mak's a muckle." And hear this example. A huge wave of the sea comes sometimes with so great violence that it sinks a ship. And the same harm is caused sometimes by the small drops of water that enter through the little opening in the seam into the bilge of the ship, if men be so negligent that they do not discharge it in time. And therefore, though there be a difference between these two ways of sinking, nevertheless the ship is sunk. Just so it is sometimes with mortal sin, and with vexatious venial sins when they multiply in a man so greatly that the worldly things he loves, for which he venially sins, have grown as great in his heart as the love for God, or greater. And therefore, the love for everything that is not fixed or rooted in God, or done principally for God's sake, though a man love it less than he love God, yet it is venial sin; and it is mortal sin when the love for anything weighs in the heart of man as much as the love for God, or more. "Mortal sin," as Saint Augustine says, "is when a man turns his heart from God, Who is the truly sovereign goodness and may not change, and gives his heart unto things that may change and pass away." And true it is that if a man give his love, the which he owes all to God, with all his heart, unto a creature, then certainly so much of his love as he gives unto the said creature he takes away from God; and thereby does he sin. For he, who is debtor to God, yields not unto God all of his debt, which is to say, all the love of his heart.

22. Now sith man understondeth generally, which is venial sinne, thanne is it covenable to tellen specially of sinnes whiche that many a man per-aventure ne demeth hem nat sinnes, and ne

Now since man understands generally what venial sin is, it is fitting to tell especially of sins which many a man perhaps holds not to be sins at all, and for which he shrives not himself; yet, nevertheless, they are sins. Truly, as clerics write, every time a man eats or drinks more than suffices for the sustenance of his body, it is certain that he thereby sins. And, too, when he speaks more than it is necessary it is sin. Also, when he hears not benignly the complaint of the poor. Also, when he is in health of body and will not fast when other folk fast, and that without a reasonable excuse. Also, when he sleeps more than he needs, or when he comes, for that reason, too late to church, or to other places where works of charity are done. Also, when he enjoys his wife without a sovereign desire to procreate children to the honour of God, or when he does it without intention to yield to his wife the duty of his body. Also, when he will not visit the sick and the imprisoned, if he may do so. Also, if he love wife or child or any other worldly thing more than reason requires. Also, if he flatter or blandish more than, of necessity, he ought. Also, if he diminish or withdraw his alms to the poor. Also, if he prepare his food more delicately than is needful, or eat it too hastily or too greedily. Also, if he talk about vain and trifling matters in a church or at God's service, or if he be a user of idle words of folly or of obscenity; for he shall yield up an accounting of it at the day of doom. Also, when he promises or assures one that he will do what he cannot perform. Also, when he, through thoughtlessness or folly, slanders or scorns his neighbour. Also, when he suspects a thing to be evil when he has no certain knowledge of it. These things, and more without number, are sins, as Saint Augustine says.

Now shall men understand that while no earthly man may avoid all venial sins, yet may he keep them down by the burning love that he has to Our Lord Jesus Christ, and by prayer and confession, and by other good deeds. For, as Saint Augustine says: "If a man love God in such manner that all that he ever does is done in the love of God, and truly for the love of God, because he burns with the love of God: behold, then, how much a drop of water falling in a furnace harms or proves troublesome; and just so much vexes the venial sin a man who is perfect in the love of Christ." Men may also keep down venial sins by receiving deservingly the precious body of Jesus Christ; also by receiving holy water; by almsgiving; by general confession of *confiteor* at mass and at compline; and by the blessings of bishops and of priests, and by other good works.

shryveth him nat of the same thinges; and yet nathelees they been sinnes. Soothly, as thise clerkes wryten, this is to seyn, that at every tyme that a man eteth or drinketh more than suffyseth to the sustenaunce of his body, in certein he dooth sinne. And eek whan he speketh more than nedeth, it is sinne. Eke whan he herkneth nat benignely the compleint of the povre. Eke whan he is in hele of body and wol nat faste, whan othere folk faste, with-outen cause resonable. Eke whan he slepeth more than nedeth, or whan he comth by thilke enchesoun to late to chirche, or to othere werkes of charite. Eke whan he useth his wyf, with-outen sovereyn desyr of engendrure, to the honour of god, or for the entente to yelde to his wyf the dette of his body. Eke whan he wol nat visite the sike and the prisoner, if he may. Eke if he love wyf or child, or other worldly thing, more than resoun requyreth. Eke if he flatere or blandishe more than him oghte for any necessitee. Eke if he amenuse or withdrawe the almesse of the povre. Eke if he apparailleth his mete more deliciously than nede is, or ete it to hastily by likerousnesse. Eke if he tale vanitees at chirche or at goddes service, or that he be a talker of ydel wordes of folye or of vileinye; for he shal yelden acountes of it at the day of dome. Eke whan he biheteth or assureth to do thinges that he may nat perfourne. Eke whan that he, by lightnesse or folie, misseyeth or scorneth his neighebore. Eke whan he hath any wikked suspecion of thing, ther he ne woot of it no soothfastnesse. Thise thinges and mo with-oute nombre been sinnes, as seith seint Augustin.

Now shal men understonde, that al-be-it so that noon erthely man may eschue alle venial sinnes, yet may he refreyne him by the brenninge love that he hath to oure lord Jesu Crist, and by preyeres and confession and othere gode werkes, so that it shal but litel greve. For, as seith seint Augustin: "if a man love god in swiche manere, that al that evere he doth is in the love of god, and for the love of god verraily, for he brenneth in the love of god: loke, how muche that a drope of water that falleth in a fourneys ful of fyr anoyeth or greveth, so muche anoyeth a venial sinne un-to a man that is parfit in the love of Jesu Crist." Men may also refreyne venial sinne by receyvinge worthily of the precious body of Jesu Crist; by receyving eek of holy water; by almesdede; by general confession of *Confiteor* at masse and at complin; and by blessinge of bisshopes and of preestes, and by othere gode werkes.

HERE ENDETH THE SECOND PART OF PENITENCE

HERE FOLLOWETH THE SEVEN DEADLY SINS AND THEIR DEPENDENCIES, CIRCUMSTANCES, AND TYPES

Now it is a needful thing to tell which are the mortal sins, that is to say, the principal sins; they are all leashed together, but are different in their ways. Now they are called principal sins because they are the chief sins and the trunk from which branch all

23. Now is it bihovely thing to telle whiche been the deedly sinnes, this is to seyn, chieftaines of sinnes; alle they renne in o lees, but in diverse maneres. Now been they cleped chieftaines for-asmuche as they been chief, and springers of alle

othere sinnes. Of the roote of thise sevene sinnes thanne is Pryde, the general rote of alle harmes; for of this rote springen certein braunches, as Ire, Envye, Accidie or Slewthe, Avarice or Coveitise (to commune understondinge), Glotonye, and Lecherye. And everich of thise chief sinnes hath hise braunches and hise twigges, as shal be declared in hir chapitres folwinge.

others. And the root of these seven sins is pride, which is the general root of all evils; for from this root spring certain branches, as anger, envy, acedia or sloth, avarice (or covetousness, for vulgar understanding), gluttony, and lechery. And each of these principal sins has its branches and its twigs, as shall be set forth and declared in the paragraphs following.

Of Pride

24. And thogh so be that no man can outrely telle the nombre of the twigges and of the harmes that cometh of Pryde, yet wol I shewe a partie of hem, as ye shul understonde. Ther is Inobedience, Avauntinge, Ipocrisie, Despyt, Arrogance, Impudence, Swellinge of herte, Insolence, Elacion, Impacience, Strif, Contumacie, Presumpcion, Irreverence, Pertinacie, Veyne Glorie; and many another twig that I can nat declare. Inobedient, is he that disobeyeth for despyt to the comandements of god and to hise sovereyns, and to his goostly fader. Avauntour, is he that bosteth of the harm or of the bountee that he hath doon. Ipocrite, is he that hydeth to shewe him swiche as he is, and sheweth him swiche as he noght is. Despitous, is he that hath desdeyn of his neighebore, that is to seyn, of his evenecristene, or hath despyt to doon that him oghte to do. Arrogant, is he that thinketh that he hath thilke bountees in him that he hath noght, or weneth that he sholde have hem by hise desertes; or elles he demeth that he be that he nis nat. Impudent, is he that for his pride hath no shame of hise sinnes. Swellinge of herte, is whan a man rejoyseth him of harm that he hath doon. Insolent, is he that despyseth in his jugement alle othere folk as to regard of his value, and of his conning, and of his speking, and of his bering. Elacion, is whan he ne may neither suffre to have maister ne felawe. Impacient, is he that wol nat been y-taught ne undernome of his vyce, and by stryf werreyeth trouthe witingly, and deffendeth his folye. *Contumax*, is he that thurgh his indignacion is agayns everich auctoritee or power of hem that been hise sovereyns. Presumpcion, is whan a man undertaketh an empryse that him oghte nat do, or elles that he may nat do; and that is called Surquidrie. Irreverence, is whan men do nat honour thereas hem oghte to doon, and waiten to be reverenced. Pertinacie is whan man deffendeth his folye, and trusteth to muchel in his owene wit. Veyne glorie, is for to have pompe and delyt in his temporel hynesse, and glorifie him in this worldly estaat. Janglinge, is whan men speken to muche biforn folk, and clappen as a mille, and taken no kepe what they seye.

And though it be true that no man can absolutely tell the number of the twigs and of the evil branches that spring from pride, yet will I show forth a number of them, as you shall understand. There are disobedience, boasting, hypocrisy, scorn, arrogance, impudence, swelling of the heart, insolence, elation, impatience, strife, contumacy, presumption, irreverence, obstinacy, vainglory; and many another twig that I cannot declare. Disobedient is he that disobeys for spite the commandments of God, of his rulers, and of his spiritual father. Braggart is he that boasts of the evil or the good that he has done. Hypocrite is he that hides his true self and shows himself such as he is not. Scorner is he who has disdain for his neighbour, that is to say, for his fellow Christian, or who scorns to do that which he ought to do. Arrogant is he who thinks he has within himself those virtues which he has not, or who holds that he should so have them as his desert; or else he deems that he is that which he is not. Impudent is he who, for his pride's sake, has no shame for his sins. Swelling of heart is what a man has when he rejoices in evil that he has done. Insolent is he that despises in his judgments all other folk in comparing theirs with his worth, and with his understanding, and with his conversation, and with his bearing. Elated is he who will suffer neither a master nor a peer. Impatient is he who will not be taught nor reproved for his vice, and who, by strife, knowingly wars on truth and defends his folly. *Contumax* is he who, because of his indignation, is against all authority or power of those that are his rulers. Presumption is when a man undertakes an enterprise that he ought not to attempt, or one which he cannot accomplish; and that is called over-confidence. Irreverence is when men do not show honour where they ought, and themselves wait to be reverenced. Obstinacy is when man defends his folly and trusts too much in his own judgment. Vainglory is delight in pomp and temporal rank, and glorification in this worldly estate. Chattering is when men speak too much before folk, clattering like a mill and taking no care of what they say.

25. And yet is ther a privee spece of Pryde, that waiteth first to be salewed er he wole salewe, al be he lasse worth than that other is, per-aventure; and eek he waiteth or desyreth to sitte, or elles to goon above him in the wey, or kisse pax, or been encensed, or goon to offring biforn his neighebore, and swiche semblable thinges; agayns his

And then there is a private species of pride that waits to be saluted before it will salute, albeit the one who has it is of less worth than is the other, perchance; also, when he attends services in church he desires to sit, or else to go, before his neighbour in the aisle, or to kiss the pax before him, or to be censed before him, or to make offering before his neighbour, and similar things; all against his necessity, peradventure, save that in his heart and his will is such proud desire to be magnified and honoured before the people.

Now there are two kinds of pride; one of them lies within the heart of man, and the other lies without. Whereof, truly, these aforesaid things, and more than I have named, appertain to that pride which is within the heart of man; for that other species of pride lies without. But notwithstanding, one of these species of pride is a sign of the existence of the other, just as the fresh bush at the tavern door is a sign of the wine that is in the cellar. And this second kind of pride shows itself in many ways: as in speech and bearing, and in extravagant array of clothing; for truly, if there had been no sin in clothing, Christ would not have noted and spoken of the clothing of that rich man in the gospel. And, as Saint Gregory says, that same precious clothing is culpable for the glory and beauty of it, and for its softness, and for its strange new modes, and its fantastic ornamentation, and for its superfluity, and for the inordinate scantiness of it. Alas! May not men see, in our days, the sinfully costly array of clothing, especially in the matter of superfluity, or else in inordinate scantiness?

As to the first sin, it lies in the superfluity of clothing, which makes cloth so dear, to the harm of the people; not only the cost of embroidering, the elaborate notching or barring, the waved lines, the stripes, the twists, the diagonal bars, and similar waste of cloth in vanity; but there is also the costly furring of gowns, so much perforating with scissors to make holes, so much slashing with shears; and then the superfluity in length of the aforesaid gowns, trailing in the dung and in the mire, a-horseback and afoot, as well of man's clothing as of woman's, until all this trailing verily, in its effect, wastes, consumes, makes threadbare and rotten with dung the superfluity that rather should be given unto the poor; to the great harm of the aforesaid poor. And that in sundry wise: this is to say, the more that cloth is wasted, the more it costs the people because of its scarcity; and furthermore, if they would give such perforated and slashed clothing to the poor folk, it would not be suitable for their wearing, what of their state, nor sufficient to help their necessity to keep themselves from the fury of the elements. On the other hand, to speak of the horrible inordinate scantiness of clothing, let us notice these short-cut smocks or jackets, which, because of their shortness, cover not the shameful members of man, to the wicked calling of them to attention. Alas! Some of them show the very boss of their penis and the horrible pushed-out testicles that look like the malady of hernia in the wrapping of their hose; and the buttocks of such persons look like the hinder parts of a she-ape in the full of the moon. And moreover, the hateful proud members that they show by the fantastic fashion of making one leg of their hose white and the other red, make it seem that half their shameful privy members are flayed. And if it be that they divide their hose in other colours, as

duetee, per-aventure, but that he hath his herte and his entente in swich a proud desyr to be magnifyed and honoured biforn the peple.

26. Now been ther two maneres of Pryde; that oon of hem is with-inne the herte of man, and that other is withoute. Of whiche soothly thise forseyde thinges, and mo than I have seyd, apertenen to pryde that is in the herte of man; and that othere speces of pryde been with-oute. But natheles that oon of thise speces of pryde is signe of that other, right as the gaye leefsel atte taverne is signe of the wyn that is in the celer. And this is in manye thinges: as in speche and contenaunce, and in outrageous array of clothing; for certes, if ther ne hadde be no sinne in clothing, Crist wolde nat have noted and spoken of the clothing of thilke riche man in the gospel. And, as seith Seint Gregorie, that precious clothing is coupable for the derthe of it, and for his softenesse, and for his strangenesse and degysinesse, and for the superfluitee, or for the inordinat scantnesse of it. Allas! may men nat seen, as in oure dayes, the sinful costlewe array of clothinge, and namely in to muche superfluitee, or elles in to desordinat scantnesse?

27. As to the firste sinne, that is in superfluitee of clothinge, which that maketh it so dere, to harm of the peple; nat only the cost of embroudinge, the degyse endentinge or barringe, oundinge, palinge, windinge, or bendinge, and semblable wast of clooth in vanitee; but ther is also costlewe furringe in hir gounes, so muche pounsoninge of chisels to maken holes, so muche dagginge of sheres; forth-with the superfluitee in lengthe of the forseide gounes, trailinge in the dong and in the myre, on horse and eek on fote, as wel of man as of womman, that al thilke trailing is verraily as in effect wasted, consumed, thredbare, and roten with donge, rather than it is yeven to the povre; to greet damage of the forseyde povre folk. And that in sondry wyse: this is to seyn, that the more that clooth is wasted, the more it costeth to the peple for the scantnesse; and forther-over, if so be that they wolde yeven swich pounsoned and dagged clothing to the povre folk, it is nat convenient to were for hir estaat, ne suffisant to bete hir necessitee, to kepe hem fro the distemperance of the firmament. Upon that other syde, to speken of the horrible disordinat scantnesse of clothing, as been thise cutted sloppes or hainselins, that thurgh hir shortnesse ne covere nat the shameful membres of man, to wikked entente. Allas! somme of hem shewen the boce of hir shap, and the horrible swollen membres, that semeth lyk the maladie of hirnia, in the wrappinge of hir hoses; and eek the buttokes of hem faren as it were the hindre part of a she-ape in the fulle of the mone. And moreover, the wrecched swollen membres that they shewe thurgh the degysinge, in departinge of hir hoses in whyt and reed, semeth that half hir shameful privee membres weren flayn. And if so

be that they departen hire hoses in othere colours, as is whyt and blak, or whyt and blew, or blak and reed, and so forth; thanne semeth it, as by variance of colour, that half the partie of hir privee membres were corrupt by the fyr of seint Antony, or by cancre, or by other swich meschaunce. Of the hindre part of hir buttokes, it is ful horrible for to see. For certes, in that partie of hir body ther-as they purgen hir stinkinge ordure, that foule partie shewe they to the peple proudly in despyt of honestetee, the which honestetee that Jesu Crist and hise freendes observede to shewen in hir lyve. Now as of the outrageous array of wommen, god woot, that though the visages of somme of hem seme ful chaast and debonaire, yet notifie they in hir array of atyr likerousnesse and pryde. I sey nat that honestetee in clothinge of man or womman is uncovenable, but certes the superfluitee or disordinat scantitee of clothinge is reprevable. Also the sinne of aornement or of apparaille is in thinges that apertenen to rydinge, as in to manye delicat horses that been holden for delyt, that been so faire, fatte, and costlewe; and also to many a vicious knave that is sustened by cause of hem; in to curious harneys, as in sadeles, in crouperes, peytrels, and brydles covered with precious clothing and riche, barres and plates of gold and of silver. For which god seith by Zakarie the prophete, "I wol confounde the ryderes of swiche horses." This folk taken litel reward of the rydinge of goddes sone of hevene, and of his harneys whan he rood up-on the asse, and ne hadde noon other harneys but the povre clothes of hise disciples; ne we ne rede nat that evere he rood on other beest. I speke this for the sinne of superfluitee, and nat for reasonable honestetee, whan reson it requyreth. And forther, certes pryde is greetly notified in holdinge of greet meinee, whan they be of litel profit or of right no profit. And namely, whan that meinee is felonous and damageous to the peple, by hardinesse of heigh lordshipe or by wey of offices. For certes, swiche lordes sellen thanne hir lordshipe to the devel of helle, whanne they sustenen the wikkednesse of hir meinee. Or elles whan this folk of lowe degree, as thilke that holden hostelries, sustenen the thefte of hir hostilers, and that is in many manere of deceites. Thilke manere of folk been the flyes that folwen the hony, or elles the houndes that folwen the careyne. Swiche forseyde folk stranglen spiritually hir lordshipes; for which thus seith David the prophete, "wikked doeth mote come up-on thilke lordshipes, and god yeve that they mote descenden in-to helle al doun; for in hir houses been iniquitees and shrewednesses," and nat god of hevene. And certes, but-if they doon amendement, right as god yaf his benison to Laban by the service of Jacob, and to Pharao by the service of Joseph, right so god wol yeve his malison to swiche lordshipes as sustenen the wikkednesse of hir servaunts, but-if they come to amendement. Pryde of the table appereth eek ful ofte; for certes, riche

white and black, or white and blue, or black and red, and so forth, then it seems, by variation of colour, that the half of their privy members are corrupted by the fire of Saint Anthony, or by cancer, or by other such misfortune. As to the hinder parts of their buttocks, the thing is horrible to see. For, indeed, in that part of their body where they purge their stinking ordure, that foul part they proudly show to the people in despite of decency, which decency Jesus Christ and His friends observed in their lives. Now, as to the extravagant array of women, God knows that though the faces of them seem chaste and gentle, yet do they advertise, by their attire, their lickerousness and pride. I say not that a moderate gaiety in clothing is unseemly, but certainly the superfluity or inordinate scantiness of clothing is reprehensible. Also, the sin of adornment or apparel lies in things that appertain to riding, as in too many fine horses that are kept for delight, that are so fair, fat, and costly; in many a vicious knave who is kept because of them; in too curious harness, as saddles, cruppers, poitrels, and bridles covered with precious caparison and rich, and with bars and plates of gold and silver. As to which God says by Zechariah the prophet: "I will confound the riders of such horses." These folk have but little regard for the riding of God of Heaven's Son and of His trappings, when He rode upon the ass and had no other caparison than the poor cloaks of His disciples; nor do we read that ever He rode upon any other beast. I say this against the sin of superfluity, and not against reasonable display when the occasion requires it. And further, certainly pride is greatly shown in keeping up a great household, when such servants are of little profit, or of no profit. And this is especially so when such an array of servants is mischievous and injurious to the people, by the insolence of high rank or by way of office. For truly, such lords sell then their lordships to the Devil of Hell when they sustain the wickedness of their following. And when folk of low degree, as those that keep and run hostelries, sustain the thievery of their servants, which is done in many ways. This kind of folk are the flies that seek honey or the dogs that seek carrion. Such folk strangle spiritually their lordships; as to which thus says David the prophet: "Wicked death shall come upon such masters, and God will give that they descend into Hell; for in their houses are iniquities and evil deeds." And God of Heaven is not there. And truly, unless they mend their ways, just as God gave His blessing to Laban for the service of Jacob and to Pharaoh for the service of Joseph, just so will God give His curse to such lordships as sustain the wickedness of their servants, unless they shall make amendment. Pride of the table is often seen; for truly, rich men are bidden to feasts and poor folk are turned away and rebuked. The sin of pride lies also in excess of divers meats and drinks; and especially in certain baked meats and made-dishes burning with spirituous liquors and decorated and castellated with paper, and in similar waste; so that it is scandalous to think upon. And also in too great preciousness of vessels and in curious instruments of minstrelsy, whereby a man is stirred the more to the delights of luxury; if it be that he thereby sets his heart the less upon Jesus Christ, certainly it is a sin; and certainly the delights might be so great in this case that a man could easily fall thereby into mortal sin. The varieties of sin that arise out of pride, truly, when they arise with malice imagined, advised, and aforethought, or from habit, are mortal sins, and of that there is no doubt. And when they arise out of frailty, unadvisedly and suddenly, and are quickly withdrawn again, albeit they are grievous sins, I think that they are not mortal. Now might men ask, whence pride arises and takes its being, and I say: sometimes it springs out of the good things of nature, and sometimes from the benefits of Fortune, and sometimes from the good of grace itself. Certainly the good things of nature consist of either physical well-being or riches of the soul. Certainly physical well-being consists of the weal of the body, as strength, activity, beauty, good blood, and generous candour. The benefits of nature to the soul are good wit, keen understanding, clever talent, natural virtue, and good memory. The benefits of Fortune are riches, high rank, and the people's praise. The good of grace consists of knowledge, power to suffer spiritual travail, benignity, virtuous contemplation, ability to withstand temptation, and similar things. Of which aforesaid things, certainly it is great folly in a man when he permits himself to be proud of any of them. As for the benefits of nature, God knows that sometimes we receive them naturally as much to our detriment as to our profit. As, to take bodily health, certainly it passes away lightly enough, and moreover it is often the reason for the wickedness of the soul; for God knows that the flesh is a great enemy to the soul; and therefore, the more sound the body is, the more are we in danger of falling into sin. Also, to feel pride in the strength of one's body is a great folly; for certainly the flesh lusts for that which is detrimental to the spirit, and ever the stronger the flesh is, the sorrier must the soul be: and above all this, strength of body and worldly boldness bring a man often into danger of mischance. Also, to be proud of his gentility is a great folly; for often the gentility of the body debases the gentility of the soul; and furthermore, we are all of one father and one mother; and we are of one nature, rotten and corrupt, both the rich and the poor. Forsooth, but one kind of gentility is praiseworthy, and that it is which clothes a man's heart with virtue and morality and makes of him Christ's child. For trust this well, that over whatsoever man sin has gained the mastery, that man is a very serf to sin.

Now there are general signs of gentility; as the eschewing of vice and ribaldry and servitude to sin,

men been cleped to festes, and povre folk been put awey and rebuked. Also in excesse of diverse metes and drinkes; and namely, swiche manere bake metes and dish-metes, brenninge of wilde fyr, and peynted and castelled with papir, and semblable wast; so that it is abusion for to thinke. And eek in to greet preciousnesse of vessel and curiositee of minstralcie, by whiche a man is stired the more to delyces of luxurie, if so be that he sette his herte the lasse up-on oure lord Jesu Crist, certein it is a sinne; and certeinly the delyces mighte been so grete in this caas, that man mighte lightly falle by hem in-to deedly sinne. The especes that sourden of Pryde, soothly whan they sourden of malice ymagined, avysed, and forncast, or elles of usage, been deedly synnes, it is no doute. And whan they sourden by freletee unavysed sodeinly, and sodeinly withdrawen ayein, al been they grevouse sinnes, I gesse that they ne been nat deedly. Now mighte men axe wher-of that Pryde sourdeth and springeth, and I seye: somtyme it springeth of the goodes of nature, and som-tyme of the goodes of fortune, and som-tyme of the goodes of grace. Certes, the goodes of nature stonden outher in goodes of body or in goodes of soule. Certes, goodes of body been hele of body, as strengthe, delivernesse, beautee, gentrye, franchise. Goodes of nature of the soule been good wit, sharp understondynge, subtil engin, vertu naturel, good memorie. Goodes of fortune been richesses, highe degrees of lordshipes, preisinges of the peple. Goodes of grace been science, power to suffre spirituel travaille, benignitee, vertuous contemplacion, withstondinge of temptacion, and semblable thinges. Of whiche forseyde goodes, certes it is a ful greet folye a man to pryden him in any of hem alle. Now as for to speken of goodes of nature, god woot that som-tyme we han hem in nature as muche to oure damage as to oure profit. As, for to speken of hele of body; certes it passeth ful lightly, and eek it is ful ofte encheson of the siknesse of oure soule; for god woot, the flesh is a ful greet enemy to the soule: and therfore, the more that the body is hool, the more be we in peril to falle. Eke for to pryde him in his strengthe of body, it is an heigh folye; for certes, the flesh coveiteth agayn the spirit, and ay the more strong that the flesh is, the sorier may the soule be: and, over al this, strengthe of body and worldly hardinesse causeth ful ofte many a man to peril and meschaunce. Eek for to pryde him of his gentrye is ful greet folye; for ofte tyme the gentrye of the body binimeth the gentrye of the soule; and eek we ben alle of o fader and of o moder; and alle we been of o nature roten and corrupt, both riche and povre. For sothe, oo manere gentrye is for to preise, that apparailleth mannes corage with vertues and moralitees, and maketh him Cristes child. For truste wel, that over what man sinne hath maistrie, he is a verray cherl to sinne.

28. Now been ther generale signes of gentilesse; as eschewinge of vyce and ribaudye and servage of

sinne, in word, in werk, and contenance; and usinge vertu, curteisye, and clennesse, and to be liberal, that is to seyn, large by mesure; for thilke that passeth mesure is folye and sinne. Another is, to remembre him of bountee that he of other folk hath receyved. Another is, to be benigne to hise goode subgetis; wherfore, as seith Senek, "ther is no-thing more covenable to a man of heigh estaat than debonairetee and pitee. And therfore thise flyes that men clepeth bees, whan they maken hir king, they chesen oon that hath no prikke wherwith he may stinge." Another is, a man to have a noble herte and a diligent, to attayne to heighe vertuouse thinges. Now certes, a man to pryde him in the goodes of grace is eek an outrageous folye; for thilke yiftes of grace that sholde have turned him to goodnesse and to medicine, turneth him to venim and to confusion, as seith seint Gregorie. Certes also, who-so prydeth him in the goodes of fortune, he is a ful greet fool; for som-tyme is a man a greet lord by the morwe, that is a caitif and a wrecche er it be night: and somtyme the richesse of a man is cause of his deeth; somtyme the delyces of a man is cause of the grevous maladye thurgh which he dyeth. Certes, the commendacion of the peple is somtyme ful fals and ful brotel for to triste; this day they preyse, tomorwe they blame. God woot, desyr to have commendacion of the peple hath caused deeth to many a bisy man.

in word, in deed, and in conduct; and as the practising of virtue, courtesy, and purity, and being generous, which is to say, bounteous within measure; for that which goes beyond a reasonable measure is folly and sin. Another such sign is, when a man remembers and bears in mind the good that he has received from others. Another is, to be benign to his good inferiors; wherefore, as Seneca says: "There is nothing more becoming a man of high estate than kindliness, courtesy, and pity. And therefore the flies that men call bees, when they make their king, they choose one that has no prick wherewith he may sting." Another is, for a man to have a good heart and a diligent, to attain to high virtuous things. Now truly, for a man to pride himself on the gifts of grace is also an extravagant folly; for these same gifts of grace that should have turned him to goodness and to alleviation, turn him to venom and confusion, as says Saint Gregory. Certainly, also, whoso prides himself on the benefits of Fortune, he is a full great fool; for sometimes a man is a great lord at morning who is a captive and a wretch ere it be night; and sometimes the wealth of a man is the cause of his death; sometimes the pleasures of a man cause the grievous malady whereof he dies. Certainly the people's commendation is sometimes false enough and brittle enough to trust; today they praise, tomorrow they blame. God knows, desire to have commendation of the people has caused death to many a busy man.

The Remedy Against the Sin of Pride

29. Now sith that so is, that ye han understonde what is pryde, and whiche been the speces of it, and whennes pride sourdeth and springeth; now shul ye understonde which is the remedie agayns the sinne of pryde, and that is, humilitee or mekenesse. That is a vertu, thurgh which a man hath verray knoweleche of him-self, and holdeth of himself no prys ne deyntee as in regard of hise desertes, consideringe evere his freletee. Now been ther three maneres of humilitee; as humilitee in herte, and another humilitee in his mouth; the thridde in hise werkes. The humilitee in herte is in foure maneres: that oon is, whan a man holdeth him-self as noght worth biforn god of hevene. Another is, whan he ne despyseth noon other man. The thridde is, whan he rekketh nat thogh men holde him noght worth. The ferthe is, whan he nis nat sory of his humiliacion. Also, the humilitee of mouth is in foure thinges: in attempree speche, and in humblesse of speche, and whan he biknoweth with his owene mouth that he is swich as him thinketh that he is in his herte. Another is, whan he preiseth the bountee of another man, and nothing ther-of amenuseth. Humilitee eek in werkes is in foure maneres: the firste is, whan he putteth othere men biforn him. The seconde is, to chese the loweste place over-al. The thridde is, gladly to assente to good conseil. The ferthe is, to stonde gladly to the award of hise sovereyns, or of him that is in hyer degree; certein, this is a greet werk of humilitee.

Now, since it has come to pass that you have understood what pride is, and what the species of it are, and whence pride arises and springs, now you shall understand what is the remedy for the sin of pride, and that is, humility or meekness. That is a virtue whereby a man may come to have a true knowledge of himself, and whereby he will hold himself to be of no price or value in regard to his deserts, but will be considering ever his frailty. Now there are three kinds of humility: as humility of heart, and another humility is of the mouth, and the third is in a man's works. The humility of heart is of four kinds: one is when a man holds himself to be of nothing worth before God in Heaven. Another is, when he despises no other man. The third is, when he recks not though men hold him as nothing worth. The fourth is when he is not sorry for his humiliation. Also, the humility of the mouth is of four kinds: temperate speech, meek speech, and when a man acknowledges with his own mouth that he is as he thinks himself to be, in his heart. Another is, when he praises the goodness of another man and nothing thereof belittles. Humility in deeds is in four manners: the first is, when a man puts other men before him. The second is, to choose the lowest place of all for himself. The third is, gladly to assent to good counsel. The fourth is, to abide gladly by the decision of his rulers, or of him that is of higher rank; certainly this is a great work of humility.

Here Followeth Envy

After pride I will speak of the foul sin of envy, which is, according to the word of the philosopher, sorrow for other men's prosperity; and according to the word of Saint Augustine, it is sorrow for other men's weal and joy for other men's harm. This foul sin is flatly against the Holy Ghost. Be it that every sin is in opposition to the Holy Ghost, yet, nevertheless, for as much as goodness appertains properly to the Holy Ghost and envy springs by nature out of malice, therefore is it especially against the goodness of the Holy Ghost. Now malice has two species, that is to say, a heart hardened in wickedness, or else the flesh of man is so blind that he does not consider himself to be in sin, or he cares not that he is in sin, which is the hardihood of the Devil. The other kind of malice is, when a man wars against the truth, knowing that it is truth. Also, when he wars against the grace that God has given to his neighbour; and all this is envy. Certainly, then, envy is the worst sin there is. For truly, all other sins are sometime against only one special virtue; but truly, envy is against all virtues and against all goodnesses; for it is sorry for all the virtues of its neighbour; and in this way it differs from all other sins. For hardly is there any sin that has not some delight in itself, save only envy, which ever has of itself but anguish and sorrow. The kinds of envy are these: there is, first, sorrow for other men's goodness and prosperity; and prosperity being naturally a thing for joy, then envy is a sin against nature. The second kind of envy is joy in other men's harm; and this is naturally like the Devil, who always rejoices in man's harm. From these two species comes backbiting; and this sin of backbiting, or detraction, has certain forms, as thus. A man praises his neighbour with a wicked intention, for he puts always a wicked twist into it at the end. Always he puts a "but" in at the end, which implies more blame than all the praise is worth. The second form is, when a man is good and does or says a thing to good intent, the backbiter turns all this goodness upside-down to his own evil end. The third is, to belittle the goodness of a neighbour. The fourth form of backbiting is this: that if a man say good of a man, then the backbiter says, "Faith, such or such a man is better than he," in disparagement of him that men praise. The fifth form is this, to assent gladly and listen gladly to the evil that folk speak of others. This sin is a great one; and it grows according to the wicked endeavours of the backbiter. After backbiting comes grumbling or murmuring; and sometimes it springs from impatience with God, and sometimes with man. Impatience with God it is when the man grumbles against the pains of Hell, or against poverty, or loss of chattels, or against rain or tempest; or else complains that scoundrels prosper, or else that good men have adversity. And all these things should men suffer patiently, for they come by the right judgment and ordinance of God. Sometimes grumbling comes of avarice; as Judas complained of the Magdalen when she anointed the head of Our

30. After Pryde wol I speken of the foule sinne of Envye, which is, as by the word of the philosophre, sorwe of other mannes prosperitee; and after the word of seint Augustin, it is sorwe of other mannes wele, and joye of othere mennes harm. This foule sinne is platly agayns the holy goost. Al-be-it so that every sinne is agayns the holy goost, yet nathelees, for as muche as bountee aperteneth proprely to the holy goost, and Envye comth proprely of malice, therfore it is proprely agayn the bountee of the holy goost. Now hath malice two speces, that is to seyn, hardnesse of herte in wikkednesse, or elles the flesh of man is so blind, that he considereth nat that he is in sinne, or rekketh nat that he is in sinne; which is the hardnesse of the devel. That other spece of malice is, whan a man werreyeth trouthe, whan he woot that it is trouthe. And eek, whan he werreyeth the grace that god hath yeve to his neighebore; and al this is by Envye. Certes, thanne is Envye the worste sinne that is. For soothly, alle othere sinnes been somtyme only agayns o special vertu; but certes, Envye is agayns alle vertues and agayns alle goodnesses; for it is sory of alle the bountees of his neighebore; and in this manere it is divers from alle othere sinnes. For wel unnethe is ther any sinne that it ne hath som delyt in itself, save only Envye, that evere hath in itself anguish and sorwe. The speces of Envye been thise: ther is first, sorwe of other mannes goodnesse and of his prosperitee; and prosperitee is kindely matere of joye; thanne is Envye a sinne agayns kinde. The seconde spece of Envye is joye of other mannes harm; and that is proprely lyk to the devel, that evere rejoyseth him of mannes harm. Of thise two speces comth bakbyting; and this sinne of bakbyting or detraccion hath certeine speces, as thus. Som man preiseth his neighebore by a wikke entente; for he maketh alwey a wikked knotte atte laste ende. Alwey he maketh a "but" atte laste ende, that is digne of more blame, than worth is al the preisinge. The seconde spece is, that if a man be good and dooth or seith a thing to good entente, the bakbyter wol turne all thilke goodnesse up-so-doun to his shrewed entente. The thridde is, to amenuse the bountee of his neighebore. The fourthe spece of bakbyting is this, that if men speke goodnesse of a man, thanne wol the bakbyter seyn, "parfey, swich a man is yet bet than he"; in dispreisinge of him that men preise. The fifte spece is this; for to consente gladly and herkne gladly to the harm that men speke of other folk. This sinne is ful greet, and ay encreseth after the wikked entente of the bakbyter. After bakbyting cometh grucching or murmuracion; and somtyme it springeth of inpacience agayns god, and somtyme agayns man. Agayns god it is, whan a man gruccheth agayn the peynes of helle, or agayns poverte, or los of catel, or agayn reyn or tempest; or elles gruccheth that shrewes han prosperitee, or elles for that goode men han adversitee. And alle thise thinges sholde men

suffre paciently, for they comen by the rightful jugement and ordinance of god. Somtyme comth grucching of avarice; as Judas grucched agayns the Magdaleyne, whan she enoynte the heved of oure lord Jesu Crist with hir precious oynement. This maner murmure is swich as whan man gruccheth of goodnesse that him-self dooth, or that other folk doon of hir owene catel. Somtyme comth murmure of Pryde; as whan Simon the Pharisee grucched agayn the Magdaleyne, whan she approched to Jesu Crist, and weep at his feet for hir sinnes. And somtyme grucching sourdeth of Envye; whan men discovereth a mannes harm that was privee, or bereth him on hond thing that is fals. Murmure eek is ofte amonges servaunts, that grucchen whan hir sovereyns bidden hem doon leveful thinges; and, for-as-muche as they dar nat openly withseye the comaundements of hir sovereyns, yet wol they seyn harm, and grucche, and murmure prively for verray despyt; whiche wordes men clepen the develes *Paternoster*, though so be that the devel ne hadde nevere *Pater-noster*, but that lewed folk yeven it swich a name. Som tyme grucching comth of ire or prive hate, that norisseth rancour in herte, as afterward I shal declare. Thanne cometh eek bitternesse of herte; thurgh which bitternesse every good dede of his neighebor semeth to him bitter and unsavory. Thanne cometh discord, that unbindeth alle manere of frendshipe. Thanne comth scorninge, as whan a man seketh occasioun to anoyen his neighebor, al do he never so weel. Thanne comth accusinge, as whan man seketh occasion to anoyen his neighebor, which that is lyk to the craft of the devel, that waiteth bothe night and day to accusen us alle. Thanne comth malignitee, thurgh which a man anoyeth his neighebor prively if he may; and if he noght may, algate his wikked wil ne shal nat wante, as for to brennen his hous prively, or empoysone or sleen hise bestes, and semblable thinges.

Lord Jesus Christ with her precious ointment. This murmuring is such as when a man grumbles at good that he himself has done, or that other folk do with their wealth. Sometimes murmuring comes of pride; as when Simon the Pharisee murmured against the Magdalen when she approached Jesus Christ and wept at His feet for her sins. And sometimes grumbling arises out of envy; as when men discover a man's secret weakness, or swear of him a thing that is false. Murmuring, too, is often found among servants, who grumble when their masters bid them to do lawful things; and for as much as they dare not openly gainsay the commands of their masters, yet do they speak evilly of them and grumble and murmur privately, for very spite; which words men call the Devil's Paternoster, though the Devil never had a Paternoster, save that vulgar folk give these murmurings that name. Sometimes grumbling comes of anger or privy hate, that nurtures rancour in its heart, as I shall hereafter set forth. Then comes bitterness of heart, through which bitterness every good deed of one's neighbour seems to one to be but bitter and unsavoury. Then comes discord, which undoes all friendship. Then comes spite, as when a man seeks occasion to annoy his neighbour, though he do never so well. Then comes accusation, as when a man seeks occasion to offend his neighbour, which is like the guile of the Devil, who watches both night and day to accuse us all. Then comes malignity, through which a man annoys his neighbour privately, if he may; and if he may not, then nevertheless his wicked will shall not want for means to harm him, as by burning his house, or poisoning or slaying his beasts, and suchlike things.

The Remedy Against the Sin of Envy

31. Now wol I speke of the remedie agayns this foule sinne of Envye. First, is the love of god principal, and loving of his neighebor as him-self; for soothly, that oon ne may nat been withoute that other. And truste wel, that in the name of thy neighebore thou shalt understonde the name of thy brother; for certes alle we have o fader fleshly, and o moder, that is to seyn, Adam and Eve; and eek o fader espirituel, and that is god of hevene. Thy neighebore artow holden for to love, and wilne him alle goodnesse; and therfore seith god, "love thy neighebore as thyselve," that is to seyn, to salvacion bothe of lyf and of soule. And more-over, thou shalt love him in word, and in benigne amonestinge, and chastysinge; and conforten him in hise anoyes, and preye for him with al thyn herte. And in dede thou shalt love him in swich wyse, that thou shalt doon to him in charitee as thou woldest that it were doon to thyn owene persone. And therfore, thou ne shalt doon him no damage in wikked

Now will I speak of the remedy for this foul sin of envy. First, is the love of God, and the love of one's neighbour as one's self; for indeed the one cannot be without the other. And trust well, that by the name of your neighbour you are to understand your brother; for certainly all of us have one fleshly father and one mother, that is to say, Adam and Eve; and even one spiritual father, and that is God in Heaven. Your neighbour you are bound to love and to wish all good things; and thereunto God says, "Love thy neighbour as thyself." That is to say, to the salvation both of life and soul. Moreover, you shall love him in word, and in benign admonition and in chastening; and comfort him in his vexations, and pray for him with all your heart. And you shall love him in deed and in such wise that you shall charitably do unto him as you would that it were done unto yourself. And therefore you shall do him no damage by wicked words, nor any harm in his body, nor in his goods, nor in his soul by the enticement of wicked example. You shall not covet his wife, nor any of his things. Understand also that in the word neighbour is included his enemy. Certainly man shall love his enemy, by the commandment of God; and truly, your friend shall you love in God. I say, you shall love your enemy for God's sake, and by His commandment. For if it were reasonable that a man should hate his enemies, then God would not receive us into His love, when we are His enemies. For three kinds of wrong that his enemy may do to a man, he shall do three things in return, thus: for hate and rancour, he shall love him in heart. For chiding and wicked words, he shall pray for his enemy. And for the wicked deed of his enemy, he shall do him kindness. For Christ says: "Love your enemies, bless them that curse you, do good to them that hate you, and pray for them which despitefully use you and persecute you." Lo, thus Our Lord Jesus Christ commands that we do to our enemies. For indeed, nature drives us to love our enemies, and, faith, our enemies have more need for love than our friends; and they that have more need, truly to them men ought to do good; and truly, in the deed thereof have we remembrance of the love of Jesus Christ Who died for His enemies. And in so much as that same love is the harder to feel and to show, in that much is the merit the greater; and therefore the loving of our enemy has confounded the venom of the Devil. For just as the Devil is discomfited by humility, so is he wounded to the death by love for our enemy. Certainly, then, love is the medicine that purges the heart of man of the poison of envy. The kinds of this degree of sin will be set forth more at large in the paragraphs following.

word, ne harm in his body, ne in his catel, ne in his soule, by entysing of wikked ensample. Thou shalt nat desyren his wyf, ne none of hise thinges. Understond eek, that in the name of neighebor is conprehended his enemy. Certes man shal loven his enemy by the comandement of god; and soothly thy frend shaltow love in God. I seye, thyn enemy shaltow love for goddes sake, by his comandement. For if it were reson that a man sholde haten his enemy, for sothe god nolde nat receiven us to his love that been hise enemys. Agayns three manere of wronges that his enemy dooth to hym, he shal doon three thinges, as thus. Agayns hate and rancour of herte, he shal love him in herte. Agayns chyding and wikkede wordes, he shal preye for his enemy. And agayn the wikked dede of his enemy, he shal doon him bountee. For Crist seith, "loveth youre enemys, and preyeth for hem that speke yow harm; and eek for hem that yow chacen and pursewen, and doth bountee to hem that yow haten." Lo, thus comaundeth us oure lord Jesu Crist, to do to oure enemys. For soothly, nature dryveth us to loven oure freendes, and parfey, oure enemys han more nede to love than our freendes; and they that more nede have, certes, to hem shal men doon goodnesse; and certes, in thilke dede have we remembrance of the love of Jesu Crist, that deyde for hise enemys. And in-as-muche as thilke love is the more grevous to perfourne, in-so-muche is the more gretter the merite; and therfore the lovinge of oure enemy hath confounded the venim of the devel. For right as the devel is disconfited by humilitee, right so is he wounded to the deeth by love of oure enemy. Certes, thanne is love the medicine that casteth out the venim of Envye fro mannes herte. The speces of this pas shullen be more largely in hir chapitres folwinge declared.

Here followeth Wrath

After envy will I describe the sin of anger. For truly, whoso has envy of his neighbour will generally find himself showing anger, in word or in deed, against him whom he envies. And anger comes as well from pride as from envy; for certainly, he that is proud or envious is easily angered.

This sin of anger, according to Saint Augustine, is a wicked determination to be avenged by word or by deed. Anger, according to the philosopher, is the hot blood of man quickened in his heart, because of which he wishes to harm him whom he hates. For truly, the heart of man, by the heating and stirring of his blood, grows so disturbed that he is put out of all ability to judge reasonably. But you shall understand that anger manifests itself in two manners; one of them is good, the other bad. The good anger is caused by zeal for goodness, whereof a man is enraged by wickedness and against wickedness; and thereupon a wise man says that "Anger is better than play." This anger is gentle and without bitterness; not felt against the man, but against the misdeed of the man, as the Prophet David says: *Iras-*

32. After Envye wol I discryven the sinne of Ire. For soothly, who-so hath envye upon his neighebor, anon he wole comunly finde him a matere of wratthe, in word or in dede, agayns him to whom he hath envye. And as wel comth Ire of Pryde, as of Envye; for soothly, he that is proude or envious is lightly wrooth.

33. This sinne of Ire, after the discryving of seint Augustin, is wikked wil to been avenged by word or by dede. Ire, after the philosophre, is the fervent blood of man y-quiked in his herte, thurgh which he wole harm to him that he hateth. For certes the herte of man, by eschaufinge and moevinge of his blood, wexeth so trouble, that he is out of alle jugement of resoun. But ye shal understonde that Ire is in two maneres; that oon of hem is good, and that other is wikked. The gode Ire is by jalousye of goodnesse, thurgh which a man is wrooth with wikkednesse and agayns wikkednesse; and therfore seith a wys man, that "Ire is bet than pley." This Ire is with debonairetee, and it is wrooth withouten bitternesse; nat wrooth agayns the man, but wrooth with the misdede of the man; as seith the prophete

David, *Irascimini et nolite peccare.* Now understondeth, that wikked Ire is in two maneres, that is to seyn, sodeyn Ire or hastif Ire, withouten avisement and consentinge of resoun. The mening and the sens of this is, that the resoun of man ne consente nat to thilke sodeyn Ire; and thanne it is venial. Another Ire is ful wikked, that comth of felonye of herte avysed and cast biforn; with wikked wil to do vengeance, and therto his resoun consenteth; and soothly this is deedly sinne. This Ire is so displesant to god, that it troubleth his hous and chaceth the holy goost out of mannes soule, and wasteth and destroyeth the lyknesse of god, that is to seyn, the vertu that is in mannes soule; and put in him the lyknesse of the devel, and binimeth the man fro god that is his rightful lord. This Ire is a ful greet plesaunce to the devel; for it is the develes fourneys, that is eschaufed with the fyr of helle. For certes, right so as fyr is more mighty to destroyen erthely thinges than any other element, right so Ire is mighty to destroyen alle spirituel thinges. Loke how that fyr of smale gledes, that been almost dede under asshen, wollen quike agayn whan they been touched with brimstoon; right so Ire wol everemo quiken agayn, whan it is touched by the pryde that is covered in mannes herte. For certes fyr ne may nat comen out of no-thing, but-if it were first in the same thing naturelly; as fyr is drawen out of flintes with steel. And right so as pryde is ofte tyme matere of Ire, right so is rancour norice and keper of Ire. Ther is a maner tree, as seith seint Isidre, that whan men maken fyr of thilke tree, and covere the coles of it with asshen, soothly the fyr of it wol lasten al a yeer or more. And right so fareth it of rancour; whan it is ones conceyved in the hertes of som men, certein, it wol lasten peraventure from oon Estre day unto another Estre-day, and more. But certes, thilke man is ful fer fro the mercy of god al thilke while.

34. In this forseyde develes fourneys ther forgen three shrewes: Pryde, that ay bloweth and encreseth the fyr by chydinge and wikked wordes. Thanne stant Envye, and holdeth the hote iren upon the herte of man with a peire of longe tonges of long rancour. And thanne stant the sinne of contumelie or stryf and cheeste, and batereth and forgeth by vileyns reprevinges. Certes, this cursed sinne anoyeth bothe to the man him-self and eek to his neighebor. For soothly, almost al the harm that any man dooth to his neighebore comth of wratthe. For certes, outrageous wratthe doth al that evere the devel him comaundeth; for he ne spareth neither Crist, ne his swete mooder. And in his outrageous anger and Ire, allas! allas! ful many oon at that tyme feleth in his herte ful wikkedly, bothe of Crist and of alle hise halwes. Is nat this a cursed vice? Yis, certes. Allas! it binimeth from man his wit and his resoun, and al his debonaire lyf espirituel that sholde kepen his soule. Certes, it binimeth eek goddes due lordshipe, and that is mannes soule, and the love of hise neighebores. It stryveth eek alday agayn trouthe. It reveth him the quiete of his herte, and subverteth his soule.

cimini et nolite peccare. Now understand, that wicked anger is manifested in two manners, that is to say, sudden or hasty anger, without the advice and counsel of reason. The meaning and the sense of this is, that the reason of man consents not to this sudden anger, and so it is venial. Another anger is full wicked, which comes of sullenness of heart, with malice aforethought and with wicked determination to take vengeance, and to which reason assents; and this, truly, is mortal sin. This form of anger is so displeasing to God that it troubles His house and drives the Holy Ghost out of man's soul, and wastes and destroys the likeness of God, that is to say, the virtue that is in man's soul; and it puts within him the likeness of the Devil, and takes the man away from God, his rightful Lord. This form of anger is a great joy to the Devil; for it is the Devil's furnace, heated with the fire of Hell. For certainly, just as fire is the mightiest of earth's engines of destruction, just so ire is mightiest to destroy things spiritual. Observe how a fire of smouldering coals, almost extinct under the ashes, will quicken again when touched by brimstone; just so will anger quicken again when it is touched by the pride that lies hidden in man's heart. For certainly fire cannot come from nothing, but must first be naturally dormant within a thing as it is drawn out of flints with steel. And just as pride is often the matter of which anger is made, just so is rancour the nurse and keeper of anger. There is a kind of tree, as Saint Isidore says, which, when men make a fire of the wood of it, and then cover over the coals with ashes, truly the embers will live and last a year or more. And just so fares it with rancour; when it is once conceived in the hearts of some men, certainly it will last, perchance, from one Easter-day to another Easter-day, and longer. But truly, such men are very far from the mercy of God all that while.

In this aforesaid Devil's furnace there are forged three evils: pride that ever fans and increases the fire by chiding and wicked words. Then stands up envy and holds the hot iron upon the heart of man with a pair of long tongs of abiding rancour. And then stands up the sin of contumely, or strife and wrangling, and strikes and hammers with villainous reproaches. Certainly, this cursed sin injures both the man who does it and his neighbour. For truly, almost all the harm that any man does to his neighbour comes from wrath. For certainly, outrageous wrath does all that the Devil orders; for it spares neither Christ nor His Sweet Mother. And in his outrageous anger and ire, alas! full many a one at that time feels in his heart right wickedly, both as to Christ and as to His saints. Is not this a cursed vice? Yes, certainly. Alas! It takes from man his wit and his reason and all the kindly spiritual life that should guard his soul. Certainly, it takes away also God's due authority, and that is man's soul and the love of his neighbour. It strives always against truth, also. It bereaves him of the peace of his heart and subverts his soul.

From anger come these stinking engenderings: first hate, which is old wrath; discord, by which a man forsakes his old friend whom he has long loved. And then come strife and every kind of wrong that man does to his neighbour, in body or in goods. Of this cursed sin of anger comes manslaughter also. And understand well that homicide, manslaughter, that is, is of different kinds. Some kinds of homicide are spiritual, and some are bodily. Spiritual manslaughter lies in six things. First, hate; and as Saint John says: "He that hateth his brother committeth homicide." Homicide is also accomplished by backbiting; and of backbiters Solomon says that "They have two swords wherewith they slay their neighbours." For truly, it is as wicked to take away a man's good name as his life. Homicide consists also in the giving of wicked counsel deceitfully, as in counselling one to levy wrongful duties and taxes. And Solomon says that cruel masters are like roaring lions and hungry bears, in withholding or diminishing the wages (or the hire) of servants; or else in usury; or in withholding alms from poor folk. As to which the wise man says: "Feed him who is dying of hunger." For indeed, unless you feed him, you slay him; and all these are mortal sins. Bodily homicide is when you slay a man with your tongue is some manner; as when you give command to slay a man, or else counsel him to the slaying of another. Homicide in deed is in four manners. One is by law; as when a judge condemns a culpable man to death. But let the judge take care that he do it rightfully, and that he do it not for delight in the spilling out of blood, but only for the doing of justice. Another kind of homicide is that which is done by necessity, as when one man slays another in his own defence, and when he may not otherwise escape his own death. But certainly, if he may escape without killing his adversary, and yet slays him, he commits sin, and he shall bear the punishment for mortal sin. Also, if a man by force of circumstances, or by chance, shoot an arrow or cast a stone with which he kill a man, he commits homicide. Also, if a woman negligently overlie her child in her sleep, it is homicide and mortal sin. Also, when a man interferes with the conception of a child, and makes a woman barren by the drinking of poisonous drugs, whereby she cannot conceive, or slays an unborn child deliberately, by drugs or by the introduction of certain substances into her secret parts with intent to slay the child; or does any unnatural sin whereby man or woman spill his or her fluid in such manner or in such place as a child cannot be conceived; or if a woman, having conceived, so hurt herself that she slays her child, it is homicide. What do we say of women that murder their children for dread of worldly shame? Certainly, such a one is called a horrible homicide. Homicide it is, also, if a man approach a woman by desire of lechery, through the accomplishing of which her child is killed in the womb, or strike a woman knowingly in such manner that she is caused to miscarry and lose her child. All these constitute homicide and are horrible mortal sins. Besides, there come from anger many more

35. Of Ire comen thise stinkinge engendrures: first hate, that is old wratthe; discord, thurgh which a man forsaketh his olde freend that he hath loved ful longe. And thanne cometh werre, and every manere of wrong that man dooth to his neighebore, in body or in catel. Of this cursed sinne of Ire cometh eek manslaughtre. And understonde wel, that homicyde, that is manslaughtre, is in dyverse wyse. Som manere of homicyde is spirituel, and som is bodily. Spirituel manslaughtre is in six thinges. First, by hate; as seint John seith, "he that hateth his brother is homicyde." Homicyde is eek by bakbytinge; of whiche bakbyteres seith Salomon, that "they han two swerdes with whiche they sleen hir neighebores." For soothly, as wikke is to binime his good name as his lyf. Homicyde is eek, in yevinge of wikked conseil by fraude; as for to yeven conseil to areysen wrongful custumes and taillages. Of whiche seith Salomon, "Leon rorynge and bere hongry been lyke to the cruel lordshipes," in withholdinge or abregginge of the shepe (or the hyre), or of the wages of servaunts, or elles in usure or in withdrawinge of the almesse of povre folk. For which the wyse man seith, "fedeth him that almost dyeth for honger"; for soothly, but-if thou fede him, thou sleest him; and alle thise been deedly sinnes. Bodily manslaughtre is, whan thow sleest him with thy tonge in other manere; as whan thou comandest to sleen a man, or elles yevest him conseil to sleen a man. Manslaughtre in dede is in foure maneres. That oon is by lawe; right as a justice dampneth him that is coupable to the deeth. But lat the justice be war that he do it rightfully, and that he do it nat for delyt to spille blood, but for kepinge of rightwisenesse. Another homicyde is, that is doon for necessitee, as whan o man sleeth another in his defendaunt, and that he ne may noon otherwise escape from his owene deeth. But certeinly, if he may escape withouten manslaughtre of his adversarie, and sleeth him, he doth sinne, and he shal bere penance as for deedly sinne. Eek if a man, by caas or aventure, shete an arwe or caste a stoon with which he sleeth a man, he is homicyde. Eek if a womman by necligence overlyeth hir child in hir sleping, it is homicyde and deedly sinne. Eek whan man destourbeth concepcion of a child, and maketh a womman outher bareyne by drinkinge venemouse herbes, thurgh which she may nat conceyve, or sleeth a child by drinkes wilfully, or elles putteth certeine material thinges in hir secree places to slee the child; or elles doth unkindely sinne, by which man or womman shedeth hir nature in manere or in place ther-as a child may nat be conceived; or elles, if a womman have conceyved and hurt hirself, and sleeth the child, yet is it homicyde. What seye we eek of wommen that mordren hir children for drede of worldly shame? Certes, an horrible homicyde. Homicyde is eek if a man approcheth to a womman by desir of lecherye, thurgh which the child is perissed, or elles smyteth a womman witingly, thurgh which she leseth hir child. Alle thise been homicydes and horrible deedly sinnes.

Yet comen ther of Ire manye mo sinnes, as wel in word as in thoght and in dede; as he that arretteth upon god, or blameth god, of thing of which he is him-self gilty; or despyseth god and alle hise halwes, as doon thise cursede hasardours in diverse contrees. This cursed sinne doon they, whan they felen in hir hertes ful wikkedly of god and of hise halwes. Also, whan they treten unreverently the sacrement of the auter, thilke sinne is so greet, that unnethe may it been relesed, but that the mercy of god passeth alle hise werkes; it is so greet and he so benigne. Thanne comth of Ire attry angre; whan a man is sharply amonested in his shrifte to forleten his sinne, than wole he be angry and answeren hokerly and angrily, and deffenden or excusen his sinne by unstedefastnesse of his flesh; or elles he dide it for to holde companye with hise felawes, or elles, he seith, the fend entyced him; or elles he dide it for his youthe, or elles his complexioun is so corageous, that he may nat forbere; or elles it is his destinee, as he seith, unto a certein age; or elles, he seith, it cometh him of gentillesse of hise auncestres; and semblable thinges. Alle this manere of folk so wrappen hem in hir sinnes, that they ne wol nat delivere hem-self. For soothly, no wight that excuseth him wilfully of his sinne may nat been delivered of his sinne, til that he mekely biknoweth his sinne. After this, thanne cometh swering, that is expres agayn the comandement of god; and this bifalleth ofte of anger and of Ire. God seith: "thou shalt nat take the name of thy lord god in veyn or in ydel." Also oure lord Jesu Crist seith by the word of seint Mathew: "*Nolite iurare omnino:* ne wol ye nat swere in alle manere; neither by hevene, for it is goddes trone; ne by erthe, for it is the bench of his feet; ne by Jerusalem, for it is the citee of a greet king; ne by thyn heed, for thou mayst nat make an heer whyt ne blak. But seyeth by youre word, 'ye, ye,' and 'nay, nay'; and what that is more, it is of yvel," seith Crist. For Cristes sake, ne swereth nat so sinfully, in dismembringe of Crist by soule, herte, bones, and body. For certes, it semeth that ye thinke that the cursede Jewes ne dismembred nat y-nough the preciouse persone of Crist, but ye dismembre him more. And if so be that the lawe compelle yow to swere, thanne rule yow after the lawe of god in youre swering, as seith Jeremye *quarto capitulo*, "*Iurabis in veritate, in iudicio et in iusticia:* thou shalt kepe three condicions; thou shalt swere in trouthe, in doom, and in rightwisnesse." This is to seyn, thou shalt swere sooth; for every lesinge is agayns Crist. For Crist is verray trouthe. And think wel this, that every greet swerere, nat compelled lawefully to swere, the wounde shal nat departe from his hous whyl he useth swich unleveful swering. Thou shalt sweren eek in doom, whan thou art constreyned by thy domesman to witnessen the trouthe. Eek thou shalt nat swere for envye ne for favour, ne for mede, but for rightwisnesse; for declaracioun of it to the worship of god and helping of thyne evenecristene. And therfore, every man that taketh goddes name in ydel, or fals-

sins, as well of word as of thought and of deed; as that of accusing God of, or blaming God for, a thing of which a man is himself guilty; or despising God and all His saints, as do wicked gamblers in divers countries. They do this cursed sin when they feel in their heart a great wickedness toward God and His saints. Also, they do it when they treat irreverently the sacraments of the altar, and then the sin is so great that scarcely may it be forgiven, save that the mercy of God passes all His works; it is so great and He is so benign. Then comes of anger, venomous anger; when a man is sharply admonished after confession to forgo his sin, then will he be angry and will answer scornfully and angrily, and will defend or excuse his sin as the result of the weakness of his flesh; or else he did it to keep the good will of his fellows, or else, he'll say, the Fiend enticed him; or else he did it because of his youth, or else his temperament is so mettled that he could not forbear; or else it was his destiny, as he says, until a certain age; or else, he says, it comes to him out of the breeding of his ancestors; and suchlike things. All this kind of folk so wrap themselves in their sins that they will not deliver themselves. For truly, no man that excuses himself for his sin may be shriven of it until he meekly acknowledges it. After this, then comes swearing, which is expressly against the commandment of God; and this comes often of anger and ire. God says: "Thou shalt not take the name of the Lord thy God in vain." Also, Our Lord Jesus Christ says, through Saint Matthew: "*Nolite iurare omnino:* neither by Heaven; for it is God's throne: nor by the earth; for it is His footstool: neither by Jersusalem; for it is the city of the great King. Neither shalt thou swear by thy head, because thou canst not make one hair white or black: but let your communication be, yea, yea, nay, nay; for whatsoever is more than these, cometh of evil." For Christ's sake, swear not so sinfully, thus dismembering Christ by soul, heart, bones, and body. For indeed it seems that you think that the cursed Jews did not dismember enough the precious body of Christ, since you dismember Him even more. And if it be that the law compel you to swear, then be governed by the rule of the law in your swearing, as Jeremiah says, *quarto capitulo:* "*Iurabis, in veritate, in iudicio et in iusticia:* thou shalt swear, the Lord liveth, in truth, in judgment, and in righteousness." That is to say, you shall swear truth, for every lie is against Christ. For Christ is utter truth. And think well on this, that every great swearer, not by law compelled to swear, the plague will not depart from his house while he continues to indulge in such forbidden swearing. You shall swear for the sake of justice also, when you are constrained by your judge to bear witness to the truth. Also, you shall swear not for envy, nor for favour, nor for reward, but for righteousness; for the declaring of it to the honour of God and the helping of your fellow Christian. And therefore, every man that takes God's name in vain, or falsely swears by word of mouth, or takes upon him the name of Christ that he may be called a Christian man, and who lives not in accordance with Christ's example of living and with His teaching, all they take God's name in vain. Behold, too, what Saint Peter says, *Actuum, quarto capitulo: "Non est aliud nomen sub celo, etc.* There is none other name under Heaven given among men whereby we must be saved." That is to say, save the name of Jesus Christ. Take heed also how in the precious name of Christ, as Saint Paul says *ad Philipenses secundo: "In nomine Iesu, etc.* In the name of Jesus every knee should bow, of things in Heaven, and things in earth, and things under the earth." For it is so high and so worshipful that the cursed Fiend in Hell must tremble to hear it named.

Then it appears that men who swear so horribly by His blessed name despise Him more boldly than all the cursed Jews, or even than the Devil, who trembles when he hears His name.

Now, certainly, since swearing, unless it be lawfully done, is so strictly forbidden, much worse is false swearing, and it is needless.

What shall we say of those that delight in swearing and hold it for an act of the gentry, or a manly thing, to swear great oaths? And what of those that, of very habit, cease not to swear great oaths, though the reason therefor be not worth a straw? Certainly this is a horrible sin. Swearing suddenly and thoughtlessly is also a sin. But let us pass now to that horrible swearing of adjuration and conjuration, as do these false enchanters or necromancers in basins full of water, or in a bright sword, in a circle, or in a fire, or in a shoulder-bone of a sheep. I can say nothing, save that they do wickedly and damnably against Christ and all the faith of Holy Church.

What shall we say of those that believe in divinations, as by the flying or the crying of birds, or of beasts, or by chance, by geomancy, by dreams, by creaking of doors, by cracking of houses, by gnawing of rats, and such kinds of wickedness? Certainly, all these things are forbidden by God and by all Holy Church. For which they are accursed, until they repent and mend their ways, who set their beliefs in such filth. Charms against wounds or maladies in men or in beasts, if they have any effect, it may be, peradventure, that God permits it that folk shall have the more faith in Him and the more reverence unto His name.

Now will I speak of lying, which generally is the using of words in false signification with intent to deceive one's fellow Christian. Some lying there is whereof there comes no advantage to anyone; and some lying is done for the ease and profit of one man, and to the uneasiness and damage of another man. Another kind of lying is done to save one's life or chattels. Another kind of lying is born of mere delight in lying, for which delight they will fabricate a long tale and adorn it with all circumstances, where all the groundwork of the tale is false. Some lying is done because one would maintain his previous word; and some lying is done out of recklessness, without forethought; and for similar reasons.

ly swereth with his mouth, or elles taketh on him the name of Crist, to be called a Cristene man, and liveth agayns Cristes livinge and his techinge, alle they taken goddes name in ydel. Loke eek what seint Peter seith, *Actuum quarto capitulo, "Non est aliud nomen sub celo,"* &c. "Ther nis noon other name," seith seint Peter, "under hevene, yeven to men, in which they mowe be saved"; that is to seyn, but the name of Jesu Crist. Take kepe eek how that the precious name of Crist, as seith seint Paul *ad Philipenses secundo, "In nomine Jesu,* &c.: that in the name of Jesu every knee of hevenely creatures, or erthely, or of helle sholden bowe"; for it is so heigh and so worshipful, that the cursede feend in helle sholde tremblen to heren it y-nempned. Thanne semeth it, that men that sweren so horribly by his blessed name, that they despyse him more boldely than dide the cursede Jewes, or elles the devel, that trembleth whan he hereth his name.

36. Now certes, sith that swering, but-if it be lawefully doon, is so heighly deffended, muche worse is forswering falsly, and yet nedelees.

37. What seye we eek of hem that delyten hem in swering, and holden it a gentrie or a manly dede to swere grete othes? And what of hem that, of verray usage, ne cesse nat to swere grete othes, al be the cause nat worth a straw? Certes, this is horrible sinne. Sweringe sodeynly with-oute avysement is eek a sinne. But lat us go now to thilke horrible swering of adjuracioun and conjuracioun, as doon thise false enchauntours or nigromanciens in bacins ful of water, or in a bright swerd, in a cercle, or in a fyr, or in a shulder-boon of a sheep. I can nat seye but that they doon cursedly and damnably, agayns Crist and al the feith of holy chirche.

38. What seye we of hem that bileven in divynailes, as by flight or by noyse of briddes, or of bestes, or by sort, by geomancie, by dremes, by chirkinge of dores, or crakkinge of houses, by gnawynge of rattes, and swich manere wrecchednesse? Certes, al this thing is deffended by god and by al holy chirche. For which they been acursed, til they come to amendement, that on swich filthe setten hir bileve. Charmes for woundes or maladye of men, or of bestes, if they taken any effect, it may be peraventure that god suffreth it, for folk sholden yeve the more feith and reverence to his name.

39. Now wol I speken of lesinges, which generally is fals significacioun of word, in entente to deceyven his evenecristene. Som lesinge is of which ther comth noon avantage to no wight: and som lesinge turneth to the ese or profit of o man, and to disese and damage of another man. Another lesinge is for to saven his lyf or his catel. Another lesinge comth of delyt for to lye, in which delyt they wol forge a long tale, and peynten it with alle circumstaunces, where al the ground of the tale is fals. Som lesinge comth, for he wole sustene his word; and som lesinge comth of recchelesnesse, with-outen avysement; and semblable thinges.

40. Lat us now touche the vyce of flateringe, which ne comth nat gladly but for drede or for coveitise. Flaterye is generally wrongful preisinge. Flatereres been the develes norices, that norissen hise children with milk of losengerie. For sothe, Salomon seith, that "flaterie is wors than detraccioun." For som-tyme detraccion maketh an hautein man be the more humble, for he dredeth detraccion; but certes flaterye, that maketh a man to enhauncen his herte and his contenaunce. Flatereres been the develes enchauntours; for they make a man to wene of him-self be lyk that he nis nat lyk. They been lyk to Judas that bitraysed [god; and thise flatereres bitraysen] a man to sellen him to his enemy, that is, to the devel. Flatereres been the develes chapelleyns, that singen evere *Placebo*. I rekene flaterye in the vyces of Ire; for ofte tyme, if o man be wrooth with another, thanne wol he flatere som wight to sustene him in his querele.

41. Speke we now of swich cursinge as comth of irous herte. Malisoun generally may be seyd every maner power of harm. Swich cursinge bireveth man fro the regne of god, as seith seint Paul. And ofte tyme swich cursinge wrongfully retorneth agayn to him that curseth, as a brid that retorneth agayn to his owene nest. And over alle thing men oghten eschewe to cursen hir children, and yeven to the devel hir engendrure, as ferforth as in hem is; certes, it is greet peril and greet sinne.

42. Lat us thanne speken of chydinge and reproche, whiche been ful grete woundes in mannes herte; for they unsowen the semes of frendshipe in mannes herte. For certes, unnethes may a man pleynly been accorded with him that hath him openly revyled and repreved in disclaundre. This is a ful grisly sinne, as Crist seith in the gospel. And tak kepe now, that he that repreveth his neighebor, outher he repreveth him by som harm of peyne that he hath on his body, as "mesel," "croked harlot," or by som sinne that he dooth. Now if he repreve him by harm of peyne, thanne turneth the repreve to Jesu Crist; for peyne is sent by the rightwys sonde of god, and by his suffrance, be it meselrie, or maheym, or maladye. And if he repreve him uncharitably of sinne, as, "thou holour," "thou dronkelewe harlot," and so forth; thanne aperteneth that to the rejoysinge of the devel, that evere hath joye that men doon sinne. And certes, chydinge may nat come but out of a vileyns herte. For after the habundance of the herte speketh the mouth ful ofte. And ye shul understonde that loke, by any wey, whan any man shal chastyse another, that he be war from chydinge or reprevinge. For trewely, but he be war, he may ful lightly quiken the fyr of angre and of wratthe, which that he sholde quenche, and per-aventure sleeth him which that he mighte chastyse with benignitee. For as seith Salomon, "the amiable tonge is the tree of lyf," that is to seyn, of lyf espirituel: and sothly, a deslavee tonge sleeth the spirites of him that repreveth, and eek of him that is repreved. Lo, what seith seint Augustin: "ther is no-thing so lyk the

Let us now touch upon the vice of flattering, which comes not gladly from the heart, but for fear or for covetousness. Flattery is generally unearned praise. Flatterers are the Devil's nurses, who nurse his children with the milk of adulation. Forsooth, as Solomon says, "Flattery is worse than detraction." For sometimes detraction causes a haughty man to be more humble, for he fears detraction; but certainly flattery—that causes a man to exalt his heart and his bearing. Flatterers are the Devil's enchanters, for they cause a man to think of himself that he is like what he is not like. They are like Judas who betrayed God; for these flatterers betray a man in order to sell him out to his enemy, that is, to the Devil. Flatterers are the Devil's chaplains, that continually sing *Placebo*. I reckon flattery among the vices of anger; for oftentimes, if one man be enraged at another, then will he flatter some other to gain an ally in his quarrel.

Let us speak now of such cursing as comes from an angry heart. Execration generally may be said to embrace every kind of evil. Such cursing deprives a man of the Kingdom of God, as says Saint Paul. And oftentimes such cursing returns again upon the head of him that curses, like a bird that returns again to its own nest. And above all things men ought to eschew the cursing of their children, and the giving to the Devil of their progeny, so far as they may; certainly it is a great danger and a great sin.

Let us now speak of chiding and reproaching, which are great evils in man's heart; for they rip up the seams of friendship in man's heart. For truly, a man can hardly be reconciled with him that has openly reviled and slandered him. This is a terrible sin, as Christ says in the gospel. And note now that he who reproaches his neighbour, either he reproaches him for some painful evil that he has in his body, as with "leper" or "hunchbacked scoundrel," or by some sin that he does. Now, if he reproach him for a painful evil, then the reproach is turned upon Jesus Christ; for pain is sent as the righteous giving of God, and by His permission, be it of leprosy or malady or bodily imperfection. And if he reproach him uncharitably for sin, as with "you whoremonger," "you drunken scoundrel," and so forth, then that appertains to the rejoicing of the Devil, who is ever rejoiced when men sin. And truly, chiding may not come, save out of a sinful heart. For according to the abundance of what is in the heart the mouth speaks. And you shall understand that when any man would correct another, let him beware of chiding or reproaching. For truly, save he beware, he may easily quicken the fire of anger and wrath, which he should quench, and perhaps will slay him whom he might have corrected gently. For, as Solomon says, "the amiable tongue is the tree of life," which is to say, of the spiritual life; and in sooth, a foul tongue drains the vital forces of him that reproaches, and also of him that is reproached. Behold what Saint Augustine says: "There is nothing so like the Devil's child as he that chideth." Saint Paul says, too: "The servant of the Lord must not strive." And though bickering be a sinful thing as between all kinds of folk, certainly it is most unsuitable between a man and his wife; for there is never rest there. Thereupon Solomon says: "A continual dropping in a very rainy day, and a contentious woman, are alike." A man who is in a house, the roof whereof leaks in many places, though he avoid the dripping in one place, it finds him in another; and so fares he who has a chiding wife. If she cannot scold him in one place, she will scold him in another. And therefore, "Better is a dinner of herbs where love is, than a stalled ox and hatred therewith," says Solomon. Saint Paul says: "Wives, submit yourselves unto your husbands, as it is fit in the Lord. Husbands, love your wives, and be not bitter against them." *Ad Colossenses, tertio.*

After that, let us speak of scorn, which is a wicked sin; especially when one scorns a man for his good works. For truly, such scorners are like the foul toad, which cannot bear to smell the sweet odour of the vine when it blossoms. These scorners are fellow-partakers with the Devil; for they rejoice when the Devil wins and sorrow when he loses. They are adversaries of Jesus Christ; for they hate what He loves, that is to say, the salvation of souls.

Now will we speak of wicked counsel; for he that gives wicked counsel is a traitor. For he deceives him that trusts in him, *ut Achitofel ad Absolonem.* Nevertheless, his wicked counsel first harms himself. For, as the wise man says, every false person living has within himself this peculiarity, that he who would harm another harms first himself. And men should understand that they should take counsel not of false folk, nor of angry folk, nor of vexatious folk nor of folk that love too much their own advantage, nor of too worldly folk, especially in the counselling of souls.

Now comes the sin of those that sow discord amongst folk, which is a sin that Christ utterly hates; and no wonder. For He died to establish concord on earth. And more shame do they do to Christ than did those that crucified Him; for God loves better that friendliness be among men than He loved His own body, the which He gave for the sake of unity. Therefore they are like the Devil, who ever goes about to make discord.

Now comes the sin of the double-tongued; such as speak fairly before folk, and wickedly behind; or they make a semblance of speaking with good intention, or in jest and play, and yet they speak with evil intention.

Now comes betraying of confidence, whereby a man is defamed: truly, the damage so done may scarcely be repaired.

Now comes menacing, which is an open folly; for he that often menaces, he often threatens more than he can perform.

Now come idle words, which sin is without profit to him that speaks and also to him that listens. Or

develes child as he that ofte chydeth." Seint Paul seith eek: "I, servant of god, bihove nat to chyde." And how that chydinge be a vileyns thing bitwixe alle manere folk, yet it is certes most uncovenable bitwixe a man and his wyf; for there is nevere reste. And therfore seith Salomon, "an hous that is uncovered and droppinge, and a chydinge wyf, been lyke." A man that is in a droppinge hous in many places, though he eschewe the droppinge in o place, it droppeth on him in another place; so fareth it by a chydinge wyf. But she chyde him in o place, she wol chyde him in another. And therfore, "bettre is a morsel of breed with joye than an hous ful of delyces, with chydinge," seith Salomon. Seint Paul seith: "O ye wommen, be ye subgetes to youre housbondes as bihoveth in god; and ye men, loveth youre wyves." *Ad Colossenses, tertio.*

43. Afterward speke we of scorninge, which is a wikked sinne; and namely, whan he scorneth a man for hise gode werkes. For certes, swiche scorneres faren lyk the foule tode, that may nat endure to smelle the sote savour of the vyne whanne it florissheth. Thise scorneres been parting felawes with the devel; for they han joye whan the devel winneth, and sorwe whan he leseth. They been adversaries of Jesu Crist; for they haten that he loveth, that is to seyn, salvacion of soule.

44. Speke we now of wikked conseil; for he that wikked conseil yeveth is a traytour. For he deceyveth him that trusteth in him, *ut Achitofel ad Absolonem.* But natheless, yet is his wikked conseil first agayn him-self. For, as seith the wyse man, every fals livinge hath this propertee in him-self, that he that wole anoye another man, he anoyeth first him-self. And men shul understonde, that man shal nat taken his conseil of fals folk, ne of angry folk, or grevous folk, ne of folk that loven specially to muchel hir owene profit, ne to muche worldly folk, namely, in conseilinge of soules.

45. Now comth the sinne of hem that sowen and maken discord amonges folk, which is a sinne that Crist hateth outrely; and no wonder is. For he deyde for to make concord. And more shame do they to Crist, than dide they that him crucifyede; for god loveth bettre, that frendshipe be amonges folk, than he dide his owene body, the which that he yaf for unitee. Therfore been they lykned to the devel, that evere been aboute to maken discord.

46. Now comth the sinne of double tonge; swiche as speken faire biforn folk, and wikkedly bihinde; or elles they maken semblant as though they speke of good entencioun, or elles in game and pley, and yet they speke of wikked entente.

47. Now comth biwreying of conseil, thurgh which a man is defamed; certes, unnethe may he restore the damage.

Now comth manace, that is an open folye; for he that ofte manaceth, he threteth more than he may perfourne ful ofte tyme.

Now cometh ydel wordes, that is withouten profit of him that speketh tho wordes, and eek of him that herkneth tho wordes. Or elles ydel wordes been tho that been nedelees, or with-outen entente of naturel profit. And al-be-it that ydel wordes been som tyme venial sinne, yet sholde men douten hem; for we shul yeve rekeninge of hem bifore god.

else idle words are those that are needless, or without an aim toward any profit. And although idle words are at times but a venial sin, yet men should distrust them; for we shall have to account for them before God.

Now comth janglinge, that may nat been withoute sinne. And, as seith Salomon, "it is a sinne of apert folye." And therfore a philosophre seyde, whan men axed him how that men sholde plese the peple; and he answerde, "do many gode werkes, and spek fewe jangles."

Now comes chattering, which cannot occur without sin. And, as Solomon says, "It is a sin of manifest folly." And therefore a philosopher said, when men asked him how to please the people: "Do many good deeds and chatter but little."

After this comth the sinne of japeres, that been the develes apes; for they maken folk to laughe at hir japerie, as folk doon at the gaudes of an ape. Swiche japeres deffendeth seint Paul. Loke how that vertuouse wordes and holy conforten hem that travaillen in the service of Crist; right so conforten the vileyns wordes and knakkes of japeris hem that travaillen in the service of the devel. Thise been the sinnes that comen of the tonge, that comen of Ire and of othere sinnes mo.

After this comes the sin of jesters, who are the Devil's apes. For they make folk laugh at their buffoonery, as they do at the pranks of an ape. Such clowning were forbidden by Saint Paul. Behold how virtuous and holy words give comfort to those that labour in the service of Christ; just so the sinful words and tricks of jesters and jokers comfort those that travail in the service of the Devil. These are the sins that come by way of the tongue, and from anger and many other sins.

Here followeth the Remedy against the Sin of Wrath

48. The remedye agayns Ire is a vertu that men clepen Mansuetude, that is Debonairetee; and eek another vertu, that men callen Pacience or Suffrance.

The remedy for anger is a virtue which men call mansuetude, which is gentleness; and even another virtue which men call patience or tolerance.

49. Debonairetee withdraweth and refreyneth the stiringes and the moevynges of mannes corage in his herte, in swich manere that they ne skippe nat out by angre ne by Ire. Suffrance suffreth swetely alle the anoyaunces and the wronges that men doon to man outward. Seint Jerome seith thus of debonairetee, that "it doth noon harm to no wight, ne seith; ne for noon harm that men doon or seyn, he ne eschaufeth nat agayns his resoun." This vertu som-tyme comth of nature; for, as seith the philosophre, "a man is a quik thing, by nature debonaire and tretable to goodnesse; but whan debonairetee is enformed of grace, thanne is it the more worth."

Gentleness withholds and restrains the stirrings and the urgings of man's impetuosity in his heart in such manner that it leaps not out in anger or in ire. Tolerance suffers sweetly all the annoyances and wrongs that men do to men bodily. Saint Jerome says thus of gentleness, that "it does harm to no one, nor says harm; nor for any harm that men do or say does it chafe against reason." This virtue is sometimes naturally implanted; for, as says the philosopher: "A man is a living thing, by nature gentle and tractable to goodness; but when gentleness is informed of grace, then is it worth the more."

50. Pacience, that is another remedye agayns Ire, is a vertu that suffreth swetely every mannes goodnesse, and is nat wrooth for noon harm that is doon to him. The philosophre seith, that "pacience is thilke vertu that suffreth debonairely alle the outrages of adversitee and every wikked word." This vertu maketh a man lyk to god, and maketh him goddes owene dere child, as seith Crist. This vertu disconfiteth thyn enemy. And therfore seith the wyse man, "if thou wolt venquisse thyn enemy, lerne to suffre." And thou shalt understonde, that man suffreth foure manere of grevances in outward thinges, agayns the whiche foure he moot have foure manere of paciences.

Patience, which is another remedy against anger, is a virtue that suffers sweetly man's goodness, and is not wroth for harm done to it. The philosopher says that "patience is that virtue which suffers meekly all the outrages of adversity and every wicked word." This virtue makes a man god-like and makes him God's own dear child, as Christ says. This virtue discomfits one's enemy. And thereupon the wise man says: "If thou wilt vanquish thy enemy, learn to endure." And you shall understand that man suffers four kinds of grievances from outward things, against the which he must have four kinds of patience.

51. The firste grevance is of wikkede wordes; thilke suffrede Jesu Crist withouten grucching, ful paciently, whan the Jewes despysed and repreved him ful ofte. Suffre thou therfore paciently; for the wyse man seith: "if thou stryve with a fool, though the fool be wrooth or though he laughe,

The first grievance is of wicked words; this suffered Jesus Christ without grumbling, and patiently, when the Jews many times reproached Him and showed how they despised Him. Suffer patiently, therefore, for the wise man says: "If thou strive with a fool, though the fool be wroth or though he laugh, nevertheless thou shalt have no rest." Another outward grievance is to suffer damage in one's chattels. In that Christ endured patiently when He was despoiled of all that He had in the world, that being His clothing.

The third grievance is for a man to suffer injury in his body. That, Christ endured full patiently throughout all His passion. The fourth grievance is in extravagant labour. Wherefore I say that folk who make their servants labour too grievously, or out of the proper time, as on holidays, truly they do great sin. Thereof endured Christ full patiently, and taught us patience when He bore upon His blessed shoulder the cross whereon He was to suffer a pitiless death. Hereof may men learn to be patient; for certainly, not only Christian man should be patient for love of Jesus Christ, and for the reward of the blessed life everlasting, but even the old pagans, who never were Christians, commended and practised the virtue of patience.

Upon a time a philosopher would have beaten a disciple for his great misdoing, at which the philosopher had been much annoyed; and he brought a rod wherewith to scourge the youth; and when the youth saw the rod he said to his master: "What do you intend to do?" "I will beat you," said the master, "for your correction." "Forsooth," said the youth, "you ought first to correct yourself who have lost all your patience at the offence of a child." "Forsooth," said the master, weeping, "you say truth; take the rod yourself, my dear son, and correct me for my impatience." From patience comes obedience, whereby a man becomes obedient to Christ and to all to whom he owes obedience in Christ. And understand well that obedience is perfect when a man does gladly and speedily, with entire good heart, all that he should do. Obedience, generally, is to put into practice the doctrine of God and of man's masters, to whom he ought to be humble in all righteousness.

algate thou shalt have no reste." That other grevance outward is to have damage of thy catel. Theragayns suffred Crist ful paciently, whan he was despoyled of al that he hadde in this lyf, and that nas but hise clothes. The thridde grevance is a man to have harm in his body. That suffred Crist ful paciently in al his passioun. The fourthe grevance is in outrageous labour in werkes. Wherfore I seye, that folk that maken hir servants to travaillen to grevously, or out of tyme, as on halydayes, soothly they do greet sinne. Heer-agayns suffred Crist ful paciently, and taughte us pacience, whan he bar up-on his blissed shulder the croys, up-on which he sholde suffren despitous deeth. Heer may men lerne to be pacient; for certes, noght only Cristen men been pacient for love of Jesu Crist, and for guerdoun of the blisful lyf that is perdurable; but certes, the olde payens, that nevere were Cristene, commendeden and useden the vertu of pacience.

52. A philosophre up-on a tyme, that wolde have beten his disciple for his grete trespas, for which he was greetly amoeved, and broghte a yerde to scourge the child; and whan this child saugh the yerde, he seyde to his maister, "what thenke ye to do?" "I wol bete thee," quod the maister, "for thy correccion." "For sothe," quod the child, "ye oghten first correcte youre-self, that han lost al youre pacience for the gilt of a child." "For sothe," quod the maister al wepinge, "thou seyst sooth; have thou the yerde, my dere sone, and correcte me for myn inpacience." Of Pacience comth Obedience, thurgh which a man is obedient to Crist and to alle hem to whiche he oghte to been obedient in Crist. And understond wel that obedience is perfit, whan that a man doth gladly and hastily, with good herte entierly, al that he sholde do. Obedience generally, is to perfourne the doctrine of god and of his sovereyns, to whiche him oghte to ben obeisaunt in alle rightwysnesse.

Here followeth Sloth

After the sins of envy and of anger, now will I speak of the sin of acedia, or sloth. For envy blinds the heart of a man and anger troubles a man; and acedia makes him heavy, thoughtful, and peevish. Envy and anger cause bitterness of heart; which bitterness is the mother of acedia, and takes from a man the love of all goodness. Then is acedia the anguish of a troubled heart; and Saint Augustine says: "It is the sadness of goodness and the joy of evil." Certainly this is a damnable sin; for it wrongs Jesus Christ in as much as it lessens the service that men ought to give to Christ with due diligence, as says Solomon. But sloth has no such diligence; it does everything sadly and with peevishness, slackness, and false excusing, and with slovenliness and unwillingness; for which the Book says: "Accursed be he that serveth God negligently." Then acedia is the enemy to every state of man; for indeed the state of man is in three degrees. One is the state of innocence, as was the condition of Adam before he fell into sin; in

53. After the sinnes of Envie and of Ire, now wol I speken of the sinne of Accidie. For Envye blindeth the herte of a man, and Ire troubleth a man; and Accidie maketh him hevy, thoghtful, and wrawe. Envye and Ire maken bitternesse in herte; which bitternesse is moder of Accidie, and binimeth him the love of alle goodnesse. Thanne is Accidie the anguissh of a trouble herte; and seint Augustin seith: "it is anoy of goodnesse and joye of harm." Certes, this is a dampnable sinne; for it doth wrong to Jesu Crist, in-as-muche as it binimeth the service that men oghte doon to Crist with alle diligence, as seith Salomon. But Accidie dooth no swich diligence; he dooth alle thing with anoy, and with wrawnesse, slaknesse, and excusacioun, and with ydelnesse and unlust, for which the book seith: "acursed be he that doth the service of god necligently." Thanne is Accidie enemy to everich estaat of man; for certes, the estaat of man is in three maneres. Outher it is th'estaat of

innocence, as was th'estaat of Adam biforn that he fil into sinne; in which estaat he was holden to wirche, as in heryinge and adouringe of god. Another estaat is the estaat of sinful men, in which estaat men been holden to laboure in preyinge to god for amendement of hir sinnes, and that he wol graunte hem to arysen out of hir sinnes. Another estaat is th'estaat of grace, in which estaat he is holden to werkes of penitence; and certes, to alle thise thinges is Accidie enemy and contrarie. For he loveth no bisinesse at al. Now certes, this foule sinne Accidie is eek a ful greet enemy to the lyflode of the body; for it ne hath no purveaunce agayn temporel necessitee; for it forsleweth and forsluggeth, and destroyeth alle goodes temporeles by reccheleesnesse.

54. The fourthe thinge is, that Accidie is lyk to hem that been in the peyne of helle, by-cause of hir slouthe and of hir hevinesse; for they that been dampned been so bounde, that they ne may neither wel do ne wel thinke. Of Accidie comth first, that a man is anoyed and encombred for to doon any goodnesse, and maketh that god hath abhominacion of swich Accidie, as seith seint Johan.

55. Now comth Slouthe, that wol nat suffre noon hardnesse ne no penaunce. For soothly, Slouthe is so tendre, and so delicat, as seith Salomon, that he wol nat suffre noon hardnesse ne penaunce, and therfore he shendeth al that he dooth. Agaynes this roten-herted sinne of Accidie and Slouthe sholde men exercise hem-self to doon gode werkes, and manly and vertuously cacchen corage wel to doon; thinkinge that oure lord Jesu Crist quyteth every good dede, be it never so lyte. Usage of labour is a greet thing; for it maketh, as seith seint Bernard, the laborer to have stronge armes and harde sinwes; and Slouthe maketh hem feble and tendre. Thanne comth drede to biginne to werke any gode werkes; for certes, he that is enclyned to sinne, him thinketh it is so greet an empryse for to undertake to doon werkes of goodnesse, and casteth in his herte that the circumstaunces of goodnesse been so grevouse and so chargeaunt for to suffre, that he dar nat undertake to do werkes of goodnesse, as seith seint Gregorie.

56. Now comth wanhope, that is despeir of the mercy of god, that comth somtyme of to muche outrageous sorwe, and somtyme of to muche drede: imagininge that he hath doon so much sinne, that it wol nat availlen him, though he wolde repenten him and forsake sinne: thurgh which despeir or drede he abaundoneth al his herte to every maner sinne, as seith seint Augustin. Which dampnable sinne, if that it continue un-to his ende, it is cleped sinning in the holy gost. This horrible sinne is so perilous, that he that is despeired, ther nis no felonye ne no sinne that he douteth for to do; as shewed wel by Judas. Certes, aboven alle sinnes thanne is this sinne most displesant to Crist, and most adversarie. Soothly, he that despeireth him is lyk the coward champioun recreant, that seith creant withoute nede. Allas! allas! nedeles is he

which state he was maintained to praise and adore his God. Another state is the condition of sinful men wherein they are obliged to labour in praying to God for the amendment of their sins. Another state is the condition of grace, in which condition man is bound to acts of penitence; and truly, to all these things acedia is the enemy and the opposite. For it loves no busyness at all. Now certainly this foul sin of acedia is also a great enemy to the livelihood of the body; for it makes no provision for temporal necessity; for it wastes, and it allows things to spoil, and it destroys all worldly wealth by its carelessness.

The fourth thing is that acedia is like those who are in the pain of Hell, because of their sloth and their sluggardliness; for those that are damned are so bound that they may neither do well nor think well. First of all, from the sin of acedia it happens that a man is too sad and hindered to be able to do anything good, wherefore God abominates acedia, as says Saint John.

Then comes that kind of sloth that will endure no hardship nor any penance. For truly, sloth is so tender and so delicate, as Solomon says, that it will endure no hardship or penance, and therefore it spoils everything that it attempts to do. To combat this rotten-hearted sin of acedia or sloth, men should be diligent to do good works and manfully and virtuously to come by the determination to do well; remembering that Our Lord Jesus Christ rewards every good deed, be it ever so little. The habit of labour is a great thing; for, as Saint Bernard says, it gives the labourer strong arms and hard thews, whereas sloth makes them feeble and tender. Then arises the dread of beginning to do any good deeds; for certainly, he that is inclined toward sin, he thinks it is so great an enterprise to start any works of goodness, and tells himself in his heart that the circumstances having to do with goodness are so wearisome and burdensome to endure, that he dare not undertake any such works, as says Saint Gregory.

Now enters despair, which is despair of the mercy of God, and comes sometimes of too extravagant sorrows and sometimes of too great fear: for the victim imagines that he has done so much sin that it will avail him not to repent and forgo sin; because of which fear he abandons his heart to every kind of sin, as Saint Augustine says. This damnable sin, if it be indulged to the end, is called sinning in the Holy Ghost. This horrible sin is so dangerous that, as for him that is so desperate, there is no felony or sin that he hesitates to do; as was well showed by Judas. Certainly, then, above all other sins, this sin is most displeasing to Christ, and most hateful. Truly he that grows so desperate is like the cowardly and recreant combatant that yields before he is beaten, and when there is no need. Alas, alas! Needlessly is he recreant and needlessly in despair. Certainly the mercy of God ys available to every penitent, and this is the greatest of all God's works. Alas! Cannot a man bethink him of the gospel of Saint Luke, 15, wherein Christ says: "Joy shall be in Heaven over one sinner that repenteth more than over ninety and nine just persons which need no repentance." Behold further, in the same gospel, the joy of and the feast given by the good man who had lost his son, when his son, repentant, returned to his father. Can they not remember, also, that, as Saint Luke says, *XXIII° capitulo*, the thief who was hanged beside Jesus Christ said: "Lord, remember me when Thou comest into Thy Kingdom." "Verily," said Christ, "I say unto thee, today shalt thou be with me in Paradise." Certainly, there is no such horrible sin of man that it may not be, in his lifetime, destroyed by penitence, by virtue of the passion and the death of Jesus Christ. Alas! Why then need a man despair, since mercy is so ready and so great? Ask, and it shall be given unto you. Then enters somnolence, that is to say, sluggish slumbering, which makes a man heavy and dull in body and in soul; and this sin comes from sloth. And truly, the time that a man should not sleep, in all reason, is the early morning, unless there be a reasonable necessity. For verily the morningtide is most suitable for a man to say his prayers, and to meditate on God and to honour God, and to give alms to the poor person who first asks in the name of Christ. Behold what Solomon says: "Whoso would awake in the dawn and seek me, me shall he find." Then enters negligence, or carelessness, that recks of nothing. And if ignorance is the mother of all evil, certainly then negligence is the nurse. Negligence cares not, when it must do a thing, whether it be well done or badly.

As to the remedies for these two sins, as the wise man says: "He that fears God spares not to do that which he ought." And he that loves God, he will be diligent to please God by his works, and will exert himself, with all his might, to do well. Then enters idleness, which is the gate to all evils. An idle man is like a house that has no walls; the devils may enter on every side and shoot at him, he being thus unprotected, and tempt him on every side. This idleness is the sink of all wicked and villainous thoughts, and of all idle chattering, and trifles, and of all filthiness. Certainly Heaven is for those that labour, and not for idle folk. Also, David says: "They are not among the harvest of men and they shall not be threshed with men," which is to say, in Purgatory. Certainly, then, it appears that they shall be tormented by the Devil in Hell, unless they soon repent.

Then enters the sin that men call *tarditas*, which is when a man is too tardy or too long-tarrying before he turns unto God; and certainly this is a great folly. He is like one that falls in the ditch and will not arise. And this vice comes of a false hope where-

recreant and nedeles despeired. Certes, the mercy of god is evere redy to every penitent, and is aboven alle his werkes. Allas! can nat a man bithinke him on the gospel of seint Luk, 15., where-as Crist seith that "as wel shal ther be joye in hevene upon a sinful man that doth penitence, as up-on nynety and nyne rightful men that neden no penitence?" Loke forther, in the same gospel, the joye and the feste of the gode man that hadde lost his sone, whan his sone with repentaunce was retourned to his fader. Can they nat remembren hem eek, that, as seith seint Luk *xxiii° capitulo*, how that the theef that was hanged bisyde Jesu Crist, seyde: "Lord, remembre of me, whan thou comest in-to thy regne?" "For sothe," seyde Crist, "I seye to thee, to-day shaltow been with me in Paradys." Certes, ther is noon so horrible sinne of man, that it ne may, in his lyf, be destroyed by penitence, thurgh vertu of the passion and of the deeth of Crist. Allas! what nedeth man thanne to been despeired, sith that his mercy so redy is and large? Axe and have. Thanne cometh Sompnolence, that is, sluggy slombringe, which maketh a man be hevy and dul, in body and in soule; and this sinne comth of Slouthe. And certes, the tyme that, by wey of resoun, men sholde nat slepe, that is by the morwe; but-if ther were cause resonable. For soothly, the morwe-tyde is most covenable, a man to seye his preyeres, and for to thinken on god, and for to honoure god, and to yeven almesse to the povre, that first cometh in the name of Crist. Lo! what seith Salomon: "who-so wolde by the morwe awaken and seke me, he shal finde." Thanne cometh Necligence, or recchelesnesse, that rekketh of no-thing. And how that ignoraunce be moder of alle harm, certes, Necligence is the norice. Necligence ne doth no fors, whan he shal doon a thing, whether he do it weel or baddely.

57. Of the remedie of thise two sinnes, as seith the wyse man, that "he that dredeth god, he spareth nat to doon that him oghte doon." And he that loveth god, he wol doon diligence to plese god by his werkes, and abaundone him-self, with al his might, wel for to doon. Thanne comth ydelnesse, that is the yate of alle harmes. An ydel man is lyk to a place that hath no walles; the develes may entre on every syde and sheten at him at discovert, by temptacion on every syde. This ydelnesse is the thurrok of alle wikked and vileyns thoghtes, and of alle jangles, trufles, and of alle ordure. Certes, the hevene is yeven to hem that wol labouren, and nat to ydel folk. Eek David seith: that "they ne been nat in the labour of men, ne they shul nat been whipped with men," that is to seyn, in purgatorie. Certes, thanne semeth it, they shul be tormented with the devel in helle, but-if they doon penitence.

58. Thanne comth the sinne that men clepen *Tarditas*, as whan a man is to latrede or taryinge, er he wole turne to god; and certes, that is a greet folye. He is lyk to him that falleth in the dich, and wol nat aryse. And this vyce comth of a fals hope,

that he thinketh that he shal live longe; but that hope faileth ful ofte.

59. Thanne comth Lachesse; that is he, that whan he biginneth any good werk, anon he shal forleten it and stinten; as doon they that han any wight to governe, and ne taken of him na-more kepe, anon as they finden any contrarie or any anoy. Thise been the newe shepherdes, that leten hir sheep witingly go renne to the wolf that is in the breres, or do no fors of hir owene governaunce. Of this comth poverte and destruccioun, bothe of spirituel and temporel thinges. Thanne comth a manere coldnesse, that freseth al the herte of man. Thanne comth undevocioun, thurgh which a man is so blent, as seith seint Bernard, and hath swiche langour in soule, that he may neither rede ne singe in holy chirche, ne here ne thinke of no devocioun, ne travaille with hise handes in no good werk, that it nis him unsavory and al apalled. Thanne wexeth he slow and slombry, and sone wol be wrooth, and sone is enclyned to hate and to envye. Thanne comth the sinne of worldly sorwe, swich as is cleped *tristicia*, that sleeth man, as seint Paul seith. For certes, swich sorwe werketh to the deeth of the soule and of the body also; for therof comth, that a man is anoyed of his owene lyf. Wherfore swich sorwe shorteth ful ofte the lyf of a man, er that his tyme be come by wey of kinde.

under a man comes to think that he shall live long; but that hope full often fails him.

Then comes laziness; that is when a man begins any work and anon forgoes it and holds his hand; as do those who have anyone to govern and who take no care of him as soon as they find any difficulty or annoyance. These are the modern shepherds who knowingly allow their sheep to run to the wolf in the briers, or have no care for their governing. Of this come poverty and the destruction of both spiritual and temporal things. Then comes a kind of dull coldness that freezes the heart of man. Then comes lack of devotion, whereby a man is so blinded, as Saint Bernard says, and has such languor of soul, that he may not read or sing in holy church, nor hear or think of anything devout, nor toil with his hands at any good work, without the labour being unsavoury and vapid to him. Then he grows slow and slumbery, and is easily angered and is easily inclined toward hate and envy. Then comes the sin of worldly sorrow, such as is called *tristicia*, which slays men, as Saint Paul says. For, verily, such sorrow works the death of the soul and of the body also; for thereof it comes to pass that a man is bored by his own life. Wherefore such sadness full often shortens a man's life before his time has naturally come.

The Remedy against the Sin of Sloth

60. Agayns this horrible sinne of Accidie, and the branches of the same, ther is a vertu that is called *Fortitudo* or Strengthe; that is, an affeccioun thurgh which a man despyseth anoyous thinges. This vertu is so mighty and so vigorous, that it dar withstonde mightily and wysely kepen him-self fro perils that been wikked, and wrastle agayn the assautes of the devel. For it enhaunceth and enforceth the soule, right as Accidie abateth it and maketh it feble. For this *Fortitudo* may endure by long suffraunce the travailles that been covenable.

61. This vertu hath manye speces; and the firste is cleped Magnanimitee, that is to seyn, greet corage. For certes, ther bihoveth greet corage agains Accidie, lest that it ne swolwe the soule by the sinne of sorwe, or destroye it by wanhope. This vertu maketh folk to undertake harde thinges and grevouse thinges, by hir owene wil, wysely and resonably. And for as muchel as the devel fighteth agayns a man more by queyntise and by sleighte than by strengthe, therfore men shal withstonden him by wit and by resoun and by discrecioun. Thanne arn ther the vertues of feith, and hope in god and in hise seintes, to acheve and acomplice the gode werkes in the whiche he purposeth fermely to continue. Thanne comth seuretee or sikernesse; and that is, whan a man ne douteth no travaille in tyme cominge of the gode werkes that a man hath bigonne. Thanne comth Magnificence, that is to seyn, whan a man dooth and perfourneth grete werkes of goodnesse that he hath bigonne; and that is the ende why that men sholde

Against this horrible sin of acedia, and the branches thereof, there is a virtue that is called *fortitudo* or strength; that is, a force of character whereby a man despises annoying things. This virtue is so mighty and so vigorous that it dares to withstand sturdily, and wisely to keep itself from dangers that are wicked, and to wrestle against the assaults of the Devil. For it enhances and strengthens the soul, just as acedia reduces it and makes it feeble. For this *fortitudo* can endure, by long suffering, the toils that are fitting.

This virtue has many species; and the first is called magnanimity, which is to say, great-heartedness. For certainly a great heart is needed against acedia, lest it swallow up the soul by the sin of sadness, or destroy it by despair. This virtue causes folk to undertake hard things, or grievous things, of their own initiative, wisely and reasonably. And for as much as the Devil fights a man more by craft and by trickery than by strength, therefore men may withstand him by wit and by reason and by discretion. Then there are the virtues of faith and of hope in God and in His saints, to achieve and accomplish the good works in which one firmly purposes to continue. Then comes security and certainness; and that is when a man shall not doubt, in time to come, the value of the toil of the good works that he has begun. Then comes munificence, which is to say, that virtue whereby a man performs great works of goodness that he has begun; and that is the goal to reach which men should do good works; for in the doing of great good works lies the great reward. Then there is constancy, that is, stability of purpose, and this should be evidenced in heart by steadfast faith, and in word and in attitude and in appearance and in deed. Also, there are other special remedies against acedia or sloth, in divers works, and in consideration of the pains of Hell and of the joys of Heaven, and in faith in the grace of the Holy Ghost, that will give to a man the strength wherewith to perform his good purpose.

do gode werkes; for in the acomplissinge of grete goode werkes lyth the grete guerdoun. Thanne is ther Constaunce, that is, stablenesse of corage; and this sholde been in herte by stedefast feith, and in mouth, and in beringe, and in chere and in dede. Eke ther been mo speciale remedies agains Accidie, in diverse werkes, and in consideracioun of the peynes of helle, and of the joyes of hevene, and in trust of the grace of the holy goost, that wole yeve him might to perfourne his gode entente.

Here followeth Avarice

After acedia I will speak of avarice and of covetousness, of which sin Saint Paul says that "The love of money is the root of all evil": *ad Timotheum, sexto capitulo*. For verily, when the heart of a man is confounded within itself, and troubled, and when the soul has lost the comforting of God, then seeks a man a vain solace in worldly things.

Avarice, according to the description of Saint Augustine, is the eagerness of the heart to have earthly things. Others say that avarice is the desire to acquire earthly goods and give nothing to those that need. And understand that avarice consists not only of greed for land and chattels, but sometimes for learning and for glory, and for every kind of immoderate thing. And the difference between avarice and covetousness is this. Covetousness is to covet such things as one has not; and avarice is to keep and withhold such things as one has when there is no need to do so. Truly, this avarice is a sin that is very damnable; for all holy writ condemns it and inveighs against that vice; for it does wrong to Jesus Christ. For it takes away from Him the love that men owe to Him and turns it backward, and this against all reason; and it causes that an avaricious man has more hope in his chattels than in Jesus Christ and is more diligent in the guarding and keeping of his treasure than in the service of Jesus Christ. And therefore Saint Paul says, *ad Ephesios*, *quinto*, that "this ye know, that no . . . covetous man, who is an idolater, hath any inheritance in the Kingdom of Christ and of God."

What difference is there between an idolater and an avaricious man, save that an idolater, peradventure, has but one idol and the avaricious man has many? For verily, every florin in his coffer is his idol. And certainly the sin of idolatry is the first thing that God forbids in the ten commandments, as witnesses *Exodi, capitulo XX°*: "Thou shalt have no other gods before me, thou shalt not make unto thee any graven image." Thus an avaricious man, who loves his treasure more than God, is an idolater, by reason of this cursed sin of avarice. Of covetousness come these hard exactions whereunder men are assessed and made to pay taxes, rents, and payments in lieu of service, more than duty requires or reason demands. Also, they take from their serfs amercements that might more reasonably be called extortions than amercements. As to which amercements and fines of serfs, some lords' stewards say that it is

62 After Accidie wol I speke of Avarice and of Coveitise, of which sinne seith seint Paule, that "the rote of alle harmes is Coveitise": *Ad Timotheum, sexto capitulo*. For soothly, whan the herte of a man is confounded in it-self and troubled, and that the soule hath lost the confort of god, thanne seketh he an ydel solas of worldly thinges.

63. Avarice, after the descripcion of seint Augustin, is likerousnesse in herte to have erthely thinges. Som other folk seyn, that Avarice is, for to purchacen manye erthely thinges, and nothing yeve to hem that han nede. And understond, that Avarice ne stant nat only in lond ne catel, but somtyme in science and in glorie, and in every manere of outrageous thing is Avarice and Coveitise. And the difference bitwixe Avarice and Coveitise is this. Coveitise is for to coveite swiche thinges as thou hast nat; and Avarice is for to withholde and kepe swiche thinges as thou hast, with-oute rightful nede. Soothly, this Avarice is a sinne that is ful dampnable; for al holy writ curseth it, and speketh agayns that vyce; for it dooth wrong to Jesu Crist. For it bireveth him the love that men to him owen, and turneth it bakward agayns alle resoun; and maketh that the avaricious man hath more hope in his catel than in Jesu Crist, and dooth more observance in kepinge of his tresor than he dooth to service of Jesu Crist. And therfore seith seint Paul *ad Ephesios*, *quinto*, that "an avaricious man is in the thraldom of ydolatrie."

64. What difference is bitwixe an ydolastre and an avaricious man, but that an ydolastre, per aventure, ne hath but o mawmet or two, and the avaricious man hath manye? For certes, every florin in his cofre is his mawmet. And certes, the sinne of Mawmetrye is the firste thing that God deffended in the ten comaundments, as bereth witnesse *Exodi, capitulo xx°*: "Thou shalt have no false goddes bifore me, ne thou shalt make to thee no grave thing." Thus is an avaricious man, that loveth his tresor biforn god, an ydolastre, thurgh this cursed sinne of Avarice. Of Coveitise comen thise harde lordshipes, thurgh whiche men been distreyned by tailages, custumes, and cariages, more than hir duetee or resoun is. And eek they taken of hir bonde-men amerciments, whiche mighten more resonably ben cleped extorcions than amerciments. Of whiche amerciments and raunsoninge of bonde-

men, somme lordes stywardes seyn, that it is rightful; for-as-muche as a cherl hath no temporel thing that it ne is his lordes, as they seyn. But certes, thise lordshipes doon wrong, that bireven hir bonde-folk thinges that they nevere yave hem: *Augustinus de Civitate, libro nomo*. Sooth is, that the condicioun of thraldom and the firste cause of thraldom is for sinne; *Genesis, quinto*.

65. Thus may ye seen that the gilt disserveth thraldom, but nat nature. Wherfore thise lordes ne sholde nat muche glorifyen hem in hir lordshipes, sith that by naturel condicion they been nat lordes of thralles; but for that thraldom comth first by the desert of sinne. And forther-over, ther-as the lawe seith, that temporel godes of bonde-folk been the godes of hir lordshipes, ye, that is for to understonde, the godes of the emperour, to deffenden hem in hir right, but nat for to robben hem ne reven hem. And therfore seith Seneca: "thy prudence sholde live benignely with thy thralles." Thilke that thou clepest thy thralles been goddes peple; for humble folk been Cristes freendes; they been contubernial with the lord.

66. Think eek, that of swich seed as cherles springeth, of swich seed springen lordes. As wel may the cherl be saved as the lord. The same deeth that taketh the cherl, swich deeth taketh the lord. Wherfore I rede, do right so with thy cherl, as thou woldest that thy lord dide with thee, if thou were in his plyt. Every sinful man is a cherl to sinne. I rede thee, certes, that thou, lord, werke in swiche wyse with thy cherles, that they rather love thee than drede. I woot wel ther is degree above degree, as reson is; and skile it is, that men do hir devoir ther-as it is due; but certes, extorcions and despit of youre underlinges is dampnable.

67. And forther-over understond wel, that thise conquerours or tiraunts maken ful ofte thralles of hem, that been born of as royal blood as been they that hem conqueren. This name of thraldom was nevere erst couth, til that Noe seyde, that his sone Canaan sholde be thral to hise bretheren for his sinne. What seye we thanne of hem that pilen and doon extorcions to holy chirche? Certes, the swerd, that men yeven first to a knight whan he is newe dubbed, signifyeth that he sholde deffenden holy chirche, and nat robben it ne pilen it; and who so dooth, is traitour to Crist. And, as seith seint Augustin, "they been the develes wolves, that stranglen the sheep of Jesu Crist"; and doon worse than wolves. For soothly, whan the wolf hath ful his wombe, he stinteth to strangle sheep. But soothly, the pilours and destroyours of goddes holy chirche ne do nat so; for they ne stinte nevere to pile. Now, as I have seyd, sith so is that sinne was first cause of thraldom, thanne is it thus; that thilke tyme that al this world was in sinne, thanne was al this world in thraldom and subjeccioun. But certes, sith the tyme of grace cam, god ordeyned that som folk sholde be more heigh in estaat and in degree, and som folk more lowe, and that everich sholde

just, because a churl has no temporal thing that does not belong to his lord, or so they say. But certainly these lordships do wrong that take away from their serfs things that they never gave them, *Augustinus de Civitate, libro nono*. The truth is that the condition of serfdom is a sin: *Genesis, quinto*.

Thus may you see that man's sin deserves thralldom, but man's origin does not. Wherefore these lords should not greatly glorify themselves in their lordships, since by natural condition, or origin, they are not lords of thralls; but thralldom came into being first as the desert of sin. And furthermore, whereas the law says that the temporal effects of bondmen are the property of their lords, verily, by that is to be understood, the property of the emperor, who defends them in their rights, but who has no right to rob or to plunder them. And thereupon says Seneca: "Thy prudence should cause thee to live benignly with thy slaves." Those whom you call your serfs are God's people; for humble folk are Christ's friends; they are at home in the house of the Lord.

Think, also, that such seed as churls come from, from such seed come the lords. As easily may the churl be saved as the lord. The same death that takes the churl takes the lord. Wherefore I advise you to do unto your churl as you would that your lord should do unto you, if you were in the churl's plight. Every sinful man is a serf to sin. I advise you, verily, that you, lord, act in such wise with your serfs that they shall rather love you than fear. I know well that there is degree above degree, and that this is reasonable; and reasonable it is that men should pay their duty where it is due; but, certainly, extortions and contempt for underlings is damnable.

And furthermore, understand well that conquerors or tyrants often make thralls of those who were born of as royal blood as those who have conquered. This word of thralldom was unknown until Noah said that his grandson Canaan should be servant to his brethren for his sin. What say we then of those that plunder and extort money from Holy Church? Certainly, the sword which men give to a knight when he is dubbed, signifies that he should defend Holy Church and not rob or pillage it; and whoever does so is a traitor to Christ. And, as Saint Augustine says: "They are the Devil's wolves that pull down the sheep of Jesus Christ." And they do worse than wolves. For truly, when the wolf has filled his belly, he ceases to kill sheep. But truly, the plunderers and destroyers of God's Holy Church do not so, for they never cease to pillage. Now, as I have said, since it was because sin was the first cause of thralldom, then it stands thus: that all the while all the world was in sin, it was in thralldom and subjection. But certainly, since the time of grace came, God ordained that some folk should be higher in rank and state and some folk lower, and that each should be served according to his rank and his state. And therefore, in some countries, where they buy slaves, when they have converted them to the faith, they set their slaves free from slavery. And therefore, certainly, the lord owes to his man that which the man owes to his lord. The pope calls himself servant of the servants of God; but in as much as the estate of Holy Church might not have come into being, nor the common advantage kept, nor any peace and rest established on earth, unless God had ordained that some men should have higher rank and some lower: therefore was sovereignty ordained to guard and maintain and defend its underlings or its subjects within reason and so far as lies in its power, and not to destroy or to confound them. Wherefore, I say that those lords that are like wolves, that devour the wealth or the possessions of poor folk wrongfully, without mercy or measure, they shall receive, by the same measure that they have used toward poor folk, the mercy of Jesus Christ, unless they mend their ways. Now comes deceit between merchant and merchant. And you shall understand that trade is of two kinds; the one is material and the other is spiritual. The one is decent and lawful and the other is indecent and unlawful. Of this material trade, that which is decent and lawful is this: that where God has ordained that a kingdom or a country is sufficient unto itself, then it is decent and lawful that of the abundance of this country men should help another country that is more needy. And therefore there are permitted to be merchants to bring from the one country to the other their merchandise. That other trade, which men barter with fraud and treachery and deceit, with lies and with false oaths, is accursed and damnable. Spiritual trade is properly simony, which is earnest desire to buy spiritual things, that is to say, things that appertain to the sanctuary of God and to the cure of the soul. This desire, if it be that a man is diligent in accomplishing it, even though his desire have no effect, yet it is a deadly sin; and if he be ordained he sins against his orders. Simony is named for Simon Magus, who would have bought, with temporal wealth, the gift that God had given, by the Holy Ghost, to Saint Peter and to the other apostles. And therefore you should understand that both he that buys and he that sells spiritual things are called simonists; be it by means of chattels, or by entreaty, or by fleshly asking of his friends—fleshly friends or spiritual friends. Fleshly friends are of two kinds, as kindred and other friends. Truly, if they ask for one who is not worthy and able, it is simony if he take the benefice; but if he be worthy and able, it is not. The other kind is when a man or woman asks folk to advance him or her, only for wicked fleshly affection that they may have for that person; and that is vile simony. But certainly, in that service for which men give spiritual things unto their servants, it must be understood that the service is honest; and also that it be done without bargaining, and that the person be able. For, as Saint Damasus says: "All the sins of the world, compared to this sin, are as naught." For it is the greatest sin that may be done, after that of Lucifer and Antichrist. For by this sin God loses the Church and

be served in his estaat and in his degree. And therfore, in somme contrees ther they byen thralles, whan they han turned hem to the feith, they maken hir thralles free out of thraldom. And therfore, certes, the lord oweth to his man that the man oweth to his lord. The Pope calleth himself servant of the servaunts of god; but for-asmuche as the estaat of holy chirche ne mighte nat han be, ne the commune profit mighte nat han be kept, ne pees and reste in erthe, but-if god hadde ordeyned that som men hadde hyer degree and som men lower: therfore was sovereyntee ordeyned to kepe and mayntene and deffenden hir underlinges or hir subgets in resoun, as ferforth as it lyth in hir power; and nat to destroyen hem ne confounde. Wherfore I seye, that thilke lordes that been lyk wolves, that devouren the possessiouns or the catel of povre folk wrongfully, withouten mercy or mesure, they shul receyven by the same mesure that they han mesured to povre folk the mercy of Jesu Crist, but-if it be amended. Now comth deceite bitwixe marchant and marchant. And thow shalt understonde, that marchandyse is in two maneres; that oon is bodily, and that other is goostly. That oon is honeste and leveful, and that other is deshoneste and unleveful. Of thilke bodily marchandyse, that is leveful and honeste, is this; that, thereas god hath ordeyned that a regne or a contree is suffisaunt to him-self, thanne is it honeste and leveful, that of habundaunce of this contree, that men helpe another contree that is more nedy. And therfore, ther mote been marchants to bringen fro that o contree to that other hire marchandyses. That other marchandise, that men haunten with fraude and trecherie and deceite, with lesinges and false othes, is cursed and dampnable. Espirituel marchandyse is proprely Symonye, that is, ententif desyr to byen thing espirituel, that is, thing that aperteneth to the seintuarie of god and to cure of the soule. This desyr, if so be that a man do his diligence to parfournen it, al-be-it that his desyr ne take noon effect, yet is it to him a deedly sinne; and if he be ordred, he is irreguler. Certes, Symonye is cleped of Symon Magus, that wolde han boght, for temporel catel, the yifte that god hadde yeven, by the holy goost, to seint Peter and to the apostles. And therfore understond, that bothe he that selleth and he that byeth thinges espirituels, been cleped Symonials; be it by catel, be it by procuringe, or by fleshly preyere of his freendes, fleshly freendes, or espirituel freendes. Fleshly, in two maneres; as by kinrede or othere freendes. Soothly, if they praye for him that is nat worthy and able, it is Symonye if he take the benefice; and if he be worthy and able, ther nis noon. That other manere is, whan a man or womman preyen for folk to avauncen hem, only for wikked fleshly affeccioun that they have un-to the persone; and that is foul Symonye. But certes, in service, for which men yeven thinges espirituels un-to hir servants, it moot been understonde that the service moot been honeste, and elles nat; and eek that it be with-outen bargayninge, and that the persone be able. For, as seith seint Damasie, "alle the sinnes of the world, at regard of this sinne, arn as thing of noght"; for it is the gretteste sinne that may be, after the sinne of Lucifer and Antecrist. For, by this sinne, god forleseth the chirche, and the soule that he boghte with his precious blood, by hem that yeven chirches to hem that been nat digne. For they putten in theves, that stelen the soules of Jesu Christ and destroyen his patrimoine. By swiche undigne preestes and curates han lewed men the lasse reverence of the sacraments of holy chirche; and swiche yeveres of chirches putten out the children of Crist, and putten in-to the chirche the develes owene sone. They sellen the soules that lambes sholde kepen to the wolf that strangleth hem. And therfore shul they nevere han part of the pasture of lambes, that is, the blisse of hevene. Now comth hasardrye with hise apurtenaunces, as tables and rafles;[1] of which comth deceite, false othes, chydinges, and alle ravines, blasphemiṅge and reneyinge of god, and hate of hise neighebores, wast of godes, misspendinge of tyme, and somtyme manslaughtre. Certes, hasardours ne mowe nat been with-outen greet sinne whyles they haunte that craft. Of avarice comen eek lesinges, thefte, fals witnesse, and false othes. And ye shul understonde that thise been grete sinnes, and expres agayn the comaundements of god, as I have seyd. Fals witnesse is in word and eek in dede. In word, as for to bireve thy neighebores goode name by thy fals witnessing, or bireven him his catel or his heritage by thy fals witnessing; whan thou, for ire or for mede, or for envye, berest fals witnesse, or accusest him or excusest him by thy fals witnesse, or elles excusest thy-self falsly. Ware yow, questemongeres and notaries! Certes, for fals witnessing was Susanna in ful gret sorwe and peyne, and many another mo. The sinne of thefte is eek expres agayns goddes heste, and that in two maneres, corporel and espirituel. Corporel, as for to take thy neighebores catel agayn his wil, be it by force or by sleighte, be it by met or by mesure. By steling eek of false enditements upon him, and in borwinge of thy neighebores catel, in entente nevere to payen it agayn, and semblable thinges. Espirituel thefte is Sacrilege, that is to seyn, hurtinge of holy thinges, or of thinges sacred to Crist, in two maneres; by reson of the holy place, as chirches or chirche-hawes, for which every vileyns sinne that men doon in swiche places may be cleped sacrilege, or every violence in the semblable places. Also, they that withdrawen falsly the rightes that longen to holy chirche. And pleynly and generally, sacrilege is to reven holy thing fro holy place, or unholy thing out of holy place, or holy thing out of unholy place.

the soul that He bought with His precious blood, because of those who give churches to those who are not worthy. For they put in thieves, who steal souls from Jesus Christ and destroy His patrimony. By reason of such unworthy priests and curates have ignorant men the less reverence for the sacraments of Holy Church; and such givers of churches put out the children of Christ and put in the Devil's own sons. They sell the souls that they watch over as lambs to the wolf that rends them. And therefore they shall never have any part in the pasture of lambs, that is, the bliss of Heaven. Now comes hazardry with its appurtenances, such as backgammon and raffles;[1] whence come deceit, false oaths, chidings, and hatred for one's neighbours, waste of wealth, mis-spending of time, and sometimes homicide. Certainly, hazarders cannot be without great sin while they continue to practise their craft. Of avarice come also lying, theft, false witnessing, and false oaths. And you must understand that these are great sins, expressly against the commandments of God, as I have said. False witnessing lies in word and also in deed. In word, as by taking away your neighbour's good name by bearing false witness against him, or by depriving him of his chattels or his heritage by such false witnessing when you, for anger or reward, bear false witness or accuse him by your false witnessing, or else when you falsely excuse yourself. Beware, you jurymen and notaries! Certainly, by false witness, was Susanna in great sorrow and pain, as have been many others. The sin of theft is also expressly against God's command, and that of two kinds, corporal and spiritual. Corporal, as taking your neighbour's chattels against his will, be it by force or by fraud, be it by short lineal measure or by short measure of capacity. By secret swearing, also, of false indictments against him, and by borrowing your neighbour's goods with intent never to return them, and by similar things. Spiritual theft is sacrilege, that is to say, injuring of holy things, or of things sacred to Christ, and is of two kinds; by reason of the fact that it is a holy place, as a church or a churchyard, every vile sin that men do in such places may be called sacrilege, or every violence done in such places. Also they who withhold what of right belongs to Holy Church are guilty of sacrilege. And plainly and generally, sacrilege is to steal a holy thing from a holy place, or an unholy thing from a holy place, or a holy thing from an unholy place.

The Relief against the Sin of Avarice

68. Now shul ye understonde, that the relevinge of Avarice is misericorde, and pitee largely taken.

Now shall you understand that the relief for avarice is mercy and pity in large doses. And men might

[1]An old game with three dice, in which that player wins the stakes who throws all three alike.

ask why mercy and pity relieve avarice. Certainly, the avaricious man shows no pity nor any mercy to the needy man; for he delights in keeping his treasure and not in the rescuing or relieving of his fellow Christian. And therefore will I speak first of mercy. Mercy, as the philosopher says, is a virtue whereby the feelings of a man are moved by the trouble of him that is in trouble. Upon which mercy follows pity and performs charitable works of mercy. And certainly, these things impel a man to the mercy of Jesus Christ—that He gave Himself for our sins, and suffered death for the sake of mercy, and forgave us our original sins; and thereby released us from the pains of Hell and lessened the pains of Purgatory by means of penitence, and gives us grace to do good, and, at the last, gives us the bliss of Heaven. The kinds of mercy are: to lend, and to give, and to forgive, and to set free, and to have pity in heart and compassion on the tribulations of one's fellow Christian, and also, to chasten, as need may be. Another kind of remedy for avarice is reasonable largess; and truly, here it behooves one to give consideration to the grace of Jesus Christ, and to one's temporal wealth, and also to the perdurable wealth that Christ gave to us; and to remember the death that he shall receive, he knows not when, where, or how, and also that he must forgo all that he has, save only that which he has invested in good works.

And men mighten axe, why that misericorde and pitee is relevinge of Avarice? Certes, the avaricious man sheweth no pitee ne misericorde to the nedeful man; for he delyteth him in the kepinge of his tresor, and nat in the rescowinge ne relevinge of his evene-cristene. And therfore speke I first of misericorde. Thanne is misericorde, as seith the philosophre, a vertu, by which the corage of man is stired by the misese of him that is misesed. Upon which misericorde folweth pitee, in parfourninge of charitable werkes of misericorde. And certes, thise thinges moeven a man to misericorde of Jesu Crist, that he yaf him-self for oure gilt, and suffred deeth for misericorde, and forgaf us oure originale sinnes; and therby relessed us fro the peynes of helle, and amenused the peynes of purgatorie by penitence, and yeveth grace wel to do, and atte laste the blisse of hevene. The speces of misericorde been, as for to lene and for to yeve and to foryeven and relesse, and for to han pitee in herte, and compassioun of the meschief of his evene-cristene, and eek to chastyse there as nede is. Another manere of remedie agayns Avarice is resonable largesse; but soothly, here bihoveth the consideracioun of the grace of Jesu Crist, and of hise temporel goodes, and eek of the godes perdurables that Crist yaf to us; and to han remembrance of the deeth that he shal receyve, he noot whanne, where, ne how; and eek that he shal forgon al that he hath, save only that he hath despended in gode werkes.

But for as much as some folk are immoderate, men ought to avoid foolish largess, which men call waste. Certainly, he that is prodigal gives not his wealth, but loses his wealth. Truly, that which he gives out of vainglory, as to minstrels and to followers, in order to have his renown carried about the world, he does sin thereby rather than gives alms. Certainly, he shamefully loses his wealth who seeks in the gift thereof nothing but sin. He is like a horse that chooses rather to drink muddy or turbid water than the clear water of a well. And for as much as they give where they should not give, to them belongs that cursing which Christ will give at the day of doom to those that shall be damned.

69. But for-as-muche as som folk been unmesurable, men oghten eschue fool-largesse, that men clepen wast. Certes, he that is fool-large ne yeveth nat his catel, but he leseth his catel. Soothly, what thing that he yeveth for veyne glorie, as to minstrals and to folk, for to beren his renoun in the world, he hath sinne ther-of and noon almesse. Certes, he leseth foule his good, that ne seketh with the yifte of his good no-thing but sinne. He is lyk to an hors that seketh rather to drinken drovy or trouble water than for to drinken water of the clere welle. And for-as-muchel as they yeven ther as they sholde nat yeven, to hem aperteneth thilke malisoun that Crist shal yeven at the day of dome to hem that shullen been dampned.

Here followeth Gluttony

After avarice comes gluttony, which also is entirely against the commandment of God. Gluttony is immoderate appetite to eat or to drink, or else to yield to the immoderate desire to eat or to drink. This sin corrupted all this world, as is well shown by the sin of Adam and Eve. Read, also, what Saint Paul says of gluttony: "For many walk, of whom I have told you often, and now tell you even weeping, that they are the enemies of the cross of Christ: whose end is destruction, whose God is their belly, and whose glory is in their shame, who mind earthly things." He that is addicted to this sin of gluttony may withstand no other sin. He may even be in the service of all the vices, for it is in the Devil's treasure house

70. After Avarice comth Glotonye, which is expres eek agayn the comandement of god. Glotonye is unmesurable appetyt to ete or to drinke, or elles to doon y-nogh to the unmesurable appetyt and desordeynee coveityse to eten or to drinke. This sinne corrumped al this world, as is wel shewed in the sinne of Adam and of Eve. Loke eek, what seith seint Paul of Glotonye. "Manye," seith seint Paul, "goon, of whiche I have ofte seyd to yow, and now I seye it wepinge, that they been the enemys of the croys of Crist; of whiche the ende is deeth, and of whiche hir wombe is hir god, and hir glorie in confusioun of hem that so saveren erthely thinges." He that is usaunt to this sinne of Glotonye, he ne may

no sinne withstonde. He moot been in servage of alle vyces, for it is the develes hord ther he hydeth him and resteth. This sinne hath manye speces. The firste is dronkenesse, that is the horrible sepulture of mannes resoun; and therfore, whan a man is dronken, he hath lost his resoun; and this is deedly sinne. But soothly, whan that a man is nat wont to strong drinke, and peraventure ne knoweth nat the strengthe of the drinke, or hath feblesse in his heed, or hath travailed, thurgh which he drinketh the more, al be he sodeynly caught with drinke, it is no deedly sinne, but venial. The seconde spece of Glotonye is, that the spirit of a man wexeth al trouble; for dronkenesse bireveth him the discrecioun of his wit. The thridde spece of Glotonye is, whan a man devoureth his mete, and hath no rightful manere of etinge. The fourthe is whan, thurgh the grete habundaunce of his mete, the humours in his body been destempred. The fifthe is, foryetelnesse by to muchel drinkinge; for which somtyme a man foryeteth er the morwe what he dide at even or on the night biforn.

71. In other manere been distinct the speces of Glotonye, after seint Gregorie. The firste is, for to ete biforn tyme to ete. The seconde is, whan a man get him to delicat mete or drinke. The thridde is, whan men taken to muche over mesure. The fourthe is curiositee, with greet entente to maken and apparaillen his mete. The fifthe is, for to eten to gredily. Thise been the fyve fingres of the develes hand, by whiche he draweth folk to sinne.

that he hides himself and rests. This sin has many species. The first is drunkenness, which is the horrible sepulture of man's reason; and therefore, when a man is drunk he has lost his reason; and this is deadly sin. But truly, when a man is not used to strong drink, and perhaps knows not the strength of the drink, or is feeble-minded, or has toiled, for which reason he drinks too much, then, though he be suddenly caught by drink, it is not deadly sin, but venial. The second kind of gluttony is when the spirit of man grows turbid, for drunkenness has robbed him of the discretion of his wit. The third kind of gluttony is when a man devours his food and has no correct manner of eating. The fourth is when, through the great abundance of his food, the humours in his body become distempered. The fifth is, forgetfulness caused by too much drinking, whereby sometimes a man forgets before the morning what he did last evening, or the night before.

In another manner are distinguished the kinds of gluttony, according to Saint Gregory. The first is, eating before it is time to eat. The second is when a man gets himself too delicate food or drink. The third is when men eat too much, and beyond measure. The fourth is fastidiousness, with great attention paid to the preparation and dressing of food. The fifth is to eat too greedily. These are the five fingers of the Devil's hand wherewith he draws folk into sin.

The Remedy against the Sin of Gluttony

72. Agayns Glotonye is the remedie Abstinence, as seith Galien; but that holde I nat meritorie, if he do it only for the hele of his body. Seint Augustin wole, that Abstinence be doon for vertu and with pacience. Abstinence, he seith, is litel worth, but-if a man have good wil ther-to, and but it be enforced by pacience and by charitee, and that men doon it for godes sake, and in hope to have the blisse of hevene.

73. The felawes of Abstinence been Attemperaunce, that holdeth the mene in alle thinges: eek Shame, that eschueth alle deshonestee: Suffisance, that seketh no riche metes ne drinkes, ne dooth no fors of to outrageous apparailinge of mete. Mesure also, that restreyneth by resoun the deslavee appetyt of etinge: Sobrenesse also, that restreyneth the outrage of drinke: Sparinge also, that restreyneth the delicat ese to sitte longe at his mete and softely; wherfore som folk stonden of hir owene wil, to eten at the lasse leyser.

Against gluttony abstinence is the remedy, as Galen says; but I hold that to be not meritorious if he do it only for the health of his body. Saint Augustine will have it that abstinence should be practised for the sake of virtue and with patience. Abstinence, he says, is little worth unless a man have a good will thereto, and save it be practised in patience and charity and that men do it for God's sake and in hope of the bliss of Heaven.

The companions of abstinence are temperance, which follows the middle course in all things; and shame, which eschews all indecency; and sufficiency, which seeks after no rich foods and drinks and cares nothing for too extravagant dressing of meats. Measure, also, which restrains within reason the unrestrained appetite for eating; sobriety, also, which restrains the luxurious desire to sit long and softly at meat, and because of which some folk, of their own will, stand, in order to spend less time at eating.

Here followeth Lechery

74. After Glotonye, thanne comth Lecherie; for thise two sinnes been so ny cosins, that ofte tyme they wol nat departe. God woot, this sinne is ful displesaunt thing to god; for he seyde himself, "do no lecherie." And therfore he putte grete peynes agayns this sinne in the olde lawe. If womman thral were taken in this sinne, she sholde be beten with

After gluttony, then comes lechery; for these two sins are such close cousins that oftentimes they will not be separated. God knows, this sin is unpleasing to God; for He said Himself, "Do no lechery." And therefore He imposed great penalties against this sin in the old law. If a bondwoman were taken in this sin, she should be beaten to death with rods. And if she were a woman of quality, she should be slain with stones. And if she were a bishop's daughter, she should be burnt, by God's commandment. Furthermore, for the sin of lechery, God drowned all the world by the deluge. And after that He burned five cities with thunderbolts and sank them into Hell.

Let us speak, then, of that stinking sin of lechery that men call adultery of wedded folk, which is to say, if one of them be wedded, or both. Saint John says that adulterers shall be in Hell "in the lake which burneth with fire and brimstone"—in the fire for the lechery, in brimstone for the stink of their filthiness. Certainly, the breaking of this sacrament is a horrible thing; it was ordained by God Himself in Paradise, and confirmed by Jesus Christ, as witness Saint Matthew in the gospel: "For this cause shall a man leave father and mother, and shall cleave to his wife; and they twain shall be one flesh." This sacrament betokens the knitting together of Christ and of Holy Church. And not only did God forbid adultery in deed, but also He commanded that "thou shalt not covet thy neighbour's wife." This behest, says Saint Augustine, contains the forbidding of all desire to do lechery. Behold what Saint Matthew says in the gospel: "Whosoever looketh on a woman to lust after her, hath committed adultery with her already in his heart." Here you may see that not only the doing of this sin is forbidden, but also the desire to do that sin. This accursed sin grievously troubles those whom it haunts. And first, it does harm to the soul; for it constrains it to sin and to the pain of everlasting death. Unto the body it is a tribulation also, for it drains it, and wastes and ruins it, and makes of its blood a sacrifice to the Fiend of Hell also it wastes wealth and substance. And certainly, if it be a foul thing for a man to waste his wealth on women, it is a yet fouler thing when, for such filthiness, women spend on men their wealth and their substance. This sin, as says the prophet, robs man and woman of good name and of all honour; and it gives great pleasure to the Devil, for thereby won he the greater part of the world. And just as a merchant delights most in that trading whereof he reaps the greater gain, just so the Fiend delights in this filth.

This is the Devil's other hand, with five fingers to catch the people into his slavery. The first finger is the foolish interchange of glances between the foolish woman and the foolish man, which slays just as the basilisk slays folk by the venom of its sight; for the lust of the eyes follows the lust of the heart. The second finger is vile touching in wicked manner; and thereupon Solomon says that he who touches and handles a woman fares like the man that handles the scorpion which stings and suddenly slays by its poisoning; even as, if any man touch warm pitch, it defiles his fingers. The third is vile words, which are like fire, which immediately burns the heart. The fourth finger is kissing; and truly he were a great fool who would kiss the mouth of a burning oven

staves to the deeth. And if she were a gentil womman, she sholde be slayn with stones. And if she were a bisshoppes doghter, she sholde been brent, by goddes comandement. Forther over, by the sinne of Lecherie, god dreynte al the world at the diluge. And after that, he brente fyve citees with thonderleyt, and sank hem in-to helle.

75. Now lat us speke thanne of thilke stinkinge sinne of Lecherie that men clepe Avoutrie of wedded folk, that is to seyn, if that oon of hem be wedded, or elles bothe. Seint John seith, that avoutiers shullen been in helle in a stank brenninge of fyr and of brimston; in fyr, for the lecherie; in brimston, for the stink of hir ordure. Certes, the brekinge of this sacrement is an horrible thing; it was maked of god him-self in paradys, and confermed by Jesu Crist, as witnesseth seint Mathew in the gospel: "A man shal lete fader and moder, and taken him to his wyf, and they shullen be two in o flesh." This sacrement bitokneth the knittinge togidre of Crist and of holy chirche. And nat only that god forbad avoutrie in dede, but eek he comanded that thou sholdest nat coveite thy neighebores wyf. In this heeste, seith seint Augustin, is forboden alle manere coveitise to doon lecherie. Lo what seith seint Mathew in the gospel: that "whoso seeth a womman to coveitise of his lust, he hath doon lecherie with hir in his herte." Here may ye seen that nat only the dede of this sinne is forboden, but eek the desyr to doon that sinne. This cursed sinne anoyeth grevousliche hem that it haunten. And first, to hir soule; for he oblygeth it to sinne and to peyne of deeth that is perdurable. Un-to the body anoyeth it grevously also, for it dreyeth him, and wasteth, and shent him, and of his blood he maketh sacrifyce to the feend of helle; it wasteth his catel and his substaunce. And certes, if it be a foul thing, a man to waste his catel on wommen, yet is it a fouler thing whan that, for swich ordure, wommen dispenden up-on men hir catel and substaunce. This sinne, as seith the prophete, bireveth man and womman hir gode fame, and al hir honour; and it is ful pleasaunt to the devel; for ther-by winneth he the moste partie of this world. And right as a marchant delyteth him most in chaffare that he hath most avantage of, right so delyteth the feend in this ordure.

76. This is that other hand of the devel, with fyve fingres, to cacche the peple to his vileinye. The firste finger is the fool lookinge of the fool womman and of the fool man, that sleeth, right as the basilicok sleeth folk by the venim of his sighte; for the coveitise of eyen folweth the coveitise of the herte. The seconde finger is the vileyns touchinge in wikkede manere; and ther-fore seith Salomon, that who-so toucheth and handleth a womman, he fareth lyk him that handleth the scorpioun that stingeth and sodeynly sleeth thurgh his enveniminge; as who-so toucheth warm pich, it shent his fingres. The thridde, is foule wordes, that fareth lyk fyr, that right anon brenneth the herte. The fourthe finger is the kissinge; and trewely he were

a greet fool that wolde kisse the mouth of a brenninge ovene or of a fourneys. And more fooles been they that kissen in vileinye; for that mouth is the mouth of helle: and namely, thise olde dotardes holours, yet wol they kisse, though they may nat do, and smatre hem. Certes, they been lyk to houndes; for an hound, whan he comth by the roser or by othere busshes, though he may nat pisse, yet wole he heve up his leg and make a contenaunce to pisse. And for that many man weneth that he may nat sinne, for no likerousnesse that he doth with his wyf; certes, that opinion is fals. God woot, a man may sleen him-self with his owene knyf, and make him-selven dronken of his owene tonne. Certes, be it wyf, be it child, or any worldly thing that he loveth biforn god, it is his maumet, and he is an ydolastre. Man sholde loven his wyf by discrecioun, paciently and atemprely; and thanne is she as though it were his suster. The fifthe finger of the develes hand is the stinkinge dede of Lecherie. Certes, the fyve fingres of Glotonie the feend put in the wombe of a man, and with hise fyve fyngres of Lecherie he gripeth him by the reynes, for to throwen him in-to the fourneys of helle; ther-as they shul han the fyr and the wormes that evere shul lasten, and wepinge and wailinge, sharp hunger and thurst, and grimnesse of develes that shullen al to-trede hem, with-outen respit and with-outen ende. Of Lecherie, as I seyde, sourden diverse speces; as fornicacioun, that is bitwixe man and womman that been nat maried; and this is deedly sinne and agayns nature. Al that is enemy and destruccioun to nature is agayns nature. Parfay, the resoun of a man telleth eek him wel that it is deedly sinne, for-as-muche as god forbad Lecherie. And seint Paul yeveth hem the regne, that nis dewe to no wight but to hem that doon deedly sinne. Another sinne of Lecherie is to bireve a mayden of hir maydenhede; for he that so dooth, certes, he casteth a mayden out of the hyeste degree that is in this present lyf, and bireveth hir thilke precious fruit that the book clepeth "the hundred fruit." I ne can seye it noon other weyes in English, but in Latin it highte *Centesimus fructus*. Certes, he that so dooth is cause of manye damages and vileinyes, mo than any man can rekene; right as he somtyme is cause of alle damages that bestes don in the feeld, that breketh the hegge or the closure; thurgh which he destroyeth that may nat been restored. For certes, na-more may maydenhede be restored than an arm that is smiten fro the body may retourne agayn to wexe. She may have mercy, this woot I wel, if she do penitence; but nevere shal it be that she nas corrupt. And al-be-it so that I have spoken somwhat of Avoutrie, it is good to shewen mo perils that longen to Avoutrie, for to eschue that foule sinne. Avoutrie in Latin is for to seyn, approchinge of other mannes bed, thurgh which tho that whylom weren o flessh abaundone hir bodyes to othere persones. Of this sinne, as seith the wyse man, folwen manye harmes. First, brekinge of feith; and certes, in feith is the keye of Cristendom. And

or of a furnace. And the more fools they are who kiss in vileness; for that mouth is the mouth of Hell; and I speak specifically of these old dotard whoremongers, who will yet kiss though they cannot do anything, and so taste them. Certainly they are like dogs, for a dog, when he passes a rosebush, or other bushes, though he cannot piss, yet will he heave up his leg and make an appearance of pissing. And as for the opinion of many that a man cannot sin for any lechery he does with his wife, certainly that opinion is wrong. God knows, a man may slay himself with his own knife, and make himself drunk out of his own tun. Certainly, be it wife, be it child, or any worldly thing that a man loves more than he loves God, it is his idol, and he is an idolater. Man should love his wife with discretion, calmly and moderately; and then she is as it were his sister. The fifth finger of the Devil's hand is the stinking act of lechery. Truly, the five fingers of gluttony the Fiend thrusts into the belly of a man, and with his five fingers of lechery he grips him by the loins in order to throw him into the furnace of Hell; wherein he shall have the fire and the everlasting worms, and weeping and wailing, sharp hunger and thirst, and horror of devils that shall trample all over him, without respite and without end. From lechery, as I said, spring divers branches; as fornication, which is between man and woman who are not married; and this is deadly sin and against nature. All that is an enemy to and destructive of nature is against nature. Faith, the reason of a man tells him well that it is mortal sin, since God forbade lechery. And Saint Paul gives him over to that kingdom which is the reward of no man save those who do mortal sin. Another sin of lechery is to bereave a maiden of her maidenhead; for he that so does, certainly, he casts a maiden out of the highest state in this present life and he bereaves her of that precious fruit that the Book calls "the hundred fruit." I can say it in no other way in English, but in Latin it is called *centesimus fructus*. Certainly, he that so acts is the cause of many inujries and villainies, more than any man can reckon; just as he sometimes is cause of all damage that beasts do in the field, who breaks down the hedge or the fence, just so does the seducer destroy that which cannot be restored. For truly, no more may a maidenhead be restored than an arm that has been smitten from the body may return thereto to grow again. She may have mercy, this I know well, if she does penance, but it shall never again be that she is uncorrupted. And though I have spoken somewhat of adultery, it is well to show forth more dangers that come of adultery, in order that men may eschew that foul sin. Adultery, in Latin, means to approach another man's bed, by reason of which those that once were one flesh abandon their bodies to other persons. Of this sin, as the wise man says, follow many evils. First, breaking of faith; and certainly, in faith lies the key to Christianity. And when faith is broken and lost truly, Christianity stands barren and without fruit. This sin is also a theft; for theft commonly is to deprive a person of his own thing against his will.

Certainly this is the vilest thievery that can be when a woman steals her body from her husband and gives it to her lecher to defile her; and steals her soul from Christ and gives it to the Devil. This is a fouler theft than to break into a church and steal the chalice; for these adulterers break into the temple of God spiritually and steal the vessel of grace, that is, the body and the soul, for which Christ will destroy them, as Saint Paul says. Truly, of this theft Joseph was much afraid when his master's wife besought him to lie with her, and he said: "Behold, my master wotteth not what is with me in the house, and he hath committed all that he hath to my hand: there is none greater in this house than I; neither hath he kept any thing from me but thee, because thou art his wife: how then can I do this great wickedness and sin against God?" Alas! All too little is such truth encountered nowadays. The third evil is the filth whereby they break the commandment of God and defame the Author of matrimony, Who is Christ. For certainly, in so far as the sacrament of marriage is so noble and honourable, so much the more is it a sin to break it; for God established marriage in Paradise, in the state of innocence, in order to multiply mankind to the service of God. And therefore is the breaking thereof the more grievous. Of which breaking come oftentimes false heirs, that wrongfully inherit. And therefore will Christ put them out of the Kingdom of Heaven, which is the heritage of good folk. From this breaking it happens oftentimes, also, that people wed or sin with their own kindred; and specially the loose-livers who haunt the brothels of prostitutes, who may be likened to a common privy wherein men purge themselves of their ordure. What shall we say, also, of whoremasters who live by the horrible sin of prostitution, yea, sometimes by the prostitution of their own wives and children, as do pimps and procurers? Certainly these are accursed sins. Understand also that adultery is fitly placed in the ten commandments between theft and homicide; for it is the greatest theft that can be, being theft of body and of soul. And it is like homicide, for it cuts in twain and breaks asunder those that were made one flesh, and therefore, by the old law of God, adulterers should be slain. But nevertheless, by the law of Jesus Christ, which is a law of pity, He said to the woman who was taken in adultery and should have been slain with stones, according to the will of the Jews, as was their law: "Go," said Jesus Christ, "and have no more will to sin," or "will no more to do sin." Truly, the punishment of adultery is given to the torment of Hell, unless it be that it is hindered by penitence. And there are yet more branches of this wicked sin; as when one of them is a religious, or else both; or folk who have entered orders, as a sub-deacon, or deacon priest, or hospitaller. And ever the higher that he is in orders, the greater is the sin. The thing that greatly aggravates their sin is the breaking of the vow of chastity, taken when they received the order. And furthermore, the truth is that the office of a holy order is chief of all the treasury of God, and His

whan that feith is broken and lorn, soothly Cristendom stant veyn and with-outen fruit. This sinne is eek a thefte; for thefte generally is for to reve a wight his thing agayns his wille. Certes, this is the fouleste thefte that may be, whan a womman steleth hir body from hir housbonde and yeveth it to hire holour to defoulen hir; and steleth hir soule fro Crist, and yeveth it to the devel. This is a fouler thefte, than for to breke a chirche and stele the chalice; for thise avoutiers breken the temple of god spiritually, and stelen the vessel of grace, that is, the body and the soule, for which Crist shal destroyen hem, as seith seint Paul. Soothly of this thefte douted gretly Joseph, whan that his lordes wyf preyed him of vileinye, whan he seyde, "lo, my lady, how my lord hath take to me under my warde al that he hath in this world; ne no-thing of hise thinges is out of my power, but only ye that been his wyf. And how sholde I thanne do this wikkednesse, and sinne so horribly agayns god, and agayns my lord? God it forbede." Allas! al to litel is swich trouthe now y-founde! The thridde harm is the filthe thurgh which they breken the comandement of god, and defoulen the auctour of matrimoine, that is Crist. For certes, in-so-muche as the sacrement of mariage is so noble and so digne, so muche is it gretter sinne for to breken it; for god made mariage in paradys, in the estaat of innocence, to multiplye man-kinde to the service of god. And therfore is the brekinge ther-of more grevous. Of which brekinge comen false heires ofte tyme, that wrongfully occupyen folkes heritages. And therfore wol Crist putte hem out of the regne of hevene, that is heritage to gode folk. Of this brekinge comth eek ofte tyme, that folk unwar wedden or sinnen with hir owene kinrede; and namely thilke harlottes that haunten bordels of thise fool wommen, that mowe be lykned to a commune gonge, where-as men purgen hir ordure. What seye we eek of putours that liven by the horrible sinne of puterie, and constreyne wommen to yelden to hem a certeyn rente of hir bodily puterie, ye, somtyme of his owene wyf or his child; as doon this baudes? Certes, thise been cursede sinnes. Understond eek, that avoutrie is set gladly in the ten comandements bitwixe thefte and manslaughtre; for it is the gretteste thefte that may be; for it is thefte of body and of soule. And it is lyk to homicyde; for it kerveth a-two and breketh a-two hem that first were maked o flesh, and therfore, by the olde lawe of god, they sholde be slayn. But nathelees, by the lawe of Jesu Crist, that is lawe of pitee, whan he seyde to the womman that was founden in avoutrie, and sholde han been slayn with stones, after the wil of the Jewes, as was hir lawe: "Go," quod Jesu Crist, "and have na-more wil to sinne"; or, "wille namore to do sinne." Soothly, the vengeaunce of avoutrie is awarded to the peynes of helle, but-if so be that it be destourbed by penitence. Yet been ther mo speces of this cursed sinne; as whan that oon of hem is religious, or elles bothe; or of folk that been entred in-to ordre, as subdekne or dekne, or preest, or hospitaliers. And evere the hyer that he is in ordre, the gretter is the sinne. The thinges that gretly agreggen hir sinne is the brekinge of hir avow of chastitee, whan they receyved the ordre. And forther-over, sooth is, that holy ordre is chief of al the tresorie of god, and his especial signe and mark of chastitee; to shewe that they been joyned to chastitee, which that is most precious lyf that is. And thise ordred folk been specially tytled to god, and of the special meynee of god; for which, whan they doon deedly sinne, they been the special traytours of god and of his peple; for they liven of the peple, to preye for the peple, and whyle they been suche traitours, hir preyers availen nat to the peple. Preestes been aungeles, as by the dignitee of hir misterye; but for sothe, seint Paul seith, that "Sathanas transformeth him in an aungel of light." Soothly, the preest that haunteth deedly sinne, he may be lykned to the aungel of derknesse transformed in the aungel of light; he semeth aungel of light, but for sothe he is aungel of derknesse. Swiche preestes been the sones of Helie, as sheweth in the book of Kinges, that they weren the sones of Belial, that is, the devel. Belial is to seyn "with-outen juge"; and so faren they; hem thinketh they been free, and han no juge, na-more than hath a free bole that taketh which cow that him lyketh in the toun. So faren they by wommen. For right as a free bole is y-nough for al a toun, right so is a wikked preest corrupcioun y-nough for al a parisshe, or for al a contree. Thise preestes, as seith the book, ne conne nat the misterie of preesthode to the peple, ne god ne knowe they nat; they ne helde hem nat apayd, as seith the book, of soden flesh that was to hem offred, but they toke by force the flesh that is rawe. Certes, so thise shrewes ne holden hem nat apayed of rosted flesh and sode flesh, with which the peple fedden hem in greet reverence, but they wole have raw flesh of folkes wyves and hir doghtres. And certes, thise wommen that consenten to hir harlotrie doon greet wrong to Crist and to holy chirche and alle halwes, and to alle soules; for they bireven alle thise him that sholde worshipe Crist and holy chirche, and preye for Cristene soules. And therfore han swiche preestes, and hir lemmanes eek that consenten to hir lecherie, the malisoun of al the court Cristen, til they come to amendement. The thridde spece of avoutrie is som-tyme bitwixe a man and his wyf; and that is whan they take no reward in hir assemblinge, but only to hire fleshly delyt, as seith seint Jerome; and ne rekken of no-thing but that they been assembled; by-cause that they been maried, al is good y-nough, as thinketh to hem. But in swich folk hath the devel power, as seyde the aungel Raphael to Thobie; for in hir assemblinge they putten Jesu Crist out of hir herte, and yeven hem-self to alle ordure. The fourthe spece is, the assemblee of hem that been of hire kinrede, or of hem that been of oon affinitee, or elles with hem with whiche hir fadres or hir kinrede han deled in the sinne of lecherie; this sinne maketh hem lyk to houndes, that taken no kepe to kinrede. And certes,

special sign and mark of chastity, to show that those who have entered it are joined to chastity, which is the most precious kind of life there is. And these folk in orders are specially dedicated to God, and are of the special household of God; for which, when they do deadly sin, they are especially traitors to God and to His people; for they live on the people in order to pray for the people, and while they are such traitors their prayers avail the people nothing at all. Priests are angels, by reason of the dignity of their ministry; but forsooth, as Saint Paul says: "Satan himself is transformed into an angel of light." Truly the priest that resorts to mortal sin, he may be likened to the angel of darkness transformed into the angel of light; he seems an angel of light, but, forsooth, he is an angel of darkness. Such priests are the sons of Eli, as is shown in the Book of the Kings, that they were the sons of Belial, that is, the Devil. Belial means, "without judge"; and so fare they; they think they are free and have no judge, any more than has a free bull that takes whatever cow pleases him on the farm. So act they with women. For just as a free bull is enough for all a farm, just so is a wicked priest corruption enough for all a parish, or for all a county. These priests, as the Book says, teach not the functions of priesthood to the people and they know not God; they held themselves but ill satisfied, as the Book says, with the flesh that was boiled and offered to them and took by force the flesh that was raw. Certainly, so these scoundrels hold themselves not pleased with roasted flesh and boiled flesh, with which the people feed them in great reverence, but they will have the raw flesh of laymen's wives and of their daughters. And certainly these women that give assent to their rascality do great wrong to Christ and to Holy Church and all saints and all souls; for they bereave all these of him that should worship Christ and Holy Church and pray for Christian souls. And therefore such priests and their lemans also, who give assent to their lechery, have the cursing of all the Christian court, until they mend their ways. The third kind of adultery is sometimes practised between a man and his wife; and that is when they have no regard to their union save only for their fleshly delight, as says Saint Jerome; and care for nothing but that they are come together; because they are married, it is all well enough, as they think. But over such folk the Devil has power, as said the Angel Raphael to Tobias; for in their union they put Jesus Christ out of mind and give themselves to all filthiness. The fourth kind is the coming together of those that are akin, or of those that are related by marriage, or else of those whose fathers or other kindred have had intercourse in the sin of lechery; this sin makes them like dogs that pay no heed to relationship. And certainly, kinship is of two kinds, either spiritual or carnal; spiritual, as when one lies with one's sponsor. For just as he that engenders a child is its fleshly father, just so is his godfather his spiritual father. For which reason a woman is in no less sin when she lies carnally with her godfather or her godson than she would be in if she coupled with her own fleshly brother. The fifth kind is that abominable sin whereof a man ought scarcely to speak or write, notwithstanding it is openly discussed in holy writ. This wickedness men and women do with divers intentions and in divers manners; but though holy writ speaks of such horrible sin, holy writ cannot be defiled, any more than can the sun that shines upon the dunghill. Another form of sin appertains to lechery, and that comes often to those who are virgin and also to those who are corrupt; and this sin men call pollution, which comes in four ways. Sometimes it is due to laxness of the body; because the humours are too rank and abundant in the body of man. Sometimes it is due to infirmity; because of the weakness of the retentive virtue, as is discussed in works on medicine. Sometimes it is due to a surfeit of food and drink. And sometimes it comes from base thoughts that were enclosed in man's mind when he fell asleep; which thing may not happen without sin. Because of this, men must govern themselves wisely, or else they may fall into grievous sin.

parentele is in two maneres, outher goostly or fleshly; goostly, as for to delen with hise godsibbes. For right so as he that engendreth a child is his fleshly fader, right so is his godfader his fader espirituel. For which a womman may in no lasse sinne assemblen with hir godsib than with hir owene fleshly brother. The fifthe spece is thilke abhominable sinne, of which that no man unnethe oghte speke ne wryte, nathelees it is openly reherced in holy writ. This cursednesse doon men and wommen in diverse entente and in diverse manere; but though that holy writ speke of horrible sinne, certes, holy writ may nat been defouled, na-more than the sonne that shyneth on the mixen. Another sinne apertenethe to lecherie, that comth in slepinge; and this sinne cometh ofte to hem that been maydenes, and eek to hem that been corrupt; and this sinne men clepen pollucioun, that comth in foure maneres. Somtyme, of languissinge of body; for the humours been to ranke and habundaunt in the body of man. Somtyme of infermetee; for the feblesse of the vertu retentif, as phisik maketh mencioun. Somtyme, for surfeet of mete and drinke. And somtyme of vileyns thoghtes, that been enclosed in mannes minde whan he goth to slepe; which may nat been with-oute sinne. For which men moste kepen hem wysely, or elles may men sinnen ful grevously.

The Remedy against the Sin of Lechery

Now comes the remedy for lechery, and that is, generally, chastity and continence, which restrain all the inordinate stirrings that come of fleshly desires. And ever the greater merit shall he have who restrains the wicked enkindlings of the ordure of this sin. And this is of two kinds, that is to say, chastity in marriage and chastity in widowhood. Now you shall understand that matrimony is the permitted coming together of man and of woman, who receive, by virtue of the sacrament, the bond of union from which they may not be freed in all their life, that is to say, while they both live. This, says the Book, is a very great sacrament. God established it, as I have said, in Paradise, and had Himself born into wedlock. And to sanctify marriage, He attended a wedding, where He turned water into wine, which was the first miracle that He wrought on earth before His disciples. The true result of marriage is the cleansing of fornication and the replenishing of Holy Church with believers of good lineage; for that is the end of marriage; and it changes deadly sin to venial sin between those who are wedded, and makes one the hearts of them, as well as the bodies. This is true marriage, which was established by God ere sin began, when natural law occupied its rightful position in Paradise; and it was ordained that one man should have but one woman, and one woman but one man, as Saint Augustine says, and that for many reasons.

First, because marriage figures the union between Christ and Holy Church. And another is, because the man is the head of the woman; at any rate it has been so ordained by ordinance. For if a woman had

77. Now comth the remedie agayns Lecherie, and that is, generally, Chastitee and Continence, that restreyneth alle the desordeynee moevinges that comen of fleshly talentes. And evere the gretter merite shal he han, that most restreyneth the wikkede eschaufinges of the ordure of this sinne. And this is in two maneres, that is to seyn, chastitee in mariage, and chastitee in widwehode. Now shaltow understonde, that matrimoine is leefful assemblinge of man and of womman, that receyven by vertu of the sacrement the bond, thurgh which they may nat be departed in al hir lyf, that is to seyn, whyl that they liven bothe. This, as seith the book, is a ful greet sacrement. God maked it, as I have seyd, in paradys, and wolde him-self be born in mariage. And for to halwen mariage, he was at a weddinge, where-as he turned water in-to wyn; which was the firste miracle that he wroghte in erthe biforn hise disciples. Trewe effect of mariage clenseth fornicacioun and replenisseth holy chirche of good linage; for that is the ende of mariage; and it chaungeth deedly sinne in-to venial sinne bitwixe hem that been y-wedded, and maketh the hertes al oon of hem that been y-wedded, as wel as the bodies. This is verray mariage, that was establissed by god er that sinne bigan, whan naturel lawe was in his right point in paradys; and it was ordeyned that o man sholde have but o womman, and o womman but o man, as seith seint Augustin, by manye resouns.

78. First, for mariage is figured bitwixe Crist and holy chirche. And that other is, for a man is heved of a womman; algate, by ordinaunce it sholde be so. For if a womman had mo men than oon, thanne

sholde she have mo hevedes than oon, and that were an horrible thing biforn god; and eek a womman ne mighte nat plese to many folk at ones. And also ther ne sholde nevere be pees ne reste amonges hem; for everich wolde axen his owene thing. And forther-over, no man ne sholde knowe his owene engendrure, ne who sholde have his heritage; and the womman sholde been the lasse biloved, fro the time that she were conjoynt to many men.

79. Now comth, how that a man sholde bere him with his wyf; and namely, in two thinges, that is to seyn in suffraunce and reverence, as shewed Crist whan he made first womman. For he ne made hir nat of the heved of Adam, for she sholde nat clayme to greet lordshipe. For ther-as the womman hath the maistrie, she maketh to muche desray; ther neden none ensamples of this. The experience of day by day oghte suffyse. Also certes, god ne made nat womman of the foot of Adam, for she ne sholde nat been holden to lowe; for she can nat paciently suffre: but god made womman of the rib of Adam, for womman sholde be felawe un-to man. Man sholde bere him to his wyf in feith, in trouthe, and in love, as seith seint Paul: that "a man sholde loven his wyf as Crist loved holy chirche, that loved it so wel that he deyde for it." So sholde a man for his wyf, if it were nede.

80. Now how that a womman sholde be subget to hir housbonde, that telleth seint Peter. First, in obedience. And eek, as seith the decree, a womman that is a wyf, as longe as she is a wyf, she hath noon auctoritee to swere ne bere witnesse with-oute leve of hir housbonde, that is hir lord; algate, he sholde be so by resoun. She sholde eek serven him in alle honestee, and been attempree of hir array. I wot wel that they sholde setten hir entente to plesen hir housbondes, but nat by hir queyntise of array. Seint Jerome seith, that wyves that been apparailled in silk and in precious purpre ne mowe nat clothen hem in Jesu Crist. What seith seint John eek in this matere? Seint Gregorie eek seith, that no wight seketh precious array but only for veyne glorie, to been honoured the more biforn the peple. It is a greet folye, a womman to have a fair array outward and in hirself be foul inward. A wyf sholde eek be mesurable in lokinge and in beringe and in laughinge, and discreet in alle hir wordes and hir dedes. And aboven alle worldly thing she sholde loven hir housbonde with al hir herte, and to him be trewe of hir body; so sholde an housbonde eek be to his wyf. For sith that al the body is the housbondes, so sholde hir herte been, or elles ther is bitwixe hem two, as in that, no parfit mariage. Thanne shal men understonde that for three thinges a man and his wyf fleshly mowen assemble. The firste is in entente of engendrure of children to the service of god, for certes that is the cause fynal of matrimoine. Another cause is, to yelden everich of hem to other the dette of hir bodies, for neither of hem hath power over his owene body. The thridde is, for to eschewe lecherye and vileinye. The ferthe is for

more men than one, then should she have more heads than one, and that were a horrible thing before God; and also, a woman could not please too many folk at once. And also, there should never be peace or rest among them; for each would demand his own thing. And furthermore, no man should know his own get, nor who should inherit his property; and the woman should be the less beloved from the time that she were joined with many men.

Now comes the question, How should a man conduct himself toward his wife? and specifically in two things, that is to say, in tolerance and reverence, as Christ showed when He first made woman. For He made her not of the head of Adam, because she should not claim to exercise great lordship. For wherever the woman has the mastery she causes too much disorder; there are needed no instances of this. The experience of every day ought to suffice. Also, certainly, God did not make woman of the foot of Adam, because she should not be held in too great contempt; for she cannot patiently endure: but God made woman of the rib of Adam, because woman should be a companion to man. Man should conduct himself toward his wife in faith, in truth, and in love; as Saint Paul says: "Husbands, love your wives, even as Christ also loved the Church, and gave Himself for it." So should a man give himself for his wife, if there be need.

Now how a woman should be subject to her husband, that is told by Saint Peter. First, by obedience. And also, as says the law, a woman who is a wife, as long as she is a wife, has no authority to make oath or to bear witness without the consent of her husband, who is her lord; in any event he should be so, in reason. She should also serve him in all honour. and be modest in her dress. I know well that they should resolve to please their husbands, but not by the finery of their array. Saint Jerome says that wives who go apparelled in silk and in precious purple cannot clothe themselves in Jesus Christ. Also, what says Saint John on this subject? Saint Gregory, also, says that a person seeks precious array only out of vainglory, to be honoured the more before the crowd. It is a great folly for a woman to have a fair outward appearance and inwardly to be foul. A wife should also be modest in glance and demeanour and in conversation, and discreet in all her words and deeds. And above all worldly things she should love her husband with her whole heart, and be true to him of her body; so, also, should a husband be to his wife. For since all the body is the husband's, so should her heart be, or else there is between them, in so far as that is concerned, no perfect marriage. Then shall men understand that for three things a man and his wife may have carnal coupling. The first is with intent to procreate children to the service of God, for certainly, that is the chief reason for matrimony. Another is, to pay, each of them to the other, the debt of their bodies, for neither of them has power over his own body. The third is, to avoid lechery and baseness. The fourth is, indeed, deadly sin. As for the first, it is meritorious; the second also, for, as the law says, she has the merit of chastity who pays to her husband the debt of her body, aye, though it be against her liking and the desire of her heart. The third is venial sin, and truly, hardly any of these unions may be without venial sin, because of the original sin and because of the pleasure. As to the fourth, be it understood that if they couple only for amorous love and for none of the aforesaid reasons, but merely to accomplish that burning pleasure, no matter how often, truly it is a mortal sin; and yet (with sorrow I say it) some folk are at pains to do it more and oftener than their appetite really demands.

The second kind of chastity is to be a clean widow and eschew the embraces of man and desire the embrace of Jesus Christ. These are those that have been wives and have lost their husbands, and also women that have fornicated and have been relieved by penitence. And truly, if a wife could keep herself always chaste with leave and license of her husband, so that she should thereby give him never an occasion to sin, it were a great merit in her. These women that observe chastity must be clean in heart as well as in body and in thought, and modest in dress and demeanour; and be abstinent in eating and drinking, in speech and in deed. They are the vessel or the box of the blessed Magdalen, which fills Holy Church with good odour. The third kind of chastity is virginity, and it behooves her to be holy in heart and clean of body; then is she the spouse of Christ and she is the beloved of the angels. She is the honour of this world, and she is the equal of martyrs; she has within her that which tongue may not tell nor the heart think. Virginity bore Our Lord Jesus Christ, and virgin was He Himself.

Another remedy for lechery is, specially to withhold oneself from such things as give rise to this baseness; as ease, and eating and drinking: for certainly, when the pot boils furiously, the best measure is to withdraw it from the fire. Sleeping long in great security from disturbance is also a nurse to lechery.

Another remedy for lechery is, that a man or woman eschew the company of those by whom he expects to be tempted; for though it be that the act itself is withstood, yet there is great temptation. Truly a white wall, though it burn not from the setting of a candle near it, yet shall the wall be made black by the flame. Often and often I counsel that no man trust in his own perfection, save he be stronger than Samson and holier than David and wiser than Solomon.

Now, since I have expounded to you, as best I could, the seven deadly sins, and some of their branches, and their remedies, truly, if I could, I would tell you of the ten commandments. But so high a doctrine I leave to the divines. Nevertheless, I hope to God that they have been touched upon in this treatise, each of them all.

sothe deedly sinne. As to the firste, it is meritorie; the seconde also; for, as seith the decree, that she hath merite of chastitee that yeldeth to hir housbonde the dette of hir body, ye, though it be agayn hir lykinge and the lust of hir herte. The thridde manere is venial sinne, and trewely scarsly may ther any of thise be with-oute venial sinne, for the corrupcion and for the delyt. The fourthe manere is for to understonde, if they assemble only for amorous love and for noon of the forseyde causes, but for to accomplice thilke brenninge delyt, they rekke nevere how ofte, sothly it is deedly sinne; and yet, with sorwe, somme folk wol peynen hem more to doon than to hir appetyt suffyseth.

81. The seconde manere of chastitee is for to been a clene widewe, and eschue the embracinges of man, and desyren the embracinge of Jesu Crist. Thise been tho that han been wyves and han forgoon hir housbondes, and eek wommen that han doon lecherie and been releeved by Penitence. And certes, if that a wyf coude kepen hir al chaast by licence of hir housbonde, so that she yeve nevere noon occasion that he agilte, it were to hire a greet merite. Thise manere wommen that observen chastitee moste be clene in herte as well as in body and in thoght, and mesurable in clothinge and in contenaunce; and been abstinent in etinge and drinkinge, in spekinge, and in dede. They been the vessel or the boyste of the blissed Magdalene, that fulfilleth holy chirche of good odour. The thridde manere of chastitee is virginitee, and it bihoveth that she be holy in herte and clene of body; thanne is she spouse to Jesu Crist, and she is the lyf of angeles. She is the preisinge of this world, and she is as thise martirs in egalitee; she hath in hir that tonge may nat telle ne herte thinke. Virginitee baar oure lord Jesu Crist, and virgine was him-selve.

82. Another remedie agayns Lecherie is, specially to withdrawen swiche thinges as yeve occasion to thilke vileinye; as ese, etinge and drinkinge; for certes, whan the pot boyleth strongly, the beste remedie is to withdrawe the fyr. Slepinge longe in greet quiete is eek a greet norice to Lecherie.

83. Another remedie agayns Lecherie is, that a man or a womman eschue the companye of hem by whiche he douteth to be tempted; for al-be-it so that the dede is withstonden, yet is ther greet temptacioun. Soothly a whyt wal, although it ne brenne noght fully by stikinge of a candele, yet is the wal blak of the leyt. Ful ofte tyme I rede, that no man truste in his owene perfeccioun, but he be stronger than Sampson, and holier than David, and wyser than Salomon.

84. Now after that I have declared yow, as I can, the sevene deedly sinnes, and somme of hir braunches and hir remedies, soothly, if I coude, I wolde telle yow the ten comandements. But so heigh a doctrine I lete to divines. Nathelees, I hope to god they been touched in this tretice, everich of hem alle.

Of Confession

85. Now for-as-muche as the second partie of Penitence stant in Confessioun of mouth, as I bigan in the firste chapitre, I seye, seint Augustin seith: sinne is every word and every dede, and al that men coveiten agayn the lawe of Jesu Crist; and this is for to sinne in herte, in mouth, and in dede, by thy fyve wittes, that been sighte, heringe, smellinge, tastinge or savouringe, and felinge. Now is it good to understonde that that agreggeth muchel every sinne. Thou shalt considere what thou art that doost the sinne, whether thou be male or femele, yong or old, gentil or thral, free or servant, hool or syk, wedded or sengle, ordred or unordred, wys or fool, clerk or seculer; if she be of thy kinrede, bodily or goostly, or noon; if any of thy kinrede have sinned with hir or noon, and manye mo thinges.

86. Another circumstaunce is this; whether it be doon in fornicacioun, or in avoutrie, or noon; incest, or noon; mayden, or noon; in manere of homicyde, or noon; horrible grete sinnes, or smale; and how longe thou hast continued in sinne. The thridde circumstaunce is the place ther thou hast do sinne; whether in other mennes hous or in thyn owene; in feeld or in chirche, or in chirche-hawe; in chirche dedicat, or noon. For if the chirche be halwed, and man or womman spille his kinde in-with that place by wey of sinne, or by wikked temptacion, the chirche is entredited til it be reconciled by the bishop; and the preest that dide swich a vileinye, to terme of al his lyf, he sholde na-more singe masse; and if he dide, he sholde doon deedly sinne at every tyme that he so songe masse. The fourthe circumstaunce is, by whiche mediatours or by whiche messagers, as for entycement, or for consentement to bere companye with felaweshipe; for many a wrecche, for to bere companye, wil go to the devel of helle. Wher-fore they that eggen or consenten to the sinne been parteners of the sinne, and of the dampnacioun of the sinner. The fifthe circumstaunce is, how manye tymes that he hath sinned, if it be in his minde, and how ofte that he hath falle. For he that ofte falleth in sinne, he despiseth the mercy of god, and encreesseth his sinne, and is unkinde to Crist; and he wexeth the more feble to withstonde sinne, and sinneth the more lightly, and the latter aryseth, and is the more eschew for to shryven him, namely, to him that is his confessour. For which that folk, whan they falle agayn in hir olde folies, outher they forleten hir olde confessours al outrely, or elles they departen hir shrift in diverse places; but soothly, swich departed shrift deserveth no mercy of god of hise sinnes. The sixte circumstaunce is, why that a man sinneth, as by whiche temptacioun; and if him-self procure thilke temptacioun, or by the excytinge of other folk; or if he sinne with a womman by force, or by hir owene assent; or if the womman, maugree hir heed, hath been afforced, or noon; this shal she telle; for coveitise, or for poverte, and if it was hir procuringe,

Now, for as much as the second part of penitence deals in oral confession, as I said in the first paragraph hereof, I say that Saint Augustine says: Sin is every word and every deed and all that men covet against the law of Jesus Christ; and that is, to sin in heart, in word, and in deed by one's five senses, which are sight, hearing, smell, taste or savour, and feeling. Now it is well to understand that which greatly aggravates every sin. You should consider what you are that do the sin, whether you are male or female, young or old, noble or thrall, free or servant, healthy or ailing, wedded or single, member of a religious order or not, wise or foolish, clerical or secular; whether she is of your kindred, bodily or spiritual, or not; whether any of your kindred has sinned with her, or not; and many other things.

Another circumstance is this: whether it be done in fornication, or in adultery, or otherwise; incest, or not; maiden, or not; in manner of homicide, or not; horrible great sins, or small; and how long you have continued in sin. The third circumstance is the place where you have done the sin; whether in other men's houses, or your own; in field, or in church or churchyard; in a dedicated church, or not. For if the church be consecrated, and man or woman spill seed within that place, by way of sin or by wicked temptation, the church is interdicted till it be reconciled by the bishop; and the priest that did such a villainy, for the term of all his life, should nevermore sing mass; and if he did, he should do deadly sin every time that he so sang mass. The fourth circumstance is, what go-betweens, or what messengers, are sent for the sake of enticement, or to gain consent to bear company in the affair; for many a wretch, for the sake of companionship, will go to the Devil of Hell. Wherefore those that egg on to or connive for the sin are partners in the sin, and shall partake of the damnation of the sinner. The fifth circumstance is, how many times has he sinned, if it be in his memory, and how often he has fallen. For he that falls often in sin, he despises the mercy of God, and increases his sin, and is ungrateful to Christ; and he grows the more feeble to withstand sin, and sins the more lightly, and the more slowly rises out of sin, and is the more reluctant to be shriven, especially by his own confessor. For the which reasons, when folk fall again into their old follies, either they avoid their old confessors altogether, or else they make parts of confession in divers places; but truly, such divided confessions deserve no mercy of God for one's sins. The sixth circumstance is, why a man sins, as by way of what sort of temptation; and whether he himself procured that temptation, or whether it came by the incitement of other folk; or whether he sin by forcing a woman or by her consent: or, if the sinner be a woman, despite all her efforts were she forced or not —this shall she tell; and whether for greed of gain or for stress of poverty, and whether it was of her own procuring, or not; and all such trappings. The seventh circumstance is, in what manner he has done his sin, or how she has suffered men to do it unto her. And the same shall the man tell fully, with all the circumstances; and whether he has sinned with common brothel-women, or not; or has done his sin in holy times, or not; in fasting times, or not; or before confession, or after his last shriving; and whether he has, peradventure, broken therefor his enjoined penance; by whose help and by whose counsel; by sorcery or cunning: all must be told. All these things, according as they are great or small, burden the conscience of a man. And, too, that the priest who is your judge shall be the better advised to his judgment in giving you penance, that is, according to your contrition. For understand well that after a man has defiled his baptism by sin, if he would gain salvation, there is no other way than by penitence and shrift and penance; and specifically by the two, if there be a confessor to shrive him; and by the third if he live to perform it.

Then shall a man reflect and consider that if he will make a true and profitable confession, there must be four conditions. First, it must be in sorrowful bitterness of heart, as said King Hezekiah to God: "I will remember all the days of my life in bitterness of heart." This condition of bitterness has five signs. The first is, that confession must be shamefaced, not to cover up nor to hide sin, for the sinner has offended his God and defiled his soul. And thereof Saint Augustine says: "The heart suffers for the shame of its sin." And if he has a great sense of shame, he is worthy of great mercy from God. Such was the confession of the publican who would not lift up his eyes to Heaven, for he had offended God in Heaven; for which shamefacedness he received straightway the mercy of God. And thereof says Saint Augustine that such shamefaced folk are to forgiveness and remission. Another sign is humility in confession; of which Saint Peter says "Humble thyself beneath the might of God." The hand of God is mighty in confession, for thereby God forgives you your sins; for He alone has the power. And this humility shall be of the heart, and shall be manifested outwardly; for just as he has humility to God in his heart, just so should he humble his body outwardly to the priest that sits in God's place. Since Christ is sovereign and the priest is means and mediator between Christ and the sinner, and the sinner is the last, in reason, the sinner should nowise sit as high as his confessor, but should kneel before him, or at his feet, unless infirmity hinder it. For he shall care not who sits there, but only in whose place he sits. A man who has offended a lord, and who comes to ask mercy and to be at peace again, and who should sit down at once by the lord's side—men would hold him to be presumptuous and not worthy so soon to have remission or mercy. The third sign is, your confession should be made in tears, if a man can weep; and if a man cannot weep with his fleshly eyes, let him weep in his heart. Such was the confession of Saint Peter;

or noon; and swiche manere harneys. The seventhe circumstaunce is, in what manere he hath doon his sinne, or how that she hath suffred that folk han doon to hir. And the same shal the man telle pleynly, with alle circumstaunces; and whether he hath sinned with comune bordel-wommen, or noon; or doon his sinne in holy tymes, or noon; in fastingtymes, or noon; or biforn his shrifte, or after his latter shrifte; and hath, peraventure, broken therfore his penance enjoyned; by whos help and whos conseil; by sorcerie or craft; al moste be told. Alle thise thinges, after that they been grete or smale, engreggen the conscience of man. And eek the preest that is thy juge, may the bettre been avysed of his jugement in yevinge of thy penaunce, and that is after thy contricioun. For understond wel, that after tyme that a man hath defouled his baptesme by sinne, if he wole come to salvacioun, ther is noon other wey but by penitence and shrifte and satisfaccioun; and namely by the two, if ther be a confessour to which he may shryven him; and the thridde, if he have lyf to parfournen it.

87. Thanne shal man looke and considere, that if he wole maken a trewe and a profitable confessioun, ther moste be foure condicious. First, it moot been in sorweful bitternesse of herte, as seyde the king Ezekias to god: "I wol remembre me alle the yeres of my lyf in bitternesse of myn herte." This condicioun of bitternesse hath fyve signes. The firste is, that confessioun moste be shamefast, nat for to covere ne hyden his sinne, for he hath agilt his god and defouled his soule. And her-of seith seint Augustin: "the herte travailleth for shame of his sinne"; and for he hath greet shamefastnesse, he is digne to have greet mercy of god. Swich was the confession of the publican, that wolde nat heven up hise eyen to hevene, for he hadde offended god of hevene; for which shamefastnesse he hadde anon the mercy of god. And ther-of seith seint Augustin, that swich shamefast folk been next foryevenesse and remissioun. Another signe is humilitee in confessioun; of which seith seint Peter, "Humbleth yow under the might of god." The hond of god is mighty in confessioun, for ther-by god foryeveth thee thy sinnes; for he allone hath the power. And this humilitee shal been in herte, and in signe outward; for right as he hath humilitee to god in his herte, right so sholde he humble his body outward to the preest that sit in goddes place. For which in no manere, sith that Crist is sovereyn and the preest mene and mediatour bitwixe Crist and the sinnere, and the sinnere is the laste by wey of resoun, thanne sholde nat the sinnere sitte as heighe as his confessour, but knele biforn him or at his feet, but-if maladie destourbe it. For he shal nat taken kepe who sit there, but in whos place that he sitteth. A man that hath trespased to a lord, and comth for to axe mercy and maken his accord, and set him doun anon by the lord, men wolde holden him outrageous, and nat worthy so sone for to have remissioun ne mercy. The thridde signe is, how that thy shrift sholde be ful of teres, if man may;

and if man may nat wepe with hise bodily eyen, lat him wepe in herte. Swich was the confessioun of seint Peter; for after that he hadde forsake Jesu Crist, he wente out and weep ful bitterly. The fourthe signe is, that he ne lette nat for shame to shewen his confessioun. Swich was the confessioun of the Magdelene, that ne spared, for no shame of hem that weren atte feste, for to go to oure lord Jesu Crist and biknowe to him hir sinnes. The fifthe signe is, that a man or a womman be obeisant to receyven the penaunce that him is enjoyned for hise sinnes; for certes Jesu Crist, for the giltes of a man, was obedient to the deeth.

88. The seconde condicion of verray confession is, that it be hastily doon; for certes, if a man hadde a deedly wounde, evere the lenger that he taried to warisshe him-self, the more wolde it corrupte and haste him to his deeth; and eek the wounde wolde be the wors for to hele. And right so fareth sinne, that longe tyme is in a man unshewed. Certes, a man oghte hastily shewen hise sinnes for manye causes; as for drede of deeth, that cometh ofte sodenly, and is in no certeyn what tyme it shal be, ne in what place; and eek the drecchinge of o synne draweth in another; and eek the lenger that he tarieth, the ferther he is fro Crist. And if he abyde to his laste day, scarsly may he shryven him or remembre him of hise sinnes, or repenten him, for the grevous maladie of his deeth. And for-as-muche as he ne hath nat in his lyf herkned Jesu Crist, whanne he hath spoken, he shal crye to Jesu Crist at his laste day, and scarsly wol he herkne him. And understond that this condicioun moste han foure thinges. Thy shrift moste be purveyed bifore and avysed; for wikked haste doth no profit; and that a man conne shryve him of hise sinnes, be it of pryde, or of envye, and so forth of the speces and circumstances; and that he have comprehended in his minde the nombre and the greetnesse of hise sinnes, and how longe that he hath leyn in sinne; and eek that he be contrit of hise sinnes, and in stedefast purpos, by the grace of god, nevere eft to falle in sinne; and eek that he drede and countrewaite him-self, that he flee the occasiouns of sinne to whiche he is enclyned. Also thou shalt shryve thee of alle thy sinnes to o man, and nat a parcel to o man and a parcel to another; that is to understonde, in entente to departe thy confessioun as for shame or drede; for it nis but stranglinge of thy soule. For certes, Jesu Crist is entierly al good; in him nis noon inperfeccioun; and therfore outher he foryeveth al parfitly or never a deel. I seye nat that if thou be assigned to the penitauncer for certein sinne, that thou art bounde to shewen him al the remenaunt of thy sinnes, of whiche thou hast be shriven to thy curat, but-if it lyke to thee of thyn humilitee; this is no departinge of shrifte. Ne I seye nat, ther-as I speke of divisioun of confessioun, that if thou have lycence for to shryve thee to a discreet and an honeste preest, where thee lyketh, and by lycence of thy curat, that thou ne mayst wel shryve thee to him of alle thy sinnes. But lat no

for after he had forsaken Jesus Christ he went out and wept full bitterly. The fourth sign is, when the sinner forgoes not for shame to make his confession. Such was the confession of the Magdalen, who did not spare, for any shame before those who were at the feast, to go to Our Lord Jesus Christ and acknowledge to Him her sins. The fifth sign is, that a man or woman shall obediently receive the penance that is imposed for the sins; for certainly, Jesus Christ, for the sins of a man, was obedient unto death.

The second condition of true confession is that it be speedily done; for truly, if a man had a dangerous wound, the longer he waited to cure himself the more would it fester and hasten him toward his death; and also the wound would be but the harder to heal. And it is even so with sin that is long carried in a man unconfessed. Certainly a man ought to confess his sins without delay, for many reasons; as, for fear of death, which often comes suddenly and whereof no man can ever be certain when it will come or in what place; and also the prolonging of one sin draws a man into another; and further, the longer he delays the farther he is from Christ. And if he live until his last day, scarcely then may he shrive himself or then remember his sins, or repent of them, because of the grievous malady about to cause his death. And for as much as he has not in his life hearkened unto Jesus Christ when He has spoken, he shall cry to Jesus Christ at the last and scarcely will He hear him. And understand that this condition must have four elements. Your shrift must be considered in advance and well advised upon, for wicked haste gives no profit; and that a man shall be able to make confession of all of his sins, be they of pride, or of envy, and so forth, according to the kind and the circumstances; and that he shall have comprehended in his mind the number and the greatness of his sins; and how long he has lain in sin; and also that he shall be contrite for his sins, and have a steadfast purpose that never again, by the grace of God, shall he fall into sin; and also that he fear and keep watch upon himself, so that he shall flee the occasions whereof he is tempted to sin. And you shall also shrive yourself of all your sins to one man, and not of some of them to one man and some to another; when, it is to be understood, the intention is to split up your shriving out of shame or fear; for this is but the strangling of your soul. For indeed, Jesus Christ is wholly good; there is no imperfection in Him; and therefore He perfectly forgives all, or nothing. I do not say that if you are sent to the director for a certain sin you are bound to show unto him all the rest of your sins, whereof you have been shriven by your own curate, save and except you wish to do so out of humility; for this does not constitute dividing your shrift. Nor do I say, in speaking of divided confession, that if you have leave to shrive yourself to a discreet and honest priest, where you wish to do so and by leave of your curate, that you may not as well shrive yourself to him of all your sins. But let no blot remain behind, let no sin be untold, so far as you have remembrance of them. And when you shall be shriven by your curate, tell him as well all of the sins that you have done since last you were shriven; and then this will be no wicked intention to divide confession.

Also, true confession asks certain other conditions. First, that you shrive yourself of your free will, not by constraint, nor for shame, nor for illness, nor for any such things; for it is only reasonable that he who trespassed of his own free will shall as freely confess it, and that no other man tell his sin, but that he himself do it, nor shall he withhold or deny his sin, nor allow himself to become angry at the priest for admonishing him to leave sin. Another condition is that your shrift be lawful; that is to say, that you, who shrive yourself, and also the priest who hears your confession, be verily of the faith of Holy Church; and that a man be not deprived of hope of the mercy of Jesus Christ, as was Cain or Judas. And also a man must himself accuse himself for his own trespass, and not another; but he shall blame and reproach himself and his own malice for his sin, and not another; nevertheless, if another man be the occasion for or enticer to his sin, or the state of a person be such that because of that person the sin is aggravated, or else if he cannot fully shrive himself without telling of the person with whom he has sinned; then he may tell; so that the intention be not to backbite such a person, but only to declare fully the confession.

Also you shall tell no lies in your confession; as to seem humble, perchance, in saying that you have done sins whereof you were never guilty. For Saint Augustine says: if thou, by reason of thy humility, liest against thyself, though thou wast not in sin before, yet art thou then in sin because of thy lying. You must also confess your sin with your own mouth, unless you grow dumb, and not by letter; for you have done the sin and you shall have the shame thereof. Also, you shall not embellish your confession with fair and subtle words, the more to cover up the sin; for then you beguile yourself and not the priest; you must tell it plainly, be it ever so foul or so horrible. You shall also shrive yourself to a priest that is discreet in counselling you, and moreover, you shall not shrive yourself for vainglory, nor hypocritically, nor for any cause other than the fear of Jesus Christ and the well-being of your soul. Also, you shall not run suddenly to the priest to tell him lightly of your sin, as one would tell a jest or a tale, but advisedly and with great devotion. And, generally speaking, shrive yourself often. If you fall often, then you rise by confession. And though you shrive yourself more than once of sin for which you have been already shriven, it is the more merit. And, as Saint Augustine says, you shall thereby the more easily obtain release from and the grace of God, both as to sin and punishment. And certainly, once a year, at the least, it is lawful to receive the Eucharist, for truly, once a year all things are renewed.

blotte be bihinde; lat no sinne been untold, as fer as thou hast remembraunce. And whan thou shalt be shriven to thy curat, telle him eek alle the sinnes that thou hast doon sin thou were last y-shriven; this is no wikked entente of divisioun of shrifte.

89. Also the verray shrifte axeth certeine condiciouns. First, that thou shryve thee by thy free wil, noght constreyned, ne for shame of folk, ne for maladie, ne swiche thinges; for it is resoun that he that trespasseth by his free wil, that by his free wil he confesse his trespas; and that noon other man telle his sinne but he him-self, ne he shal nat nayte ne denye his sinne, ne wratthe him agayn the preest for his amonestinge to leve sinne. The seconde condicioun is, that thy shrift be laweful; that is to seyn, that thou that shryvest thee, and eek the preest that hereth thy confessioun, been verraily in the feith of holy chirche; and that a man ne be nat despeired of the mercy of Jesu Crist, as Caym or Judas. And eek a man moot accusen him-self of his owene trespas, and nat another; but he shal blame and wyten him-self and his owene malice of his sinne, and noon other; but nathelees, if that another man be occasioun or entycer of his sinne, or the estaat of a persone be swich thurgh which his sinne is agregged, or elles that he may nat pleynly shryven him but he telle the persone with which he hath sinned; thanne may he telle; so that his entente ne be nat to bakbyte the persone, but only to declaren his confessioun.

90. Thou ne shalt nat eek make no lesinges in thy confessioun; for humilitee, per-aventure, to seyn that thou hast doon sinnes of whiche that thou were nevere gilty. For seint Augustin seith: if thou, by cause of thyn humilitee, makest lesinges on thyself, though thou ne were nat in sinne biforn, yet artow thanne in sinne thurgh thy lesinges. Thou most eek shewe thy sinne by thyn owene propre mouth, but thou be wexe doumb, and nat by no lettre; for thou that hast doon the sinne, thou shalt have the shame therfore. Thou shalt nat eek peynte thy confessioun by faire subtile wordes, to covere the more thy sinne; for thanne bigylestow thy-self and nat the preest; thou most tellen it pleynly, be it nevere so foul ne so horrible. Thou shalt eek shryve thee to a preest that is discreet to conseille thee, and eek thou shalt nat shryve thee for veyne glorie, ne for ypocrisye, ne for no cause, but only for the doute of Jesu Crist and the hele of thy soule. Thou shalt nat eek renne to the preest sodeynly, to tellen him lightly thy sinne, as who-so telleth a jape or a tale, but avysely and with greet devocioun. And generally, shryve thee ofte. If thou ofte falle, ofte thou aryse by confessioun. And thogh thou shryve thee ofter than ones of sinne, of which thou hast be shriven, it is the more merite. And, as seith seint Augustin, thou shalt have the more lightly relesing and grace of god, bothe of sinne and of peyne. And certes, ones a yere atte leeste wey it is laweful for to been housled; for certes ones a yere alle thinges renovellen.

HERE ENDETH THE SECOND PART OF PENITENCE

HERE FOLLOWETH THE THIRD PART OF SATISFACTION

91. Now have I told you of verray Confessioun, that is the seconde partie of Penitence.

The thridde partie of Penitence is Satisfaccioun; and that stant most generally in almesse and in bodily peyne. Now been ther three manere of almesses; contricion of herte, where a man offreth himself to god; another is, to han pitee of defaute of hise neighebores; and the thridde is, in yevinge of good conseil goostly and bodily, where men han nede, and namely in sustenaunce of mannes fode. And tak keep, that a man hath need of thise thinges generally; he hath need of fode, he hath nede of clothing, and herberwe, he hath nede of charitable conseil, and visitinge in prisone and in maladie, and sepulture of his dede body. And if thou mayst nat visite the nedeful with thy persone, visite him by thy message and by thy yiftes. Thise been generally almesses or werkes of charitee of hem that han temporel richesses or discrecioun in conseilinge. Of thise werkes shaltow heren at the day of dome.

92. Thise almesses shaltow doon of thyne owene propre thinges, and hastily, and prively if thou mayst; but nathelees, if thou mayst nat doon it prively, thou shalt nat forbere to doon almesse though men seen it; so that it be nat doon for thank of the world, but only for thank of Jesu Crist. For as witnesseth seint Mathew, *capitulo quinto*, "A citee may nat been hid that is set on a montayne; ne men lighte nat a lanterne and put it under a busshel; but men sette it on a candle-stikke, to yeve light to the men in the hous. Right so shal youre light lighten bifore men, that they may seen youre gode werkes, and glorifie youre fader that is in hevene."

93. Now as to speken of bodily peyne, it stant in preyeres, in wakinges, in fastinges, in vertuouse techinges of orisouns. And ye shul understonde, that orisouns or preyeres is for to seyn a pitous wil of herte, that redresseth it in god and expresseth it by word outward, to remoeven harmes and to han thinges espirituel and durable, and somtyme temporel thinges; of whiche orisouns, certes, in the orisoun of the *Pater-noster*, hath Jesu Crist enclosed most thinges. Certes, it is privileged of three thinges in his dignitee, for which it is more digne than any other preyere; for that Jesu Crist him-self maked it; and it is short, for it sholde be coud the more lightly, and for to withholden it the more esily in herte, and helpen him-self the ofter with the orisoun; and for a man sholde be the lasse wery to seyen it, and for a man may nat excusen him to lerne it, it is so short and so esy; and for it comprehendeth in it-self alle gode preyeres. The exposicioun of this holy preyere, that is so excellent and digne, I bitake to thise maistres of theologie; save thus muchel wol I seyn: that, whan thou prayest that god sholde foryeve thee thy giltes as thou foryevest hem that agilten to thee, be ful wel war that thou be nat out of charitee. This holy orisoun amenuseth eek venial sinne; and therfore it aperteneth specially to penitence.

Now have I told you of true confession, which is the second part of penitence. The third part of penitence is expiation; and that is generally achieved through alms-giving and bodily pain. Now there are three kinds of alms-givings: contrition of heart, where a man offers himself to God; another is, to have pity on the weaknesses of one's neighbours; and the third is, the giving of good counsel, spiritual and material, where men have need of it, and especially in the procuring of men's food. And take note that a man has need of these things, generally; he has need of food, he has need of clothing and shelter, he has need of charitable counsel, and of visiting in prison and in illness, and sepulture for his dead body. And if you cannot visit the needy in person, visit him by your message and by your gifts. These are general alms-givings, or works of charity, by those who have temporal riches or discretion in counselling. Of these works you shall hear at the day of doom.

These alms-doings shall you do with your own proper things, and without delay, and privately, if you can; but nevertheless, if you cannot do it privately, you shall not forbear to do such works though men may see you, so long as they be done not for the world's approbation, but for the pleasing of Jesus Christ. For take witness of Saint Matthew, *capitulo quinto*: "A city that is set on a hill cannot be hid. Neither do men light a candle and put it under a bushel, but on a candlestick; and it giveth light unto all that are in the house. Let your light so shine before men, that they may see your good works, and glorify your Father which is in Heaven."

Now, to speak of bodily pain, it consists of prayers, of vigils, of fasts, of virtuous teaching of orisons. And you shall understand that orisons or prayers consist of a pious will of the heart that has made amends to God and expresses itself by spoken word, asking for the removal of evils and to obtain things spiritual and durable, as well as temporal things, sometimes; of which orisons, truly, in the prayer of the paternoster has Christ included most things. Certainly, it is invested with three things pertaining to His dignity, wherefore it is more dignified than any other prayer; Jesus Christ made it Himself; and it is short, so that it may be learned the more easily, and be held the more easily in the heart of memory, that man may the oftener help himself by repeating the prayer; and in order that a man may the less grow weary of saying it, and that he may not excuse himself from learning it; it is so short and so easy; and because it comprises within itself all good prayers. The expounding of this holy prayer I commit to these masters of theology; save that thus much will I say: that, when you pray that God forgive your trespasses as you forgive those that trespass against you, beware that you are not uncharitable. This holy orison diminishes each venial sin, and therefore it appertains specially to penitence.

This prayer must be truly said and in utter faith, in order that men may pray to God ordinately and discreetly and devoutly; and always a man shall subject his own will to the will of God. This prayer must also be said with great humility and all innocently; honourably and not to the annoyance of any man or woman. It must also be followed by works of charity. It is of avail also even against the vices of the soul; for, as Saint Jerome says, "By fasting we are saved from the vices of the flesh, and by prayer from the vices of the soul."

After the foregoing you shall understand that bodily pain lies in vigils; for Jesus Christ says, "Watch and pray, that ye enter not into temptation." You shall understand, also, that fasting stands in three things; in the forgoing of material food and drink, and in forgoing worldly pleasures, and in forgoing the doing of mortal sin; this is to say, that a man shall guard himself from deadly sin with all his might.

And you shall understand, also, that God ordained fasting; and to fasting pertain four things: Largess to poor folk, gladness of the spiritual heart in order not to be angry or vexed, nor to grumble because you fast; and also reasonable hours wherein to eat moderately; that is to say, a man shall not eat out of season, nor sit and eat longer at his table because he has fasted.

Then you shall understand that bodily pain lies in disciplining or teaching, by word or by writing, or by example. Also, in wearing shirts of hair or coarse wool, or habergeons next the naked flesh, for Christ's sake, and such other kinds of penance. But beware that such kinds of penance on your flesh do not make your heart bitter or angry or vexed with yourself; for it is better to cast away your hair shirt than to cast away the security of Jesus Christ. And therefore Saint Paul says: "Clothe yourselves as those that are the chosen of God, in heart of mercy, gentleness, long-suffering, and such manner of clothing." Whereof Jesus Christ is more pleased than of hair shirts, or habergeons, or hauberks.

Then, discipline lies also in beating of the breast, in scourging with rods, in kneelings, in tribulations, in suffering patiently the wrongs that are done unto one, and also in patient endurance of illnesses, or losing of worldly chattels, or of wife or of child or other friends.

Then shall you understand which things hinder penance; and these are four, that is to say, fear, shame, hope, and despair. And, to speak first of fear, since a man sometimes thinks that he cannot endure penance, against this thought may be set, as remedy, the thought that such bodily penance is short and mild compared with the pain of Hell, which is so cruel and so long that it lasts for ever.

Now against the shame that a man has in confession, and especially of these hypocrites that would be held so perfect that they have no need for shrift—against that shame should a man think, and reasonably enough, that he who has not been ashamed to

94. This preyere moste be trewely seyd and in verray feith, and that men preye to god ordinatly and discreetly and devoutly; and alwey a man shal putten his wil to be subget to the wille of god. This orisoun moste eek been seyd with greet humblesse and ful pure; honestly, and nat to the anoyaunce of any man or womman. It moste eek been continued with the werkes of charitee. It avayleth eek agayn the vyces of the soule; for, as seith seint Jerome, "By fastinge been saved the vyces of the flesh, and by preyere the vyces of the soule."

95. After this, thou shalt understonde, that bodily peyne stant in wakinge; for Jesu Crist seith, "waketh, and preyeth that ye ne entre in wikked temptacioun." Ye shul understanden also, that fastinge stant in three thinges; in forberinge of bodily mete and drinke, and in forberinge of worldly jolitee, and in forberinge of deedly sinne; this is to seyn, that a man shal kepen him fro deedly sinne with al his might.

96. And thou shalt understanden eek, that god ordeyned fastinge; and to fastinge appertenen foure thinges. Largenesse to povre folk, gladnesse of herte espirituel, nat to been angry ne anoyed, ne grucche for he fasteth; and also resonable houre for to ete by mesure; that is for to seyn, a man shal nat ete in untyme, ne sitte the lenger at his table to ete for he fasteth.

97. Thanne shaltow understonde, that bodily peyne stant in disciplyne or techinge, by word or by wrytinge, or in ensample. Also in weringe of heyres or of stamin, or of haubergeons on hir naked flesh, for Cristes sake, and swiche manere penances. But war thee wel that swiche manere penances on thy flesh ne make nat thyn herte bitter or angry or anoyed of thy-self; for bettre is to caste awey thyn heyre, than for to caste away the sikernesse of Jesu Crist. And therfore seith seint Paul: "Clothe yow, as they that been chosen of god, in herte of misericorde, debonairetee, suffraunce, and swich manere of clothinge"; of whiche Jesu Crist is more apayed than of heyres, or haubergeons, or hauberkes.

98. Thanne is disciplyne eek in knokkinge of thy brest, in scourginge with yerdes, in knelinges, in tribulacions; in suffringe paciently wronges that been doon to thee, and eek in pacient suffraunce of maladies, or lesinge of worldly catel, or of wyf, or of child, or othere freendes.

99. Thanne shaltow understonde, whiche thinges destourben penaunce; and this is in four maneres, that is, drede, shame, hope, and wanhope, that is, desperacion. And for to speke first of drede; for which he weneth that he may suffre no penaunce; ther-agayns is remedie for to thinke, that bodily penaunce is but short and litel at regard of the peyne of helle, that is so cruel and so long, that it lasteth with-outen ende.

100. Now again the shame that a man hath to shryven him, and namely, thise ypocrites that wolden been holden so parfite that they han no nede to shryven hem; agayns that shame, sholde a man thinke that, by wey of resoun, that he that hath nat

been ashamed to doon foule thinges, certes him oghte nat been ashamed to do faire thinges, and that is confessiouns. A man sholde eek thinke, that god seeth and woot alle hise thoghtes and alle hise werkes; to him may no thing been hid ne covered. Men sholden eek remembren hem of the shame that is to come at the day of dome, to hem that been nat penitent and shriven in this present lyf. For alle the creatures in erthe and in helle shullen seen apertly al that they hyden in this world.

101. Now for to speken of the hope of hem that been necligent and slowe to shryven hem, that stant in two maneres. That oon is, that he hopeth for to live longe and for to purchacen muche richesse for his delyt, and thanne he wol shryven him; and, as he seith, him semeth thanne tymely y-nough to come to shrifte. Another is, surquidrie that he hath in Cristes mercy. Agayns the firste vyce, he shal thinke, that oure lyf is in no sikernesse; and eek that alle the richesses in this world ben in aventure, and passen as a shadwe on the wal. And, as seith seint Gregorie, that it aperteneth to the grete rightwisnesse of god, that nevere shal the peyne stinte of hem that nevere wolde withdrawen hem fro sinne, hir thankes, but ay continue in sinne; for thilke perpetuel wil to do sinne shul they han perpetuel peyne.

102. Wanhope is in two maneres: the firste wanhope is in the mercy of Crist; that other is that they thinken, that they ne mighte nat longe persevere in goodnesse. The firste wanhope comth of that he demeth th[illegible]he hath sinned so greetly and so ofte, and so long[illegible]yn in sinne, that he shal nat be saved. Certes, ag[illegible]s that cursed wanhope sholde he thinke, that [illegible] passion of Jesu Crist is more strong for to unbi[illegible] than sinne is strong for to binde. Agayns the s[illegible]nde wanhope, he shal thinke, that as ofte as he [illegible]leth he may aryse agayn by penitence. And t[illegible]h he never so longe have leyn in sinne, the me[illegible] of Crist is alwey redy to receiven him to mercy. [illegible]ayns the wanhope, that he demeth that he sho[illegible] nat longe persevere in goodnesse, he shal thinke, [illegible]t the feblesse of the devel may no-thing doon [illegible] if men wol suffren him; and eek he shal han stre[illegible]he of the help of god, and of al holy chirche, an[illegible] the proteccioun of aungels, if him list.

103. Thanne s[illegible] men understonde what is the fruit of penaunce; [illegible], after the word of Jesu Crist, it is the endelees [illegible]e of hevene, ther joye hath no contrarioustee [illegible]wo ne grevaunce, ther alle harmes been passe[illegible] this present lyf; ther-as is the sikernesse fro t[illegible]eyne of helle; ther-as is the blisful companye th[illegible]oysen hem everemo, everich of otheres joye; [illegible]as the body of man, that whylom was foul an[illegible]k, is more cleer than the sonne; ther-as the bod[illegible]t whylom was syk, freele, and feble, and morta[illegible]nmortal, and so strong and so hool that ther m[illegible]-thing apeyren it; ther-as ne is neither hunge[illegible]rst, ne cold, but every soule replenissed with t[illegible]hte of the parfit knowinge of god. This blisfu[illegible]e may men purchace

do foul things, certainly he ought not to be ashamed to do fair things, and of such is confession. A man should also think that God sees and knows all his thoughts and all his deeds; from Him nothing may be hidden nor covered. Men should even bear in mind the shame that is to come at the day of judgment to those who are not penitent and shriven in this present life. For all the creatures on earth and in Hell shall openly behold all that sinners hide in this world.

Now to speak of the hope of those who are negligent and slow in shriving themselves—that is of two sorts. The one is, that he hopes to live long and to acquire riches for his delight, and then he will shrive himself; and as he tells himself, it seems to him that it will then be time enough to go to confession. Another is the over-confidence that he has in Christ's mercy. Against the first vice he shall think, that our life is in no security; and also that all the riches in this world are at hazard, and pass as does a shadow on the wall. And, as Saint Gregory says, it is part of the great righteousness of God that never shall the torment cease of those that would never withdraw themselves willingly from sin, but have always continued in sin; because, for the perpetual will to sin, they shall have perpetual torment.

Despair is of two sorts: the first is of the mercy of Christ; the other is the thought of sinners that they cannot long persevere in goodness. The first despair comes of the thought that he has sinned so greatly and so often, and has lain so long in sin, that he shall not be saved. Certainly, against that accursed despair should be set the thought that the passion of Jesus Christ is stronger to loose than sin is strong to bind. Against the second despair, let him think that as often as he falls he may rise again by penitence. And though he may have lain in sin ever so long, the mercy of Christ is ever ready to receive him into grace. Against that form of despair wherein he deems that he should not long persevere in goodness, he shall think that the feebleness of the Devil can do nothing unless men allow him to; and also that he shall have strength of the help of God and of all Holy Church and of the protection of angels, if he will.

Then shall men understand what is the fruit of penance; and according to the word of Jesus Christ, it is the endless bliss of Heaven, where joy has no opposite of woe or grievance, where all evils of this present life are past; wherein is security from the torments of Hell; wherein is the blessed company that rejoices evermore, each of the others' joy; wherein the body of man, that formerly was foul and dark, is more bright than the sun; wherein the body, that lately was ailing, frail, and feeble, and mortal, is immortal, and so strong and so whole that nothing may impair it; wherein is no hunger nor thirst, nor cold, but every soul is replenished with the ability to perceive the perfect knowing of God. This blessed kingdom may man acquire by poverty of spirit, and the glory of humbleness, and the plenitude of joy by hunger and thirst, and the ease and rest by labour, and life by death and the mortification of sin.

by poverte espirituel, and the glorie by lowenesse the plentee of joye by hunger and thurst, and th reste by travaille; and the lyf by deeth and morti ficacion of sinne.

L'Envoi

Now do I pray all those who hear this little treatise, or read it, that, if there be within it anything that pleases them, they thank Our Lord Jesus Christ, from Whom proceeds all understanding and all goodness. And if there be anything that displeases them, I pray them, also, that they impute it to the fault of my ignorance and not to my intention, which would fain have better said if I had had the knowledge. For our Book says, "All that is written is written for our instruction"; and that was my intention. Wherefore I meekly beseech you that, for the sake of God's mercy, you pray for me that Christ have mercy upon me and forgive me my trespasses—and especially for my translations and the writing of worldly vanities, the which I withdraw in my retractations: as, The Book of Troilus; also The Book of Fame; The Book of the Nineteen Ladies; The Book of the Duchess; The Book of Saint Valentine's Day, Of the Parliament of Birds; The Tales of Canterbury, those that tend toward sin; The Book of the Lion; and many another book, were they in my remembrance; and many a song and many a lecherous lay,—as to which may Christ, of His great mercy, forgive me the sin. But for the translation of Boethius's *de Consolatione*, and other books of legends of saints, and homilies, and of morality and devotion—for those I thank Our Lord Jesus Christ and His Blessed Mother and all the saints of Heaven; beseeching them that they, henceforth unto my life's end, send me grace whereof to bewail my sins, and to study for the salvation of my soul:—and grant me the grace of true penitence, confession, and expiation in this present life; through the benign grace of Him Who is King of kings and Priest over all priests, Who redeemed us with the precious blood of His heart; so that I may be one of those, at the day of doom, that shall be saved: *Qui cum patre, etc.*

104. Now preye I to hem alle that herkne thi litel tretis or rede, that if ther be any thing in i that lyketh hem, that ther-of they thanken our lord Jesu Crist, of whom procedeth al wit and a goodnesse. And if ther be any thing that disples hem, I preye hem also that they arrette it to the de faute of myn unconninge, and nat to my wil, tha wolde ful fayn have seyd bettre if I hadde had conninge. For oure boke seith, "al that is writen is writen for oure doctrine"; and that is myn entente Wherfore I biseke yow mekely for the mercy o god, that ye preye for me, that Crist have mercy on me and foryeve me my giltes:—and namely, o my translacions and endytinges of worldly vanitees, the whiche I revoke in my retracciouns: as is the book of Troilus; The book also of Fame; The book of the nynetene Ladies; The book of the Duchesse; The book of seint Valentynes day of the Parlement of Briddes; The tales of Caunterbury, thilke that sounen in-to sinne; The book of the Leoun; and many another book, if they were in my remembrance; and many a song and many a lecherous lay; that Crist for his grete mercy foryeve me the sinne. But of the translacion of Boece de Consolacione, and othere bokes of Legendes of seintes, and omelies, and moralitee, and devocioun, that thanke I oure lord Jesu Crist and his blisful moder, and alle the seintes of hevene; bisekinge hem that they from hennesforth, un-to my lyves ende, sende me grace to biwayle my giltes, and to studie to the salvacioun of my soule:—and graunte me grace of verray penitence, confessioun and satisfaccioun to doon in this present lyf; thurgh the benigne grace of him that is king of kinges and preest over alle preestes, that boghte us with the precious blood of his herte; so that I may been oon of hem at the day of dome that shulle be saved: *Qui cum patre, &c.*

HERE IS ENDED THE BOOK OF THE TALES OF CANTERBURY, COMPILED BY GEOFFREY CHAUCER, ON WHOSE SOUL JESUS CHRIST HAVE MERCY

∴

AMEN

PRINTED IN THE U. S. A.